create.mheducation.com

ISBN-13: 9781307334548

ISBN-10: 1307334547

Contents

i. About the Author 1
ii. Preface 2
iii. Learning Resources for Instructors and Students 6
iv. Acknowledgments 8
v. List of How To's 9
vi. List of Applications 11
1. Matter and Measurement 15
2. Atoms and the Periodic Table 50
3. Ionic Compounds 90
4. Covalent Compounds 121
5. Chemical Reactions 151
6. Energy Changes, Reaction Rates, and Equilibrium 203
7. Gases, Liquids, and Solids 238
8. Solutions 286
9. Acids and Bases 324
10. Nuclear Chemistry 369
11. Introduction to Organic Molecules and Functional Groups 399
12. Alkanes 439
13. Unsaturated Hydrocarbons 467
14. Organic Compounds That Contain Oxygen, Halogen, or Sulfur 510
15. The Three-Dimensional Shape of Molecules 544
16. Aldehydes and Ketones 574
17. Carboxylic Acids, Esters, and Amides 606
18. Amines and Neurotransmitters 646
19. Lipids 677
20. Carbohydrates 720
21. Amino Acids, Proteins, and Enzymes 761
22. Nucleic Acids and Protein Synthesis 808
23. Metabolism and Energy Production 846
24. Carbohydrate, Lipid, and Protein Metabolism 875
25. Body Fluids 907
26. Index for Body Fluids (Create Only) 929
A. Appendix: Useful Mathematical Concepts 931
B. Appendix: Answers to Selected In-Chapter and End-of-Chapter Problems 937

C. Glossary 991

D. Index 1003

E. Periodic Table of the Elements 1027

F. Common Functional Groups in Organic Chemistry 1029

Credits 1031

Online Supplements 1033

Connect One Semester Online Access for General, Organic, & Biological Chemistry, Fourth Edition 1034

Access Code for the Online Supplements 1035

About the Author

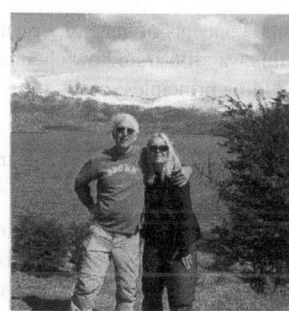

©Daniel C. Smith

Janice Gorzynski Smith was born in Schenectady, New York. She became interested in chemistry in high school, and went on to major in chemistry at Cornell University where she received an A.B. degree *summa cum laude*. Jan earned a Ph.D. in Organic Chemistry from Harvard University under the direction of Nobel Laureate E. J. Corey, and she also spent a year as a National Science Foundation National Needs Postdoctoral Fellow at Harvard. During her tenure with the Corey group, she completed the total synthesis of the plant growth hormone gibberellic acid.

Following her postdoctoral work, Jan joined the faculty of Mount Holyoke College where she was employed for 21 years. During this time she was active in teaching chemistry lecture and lab courses, conducting a research program in organic synthesis, and serving as department chair. Her organic chemistry class was named one of Mount Holyoke's "Don't-miss courses" in a survey by *Boston* magazine. After spending two sabbaticals amidst the natural beauty and diversity in Hawai'i in the 1990s, Jan and her family moved there permanently in 2000. Most recently, she has served as a faculty member at the University of Hawai'i at Mānoa, where she has taught a one-semester organic and biological chemistry course for nursing students, as well as the two-semester organic chemistry lecture and lab courses. She has also served as the faculty advisor to the student affiliate chapter of the American Chemical Society. In 2003, she received the Chancellor's Citation for Meritorious Teaching.

Jan resides in Hawai'i with her husband Dan, an emergency medicine physician, pictured with her hiking in Patagonia in 2016. She has four children and five grandchildren. When not teaching, writing, or enjoying her family, Jan bikes, hikes, snorkels, and scuba dives in sunny Hawai'i, and time permitting, enjoys travel and Hawaiian quilting.

Dedicated to my family

Preface

My goal in writing this text was to relate the fundamental concepts of general, organic, and biological chemistry to the world around us, and in this way illustrate how chemistry explains many aspects of everyday life. I have followed two guiding principles:

- use relevant and interesting applications for all basic chemical concepts
- present the material in a student-friendly fashion using bulleted lists, extensive illustrations, and step-by-step problem solving

This text is different—by design. Since today's students rely more heavily on visual imagery to learn than ever before, this text uses less prose and more diagrams and figures to reinforce the major themes of chemistry. A key feature is the use of molecular art to illustrate and explain common phenomena we encounter every day. Each topic is broken down into small chunks of information that are more manageable and easily learned. Students are given enough detail to understand basic concepts, such as how soap cleans away dirt and why trans fats are undesirable in the diet, without being overwhelmed.

This textbook is written for students who have an interest in nursing, nutrition, environmental science, food science, and a wide variety of other health-related professions. The content of this book is designed for an introductory chemistry course with no chemistry prerequisite, and is suitable for either a two-semester sequence or a one-semester course. I have found that by introducing one new concept at a time, keeping the basic themes in focus, and breaking down complex problems into small pieces, many students in these chemistry courses acquire a new appreciation of both the human body and the larger world around them.

Building the Text

Writing a textbook is a multifaceted process. McGraw-Hill's 360° Development Process is an ongoing, never-ending market-oriented approach to building accurate and innovative print and digital products. It is dedicated to continual large-scale and incremental improvement, driven by multiple customer feedback loops and checkpoints. This is initiated during the early planning stages of new products, intensifies during the development and production stages, and then begins again upon publication, in anticipation of the next edition. This process is designed to provide a broad, comprehensive spectrum of feedback for refinement and innovation of learning tools, for both student and instructor. The 360° Development Process includes market research, content reviews, faculty and student focus groups, course- and product-specific symposia, accuracy checks, and art reviews.

The Learning System Used in *General, Organic, & Biological Chemistry*

- **Writing Style** A concise writing style allows students to focus on learning major concepts and themes of general, organic, and biological chemistry. Relevant materials from everyday life are used to illustrate concepts, and topics are broken into small chunks of information that are more easily learned.
- **Chapter Outline** The chapter outline lists the main headings of the chapter, to help students map out the organization of each chapter's content.

- **Chapter Goals, tied to end-of-chapter Key Concepts**   The Chapter Goals at the beginning of each chapter identify what students will learn, and are tied numerically to the end-of-chapter Key Concepts, which serve as bulleted summaries of the most important concepts for study.
- **Macro-to-Micro Illustrations**   Because today's students are visual learners, and because visualizing molecular-level representations of macroscopic phenomena is critical to the understanding of any chemistry course, many illustrations in this text include photos or drawings of everyday objects, paired with their molecular representation, to help students understand the chemistry behind ordinary occurrences.
- **Problem Solving**   Sample Problems lead students through the thought process tied to successful problem solving by employing Analysis and Solution parts. Sample Problems are paired with Practice Problems to allow students to apply what they have just learned. The Practice Problems are followed by More Practice lists to point students to end-of-chapter Problems that are similar in concept. Other Problems within the chapter build on the concepts learned in the Sample and Practice Problems. Students can verify their answers to the Practice Problems and selected in-chapter Problems in the appendix at the end of the book.
- *How To's*   Key processes are taught to students in a straightforward and easy-to-understand manner by using examples and multiple, detailed steps to solving problems.
- **Applications**   Common applications of chemistry to everyday life are found in margin-placed Health Notes, Consumer Notes, and Environmental Notes, as well as sections titled "Focus on Health & Medicine," "Focus on the Environment," and "Focus on the Human Body."

A Student-Focused Revision

For the fourth edition, real student data points and input, derived from thousands of our LearnSmart users, were used to guide the revision. LearnSmart Heat Maps provided a quick visual snapshot of usage of portions of the text and the relative difficulty students experienced in mastering the content. With these data, the text content was honed:

- If the data indicated that the subject covered was more difficult than other parts of the book, as evidenced by a high proportion of students responding incorrectly to LearnSmart probes, the text content was substantively revised or reorganized to be as clear and illustrative as possible.
- When the data showed that a smaller percentage of the students had difficulty learning the material, the text was revised to provide a clearer presentation by rewriting the section or providing additional sample problems to strengthen student problem-solving skills.

This process was used to direct all of the revisions for this new edition. The following "New to This Edition" summary lists the major additions and refinements.

New To This Edition
General

NEW PROBLEM-SOLVING APPROACH   Sample Problems lead students through the thought process tied to successful problem solving by employing Analysis and Solution parts. Sample Problems are categorized sequentially by topic to match chapter organization, with a title so students know what they should be learning from each Sample Problem. Sample Problems are now paired with Practice Problems to allow students to apply what they have just learned. The Practice Problems are followed by More Practice lists to point students to end-of-chapter Problems that are similar in concept.

PHOTOS   Roughly one-half of the chapter-opening photos have been replaced with photos emphasizing relevant material within the chapter. More marginal photos of applications have also been added.

ART   The colors in artwork throughout the text were revised for emphasis, clarity, and consistency. Many chemical structures in Chapters 11 through 24 were updated for a cleaner appearance to help student understanding.

PROBLEMS   Over 180 new problems have been added, many of which incorporate molecular art or photographs.

Chapter Specific

- **Chapter 1**   Two new Sample Problems were added: Sample Problem 1.2 (Translating a Measurement into a Metric Unit) and Sample Problem 1.10, which uses an environmental example to solve a problem with a conversion factor.
- **Chapter 2**   New Sample Problem 2.2 uses a more complex ball-and-stick model to illustrate structure, and new Sample Problem 2.17 uses molecular art to predict periodic trends.
- **Chapter 3**   A revised Section 3.1 includes images to visually show the difference between ionic and covalent bonding. New material was added to Section 3.2 on the relative size of anions, cations, and atoms. A new Sample Problem 3.12 on deriving a formula for a compound with a polyatomic ion was also added.
- **Chapter 4**   Each of the chapter's Sample Problems on drawing Lewis structures was revised to emphasize how electrons are counted. All dashed bonds were updated to dashed wedges.
- **Chapter 5**   To assist understanding with number calculations, more molecular art was added as a visual aid within the body of the text, in the *How To*'s, and in the Sample Problems.
- **Chapters 6 through 9**   Molecular art has been added to visually aid students in their understanding of difficult concepts. Figure 6.6 shows what an equilibrium constant means in molecular art. Figure 6.7 shows Le Châtelier's principle in molecular art, so that students can better understand what species increase and decrease in concentration. New Sample Problem 6.10 relates the equilibrium constant through counting molecules in molecular art. New Sample Problem 6.14 uses molecular art to show how temperature affects the amount of product. Ball-and-stick models have been added to Section 7.7, including a new problem that uses models. More molecular art and a new Sample Problem 8.17 appear in Sections 8.8 and 8.9 on colligative properties and osmotic pressure. New molecular art has also been added to several sections and problems: Section 9.1A and 9.1B to help visualize acid–base reactions; Section 9.5 to show how two molecules of water react; and Section 9.11 on buffers in the blood. New Sample Problem 9.7 uses molecular art to visualize acid strength.
- **Chapter 10**   Two new Sample Problems were added: Sample Problem 10.4 on half-lives and Sample Problem 10.8 on nuclear fusion. There is also new material in Section 10.4B on smoking and radioisotopes in the lungs.
- **Chapter 11**   This chapter has been revised to increase early familiarity with skeletal structures. Section 11.4 has been expanded, with more material on skeletal structures, including using them with acyclic molecules. A *How To* on interpreting skeletal structures in Section 11.4 and Figure 11.4, which interprets skeletal structures in rings, were added to expand the coverage on skeletal structures.
- **Chapter 12**   This chapter has also been revised to increase familiarity with skeletal structures. Material added on skeletal structures includes a new Figure 12.1 on identifying alkyl groups in skeletal structures and a new Sample Problem 12.5 on naming a skeletal structure. The information on CO_2 concentration in the atmosphere has also been updated in Section 12.8 and Figure 12.4.
- **Chapter 13**   New sample problems were added: Sample Problem 13.6 on stereoisomers versus constitutional isomers and Sample Problem 13.9 on hydration of alkenes. To again increase familiarity with skeletal structures, a new Sample Problem 13.3 on naming a skeletal structure was included, and skeletal structures were added to Table 13.1.
- **Chapter 15**   Three new Sample Problems have been added to aid student understanding of the chapter concepts: Sample Problem 15.1 on isomers; Sample Problem 15.3 on finding chirality centers; and Sample Problem 15.4 on drawing an enantiomer and constitutional isomer for compounds with chirality centers on rings.
- **Chapter 16**   This revised chapter includes a new Sample Problem 16.8 on locating an acetal, hemiacetal, and ether in a cyclic compound and a new example in Section 16.8C on acetal hydrolysis.
- **Chapter 17**   Two new Sample Problems have been added to aid student understanding of the chapter concepts: Sample Problem 17.4 on the solubility of carboxylic acids and carboxylate anions and Sample Problem 17.10 on polymer components. The coverage of aspirin solubility in Section 17.7 was also expanded for clarity.
- **Chapter 18**   There is a new Sample Problem 18.6 on solubility.
- **Chapter 19**   A new Figure 19.8 on the structure of HDL and LDL particles was added, and more skeletal structures for fatty acids and triacylglycerols are used throughout.

- **Chapter 20**   This revised chapter includes a new Section 20.5C on human milk oligosaccharides in breast milk and a new Sample Problem 20.4 on locating anomers.
- **Chapter 21**   Two new Sample Problems were added for better student understanding of peptides—Sample Problem 21.3 and Sample Problem 21.4.
- **Chapter 22**   The revised chapter includes a new Section 22.10D on the Human Genome Project.
- **Chapter 23**   A new Figure 23.6 on the structure of acetyl CoA was added. The coverage of the citric acid cycle was expanded with new art in Figure 23.8 and material added in Section 23.5.

Our Commitment to Serving Teachers and Learners

TO THE INSTRUCTOR   Writing a chemistry textbook is a colossal task. Teaching chemistry for over 25 years at both a private, liberal arts college and a large state university has given me a unique perspective with which to write this text. I have found that students arrive with vastly different levels of preparation and widely different expectations for their college experience. As an instructor and now an author, I have tried to channel my love and knowledge of chemistry into a form that allows this spectrum of students to understand chemical science more clearly, and then see everyday phenomena in a new light.

TO THE STUDENT   I hope that this text and its ancillary program will help you to better understand and appreciate the world of chemistry. My interactions with thousands of students in my long teaching career have profoundly affected the way I teach and write about chemistry, so please feel free to email me with any comments or questions at jgsmith@hawaii.edu.

Learning Resources for Instructors and Students

Student Study Guide/Solutions Manual

The Student Solutions Manual, prepared by Erin R. Smith and Janice Gorzynski Smith, begins each chapter with a detailed chapter review that is organized around the chapter goals and key concepts. The Problem Solving section provides a number of examples for solving each type of problem essential to that chapter. The Self-Test section of each chapter quizzes chapter highlights, with answers provided. Finally, each chapter ends with the solutions to all in-chapter problems, as well as the solutions to all odd-numbered end-of-chapter problems.

Instructor's Solutions Manual

This supplement contains complete, worked-out solutions for all the end-of-chapter problems in the text. It can be found within the Instructor's Resources on the text's online learning center.

Computerized Test Bank Online

A comprehensive bank of test questions prepared by Andrea Leonard is provided within a computerized test bank enabling you to create paper and online tests or quizzes in an easy-to-use program that allows you to prepare and access your test or quiz anywhere, at anytime. Instructors can create or edit questions, or drag-and-drop questions, to prepare tests quickly and easily. Tests may be published to an online course, or printed for paper-based assignments.

McGraw-Hill LearnSmart Prep™ for General Chemistry

Fueled by LearnSmart—the most widely used and intelligent adaptive learning resource—LearnSmart Prep is designed to get students ready for a forthcoming course by quickly and effectively addressing prerequisite knowledge gaps that may cause problems down the road. By distinguishing what students know from what they don't, and honing in on concepts they are most likely to forget, LearnSmart Prep maintains a continuously adapting learning path individualized for each student, and tailors content to focus on what the student needs to master in order to have a successful start in the new class.

ALEKS® Preparation for General Chemistry

Assessment and LEarning in Knowledge Spaces is a web-based, artificially intelligent assessment and learning system. ALEKS uses adaptive questioning to quickly and accurately determine exactly what students know and don't know in a course. ALEKS then instructs students on the topics they are most ready to learn. As students work through a course, ALEKS periodically reassesses them to ensure that topics learned are also retained. ALEKS courses are very complete in their topic coverage, and ALEKS avoids multiple-choice questions. Students who show a high level of mastery of an ALEKS course will be successful in the actual course they are taking.

The ALEKS Preparation for General Chemistry course covers material usually taught in a one-term, preparatory chemistry course. By default, the topics listed below are all available. However, instructors can customize the course to align with their teaching goals using *any* topics from the Preparation for General Chemistry course or the complete ALEKS curriculum (other topics available), using the content editor in the Teacher Module.

Preparation for General Chemistry

- Math and Physics (55 topics)
- Measurement and Matter (62 topics)
- Chemical Reactions (47 topics)
- Structure and Bonding (31 topics)
- Gases, Liquids, and Solids (6 topics)

Other Topics Available (259 additional topics)

—Chemical Reactions (12 topics)
—Structure and Bonding (37 topics)
—Gases, Liquids, and Solids (24 topics)
—Solutions (9 topics)
—Kinetics and Equilibrium (40 topics)
—Acids and Bases (46 topics)
—Entropy and Free Energy (14 topics)
—Electrochemistry (19 topics)
—The Transition Metals (28 topics)
—Nuclear and Organic Chemistry (30 topics)

Presentation Tools

Accessed from your textbook's Connect Instructor's Resources, **Presentation Tools** is an online digital library containing photos, artwork, animations, and other media types that can be used to create customized lectures, visually enhanced tests and quizzes, compelling course websites, or attractive printed support materials. All assets are copyrighted by McGraw-Hill Higher Education but can be used by instructors for classroom purposes. The visual resources in this collection include:

- **Art, Photo, and Table Library:** Full-color digital files of all of the illustrations and tables and many of the photos in the text can be readily incorporated into lecture presentations, exams, or custom-made classroom materials.
- **Animations Library:** Files of animations and videos covering the many topics in *Integrated Science* are included so that you can easily make use of these animations in a lecture or classroom setting.

Also residing on your textbook's Connect Instructor's Resources site are:

- **PowerPoint Slides:** For instructors who prefer to create their lectures from scratch, all illustrations, photos, and tables are pre-inserted by chapter into PowerPoint slides.
- **Lecture Outlines:** Lecture notes, incorporating illustrations, have been written to the fourth edition text. They are provided in PowerPoint format so that you may use these lectures as written or customize them to fit your lecture.

Acknowledgments

Publishing a modern chemistry textbook requires a team of knowledgeable and hard-working individuals who are able to translate an author's vision into a reality. I am thankful to work with such a group of dedicated publishing professionals at McGraw-Hill.

I am especially grateful to once again work with Senior Product Developer Mary Hurley, who managed the day-to-day details of the project with timeliness and professionalism. Mary always knew what needed to get done and how best to meet the deadlines, which seem to get earlier with each edition. Much thanks also go to Director David Spurgeon, Ph.D., and Sherry Kane, Senior Content Project Manager, who skillfully directed the production process. I also appreciate the work of freelance Developmental Editor John Murdzek in the creation of both the text and the student solutions manual. I have greatly benefited from a team of advisors who helped guide me through the preparation of the first edition, as well as a panel of art reviewers who oversaw the creation of the beautiful figures present in the finished text.

Finally, I thank my family for their support and patience during the long process of publishing a textbook. My husband Dan, an emergency medicine physician, took several photos that appear in the text, and served as a consultant for many medical applications. My daughter Erin co-authored the *Student Study Guide/Solutions Manual* with me, which was written while she was busy parenting energetic sons and working as a full-time physician in emergency medicine.

REVIEWERS

The following people were instrumental in reading and providing feedback on previous editions of the text, which helped to shape my ideas into cohesive pages:

Madeline Adamczeski, *San Jose City College*
Edward Alexander, *San Diego Mesa College*
Julie Bezzerides, *Lewis–Clark State College*
John Blaha, *Columbus State Community College*
Nicholas Burgis, *Eastern Washington University*
Mitchel Cottenoir, *South Plains College*
Anne Distler, *Cuyahoga Community College*
Stacie Eldridge, *Riverside City College*
Daniel Eves, *Southern Utah University*
Fred Omega Garces, *San Diego Miramar College, SDCCD*
Bobbie Grey, *Riverside City College*
Peng Jing, *Indiana University–Fort Wayne University*
Kenneth O'Connor, *Marshall University*
Shadrick Paris, *Ohio University*
Julie Pigza, *Queensborough Community College*
Mike Rennekamp, *Columbus State Community College*
Raymond Sadeghi, *The University of Texas at San Antonio*
Hussein Samha, *Southern Utah University*
Susan T. Thomas, *The University of Texas at San Antonio*
Tracy Thompson, *Alverno College*
James Zubricky, *University of Toledo*

Thanks go to David G. Jones, Vistamar School, who helped write and review learning goal-oriented content for McGraw-Hill LearnSmart™ for *General, Organic, & Biological Chemistry*. We are also extremely grateful to the authors of the other ancillaries to accompany *General, Organic, & Biological Chemistry,* Fourth Edition: Lauren McMills of Ohio University–Athens for her authoring of the Instructor's Solutions Manual; Harpreet Malhotra of Florida State College, Jacksonville, for her authoring of the PowerPoint Lecture Outlines; and Andrea Leonard of the University of Louisiana, Lafayette, for her authoring of the Test Bank.

List of *How To*'s

Chapter 1   Matter and Measurement   1
How To Convert a Standard Number to Scientific Notation   17
How To Solve a Problem Using Conversion Factors   21

Chapter 2   Atoms and the Periodic Table   36
How To Determine the Atomic Weight of an Element   49
How To Draw an Orbital Diagram for the Ground State Electronic Configuration of an Element   62

Chapter 3   Ionic Compounds   76
How To Write a Formula for an Ionic Compound   89
How To Name an Ionic Compound That Contains a Metal with Variable Charge   93
How To Derive a Formula from the Name of an Ionic Compound   95

Chapter 4   Covalent Compounds   107
How To Draw a Lewis Structure   112
How To Name a Covalent Molecule with Two Elements   120

Chapter 5   Chemical Reactions   137
How To Balance a Chemical Equation   143
How To Calculate the Formula Weight of a Compound   160
How To Convert Moles of Reactant to Grams of Product   165
How To Convert Grams of Reactant to Grams of Product   168

Chapter 6   Energy Changes, Reaction Rates, and Equilibrium   189
How To Calculate the Equilibrium Constant for a Reaction   208

Chapter 7   Gases, Liquids, and Solids   224
How To Use Boyle's Law to Calculate a New Gas Volume or Pressure   230
How To Convert Moles of Gas to Volume at STP   238
How To Carry Out Calculations with the Ideal Gas Law   241

Chapter 8   Solutions   272
How To Calculate Molarity from a Given Number of Grams of Solute   230

Chapter 9   Acids and Bases   310
How To Predict the Direction of Equilibrium in an Acid–Base Reaction   325
How To Draw a Balanced Equation for a Neutralization Reaction Between HA and MOH   336
How To Determine the Molarity of an Acid Solution from a Titration   341

Chapter 10   Nuclear Chemistry   355
How To Balance an Equation for a Nuclear Reaction   359
How To Use a Half-Life to Determine the Amount of Radioisotope Present   365

Chapter 11   Introduction to Organic Molecules and Functional Groups   385
How To Interpret a Skeletal Structure   399

Chapter 12   Alkanes   425
How To Name an Alkane Using the IUPAC System   435
How To Name a Cycloalkane Using the IUPAC System   441

Chapter 13   Unsaturated Hydrocarbons   453
How To Name an Alkene or an Alkyne   456

xxx   List of *How To*'s

Chapter 14   Organic Compounds That Contain Oxygen, Halogen, or Sulfur   496
How To Name an Alcohol Using the IUPAC System   501
How To Name an Alkyl Halide Using the IUPAC System   517

Chapter 15   The Three-Dimensional Shape of Molecules   530
How To Draw Two Enantiomers of a Chiral Compound   539

Chapter 16   Aldehydes and Ketones   560
How To Draw a Hemiacetal and Acetal from a Carbonyl Compound   578

Chapter 17   Carboxylic Acids, Esters, and Amides   592
How To Name an Ester (RCO_2R') Using the IUPAC System   597
How To Name a 2° or 3° Amide   598

Chapter 18   Amines and Neurotransmitters   632
How To Name 2° and 3° Amines with Different Alkyl Groups   636

Chapter 20   Carbohydrates   706
How To Draw a Haworth Projection from an Acyclic Aldohexose   717

Chapter 21   Amino Acids, Proteins, and Enzymes   747
How To Draw a Dipeptide from Two Amino Acids   756

Chapter 22   Nucleic Acids and Protein Synthesis   794
How To Use the Polymerase Chain Reaction to Amplify a Sample of DNA   821

Chapter 24   Carbohydrate, Lipid, and Protein Metabolism   861
How To Determine the Number of Molecules of ATP Formed from a Fatty Acid   880

List of Applications

Chapter 1   Matter and Measurement   1
Focus on Health & Medicine: Problem Solving Using Clinical Conversion Factors   24
Consumer Note: Digital and Tympanic Thermometers   26
Health Note: Specific Gravity of a Urine Sample   29

Chapter 2   Atoms and the Periodic Table   36
Focus on the Human Body: The Elements of Life   39
Health Note: Platinum-Containing Drugs Used to Treat Cancer   48
Focus on Health & Medicine: Isotopes in Medicine   50
Health Note: Zinc Tablets Used to Prevent Diarrhea   52
Consumer Note: Recycling Aluminum Cans   52
Health Note: Mercury in Dental Amalgam   65

Chapter 3   Ionic Compounds   76
Focus on the Human Body: Important Ions in the Body   86
Focus on Health & Medicine: Ionic Compounds in Consumer Products   91
Health Note: Potassium in Electrolyte Replacement Beverages   91
Consumer Note: Zinc Oxide in Sunblock   92
Focus on Health & Medicine: Useful Ionic Compounds   100
Focus on Health & Medicine: Treating Osteoporosis   101
Health Note: Normal Bone vs. Brittle Bone   101

Chapter 4   Covalent Compounds   107
Focus on the Human Body: Covalent Molecules and the Cardiovascular
    System   111
Focus on the Environment: Ozone   119
Health Note: Cassava Root   121
Consumer Note: Dihydroxyacetone in Tanning Agents   124
Focus on Health & Medicine: Covalent Drugs and Medical Products   128

Chapter 5   Chemical Reactions   137
Environmental Note: Nitrogen Dioxide in Polluted Air   149
Consumer Note: Benzoyl Peroxide in Acne Medications   152
Focus on Health & Medicine: Pacemakers   156
Health Note: Vitamin C   163
Environmental Note: Nitrogen Monoxide from Car Exhaust   164
Environmental Note: Ethanol in Gasohol   170
Focus on Health & Medicine: The Importance of Percent Yield in the
    Pharmaceutical Industry   174

Chapter 6   Energy Changes, Reaction Rates, and Equilibrium   189
Focus on the Human Body: Energy and Nutrition   191
Consumer Note: Estimating the Number of Calories in Food   192
Environmental Note: Methane from Decomposing Waste   195
Focus on the Human Body: Lactase, a Biological Catalyst   202
Focus on the Environment: Catalytic Converters   203
Focus on the Human Body: Body Temperature   216
Health Note: Shivering   216

Chapter 7   Gases, Liquids, and Solids   224
Focus on Health & Medicine: Blood Pressure   228
Focus on the Environment: How Charles's Law Explains Wind Currents   233
Focus on the Human Body: The Lungs   240
Health Note: The Local Anesthetic Ethyl Chloride   249

Chapter 8   Solutions   272
Health Note: Blood, a Suspension   274
Health Note: The Anesthetic Ketamine   285
Consumer Note: Alcohol-Based Hand Sanitizers   286
Environmental Note: DDT Accumulation   287
Health Note: The Many Uses of Saline Solutions   290
Focus on the Human Body: Osmosis and Biological Membranes   299
Focus on Health & Medicine: Dialysis   300

Chapter 9   Acids and Bases   310
Focus on the Human Body: Hydrochloric Acid in the Stomach   321
Health Note: Lactic Acid in Tissues   326
Health Note: Sports Drinks and Dental Erosion   334
Focus on the Human Body: The pH of Body Fluids   335
Focus on the Environment: Acid Rain and a Naturally Buffered Lake   346
Focus on the Human Body: Buffers in Blood   347
Health Note: Cystic Fibrosis   347
Health Note: Blood pH During Strenuous Exercise   347

Chapter 10   Nuclear Chemistry   355
Focus on Health & Medicine: External Radiation Treatment for Tumors   363
Focus on Health & Medicine: The Effects of Radioactivity   370
Health Note: Radioactive Substances in Secondhand Smoke   370
Focus on Health & Medicine: Medical Uses of Radioisotopes   371
Health Note: Radioactive Seeds Implanted to Treat Cancer   373
Focus on Health & Medicine: Medical Imaging Without Radioactivity   378

Chapter 11   Introduction to Organic Molecules and Functional Groups   385
Health Note: Lidocaine   394
Health Note: Treating Type 2 Diabetes   401
Health Note: Tetrahydrocannabinol in Marijuana   403
Health Note: Tamiflu   407
Health Note: Drugs Used to Treat High Blood Pressure   408
Focus on the Environment: Environmental Pollutants   414
Focus on Health & Medicine: Vitamins   415
Health Note: Scurvy Grass as a Source of Vitamin C   416

Chapter 12   Alkanes   425
Focus on Health & Medicine: Naming New Drugs   433
Focus on the Environment: Fossil Fuels   442
Environmental Note: Crude Oil Leaks   444
Focus on the Environment: Combustion   444
Environmental Note: Carbon Dioxide from Automobiles   445

Chapter 13   Unsaturated Hydrocarbons   453
Focus on Health & Medicine: Saturated and Unsaturated Fatty Acids   463
Health Note: Essential Fatty Acids   464
Health Note: The Antioxidant Lycopene   466
Focus on Health & Medicine: Oral Contraceptives   467
Focus on Health & Medicine: Margarine or Butter?   473
Consumer Note: HDPE vs. LDPE   475
Consumer Note: Disposable Diapers   478
Focus on the Environment: Polymer Recycling   478
Focus on Health & Medicine: Aromatic Drugs, Sunscreens, and Carcinogens   482

Health Note: SPF Ratings in Sunscreens 482
Focus on Health & Medicine: Phenols as Antioxidants 484
Focus on Health & Medicine: Nitration and Sulfa Drugs 486

Chapter 14   Organic Compounds That Contain Oxygen, Halogen, or Sulfur 496
Focus on the Human Body: Oxidation and Blood Alcohol Screening 509
Focus on Health & Medicine: Ethanol, the Most Widely Abused Drug 510
Focus on Health & Medicine: Ethers as Anesthetics 515
Health Note: Fluticasone, a Drug Used to Treat Seasonal Allergies and Asthma 519
Focus on the Environment: Alkyl Halides and the Ozone Layer 519
Environmental Note: The Antarctic Ozone Hole 520

Chapter 15   The Three-Dimensional Shape of Molecules 530
Focus on Health & Medicine: The Unforgettable Legacy of Thalidomide 542
Focus on Health & Medicine: Chiral Drugs 543
Health Note: Naproxen, a Widely Used Pain Reliever 544
Focus on the Human Body: The Sense of Smell 552

Chapter 16   Aldehydes and Ketones 560
Focus on Health & Medicine: Interesting Aldehydes and Ketones 567
Focus on the Human Body: Biological Reductions 574
Focus on the Human Body: The Chemistry of Vision 575
Health Note: Oleandrin, a Compound from Oleander Used to
   Treat Congestive Heart Failure 581
Health Note: Digoxin 582

Chapter 17   Carboxylic Acids, Esters, and Amides 592
Focus on Health & Medicine: Skin Care Products 601
Focus on Health & Medicine: Aspirin and Anti-Inflammatory Agents 602
Consumer Note: Preservatives in Packaged Breads 607
Focus on Health & Medicine: Aspirin 609
Environmental Note: Pheromone-Baited Traps for Cockroaches 613
Health Note: DEET Insect Repellant 613
Focus on Health & Medicine: Olestra, a Synthetic Fat 617
Consumer Note: Kevlar Bike Tires 620
Focus on Health & Medicine: Dissolving Sutures 622
Focus on the Environment: Polymer Recycling 623
Focus on Health & Medicine: Penicillin 623

Chapter 18   Amines and Neurotransmitters 632
Health Note: Scopolamine for Motion Sickness 635
Focus on Health & Medicine: Caffeine and Nicotine 639
Consumer Note: Morphine in Poppy Seeds 642
Focus on Health & Medicine: Ammonium Salts as Useful Drugs 648
Focus on the Human Body: Epinephrine and Related Compounds 653
Focus on Health & Medicine: Histamine and Antihistamines 656
Health Note: Scombroid Fish Poisoning 656

Chapter 19   Lipids 663
Health Note: Coconut Oil 673
Health Note: Fish Oils 674
Focus on Health & Medicine: Fats and Oils in the Diet 675
Focus on the Human Body: Metabolism of Triacylglycerols 678
Environmental Note: Biofuels 679
Focus on Health & Medicine: Nerve Cells and Multiple Sclerosis 684
Focus on Health & Medicine: Cholesterol, the Most Prominent Steroid 688
Health Note: Lovastatin, a Cholesterol-Lowering Drug 691
Focus on Health & Medicine: Fat-Soluble Vitamins 694
Focus on Health & Medicine: Prostaglandins and Leukotrienes 696
Health Note: Celecoxib, a Pain Reliever That Blocks the COX-2 Enzyme 697

Chapter 20   Carbohydrates   706
    Focus on Health & Medicine: Monitoring Glucose Levels   724
    Focus on Health & Medicine: Lactose Intolerance   728
    Focus on Health & Medicine: Sucrose and Artificial Sweeteners   729
    Consumer Note: Rebaudioside A, a Natural Sweetener   731
    Focus on Health & Medicine: Human Milk Oligosaccharides   731
    Health Note: Breast Feeding   732
    Focus on the Human Body: Useful Carbohydrate Derivatives   736
    Health Note: Chondroitin and Glucosamine Supplements   737
    Focus on the Human Body: Blood Type   738

Chapter 21   Amino Acids, Proteins, and Enzymes   747
    Health Note: Combining Foods to Get All of the Essential Amino Acids   751
    Focus on the Human Body: Biologically Active Peptides   760
    Focus on the Human Body: Common Proteins   769
    Health Note: Sickle Cell Anemia   771
    Focus on Health & Medicine: Using Enzymes to Diagnose and Treat Diseases   785

Chapter 22   Nucleic Acids and Protein Synthesis   794
    Health Note: Cystic Fibrosis   818
    Consumer Note: Genetically Modified Crops   820
    Focus on the Human Body: DNA Fingerprinting   822
    Health Note: Newborn Screening   823
    Focus on Health & Medicine: Viruses   823

Chapter 23   Metabolism and Energy Production   832
    Focus on the Human Body: Creatine and Athletic Performance   842
    Health Note: Sources of Vitamin B_2 846
    Health Note: A Source of Vitamin B_5 847
    Focus on Health & Medicine: Hydrogen Cyanide   855

Chapter 24   Carbohydrate, Lipid, and Protein Metabolism   861
    Focus on Health & Medicine: Glycolysis and Cancer Cells   870
    Focus on Health & Medicine: Conversion to Lactate   871
    Focus on Health & Medicine: Conversion to Ethanol   873
    Health Note: Low Carbohydrate Diets   882

1

Matter and Measurement

CHAPTER OUTLINE

1.1 Chemistry—The Science of Everyday Experience

1.2 States of Matter

1.3 Classification of Matter

1.4 Measurement

1.5 Significant Figures

1.6 Scientific Notation

1.7 Problem Solving Using Conversion Factors

1.8 FOCUS ON HEALTH & MEDICINE: Problem Solving Using Clinical Conversion Factors

1.9 Temperature

1.10 Density and Specific Gravity

CHAPTER GOALS

In this chapter you will learn how to:

1. Describe the three states of matter

2. Classify matter as a pure substance, mixture, element, or compound

3. Report measurements using the metric units of length, mass, and volume

4. Use significant figures

5. Use scientific notation for very large and very small numbers

6. Use conversion factors to convert one unit to another

7. Convert temperature from one scale to another

8. Define density and specific gravity and use density to calculate the mass or volume of a substance

Why Study Matter and Measurement?

Everything you touch, feel, or taste is composed of chemicals—that is, **matter**—so an understanding of its composition and properties is crucial to our appreciation of the world around us. Some matter—lakes, trees, sand, and soil—is naturally occurring, while other examples of matter—aspirin, CDs, nylon fabric, plastic syringes, and vaccines—are made by humans. To understand the properties of matter, as well as how one form of matter is converted to another, we must also learn about measurements. Following a recipe, pumping gasoline, and figuring out drug dosages involve manipulating numbers. Thus, Chapter 1 begins our study of chemistry by examining the key concepts of matter and measurement.

1.1   Chemistry—The Science of Everyday Experience

What activities might occupy the day of a typical student? You may have done some or all of the following tasks: eaten some meals, drunk coffee or cola, taken a shower with soap, taken notes in a class, checked email on a computer, watched some television, ridden a bike or car to a part-time job, taken an aspirin to relieve a headache, and spent some of the evening having snacks and refreshments with friends. Perhaps, without your awareness, your life was touched by chemistry in each of these activities. What, then, is this discipline we call **chemistry?**

• *Chemistry* is the study of matter—its composition, properties, and transformations.

What is **matter?**

• *Matter* is anything that has mass and takes up volume.

In other words, **chemistry studies anything that we touch, feel, see, smell, or taste,** from simple substances like water and salt, to complex substances like proteins and carbohydrates that combine to form the human body. Some matter—cotton, sand, an apple, and the cardiac drug digoxin—is **naturally occurring,** meaning it is isolated from natural sources. Other substances—nylon, Styrofoam, the plastic used in soft drink bottles, and the pain reliever ibuprofen—are **synthetic,** meaning they are produced by chemists in the laboratory (Figure 1.1).

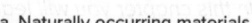

Figure 1.1   Naturally Occurring and Synthetic Materials

a. Naturally occurring materials

b. Synthetic materials

Matter occurs in nature or is synthesized in the lab. (a) Sand and apples are two examples of natural materials. Cotton fabric is woven from cotton fiber, obtained from the cotton plant. The drug digoxin (trade name Lanoxin), widely prescribed for decades for patients with congestive heart failure, is extracted from the leaves of the woolly foxglove plant. (b) Nylon was the first synthetic fiber made in the laboratory. It quickly replaced the natural fiber silk in parachutes and ladies' stockings. Styrofoam and PET (polyethylene terephthalate), the plastic used for soft drink bottles, are strong yet lightweight synthetic materials used for food storage. Over-the-counter pain relievers like ibuprofen are synthetic. The starting materials for all of these useful products are obtained from petroleum.
(a–b): ©McGraw-Hill Education/Jill Braaten, photographer

Figure 1.2   Transforming Natural Materials into Useful Synthetic Products

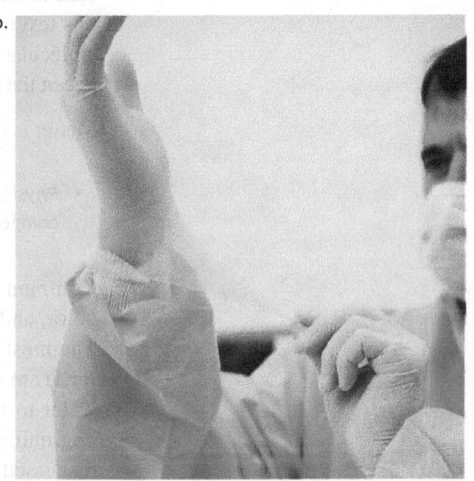

(a) Latex, the sticky liquid that oozes from a rubber tree when it is cut, is too soft for most applications. (b) Vulcanization converts latex into the stronger, elastic rubber used in tires and other products. *(a): ©Suphatthra China/Shutterstock RF; (b): ©Fuse/Corbis/Getty Images RF*

Sometimes a chemist studies what a substance is made of, whereas at other times he or she might be interested in its properties. Alternatively, the focus may be how to convert one material into a new material with unique and useful properties. As an example, naturally occurring rubber exists as the sticky liquid latex, which is too soft for most applications. The laboratory process of vulcanization converts it into the stronger, more elastic material used in tires and other products (Figure 1.2).

Chemistry is truly the science of everyday experience. Soaps and detergents, newspapers and CDs, condoms and oral contraceptives, Tylenol and penicillin—all of these items are products of chemistry. Without a doubt, advances in chemistry have transformed life in modern times.

PROBLEM 1.1

Imagine that your job as a healthcare professional is to take a blood sample from a patient and store it in a small container in a refrigerator until it is picked up for analysis in the hospital lab. You might have to put on gloves and a mask, use a plastic syringe with a metal needle, store the sample in a test tube or vial, and place it in a cold refrigerator. Pick five objects you might encounter during the process and decide if they are made of naturally occurring or synthetic materials.

1.2   States of Matter

Matter exists in three common states—solid, liquid, and gas.

- A *solid* has a definite volume, and maintains its shape regardless of the container in which it is placed. The particles of a solid lie close together, and are arranged in a regular three-dimensional array.
- A *liquid* has a definite volume, but takes on the shape of the container it occupies. The particles of a liquid are close together, but they can randomly move around, sliding past one another.
- A *gas* has no definite shape or volume. The particles of a gas move randomly and are separated by a distance much larger than their size. The particles of a gas expand to fill the volume and assume the shape of whatever container they are put in.

For example, water exists in its solid state as ice or snow, liquid state as liquid water, and gaseous state as steam or water vapor. Blow-up circles like those in Figure 1.3 will be used commonly in this text to indicate the composition and state of the particles that compose a substance. In this molecular art, different types of particles are shown in color-coded spheres, and the distance between the spheres signals its state—solid, liquid, or gas.

Matter is characterized by its **physical properties** and **chemical properties.**

> • *Physical properties* are those that can be observed or measured without changing the composition of the material.

Common physical properties include melting point (mp), boiling point (bp), solubility, color, and odor. **A *physical change* alters a substance without changing its composition.** The most common physical changes are **changes in state**—that is, the **conversion of matter from one state to another.** Melting an ice cube to form liquid water, and boiling liquid water to form steam, are two examples of physical changes. Water is the substance at the beginning and end of both physical changes. More details about physical changes are discussed in Chapter 7.

Figure 1.3   The Three States of Water—Solid, Liquid, and Gas

a. Solid water

b. Liquid water

c. Gaseous water

• The particles of a solid are close together and highly organized. (Photo: snow-capped Mauna Kea on the Big Island of Hawaii)

• The particles of a liquid are close together but more disorganized than the solid. (Photo: Akaka Falls on the Big Island of Hawaii)

• The particles of a gas are far apart and disorganized. (Photo: steam formed by a lava flow on the Big Island of Hawaii)

Each red sphere joined to two gray spheres represents a single water particle. In proceeding from left to right, from solid to liquid to gas, the molecular art shows that the level of organization of the water particles decreases. Color-coding and the identity of the spheres within the particles will be addressed in Chapter 2. *(a): ©Alvis Upitis/SuperStock/Alamy; (b): ©Daniel C. Smith; (c): Source: T.J. Takahashi/USGS* solid water   melting — physical change   liquid water   boiling — physical change   water vapor

- *Chemical properties* are those that determine how a substance can be converted to another substance.

A *chemical change,* **or a** *chemical reaction,* **converts one material into another.** The conversion of hydrogen and oxygen into water is a chemical reaction because the composition of the material is different at the beginning and end of the process. Chemical reactions are discussed in Chapters 5 and 6.

oxygen   water   chemical reaction   hydrogen

PROBLEM 1.2

Characterize each process as a physical change or a chemical change: (a) making ice cubes; (b) burning natural gas; (c) silver jewelry tarnishing; (d) a pile of snow melting; (e) fermenting grapes to produce wine.

PROBLEM 1.3

Does the molecular art represent a chemical change or a physical change? Explain your choice.

1.3   Classification of Matter

All matter can be classified as either a **pure substance** or a **mixture.**

- A *pure substance* is composed of a single component and has a constant composition, regardless of the sample size and the origin of the sample.

A pure substance, such as water or table sugar, can be characterized by its physical properties, because these properties do not change from sample to sample. **A pure substance cannot be broken down to other pure substances by any physical change.**

- A *mixture* is composed of more than one substance. The composition of a mixture can vary depending on the sample.

The physical properties of a mixture may also vary from one sample to another. **A mixture can be separated into its components by physical changes.** Dissolving table sugar in water forms a mixture, whose sweetness depends on the amount of sugar added. If the water is allowed to evaporate from the mixture, pure table sugar and pure water are obtained.

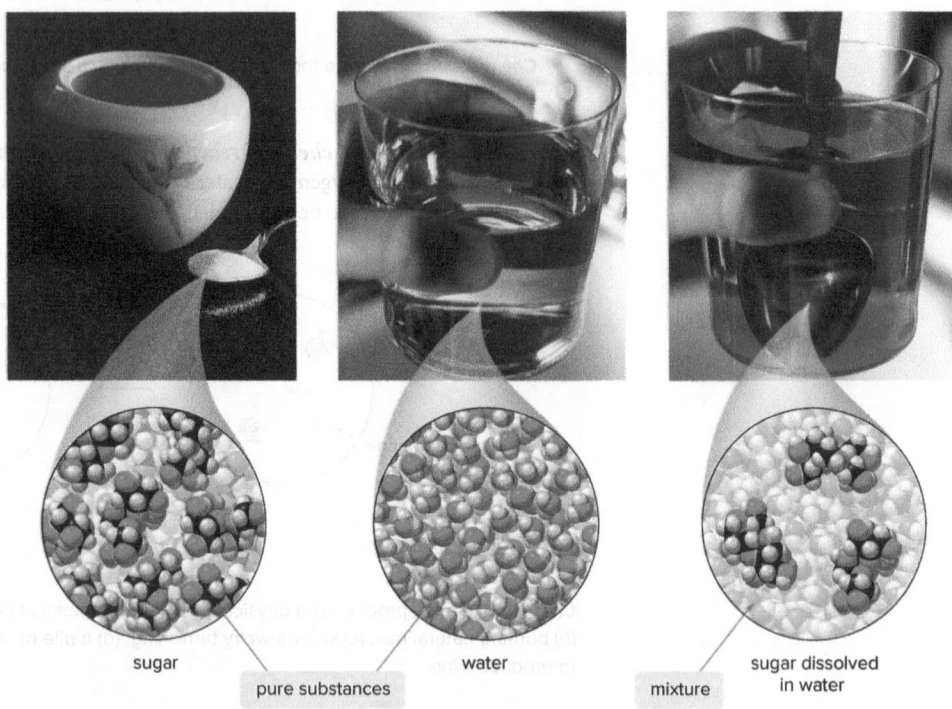

sugar

pure substances

water

mixture

sugar dissolved in water

(left): ©Daniel C. Smith; (middle & right): ©McGraw-Hill Education/Jill Braaten, photographer

Mixtures can be formed from solids, liquids, and gases, as shown in Figure 1.4. The compressed air breathed by a scuba diver consists mainly of the gases oxygen and nitrogen. A saline solution used in an IV bag contains solid sodium chloride (table salt) dissolved in liquid water.

Figure 1.4   Two Examples of Mixtures

a. Two gases

b. A solid and a liquid

oxygen   nitrogen

water   sodium

chloride (from chlorine)

(a): ©Daniel C. Smith; (b): ©Richard T. Nowitz/Science Source

Figure 1.5   Elements and Compounds

a. Aluminum foil

b. Nitrogen gas

c. Water

d. Table salt

aluminum   nitrogen   hydrogen   oxygen   chloride   sodium
(from chlorine)

- Aluminum foil and nitrogen gas are elements. **The molecular art for an element shows spheres of *one* color only.** Thus, aluminum is a solid shown with gray spheres, whereas nitrogen is a gas shown with blue spheres. Water and table salt are compounds. Color-coding of the spheres used in the molecular art indicates that water is composed of two elements—hydrogen shown as gray spheres, and oxygen shown in red. Likewise, the gray (sodium) and green (chlorine) spheres illustrate that sodium chloride is formed from two elements as well.
  (a): ©Daniel C. Smith; (b): ©Keith Eng, 2008; (c): ©McGraw-Hill Education/Jill Braaten, photographer; (d): ©Daniel C. Smith

A pure substance is classified as either an **element** or a **compound.**

- An *element* is a pure substance that cannot be broken down into simpler substances by a chemical reaction.
- A *compound* is a pure substance formed by chemically combining (joining together) two or more elements.

An alphabetical list of elements is located on the inside front cover of this text. The elements are commonly organized into a periodic table, also shown on the inside front cover, and discussed in much greater detail in Section 2.4.

Nitrogen gas, aluminum foil, and copper wire are all elements. Water is a compound because it is composed of the elements hydrogen and oxygen. Table salt, sodium chloride, is also a compound because it is formed from the elements sodium and chlorine (Figure 1.5). Although only 118 elements are currently known, over 50 million compounds occur naturally or have been synthesized in the laboratory. We will learn much more about elements and compounds in Chapter 2. Figure 1.6 summarizes the categories into which matter is classified.

SAMPLE PROBLEM 1.1 USING MOLECULAR ART FOR AN ELEMENT
AND A COMPOUND

Classify each example of molecular art as an element or a compound:

a.

b.

Analysis

In molecular art, an element is composed of spheres of the same color, whereas a compound is composed of spheres of different colors.

Solution

Representation (a) is an element because each particle contains only gray spheres.
Representation (b) is a compound because each particle contains both red and black spheres.

PRACTICE PROBLEM 1.1

Classify each example of molecular art as a pure substance or a mixture:

More Practice: Try Problems 1.19–1.23.

PROBLEM 1.4

(a) Which representation(s) of molecular art illustrate pure elements? (b) Which representation(s) illustrate a mixture of a compound and an element? (c) Which representation(s) illustrate a mixture of two compounds?

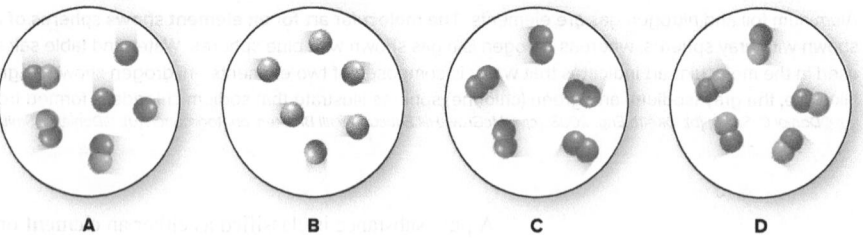

PROBLEM 1.5

Classify each item as a pure substance or a mixture: (a) blood; (b) ocean water; (c) a piece of wood; (d) a chunk of ice.

PROBLEM 1.6

Classify each item as an element or a compound: (a) the gas inside a helium balloon; (b) table sugar; (c) the rust on an iron nail; (d) aspirin. All elements are listed alphabetically on the inside front cover.

Figure 1.6

Classification of Matter

1.4 Measurement

Any time you check your weight on a scale, measure the ingredients of a recipe, or figure out how far it is from one location to another, you are measuring a quantity. Measurements are routine for healthcare professionals who use weight, blood pressure, pulse, and temperature to chart a patient's progress.

Length:
21.0 in.
or
53.3 cm

number   unit

Mass
(Weight):
8 lb 8 oz
or
3.9 kg

number   unit

©Roy Hsu/Photographers Choice/Getty Images RF

In 1960, the **International System of Units** was formally adopted as the uniform system of units for the sciences. **SI units,** as they are called, are based on the metric system, but the system recommends the use of some metric units over others. SI stands for the French words *Système Internationale.*

• **Every measurement is composed of a *number* and a *unit*.**

Reporting the value of a measurement is meaningless without its unit. For example, if you were told to give a patient an aspirin dosage of 325, does this mean 325 ounces, pounds, grams, milligrams, or tablets? Clearly there is a huge difference among these quantities.

1.4A The Metric System

In the United States, most measurements are made with the **English system,** using units like miles (mi), gallons (gal), pounds (lb), and so forth. A disadvantage of this system is that the units are not systematically related to each other and require memorization. For example, 1 lb = 16 oz, 1 gal = 4 qt, and 1 mi = 5,280 ft.

Scientists, health professionals, and people in most other countries use the **metric system,** with units like meter (m) for length, gram (g) for mass, and liter (L) for volume. The metric system is slowly gaining popularity in the United States. The weight of packaged foods is often given in both ounces and grams. Distances on many road signs are shown in miles and kilometers. Most measurements in this text will be reported using the metric system, but learning to convert English units to metric units is also a necessary skill that will be illustrated in Section 1.7.

The important features of the metric system are the following:

The metric system is slowly gaining acceptance in the United States, as seen in the gallon jug of milk and the two-liter bottle of soda. ©Jill Braaten RF

• Each type of measurement has a base unit—the meter (m) for length; the gram (g) for mass; the liter (L) for volume; the second (s) for time.
• All other units are related to the base unit by powers of 10.
• The prefix of the unit name indicates if the unit is larger or smaller than the base unit.

The base units of the metric system are summarized in Table 1.1, and the most common prefixes used to convert the base units to smaller or larger units are summarized in Table 1.2. **The same prefixes are used for all types of measurement.** For example, the prefix *kilo-* means 1,000 times as large. Thus,

Table 1.1 Metric Units

Quantity	Metric Base Unit	Symbol
Length	Meter	m
Mass	Gram	g
Volume	Liter	L
Time	Second	s

1 **kilo**meter = **1,000** meters   or   1 km = 1,000 m

1 **kilo**gram = **1,000** grams   or   1 kg = 1,000 g

1 **kilo**liter = **1,000** liters   or   1 kL = 1,000 L

Table 1.2 Common Prefixes Used for Metric Units

Prefix	Symbol	Meaning	Numerical Value[a]	Scientific Notation[b]
Giga-	G	Billion	1,000,000,000.	10^9
Mega-	M	Million	1,000,000.	10^6
Kilo-	k	Thousand	1,000.	10^3
Deci-	d	Tenth	0.1	10^{-1}
Centi-	c	Hundredth	0.01	10^{-2}
Milli-	m	Thousandth	0.001	10^{-3}
Micro-	μ[c]	Millionth	0.000 001	10^{-6}
Nano-	n	Billionth	0.000 000 001	10^{-9}

The metric symbols are all lowercase except for the unit **liter** (L) and the prefixes **mega-** (M) and **giga-** (G). Liter is capitalized to distinguish it from the number *one*. Mega is capitalized to distinguish it from the symbol for the prefix *milli-*. Giga is capitalized to distinguish it from the abbreviation for gram (g).

[a]Numbers that contain five or more digits to the right of the decimal point are written with a small space separating each group of three digits.
[b]How to express numbers in scientific notation is explained in Section 1.6.
[c]The symbol μ is the lowercase Greek letter mu. The prefix *micro-* is sometimes abbreviated as **mc.**

The prefix *milli-* means one-thousandth as large (1/1,000 or 0.001). Thus,

1 **milli**meter = **0.001** meter	or	1 mm = 0.001 m
1 **milli**gram = **0.001** gram	or	1 mg = 0.001 g
1 **milli**liter = **0.001** liter	or	1 mL = 0.001 L

SAMPLE PROBLEM 1.2 TRANSLATING A MEASUREMENT INTO A METRIC UNIT

What term is used for each of the following units: (a) a thousand seconds; (b) a millionth of a gram?

Analysis

Use Table 1.2 to determine the prefix, and add the prefix before the base unit.

Solution

a. The prefix *kilo-* means 1,000 times as large, so 1,000 seconds = 1 kilosecond.

b. The prefix *micro-* means one-millionth as large (0.000 001), so 0.000 001 gram = 1 microgram.

PRACTICE PROBLEM 1.2

What term is used for each of the following units: (a) a million liters; (b) a thousandth of a second; (c) a hundredth of a gram; (d) a tenth of a liter?

More Practice: Try Problem 1.8.

1.4B   Measuring Length

©Chuck Savage/Corbis/Getty Images

The base unit of length in the metric system is the *meter* (m). A meter, 39.4 inches in the English system, is slightly longer than a yard (36 inches). The three most common units derived from a meter are the kilometer (km), centimeter (cm), and millimeter (mm).

$$1,000 \ m = 1 \ km$$
$$1 \ m = 100 \ cm$$
$$1 \ m = 1,000 \ mm$$

Note how these values are related to those in Table 1.2. Since a centimeter is one *hundredth* of a meter (0.01 m), there are *100* centimeters in a meter.

PROBLEM 1.7

If a nanometer is one-billionth of a meter (0.000 000 001 m), how many nanometers are there in one meter?

1.4C Measuring Mass

Although the terms mass and weight are often used interchangeably, they really have different meanings.

- *Mass* is a measure of the amount of matter in an object.
- *Weight* is the force that matter feels due to gravity.

The mass of an object is independent of its location. The weight of an object changes slightly with its location on the earth, and drastically when the object is moved from the earth to the moon, where the gravitational pull is only one-sixth that of the earth. Although we often speak of *weighing* an object, we are really *measuring its mass.*

The base unit of mass in the metric system is the *gram* **(g),** a small quantity compared to the English pound (1 lb = 454 g). The two most common units derived from a gram are the kilogram (kg) and milligram (mg).

$$1,000 \text{ g} = 1 \text{ kg}$$
$$1 \text{ g} = 1,000 \text{ mg}$$

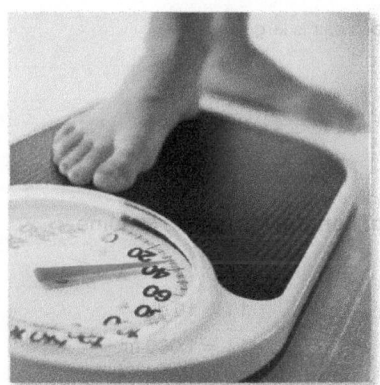
©PhotoDisc/Getty Images RF

PROBLEM 1.8

What term is used for each quantity? (For example, 0.001 g = one milligram.)

a. 0.000 001 g   c. 0.000 000 001 s

b. 1,000,000,000 m   d. 0.01 g

1.4D Measuring Volume

Note the difference between the units **cm** and **cm³.** The centimeter (cm) is a unit of length. A cubic centimeter (cm³ or cc) is a unit of volume.

The base unit of volume in the metric system is the *liter* **(L),** which is slightly larger than the English quart (1 L = 1.06 qt). One liter is defined as the volume of a cube 10 cm on an edge.

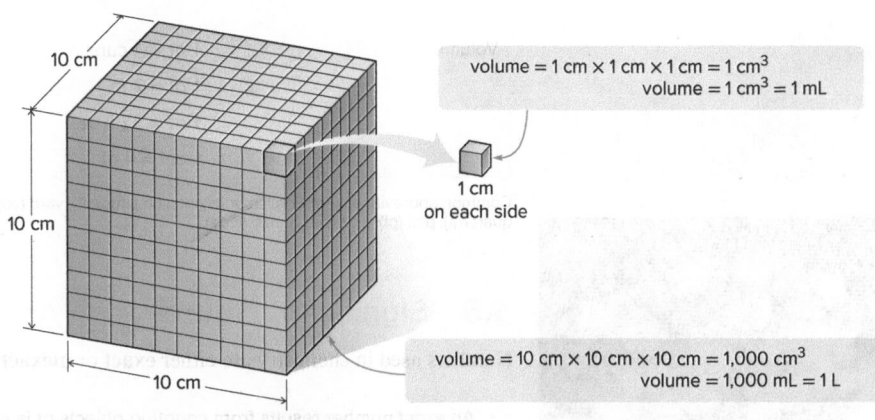

Three common units derived from a liter used in medicine and laboratory research are the deciliter (dL), milliliter (mL), and microliter (μL). **One milliliter is the same as one cubic centimeter (cm³), which is abbreviated as cc.**

©Steve Cole, Vetta/Getty Images RF

$$1 \text{ L} = 10 \text{ dL}$$
$$1 \text{ L} = 1,000 \text{ mL}$$
$$1 \text{ L} = 1,000,000 \text{ μL}$$
$$1 \text{ mL} = 1 \text{ cm}^3 = 1 \text{ cc}$$

Table 1.3 summarizes common metric units of length, mass, and volume. Table 1.4 lists English units of measurement, as well as their metric equivalents.

PROBLEM 1.9

Using the prefixes in Table 1.2, determine which quantity in each pair is larger.

a. 3 mL or 3 cL   c. 5 km or 5 cm
b. 1 ng or 1 µg   d. 2 mL or 2 µL

Table 1.3 Summary of the Common Metric Units of Length, Mass, and Volume

Length	Mass	Volume
1 km = 1,000 m	1 kg = 1,000 g	1 L = 10 dL
1 m = 100 cm	1 g = 1,000 mg	1 L = 1,000 mL
1 m = 1,000 mm	1 mg = 1,000 µg	1 L = 1,000,000 µL
1 cm = 10 mm		1 dL = 100 mL
		1 mL = 1 cm^3 = 1 cc

Table 1.4 English Units and Their Metric Equivalents

Quantity	English Unit	Metric–English Relationship
Length	1 ft = 12 in.	2.54 cm = 1 in.
	1 yd = 3 ft	1 m = 39.4 in.
	1 mi = 5,280 ft	1 km = 0.621 mi
Mass	1 lb = 16 oz	1 kg = 2.20 lb
	1 ton = 2,000 lb	454 g = 1 lb
		28.3 g = 1 oz
Volume	1 qt = 4 cups	946 mL = 1 qt
	1 qt = 2 pt	1 L = 1.06 qt
	1 qt = 32 fl oz	29.6 mL = 1 fl oz
	1 gal = 4 qt	

Common abbreviations for English units: inch (in.), foot (ft), yard (yd), mile (mi), pound (lb), ounce (oz), gallon (gal), quart (qt), pint (pt), and fluid ounce (fl oz).

1.5   Significant Figures

Numbers used in chemistry are either **exact** or **inexact.**

- An *exact* number results from counting objects or is part of a definition.

Our bodies have 10 fingers, 10 toes, and two kidneys. A meter is composed of 100 centimeters. These numbers are exact because there is no uncertainty associated with them.

- An *inexact* number results from a measurement or observation and contains some uncertainty.

Whenever we measure a quantity there is a degree of uncertainty associated with the result. The last number (farthest to the right) is an estimate, and it depends on the type of measuring device

A container of 71 macadamia nuts weighs 125 g. The number of nuts (71) is exact, whereas the mass of the nuts (125 g) is inexact. ©*Zachary D.-K. Smith*

we use to obtain it. For example, the length of a fish caught on a recent outing could be reported as 53 cm or 53.5 cm depending on the tape measure used.

©Daniel C. Smith

- **Significant figures** are all the digits in a measured number including *one* estimated digit.

Thus, the length 53 cm has two significant figures, and the length 53.5 cm has three significant figures.

1.5A Determining the Number of Significant Figures

How many significant figures are contained in a number?

- **All nonzero digits are always significant.**

65.2 g	three significant figures
1,265 m	four significant figures
25 µL	two significant figures
255.345 g	six significant figures

Whether a zero counts as a significant figure depends on its location in the number.

Rules to Determine When a Zero Is a Significant Figure

Rule [1] A zero *counts* as a significant figure when it occurs:

- Between two nonzero digits
  - 29.05 g—four significant figures
  - 1.0087 mL—five significant figures
- At the end of a number with a decimal point
  - 25.70 cm—four significant figures
  - 3.7500 g—five significant figures
  - 620. lb—three significant figures

Rule [2] A zero does *not* count as a significant figure when it occurs:

- At the beginning of a number
  - 0.0245 mg—three significant figures
  - 0.008 mL—one significant figure
- At the end of a number that does *not* have a decimal point
  - 2,570 m—three significant figures
  - 1,245,500 m—five significant figures

In reading a number with a decimal point from left to right, all digits starting with the first nonzero number are significant figures. The number 0.003 450 120 has seven significant figures, shown in red.

SAMPLE PROBLEM 1.3 DETERMINING THE NUMBER OF SIGNIFICANT FIGURES

How many significant figures does each number contain?

a. 34.08   b. 0.0054   c. 260.00   d. 260

Analysis

All nonzero digits are significant. A zero is significant when it occurs between two nonzero digits, or at the end of a number with a decimal point.

Solution

Significant figures are shown in red.

a. 34.08 (four)   b. 0.0054 (two)   c. 260.00 (five)   d. 260 (two)

PRACTICE PROBLEM 1.3

How many significant figures does each number contain?

a. 23.45   c. 230   e. 0.202   g. 1,245,006   i. 10,040
b. 23.057   d. 231.0   f. 0.003 60   h. 1,200,000   j. 10,040.

More Practice: Try Problems 1.35, 1.36.

PROBLEM 1.10

Indicate whether each zero in the following numbers is significant.

a. 0.003 04   b. 26,045   c. 1,000,034   d. 0.304 00

1.5B   Using Significant Figures in Multiplication and Division

We often must perform calculations with numbers that contain a different number of significant figures. The number of significant figures in the answer of a problem depends on the type of mathematical calculation—multiplication (and division) or addition (and subtraction).

> • In multiplication and division, the answer has the same number of significant figures as the original number with the *fewest* significant figures.

Let's say you drove a car 351.2 miles in 5.5 hours, and you wanted to calculate how many miles per hour you traveled. Entering these numbers on a calculator would give the following result:

four significant figures

$$\text{Miles per hour} = \frac{351.2 \text{ miles}}{5.5 \text{ hours}} = 63.854\,545 \text{ miles per hour}$$

two significant figures

The answer must contain only two significant figures.

The answer to this problem can have only *two* significant figures, because one of the original numbers (5.5 hours) has only *two* significant figures. To write the answer in proper form, we must **round off the number** to give an answer with only two significant figures. Two rules are used in rounding off numbers.

> • If the first number that must be dropped is 4 or fewer, drop it and all remaining numbers.
> • If the first number that must be dropped is 5 or greater, *round the number up* by adding one to the last digit that will be retained.

In this problem:

These digits must be retained.

first digit to be dropped

63.854 545

These digits must be dropped.

> • Since the first digit to be dropped is 8 (5 or greater), add 1 to the digit to its left.
> • The answer 63.854 545 rounded to two digits is **64 miles per hour.**

Table 1.5 Rounding Off Numbers

Original Number	Rounded To	Rounded Number
61.2537	Two places	61
61.2537	Three places	61.3
61.2537	Four places	61.25
61.2537	Five places	61.254

The first number to be dropped is indicated in red in each original number. When this number is 4 or fewer, it and all other digits to its right are dropped. When this number is 5 or greater, 1 is added to the digit to its left.

Table 1.5 gives other examples of rounding off numbers.

When a calculator is used in calculations, sometimes the display shows more digits than are significant and sometimes it shows fewer digits. For example, in multiplying 23.2 by 1.1, the calculator displays the answer as 25.52. Since the quantity 1.1 has only two significant figures, the answer must contain only two significant figures and be rounded to 26.

$$23.2 \quad \times \quad 1.1 \quad = \quad 25.52 \quad \xrightarrow{\text{round off}} \quad 26$$

three significant figures $\quad$ two significant figures $\quad$ calculator display $\quad\quad\quad$ two significant figures

Answer

In contrast, dividing 25.0 by 0.50 displays the answer as 50, a quantity with only one significant figure. Since 0.50 has two significant figures, the answer must contain two significant figures, and this is achieved by adding a decimal point (50.).

$$25.0 \quad \times \quad 0.50 \quad = \quad 50 \quad \xrightarrow{\text{add decimal}} \quad 50.$$

three significant figures $\quad$ two significant figures $\quad$ calculator display $\quad\quad\quad$ two significant figures

Answer

SAMPLE PROBLEM 1.4 ROUNDING OFF NUMBERS

Round off each number to three significant figures.

a. 1.2735   b. 0.002 536 22   c. 3,836.9

Analysis

If the answer is to have *three* significant figures, look at the *fourth* number from the left. If this number is 4 or fewer, drop it and all remaining numbers to the right. If the fourth number from the left is 5 or greater, round the number up by adding one to the third digit.

Solution

a. 1.27   b. 0.002 54   c. 3,840 (Omit the decimal point after the 0. The number 3,840. has four significant figures.)

PRACTICE PROBLEM 1.4

Round off each number in Sample Problem 1.4 to two significant figures.

More Practice: Try Problems 1.37, 1.38.

SAMPLE PROBLEM 1.5 DETERMINING SIGNIFICANT FIGURES IN MULTIPLICATION AND DIVISION

Carry out each calculation and give the answer using the proper number of significant figures.

a. 3.81 × 0.046   b. 120.085 ÷ 106

Analysis

Since these calculations involve multiplication and division, the answer must have the same number of significant figures as the original number with the fewer number of significant figures.

Solution

a. 3.81 × 0.046 = 0.1753

• Since 0.046 has only two significant figures, round the answer to give it two significant figures.

0.1753   Since this number is 5 (5 or greater), round the 7 to its left up by one.

Answer: 0.18

b. $120.085 \div 106 = 1.132\,877\,36$

• Since 106 has three significant figures, round the answer to give it three significant figures.

1.132 877 36   Since this number is 2 (4 or fewer), drop it and all numbers to its right.

Answer: 1.13

PRACTICE PROBLEM 1.5

Carry out each calculation and give the answer using the proper number of significant figures.

  a. 10.70×3.5 b. $0.206 \div 25{,}993$ c. $1{,}300 \div 41.2$ d. 120.5×26

More Practice: Try Problems 1.39a, c, e; 1.40a, c, e.

1.5C   Using Significant Figures in Addition and Subtraction

In determining significant figures in addition and subtraction, the decimal place of the last significant digit determines the number of significant figures in the answer.

> • In addition and subtraction, the answer has the same number of decimal places as the original number with the *fewest* decimal places.

Suppose a baby weighed 3.6 kg at birth and 10.11 kg on his first birthday. To figure out how much weight the baby gained in his first year of life, we subtract these two numbers and report the answer using the proper number of significant figures.

weight at one year = 10.11 kg

weight at birth = 3.6 kg

weight gain = 6.51 kg

10.11 kg   two digits after the decimal point

− 3.6 kg   one digit after the decimal point

last significant digit

> • The answer can have only one digit after the decimal point.
> • Round 6.51 to 6.5.
> • The baby gained 6.5 kg during his first year of life.

Since 3.6 kg has only one significant figure after the decimal point, the answer can have only one significant figure after the decimal point as well.

SAMPLE PROBLEM 1.6 DETERMINING SIGNIFICANT FIGURES IN ADDITION AND SUBTRACTION

While on a diet, a woman lost 3.52 lb the first week, 2.2 lb the second week, and 0.59 lb the third week. How much weight did she lose in all?

Analysis

Add up the amount of weight loss each week to get the total weight loss. When adding, the answer has the same number of decimal places as the original number with the fewest decimal places.

Solution

3.52 lb

2.2 lb   one digit after the decimal point

0.59 lb

6.31 lb   - - - - → 6.3 lb

round off

last significant digit

• Since 2.2 lb has only one digit after the decimal point, the answer can have only one digit after the decimal point.

• Round 6.31 to 6.3.

• Total weight loss: 6.3 lb.

PRACTICE PROBLEM 1.6

Carry out each calculation and give the answer using the proper number of significant figures.

a. 27.8 cm + 0.246 cm

b. 102.66 mL + 0.857 mL + 24.0 mL

c. 54.6 mg − 25 mg

d. 2.35 s − 0.266 s

More Practice: Try Problems 1.39b, d, f; 1.40b, d, f.

1.6 Scientific Notation

Healthcare professionals and scientists must often deal with very large and very small numbers. For example, the blood platelet count of a healthy adult might be 250,000 platelets per mL. At the other extreme, the level of the female sex hormone estriol during pregnancy might be 0.000 000 250 g per mL of blood plasma. Estriol is secreted by the placenta and its concentration is used as a measure of the health of the fetus.

To write numbers that contain many leading zeros (at the beginning) or trailing zeros (at the end), scientists use **scientific notation.**

- In scientific notation, a number is written as $y \times 10^x$.
- The term y, called the coefficient, is a number between 1 and 10.
- The value x is an exponent, which can be any positive or negative whole number.

First, let's recall what powers of 10 with *positive* exponents, such as 10^2 or 10^5, mean. These correspond to numbers greater than one, and the positive exponent tells how many zeros are to be written after the number one. Thus, $10^2 = 100$, a number with two zeros after the number one.

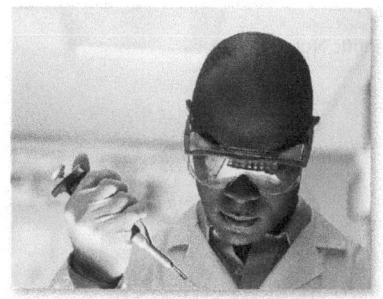

Hospital laboratory technicians determine thousands of laboratory results each day. ©Stockbyte/Getty Images RF

The product has two zeros.

$$10^2 = 10 \times 10 = 100$$

The exponent 2 means "multiply two 10s."

The product has five zeros.

$$10^5 = 10 \times 10 \times 10 \times 10 \times 10 = 100,000$$

The exponent 5 means "multiply five 10s."

Powers of 10 that contain *negative* exponents, such as 10^{-3}, correspond to numbers less than one. In this case the exponent tells how many places (*not* zeros) are located to the right of the decimal point.

The answer has three places to the right of the decimal point, including the number one.

$$10^{-3} = \frac{1}{10 \times 10 \times 10} = 0.001$$

The exponent −3 means "divide by three 10s."

To write a number in scientific notation, we follow a stepwise procedure.

How To Convert a Standard Number to Scientific Notation

Example: Write each number in scientific notation: (a) 2,500; (b) 0.036.

Step [1] Move the decimal point to give a number between 1 and 10.

a. 2500.

Move the decimal point three places to the left to give the number 2.5.

b. 0.036

Move the decimal point two places to the right to give the number 3.6.

—Continued

How To, continued . . .

Step [2]   **Multiply the result by 10^x, where x is the number of places the decimal point was moved.**

- If the decimal point is moved to the **left,** x is **positive.**
- If the decimal point is moved to the **right,** x is **negative.**

a. Since the decimal point was moved three places to the **left,** the exponent is +3, and the coefficient is multiplied by 10^3.

   Answer: 2,500 = 2.5 × 10^3

b. Since the decimal point was moved two places to the **right,** the exponent is −2, and the coefficient is multiplied by 10^{-2}.

   Answer: 0.036 = 3.6 × 10^{-2}

Notice that the number of significant figures in the coefficient in scientific notation must equal the number of significant figures in the original number. Thus, the coefficients for both 2,500 and 0.036 need two significant figures and no more. Figure 1.7 shows two more examples of numbers written in standard form and scientific notation.

$$2,500 = 2.5 \times 10^3 \quad \textit{not} \quad 2.50 \times 10^3 \text{ (three significant figures)}$$
$$\textit{not} \quad 2.500 \times 10^3 \text{ (four significant figures)}$$

two significant figures

Figure 1.7   Numbers in Standard Form and Scientific Notation

The human body contains 2 × 10^{13} red blood cells.

A single red blood cell has a diameter of 6 × 10^{-6} m.

©Creative Studios/Alamy RF

Very large and very small numbers are more conveniently written in scientific notation.

Quantity	Number	Scientific Notation
Number of red blood cells	20,000,000,000,000	2 × 10^{13}
Diameter of a red blood cell	0.000 006 m	6 × 10^{-6} m

SAMPLE PROBLEM 1.7 WRITING A NUMBER IN SCIENTIFIC NOTATION

Write the recommended daily dietary intake of each nutrient in scientific notation: (a) sodium, 2,400 mg; (b) vitamin B$_{12}$, 0.000 006 g.

Analysis

Move the decimal point to give a number between 1 and 10. Multiply the number by 10^x, where x is the number of places the decimal point was moved. The exponent x is (+) when the decimal point moves to the left and (−) when it moves to the right.

Solution

a.

$$2400 = 2.4 \times 10^3$$

the number of places the decimal point was moved to the left

Move the decimal point three places to the left.

- Write the coefficient as 2.4 (two significant figures), because 2,400 contains two significant figures.

b.

$$0.000\,006 = 6 \times 10^{-6}$$

the number of places the decimal point was moved to the right

Move the decimal point six places to the right.

- Write the coefficient as 6 (one significant figure), because 0.000 006 contains one significant figure.

PRACTICE PROBLEM 1.7

Write each number in scientific notation.

a. 93,200
b. 0.000 725
c. 6,780,000
d. 0.000 030
e. 4,520,000,000,000
f. 0.000 000 000 028

More Practice: Try Problems 1.41, 1.42, 1.47.

PROBLEM 1.11

Lab results for a routine check-up showed an individual's iron level in the blood to be 0.000 098 g per deciliter, placing it in the normal range. Convert this number to scientific notation.

To convert a number in scientific notation to a standard number, reverse the procedure, as shown in Sample Problem 1.8. It is often necessary to add leading or trailing zeros to write the number.

- When the exponent x is positive, move the decimal point x places to the *right*.

$$2.800 \times 10^2 \qquad 2,800 \quad ---\rightarrow \quad 280.0$$

Move the decimal point to the right two places.

- When the exponent x is negative, move the decimal point x places to the *left*.

$$2.80 \times 10^{-2} \qquad 002,80 \quad ---\rightarrow \quad 0.0280$$

Move the decimal point to the left two places.

SAMPLE PROBLEM 1.8 CONVERTING A NUMBER IN SCIENTIFIC NOTATION TO A STANDARD NUMBER

The average diameter of a human hair is about 1.2×10^{-4} m. Convert this value to a standard number.

Analysis

The exponent in 10^x tells how many places to move the decimal point in the coefficient to generate a standard number. The decimal point goes to the *right* when x is positive and to the *left* when x is negative.

Solution

$$1.21 \times 10^{-4} \qquad 000\,01,2 \quad ---\rightarrow \quad 0.000\,12 \text{ m}$$

Move the decimal point to the *left* four places.

Answer

The answer, 0.000 12, has two significant figures, just like 1.2×10^{-4}.

Anatomy of a hair

Hair is a protein that grows from follicles in the skin. We will learn more about the proteins in hair in Section 21.7.

hair shaft

skin surface

hair follicle

PRACTICE PROBLEM 1.8

Convert each number to its standard form.

a. 6.5×10^3 c. 3.780×10^{-2} e. 2.221×10^6

b. 3.26×10^{-5} d. 1.04×10^8 f. 4.5×10^{-10}

More Practice: Try Problems 1.43, 1.44.

1.7   Problem Solving Using Conversion Factors

Often a measurement is recorded in one unit, and then it must be converted to another unit. For example, a patient may weigh 130 lb, but we may need to know her weight in kilograms to calculate a drug dosage. The recommended daily dietary intake of potassium is 3,500 mg, but we may need to know how many grams this corresponds to.

1.7A   Conversion Factors

To convert one unit to another we use one or more **conversion factors.**

These two quantities are equivalent.
Only the units are different.

• A *conversion factor* is a term that converts a quantity in one unit to a quantity in another unit.

A conversion factor is formed by taking an equality, such as 2.20 lb = 1 kg, and writing it as a ratio. We can always write a conversion factor in two different ways.

$$\frac{2.20\ lb}{1\ kg} \quad or \quad \frac{1\ kg}{2.20\ lb} \quad \begin{array}{l}numerator \\ \\ denominator\end{array}$$

conversion factors for pounds and kilograms

Refer to Tables 1.3 and 1.4 for metric and English units needed in problem solving. Common metric and English units are also listed on the inside back cover.

With pounds and kilograms, either of these values can be written above the division line of the fraction (the **numerator**) or below the division line (the **denominator**). The way the conversion factor is written will depend on the problem.

SAMPLE PROBLEM 1.9 WRITING CONVERSION FACTORS FOR A PAIR OF UNITS

Write two conversion factors for each pair of units: (a) kilograms and grams; (b) quarts and liters.

Analysis

Use the equalities in Tables 1.3 and 1.4 to write a ratio that shows the relationship between the two units.

Solution

a. Conversion factors for kilograms and grams:

$$\frac{1000\ g}{1\ kg} \quad or \quad \frac{1\ kg}{1000\ g}$$

b. Conversion factors for quarts and liters:

$$\frac{1.06\ qt}{1\ L} \quad or \quad \frac{1\ L}{1.06\ qt}$$

PRACTICE PROBLEM 1.9

Write two conversion factors for each pair of units.

a. miles and kilometers   c. grams and pounds

b. meters and millimeters   d. milligrams and micrograms

1.7B   Solving a Problem Using One Conversion Factor

When using conversion factors to solve a problem, if a unit appears in the numerator in one term and the denominator in another term, the units *cancel*. **The goal in setting up a problem is to make sure *all unwanted units cancel*.**

Let's say we want to convert 130 lb to kilograms.

$$130 \text{ lb} \quad \times \quad \boxed{\text{conversion factor}} \quad = \quad ? \text{ kg}$$
$$\text{original quantity} \qquad\qquad\qquad\qquad\quad \text{desired quantity}$$

Two possible conversion factors: $\dfrac{2.20 \text{ lb}}{1 \text{ kg}}$ or $\dfrac{1 \text{ kg}}{2.20 \text{ lb}}$

To solve this problem we must use a conversion factor that satisfies two criteria.

- The conversion factor must contain the two quantities in question—pounds and kilograms.
- The conversion factor must cancel out the unwanted unit—pounds.

This means choosing the conversion factor with the unwanted unit—pounds—*in the denominator* to cancel out pounds in the original quantity. This leaves kilograms as the only remaining unit, and the problem is solved.

$$\boxed{\text{conversion factor}}$$
$$130 \text{ lb} \quad \times \quad \frac{1 \text{ kg}}{2.20 \text{ lb}} \quad = \quad \boxed{59 \text{ kg}} \quad \textbf{answer in kilograms}$$

Pounds (lb) must be the denominator to cancel the unwanted unit (lb) in the original quantity.

We must use the correct number of significant figures in reporting an answer to each problem. In this case, the value 1 kg is *defined* as 2.20 lb; in other words, 1 kg contains the exact number "1" with *no* uncertainty, so it does not limit the number of digits in the answer. Since 130 lb has two significant figures, the answer is rounded to two significant figures (59 kg).

As problems with units get more complicated, keep in mind the following general steps that are useful for solving any problem using conversion factors.

How many grams of aspirin are contained in a 325-mg tablet? ©McGraw-Hill Education/ Mark Dierker, photographer

---

How To Solve a Problem Using Conversion Factors

Example: How many grams of aspirin are contained in a 325-mg tablet?

Step [1] Identify the original quantity and the desired quantity, including units.

- In this problem the original quantity is reported in milligrams and the desired quantity is in grams.

$$325 \text{ mg} \qquad\qquad\qquad\qquad ? \text{ g}$$
$$\text{original quantity} \qquad\qquad\qquad \text{desired quantity}$$

Step [2] Write out the conversion factor(s) needed to solve the problem.

- We need a conversion factor that relates milligrams and grams (Table 1.3). Since the unwanted unit is in milligrams, **choose the conversion factor that contains milligrams in the denominator so that the *units cancel*.**

Two possible conversion factors: $\dfrac{1000 \text{ mg}}{1 \text{ g}}$ or $\boxed{\dfrac{1 \text{ g}}{1000 \text{ mg}}}$ — Choose this factor to cancel the unwanted unit, mg.

- Sometimes one conversion factor is all that is needed in a problem. At other times (Section 1.7C) more than one conversion factor is needed.
- If the desired answer has a single unit (grams in this case), **the conversion factor must contain the desired unit in the numerator and the unwanted unit in the denominator.**

—Continued

How To, continued . . .

Step [3] **Set up and solve the problem.**
- Multiply the original quantity by the conversion factor to obtain the desired quantity.

conversion factor

$$325 \ \text{mg} \quad \times \quad \frac{1 \ \text{g}}{1000 \ \text{mg}} \quad = \quad 0.325 \ \text{g of aspirin}$$

original quantity   desired quantity

The number of mg (unwanted unit) cancels.

Step [4] **Write the answer using the correct number of significant figures and check it by estimation.**
- Use the number of significant figures in each inexact (measured) number to determine the number of significant figures in the answer. In this case the answer is limited to three significant figures by the original quantity (325 mg).
- Estimate the answer using a variety of methods. In this case we knew our answer had to be less than one, because it is obtained by dividing 325 by a number larger than itself.

ENVIRONMENTAL NOTE

As we will learn in Chapter 13, PET, the plastic used in water bottles, can be recycled into bags, containers, fleece jackets, and carpeting. ©*Angela Hampton Picture Library/Alamy*

SAMPLE PROBLEM 1.10 SOLVING A PROBLEM USING CONVERSION FACTORS

If 1.65×10^9 lb of PET (polyethylene terephthalate), the plastic used in water and soft drink bottles, is recycled in a year, how many kilograms of PET does this represent?

Analysis and Solution

[1] Identify the original quantity and the desired quantity.

1.65×10^9 lb   ? kg

original quantity   desired quantity

[2] Write out the conversion factors.
- We need a conversion factor that relates pounds and kilograms (Table 1.3). Choose the conversion factor that places pounds in the denominator, so that the units cancel.

$$\frac{2.20 \ \text{lb}}{1 \ \text{kg}} \quad \text{or} \quad \boxed{\frac{1 \ \text{kg}}{2.20 \ \text{lb}}} \quad \text{Choose this factor to cancel the unwanted unit, lb.}$$

[3] Solve the problem.
- Multiply the original quantity by the conversion factor to obtain the desired quantity. Set up the problem, so that the unwanted unit, pounds, cancels.

conversion factor

$$1.65 \times 10^9 \ \text{lb} \quad \times \quad \frac{1 \ \text{kg}}{2.20 \ \text{lb}} \quad = \quad 7.50 \times 10^8 \ \text{kg of PET}$$

The number of lb (unwanted unit) cancels.

PRACTICE PROBLEM 1.10

Carry out each of the following conversions.
   a. 25 L to dL   b. 40.0 oz to g   c. 32 in. to cm   d. 10 cm to mm

More Practice: Try Problems 1.49–1.51, 1.54, 1.55a, 1.56a, 1.57.

PROBLEM 1.12

On a flight from Bangkok, Thailand, to Taipei, Taiwan, flight data showed the plane's altitude was 11,277 m when the plane was 1,813 km from its destination. (a) Convert the altitude from meters to kilometers. (b) Convert the distance to travel from kilometers to miles.

PROBLEM 1.13

(a) What is the volume of liquid contained in the given 0.5-mL syringe? (b) Convert this value to microliters.

1.7C   Solving a Problem Using Two or More Conversion Factors

Some problems require the use of more than one conversion factor to obtain the desired units in the answer. The same stepwise procedure is followed no matter how many conversion factors are needed. Keep in mind:

- **Always arrange the factors so that the denominator in one term cancels the numerator in the preceding term.**

Sample Problem 1.11 illustrates how to solve a problem with two conversion factors.

SAMPLE PROBLEM 1.11 SOLVING A PROBLEM USING MORE THAN ONE CONVERSION FACTOR

An individual donated 1.0 pt of blood at the local blood bank. How many liters of blood does this correspond to?

Analysis and Solution

[1] Identify the original quantity and the desired quantity.

$$1.0 \text{ pt} \qquad\qquad ? \text{ L}$$
original quantity   desired quantity

[2] Write out the conversion factors.

- We have no conversion factor that relates pints to liters directly. We do, however, know conversions for pints to quarts, and quarts to liters.

pint–quart conversion

$$\frac{2 \text{ pt}}{1 \text{ qt}} \quad \text{or} \quad \boxed{\frac{1 \text{ qt}}{2 \text{ pt}}}$$

quart–liter conversion

$$\frac{1.06 \text{ qt}}{1 \text{ L}} \quad \text{or} \quad \boxed{\frac{1 \text{ L}}{1.06 \text{ qt}}}$$

Choose the conversion factors with the unwanted units—pt and qt—in the denominator.

[3] Solve the problem.

- To set up the problem so that unwanted units cancel, arrange each term so that the units in the numerator of one term cancel the units in the denominator of the adjacent term. In this problem we need to cancel both pints and quarts to get liters.
- The single desired unit, liters, must be in the **numerator** of one term.

Liters do not cancel.

$$1.0 \text{ pt} \times \frac{1 \text{ qt}}{2 \text{ pt}} \times \frac{1 \text{ L}}{1.06 \text{ qt}} = 0.47 \text{ L}$$

Pints cancel.   Quarts cancel.

[4] Check.

- Since there are two pints in a quart and a quart is about the same size as a liter, one pint should be about half a liter. The answer, 0.47, is just about 0.5.
- Write the answer with two significant figures because one term, 1.0 pt, has two significant figures.

PRACTICE PROBLEM 1.11

Carry out each of the following conversions.

  a. 6,250 ft to km   b. 3 cups to L   c. 4.5 ft to cm

More Practice: Try Problems 1.53, 1.55b, 1.56b, 1.58, 1.74, 1.76–1.78, 1.80, 1.81.

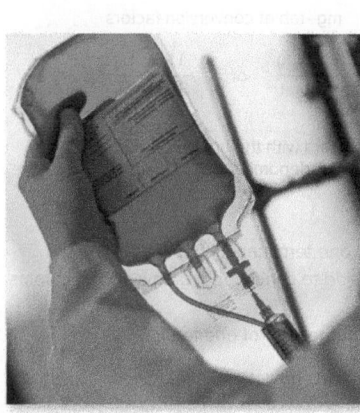

How many liters of blood does this pint of blood contain? ©Keith Brofsky/Getty Images RF

1.8 FOCUS ON HEALTH & MEDICINE
Problem Solving Using Clinical Conversion Factors

The active ingredient in Children's Tylenol is acetaminophen. ©McGraw-Hill Education/Jill Braaten, photographer

Sometimes conversion factors don't have to be looked up in a table; they are stated in the problem. If a drug is sold as a 250-mg tablet, this fact becomes a conversion factor relating milligrams to tablets.

$$\frac{250 \text{ mg}}{1 \text{ tablet}} \quad \text{or} \quad \frac{1 \text{ tablet}}{250 \text{ mg}}$$

mg–tablet conversion factors

Alternatively, a drug could be sold as a liquid solution with a specific concentration. For example, Children's Tylenol contains 80 mg of the active ingredient acetaminophen in 2.5 mL. This fact becomes a conversion factor relating milligrams to milliliters.

$$\frac{80 \text{ mg}}{2.5 \text{ mL}} \quad \text{or} \quad \frac{2.5 \text{ mL}}{80 \text{ mg}}$$

mg of acetaminophen–mL conversion factors

Sample Problems 1.12 and 1.13 illustrate how these conversion factors are used in determining drug dosages.

SAMPLE PROBLEM 1.12 USING CLINICAL CONVERSION FACTORS TO SOLVE A PROBLEM

A patient is prescribed 1.25 g of amoxicillin, which is available in 250-mg tablets. How many tablets are needed?

Analysis and Solution

[1] Identify the original quantity and the desired quantity.

- We must convert the number of grams of amoxicillin needed to the number of tablets that must be administered.

$$\underset{\text{original quantity}}{1.25 \text{ g}} \qquad \underset{\text{desired quantity}}{? \text{ tablets}}$$

[2] Write out the conversion factors.

- We have no conversion factor that relates grams to tablets directly. We do know, however, how to relate grams to milligrams, and milligrams to tablets.

g–mg conversion factors

$$\frac{1 \text{ g}}{1000 \text{ mg}} \quad \text{or} \quad \boxed{\frac{1000 \text{ mg}}{1 \text{ g}}}$$

mg–tablet conversion factors

$$\frac{250 \text{ mg}}{1 \text{ tablet}} \quad \text{or} \quad \boxed{\frac{1 \text{ tablet}}{250 \text{ mg}}}$$

Choose the conversion factors with the unwanted units–g and mg–in the denominator.

[3] Solve the problem.

- Arrange each term so that the units in the numerator of one term cancel the units in the denominator of the adjacent term. In this problem we need to cancel both grams and milligrams to get tablets.
- The single desired unit, tablets, must be located in the **numerator** of one term.

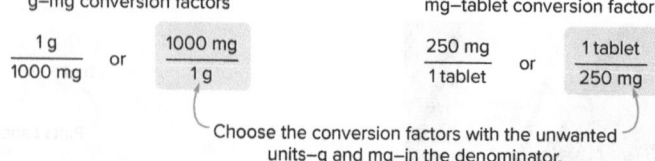

$$1.25 \text{ g} \times \frac{1000 \text{ mg}}{1 \text{ g}} \times \frac{1 \text{ tablet}}{250 \text{ mg}} = 5 \text{ tablets}$$

Grams cancel.   Milligrams cancel.   Tablets do not cancel.

[4] Check.

- The answer of 5 tablets of amoxicillin (not 0.5 or 50) is reasonable. Since the dose in a single tablet (250 mg) is a fraction of a gram, and the required dose is more than a gram, the answer must be greater than one.

PRACTICE PROBLEM 1.12

A patient is prescribed 0.100 mg of a drug that is available in 25-µg tablets. How many tablets are needed?

More Practice: Try Problem 1.83.

SAMPLE PROBLEM 1.13   USING A CLINICAL CONVERSION FACTOR TO SOLVE A PROBLEM

A dose of 240 mg of acetaminophen is prescribed for a 20-kg child. How many mL of Children's Tylenol (80. mg of acetaminophen per 2.5 mL) are needed?

Analysis and Solution

[1] Identify the original quantity and the desired quantity.

- We must convert the number of milligrams of acetaminophen needed to the number of mL that must be administered.

<table>
<tr><td>240 mg</td><td>? mL</td></tr>
<tr><td>original quantity</td><td>desired quantity</td></tr>
</table>

[2] Write out the conversion factors.

mg of acetaminophen–mL conversion factors

$$\frac{80.\ mg}{2.5\ mL} \quad or \quad \frac{2.5\ mL}{80.\ mg}$$

Choose the conversion factor to cancel mg.

[3] Solve the problem.

- Arrange the terms so that the units in the numerator of one term cancel the units of the denominator of the adjacent term. In this problem we need to cancel milligrams to obtain milliliters.
- In this problem we are given a fact we don't need to use—the child weighs 20 kg. We can ignore this quantity in carrying out the calculation.

$$240\ mg \quad \times \quad \frac{2.5\ mL}{80.\ mg} \quad = \quad 7.5\ mL\ of\ Children's\ Tylenol$$

Milligrams cancel.

[4] Check.

- The answer of 7.5 mL (not 0.75 or 75) is reasonable. Because the required dose is larger than the dose in 2.5 mL, the answer must be larger than 2.5 mL.

PRACTICE PROBLEM 1.13

(a) How many milliliters are contained in the dose of Children's Tylenol shown in the adjacent photo (1 teaspoon = 5 mL)? (b) If Children's Tylenol contains 80. mg of acetaminophen per 2.5 mL, how much acetaminophen (in mg) is contained in the dose?

More Practice: Try Problems 1.52, 1.73, 1.75, 1.79, 1.82, 1.84.

PROBLEM 1.14

How many milliliters of Children's Motrin (100 mg of ibuprofen per 5 mL) are needed to give a child a dose of 160 mg?

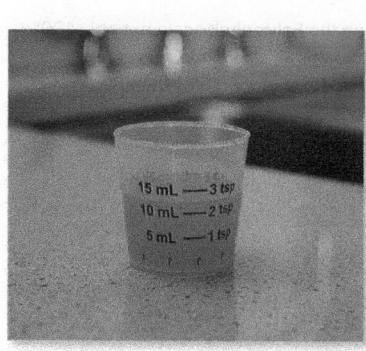

©McGraw-Hill Education/Mark Dierker, photographer

1.9 Temperature

Temperature **is a measure of how hot or cold an object is.** Three temperature scales are used: **Fahrenheit** (most common in the United States), **Celsius** (most commonly used by scientists and countries other than the United States), and **Kelvin** (Figure 1.8).

The Fahrenheit and Celsius scales are both divided into **degrees.** On the Fahrenheit scale, water freezes at 32 °F and boils at 212 °F. On the Celsius scale, water freezes at 0 °C and boils at 100 °C. To convert temperature values from one scale to another, we use two equations, where T_C is the Celsius temperature and T_F is the Fahrenheit temperature.

To convert from Celsius to Fahrenheit:

$$T_F = 1.8(T_C) + 32$$

To convert from Fahrenheit to Celsius:

$$T_C = \frac{T_F - 32}{1.8}$$

The Kelvin scale is divided into **kelvins** (K), not degrees. The only difference between the Kelvin scale and the Celsius scale is the zero point. A temperature of −273 °C corresponds to 0 K. The zero point on the Kelvin scale is called **absolute zero,** the lowest temperature possible. To convert temperature values from Celsius to Kelvin, or vice versa, use two equations.

To convert from Celsius to Kelvin:

$$T_K = T_C + 273$$

To convert from Kelvin to Celsius:

$$T_C = T_K - 273$$

CONSUMER NOTE

Although mercury thermometers were used in hospitals to measure temperature for many years, temperature is now more commonly recorded with a digital thermometer. Tympanic thermometers, which use an infrared sensing device placed in the ear, are also routinely used.
©McGraw-Hill Education/Jill Braaten, photographer

Figure 1.8   Fahrenheit, Celsius, and Kelvin Temperature Scales Compared

Since the freezing point and boiling point of water span 180° on the Fahrenheit scale but only 100° on the Celsius scale, a Fahrenheit degree and a Celsius degree differ in size. The Kelvin scale is divided into kelvins (K), not degrees. Since the freezing point and boiling point of water span 100 kelvins, one kelvin is the same size as one Celsius degree.

SAMPLE PROBLEM 1.14 CONVERTING TEMPERATURE FROM ONE SCALE TO ANOTHER

An infant had a temperature of 104 °F. Convert this temperature to both T_C and T_K.

Analysis

First convert the Fahrenheit temperature to degrees Celsius using the equation $T_C = (T_F - 32)/1.8$. Then convert the Celsius temperature to kelvins by adding 273.

Solution

[1] Convert T_F to T_C:	**[2] Convert T_C to T_K:**
$$T_C = \frac{T_F - 32}{1.8}$$ $$= \frac{104 - 32}{1.8} = 40.\ °C$$	$$T_K = T_C + 273$$ $$= 40. + 273 = 313\ K$$

PRACTICE PROBLEM 1.14

When the human body is exposed to extreme cold, hypothermia can result and the body's temperature can drop to 28.5 °C. Convert this temperature to T_F and T_K.

More Practice: Try Problems 1.55c, 1.56c, 1.59–1.62.

PROBLEM 1.15

Convert each temperature to the requested temperature scale.

a. 20. °C to T_F b. 150. °F to T_C c. 298 K to T_F d. 75 °C to T_K

1.10   Density and Specific Gravity

Two additional quantities used to characterize substances are **density** and **specific gravity.**

1.10A   Density

Density **is a physical property that relates the mass of a substance to its volume.** Density is the ratio of mass (in grams) to volume (in milliliters or cubic centimeters).

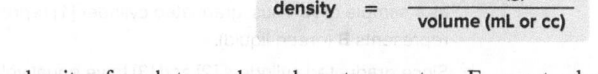

$$\text{density} = \frac{\text{mass (g)}}{\text{volume (mL or cc)}}$$

The density of a substance depends on temperature. For most substances, the solid state is more dense than the liquid state, and as the temperature increases, the density decreases. This phenomenon occurs because the volume of a sample of a substance generally increases with temperature but the mass is always constant.

Water is an exception to this generalization. Solid water, ice, is *less* dense than liquid water, and from 0 °C to 4 °C, the density of water *increases*. Above 4 °C, water behaves like other liquids and its density decreases. Thus, water's maximum density of 1.00 g/mL occurs at 4 °C. Some representative densities are reported in Table 1.6.

The density (not the mass) of a substance determines whether it floats or sinks in a liquid.

• A less dense substance floats on a more dense liquid.

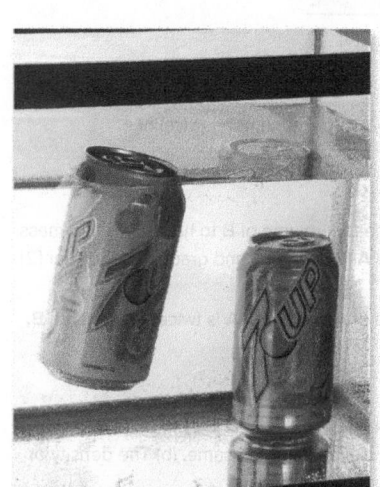

Although a can of a diet soft drink floats in water because it is less dense, a can of a regular soft drink that contains sugar is more dense than water so it sinks.
©McGraw-Hill Education/Jill Braaten, photographer

Table 1.6 Representative Densities at 25 °C

Substance	Density [g/(mL or cc)]	Substance	Density [g/(mL or cc)]
Oxygen (0 °C)	0.001 43	Urine	1.003–1.030
Gasoline	0.66	Blood plasma	1.03
Ice (0 °C)	0.92	Table sugar	1.59
Water (4 °C)	1.00	Bone	1.80

Ice floats on water because it is less dense. When petroleum leaks from an oil tanker or gasoline is spilled when fueling a boat, it floats on water because it is less dense. In contrast, a cannonball or torpedo sinks because it is more dense than water.

SAMPLE PROBLEM 1.15 USING DENSITY TO SOLVE A PROBLEM

The density of liquid **A** is twice the density of liquid **B**. (a) If you have an equal mass of **A** and **B**, which graduated cylinder ([1] or [2]) corresponds to **A** and which corresponds to **B**? (b) How do the masses of the liquids in graduated cylinders [2] and [3] compare?

Analysis

Density is the number of grams per milliliter (g/mL) or grams per cubic centimeter (g/cc) of a substance.

Solution

a. If the density of **A** is twice the density of **B,** you need twice the volume of **B** to have the same mass as a sample of **A**. Thus, graduated cylinder [1] represents **A** (gold liquid) and graduated cylinder [2] represents **B** (green liquid).

b. Since graduated cylinders [2] and [3] have equal volumes of **A** and **B** but **A** is twice as dense as **B,** the mass of [3] (**A**) must be twice the mass of [2] (**B**).

PRACTICE PROBLEM 1.15

How does the mass of liquid **A** in cylinder [1] compare with the mass of liquid **B** in cylinder [2] in each case (greater than, less than, or equal to)? (a) The densities of **A** and **B** are the same. (b) The density of **A** is twice the density of **B**. (c) The density of **B** is twice the density of **A**.

More Practice: Try Problems 1.63–1.66, 1.71.

Knowing the density of a liquid allows us to convert the volume of a substance to its mass, or the mass of a substance to its volume.

To convert volume (mL) to mass (g):

density

$$mL \times \frac{g}{mL} = g$$

Milliliters cancel.

To convert mass (g) to volume (mL):

inverse of the density

$$g \times \frac{mL}{g} = mL$$

Grams cancel.

For example, one laboratory synthesis of aspirin uses the liquid acetic acid, which has a density of 1.05 g/mL. If we need 5.0 g for a synthesis, we could use density to convert this mass to a volume that could then be easily measured out using a syringe or pipette.

$$5.0 \text{ g acetic acid} \times \frac{1 \text{ mL}}{1.05 \text{ g}} = 4.8 \text{ mL of acetic acid}$$

Grams cancel.

A scuba diver uses lead weights (Problem 1.16) on a belt around the waist in order to descend to a desired depth while diving. ©Redzaal/iStock RF

SAMPLE PROBLEM 1.16 USING DENSITY AND VOLUME TO DETERMINE MASS

Calculate the mass in grams of 15.0 mL of a saline solution that has a density of 1.05 g/mL.

Analysis

Use density (g/mL) to interconvert the mass and volume of a liquid.

Solution

density

$$15.0 \text{ mL} \times \frac{1.05 \text{ g}}{1 \text{ mL}} = 15.8 \text{ g of saline solution}$$

Milliliters cancel.

The answer, 15.8 g, is rounded to three significant figures to match the number of significant figures in both factors in the problem.

PRACTICE PROBLEM 1.16

Calculate the mass in grams of 10.0 mL of diethyl ether, an anesthetic that has a density of 0.713 g/mL.

More Practice: Try Problems 1.67–1.70.

PROBLEM 1.16

If a 120-lb woman uses five 2.0-lb lead weights in order to submerge during a recent scuba dive, what volume (in cubic centimeters) do the weights occupy if lead has a density of 11.3 g/cc?

PROBLEM 1.17

If a household recycles 10.5 kg of plastic bottles composed of PET in a month, and the density of PET is 1.38 g/mL, what volume in liters does this represent?

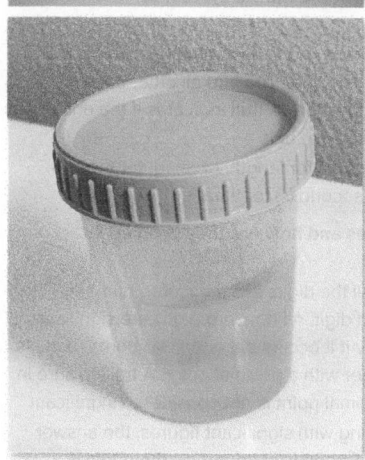

The specific gravity of a urine sample is measured to check if a patient has an imbalance in metabolism. ©PhotoDisc/Getty Images RF

HEALTH NOTE

1.10B Specific Gravity

Specific gravity **is a quantity that compares the density of a substance with the density of water at 4 °C.**

$$\text{specific gravity} = \frac{\text{density of a substance (g/mL)}}{\text{density of water (g/mL)}}$$

Unlike most other quantities, specific gravity is a quantity without units, because the units in the numerator (g/mL) cancel the units in the denominator (g/mL). Since the density of water is 1.00 g/mL at 4 °C, **the specific gravity of a substance equals its density, but it contains no units.** For example, if the density of a liquid is 1.5 g/mL, its specific gravity is 1.5.

The specific gravity of urine samples is often measured in a hospital lab. Normal urine has a density in the range of 1.003–1.030 g/mL (Table 1.6), so it has a specific gravity in the range of 1.003–1.030. Consistently high or low values can indicate an imbalance in metabolism. For example, the specific gravity of urine samples from patients with poorly controlled diabetes is abnormally high, because a large amount of glucose is excreted in the urine.

PROBLEM 1.18

(a) If the density of a liquid is 0.80 g/mL, what is its specific gravity? (b) If the specific gravity of a substance is 2.3, what is its density?

CHAPTER HIGHLIGHTS

KEY TERMS

Celsius scale (1.9)
Chemical properties (1.2)
Chemistry (1.1)
Compound (1.3)
Conversion factor (1.7)
Cubic centimeter (1.4)
Density (1.10)
Element (1.3)
English system of measurement (1.4)
Exact number (1.5)
Fahrenheit scale (1.9)

Gas (1.2)
Gram (1.4)
Inexact number (1.5)
Kelvin scale (1.9)
Liquid (1.2)
Liter (1.4)
Mass (1.4)
Matter (1.1)
Meter (1.4)
Metric system (1.4)
Mixture (1.3)

Physical properties (1.2)
Pure substance (1.3)
Scientific notation (1.6)
SI units (1.4)
Significant figures (1.5)
Solid (1.2)
Specific gravity (1.10)
States of matter (1.2)
Temperature (1.9)
Weight (1.4)

KEY CONCEPTS

1 **Describe the three states of matter. (1.1, 1.2)**
- Matter is anything that has mass and takes up volume. Matter has three common states:
  - The solid state is composed of highly organized particles that lie close together. A solid has a definite shape and volume.
  - The liquid state is composed of particles that lie close together but are less organized than the solid state. A liquid has a definite volume but not a definite shape.
  - The gas state is composed of highly disorganized particles that lie far apart. A gas has no definite shape or volume.

2 **How is matter classified? (1.3)**
- Matter is classified in one of two categories:
  - A pure substance is composed of a single component with a constant composition. A pure substance is either an element, which cannot be broken down into simpler substances by a chemical reaction, or a compound, which is formed by combining two or more elements.
  - A mixture is composed of more than one substance and its composition can vary depending on the sample.

3 **What are the key features of the metric system of measurement? (1.4)**
- The metric system is a system of measurement in which each type of measurement has a base unit and all other units are related to the base unit by a prefix that indicates if the unit is larger or smaller than the base unit.
- The base units are meter (m) for length, gram (g) for mass, liter (L) for volume, and second (s) for time.

4 **What are significant figures and how are they used in calculations? (1.5)**
- Significant figures are all the digits in a measured number, including one estimated digit. All nonzero digits are significant. A zero is significant only if it occurs between two nonzero digits, or at the end of a number with a decimal point. A trailing zero in a number without a decimal point is not considered significant.
- In multiplying and dividing with significant figures, the answer has the same number of significant figures as the original number with the fewest significant figures.
- In adding or subtracting with significant figures, the answer has the same number of decimal places as the original number with the fewest decimal places.

5 **What is scientific notation? (1.6)**
- Scientific notation is a method of writing a number as $y \times 10^x$, where y is a number between 1 and 10, and x is a positive or negative exponent.
- To convert a standard number to a number in scientific notation, move the decimal point to give a number between 1 and 10. Multiply the result by 10^x, where x is the number of places the decimal point was moved. When the decimal point is moved to the left, x is positive. When the decimal point is moved to the right, x is negative.

6 **How are conversion factors used to convert one unit to another? (1.7, 1.8)**
- A conversion factor is a term that converts a quantity in one unit to a quantity in another unit. To use conversion factors to solve a problem, set up the problem with any unwanted unit in the numerator of one term and the denominator of another term, so that unwanted units cancel.

7 **What is temperature and how are the three temperature scales related? (1.9)**
- Temperature is a measure of how hot or cold an object is. The Fahrenheit and Celsius temperature scales are divided into degrees. Both the size of the degree and the zero point of these scales differ. The Kelvin scale is divided into kelvins, and one kelvin is the same size as one degree Celsius.

8 **What are density and specific gravity? (1.10)**
- Density is a physical property reported in g/mL or g/cc that relates the mass of an object to its volume. A less dense substance floats on top of a more dense liquid.
- Specific gravity is a unitless quantity that relates the density of a substance to the density of water at 4 °C. Since the density of water is 1.00 g/mL at this temperature, the specific gravity of a substance equals its density, but it contains no units.

PROBLEMS

Selected in-chapter and odd-numbered end-of-chapter problems have brief answers in Appendix B. The *Student Study Guide and Solutions Manual* contains detailed solutions to all in-chapter and odd-numbered end-of-chapter problems, as well as additional worked examples and a chapter self-test.

Matter

1.19 Classify each example of molecular art as a pure element, a pure compound, or a mixture.

a.
c.

b.
d.

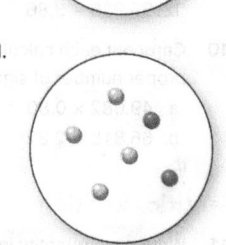

1.20 (a) Which representation(s) in Problem 1.19 illustrate a mixture of two elements? (b) Which representation(s) in Problem 1.19 illustrate a mixture of a compound and an element?

1.21 Label each component in the molecular art as an element or a compound.

1.22 Label each component in the molecular art as an element or a compound.

1.23 (a) Which representation(s) illustrate a mixture of two elements? (b) Which representation(s) illustrate a mixture of a compound and an element?

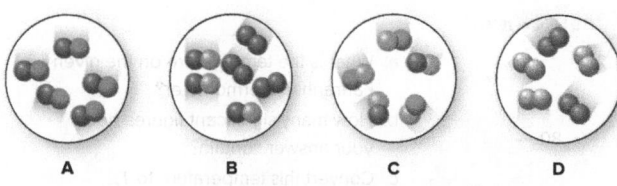

A   B   C   D

1.24 Label each of the following conversions as a chemical change or a physical change: (a) **A → B**; (b) **A → C**; (c) **A → D.**

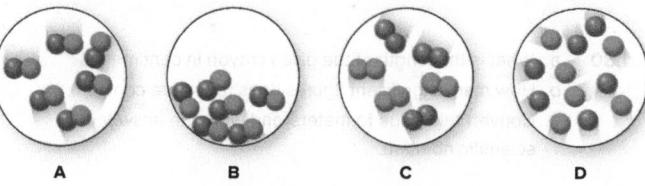

A   B   C   D

1.25 Classify each process as a chemical or physical change.
   a. dissolving calcium chloride in water
   b. burning gasoline to power a car
   c. heating wax so that it melts

1.26 Classify each process as a chemical or physical change.
 a. the condensation of water on the outside of a cold glass
 b. mixing a teaspoon of instant coffee with hot water
 c. baking a cake

1.27 When a chunk of dry ice (solid carbon dioxide) is placed out in the air, the solid gradually disappears and a gas is formed above the solid. Does the molecular art drawn below indicate that a chemical or physical change has occurred? Explain your choice.

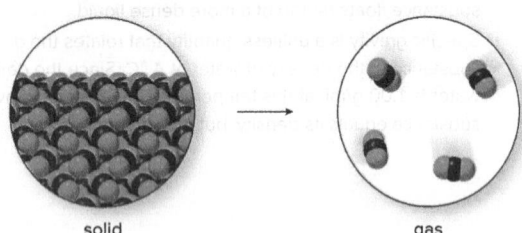

solid   gas

1.28 The inexpensive preparation of nitrogen-containing fertilizers begins with mixing together two elements, hydrogen and nitrogen, at high temperature and pressure in the presence of a metal. Does the molecular art depicted below indicate that a chemical or physical change occurs under these conditions? Explain your choice.

metal
heat

Measurement

1.29

 a. What is the temperature on the given Fahrenheit thermometer?
 b. How many significant figures does your answer contain?
 c. Convert this temperature to T_C.

1.30 a. What is the length of the given crayon in centimeters?
 b. How many significant figures does this value contain?
 c. Convert this value to meters, and write the answer in scientific notation.

1.31 Label each quantity as an exact or inexact number.
 a. A recipe requires 10 cloves of garlic and two tablespoons of oil.
 b. A dog had five puppies whose combined weight was 10 lb.

1.32 Label each quantity as an exact or inexact number.
 a. The four bicycles in the family have been ridden for a total of 250 mi.
 b. A child fell and had a 4-cm laceration that required 12 stitches.

1.33 Which quantity in each pair is larger?
 a. 5 mL or 5 dL   c. 5 cm or 5 mm
 b. 10 mg or 10 μg   d. 10 Ms or 10 ms

1.34 Which quantity in each pair is larger?
 a. 10 km or 10 m   c. 10 g or 10 μg
 b. 10 L or 10 mL   d. 10 cm or 10 mm

Significant Figures

1.35 How many significant figures does each number contain?
 a. 16.00   c. 0.001 60   e. 1.06   g. 1.060×10^{10}
 b. 160   d. 1,600,000 f. 0.1600 h. 1.6×10^{-6}

1.36 How many significant figures does each number contain?
 a. 160.   c. 0.000 16   e. 1,600   g. 1.600×10^{-10}
 b. 160.0   d. 1.60   f. 1.060   h. 1.6×10^6

1.37 Round each number to three significant figures.
 a. 25,401   c. 0.001 265 982   e. 195.371
 b. 1,248,486   d. 0.123 456   f. 196.814

1.38 Round each number in Problem 1.37 to four significant figures.

1.39 Carry out each calculation and report the answer using the proper number of significant figures.
 a. 53.6×0.41 c. $65.2 \div 12$ e. 694.2×0.2
 b. $25.825 - 3.86$ d. $41.0 + 9.135$ f. $1,045 - 1.26$

1.40 Carry out each calculation and report the answer using the proper number of significant figures.
 a. $49,682 \times 0.80$ c. $1,000 \div 2.34$ e. $25,000 \div 0.4356$
 b. $66.815 + 2.82$ d. $21 - 0.88$ f. $21.5381 + 26.55$

Scientific Notation

1.41 Write each quantity in scientific notation.
 a. 1,234 g   c. 5,244,000 L   e. 44,000 km
 b. 0.000 016 2 m   d. 0.005 62 g

1.42 Write each quantity in scientific notation.
 a. 0.001 25 m   c. 54,235.6 m   e. 4,440 s
 b. 8,100,000,000 lb   d. 0.000 001 899 L

1.43 Convert each number to its standard form.
 a. 3.4×10^8 c. 3×10^2
 b. 5.822×10^{-5} d. 6.86×10^{-8}

1.44 Convert each number to its standard form.
 a. 4.02×10^{10} c. 6.86×10^9
 b. 2.46×10^{-3} d. 1.00×10^{-7}

1.45 Which number in each pair is larger?
   a. 4.44×10^3 or 4.8×10^2
   b. 5.6×10^{-6} or 5.6×10^{-5}
   c. 1.3×10^8 or $52{,}300{,}000$
   d. 9.8×10^{-4} or $0.000\,089$

1.46 Rank the numbers in each group from smallest to largest.
   a. 5.06×10^6, 7×10^4, and 2.5×10^8
   b. 6.3×10^{-2}, 2.5×10^{-4}, and 8.6×10^{-6}

1.47 Write the recommended daily intake of each nutrient in scientific notation.
   a. 0.000 400 g of folate
   c. 0.000 080 g of vitamin K
   b. 0.002 g of copper
   d. 3,400 mg of chloride

1.48 A blood vessel is 0.40 μm in diameter. (a) Convert this quantity to meters and write the answer in scientific notation. (b) Convert this quantity to inches and write the answer in scientific notation.

Problem Solving and Unit Conversions

1.49 What is the mass in kilograms of an individual whose weight in pounds is shown on the given scale?

1.50   a. What is the volume of liquid contained in the given 3-mL syringe?
   b. Convert this value to liters and write the answer in scientific notation.

1.51 The average mass of a human liver is 1.5 kg. Convert this quantity to (a) grams; (b) pounds; (c) ounces.

1.52 (a) If there are 15 mL in one tablespoon, how many milliliters are contained in 3.5 tablespoons of a liquid medication? (b) How many milliliters would a patient receive if he took this dosage four times a day for one week? (c) How many liters does this correspond to?

1.53 The concentration of mercury, a toxic pollutant, in some yellowfin tuna is 354 mg in 1.0×10^6 g of fish. The Food and Drug Administration recommends that women who are pregnant should eat no more the 6.0 oz of yellowfin tuna per

week. How much mercury (in milligrams) would an individual ingest in one serving of fish?

©Nishihama/Shutterstock RF

1.54 Honeydew melons are high in potassium, a nutrient needed for proper fluid balance [875 mg in one serving (one-quarter of a medium melon)]. If an individual eats one serving each day for a week, how many grams of potassium are obtained?

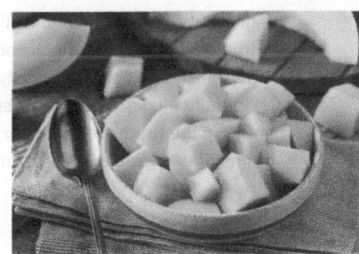

©Brent Hofacker/Shutterstock RF

1.55 Carry out each of the following conversions.
   a. What is the height in centimeters of a child who is 50. in. tall?
   b. A patient required 3.0 pt of blood during surgery. How many liters does this correspond to?
   c. A patient had a body temperature of 37.7 °C. What is his body temperature in T_F?

1.56 Carry out each of the following conversions.
   a. What is the mass in pounds of an individual who weighs 53.2 kg?
   b. How many mL are contained in the 5.0 qt of blood in the average adult human body?
   c. A patient had a body temperature of 103.5 °F. What is his body temperature in T_C?

1.57 We use conversion factors when traveling in countries that use different currencies. On a recent trip to Asia, a traveler returned to the United States with currency from Bhutan and Thailand. If she had 1,420 Bhutanese ngultrum (65 ngultrum in one U.S. dollar) and 5,750 Thai bhat (35 bhat in one U.S. dollar), how much is this foreign currency worth in U.S. dollars?

1.58 In addition to the common prefixes listed in Table 1.2, the prefix *tera-* (symbolized by T) means a trillion times as large—that is, 1,000,000,000,000 times as large. (a) How many bytes of information can a four-terabyte computer hard drive store, written in scientific notation? (b) How many gigabytes are present in four terabytes?

34   **Chapter 1**   Matter and Measurement

Temperature

1.59   Carry out each of the following temperature conversions.

   a. An over-the-counter pain reliever melts at 53 °C. Convert this temperature to T_F and T_K.

   b. A cake is baked at 350. °F. Convert this temperature to T_C and T_K.

1.60   (a) The highest air temperature recorded in Antarctica is 17.5 °C (March 24, 2015). Convert this value to T_F. (b) The lowest air temperature recorded in Antarctica is −128.6 °F (July 21, 1983). Convert this value to T_C.

1.61   Which temperature in each pair is higher?

   a. −10 °C or 10 °F   b. −50 °C or −50 °F

1.62   Rank the temperatures in each group from lowest to highest.

   a. 0 °F, 0 °C, 0 K   b. 100 K, 100 °C, 100 °F

Density and Specific Gravity

1.63   A graduated cylinder contains three liquids: water (density = 1.00 g/mL), corn syrup (density = 1.37 g/mL), and corn oil (density = 0.93 g/mL). (a) Identify the liquid that corresponds to **A, B,** and **C** in the graduated cylinder. (b) How many grams of each liquid are present?

1.64   Draw a graduated cylinder similar to Problem 1.63 that contains three liquids in the given amounts: water (25 g, density = 1.00 g/mL), gasoline (15.0 g, density = 0.75 g/mL), and honey (42.6 g, 1.42 g/mL).

1.65   The given beaker contains 100 mL of water. Draw an illustration for what would be observed in each circumstance. (a) Hexane (50 mL, density = 0.65 g/mL) is added. (b) Dichloromethane (50 mL, density = 1.33 g/mL) is added.

1.66   (a) What can be said about the density of the liquid in beaker **A**, if the object in the beaker has a density of 2.0 g/cc? (b) What can be said about the density of the liquid in beaker **B**, if the object has a density of 0.90 g/cc?

A   B

1.67   If a urine sample has a mass of 122 g and a volume of 121 mL, what is its density in g/mL?

1.68   A volume of saline solution had a mass of 25.6 g at 4 °C. An equal volume of water at the same temperature had a mass of 24.5 g. What is the density of the saline solution?

1.69   If milk has a density of 1.03 g/mL, what is the mass of one quart, reported in kilograms?

1.70   If gasoline has a density of 0.66 g/mL, what is the mass of one gallon, reported in kilograms?

1.71   Which is the upper layer when each of the following liquids is added to water?

   a. heptane (density = 0.684 g/mL)

   b. olive oil (density = 0.92 g/mL)

   c. chloroform (density = 1.49 g/mL)

   d. carbon tetrachloride (density = 1.59 g/mL)

1.72   (a) What is the specific gravity of mercury, the liquid used in thermometers, if it has a density of 13.6 g/mL? (b) What is the density of ethanol if it has a specific gravity of 0.789?

Applications

1.73   A lab test showed an individual's cholesterol level to be 186 mg/dL. (a) Convert this quantity to g/dL. (b) Convert this quantity to mg/L.

1.74   Hemoglobin is a protein that transports oxygen from the lungs to the rest of the body. Lab results indicated a patient had a hemoglobin concentration in the blood of 15.5 g/dL, which is in the normal range. (a) Convert the number of grams to milligrams and write the answer in scientific notation. (b) Convert the number of grams to micrograms and write the answer in scientific notation.

1.75   A woman was told to take a dose of 1.5 g of calcium daily. How many 500-mg tablets should she take?

1.76   A soccer player weighed 70.7 kg before a match, drank 1.8 L of liquid (density 1.05 g/mL) during the match, and weighed 69.3 kg after the match. How many pounds of sweat did the soccer player lose?

1.77   Liposuction is a cosmetic procedure used to remove excess fat from the abdomen, thigh, or buttocks of a patient. (a) If 2.0 L of fat (density = 0.94 g/mL) is removed, what is the mass (in kg) of this fat? (b) How many pounds of fat have been removed?

1.78   A single 1-oz serving of tortilla chips contains 250 mg of sodium. If an individual ate the entire 13-oz bag, how many grams of sodium would he ingest? If the recommended daily intake of sodium is 2.4 g, does this provide more or less than the recommended daily value, and by how much?

1.79   A bottle of liquid medication contains 300. mL and costs $10.00. (a) If the usual dose is 20. mL, how much does each dose cost? (b) If the usual dose is two tablespoons (1 tablespoon = 15 mL), how much does each dose cost?

1.80   The average nicotine content of a Camel cigarette is 1.93 mg. (a) Convert this quantity to both grams and micrograms. (b) Nicotine patches, which are used to help quit smoking, release nicotine into the body by absorption through the skin. The patches come with different amounts of nicotine. A smoker begins with the amount of nicotine that matches his typical daily intake. The maximum amount of nicotine in one brand of patch supplies a smoker with 21 mg of nicotine per day. If an individual smoked one pack of 20 Camel cigarettes each day, would a smoker get more or less nicotine per day using this patch?

1.81 A chemist synthesized 0.510 kg of aspirin in the lab. If the normal dose of aspirin is two 325-mg tablets, how many doses did she prepare?

1.82 Maalox is the trade name for an antacid and antigas medication used for relief of heartburn, bloating, and acid indigestion. Each 5.0-mL portion of Maalox contains 400. mg of aluminum hydroxide, 400. mg of magnesium hydroxide, and 40. mg of

simethicone. If the recommended dose is two teaspoons four times a day, how many grams of each substance would an individual take in a 24-hour period? (1 teaspoon = 5.0 mL.)

1.83 A patient is prescribed 2.0 g of a medication to be taken four times a day. If the medicine is available in 500.-mg tablets, how many tablets are needed in a 24-hour period?

1.84 A patient receives an intravenous (IV) solution that flows at the rate of 150 mL per hour. (a) How much fluid does the patient receive in 20. min? (b) How long does it take for the patient to receive 90. mL of fluid? (c) If the IV bag holds 600. mL of fluid, how many minutes does it take to empty the bag? (d) If the solution contains 90. mg of glucose per mL, how long will it take to give the patient 2.0 g of glucose?

CHALLENGE PROBLEMS

1.85 Often the specific amount of a drug to be administered must be calculated from a given dose in mg per kilogram of body weight. This ensures that individuals who have very different body mass get the proper dose. If the proper dosage of a drug is 2.0 mg/kg of body weight, how many milligrams would a 110-lb individual need?

1.86 Quinine, a drug isolated from the bark of the cinchona tree native to the Andes Mountains, is an effective treatment for malaria. Children typically receive a dose of 10. mg/kg three times a day for seven days. How many grams would a 28-kg child receive during the course of a treatment?

1.87 One measure of whether an individual has a healthy weight is to determine his body mass index (BMI), defined as the mass of an individual (in kilograms) divided by the square of his height (in meters); BMI = (mass in kg)/(height in m)^2. A BMI in the range of 18.5–25 is considered the normal range. When BMI is less than 18.5 an individual is underweight, whereas a BMI greater than 25 means an individual is overweight. Calculate the BMI for a 180-lb individual who is six feet one inch tall, and state whether he is underweight, normal in weight, or overweight.

1.88 (a) If the proper dose of ibuprofen for a 150.-lb adult is three 200.-mg tablets, calculate the dosage in mg per kg of body

weight. (b) How many milligrams of ibuprofen would a 45-kg individual receive if he were given the same dose?

1.89 Children's Chewable Tylenol contains 80 mg of acetaminophen per tablet. If the recommended dosage is 10 mg/kg, how many tablets are needed for a 42-lb child?

1.90 Artemether, an antimalarial drug prepared from the Chinese antimalarial plant *Artemisia annua*, can be given either orally or by injection. When the drug is given in pill form, the patient receives 160 mg on the first day, and then 80. mg daily for the next four days. When the drug is given by injection, the patient receives 3.2 mg/kg of body weight on the first day, and then 1.6 mg/kg daily for the next four days. (a) Which method gives a 40.-kg individual the larger dose? (b) Which method gives a 100.-kg individual the larger dose?

1.91 Children's Liquid Motrin contains 100. mg of the pain reliever ibuprofen per 5 mL. If the dose for a 45-lb child is 1.5 teaspoons, how many grams of ibuprofen would the child receive? (1 teaspoon = 5.0 mL.)

1.92 If the proper dosage of a medication is 10 µg/kg of body weight, how many milligrams would a 200-lb individual need?

2

Because the element helium is lighter than air, balloons filled with helium must be secured with strings so they don't float away.
©Stockbyte/Getty Images RF

Atoms and the Periodic Table

CHAPTER OUTLINE

2.1 Elements
2.2 Structure of the Atom
2.3 Isotopes
2.4 The Periodic Table
2.5 Electronic Structure
2.6 Electronic Configurations
2.7 Valence Electrons
2.8 Periodic Trends

CHAPTER GOALS

In this chapter you will learn how to:

1 Identify an element by its symbol and classify it as a metal, nonmetal, or metalloid

2 Describe the basic parts of an atom

3 Distinguish isotopes and calculate atomic weight

4 Describe the basic features of the periodic table

5 Understand the electronic structure of an atom

6 Write an electronic configuration for an element

7 Relate the location of an element in the periodic table to its electronic configuration

8 Draw an electron-dot symbol for an atom

9 Use the periodic table to predict the relative size and ionization energy of atoms

Examine the ingredients listed on a box of crackers. They may include flour, added vitamins, sugar for sweetness, a natural or synthetic coloring agent, baking soda, salt for flavor, and BHT as a preservative. No matter how simple or complex each of these substances is, it is composed of the basic building block, the **atom.** The word *atom* comes from the Greek word *atomos* meaning "unable to cut." In Chapter 2, we examine the structure and properties of atoms, the building blocks that comprise all forms of matter.

2.1 Elements

Elements are named for people, places, and things. For example, *carbon* (C) comes from the Latin word *carbo*, meaning "coal" or "charcoal;" *neptunium* (Np) was named for the planet Neptune; *einsteinium* (Es) was named for scientist Albert Einstein; and *californium* (Cf) was named for the state of California.

You were first introduced to elements in Section 1.3.

> • An *element* is a pure substance that cannot be broken down into simpler substances by a chemical reaction.

Of the 118 elements currently known, 90 are naturally occurring and the remaining 28 have been prepared by scientists in the laboratory. Some elements, like oxygen in the air we breathe and aluminum in a soft drink can, are familiar to you, while others, like samarium and seaborgium, are probably not. An alphabetical list of all elements appears on the inside front cover.

Each element is identified by a one- or two-letter symbol. The element carbon is symbolized by the single letter **C,** whereas the element chlorine is symbolized by **Cl.** When two letters are used in the element symbol, the first is upper case and the second is lower case. Thus, **Co** refers to the element cobalt, but CO is carbon monoxide, which is composed of the elements carbon (C) and oxygen (O). Table 2.1 lists common elements and their symbols.

While most element symbols are derived from the first one or two letters of the element name, 11 elements have symbols derived from Latin or German origins. Table 2.2 lists these elements and their symbols.

ENVIRONMENTAL NOTE

Carbon monoxide (CO), formed in small amounts during the combustion of fossil fuels like gasoline, is a toxic component of the smoggy air in many large cities. Carbon monoxide contains the elements carbon (C) and oxygen (O). We will learn about carbon monoxide in Section 12.8.
©*Alessandro Rizzi/Photonica/Getty Images*

PROBLEM 2.1

Give the symbol for each element.

a. calcium, a nutrient needed for strong teeth and bones

b. radon, a radioactive gas produced in the soil

c. nitrogen, the main component of the earth's atmosphere

d. gold, a precious metal used in coins and jewelry

Table 2.1 Common Elements and Their Symbols

Element	Symbol	Element	Symbol
Bromine	Br	Magnesium	Mg
Calcium	Ca	Manganese	Mn
Carbon	C	Molybdenum	Mo
Chlorine	Cl	Nitrogen	N
Chromium	Cr	Oxygen	O
Cobalt	Co	Phosphorus	P
Copper	Cu	Potassium	K
Fluorine	F	Sodium	Na
Hydrogen	H	Sulfur	S
Iodine	I	Zinc	Zn
Lead	Pb		

Table 2.2 Unusual Element Symbols

Element	Symbol
Antimony	Sb (stibium)
Copper	Cu (cuprum)
Gold	Au (aurum)
Iron	Fe (ferrum)
Lead	Pb (plumbum)
Mercury	Hg (hydrargyrum)
Potassium	K (kalium)
Silver	Ag (argentum)
Sodium	Na (natrium)
Tin	Sn (stannum)
Tungsten	W (wolfram)

PROBLEM 2.2

Give the name corresponding to each element symbol: (a) Ne; (b) S; (c) I; (d) Si; (e) B; (f) Hg; (g) Sn; (h) Sb.

2.1A   Elements and the Periodic Table

A periodic table appears on the inside front cover for easy reference.

Long ago it was realized that groups of elements have similar properties, and that these elements could be arranged in a schematic way called the **periodic table** (Figure 2.1). The position of an element in the periodic table tells us much about its chemical properties.

The elements in the periodic table are divided into three categories—**metals, nonmetals,** and **metalloids.** The solid line that begins with boron (B) and angles in steps down to astatine (At) marks the three regions corresponding to these groups. All metals are located to the *left* of the line. All nonmetals except hydrogen are located to the *right*. Metalloids are located along the steps.

Figure 2.1   The Periodic Table of the Elements

- **Metals** are shiny substances that conduct heat and electricity. Metals are ductile, meaning they can be drawn into wires, and malleable, meaning they can be hammered into shapes.
- **Metalloids** have properties intermediate between metals and nonmetals.
- **Nonmetals** are poor conductors of heat and electricity.

- *Metals* are shiny materials that are good conductors of heat and electricity. All metals are solids at room temperature except for mercury, which is a liquid.
- *Nonmetals* do not have a shiny appearance, and they are generally poor conductors of heat and electricity. Nonmetals like sulfur and carbon are solids at room temperature; bromine is a liquid; and nitrogen, oxygen, and nine other elements are gases.
- *Metalloids* have properties intermediate between metals and nonmetals. Only seven elements are categorized as metalloids: boron (B), silicon (Si), germanium (Ge), arsenic (As), antimony (Sb), tellurium (Te), and astatine (At).

PROBLEM 2.3

Locate each element in the periodic table and classify it as a metal, nonmetal, or metalloid.

a. titanium	c. krypton	e. arsenic	g. selenium
b. chlorine	d. palladium	f. cesium	h. osmium

2.1B FOCUS ON THE HUMAN BODY
The Elements of Life

Because living organisms selectively take up elements from their surroundings, the abundance of elements in the human body is very different from the distribution of elements in the earth's crust. **Four nonmetals—oxygen, carbon, hydrogen, and nitrogen—comprise 96% of the mass of the human body, and are called the** *building-block elements* (Figure 2.2). Hydrogen and oxygen are the elements that form water, the most prevalent substance in the body. Carbon, hydrogen, and oxygen are found in the four main types of biological molecules—proteins, carbohydrates, lipids, and nucleic acids. Proteins and nucleic acids contain the element nitrogen as well. These biological molecules are discussed in Chapters 19–22.

Seven other elements, called the **major minerals** or **macronutrients,** are also present in the body in much smaller amounts (0.1–2% by mass). Sodium, potassium, and chlorine are present

Figure 2.2   The Elements of Life

Building-Block Elements

Oxygen (O)
Carbon (C)
Hydrogen (H)
Nitrogen (N)

These four elements compose almost 96% of the mass of the human body. Muscle tissue contains all four building-block elements.

Major Minerals

Potassium (K), sodium (Na), and chlorine (Cl) are present in body fluids.

Magnesium (Mg) and sulfur (S) are present in the proteins found in muscle.

Calcium (Ca) and phosphorus (P) are present in teeth and bones.

Each major mineral is present in 0.1–2% by mass. At least 100 mg of each mineral is needed in the daily diet.

Trace Elements

Arsenic (As)	Fluorine (F)	Nickel (Ni)
Boron (B)	Iodine (I)	Selenium (Se)
Chromium (Cr)	Iron (Fe)	Silicon (Si)
Cobalt (Co)	Manganese (Mn)	Zinc (Zn)
Copper (Cu)	Molybdenum (Mo)	

Each trace element is present in less than 0.1% by mass. A small quantity (15 mg or less) of each element is needed in the daily diet.

Nutrition Facts
Serving Size 3/4 cup (30g)
Servings Per Container about 17

Amount Per Serving	Cereal	Cereal with 1/2 cup Fat Free Milk
Calories	120	160
Calories from Fat	15	15
	% Daily Value**	
Vitamin A	15%	20%
Vitamin C	0%	0%
Calcium	0%	15%
Iron	60%	60%
Vitamin D	10%	25%
Thiamin	25%	30%
Riboflavin	25%	35%
Niacin	25%	25%
Vitamin B6	25%	25%
Folic Acid	50%	50%
Vitamin B12	25%	35%
Phosphorus	4%	15%
Magnesium	4%	8%
Zinc	2%	6%
Copper	2%	2%

INGREDIENTS: CORN, WHOLE GRAIN WHEAT, SUGAR, WHOLE GRAIN ROLLED OATS, BROWN SUGAR, HIGH OLEIC VEGETABLE OIL¹ (CANOLA OR SUNFLOWER OIL), RICE FLOUR, WHEAT FLOUR, MALTED BARLEY FLOUR, SALT, RICE, CORN SYRUP, WHEY (FROM MILK¹), HONEY, MALTED CORN AND BARLEY SYRUP, CARAMEL COLOR, ARTIFICIAL FLAVOR, ANNATTO EXTRACT (COLOR), BHT ADDED TO PACKAGING MATERIAL TO PRESERVE PRODUCT FRESHNESS.
VITAMINS AND MINERALS: REDUCED IRON, NIACINAMIDE, VITAMIN B6, VITAMIN A PALMITATE, RIBOFLAVIN (VITAMIN B2), THIAMIN MONONITRATE (VITAMIN B1), ZINC OXIDE (SOURCE OF ZINC), FOLIC ACID, VITAMIN B12, VITAMIN D.

Many breakfast cereals are fortified with iron to provide the consumer with this essential micronutrient.

in body fluids. Magnesium and sulfur occur in proteins, and calcium and phosphorus are present in teeth and bones. Phosphorus is also contained in all nucleic acids, such as the DNA that transfers genetic information from one generation to another. At least 100 mg of each macronutrient is needed in the daily diet.

Many other elements occur in very small amounts in the body, but are essential to good health. These **trace elements** or **micronutrients** are required in the daily diet in small quantities, usually less than 15 mg. Each trace element has a specialized function that is important for proper cellular function. For example, iron is needed for hemoglobin, the protein that carries oxygen in red blood cells, and myoglobin, the protein that stores oxygen in muscle. Zinc is needed for the proper functioning of many enzymes in the liver and kidneys, and iodine is needed for proper thyroid function. Although most of the trace elements are metals, nonmetals like fluorine and selenium are micronutrients as well.

PROBLEM 2.4

Label each micronutrient in Figure 2.2 in the following periodic table, and classify it as a metal, nonmetal, or metalloid.

2.1C Compounds

In Section 1.3 we learned that a *compound* **is a pure substance formed by chemically combining two or more elements together.** Element symbols are used to write chemical formulas for compounds.

- A *chemical formula* uses element symbols to show the identity of the elements forming a compound and subscripts to show the ratio of atoms contained in the compound.

For example, table salt is formed from sodium (Na) and chlorine (Cl) in a ratio of 1:1, so its formula is NaCl. Water, on the other hand, is formed from two hydrogens for each oxygen, so its formula is H_2O. The subscript "1" is understood when no subscript is written. Other examples of chemical formulas are shown below.

H_2O — 2 H's for each O
water

CO_2 — 2 O's for each C
carbon dioxide
(dry ice)

C_3H_8 — 3 C's, 8 H's
propane

As we learned in Section 1.2, molecular art will often be used to illustrate the composition and state of elements and compounds. Color-coded spheres, shown in Figure 2.3, are used to identify the common elements that form compounds.

Figure 2.3   Common Element Colors Used in Molecular Art

C   H   O   N   F   Cl   Br   I   S   P

For example, a red sphere is used for the element oxygen and gray is used for the element hydrogen, so H_2O is represented as a red sphere joined to two gray spheres. Sometimes the spheres will be connected by "sticks" to generate a **ball-and-stick** representation for a compound. At other times, the spheres will be drawn close together to form a **space-filling** representation. No matter how the spheres are depicted, H_2O always consists of one red sphere for the oxygen and two gray spheres for the two hydrogens.

No matter how it is depicted, water is a compound that contains two hydrogens for each oxygen. ©Pixtal/SuperStock RF

SAMPLE PROBLEM 2.1 IDENTIFYING ELEMENTS IN MOLECULAR ART

Identify the elements used in each example of molecular art.

a.   b.

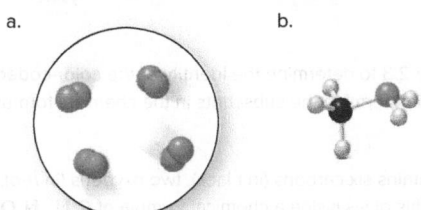

Analysis

Use Figure 2.3 to determine the identity of the color-coded spheres.

Solution

a. The blue spheres in this space-filling representation correspond to the element nitrogen and the red spheres correspond to the element oxygen. Thus, one "particle" contains two nitrogens, one contains two oxygens, and two contain one oxygen and one nitrogen.

b. This ball-and-stick representation contains the elements carbon (black), nitrogen (blue), and hydrogen (gray).

PRACTICE PROBLEM 2.1

Identify the elements used in each example of molecular art.

a.   b.   c.

More Practice: Try Problems 2.17, 2.18.

PROBLEM 2.5

Identify the elements in each chemical formula, and give the number of atoms of each element.

a. NaCN (sodium cyanide)   c. C_2H_6 (ethane)   e. CO (carbon monoxide)

b. H_2S (hydrogen sulfide)   d. SnF_2 (stannous fluoride)   f. $C_3H_8O_3$ (glycerol)

PROBLEM 2.6

Halothane is an inhaled general anesthetic, commonly used since the 1950s. Identify the elements in the ball-and-stick representation of halothane.

halothane

SAMPLE PROBLEM 2.2 DETERMINING A CHEMICAL FORMULA FROM A MORE COMPLEX BALL-AND-STICK MODEL

Determine the chemical formula of lysine from the given ball-and-stick model. Lysine is an essential amino acid needed for protein synthesis that must be ingested regularly because it is not synthesized by humans.

lysine

Analysis

Use Figure 2.3 to determine the identity of the color-coded spheres. Use the number of atoms of an element to determine the subscripts in the chemical formula.

Solution

Lysine contains six carbons (in black), two oxygens (in red), two nitrogens (in blue), and 14 hydrogens (in gray). This gives lysine a chemical formula of $C_6H_{14}N_2O_2$.

PRACTICE PROBLEM 2.2

Determine the chemical formula of caffeine from the given ball-and-stick model.

caffeine

More Practice: Try Problems 2.79, 2.80.

Quinoa, a grain relatively high in lysine content, is a good source of essential amino acids like lysine in vegetarian diets.
©Sarka Babicka/Getty Images RF

2.2   Structure of the Atom

All matter is composed of the same basic building blocks called *atoms.* An atom is much too small to be seen even by the most powerful light microscopes. The period at the end of this sentence holds about 1×10^8 atoms, and a human cheek cell contains about 1×10^{16} atoms. An atom is composed of three subatomic particles.

- A proton, symbolized by p, has a positive (+) charge.
- An electron, symbolized by e⁻, has a negative (−) charge.
- A neutron, symbolized by n, has no charge.

Protons and neutrons have approximately the same, exceedingly small mass, as shown in Table 2.3. The mass of an electron is much less, 1/1,836 the mass of a proton. These subatomic particles are not evenly distributed in the volume of an atom. There are two main components of an atom.

- The *nucleus* is a dense core that contains the protons and neutrons. Most of the mass of an atom resides in the nucleus.
- The *electron cloud* is composed of electrons that move rapidly in the almost-empty space surrounding the nucleus. The electron cloud comprises most of the volume of an atom.

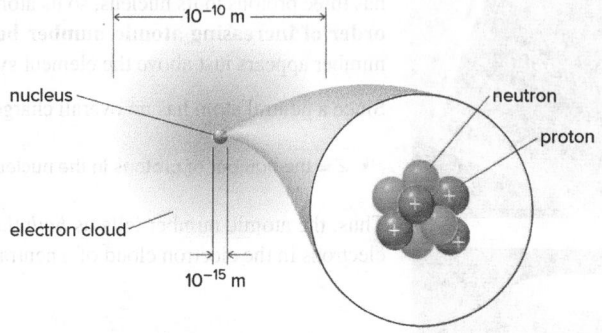

main components of an atom

While the diameter of an atom is about 10^{-10} m, the diameter of a nucleus is only about 10^{-15} m. For a macroscopic analogy, if the nucleus were the size of a baseball, an atom would be the size of Yankee Stadium!

Table 2.3 Summary: The Properties of the Three Subatomic Particles

Subatomic Particle	Charge	Mass (g)	Mass (amu)
Proton	+1	1.6726×10^{-24}	1
Neutron	0	1.6749×10^{-24}	1
Electron	−1	9.1093×10^{-28}	Negligible

The charged particles of an atom can either attract or repel each other.

- Opposite charges attract whereas like charges repel each other.

Thus, two electrons or two protons repel each other, while a proton and an electron attract each other.

Positive charges repel.   Negative charges repel.   Opposite charges attract.

Since the mass of an individual atom is so small (on the order of 10^{-24} g), chemists use a standard mass unit, the **atomic mass unit,** which defines the mass of individual atoms relative to a standard mass.

- One atomic mass unit (amu) equals one-twelfth the mass of a carbon atom that has six protons and six neutrons; 1 amu = 1.661×10^{-24} g.

The element lithium is found in many consumer products, from long-lasting lithium batteries to the prescription medication lithium carbonate, used to treat individuals with bipolar disorder.

(top): ©Jill Braaten RF; (bottom): ©McGraw-Hill Education/Charles D. Winters/Timeframe Photography, Inc.

Using this scale, one proton has a mass of 1.0073 amu, a value typically rounded to 1 amu. One neutron has a mass of 1.0087 amu, a value also typically rounded to 1 amu. The mass of an electron is so small that it is ignored.

Every atom of a given type of element always has the *same* number of protons in the nucleus, a value called the *atomic number,* symbolized by **Z.** Conversely, two *different* elements have *different* atomic numbers.

- The *atomic number* (**Z**) = the number of protons in the nucleus of an atom.

Thus, the element hydrogen has one proton in its nucleus, so its atomic number is one. Lithium has three protons in its nucleus, so its atomic number is three. **The periodic table is arranged in order of increasing atomic number beginning at the upper left-hand corner.** The atomic number appears just above the element symbol for each entry in the table.

Since a neutral atom has no overall charge:

- **Z** = the number of protons in the nucleus = the number of electrons.

Thus, the atomic number tells us *both* the number of protons in the nucleus and the number of electrons in the electron cloud of a neutral atom.

SAMPLE PROBLEM 2.3 DETERMINING THE ATOMIC NUMBER AND THE IDENTITY
OF AN ELEMENT FROM MOLECULAR ART

For the given atom: (a) determine the number of protons, neutrons, and electrons in the neutral atom; (b) give the atomic number; (c) identify the element.

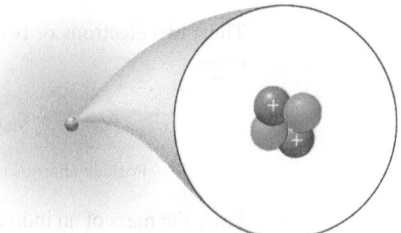

Analysis

- The number of protons = the number of positively charged particles = the atomic number.
- The number of neutrons = the number of uncharged particles.
- The number of protons = the number of electrons in a neutral atom.
- The atomic number determines the identity of an element.

Solution

a. The element contains two protons and two neutrons. Since a neutral atom has the same number of protons and electrons, the element has two electrons.

b. The two protons give the element an atomic number of two.

c. The element with two protons in the nucleus is **helium.**

PRACTICE PROBLEM 2.3

An element has nine protons and 10 neutrons in the neutral atom. (a) How many electrons are present in the neutral atom? (b) What is the atomic number of this element? (c) Identify the element.

More Practice: Try Problems 2.27, 2.28.

SAMPLE PROBLEM 2.4 USING THE ATOMIC NUMBER TO DETERMINE THE NUMBER OF PROTONS AND ELECTRONS

Identify the element that has an atomic number of 19, and give the number of protons and electrons in the neutral atom.

Analysis

The atomic number is unique to an element and tells the number of protons in the nucleus and the number of electrons in the electron cloud of a neutral atom.

Solution

According to the periodic table, the element potassium has atomic number 19. A neutral potassium atom has 19 protons and 19 electrons.

PRACTICE PROBLEM 2.4

Identify the element with each atomic number, and give the number of protons and electrons in the neutral atom: (a) 2; (b) 11; (c) 20; (d) 47; (e) 78.

Both protons and neutrons contribute to the mass of an atom. The **mass number,** symbolized by A, is the sum of the number of protons and neutrons.

- **Mass number (A) = the number of protons (Z) + the number of neutrons.**

For example, a fluorine atom with nine protons and 10 neutrons in the nucleus has a mass number of 19.

SAMPLE PROBLEM 2.5 DETERMINING ATOMIC NUMBER, MASS NUMBER, AND THE IDENTITY OF AN ELEMENT

For the given atom: (a) determine the number of protons and neutrons; (b) give the atomic number and the mass number; (c) identify the element.

Analysis

- The number of protons = the number of positively charged particles = the atomic number. **The atomic number determines the identity of an element.**
- The number of neutrons = the number of uncharged particles.
- The mass number = the number of protons + the number of neutrons.

Solution

a. The element contains six protons and seven neutrons.

b. The six protons give the element an atomic number of six. The mass number = the number of protons + the number of neutrons = 6 + 7 = 13.

c. The element with six protons in the nucleus is **carbon.**

PRACTICE PROBLEM 2.5

For the given atom: (a) determine the number of protons and neutrons; (b) give the atomic number and the mass number; (c) identify the element.

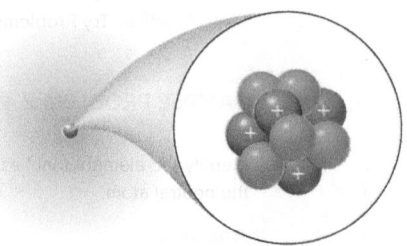

More Practice: Try Problems 2.29, 2.30.

SAMPLE PROBLEM 2.6 USING THE ATOMIC NUMBER AND MASS NUMBER TO DETERMINE THE NUMBER OF PROTONS, NEUTRONS, AND ELECTRONS

How many protons, neutrons, and electrons are contained in an atom of argon, which has an atomic number of 18 and a mass number of 40?

Analysis

- In a neutral atom, the atomic number (Z) = the number of protons = the number of electrons.
- The mass number (A) = the number of protons + the number of neutrons.

Solution

The atomic number of 18 means that argon has 18 protons and 18 electrons. To find the number of neutrons, subtract the atomic number (Z) from the mass number (A).

$$\text{number of neutrons} = \text{mass number} - \text{atomic number}$$
$$= \quad 40 \quad - \quad 18$$
$$= \quad 22 \text{ neutrons}$$

PRACTICE PROBLEM 2.6

How many protons, neutrons, and electrons are contained in each atom with the given atomic number and mass number?

a. $Z = 17, A = 35$ b. $Z = 14, A = 28$ c. $Z = 92, A = 238$

More Practice: Try Problems 2.31, 2.32.

PROBLEM 2.7

What is the mass number of an atom that contains

a. 42 protons, 42 electrons, and 53 neutrons?   b. 24 protons, 24 electrons, and 28 neutrons?

2.3   Isotopes

Two atoms of the same element always have the same number of protons, but the number of neutrons can vary.

- *Isotopes* are atoms of the same element having a different number of neutrons.

2.3A   Isotopes, Atomic Number, and Mass Number

Most elements in nature exist as a mixture of isotopes. For example, all atoms of the element chlorine contain 17 protons in the nucleus, but some of these atoms have 18 neutrons in the nucleus and some have 20 neutrons. Thus, chlorine has two isotopes with different mass numbers, 35 and 37. These isotopes are often referred to as chlorine-35 and chlorine-37.

An **isotope symbol** is also written using the element symbol with the atomic number as a subscript and the mass number as a superscript, both to the left.

Two isotopes of the element chlorine

mass number $\longrightarrow$ $^{35}_{17}Cl$ $^{37}_{17}Cl$
atomic number $\longrightarrow$

chlorine-35   chlorine-37

Because all chlorine atoms have the same atomic number (17), the subscript is sometimes omitted. Thus, chlorine-35 and chlorine-37 can be written as ^{35}Cl and ^{37}Cl, respectively.

The element hydrogen has three isotopes. Most hydrogen atoms have one proton and no neutrons, giving them a mass number of one. About 1% of hydrogen atoms have one proton and one neutron, giving them a mass number of two. This isotope is called **deuterium,** and it is often symbolized as **D.** An even smaller number of hydrogen atoms contain one proton and two neutrons, giving them a mass number of three. This isotope is called **tritium,** symbolized as **T.**

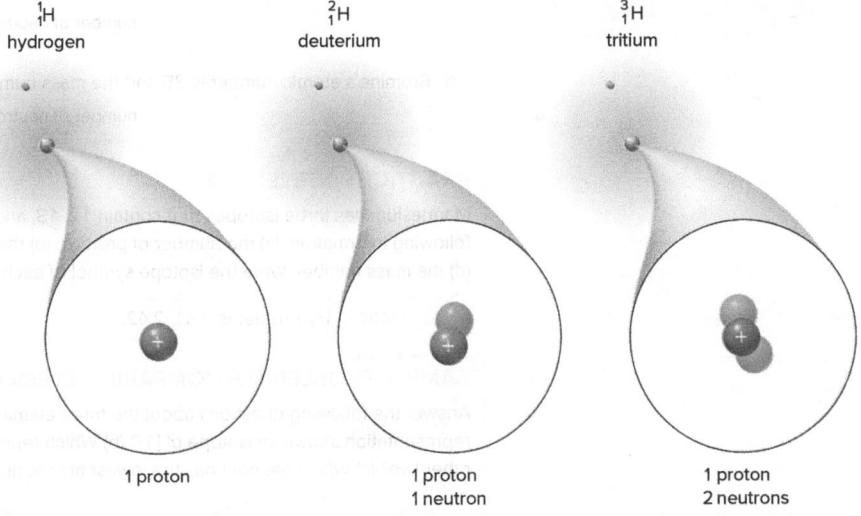

$^{1}_{1}H$ $^{2}_{1}H$ $^{3}_{1}H$
hydrogen   deuterium   tritium

1 proton   1 proton   1 proton
                1 neutron   2 neutrons

SAMPLE PROBLEM 2.7 USING AN ISOTOPE SYMBOL TO DETERMINE THE NUMBER OF PROTONS, NEUTRONS, AND ELECTRONS

For each atom give the following information: [1] the atomic number; [2] the mass number; [3] the number of protons; [4] the number of neutrons; [5] the number of electrons.

a. $^{118}_{50}Sn$ b. ^{195}Pt

Analysis

- The superscript gives the mass number and the subscript gives the atomic number for each element. When the subscript is omitted, use the identity of the element to determine the atomic number.
- The atomic number = the number of protons = the number of electrons.
- The mass number = the number of protons + the number of neutrons.

HEALTH NOTE

Eloxatin is a platinum-containing drug used to treat cancer patients.
©Dr. P. Marazzi/Science Source

Solution

	Atomic Number	Mass Number	Number of Protons	Number of Neutrons	Number of Electrons
a. $^{118}_{50}$Sn	50	118	50	118 − 50 = 68	50
b. ^{195}Pt	78	195	78	195 − 78 = 117	78

PRACTICE PROBLEM 2.7

For each atom give the following information: [1] the atomic number; [2] the mass number; [3] the number of protons; [4] the number of neutrons; [5] the number of electrons.

a. $^{13}_{6}$C   b. ^{121}Sb

More Practice: Try Problems 2.39, 2.40.

PROBLEM 2.8

Write an isotope symbol for the isotope of platinum that contains 116 neutrons.

SAMPLE PROBLEM 2.8 DETERMINING THE NUMBER OF NEUTRONS IN AN ISOTOPE

Determine the number of neutrons in each isotope: (a) carbon-14; (b) ^{81}Br.

Analysis

- The identity of the element tells us the atomic number.
- The number of neutrons = mass number (A) − atomic number (Z).

Solution

a. Carbon's atomic number (Z) is 6. Carbon-14 has a mass number (A) of 14.

$$\text{number of neutrons} = A - Z$$
$$= 14 - 6 = 8 \text{ neutrons}$$

b. Bromine's atomic number is 35 and the mass number of the given isotope is 81.

$$\text{number of neutrons} = A - Z$$
$$= 81 - 35 = 46 \text{ neutrons}$$

PRACTICE PROBLEM 2.8

Magnesium has three isotopes that contain 12, 13, and 14 neutrons. For each isotope give the following information: (a) the number of protons; (b) the number of electrons; (c) the atomic number; (d) the mass number. Write the isotope symbol of each isotope.

More Practice: Try Problems 2.41, 2.42.

SAMPLE PROBLEM 2.9 COMPARING ELEMENTS AND ISOTOPES

Answer the following questions about the three elements whose nuclei are drawn below. (a) Which representation shows an isotope of [1]? (b) Which representation shows a different element from the other two? (c) Which element has the lowest atomic number?

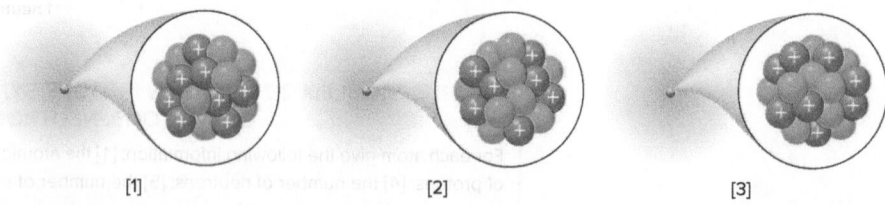

[1]   [2]   [3]

Analysis

- Two isotopes have the same number of protons but a different number of neutrons.
- Two different elements have different numbers of protons.
- The number of protons in the nucleus gives the atomic number.

Solution

a. Representation [1] has eight protons and eight neutrons in the nucleus. Representation [3] is an isotope because it has the same number of protons (eight), but it contains a different number of neutrons (nine).

b. Representation [2] is a different element because it contains only seven protons and representations [1] and [3] each have eight protons.

c. Since the number of protons determines the atomic number, representation [2] has the lowest atomic number (seven) because it has only seven protons in its nucleus.

PRACTICE PROBLEM 2.9

Use the representations ([1]–[3]) in Sample Problem 2.9 to answer the following questions.

a. Which species has the highest mass number?

b. How many electrons are present in the neutral atom of each element?

c. Give the isotope symbol for each species.

More Practice: Try Problems 2.43, 2.44.

ENVIRONMENTAL NOTE

Although gasoline sold in the United States no longer contains lead, leaded gasoline is still used extensively in Asia, Africa, and Latin America. Gasoline exhaust containing lead pollutes the air and soil, and individuals exposed to high lead levels can suffer from circulatory, digestive, and nervous disorders. Lead (Pb) is a metal with atomic number 82 and atomic weight 207.2, as shown in the periodic table. ©Steve Snodgrass

2.3B Atomic Weight

Some elements like fluorine occur naturally as a single isotope. More commonly, an element is a mixture of isotopes, and it is useful to know the average mass, called the **atomic weight** (or **atomic mass**), of the atoms in a sample.

- The *atomic weight* is the weighted average of the mass of the naturally occurring isotopes of a particular element reported in atomic mass units.

The atomic weights of the elements appear in the alphabetical list of elements on the inside front cover. The atomic weight is also given under the element symbol in the periodic table on the inside front cover.

82	← atomic number
Pb	← element symbol
207.2	← atomic weight

lead

To determine the atomic weight of an element, two quantities must be known: the mass of each isotope in atomic mass units, and the abundance with which each isotope occurs.

How To **Determine the Atomic Weight of an Element**

Example: What is the atomic weight of the element chlorine?

Step [1] List each isotope, along with its mass in atomic mass units (amu) and the percentage that each isotope occurs in nature.

- Chlorine has two isotopes—^{35}Cl and ^{37}Cl.
- To solve the problem, the masses and abundances of the isotopes must be known.

	Mass (amu)	Isotopic Abundance
^{35}Cl	34.97	75.78% = 0.7578
^{37}Cl	36.97	24.22% = 0.2422

- The mass of any isotope is very close to the mass number of the isotope.
- To convert a percent to a decimal, divide by 100, which is the same as moving the decimal point two places to the left; thus,

75.78% = 0.7578

Step [2] Multiply the isotopic abundance by the mass of each isotope, and add up the products. The sum is the atomic weight for the element.

Mass due to ^{35}Cl: 0.7578 × 34.97 amu = 26.5003 amu

Mass due to ^{37}Cl: 0.2422 × 36.97 amu = 8.9541 amu

Atomic weight = 35.4544 amu rounded to 35.45 amu

Answer

SAMPLE PROBLEM 2.10 CALCULATING ATOMIC WEIGHT

Calculate the atomic weight of copper, which has two isotopes with the following properties: copper-63 (62.93 amu, 69.17% natural occurrence) and copper-65 (64.93 amu, 30.83% natural occurrence).

Analysis

Multiply the isotopic abundance by the mass of each isotope, and add up the products to give the atomic weight for the element.

Solution

Mass due to ^{63}Cu: 0.6917×62.93 amu $= 43.5287$ amu

Mass due to ^{65}Cu: 0.3083×64.93 amu $= \underline{20.0179}$ amu

Atomic weight $= 63.5466$ amu rounded to 63.55 amu

Answer

PRACTICE PROBLEM 2.10

Calculate the atomic weight of each element given the mass and natural occurrence of each isotope.

	Mass (amu)	Isotopic Abundance		Mass (amu)	Isotopic Abundance
a. Magnesium			b. Vanadium		
Magnesium-24	23.99	78.99%	Vanadium-50	49.95	0.250%
Magnesium-25	24.99	10.00%	Vanadium-51	50.94	99.750%
Magnesium-26	25.98	11.01%			

More Practice: **Try Problems 2.45, 2.46.**

2.3C   FOCUS ON HEALTH & MEDICINE
Isotopes in Medicine

Generally the chemical properties of isotopes are identical. Sometimes, however, one isotope of an element is radioactive—that is, it emits particles or energy as some form of radiation. Radioactive isotopes have both diagnostic and therapeutic uses in medicine.

As an example, iodine-131 is used in at least two different ways for thyroid disease. Iodine is a micronutrient needed by the body to synthesize the thyroid hormone thyroxine, which contains four iodine atoms. To evaluate the thyroid gland, a patient can be given sodium iodide (NaI) that contains radioactive iodine-131. Iodine-131 is taken up in the thyroid gland and as it emits radiation, it produces an image in a thyroid scan, which is then used to determine the condition of the thyroid gland, as shown in Figure 2.4.

Other applications of radioactive isotopes in medicine are discussed in Chapter 10.

Higher doses of iodine-131 can also be used to treat thyroid disease. Since the radioactive isotope is taken up by the thyroid gland, the radiation it emits can kill overactive or cancerous cells in the thyroid.

Figure 2.4   Iodine-131 in Medicine

a.
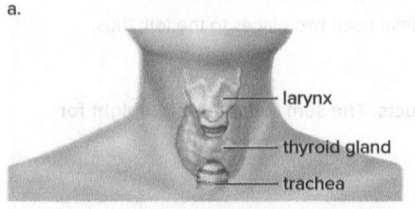
larynx
thyroid gland
trachea

b.

c.

The thyroid gland is a butterfly-shaped gland in the neck, shown in (a). Uptake of radioactive iodine-131 can reveal the presence of a healthy thyroid as in (b), or an unsymmetrical thyroid gland with dense areas of iodine uptake as in (c), which may be indicative of cancer or other thyroid disease.
(b–c): ©Dr. A. Leger/Phototake

2.4 The Periodic Table

Every beginning chemistry text has a periodic table in a prominent location—often the inside front cover—because it is a valuable list of all known elements organized so that groups of elements with similar characteristics are arranged together. The periodic table evolved over many years, and it resulted from the careful observations and experiments of many brilliant scientists in the nineteenth century. Most prominent was Russian chemist Dmitri Mendeleev, whose arrangement in 1869 of the 60 known elements into groups having similar properties became the precursor of the modern periodic table (inside front cover and Figure 2.5).

Figure 2.5 Basic Features of the Periodic Table

- Each element of the periodic table is part of a horizontal row and a vertical column.
- The periodic table consists of seven rows, labeled periods 1–7, and 18 columns that are assigned a group number. Two different numbering systems are indicated.
- Elements are divided into three categories: **main group elements** (groups 1A–8A, shown in light blue), **transition metals** (groups 1B–8B, shown in tan), and **inner transition metals** (shown in light green).

2.4A Basic Features of the Periodic Table

The periodic table is arranged into seven horizontal rows and 18 vertical columns. The particular row and column tell us much about the properties of an element.

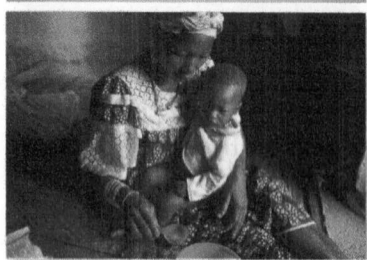

Administering a zinc tablet dissolved in water to a child with diarrhea can save his life. Diarrhea kills more children worldwide than malaria or AIDS. Zinc is a metal located in group 2B (12) in the periodic table. ©Anna Karl-Photojournalist

- A row in the periodic table is called a *period*. Elements in the same row are similar in size.
- A column in the periodic table is called a *group*. Elements in the same group have similar electronic and chemical properties.

The rows in the periodic table are numbered 1–7. The number of elements in each row varies. The first period has just two elements, hydrogen and helium. The second and third rows have eight elements each, and the fourth and fifth rows have 18 elements. Also note that two rows of 14 elements appear at the bottom of the periodic table. The **lanthanides,** beginning with the element cerium ($Z = 58$), immediately follow the element lanthanum (La). The **actinides,** beginning with thorium ($Z = 90$), immediately follow the element actinium (Ac).

Each column in the periodic table is assigned a **group number.** Groups are numbered in two ways. In one system, the 18 columns of the periodic table are assigned the numbers 1–18, beginning with the column farthest to the left. An older but still widely used system numbers the groups 1–8, followed by the letter A or B.

- The *main group elements* consist of the two columns on the far left and the six columns on the far right of the table. These groups are numbered 1A–8A (1, 2, 13–18).
- The *transition metal elements* are contained in the 10 short columns in the middle of the table, numbered 1B–8B (3–12).
- The *inner transition metal elements* consist of the lanthanides and actinides, and they are not assigned group numbers.

The periodic table in Figure 2.5 has both systems of numbering groups. For example, the element carbon (C) is located in the second row (period 2) of the periodic table. Its group number is 4A (or 14).

One group and one period are highlighted in the periodic table in Figure 2.6.

Figure 2.6   A Group and a Period in the Periodic Table

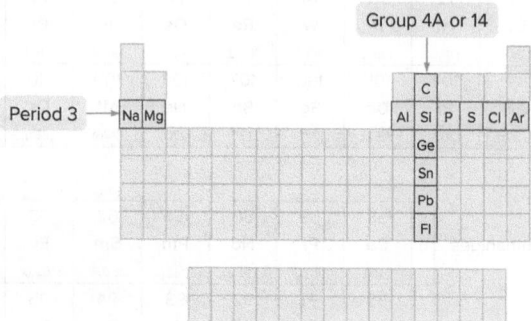

- The elements C, Si, Ge, Sn, Pb, and Fl are part of group 4A (or 14) in the periodic table.
- The elements Na, Mg, Al, Si, P, S, Cl, and Ar are part of the third row, period 3, of the periodic table.

PROBLEM 2.9

(a) How many elements are found in period 4 in the periodic table? (b) How many elements are found in group 5A (or 15)?

SAMPLE PROBLEM 2.11 DETERMINING THE GROUP NUMBER AND PERIOD OF AN ELEMENT

Give the period and group number for each element: (a) aluminum; (b) manganese.

Analysis

Use the element symbol to locate an element in the periodic table. Count down the rows of elements to determine the period. The group number is located at the top of each column.

Most food and beverage cans are made from the element aluminum (Sample Problem 2.11). Although currently over 60% of the aluminum cans used in the United States are recycled, estimates suggest that Americans discard aluminum valued at one billion dollars each year.
©FogStock/Alamy RF

Solution

a. Aluminum (Al) is located in the third row (period 3), and has group number 3A (or 13).

b. Manganese (Mn) is located in the fourth row (period 4), and has group number 7B (or 7).

PRACTICE PROBLEM 2.11

Label each macronutrient in Figure 2.2 in the following periodic table, and give its period and group number.

More Practice: Try Problems 2.23b–d, 2.24d, f, 2.82b.

2.4B   Characteristics of Groups 1A, 2A, 7A, and 8A

Four columns of main group elements illustrate an important fact about the periodic table.

• Elements that comprise a particular group have similar chemical properties.

Alkali Metals (Group 1A) and Alkaline Earth Elements (Group 2A)

The alkali metals and the alkaline earth elements are located on the far left side of the periodic table.

Although hydrogen is also located in group 1A, it is *not* an alkali metal.

The **alkali metals,** located in group 1A (group 1), include lithium (Li), sodium (Na), potassium (K), rubidium (Rb), cesium (Cs), and francium (Fr). Alkali metals share the following characteristics:

• They are soft and shiny and have low melting points.
• They are good conductors of heat and electricity.
• They react readily with water to form basic solutions.

The **alkaline earth elements,** located in group 2A (group 2), include beryllium (Be), magnesium (Mg), calcium (Ca), strontium (Sr), barium (Ba), and radium (Ra). Alkaline earth metals are also shiny solids but less reactive than the alkali metals.

None of the metals in groups 1A and 2A exist in nature as pure elements; rather, they are always combined with other elements to form compounds. Examples of compounds from group 1A elements include sodium chloride (NaCl), table salt, and potassium iodide (KI), an essential nutrient added to make iodized salt. Examples of compounds from group 2A elements include magnesium sulfate ($MgSO_4$), an anticonvulsant used to prevent seizures in pregnant women, and barium sulfate ($BaSO_4$), which is used to improve the quality of X-ray images of the gastro-intestinal tract.

Halogens (Group 7A) and Noble Gases (Group 8A)

The halogens and noble gases are located on the far right side of the periodic table.

Chlorpheniramine is an antihistamine that contains the halogen chlorine. Antihistamines are drugs used to treat the symptoms of the common cold and allergies. We will learn more about antihistamines in Chapter 18.
©Jill Braaten RF

The **halogens,** located in group 7A (group 17), include fluorine (F), chlorine (Cl), bromine (Br), iodine (I), and the rare radioactive element astatine (At). In their elemental form, halogens contain two atoms joined together—F_2, Cl_2, Br_2, and I_2. Fluorine and chlorine are gases at room temperature, bromine is a liquid, and iodine is a solid. Halogens are very reactive and combine with many other elements to form compounds. In Chapter 14, we will learn about carbon compounds that contain halogen atoms.

The **noble gases,** located in group 8A (group 18), include helium (He), neon (Ne), argon (Ar), krypton (Kr), xenon (Xe), and radon (Rn). Unlike other elements, the noble gases are especially stable as atoms, and so they rarely combine with other elements to form compounds.

The noble gas radon has received attention in recent years. Radon is a radioactive gas, and generally its concentration in the air is low and therefore its presence harmless. In some types of soil, however, radon levels can be high and radon detectors are recommended for the basement of homes to monitor radon levels.

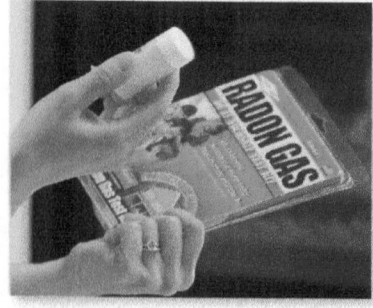

Radon detectors are used to measure high levels of radon, a radioactive noble gas linked to an increased incidence of lung cancer. ©Keith Eng, 2008

PROBLEM 2.10

Identify the element fitting each description.

  a. an alkali metal in period 4
  b. a second-row element in group 7A
  c. a noble gas in the third period
  d. a main group element in period 5 and group 2A
  e. a transition metal in group 12, period 4
  f. a transition metal in group 5, period 5

PROBLEM 2.11

Identify each highlighted element in the periodic table and give its [1] element name and symbol; [2] group number; [3] period; [4] classification (main group element, transition metal, or inner transition metal).

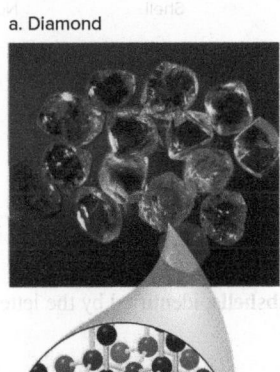

2.4C The Unusual Nature of Carbon

Carbon, a second-row element in group 4A (group 14) of the periodic table, is different from most other elements in that it has three elemental forms (Figure 2.7). The two most common forms of carbon are diamond and graphite. **Diamond** is hard because it contains a dense three-dimensional network of carbon atoms in six-membered rings. **Graphite,** on the other hand, is a slippery black substance used as a lubricant. It contains parallel sheets of carbon atoms in flat six-membered rings.

Buckminsterfullerene, also referred to as a bucky ball, is a third form that contains 60 carbon atoms joined together in a sphere of 20 hexagons and 12 pentagons in a pattern that resembles a soccer ball. A component of soot, this form of carbon was not discovered until 1985. Its unusual name stems from its shape, which resembles the geodesic dome invented by R. Buckminster Fuller.

Carbon's ability to join with itself and other elements gives it versatility not seen with any other element in the periodic table. In the unscientific but eloquent description by writer Bill Bryson in *A Short History of Nearly Everything,* carbon is described as "the party animal of the atomic world, latching on to many other atoms (including itself) and holding tight, forming

Figure 2.7 Three Elemental Forms of Carbon

a. Diamond

b. Graphite

c. Buckminsterfullerene

- Diamond consists of an intricate three-dimensional network of carbon atoms.

- Graphite contains parallel sheets of carbon atoms.

- Buckminsterfullerene contains a sphere with 60 carbon atoms.

(a): ©Charles O'Rear/Corbis Documentary/Getty Images; (b): ©Lester V. Bergman/Corbis Documentary/Getty Images; (c): ©McGraw-Hill Education/Jill Braaten, photographer

molecular conga lines of hearty robustness—the very trick of nature necessary to build proteins and DNA." As a result, millions of compounds that contain the element carbon are known. The chemistry of these compounds is discussed at length in Chapters 11–24.

2.5   Electronic Structure

Why do elements in a group of the periodic table have similar chemical properties? **The chemical properties of an element are determined by the number of *electrons* in an atom.** To understand the properties of an element, therefore, we must learn more about the electrons that surround the nucleus.

The modern description of the electronic structure of an atom is based on the following principles.

- Electrons do not move freely in space; rather, an electron is confined to a specific region, giving it a particular energy.
- Electrons occupy discrete energy levels. The energy of electrons is *quantized;* that is, the energy is restricted to specific values.

The electrons that surround a nucleus are confined to regions called the **principal energy levels** or **shells.**

- The shells are numbered, $n = 1, 2, 3, 4$, and so forth, beginning closest to the nucleus.
- Electrons closer to the nucleus are held more tightly and are lower in energy.
- Electrons farther from the nucleus are held less tightly and are higher in energy.

The number of electrons that can occupy a given shell is determined by the value of n. **The farther a shell is from the nucleus, the larger its volume becomes, and the more electrons it can hold.** Thus, the first shell can hold only two electrons, the second holds eight, the third 18, and so forth. The maximum number of electrons is given by the formula $2n^2$, where n = the shell number.

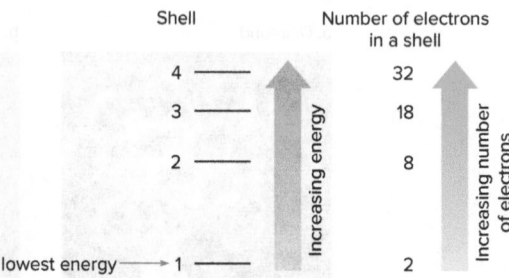

Shells are divided into **subshells,** identified by the letters *s, p, d,* and *f.* The subshells consist of **orbitals.**

- An *orbital* is a region of space where the probability of finding an electron is high. Each orbital can hold *two* electrons.

The two electrons in an orbital must have opposite spins. If one electron has a clockwise spin, the second electron in the orbital must have a counterclockwise spin.

A particular type of subshell contains a specific number of orbitals. An *s* subshell contains only **one** *s* orbital. A *p* subshell has **three** *p* orbitals. A *d* subshell has **five** *d* orbitals. An *f* subshell has **seven** *f* orbitals. The number of subshells in a given shell equals the value of *n*. The energy of orbitals shows the following trend:

| *s* orbital | *p* orbital | *d* orbital | *f* orbital |
| lowest energy | | | highest energy |

Increasing energy

The first shell of electrons around a nucleus ($n = 1$) has only one s orbital. This orbital is called the $1s$ orbital because it is the s orbital in the first shell. Since each orbital can hold two electrons and the first shell has only one orbital, the **first shell can hold two electrons.**

shell number (principal energy level) $\overset{1s}{\longrightarrow}$ = the s orbital in the first shell

The second shell of electrons ($n = 2$) has two types of orbitals—one s and three p orbitals. These orbitals are called the $2s$ and $2p$ orbitals because they are located in the second shell. Since each orbital can hold two electrons and there are four orbitals, the **second shell can hold eight electrons.**

one 2s orbital three 2p orbitals

2s   2p 2p 2p = **4 orbitals** in the second shell

Each orbital holds **two** electrons.

$$4 \text{ orbitals} \times \frac{2 \text{ electrons}}{1 \text{ orbital}} =$$

8 electrons in the second shell

The third shell of electrons ($n = 3$) has three types of orbitals—one s, three p, and five d orbitals. These orbitals are called the $3s$, $3p$, and $3d$ orbitals because they are located in the third shell. Since each orbital can hold two electrons and the third shell has a total of nine orbitals, the **third shell can hold 18 electrons.**

one 3s orbital three 3p orbitals   five 3d orbitals

3s   3p 3p 3p   3d 3d 3d 3d 3d = **9 orbitals** in the third shell

Each orbital holds **two** electrons.

$$9 \text{ orbitals} \times \frac{2 \text{ electrons}}{1 \text{ orbital}} =$$

18 electrons in the third shell

The fourth shell of electrons ($n = 4$) has four types of orbitals—one s, three p, five d, and seven f orbitals. These orbitals are called the $4s$, $4p$, $4d$, and $4f$ orbitals because they are located in the fourth shell. Since each orbital can hold two electrons and the fourth shell has a total of 16 orbitals, the **fourth shell can hold 32 electrons.**

one 4s orbital   three 4p orbitals   five 4d orbitals   seven 4f orbitals

4s   4p 4p 4p   4d 4d 4d 4d 4d   4f 4f 4f 4f 4f 4f 4f = **16 orbitals** in the fourth shell

$$16 \text{ orbitals} \times \frac{2 \text{ electrons}}{1 \text{ orbital}} =$$ **32 electrons** in the fourth shell

Thus, the maximum number of electrons that can occupy a shell is determined by the number of orbitals in the shell. Table 2.4 summarizes the orbitals and electrons in the first four shells.

Table 2.4 Orbitals and Electrons Contained in the Principal Energy Levels ($n = 1–4$)

Shell	Orbitals	Electrons in Each Subshell	Maximum Number of Electrons
1	1s	2	2
2	2s	2	8
	2p 2p 2p	$3 \times 2 = 6$	
3	3s	2	18
	3p 3p 3p	$3 \times 2 = 6$	
	3d 3d 3d 3d 3d	$5 \times 2 = 10$	
4	4s	2	32
	4p 4p 4p	$3 \times 2 = 6$	
	4d 4d 4d 4d 4d	$5 \times 2 = 10$	
	4f 4f 4f 4f 4f 4f 4f	$7 \times 2 = 14$	

Each type of orbital has a particular shape.

- An *s* orbital has a sphere of electron density. It is lower in energy than other orbitals in the same shell because electrons are kept closer to the positively charged nucleus.
- A *p* orbital has a dumbbell shape. A *p* orbital is higher in energy than an *s* orbital in the same shell because its electron density is farther from the nucleus.

All *s* orbitals are spherical, but the orbital gets larger in size as the shell number increases. Thus, both a 1*s* orbital and a 2*s* orbital are spherical, but the 2*s* orbital is larger. The three *p* orbitals in a shell are perpendicular to each other along the *x*, *y*, and *z* axes.

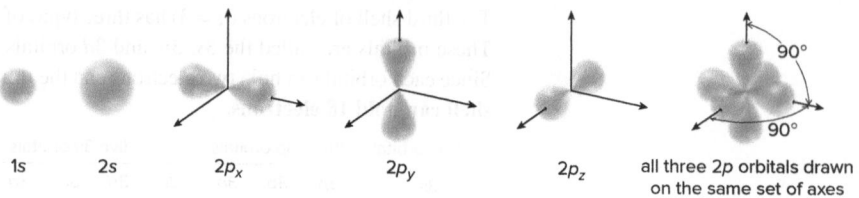

PROBLEM 2.12

How many electrons are present in each shell, subshell, or orbital?

a. a 2*p* orbital   b. the 3*d* subshell   c. a 3*d* orbital   d. the third shell

2.6   Electronic Configurations

We can now examine the **electronic configuration** of an individual atom—that is, how the electrons are arranged in an atom's orbitals. **The lowest energy arrangement of electrons is called the** *ground state*. Three rules are followed.

Rules to Determine the Ground State Electronic Configuration of an Atom

Rule [1] **Electrons are placed in the lowest energy orbitals beginning with the 1*s* orbital.**

- In comparing similar types of orbitals from one shell to another (e.g., 2*s* and 3*s*), an orbital closer to the nucleus is lower in energy. Thus, the energy of a 2*s* orbital is lower than a 3*s* orbital.
- Within a shell, orbital energies increase in the following order: *s*, *p*, *d*, *f*. These guidelines result in the following order of energies in the first three periods: 1*s*, 2*s*, 2*p*, 3*s*, 3*p*. Above the 3*p* level, however, all orbitals of one shell do *not* have to be filled before any orbital in the next higher shell gets electrons. For example, a 4*s* orbital is lower in energy than a 3*d* orbital, so it is filled first. Figure 2.8 lists the relative energies of the orbitals used by atoms in the periodic table.

Rule [2] **Each orbital holds a maximum of two electrons.**

Rule [3] **When orbitals are equal in energy, one electron is added to each orbital until the orbitals are half-filled, before any orbital is completely filled.**

- For example, one electron is added to each of the three *p* orbitals before filling any *p* orbital with two electrons.
- Because like charges repel each other (Section 2.2), adding electrons to *different p* orbitals keeps them farther away from each other, which is energetically favorable.

To illustrate how these rules are used, we can write the electronic configuration for several elements using **orbital diagrams.** An orbital diagram uses a box to represent each orbital and

Figure 2.8

Relative Energies of Orbitals

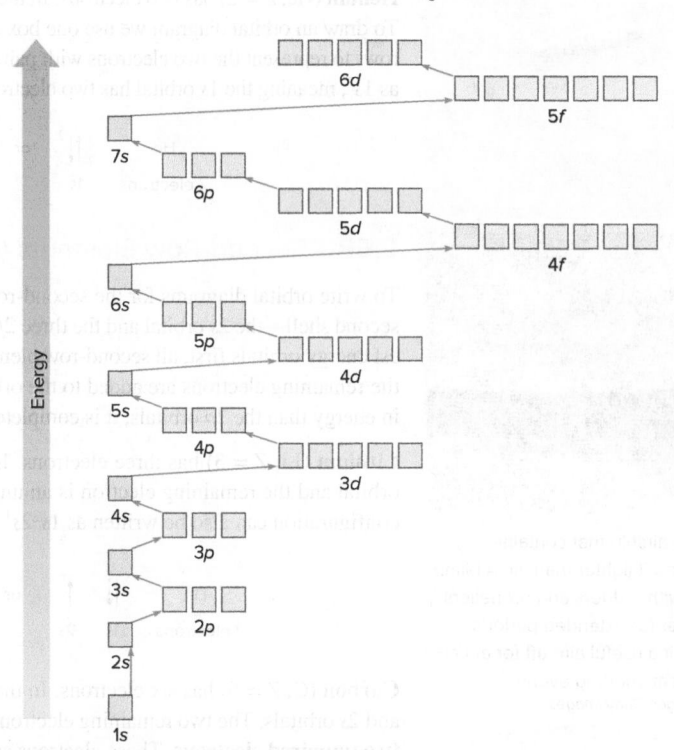

Order of orbital filling

Energy

- Electrons are added to orbitals in order of increasing energy, beginning with the 1s orbital. The arrows drawn between orbitals (i.e., 1s ⟶ 2s) show the order in which they are filled. The three p orbitals, five d orbitals, and seven f orbitals are also shown.
- The 4s orbital is filled with electrons before the 3d orbitals because it is lower in energy. The same is true for filling the 5s orbital with electrons before the 4d orbitals. Likewise, the 6s orbital is filled before both the 4f and 5d orbitals, and the 7s orbital is filled before both the 5f and 6d orbitals.

arrows to represent electrons. A single electron, called an **unpaired electron,** is shown with a single arrow pointing up (↑). Two electrons in an orbital have **paired spins**—that is, the spins are opposite in direction—so up and down arrows (↑↓) are used.

Finally, it is not necessary to memorize the order of orbital filling that appears in Figure 2.8. Rather, **the periodic table can be used to determine the electronic configuration of an element,** as shown in Section 2.6C. This method is especially useful for elements in the fourth row and later, in which an orbital of a higher shell gets electrons before filling a lower shell completely.

2.6A   First-Row Elements (Period 1)

The first row of the periodic table contains only two elements—hydrogen and helium. Since the number of protons in the nucleus equals the number of electrons in a neutral atom, the **atomic number tells us how many electrons must be placed in orbitals.**

Hydrogen (H, $Z = 1$) has one electron. In the ground state, this electron is added to the lowest energy orbital, the 1s orbital. To draw an orbital diagram we use one box to represent the 1s orbital, and one up arrow to represent the electron. We can also write out the electron configuration without boxes and arrows, using a superscript with each orbital to show how many electrons it contains.

H   ↑   or $1s^1$ one electron in the 1s orbital

1 electron   1s

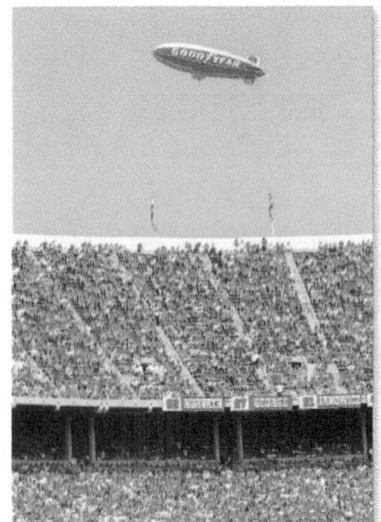

A blimp is an airship that contains helium, making it lighter than air. A blimp maneuvers with rudders and propellers and can hover for extended periods, thus making it a useful aircraft for aerial photography at sporting events.
©*Diamond Images/Getty Images*

Helium (He, $Z = 2$) has two electrons. In the ground state, both electrons are added to the $1s$ orbital. To draw an orbital diagram we use one box to represent the $1s$ orbital, and a set of up and down arrows to represent the two electrons with paired spins. The electron configuration can also be written as $1s^2$, meaning the $1s$ orbital has two electrons. Helium has a filled first shell of electrons.

He   ↑↓   or $1s^2$ two electrons in the 1s orbital
2 electrons   1s

2.6B Second-Row Elements (Period 2)

To write orbital diagrams for the second-row elements, we must now use the four orbitals in the second shell—the $2s$ orbital and the three $2p$ orbitals. Since electrons are always added to the lowest energy orbitals first, all second-row elements have the $1s$ orbital filled with electrons, and then the remaining electrons are added to the orbitals in the second shell. Since the $2s$ orbital is lower in energy than the $2p$ orbitals, it is completely filled before adding electrons to the $2p$ orbitals.

Lithium (Li, $Z = 3$) has three electrons. In the ground state, two electrons are added to the $1s$ orbital and the remaining electron is an unpaired electron in the $2s$ orbital. Lithium's electronic configuration can also be written as $1s^2 2s^1$ to show the placement of its three electrons.

Li   ↑↓ ↑   or $1s^2 2s^1$ two electrons in the 1s orbital
3 electrons   1s   2s   one electron in the 2s orbital

Carbon (C, $Z = 6$) has six electrons. In the ground state, two electrons are added to both the $1s$ and $2s$ orbitals. The two remaining electrons are added to two different $2p$ orbitals, giving carbon **two unpaired electrons.** These electrons spin in the same direction, so the arrows used to represent them are drawn in the same direction as well (both ↑ in this case). Carbon's electronic configuration is also written as $1s^2 2s^2 2p^2$. This method of writing an electronic configuration indicates that carbon has two electrons in its $2p$ orbitals, but it does not explicitly show that the two $2p$ electrons occupy *different* $2p$ orbitals.

two electrons in two *different* 2p orbitals
C   ↑↓ ↑↓ ↑ ↑   or $1s^2 2s^2 2p^2$
6 electrons   1s   2s   2p

Oxygen (O, $Z = 8$) has eight electrons. In the ground state, two electrons are added to both the $1s$ and $2s$ orbitals. The remaining four electrons must be distributed among the three $2p$ orbitals to give the lowest energy arrangement. This is done by pairing two electrons in one $2p$ orbital, and giving the remaining $2p$ orbitals one electron each. Oxygen has two unpaired electrons.

two electrons in two *different* 2p orbitals
O   ↑↓ ↑↓ ↑↓ ↑ ↑   or $1s^2 2s^2 2p^4$
8 electrons   1s   2s   2p

Neon (Ne, $Z = 10$) has 10 electrons. In the ground state, two electrons are added to the $1s$, $2s$, and each of the three $2p$ orbitals, so that the second shell of orbitals is now completely filled with electrons.

Ne   ↑↓ ↑↓ ↑↓ ↑↓ ↑↓   or $1s^2 2s^2 2p^6$
10 electrons   1s   2s   2p

Sometimes the electronic configuration of an element is shortened by using the name of the noble gas that has a filled shell of electrons from the preceding row, and then adding the electronic configuration of all remaining electrons using orbitals and superscripts. For example, each second-row element has a $1s^2$ configuration like the noble gas helium in the preceding row, so the electronic configuration for carbon can be shortened to $[He]2s^22p^2$.

Electronic configuration for helium: [He] = $1s^2$

For carbon: $1s^22s^22p^2$ $[He]2s^22p^2$

replace

carbon's electronic configuration using noble gas notation

The electronic configurations of all the first- and second-row elements are listed in Table 2.5.

Table 2.5 Electronic Configurations of the First- and Second-Row Elements

Atomic Number	Element	Orbital Diagram 1s	2s	2p	Electronic Configuration	Noble Gas Notation
1	H	↑			$1s^1$	
2	He	↑↓			$1s^2$	
3	Li	↑↓	↑		$1s^22s^1$	$[He]2s^1$
4	Be	↑↓	↑↓		$1s^22s^2$	$[He]2s^2$
5	B	↑↓	↑↓	↑	$1s^22s^22p^1$	$[He]2s^22p^1$
6	C	↑↓	↑↓	↑ ↑	$1s^22s^22p^2$	$[He]2s^22p^2$
7	N	↑↓	↑↓	↑ ↑ ↑	$1s^22s^22p^3$	$[He]2s^22p^3$
8	O	↑↓	↑↓	↑↓ ↑ ↑	$1s^22s^22p^4$	$[He]2s^22p^4$
9	F	↑↓	↑↓	↑↓ ↑↓ ↑	$1s^22s^22p^5$	$[He]2s^22p^5$
10	Ne	↑↓	↑↓	↑↓ ↑↓ ↑↓	$1s^22s^22p^6$	$[He]2s^22p^6$

PROBLEM 2.13

What element has each electronic configuration?

a. $1s^22s^22p^63s^23p^2$ b. $1s^22s^22p^63s^23p^64s^23d^1$ c. $[Ar]4s^23d^{10}$

PROBLEM 2.14

What element(s) in the first and second period fit each description?

a. The element has one electron in the second energy level.

b. There are two electrons in the 2s orbital.

c. The electronic configuration is $1s^22s^22p^5$.

d. The element contains six electrons in the second energy level.

2.6C   Electronic Configurations of Other Elements Using the Periodic Table

Orbital diagrams can be written for every element in the periodic table. We can use the location of an element in the periodic table to determine what orbitals are filled with electrons.

Considering electronic configuration, the periodic table can be divided into four regions called **blocks,** labeled *s, p, d,* and *f,* and illustrated in Figure 2.9. **The blocks are labeled according to the subshells that are filled with electrons *last.***

Figure 2.9   The Blocks of Elements in the Periodic Table

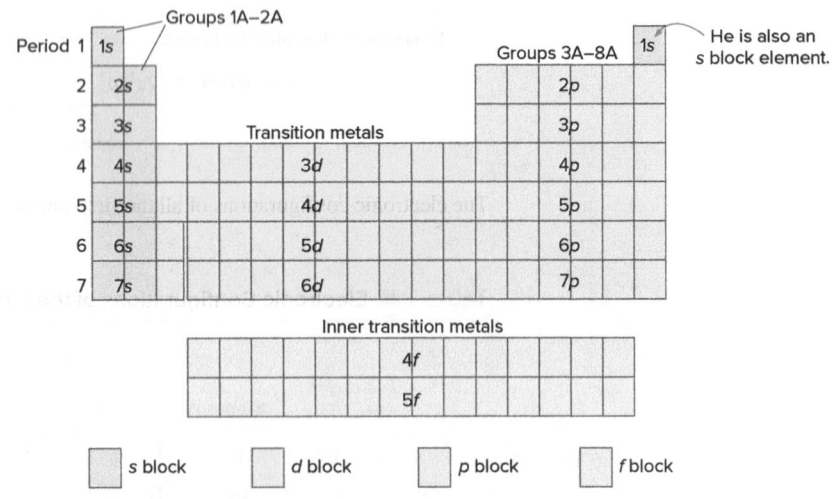

- The *s block* consists of groups 1A and 2A and the element helium. The *s* subshell is filled last in these elements.
- The *p block* consists of groups 3A–8A (except helium). The *p* subshell is filled last in these elements.
- The *d block* consists of the 10 columns of transition metals. The *d* subshell is filled last in these elements.
- The *f block* consists of the two groups of 14 inner transition metals. The *f* subshell is filled last in these elements.

How to use the blocks in Figure 2.9 to write the electronic configuration is shown in the stepwise procedure, and then illustrated with an example in Sample Problem 2.12.

How To   **Draw an Orbital Diagram for the Ground State Electronic Configuration of an Element**

Example: Give the orbital diagram for the electronic configuration of the element sulfur.

Step [1]   **Use the atomic number to determine the number of electrons.**
- Sulfur has an atomic number of 16, so 16 electrons must be placed in orbitals.

Step [2]   **Locate the element in the periodic table and use Figure 2.9 to determine the order of orbital filling.**
- Read the table in blocks from left-to-right, row-by-row, beginning at the upper left corner and ending with the element in question.
- Sulfur is located in the *p* block, so its 3*p* orbitals are filled with electrons last.

Sulfur is a *p* block element. Its 3*p* orbitals are filled with electrons last.

—Continued

Step [3] **Give each orbital two electrons until all electrons are used. In filling orbitals of the same energy, place electrons one at a time in the orbitals until they are half-filled.**

- For sulfur, add two electrons to each of the 1s, 2s, three 2p, and 3s orbitals (12 electrons used).
- To add the remaining four electrons to the 3p orbitals, give one orbital two electrons and place one unpaired electron in the remaining two orbitals.

Answer:

two unpaired electrons

S					
sulfur	1s	2s	2p	3s	3p
16 electrons					

SAMPLE PROBLEM 2.12 WRITING THE ELECTRONIC CONFIGURATION OF AN ELEMENT

Give the ground state electronic configuration of the element calcium. Convert the electronic configuration to noble gas notation.

Analysis

- Use the atomic number to determine the number of electrons.
- Locate the element in the periodic table and use Figure 2.9 to determine the order of orbitals filled with electrons.
- To convert the electronic configuration to noble gas notation, replace the electronic configuration corresponding to the noble gas in the preceding row by the symbol for the noble gas in brackets.

Solution

The atomic number of calcium is 20, so 20 electrons must be placed in orbitals. Figure 2.9 shows the following order of orbitals to be filled: 1s, 2s, 2p (three orbitals), 3s, 3p (three orbitals), and 4s. Give each orbital two electrons. Since calcium is an element in period 4, use the noble gas argon in period 3 to write the noble gas configuration. **Substitute [Ar] for all of the electrons in the first three shells.**

$$\text{Electronic configuration for Ca} \quad = \quad 1s^2 2s^2 2p^6 3s^2 3p^6 4s^2 \quad = \quad [Ar]4s^2$$

(20 electrons)   The noble gas argon contains   noble gas notation
these 18 electrons.

Replace with [Ar].

PRACTICE PROBLEM 2.12

Draw an orbital diagram for each element: (a) magnesium; (b) aluminum; (c) bromine.

More Practice: Try Problems 2.49–2.52.

PROBLEM 2.15

Give the electronic configuration for each element and then convert it to noble gas notation: (a) sodium; (b) silicon; (c) iodine.

2.7 Valence Electrons

The chemical properties of an element depend on the most loosely held electrons—that is, those electrons in the outermost shell, called the **valence shell.** The period number tells the number of the valence shell.

- **The electrons in the outermost shell are called the *valence electrons*.**

2.7A Relating Valence Electrons to Group Number

To identify the electrons in the valence shell, always look for the shell with the *highest* number. Thus, beryllium has two valence electrons that occupy the 2*s* orbital. Chlorine has seven valence electrons because it has a total of seven electrons in the third shell, two in the 3*s* orbital and five in the 3*p* orbitals.

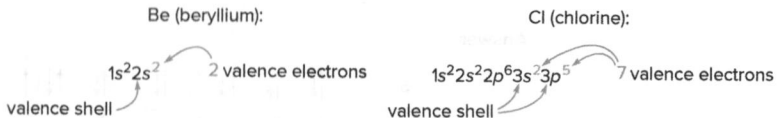

If we examine the electronic configuration of a group in the periodic table, two facts become apparent.

> - Elements in the same group have the same number of valence electrons and similar electronic configurations.
> - The group number (using the 1A–8A system) equals the number of valence electrons for main group elements (except helium).

As an example, the alkali metals in group 1A all have one valence electron that occupies an *s* orbital. Thus, a general electronic configuration for the valence electrons of an alkali metal is ns^1, where n = the period in which the element is located.

Thus, the periodic table is organized into groups of elements with similar valence electronic configurations in the same column. The valence electronic configurations of the main group elements in the first three rows of the periodic table are given in Table 2.6.

> - The chemical properties of a group are similar because these elements contain the same electronic configuration of valence electrons.

Take particular note of the electronic configuration of the noble gases in group 8A. **All of these elements have a completely filled outer shell of valence electrons.** Helium has a filled first shell ($1s^2$ configuration). The remaining elements have a completely filled valence shell of *s* and *p* orbitals (s^2p^6). This electronic arrangement is especially stable, and as a result, these elements exist in nature as single atoms. We will learn about the consequences of having a completely filled valence shell in Chapter 3.

Table 2.6 Valence Electronic Configurations for the Main Group Elements in Periods 1–3

Group Number	1A	2A	3A	4A	5A	6A	7A	8A[a]
Period 1	H $1s^1$							He $1s^2$
Period 2	Li $2s^1$	Be $2s^2$	B $2s^22p^1$	C $2s^22p^2$	N $2s^22p^3$	O $2s^22p^4$	F $2s^22p^5$	Ne $2s^22p^6$
Period 3	Na $3s^1$	Mg $3s^2$	Al $3s^23p^1$	Si $3s^23p^2$	P $3s^23p^3$	S $3s^23p^4$	Cl $3s^23p^5$	Ar $3s^23p^6$
General configuration	ns^1	ns^2	ns^2np^1	ns^2np^2	ns^2np^3	ns^2np^4	ns^2np^5	ns^2np^6

[a]The general electronic configuration in group 8A applies to all of the noble gases except helium. Since helium is a first-row element, it has only two electrons, and these occupy the only available orbital in the first shell, the $1s$ orbital.

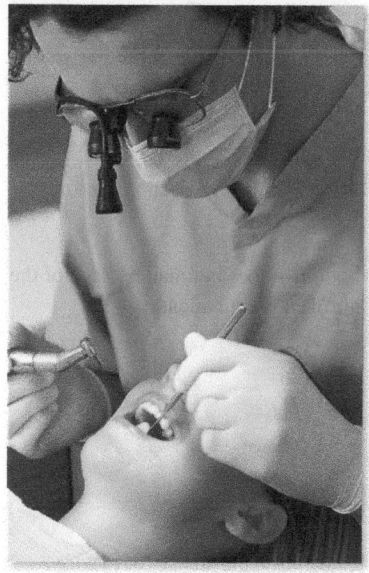

Mercury (Sample Problem 2.13) is safely used in dental amalgam to fill cavities in teeth. Mercury released into the environment, however, is converted to toxic methylmercury by microorganisms in water, so hazardous levels of this soluble mercury compound can accumulate in fish at the top of the food chain, such as sharks and swordfish. See also Problem 1.53.
©Fancy Photography/SuperStock RF

SAMPLE PROBLEM 2.13 IDENTIFYING THE NUMBER OF VALENCE ELECTRONS

Identify the total number of electrons, the number of valence electrons, and the name of the element with each electronic configuration.

a. $1s^22s^22p^63s^23p^2$

b. $1s^22s^22p^63s^23p^64s^23d^{10}4p^65s^24d^{10}5p^66s^24f^{14}5d^{10}$

Analysis

To obtain the total number of electrons, add up the superscripts. This gives the atomic number and identifies the element. **To determine the number of valence electrons, add up the number of electrons in the shell with the *highest* number.**

Solution

a. valence shell
$1s^22s^22p^63s^23p^2$
4 valence electrons

Total number of electrons =
$2 + 2 + 6 + 2 + 2 = $ **14**

Answer: Silicon (Si), 14 total electrons and 4 valence electrons

b. valence shell
$1s^22s^22p^63s^23p^64s^23d^{10}4p^65s^24d^{10}5p^66s^24f^{14}5d^{10}$
2 valence electrons

Total number of electrons = **80**

Answer: Mercury (Hg), 80 total electrons and 2 valence electrons

PRACTICE PROBLEM 2.13

Identify the total number of electrons, the number of valence electrons, and the name of the element with each electronic configuration.

a. $1s^22s^22p^63s^2$

b. $1s^22s^22p^63s^23p^3$

c. $1s^22s^22p^63s^23p^64s^23d^{10}4p^65s^24d^2$

d. $[Ar]4s^23d^6$

More Practice: Try Problems 2.55, 2.56, 2.81g, 2.84g.

SAMPLE PROBLEM 2.14 DETERMINING THE ELECTRONIC CONFIGURATION OF VALENCE ELECTRONS

Determine the number of valence electrons and give the electronic configuration of the valence electrons of each element: (a) nitrogen; (b) potassium.

Analysis

The group number of a main group element = the number of valence electrons. Use the general electronic configurations in Table 2.6 to write the configuration of the valence electrons.

Solution

a. Nitrogen is located in group 5A, so it has five valence electrons. Since nitrogen is a second-period element, its valence electronic configuration is $2s^2 2p^3$.

b. Potassium is located in group 1A, so it has one valence electron. Since potassium is a fourth-period element, its valence electronic configuration is $4s^1$.

PRACTICE PROBLEM 2.14

Determine the number of valence electrons and give the electronic configuration of the valence electrons of each element: (a) fluorine; (b) krypton; (c) magnesium; (d) germanium.

More Practice: Try Problems 2.57–2.60, 2.63, 2.64.

2.7B   Electron-Dot Symbols

The number of valence electrons around an atom is often represented by an **electron-dot symbol.** Representative examples are shown.

	H	C	O	Cl
Number of valence electrons:	1	4	6	7
Electron-dot symbol:	H·	·Ċ·	·Ö·	·Ċl:

- Each dot represents one valence electron.
- The dots are placed on the four sides of an element symbol.
- For one to four valence electrons, single dots are used. With more than four electrons, the dots are paired.

The location of the dots around the symbol—side, top, or bottom—does not matter. Each of the following representations for the five valence electrons of nitrogen is equivalent.

·N̈·   ·N̈·   :N̈·   ·N̈:

SAMPLE PROBLEM 2.15 WRITING AN ELECTRON-DOT SYMBOL

Write an electron-dot symbol for each element: (a) sodium; (b) phosphorus.

Analysis

Write the symbol for each element and use the group number to determine the number of valence electrons for a main group element. Represent each valence electron with a dot.

Solution

a. The symbol for sodium is Na. Na is in group 1A and has one valence electron. Electron-dot symbol:

Na·

b. The symbol for phosphorus is P. P is in group 5A and has five valence electrons. Electron-dot symbol:

·P̈·

PRACTICE PROBLEM 2.15

Give the electron-dot symbol for each element: (a) bromine; (b) lithium; (c) aluminum; (d) sulfur; (e) neon.

More Practice: Try Problems 2.65, 2.66.

2.8   Periodic Trends

Many properties of atoms exhibit **periodic trends;** that is, they change in a regular way across a row or down a column of the periodic table. Two properties that illustrate this phenomenon are **atomic size** and **ionization energy.**

2.8A   Atomic Size

The size of an atom is measured by its atomic radius—that is, the distance from the nucleus to the outer edge of the valence shell. Two periodic trends characterize the size of atoms.

- **The size of atoms increases down a column of the periodic table, as the valence electrons are farther from the nucleus.**

For group 7A:

- **The size of atoms decreases across a row of the periodic table as the number of protons in the nucleus increases. An increasing number of protons pulls the electrons closer to the nucleus, so the atom gets smaller.**

For period 2:

SAMPLE PROBLEM 2.16 USING PERIODIC TRENDS TO DETERMINE THE RELATIVE SIZE OF ATOMS

(a) Which of the labeled atoms has the larger atomic radius? (b) Identify the elements.

Analysis

Atomic radius (size) decreases across a row of the periodic table as the number of protons in the nucleus increases.

Solution

a. Element [1] is farther to the left in the third row, so it has the larger atomic radius.

b. Element [1] is silicon (period 3, group 4A) and element [2] is phosphorus (period 3, group 5A).

PRACTICE PROBLEM 2.16

Which element in each pair has the larger atomic radius?

a. nitrogen or arsenic   b. silicon or sulfur   c. fluorine or phosphorus

More Practice: Try Problems 2.69, 2.70, 2.73, 2.75, 2.76.

2.8B   Ionization Energy

Since a negatively charged electron is attracted to a positively charged nucleus, energy is required to remove an electron from a neutral atom. The more tightly the electron is held, the greater the energy required to remove it. Removing an electron from a neutral atom forms a **cation.**

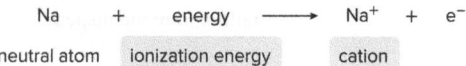

Na   +   energy ⟶ Na$^+$ + e$^-$

neutral atom   ionization energy   cation

- The *ionization energy* is the energy needed to remove an electron from a neutral atom.
- A *cation* is positively charged, and has fewer electrons than the neutral atom.

Two periodic trends characterize ionization energy.

- Ionization energies decrease down a column of the periodic table as the valence electrons get farther from the positively charged nucleus.

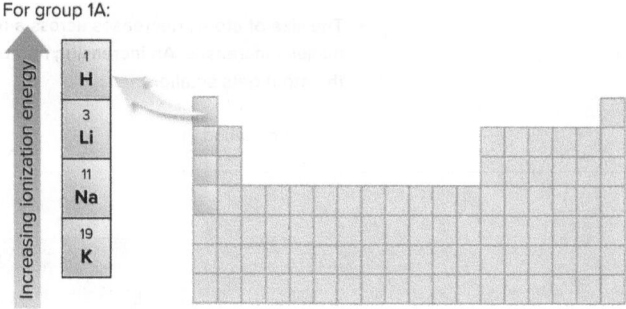

- Ionization energies generally increase across a row of the periodic table as the number of protons in the nucleus increases.

PROBLEM 2.16

Which element in each pair has the higher ionization energy?

a. silicon or sodium   b. carbon or silicon   c. sulfur or fluorine

SAMPLE PROBLEM 2.17 USING MOLECULAR ART TO DETERMINE PERIODIC TRENDS

Consider spheres **A** and **B**, which represent atoms in the same group in the periodic table. (a) Which atom has the higher atomic number? (b) Which atom has the larger ionization energy? (c) Which atom gives up an electron more easily?

Analysis

- In the same group (same column), atomic number and atomic radius *increase* down the column.
- Ionization energy *decreases* down the column.
- The lower the ionization energy, the more easily an atom gives up an electron.

Solution

a. **B** has the larger atomic radius, so it has the higher atomic number.

b. **A** has the larger ionization energy because it is above **B** in the same column.

c. **B** more easily gives up an electron because its ionization energy is lower.

PRACTICE PROBLEM 2.17

Consider spheres **A** and **B**, which represent atoms in the same period in the periodic table. (a) Which atom has the higher atomic number? (b) Which atom has the larger ionization energy? (c) Which atom gives up an electron more easily?

More Practice: Try Problems 2.67, 2.68.

SAMPLE PROBLEM 2.18 DETERMINING PERIODIC TRENDS

(a) Which of the indicated atoms has the larger atomic radius? (b) Which of the indicated atoms has the higher ionization energy?

Analysis

- Atomic size decreases across a row and increases down a column of the periodic table.
- Ionization energy increases across a row and decreases down a column of the periodic table.

Solution

a. Element [2] is farther to the left and farther down the column, so it has the larger atomic radius.

b. Element [1] is farther to the right and closer to the top of the column (lower period number), so it has the higher ionization energy.

PRACTICE PROBLEM 2.18

(a) Which of the indicated atoms has the smaller atomic radius? (b) Which of the indicated atoms has the lower ionization energy? (c) Identify the elements.

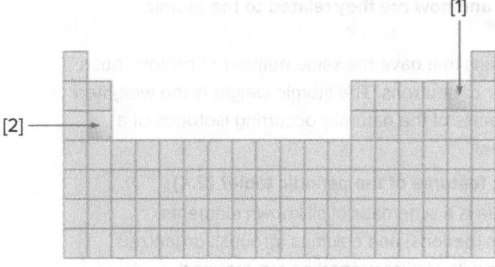

More Practice: Try Problems 2.71, 2.72, 2.74, 2.77, 2.78, 2.84b–f.

CHAPTER HIGHLIGHTS

KEY TERMS

Actinide (2.4)
Alkali metal (2.4)
Alkaline earth element (2.4)
Atom (2.2)
Atomic mass unit (2.2)
Atomic number (2.2)
Atomic weight (Atomic mass, 2.3)
Building-block element (2.1)
Cation (2.8)
Chemical formula (2.1)
Compound (2.1)
d Block (2.6)
Deuterium (2.3)
Electron (2.2)
Electron cloud (2.2)
Electron-dot symbol (2.7)
Electronic configuration (2.6)

Element (2.1)
f Block (2.6)
Ground state (2.6)
Group (2.4)
Group number (2.4)
Halogen (2.4)
Inner transition metal element (2.4)
Ionization energy (2.8)
Isotope (2.3)
Lanthanide (2.4)
Main group element (2.4)
Major mineral (Macronutrient, 2.1)
Mass number (2.2)
Metal (2.1)
Metalloid (2.1)
Neutron (2.2)
Noble gas (2.4)

Nonmetal (2.1)
Nucleus (2.2)
Orbital (2.5)
p Block (2.6)
Period (2.4)
Periodic table (2.1)
p Orbital (2.5)
Proton (2.2)
s Block (2.6)
Shell (Principal energy level, 2.5)
s Orbital (2.5)
Subshell (2.5)
Trace element (Micronutrient, 2.1)
Transition metal element (2.4)
Tritium (2.3)
Unpaired electron (2.6)
Valence electron (2.7)

KEY CONCEPTS

❶ How is the name of an element abbreviated and how does the periodic table help to classify it as a metal, nonmetal, or metalloid? (2.1)

- An element is abbreviated by a one- or two-letter symbol. The periodic table contains a stepped line from boron to astatine. All metals are located to the left of the line. All nonmetals except hydrogen are located to the right of the line. The seven elements located along the line are metalloids.

❷ What are the basic components of an atom? (2.2)

- An atom is composed of two parts: a dense nucleus containing positively charged protons and neutral neutrons, and an electron cloud containing negatively charged electrons. Most of the mass of an atom resides in the nucleus, whereas the electron cloud contains most of its volume.
- The atomic number (Z) of a neutral atom tells the number of protons and the number of electrons. The mass number (A) is the sum of the number of protons (Z) and the number of neutrons.

❸ What are isotopes and how are they related to the atomic weight? (2.3)

- Isotopes are atoms that have the same number of protons but a different number of neutrons. The atomic weight is the weighted average of the mass of the naturally occurring isotopes of a particular element.

❹ What are the basic features of the periodic table? (2.4)

- The periodic table is a schematic of all known elements, arranged in rows (periods) and columns (groups), organized so that elements with similar properties are grouped together.

- The vertical columns are assigned group numbers using two different numbering schemes: 1–8 plus the letter A or B; or 1–18.
- The periodic table is divided into the main group elements (groups 1A–8A), the transition metals (groups 1B–8B), and the inner transition metals located at the bottom.

❺ How are electrons arranged around an atom? (2.5)

- Electrons occupy discrete energy levels, organized into shells (numbered 1, 2, 3, and so on), subshells (s, p, d, and f), and orbitals.
- Each orbital can hold two electrons.

❻ What rules determine the electronic configuration of an atom? (2.6)

- To write the ground state electronic configuration of an atom, electrons are added to the lowest energy orbitals, giving each orbital two electrons. When two orbitals are equal in energy, one electron is added to each orbital until the orbitals are half-filled.
- Orbital diagrams that use boxes for orbitals and arrows for electrons indicate electronic configuration. Electron configuration can also be shown using superscripts to show how many electrons an orbital contains. For example, the electron configuration of the six electrons in a carbon atom is $1s^2 2s^2 2p^2$.

7 **How is the location of an element in the periodic table related to its electronic configuration? (2.6, 2.7)**

- The periodic table is divided into four regions—the *s* block, *p* block, *d* block, and *f* block—based on the subshells that are filled with electrons last.

- Elements in the same group have the same number of valence electrons and similar electronic configurations.

8 **What is an electron-dot symbol? (2.7)**

- An electron-dot symbol uses a dot to represent each valence electron around the symbol for an element.

9 **How are atomic size and ionization energy related to location in the periodic table? (2.8)**

- The size of an atom decreases across a row and increases down a column.

- Ionization energy—the energy needed to remove an electron from an atom—increases across a row and decreases down a column.

PROBLEMS

Selected in-chapter and odd-numbered end-of-chapter problems have brief answers in Appendix B. The *Student Study Guide and Solutions Manual* contains detailed solutions to all in-chapter and odd-numbered end-of-chapter problems, as well as additional worked examples and a chapter self-test.

Elements

2.17 Identify the elements used in each example of molecular art.

a.   b.

2.18 Write a chemical formula for each example of molecular art.

a.   b.   c.

2.19 Give the name of the elements in each group of three element symbols.

a. Au, At, Ag   d. Ca, Cr, Cl
b. N, Na, Ni   e. P, Pb, Pt
c. S, Si, Sn   f. Ti, Ta, Tl

2.20 What element(s) are designated by each symbol or group of symbols?

a. CU and Cu   c. Ni and NI
b. Os and OS   d. BIN, BiN, and BIn

2.21 Does each chemical formula represent an element or a compound?

a. H_2 b. H_2O_2 c. S_8 d. Na_2CO_3 e. C_{60}

2.22 Identify the elements in each chemical formula and tell how many atoms of each are present.

a. $K_2Cr_2O_7$
b. $C_5H_8NNaO_4$ (MSG, flavor enhancer)
c. $C_{10}H_{16}N_2O_3S$ (vitamin B_7)

2.23 Identify the element that fits each description.

a. an alkali metal in period 6
b. a transition metal in period 5, group 8
c. a main group element in period 3, group 7A
d. a main group element in period 2, group 2A
e. a halogen in period 2
f. an inner transition metal with one 4*f* electron

2.24 Identify the element that fits each description.

a. an alkaline earth element in period 3
b. a noble gas in period 6
c. a main group element in period 3 that has *p* orbitals half-filled with electrons
d. a transition metal in period 4, group 11
e. an inner transition metal with its 5*f* orbitals completely filled with electrons
f. a transition metal in period 6, group 10

2.25 Give all of the terms that apply to each element: [1] metal; [2] nonmetal; [3] metalloid; [4] alkali metal; [5] alkaline earth element; [6] halogen; [7] noble gas; [8] main group element; [9] transition metal; [10] inner transition metal.

a. sodium   c. xenon   e. uranium
b. silver   d. platinum   f. tellurium

2.26 Give all of the terms that apply to each element: [1] metal; [2] nonmetal; [3] metalloid; [4] alkali metal; [5] alkaline earth element; [6] halogen; [7] noble gas; [8] main group element; [9] transition metal; [10] inner transition metal.

a. bromine   c. cesium   e. calcium
b. silicon   d. gold   f. chromium

72   **Chapter 2**   Atoms and the Periodic Table

Atomic Structure

2.27 Give the following information about the atom shown: (a) the number of protons and neutrons in the nucleus; (b) the atomic number; (c) the mass number; (d) the number of electrons in the neutral atom; and (e) the element symbol.

2.28 Give the following information about the atom shown: (a) the number of protons and neutrons in the nucleus; (b) the atomic number; (c) the mass number; (d) the number of electrons in the neutral atom; and (e) the element symbol.

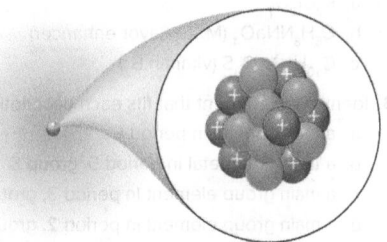

2.29 Complete the following table for neutral elements.

	Element Symbol	Atomic Number	Mass Number	Number of Protons	Number of Neutrons	Number of Electrons
a.	C		12			
b.		31				15
c.					35	30
d.	Mg	24				
e.			53		74	
f.		4			5	
g.		40	91			
h.				16		16

2.30 For the given atomic number (Z) and mass number (A): [1] identify the element; [2] give the element symbol; [3] give the number of protons, neutrons, and electrons.

a. $Z = 10, A = 20$ d. $Z = 55, A = 133$
b. $Z = 13, A = 27$ e. $Z = 28, A = 59$
c. $Z = 38, A = 88$ f. $Z = 79, A = 197$

2.31 Consider the four atoms—A, E, G, and J—with the given isotope symbols:

$^{20}_{10}A$ $^{21}_{10}E$ $^{22}_{11}G$ $^{22}_{10}J$

a. Which atoms have the same number of neutrons?
b. Which atoms are isotopes?
c. Which atom has the highest atomic number?
d. Which atoms have the same number of electrons in the neutral atom?

2.32 Consider the four atoms—L, M, N, and X—with the given isotope symbols:

$^{124}_{47}L$ $^{116}_{48}M$ $^{124}_{50}N$ $^{114}_{50}X$

a. Which atom has the smallest mass number?
b. Which atoms are isotopes?
c. Which atom has the smallest number of electrons in the neutral atom?
d. Which atom has the largest number of neutrons?

Periodic Table

2.33 Label each region on the periodic table.

a. noble gases   e. alkaline earth elements
b. period 3   f. f block elements
c. group 4A   g. transition metals
d. s block elements   h. group 10

2.34 Identify each highlighted element in the periodic table and give its [1] element name and symbol; [2] group number; [3] period; [4] classification (i.e., main group element, transition metal, or inner transition metal).

2.35 What element is located in group 1A but is not an alkali metal?

2.36 (a) Are the elements calcium, barium, and radium in the same group or same period in the periodic table? (b) Are the elements rhodium, cadmium, and tin in the same group or period?

2.37 Classify each element in the fourth row of the periodic table as a metal, nonmetal, or metalloid.

2.38 To which blocks do the elements in the fifth period belong?

Isotopes and Atomic Weight

2.39 Complete the following table for the two most widely occurring isotopes of the element nickel (Ni). The five-cent nickel coin minted in the United States contains the metals nickel and copper in a 1:3 ratio.

©McGraw-Hill Education/Ken Cavanagh, photographer

	^{58}Ni	^{60}Ni
a. Atomic number	28	
b. Mass number	58	
c. Number of protons	28	
d. Number of neutrons	30	

2.40 Complete the following table for the two most widely occurring isotopes of the element mercury (Hg). Compact fluorescent bulbs each contain about 4 mg of the toxic metal mercury, so used bulbs should not be discarded in the household trash.

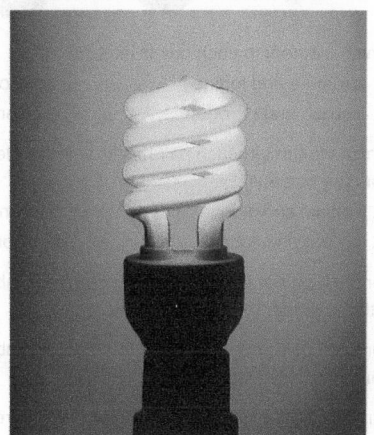

©Kelly Redinger/Getty Images RF

	^{202}Hg	^{200}Hg
a. Atomic number		
b. Mass number		
c. Number of protons		
d. Number of neutrons		

2.41 How many protons, neutrons, and electrons are contained in each element?

a. $^{27}_{13}$Al   b. $^{35}_{17}$Cl   c. ^{34}S

2.42 Give the number of protons, neutrons, and electrons in each element: (a) silver-115; (b) ^{197}Au; (c) ^{222}Rn; (d) ^{192}Os.

2.43 Write the element symbol that fits each description, using a superscript for the mass number and a subscript for the atomic number.

a. an element that contains 53 protons and 74 neutrons
b. an element with 35 electrons and a mass number of 79
c. an element with 47 protons and 60 neutrons

2.44 Write the element symbol that fits each description. Use a superscript for the mass number and a subscript for the atomic number.

a. an element that contains 10 protons and 12 neutrons
b. an element with atomic number 24 and mass number 52
c. an element with 10 electrons and 10 neutrons

2.45 Calculate the atomic weight of silver, which has two isotopes with the following properties: silver-107 (106.91 amu, 51.84% natural occurrence) and silver-109 (108.90 amu, 48.16% natural occurrence).

2.46 Calculate the atomic weight of antimony, which has two isotopes with the following properties: antimony-121 (120.90 amu, 57.21% natural occurrence) and antimony-123 (122.90 amu, 42.79% natural occurrence).

Electronic Configuration

2.47 How many orbitals are contained in each of the following shells of electrons: (a) first shell ($n = 1$); (b) second shell ($n = 2$); (c) third shell ($n = 3$); (d) fourth shell ($n = 4$)?

2.48 What is the maximum number of electrons that can be contained in each shell, subshell, or orbital?

a. second shell   c. 3p subshell   e. fourth shell
b. 3s orbital   d. 4f orbital   f. 5p orbital

2.49 Use an orbital diagram to write the electronic configuration of each element whose location is shown in the periodic table.

2.50 Use an orbital diagram to write the electronic configuration of each element whose location is shown in the periodic table.

2.51 For each element in Problem 2.49: (a) Write out the electronic configuration using a superscript with each orbital; (b) write out the electronic configuration using noble gas notation.

2.52 For each element in Problem 2.50: (a) Write out the electronic configuration using a superscript with each orbital; (b) write out the electronic configuration using noble gas notation.

2.53 How many unpaired electrons are contained in each element: (a) Al; (b) P; (c) Na?

2.54 How many unpaired electrons are contained in each element: (a) Cl; (b) Se; (c) Cs?

2.55 Give the total number of electrons, the number of valence electrons, and the identity of the element with each electronic configuration.
  a. $1s^22s^22p^63s^23p^64s^23d^{10}4p^65s^2$ c. $1s^22s^22p^63s^1$
  b. $1s^22s^22p^63s^23p^4$ d. [Ne]$3s^23p^5$

2.56 Give the total number of electrons, the number of valence electrons, and the identity of the element with each electronic configuration.
  a. $1s^22s^22p^63s^23p^6$ c. $1s^22s^22p^3$
  b. $1s^22s^22p^63s^23p^64s^23d^7$ d. [Kr]$5s^24d^{10}5p^2$

2.57 For each element, give the following information: [1] total number of electrons; [2] group number; [3] number of valence electrons; [4] period; [5] number of the valence shell.
  a. carbon   b. calcium   c. krypton

2.58 For each element, give the following information: [1] total number of electrons; [2] group number; [3] number of valence electrons; [4] period; [5] number of the valence shell.
  a. oxygen   b. sodium   c. phosphorus

2.59 For each element in Problem 2.57, first write the electronic configuration of all the electrons. Then give the electronic configuration of the valence electrons only.

2.60 For each element in Problem 2.58, first write the electronic configuration of all the electrons. Then give the electronic configuration of the valence electrons only.

2.61 Which of the following orbital diagrams are possible? Explain your reasoning.

2.62 Which of the following orbital diagrams are possible? Explain your reasoning.

2.63 Give the number of valence electrons in each element. Write out the electronic configuration for the valence electrons.
  a. sulfur b. chlorine c. barium d. titanium e. tin

2.64 Give the number of valence electrons in each element. Write out the electronic configuration for the valence electrons.
  a. neon   c. aluminum   e. zirconium
  b. rubidium   d. manganese

2.65 Write an electron-dot symbol for each element: (a) beryllium; (b) silicon; (c) iodine; (d) magnesium; (e) argon.

2.66 Write an electron-dot symbol for each element: (a) K; (b) B; (c) F; (d) Ca; (e) Se.

Periodic Trends

2.67 Consider the following three spheres, which represent atoms in the same group in the periodic table. (a) Which atom has the highest atomic number? (b) Which atom has the largest ionization energy? (c) Which atom gives up an electron most easily?

2.68 Consider the following three spheres, which represent atoms in the same period in the periodic table. (a) Which atom has the highest atomic number? (b) Which atom has the largest ionization energy? (c) Which atom gives up an electron most easily?

2.69 Which element in each pair is larger?
  a. bromine and iodine   c. silicon and potassium
  b. carbon and nitrogen   d. chlorine and selenium

2.70 Which element in each pair has its valence electrons farther from the nucleus?
  a. sodium and magnesium   c. neon and krypton
  b. carbon and fluorine   d. argon and bromine

2.71 For each pair of elements in Problem 2.69, label the element with the higher ionization energy.

2.72 For each pair of elements in Problem 2.70, label the element from which it is easier to remove an electron.

2.73 Rank the atoms in each group in order of increasing size.
  a. boron, carbon, neon
  b. calcium, magnesium, beryllium
  c. silicon, sulfur, magnesium
  d. krypton, neon, xenon
  e. sulfur, oxygen, silicon
  f. fluorine, sulfur, aluminum

2.74 Arrange the elements in each group in order of increasing ionization energy.
  a. phosphorus, silicon, sulfur
  b. magnesium, calcium, beryllium
  c. carbon, fluorine, beryllium
  d. neon, krypton, argon
  e. tin, silicon, sulfur
  f. calcium, aluminum, nitrogen

2.75 Rank the following elements in order of increasing size: sulfur, silicon, oxygen, magnesium, and fluorine.

2.76 Rank the following elements in order of increasing size: aluminum, nitrogen, potassium, oxygen, and phosphorus.

2.77 Rank the following elements in order of increasing ionization energy: nitrogen, fluorine, magnesium, sodium, and phosphorus.

2.78 Rank the following elements in order of decreasing ionization energy: calcium, silicon, oxygen, magnesium, and carbon.

Applications

2.79 (a) What is the chemical formula for bupropion (trade name Zyban), an antidepressant also used to reduce nicotine cravings? (b) Which element in bupropion has valence electrons that are farthest from the nucleus?

bupropion

2.80 (a) What is the chemical formula for brompheniramine, an antihistamine used to relieve the runny nose and sneezing associated with allergies? (b) Which element in brompheniramine has valence electrons that are farthest from the nucleus?

brompheniramine

2.81 Answer the following questions about the macronutrients sodium, potassium, and chlorine.
   a. Is each element classified as a metal, nonmetal, or metalloid?
   b. In which block does each element reside?
   c. Which element has the smallest atomic radius?
   d. Which element has the largest atomic radius?
   e. Which element has the largest ionization energy?
   f. Which element has the smallest ionization energy?
   g. How many valence electrons does each element possess?

2.82 Platinum is a precious metal used in a wide variety of products. Besides being used in fine jewelry, platinum is the catalyst found in the catalytic converters of automobile exhaust systems, and platinum-containing drugs like cisplatin are used to treat some lung and ovarian cancers. Answer the following questions about the element platinum.
   a. What is its element symbol?
   b. What group number and period are assigned to platinum?
   c. What is its atomic number?
   d. Is platinum classified as a main group element, transition metal, or inner transition metal?
   e. In what block does platinum reside?
   f. What is unusual about the electronic configuration for platinum: $[Xe]6s^14f^{14}5d^9$?

2.83 Carbon-11 is an unnatural isotope used in positron emission tomography (PET) scans. PET scans are used to monitor brain activity and diagnose dementia. How does carbon-11 compare to carbon-12 in terms of the number of protons, neutrons, and electrons? Write the element symbol of carbon-11 using superscripts and subscripts.

2.84 Answer the following questions about the macronutrients calcium, magnesium, and sulfur.
   a. Is each element classified as a metal, nonmetal, or metalloid?
   b. In which block does each element reside?
   c. Which element has the smallest atomic radius?
   d. Which element has the largest atomic radius?
   e. Which element has the largest ionization energy?
   f. Which element has the smallest ionization energy?
   g. How many valence electrons does each element possess?

CHALLENGE PROBLEMS

2.85 If one gallon of gasoline contains about 2.0 g of lead, how much lead (in kg) is emitted into the atmosphere from a car that travels 10,000. miles a year and averages 25 miles per gallon of gasoline?

2.86 Strontium-90 is a radioactive element formed in nuclear reactors. When an unusually high level of strontium is released into the air, such as occurred during the Chernobyl nuclear disaster in 1986, the strontium can be incorporated into the bones of exposed individuals. High levels of strontium can cause bone cancer and leukemia. Why does Sr-90 cause this particular health problem?

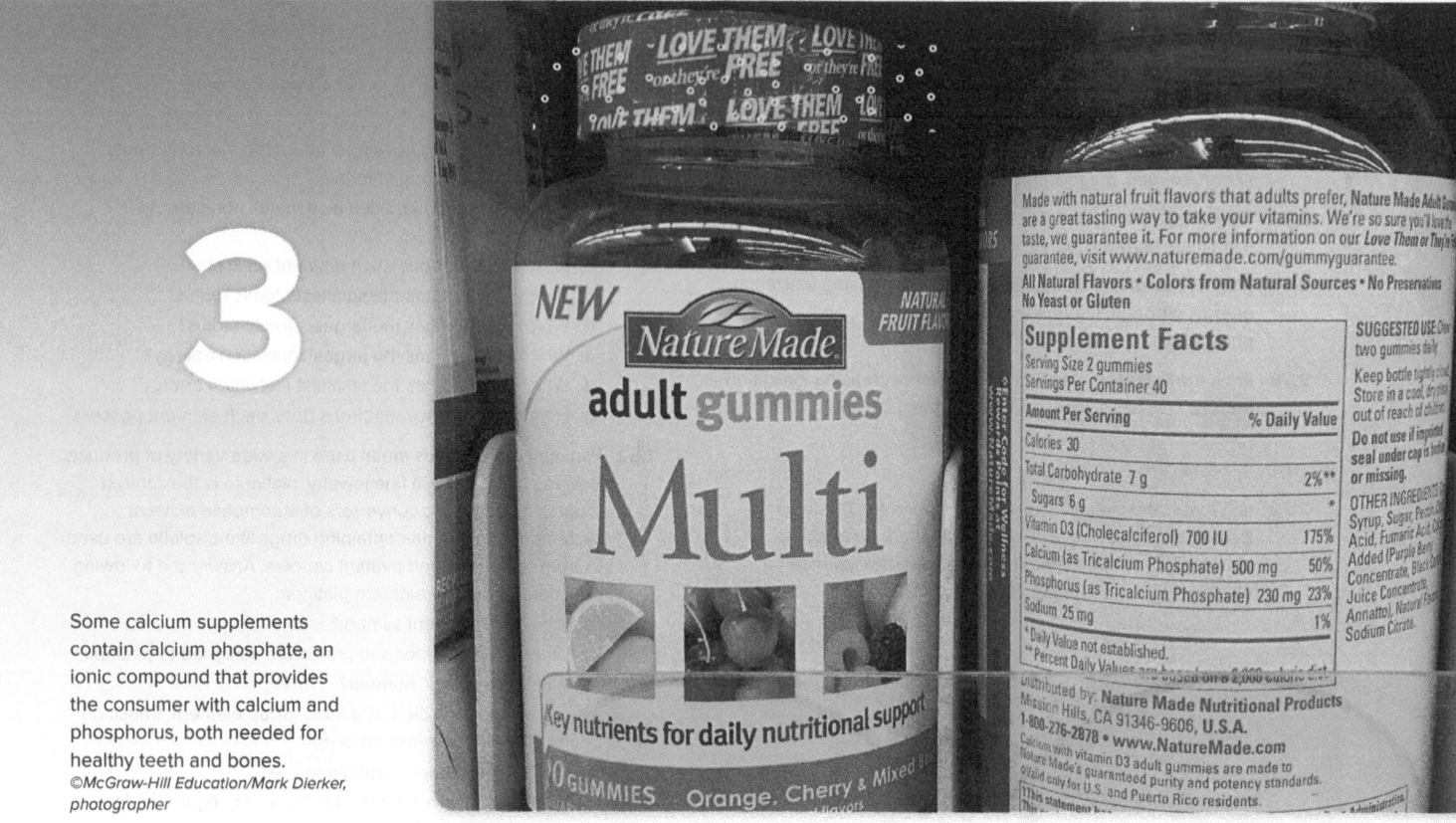

3

Some calcium supplements contain calcium phosphate, an ionic compound that provides the consumer with calcium and phosphorus, both needed for healthy teeth and bones.
©McGraw-Hill Education/Mark Dierker, photographer

Ionic Compounds

CHAPTER OUTLINE

3.1 Introduction to Bonding

3.2 Ions

3.3 Ionic Compounds

3.4 Naming Ionic Compounds

3.5 Physical Properties of Ionic Compounds

3.6 Polyatomic Ions

CHAPTER GOALS

In this chapter you will learn how to:

1. Describe the basic features of ionic and covalent bonds

2. Use the periodic table to determine whether an atom forms a cation or an anion, and determine its charge using the group number

3. Describe the octet rule

4. Write the formula for an ionic compound

5. Name ionic compounds

6. Describe the properties of ionic compounds

7. Recognize the structures of common polyatomic ions and name compounds that contain them

8. List useful consumer products and drugs that are composed of ionic compounds

**Why Study
Ionic Compounds?**

Although much of the discussion in Chapter 2 focused on atoms, individual atoms are rarely encountered in nature. Instead, atoms are far more commonly joined together to form compounds. There are two types of chemical compounds, **ionic** and **covalent. Ionic compounds** are composed of positively and negatively charged ions held together by strong **electrostatic forces**—the electrical attraction between oppositely charged ions. Examples of ionic compounds include the sodium chloride (NaCl) in table salt and the calcium carbonate ($CaCO_3$) in snail shells. **Covalent compounds** are composed of individual molecules, discrete groups of atoms that share electrons. Covalent compounds include water (H_2O) and methane (CH_4), the main component of natural gas. Chapters 3 and 4 focus on the structure and properties of ionic and covalent compounds, respectively.

3.1   Introduction to Bonding

It is rare in nature to encounter individual atoms. Instead, anywhere from two to hundreds or thousands of atoms tend to join together to form compounds. The oxygen we breathe, for instance, consists of two oxygen atoms joined together, whereas the hemoglobin that transports it to our tissues consists of thousands of carbon, hydrogen, oxygen, nitrogen, and sulfur atoms joined together. We say **two atoms are** *bonded* **together.**

- *Bonding* **is the joining of two atoms in a stable arrangement.**

Bonding is a favorable process because it always forms a compound that is more stable than the atoms from which it is made. Only the noble gases in group 8A of the periodic table are particularly stable as individual atoms; that is, the **noble gases do** *not* **readily react to form bonds,** because the electronic configuration of the noble gases is especially stable to begin with. As a result, one overriding principle explains the process of bonding.

- **In bonding, elements gain, lose, or share electrons to attain the electronic configuration of the noble gas closest to them in the periodic table.**

Bonding involves only the valence electrons of an atom. There are two different kinds of bonding: **ionic** and **covalent.**

- *Ionic bonds* **result from the transfer of electrons from one element to another.**

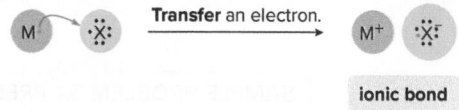

- *Covalent bonds* **result from the sharing of electrons between two atoms.**

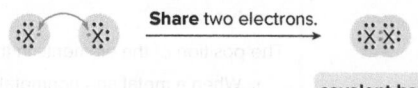

The position of an element in the periodic table determines the type of bonds it makes.

- **Ionic bonds form between a metal on the left side of the periodic table and a nonmetal on the right side.**

As shown in Figure 3.1, when the metal sodium (Na) bonds to the nonmetal chlorine (Cl_2), the ionic compound sodium chloride (NaCl) forms. Since ionic compounds are composed of *ions*—**charged species in which the number of protons and electrons in an atom is** *not* **equal**—we begin our discussion of ionic compounds with how ions are formed in Section 3.2.

- **Covalent bonds are formed when two nonmetals combine, or when a metalloid bonds to a nonmetal.**

78   **Chapter 3**   Ionic Compounds

Figure 3.1

Sodium Chloride, an Ionic Compound

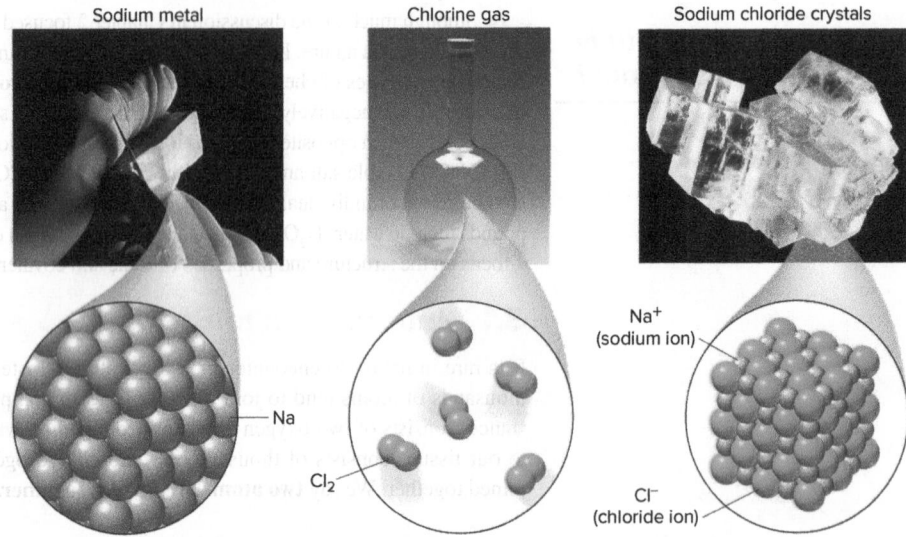

Sodium metal and chlorine gas are both elements. Sodium chloride is an ionic compound composed of sodium ions and chloride ions. *(left & middle): ©McGraw-Hill Education/Stephen Frisch, photographer; (right): ©M. Claye/Science Source*

A *molecule* **is a compound or element containing two or more atoms joined together with covalent bonds.** For example, when two hydrogen atoms bond they form the molecule H_2, and two electrons are shared. Covalent bonds and molecules are discussed in Chapter 4.

Two electrons are shared in a covalent bond.

hydrogen molecule

SAMPLE PROBLEM 3.1 PREDICTING WHETHER A BOND IS IONIC OR COVALENT

Predict whether the bonds in the following compounds are ionic or covalent: (a) NaI (sodium iodide); (b) H_2O_2 (hydrogen peroxide).

Analysis

The position of the elements in the periodic table determines the type of bonds they form.

- When a metal and nonmetal combine, the bond is ionic.
- When two nonmetals combine, or a metalloid bonds to a nonmetal, the bond is covalent.

Solution

a. Since Na is a metal on the left side and I is a nonmetal on the right side of the periodic table, the bonds in NaI are ionic.

b. Since H_2O_2 contains only the nonmetals hydrogen and oxygen, the bonds must be covalent.

PRACTICE PROBLEM 3.1

Predict whether the bonds in the following species are ionic or covalent.

a. CO   b. CaF_2 c. MgO   d. Cl_2 e. HF   f. C_2H_6

More Practice: Try Problems 3.17, 3.18.

SAMPLE PROBLEM 3.2 USING MOLECULAR ART TO PREDICT BONDING

(a) Classify each example of molecular art as a compound or an element. (b) Which of the species are molecules?

A   B

Analysis

- In molecular art, an element is composed of spheres of the same color, whereas a compound is composed of spheres of different colors. The common element colors are shown in Figure 2.3 (and on the inside back cover).
- A molecule is a compound or element that contains covalent bonds.

Solution

a. **A** is an element composed of two fluorines, whereas **B** is a compound composed of hydrogen and fluorine.

b. Both **A** and **B** are molecules because they are composed solely of covalent bonds between nonmetals.

PRACTICE PROBLEM 3.2

(a) Classify each example of molecular art as a compound or element. (b) Which of the species are molecules?

A   B   C   D   E   F

More Practice: Try Problems 3.19, 3.20.

PROBLEM 3.1

Label each of the following as a compound, element, or molecule. In some cases, more than one term applies.

a. CO_2 b. H_2O c. NaF   d. $MgBr_2$ e. F_2 f. CaO

PROBLEM 3.2

Vitamin C has the chemical formula $C_6H_8O_6$. Even if you know nothing about how the atoms in vitamin C are arranged, what type of bonds are likely to be present in vitamin C?

3.2 Ions

Ionic compounds consist of oppositely charged **ions** that have a strong **electrostatic attraction**—electrical attraction between oppositely charged ions—for each other.

3.2A Cations and Anions

There are two types of ions called **cations** and **anions.**

- *Cations* are positively charged ions. A cation has fewer electrons than protons.
- *Anions* are negatively charged ions. An anion has more electrons than protons.

The nature and magnitude of the charge on an ion depend on the position of an element in the periodic table. In forming an ion, an atom of a main group element loses or gains electrons to obtain the electronic configuration of the noble gas closest to it in the periodic table. This gives the ion an especially stable electronic arrangement with a **completely filled shell of electrons;** that is, the electrons completely fill the shell farthest from the nucleus.

For example, sodium (group 1A) has an atomic number of 11, giving it 11 protons and 11 electrons in the neutral atom. This gives sodium one *more* electron than neon, the noble gas closest to it in the periodic table. In losing one electron, sodium forms a cation with a +1 charge, which still has 11 protons, but now has only 10 electrons in its electron cloud.

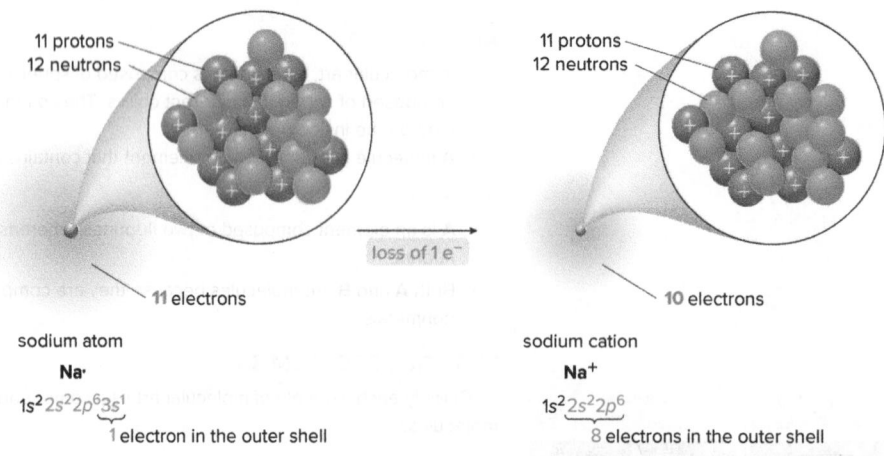

What does this mean in terms of valence electrons? A neutral sodium atom, with an electronic configuration of $1s^2 2s^2 2p^6 3s^1$, has a single valence electron. Loss of this valence electron forms a **sodium cation,** symbolized as **Na⁺,** which has the especially stable electronic configuration of the noble gas neon, $1s^2 2s^2 2p^6$. The sodium cation now has **eight electrons** that fill the $2s$ and three $2p$ orbitals.

Magnesium (group 2A) has 12 protons and 12 electrons in the neutral atom. This gives magnesium two *more* electrons than neon, the noble gas closest to it in the periodic table. In losing two electrons, magnesium forms a cation with a +2 charge, which still has 12 protons, but now has only 10 electrons in its electron cloud.

In terms of valence electrons, a neutral magnesium atom, with an electronic configuration of $1s^2 2s^2 2p^6 3s^2$, has two valence electrons. Loss of these valence electrons forms a **magnesium cation,** symbolized as **Mg²⁺,** which has the especially stable electronic configuration of the noble gas neon, $1s^2 2s^2 2p^6$. The magnesium cation now has **eight electrons** that fill the $2s$ and three $2p$ orbitals.

Sodium and magnesium are examples of metals.

Some metals—notably tin and lead—can lose *four* electrons to form cations.

- Metals form *cations.*
- By losing one, two, or three electrons, an atom forms a cation with a completely filled outer shell of electrons.
- Cations are smaller in size than the atoms from which they are formed. Because a cation has more protons than electrons, the positively charged nucleus pulls the remaining electrons closer.

A neutral chlorine atom (group 7A), on the other hand, has 17 protons and 17 electrons. This gives it one *fewer* electron than argon, the noble gas closest to it in the periodic table. By gaining one electron, chlorine forms an anion with a −1 charge because it still has 17 protons, but now has 18 electrons in its electron cloud.

chlorine atom	chloride anion
$:\overset{..}{\underset{..}{Cl}}\cdot$	$:\overset{..}{\underset{..}{Cl}}:^-$
$1s^2 2s^2 2p^6 \underbrace{3s^2 3p^5}$	$1s^2 2s^2 2p^6 \underbrace{3s^2 3p^6}$
7 electrons in the outer shell	8 electrons in the outer shell

In terms of valence electrons, a neutral chlorine atom, with an electronic configuration of $1s^2 2s^2 2p^6 3s^2 3p^5$, has seven valence electrons. Gain of one electron forms a **chloride anion,** symbolized as **Cl⁻,** which has the especially stable electronic configuration of the noble gas argon, $1s^2 2s^2 2p^6 3s^2 3p^6$. The chloride anion now has **eight valence electrons** that fill the $3s$ and three $3p$ orbitals.

Chlorine is an example of a nonmetal.

- Nonmetals form *anions.*
- By gaining one, two, or sometimes three electrons, an atom forms an anion with a completely filled outer shell of electrons.
- Anions are larger than the atoms from which they are formed. Because an anion has more electrons than protons, the electrons are held less tightly by the positively charged nucleus, and the anion size is larger than the atom size.

Ions are written with the element symbol followed by a superscript to indicate the charge. The number "1" is omitted in ions that have a +1 or −1 charge, as in Na⁺ or Cl⁻. When the charge is "2" or greater, it is written as 2+ or 2−, as in Mg²⁺ or O²⁻.

Each of these ions formed from a main group element has the s and three p orbitals filled with **eight electrons.** This illustrates the **octet rule.**

- A main group element is especially stable when it possesses an *octet* of electrons in its outer shell.

SAMPLE PROBLEM 3.3 WRITING AN ION SYMBOL BY COUNTING PROTONS AND ELECTRONS

Identify the ion shown in the molecular art and give its ion symbol.

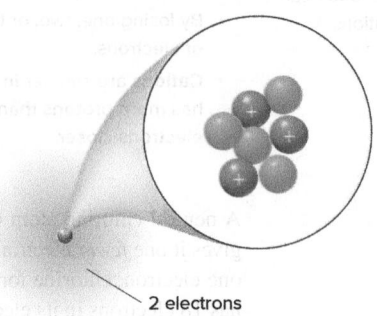

2 electrons

Analysis

- Count the number of protons to determine the atomic number and the identity of the element.
- Compare the number of protons with the number of electrons to determine the charge. When the number of protons is greater than the number of electrons, the ion has a net positive charge. When the number of electrons is greater than the number of protons, the ion has a net negative charge.

Solution

The element with three protons in the nucleus is lithium. Since there are three protons in the nucleus and only two electrons in the electron cloud, the ion has a net +1 charge. **Answer:** Li^+.

PRACTICE PROBLEM 3.3

Give the ion symbol for the ion shown in the molecular art.

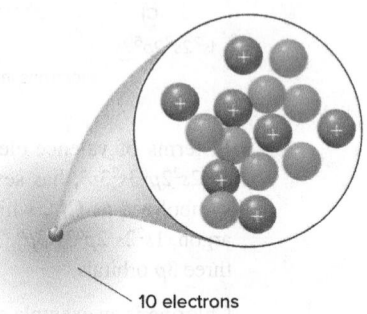

10 electrons

More Practice: Try Problems 3.21, 3.22.

SAMPLE PROBLEM 3.4 WRITING AN ION SYMBOL

Write the ion symbol for an atom with nine protons and 10 electrons.

Analysis

Since the number of protons equals the atomic number (Section 2.2), this quantity identifies the element. The charge is determined by comparing the number of protons and electrons. If the number of electrons is greater than the number of protons, the charge is negative (an anion). If the number of protons is greater than the number of electrons, the charge is positive (a cation).

Solution

An element with nine protons has an atomic number of nine, identifying it as fluorine (F). Since there is one more electron than proton (10 vs. 9), the charge is −1. **Answer:** F^-.

PRACTICE PROBLEM 3.4

Write the ion symbol for an atom with the given number of protons and electrons.

a. 19 protons and 18 electrons K^+

b. 35 protons and 36 electrons

c. 23 protons and 21 electrons

More Practice: Try Problems 3.23, 3.25, 3.26.

SAMPLE PROBLEM 3.5 USING AN ION SYMBOL TO COUNT PROTONS AND ELECTRONS

How many protons and electrons are present in each ion: (a) Ca^{2+}; (b) O^{2-}?

Analysis

Use the identity of the element to determine the number of protons. The charge tells how many more or fewer electrons there are compared to the number of protons. A positive charge means more protons than electrons, whereas a negative charge means more electrons than protons.

Solution

a. Ca^{2+}: The element calcium (Ca) has an atomic number of 20, so it has 20 protons. Since the charge is +2, there are two more protons than electrons, giving the ion 18 electrons.

b. O^{2-}: The element oxygen (O) has an atomic number of eight, so it has eight protons. Since the charge is −2, there are two more electrons than protons, giving the ion 10 electrons.

PRACTICE PROBLEM 3.5

How many protons and electrons are present in each ion?

a. Ni^{2+} b. Se^{2-} c. Fe^{3+}

More Practice: Try Problem 3.24.

PROBLEM 3.3

(a) Which sphere (**A** or **B**) represents S and which represents S^{2-}? (b) Which sphere (**C** or **D**) represents Li and which represents Li^+?

3.2B Relating Group Number to Ionic Charge for Main Group Elements

Since elements with similar electronic configurations are grouped together in the periodic table, **elements in the same group form ions of similar charge.** The group number of a main group element can be used to determine the charge on an ion derived from that element.

- Metals form cations. For metals in groups 1A, 2A, and 3A, the group number = the charge on the cation.

Group 1A	$M\cdot$ ⟶ M^+ + 1 e^-	M = Li, Na, K, Rb, Cs

one valence electron

Group 2A	$M\cdot$ ⟶ M^{2+} + 2 e^-	M = Be, Mg, Ca, Sr, Ba

two valence electrons

Group 3A	$\cdot M\cdot$ ⟶ M^{3+} + 3 e^-	M = Al, Ga, In, Tl

three valence electrons

Group **1**A elements (Li, Na, K, Rb, and Cs) have **one** valence electron. Loss of this electron forms a cation with a +**1** charge. Group **2**A elements (Be, Mg, Ca, Sr, and Ba) have **two** valence electrons. Loss of both electrons forms a cation with a +**2** charge. Group **3**A elements (Al, Ga, In, and Tl) form cations, too, but only aluminum is commonly found in ionic compounds. It has **three** valence electrons, so loss of three electrons from aluminum forms a cation with a +**3** charge.

All of the cations derived from group 1A–3A elements have an octet of outer shell electrons except for Li^+ and Be^{2+}. Li^+ and Be^{2+} have a $1s^2$ electronic configuration like helium, the noble gas to which they are closest in the periodic table. Thus, these cations are especially stable because they have a filled outer shell of electrons, although they do *not* have an octet of electrons.

- **Nonmetals form anions. For nonmetals in groups 5A, 6A, and 7A, the anion charge = 8 − (the group number).**

Group 5A	$\cdot \ddot{X} \cdot$ + 3 e⁻ ⟶	$[:\ddot{X}:]^{3-}$	X = N, P
	five valence electrons		anion charge = 8 − (group number) = 8 − 5 = 3
Group 6A	$\cdot \ddot{X} : $ + 2 e⁻ ⟶	$[:\ddot{X}:]^{2-}$	X = O, S, Se
	six valence electrons		anion charge = 8 − (group number) = 8 − 6 = 2
Group 7A	$:\ddot{X} \cdot$ + 1 e⁻ ⟶	$[:\ddot{X}:]^{-}$	X = F, Cl, Br, I
	seven valence electrons		anion charge = 8 − (group number) = 8 − 7 = 1

Group **5**A elements have **five** valence electrons. A gain of **three** electrons forms an anion with a −**3** charge (anion charge = 8 − 5). Group **6**A elements have **six** valence electrons. A gain of **two** electrons forms an anion with a −**2** charge (anion charge = 8 − 6). Group **7**A elements have **seven** valence electrons. A gain of one electron forms an anion with a −**1** charge (anion charge = 8 − 7).

Table 3.1 summarizes the ionic charges of the main group elements. The periodic table in Figure 3.2 gives the common ions formed by the main group elements.

Table 3.1 Ionic Charges of the Main Group Elements

Group Number	Number of Valence Electrons	Number of Electrons Gained or Lost	General Structure of the Ion
1A (1)	1	1 e⁻ lost	M^+
2A (2)	2	2 e⁻ lost	M^{2+}
3A (3)	3	3 e⁻ lost	M^{3+}
5A (15)	5	3 e⁻ gained	X^{3-}
6A (16)	6	2 e⁻ gained	X^{2-}
7A (17)	7	1 e⁻ gained	X^-

Figure 3.2 Common Ions Formed by Main Group Elements

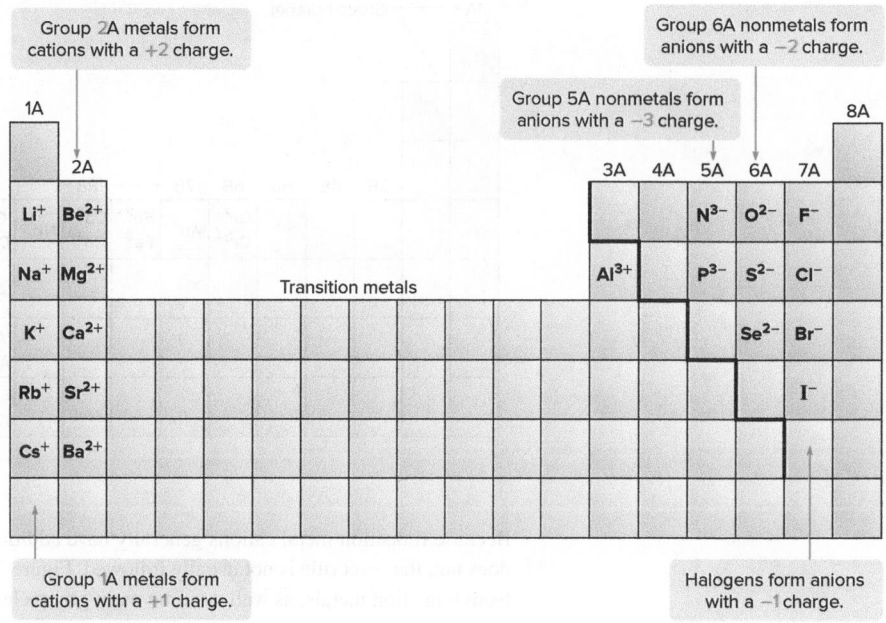

Group 2A metals form cations with a +2 charge.

Group 6A nonmetals form anions with a −2 charge.

Group 5A nonmetals form anions with a −3 charge.

Group 1A metals form cations with a +1 charge.

Halogens form anions with a −1 charge.

Transition metals

SAMPLE PROBLEM 3.6 DETERMINING ION CHARGE FROM THE GROUP NUMBER

Use the group number to determine the charge on an ion derived from each element: (a) barium; (b) sulfur.

Analysis

Locate the element in the periodic table. A metal in groups 1A, 2A, and 3A forms a cation equal in charge to the group number. A nonmetal in groups 5A, 6A, and 7A forms an anion whose charge equals 8 − (the group number).

Solution

a. Barium (Ba) is located in group 2A, so it forms a cation with a +2 charge; Ba^{2+}.

b. Sulfur (S) is located in group 6A, so it forms an anion with a negative charge of 8 − 6 = 2; S^{2-}.

PRACTICE PROBLEM 3.6

Use the group number to determine the charge on an ion derived from each element.

a. magnesium   b. iodine   c. selenium   d. rubidium

More Practice: Try Problems 3.27, 3.28, 3.36a–d.

PROBLEM 3.4

What noble gas has the same electronic configuration as each ion derived from the elements in Practice Problem 3.6?

3.2C Metals with Variable Charge

The transition metals form cations like other metals, but the magnitude of the charge on the cation is harder to predict. Some transition metals, and a few main group metals as well, form more than one type of cation. For example, iron forms two different cations, Fe^{2+} and Fe^{3+}. Fe^{2+} is formed by losing two valence electrons from the 4s orbital. Fe^{3+} is formed by loss of three electrons, two from a 4s orbital and one from a 3d orbital.

Figure 3.3   Common Cations Derived from Transition Metals and Group 4A Metals

Because transition metal cations generally have additional d electrons that the nearest noble gas does not, the octet rule is not usually followed. Figure 3.3 illustrates the common cations formed from transition metals, as well as some main group elements that form more than one cation.

PROBLEM 3.5

How many electrons and protons are contained in each cation?

   a. Au^+ b. Au^{3+} c. Sn^{2+} d. Sn^{4+}

PROBLEM 3.6

Identify each ion.

a.

27 protons
32 neutrons

24 electrons

b.

24 protons
28 neutrons

22 electrons

3.2D   FOCUS ON THE HUMAN BODY
Important Ions in the Body

Many different ions are required for proper cellular and organ function (Figure 3.4). The major cations in the body are Na^+, K^+, Ca^{2+}, and Mg^{2+}. K^+ and Mg^{2+} are present in high concentrations inside cells, while Na^+ and Ca^{2+} are present in a higher concentration outside cells, in the extracellular fluids. Na^+ is the major cation present in blood and extracellular bodily fluids, and its concentration is carefully regulated through a number of mechanisms to maintain blood volume and blood pressure within acceptable ranges that permit organ function. Ca^{2+} is found mainly in solid body parts such as teeth and bones, but it is also needed for proper nerve conduction and muscle contraction, as is Mg^{2+}.

In addition to these four cations, Fe^{2+} and Cl^- are also important ions. Fe^{2+} is essential for oxygen transport by red blood cells. Cl^- is present in red blood cells, gastric juices, and other body fluids. Along with Na^+, it plays a major role in regulating the fluid balance in the body.

Figure 3.4

Common Ions in the Human Body

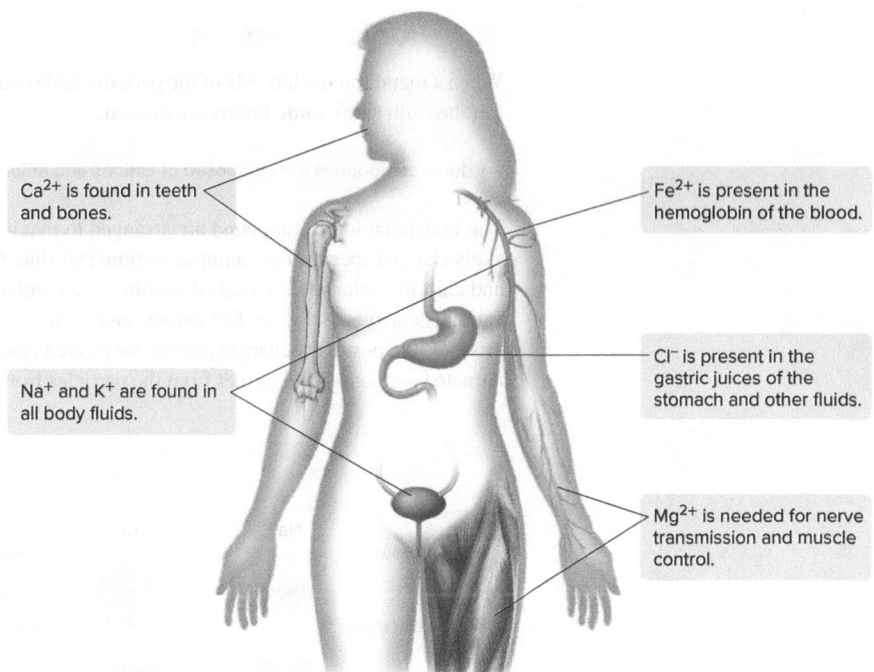

Ca²⁺ is found in teeth and bones.

Fe²⁺ is present in the hemoglobin of the blood.

Cl⁻ is present in the gastric juices of the stomach and other fluids.

Na⁺ and K⁺ are found in all body fluids.

Mg²⁺ is needed for nerve transmission and muscle control.

Na⁺, K⁺, Ca²⁺, Mg²⁺, Fe²⁺, and Cl⁻ are all common ions present throughout the organs of the human body.

Although Na⁺ is an essential mineral needed in the daily diet, the average American consumes three to five times the recommended daily allowance (RDA) of 2,400 mg. Excess sodium intake is linked to high blood pressure and heart disease. Dietary Na⁺ comes from salt, NaCl, added during cooking or at the table. Na⁺ is also added during the preparation of processed foods and canned products. For example, one 3.5-oz serving of fresh asparagus has only 1 mg of Na⁺, but the same serving size of canned asparagus contains 236 mg of Na⁺. Potato chips, snack foods, ketchup, processed meats, and many cheeses are particularly high in Na⁺. Table 3.2 lists the Na⁺ content of some common foods.

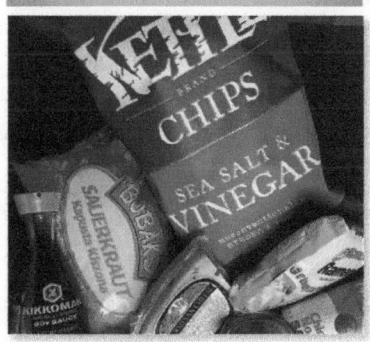

HEALTH NOTE

Many processed foods and snacks are high in sodium. ©*McGraw-Hill Education/Jill Braaten, photographer*

Table 3.2 Na⁺ Content in Common Foods

Foods High in Na⁺		Foods Low in Na⁺	
Food	Na⁺ (mg)	Food	Na⁺ (mg)
Potato chips (30)	276	Banana (1)	1
Hot dog (1)	504	Orange juice (1 cup)	2
Ham, smoked (3 oz)	908	Oatmeal, cooked (1 cup)	2
Chicken soup, canned (1 cup)	1,106	Cereal, shredded wheat (3.5 oz)	3
Tomato sauce, canned (1 cup)	1,402	Raisins, dried (3.5 oz)	27
Parmesan cheese (1 cup)	1,861	Salmon (3 oz)	55

PROBLEM 3.7

Mn²⁺ is an essential nutrient needed for blood clotting and the formation of the protein collagen. (a) How many protons and electrons are found in a neutral manganese atom? (b) How many electrons and protons are found in the cation Mn²⁺? (c) Write the electronic configuration of the element manganese and suggest which electrons are lost to form the Mn²⁺ cation.

3.3 Ionic Compounds

When a metal (on the left side of the periodic table) transfers one or more electrons to a nonmetal (on the right side), **ionic bonds** are formed.

> • **Ionic compounds are composed of cations and anions.**

The ions in an ionic compound are arranged to maximize the attractive force between the oppositely charged species. For example, sodium chloride, NaCl, is composed of sodium cations (Na^+) and chloride anions (Cl^-), packed together in a regular arrangement in a crystal lattice. Each Na^+ cation is surrounded by six Cl^- anions, and each Cl^- anion is surrounded by six Na^+ cations. In this way, the positively charged cations are located closer to the charged particles to which they are attracted—anions—and farther from the particles from which they are repelled—cations.

> • **The sum of the charges in an ionic compound must always be zero overall.**

The formula for an ionic compound shows the ratio of ions that combine to give zero charge. Since the sodium cation has a +1 charge and the chloride anion has a −1 charge, there must be one Na^+ cation for each Cl^- anion; thus, the formula is **NaCl**.

When cations and anions having charges of different magnitude combine, the number of cations per anion is *not* equal. Consider an ionic compound formed from calcium (Ca) and fluorine (F). Since calcium is located in group 2A, it loses two valence electrons to form Ca^{2+}. Since fluorine is located in group 7A, it gains one electron to form F^- like other halogens. When Ca^{2+} combines with the fluorine anion F^-, **there must be two F^- anions for each Ca^{2+} cation to have an overall charge of zero.**

Two F^- anions are needed for each Ca^{2+}.

In writing a formula for an ionic compound, we use subscripts when the number of ions needed to achieve zero charge is greater than one. Since two F^- anions are needed for each calcium cation, the formula is **CaF$_2$**. Figure 3.5 illustrates additional examples of how cations and anions combine to give zero overall charge.

Figure 3.5

Examples of Ionic Compounds with Zero Overall Charge

NaCl	Li$_2$O	BaI$_2$	Al$_2$O$_3$
Na$^+$ Cl$^-$	Li$^+$ O^{2-}	Ba^{2+} I$^-$	Al^{3+} O^{2-}
+1 −1	+2 −2	+2 −2	+6 −6

The ratio of oppositely charged ions that combine to form an ionic compound depends on the charge of the ions.

- NaCl: One Na$^+$ cation (+1 charge) combines with one Cl$^-$ anion (−1 charge).
- Li$_2$O: Two Li$^+$ cations (+2 charge total) combine with one O^{2-} anion (−2 charge).
- BaI$_2$: One Ba^{2+} cation (+2 charge) combines with two I$^-$ anions (−2 charge total).
- Al$_2$O$_3$: Two Al^{3+} cations (+6 charge total) combine with three O^{2-} anions (−6 charge total).

3.3A   Formulas for Ionic Compounds

Writing a formula for an ionic compound from two elements is a useful skill that can be practiced by following a series of steps.

How To   Write a Formula for an Ionic Compound

Step [1] Identify which element is the cation and which is the anion.

- **Metals form *cations* and nonmetals form *anions*.**
- Use the group number of a main group element to determine the charge.

An ionic compound derived from calcium and oxygen has the metal calcium as the cation and the nonmetal oxygen as the anion. Calcium (group 2A) loses two electrons to form Ca^{2+}. Oxygen (group 6A) gains two electrons to form O^{2-}.

Step [2] Determine how many of each ion type are needed for an overall charge of zero.

- When the cation and anion have the *same* charge, only *one* of each is needed.

The charges are equal in magnitude,
+2 and −2.

$$Ca^{2+} \ + \ O^{2-} \longrightarrow \quad \textbf{CaO}$$

One of each ion is needed
to balance charge.

- When the cation and anion have different charges, as is the case with the Ca^{2+} cation and Cl$^-$ anion, use the ion charges to determine the number of ions of each needed. **The charges on the ions tell us how many of the *oppositely* charged ions are needed to balance charge.**
- Write a subscript for the cation that is equal in magnitude to the charge on the anion. Write a subscript for the anion that is equal in magnitude to the charge on the cation.

The charges are not equal in
magnitude, +2 and −1.

$$Ca^{2+} \quad Cl^{1-} \qquad \text{The "1" is written for emphasis.}$$

$$Ca_1Cl_2 \ = \ \textbf{CaCl}_2 \qquad 2\ Cl^- \text{ anions for each } Ca^{2+}$$

Step [3] To write the formula, place the cation first and then the anion, and omit charges.

- Use subscripts to show the number of each ion needed to have zero overall charge. When no subscript is written, it is assumed to be "1."

As shown in step [2], the formula for the ionic compound formed from one calcium cation (Ca^{2+}) and one oxygen anion (O^{2-}) is **CaO**. The formula for the ionic compound formed from one calcium cation (Ca^{2+}) and two chlorine anions (Cl$^-$) is **CaCl$_2$**.

The tarnish on sterling silver is composed of an ionic compound formed from silver and sulfur (Sample Problem 3.7).
©Alejandro Rivera/iStockphoto/Getty Images RF

SAMPLE PROBLEM 3.7 WRITING THE FORMULA FOR AN IONIC COMPOUND

When sterling silver tarnishes, it forms an ionic compound derived from silver and sulfur. Write the formula for this ionic compound.

Analysis and Solution

[1] Identify the cation and the anion and use the periodic table to determine their charges.

- Silver is a metal, so it forms the cation, and from Figure 3.3, the charge on silver is +1 (Ag^+).
- Sulfur (group 6A) is a main group element with a −2 charge (S^{2-}).

[2] Balance charges.

- Because the charges are unequal, use their magnitudes to determine the relative number of each ion to give an overall charge of zero.
- **The charges on the ions tell us how many of the *oppositely* charged ions are needed to balance charge.**

The "1" is written for emphasis. Ag^{1+} S^{2-}

Ag_2S 2 Ag^+ cations for each S^{2-}

[3] Write the formula with the cation first and then the anion, and use subscripts to show the number of each ion needed.

- To balance charge, two Ag^+ cations are needed for each S^{2-} anion, so the formula is **Ag_2S.**

PRACTICE PROBLEM 3.7

Write the formula for the ionic compound formed from each pair of elements.

a. sodium and bromine

b. barium and oxygen

c. magnesium and iodine

d. lithium and oxygen

More Practice: Try Problems 3.47, 3.48.

SAMPLE PROBLEM 3.8 ASSIGNING IONIC FORMULAS TO ACHIEVE ZERO OVERALL CHARGE

Match the given representations of two ionic compounds dissolved in water with the following formulas: (a) KCl; (b) $CaCl_2$.

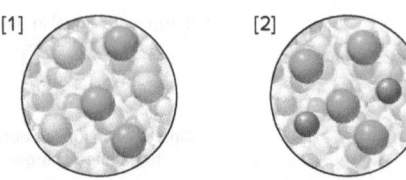

[1]   [2]

Analysis

Determine the charges on the cation and anion. When the cation and anion have the same charge, an equal number of cations and anions must be present for an overall charge of zero. When the cation and anion have different charges, use the charges on the ions to tell how many of the oppositely charged ions are needed so that the solution has an overall charge of zero.

Solution

a. Because KCl contains a cation (K^+) and anion (Cl^-) with charges of the same magnitude (+1 and −1), an equal number of cations and anions must be present in solution. Representation [1] contains an equal number of yellow and green spheres.

b. Because $CaCl_2$ contains a cation (Ca^{2+}) and anion (Cl^-) with charges of different magnitude (+2 and −1), the solution must contain twice as many anions as cations to have an overall charge of zero. Representation [2] contains twice as many green spheres (Cl^-) as purple spheres (Ca^{2+}).

PRACTICE PROBLEM 3.8

Draw a representation using molecular art for a solution of each of the following ionic compounds dissolved in water: (a) Na_2S; (b) $MgCl_2$.

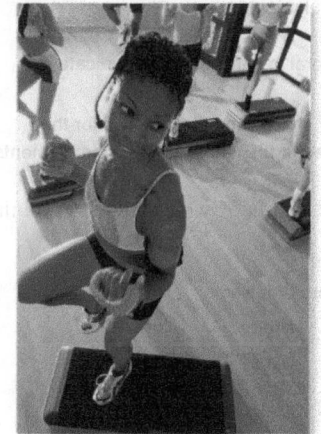

Potassium is a critical cation for normal heart and skeletal muscle function and nerve impulse conduction. Drinking electrolyte replacement beverages like Gatorade or Powerade can replenish K⁺ lost in sweat. ©Corbis VCG/Getty Images RF

Many sunblocks contain zinc oxide crystals (Problem 3.8), which reflect sunlight away from the skin to protect it from sun exposure. ©McGraw-Hill Education/ Jill Braaten, photographer

3.3B FOCUS ON HEALTH & MEDICINE
Ionic Compounds in Consumer Products

Simple ionic compounds are added to food or consumer products to prevent disease or maintain good health. For example, **potassium iodide** (KI) is an essential nutrient added to table salt. Iodine is needed to synthesize thyroid hormones. A deficiency of iodine in the diet can lead to insufficient thyroid hormone production. In an attempt to compensate, the thyroid gland may become enlarged, producing a swollen thyroid referred to as a goiter. **Sodium fluoride** (NaF) is added to toothpaste to strengthen tooth enamel and help prevent tooth decay.

K⁺ potassium iodide   sodium fluoride   Na⁺
I⁻   in table salt   in toothpaste   F⁻

©McGraw-Hill Education/Jill Braaten, photographer

Potassium chloride (KCl), sold under trade names such as K–Dur, Klor–Con, and Micro–K, is an ionic compound used for patients whose potassium levels are low. Potassium chloride can be given as tablets, an oral suspension, or intravenously. Adequate potassium levels are needed for proper fluid balance and organ function. Although potassium is readily obtained from many different food sources (e.g., potatoes, beans, melon, bananas, and spinach), levels can become low when too much potassium is lost in sweat and urine or through the use of certain medications.

PROBLEM 3.8

Zinc oxide, an ionic compound formed from zinc and oxygen, is a common component of sunblocks. What is the ionic formula for zinc oxide?

3.4 Naming Ionic Compounds

Now that we have learned how to write the formulas of some simple ionic compounds, we must learn how to name them. Assigning an unambiguous name to each compound is called chemical **nomenclature.**

3.4A Naming Cations

- **Cations of main group metals are given the name of the element from which they are formed.**

Na⁺	K⁺	Ca²⁺	Mg²⁺
sodium	potassium	calcium	magnesium

It is common to add the word "ion" after the name of the metal cation to distinguish it from the neutral metal itself. For example, when the concentration of sodium in a blood sample is determined, what is really measured is the concentration of sodium *ions* (Na⁺).

When a metal is able to form two different cations, a method is needed to distinguish these cations. Two systems are used, the systematic method and the common method. The systematic method (Method [1]) will largely be followed in this text. Since many ions are still identified by older names, however, the common method (Method [2]) is also given.

- **Method [1]:** Follow the name of the cation by a Roman numeral in parentheses to indicate its charge.
- **Method [2]:** Use the suffix *-ous* for the cation with the lesser charge and the suffix *-ic* for the cation with the higher charge. These suffixes are often added to the Latin names of the elements.

For example, the element iron (Fe) forms two cations, Fe^{2+} and Fe^{3+}, which are named in the following way:

	Systematic Name	Common Name
Fe^{2+}	iron(II)	ferr**ous**
Fe^{3+}	iron(III)	ferr**ic**

Table 3.3 lists the systematic and common names for several cations.

3.4B   Naming Anions

- Anions are named by replacing the ending of the element name by the suffix *-ide*.

Cl	$---\rightarrow$	Cl^-	[Change *-ine* to *-ide*.]
chlor*ine*		chlor**ide**	
O	$---\rightarrow$	O^{2-}	[Change *-ygen* to *-ide*.]
ox*ygen*		ox**ide**	

Table 3.4 lists the names of common anions derived from nonmetal elements.

PROBLEM 3.9

Give the name of each ion.

a. S^{2-} b. Cu^+ c. Cs^+ d. Al^{3+} e. Sn^{4+}

PROBLEM 3.10

Give the symbol for each ion.

a. stannous   b. iodide   c. manganese ion   d. lead(II)   e. selenide

Table 3.3 Systematic and Common Names for Some Metal Ions

Element	Ion Symbol	Systematic Name	Common Name
Chromium	Cr^{2+}	Chromium(II)	Chromous
	Cr^{3+}	Chromium(III)	Chromic
Copper	Cu^+	Copper(I)	Cuprous
	Cu^{2+}	Copper(II)	Cupric
Iron	Fe^{2+}	Iron(II)	Ferrous
	Fe^{3+}	Iron(III)	Ferric
Mercury	Hg_2^{2+}	Mercury(I)[a]	Mercurous
	Hg^{2+}	Mercury(II)	Mercuric
Tin	Sn^{2+}	Tin(II)	Stannous
	Sn^{4+}	Tin(IV)	Stannic

[a]Mercury(I) exists as Hg_2^{2+}, containing two atoms of mercury, each with a +1 charge.

Table 3.4 Names of Common Anions

Element	Ion Symbol	Name
Bromine	Br^-	Bromide
Chlorine	Cl^-	Chloride
Fluorine	F^-	Fluoride
Iodine	I^-	Iodide
Nitrogen	N^{3-}	Nitride
Oxygen	O^{2-}	Oxide
Phosphorus	P^{3-}	Phosphide
Sulfur	S^{2-}	Sulfide

3.4C Naming Ionic Compounds with Cations from Main Group Metals

To name an ionic compound with a main group metal cation whose charge never varies, **name the cation and then the anion.** Do *not* specify the charge on the cation. Do *not* specify how many ions of each type are needed to balance charge.

Na^+	F^-	$- - - \rightarrow$	NaF
sodium	fluoride		sodium fluoride
Mg^{2+}	Cl^-	$- - - \rightarrow$	$MgCl_2$
magnesium	chloride		magnesium chloride

Thus, $BaCl_2$ is named barium chloride (*not* barium *di*chloride). The number of ions of each type is inferred in the name because the net charge must be zero.

SAMPLE PROBLEM 3.9 NAMING AN IONIC COMPOUND THAT CONTAINS A MAIN GROUP METAL

Name each ionic compound: (a) Na_2S; (b) $AlBr_3$.

Analysis
Name the cation and then the anion.

Solution
a. Na_2S: The cation is sodium and the anion is sulfide (derived from sulfur); thus, the name is sodium sulfide.

b. $AlBr_3$: The cation is aluminum and the anion is bromide (derived from bromine); thus, the name is aluminum bromide.

PRACTICE PROBLEM 3.9

Name each ionic compound.

a. NaF   b. MgO   c. $SrBr_2$ d. Li_2O e. TiO_2 f. $AlCl_3$

More Practice: Try Problems 3.61a, b, d, f; 3.62a, b, f.

3.4D Naming Ionic Compounds Containing Metals with Variable Charge

To name an ionic compound that contains a metal with variable charge, we must specify the charge on the cation. The formula of the ionic compound—that is, how many cations there are per anion—allows us to determine the charge on the cation.

How To Name an Ionic Compound That Contains a Metal with Variable Charge

Example: Give the name for $CuCl_2$.

Step [1] Determine the charge on the cation.

- Since there are two Cl^- anions, each of which has a -1 charge, the copper cation must have a $+2$ charge to make the overall charge zero.

$CuCl_2$ 2 Cl^- anions $- - - \rightarrow$ The total negative charge is -2.

Cu must have a $+2$ charge to balance the -2 charge of the anions.

Cu^{2+}

—Continued

How To, continued . . .

Step [2]   **Name the cation and anion.**
  • Name the cation using its element name followed by a Roman numeral to indicate its charge. In the common system, use the suffix *-ous* or *-ic* to indicate charge.
  • Name the anion by changing the ending of the element name to the suffix *-ide*.

$$Cu^{2+} \ \text{---→} \quad \text{copper(II)} \quad \text{or} \quad \text{cupric}$$
$$Cl^- \ \text{---→} \quad \text{chloride}$$

Step [3]   **Write the name of the cation first, then the anion.**
  • **Answer:** Copper(II) chloride or cupric chloride

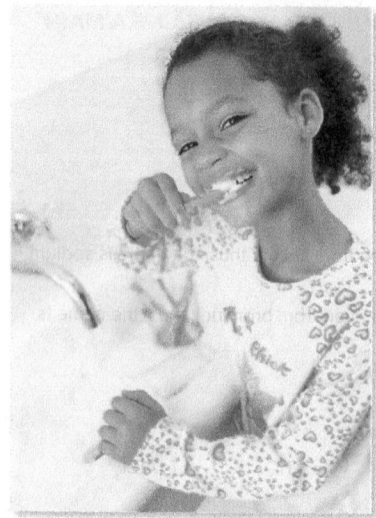

HEALTH NOTE

Some toothpastes contain the ionic compounds SnF_2 as a source of fluoride and Al_2O_3 as an abrasive. ©*Daniel Pangbourne/Digital Vision/Getty Images RF*

Sample Problem 3.10 illustrates the difference in naming ionic compounds derived from metals that have fixed or variable charge.

SAMPLE PROBLEM 3.10 NAMING AN IONIC COMPOUND

SnF_2 and Al_2O_3 are both ingredients in commercial toothpastes. SnF_2 contains fluoride, which strengthens tooth enamel. Al_2O_3 is an abrasive that helps to scrub the teeth clean when they are brushed. Give names for (a) SnF_2; (b) Al_2O_3.

Analysis

First determine if the cation has a fixed or variable charge. To name an ionic compound that contains a cation that always has the same charge, name the cation and then the anion (using the suffix *-ide*). When the metal has a variable charge, use the overall anion charge to determine the charge on the cation. Then name the cation (using a Roman numeral or the suffix *-ous* or *-ic*), followed by the anion.

Solution

a. SnF_2: Sn cations have variable charge so the overall anion charge determines the cation charge.

SnF_2 2 F^- anions   ---→   The total negative charge is −2.

Sn must have a +2 charge to balance the −2 charge of the anions.

         tin(II) or stannous   fluoride

Answer: tin(II) fluoride or stannous fluoride

b. Al_2O_3: Al has a fixed charge of +3. To name the compound, name the cation as the element (aluminum), and the anion by changing the ending of the element name to the suffix *-ide* (oxygen → oxide).

Al_2O_3 aluminum   **Answer:** aluminum oxide
            oxide

PRACTICE PROBLEM 3.10

Name each ionic compound.

  a. $CrCl_3$ b. PbS   c. SnF_4 d. PbO_2 e. $FeBr_2$ f. $AuCl_3$

More Practice: Try Problems 3.61c, e, g; 3.62c–e, g; 3.63; 3.64.

PROBLEM 3.11

Several copper salts are brightly colored. Give the name for each of the following ionic copper compounds.

  a. Cu_2O (brown)   b. CuO (black)   c. CuCl (green)   d. $CuCl_2$ (blue)

PROBLEM 3.12

When iron rusts it forms Fe_2O_3. Name this product of air oxidation.

3.4E   Writing a Formula from the Name of an Ionic Compound

Thus far, we have focused on assigning a name to a formula for an ionic compound. Writing a formula from a name is also a useful skill.

How To   **Derive a Formula from the Name of an Ionic Compound**

Example: Write the formula for tin(IV) oxide.

Step [1]   Identify the cation and the anion and determine their charges.
- The name of the cation appears first, followed by the anion.
- For metals with variable charge, the Roman numeral gives the charge on the cation.

In this example, tin is the cation. The Roman numeral tells us that its charge is +4, making the cation Sn^{4+}. Oxide is the name of the oxygen anion, O^{2-} (Table 3.4).

Step [2]   Balance charges.
- Use the charge on the cation to determine the number of ions of the anion needed to balance charge.

$$Sn^{4+} \qquad O^{2-}$$

Two −2 anions are needed
for each +4 cation.

cation   anion

Step [3]   Write the formula with the cation first, and use subscripts to show the number of each ion needed to have zero overall charge.
Answer: SnO_2

SAMPLE PROBLEM 3.11 DERIVING A FORMULA FROM THE NAME OF AN IONIC COMPOUND

Write the formula for sodium oxide.

Analysis and Solution

[1]   Identify the cation and the anion and determine their charges.
- Because the name of the cation appears first, sodium is the cation and oxide is the anion.
- Sodium has a fixed charge of +1 (Na^+) and oxide has a charge of −2 (O^{2-}).

[2]   Balance charges.
- Use the charge on the anion to determine the number of ions of the cation needed to balance charge.

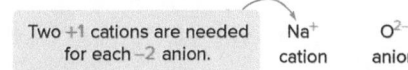

Two +1 cations are needed
for each −2 anion.

Na^+ O^{2-}

cation   anion

[3]   Write the formula with the cation first, and use subscripts to show the number of each ion needed.
- To balance charge, two Na^+ cations are needed for each oxide anion (O^{2-}), so the formula of sodium oxide is **Na_2O.**

PRACTICE PROBLEM 3.11

Write the formula for each ionic compound.

a. calcium bromide   c. ferric bromide   e. chromium(II) chloride

b. copper(I) iodide   d. magnesium sulfide

More Practice: Try Problems 3.65, 3.66.

3.5   Physical Properties of Ionic Compounds

Ionic compounds are crystalline solids composed of ions packed to maximize the interaction of the positive charge of the cations and negative charge of the anions. The relative size and charge of the ions determine the way they are packed in the crystal lattice. Ionic solids are held together by extremely strong interactions of the oppositely charged ions. How is this reflected in the melting point and boiling point of an ionic compound?

When a compound melts to form a liquid, energy is needed to overcome some of the attractive forces of the ordered solid to form the less ordered liquid phase. Since an ionic compound is held together by very strong electrostatic interactions, it takes a great deal of energy to separate the ions from each other. As a result, **ionic compounds have very high melting points.** For example, the melting point of NaCl is 801 °C.

A great deal of energy is needed to overcome the attractive forces present in the liquid phase, too, to form ions that are far apart and very disorganized in the gas phase, so **ionic compounds have extremely high boiling points.** The boiling point of liquid NaCl is 1413 °C.

A great many ionic compounds are soluble in water. When an ionic compound dissolves in water, the ions are separated, and each anion and cation is surrounded by water molecules, as shown in Figure 3.6. The interaction of the water solvent with the ions provides the energy needed to overcome the strong ion–ion attractions of the crystalline lattice. We will learn much more about solubility in Chapter 8.

An **aqueous solution** contains a substance dissolved in liquid water.

When an ionic compound dissolves in water, the resulting aqueous solution conducts an electric current. This distinguishes ionic compounds from other compounds discussed in Chapter 4, some of which dissolve in water but do not form ions and therefore do not conduct electricity.

Figure 3.6   Dissolving NaCl in Water

When NaCl dissolves in water, each Na$^+$ ion and each Cl$^-$ ion are surrounded by water molecules. The interactions of these ions with water molecules provide the energy needed to break apart the ions of the crystal lattice. *©McGraw-Hill Education/Jill Braaten, photographer*

3.6   Polyatomic Ions

Sometimes ions are composed of more than one element. The ion bears a charge because the total number of electrons it contains is different from the total number of protons in the nuclei of all of the atoms.

- A *polyatomic ion* is a cation or anion that contains more than one atom.

The atoms in the polyatomic ion are held together by covalent bonds, but since the ion bears a charge, it bonds to other ions by ionic bonding. For example, calcium sulfate, $CaSO_4$, is composed of a calcium cation, Ca^{2+}, and the polyatomic anion sulfate, SO_4^{2-}. $CaSO_4$ is used to make plaster casts for broken bones.

We will encounter only two polyatomic cations: H_3O^+, **the hydronium ion,** which will play a key role in the acid–base chemistry discussed in Chapter 9, and NH_4^+, **the ammonium ion.**

In contrast, there are several common polyatomic anions, most of which contain a nonmetal like carbon, sulfur, or phosphorus, usually bonded to one or more oxygen atoms. Common examples include **carbonate (CO_3^{2-}), sulfate (SO_4^{2-}),** and **phosphate (PO_4^{3-}).** Table 3.5 lists the most common polyatomic anions.

The names of most polyatomic anions end in the suffix *-ate.* Exceptions to this generalization include hydroxide (OH^-) and cyanide (CN^-). Two other aspects of nomenclature are worthy of note.

- The suffix *-ite* is used for an anion that has one fewer oxygen atom than a similar anion named with the *-ate* ending. Thus, SO_4^{2-} is sul*fate*, but SO_3^{2-} is sul*fite*.
- When two anions differ in the presence of a hydrogen, the word *hydrogen* or the prefix *bi-* is added to the name of the anion. Thus, SO_4^{2-} is sulfate, but HSO_4^- is *hydrogen* sulfate or *bi*sulfate.

H_3O^+
hydronium ion

NH_4^+
ammonium ion

SO_4^{2-}
sulfate

SO_3^{2-}
sulfite

HSO_4^-
hydrogen sulfate
(bisulfate)

Table 3.5   Names of Common Polyatomic Anions

Nonmetal	Formula	Name
Carbon	CO_3^{2-}	Carbonate
	HCO_3^-	Hydrogen carbonate or bicarbonate
	$CH_3CO_2^-$	Acetate
	CN^-	Cyanide
Nitrogen	NO_3^-	Nitrate
	NO_2^-	Nitrite
Oxygen	OH^-	Hydroxide
Phosphorus	PO_4^{3-}	Phosphate
	HPO_4^{2-}	Hydrogen phosphate
	$H_2PO_4^-$	Dihydrogen phosphate
Sulfur	SO_4^{2-}	Sulfate
	HSO_4^-	Hydrogen sulfate or bisulfate
	SO_3^{2-}	Sulfite
	HSO_3^-	Hydrogen sulfite or bisulfite

Spam, a canned meat widely consumed in Alaska, Hawaii, and other parts of the United States, contains the preservative sodium nitrite, $NaNO_2$. Sodium nitrite inhibits the growth of *Clostridium botulinum*, a bacterium responsible for a lethal form of food poisoning.
©McGraw-Hill Education/Elite Images

Barium sulfate is used to visualize the digestive system during an X-ray procedure. ©CNRI/Science Source

3.6A   Writing Formulas for Ionic Compounds with Polyatomic Ions

Writing the formula for an ionic compound with a polyatomic ion is no different than writing a formula for an ion with a single charged atom, so we follow the procedure outlined in Section 3.3A.

When the cation and anion have the *same* charge, only *one* of each ion is needed for an overall charge of zero.

The charges are equal in magnitude, +1 and −1.

$$Na^+ + NO_2^- \longrightarrow NaNO_2$$
sodium   nitrite   sodium nitrite

One of each ion is needed to balance charge.

The charges are equal in magnitude, +2 and −2.

$$Ba^{2+} + SO_4^{2-} \longrightarrow BaSO_4$$
barium   sulfate   barium sulfate

One of each ion is needed to balance charge.

In a compound formed from ions of unequal charge, such as magnesium (Mg^{2+}) and hydroxide (OH^-), **the charges on the ions tell us how many of the *oppositely* charged ions are needed to balance the charge.**

The charges are not equal in magnitude, +2 and −1.

$$Mg^{2+} + OH^- \longrightarrow Mg(OH)_2$$

Use a subscript outside the parentheses.

Two OH^- anions are needed to balance charge.   Use parentheses around all atoms of the ion.

Parentheses are used around the polyatomic ion, and a subscript indicates how many of each are needed to balance charge. The formula is written as $Mg(OH)_2$ (*not* MgO_2H_2 or $MgOH_2$).

SAMPLE PROBLEM 3.12 WRITING THE FORMULA FOR AN IONIC COMPOUND THAT CONTAINS A POLYATOMIC ION

A dietary supplement used to prevent and treat calcium deficiencies consists of an ionic compound formed from calcium and phosphate. What is its formula?

Analysis and Solution

[1] **Identify the cation and the anion and determine their charges.**
   - Calcium forms the cation, and from Figure 3.3, the charge on calcium is +2 (Ca^{2+}).
   - Phosphate is a polyatomic anion with a −3 charge (PO_4^{3-}).

[2] **Balance charges.**
   - The charges are unequal, so use their magnitudes to determine the relative number of each ion to give an overall charge of zero.
   - **The charges on the ions tell us how many of the *oppositely* charged ions are needed to balance charge.**

$$Ca^{2+} \qquad PO_4^{3-}$$

$$Ca_3(PO_4)_2 \qquad \text{parentheses around the anion}$$

[3] **Write the formula with the cation first and then the anion, and use subscripts to show the number of each ion needed.**

- To balance charge, three Ca^{2+} cations are needed for two PO_4^{3-} anions, so the formula is $Ca_3(PO_4)_2$.

PRACTICE PROBLEM 3.12

Write the formula for the compound formed when the sulfate anion (SO_4^{2-}) combines with a cation from each of the following elements: (a) magnesium; (b) sodium; (c) nickel; (d) aluminum; (e) lithium.

More Practice: Try Problems 3.49, 3.50, 3.57–3.60, 3.71, 3.72.

PROBLEM 3.14

Write the formula of the ionic compound formed from each pair of cations and anions.

a. sodium and bicarbonate   c. ammonium and sulfate   e. calcium and bisulfate

b. potassium and nitrate   d. magnesium and phosphate   f. barium and hydroxide

PROBLEM 3.15

Write the formula for the compound formed when K^+ combines with each anion.

a. OH^- b. NO_2^- c. SO_4^{2-} d. HSO_3^- e. PO_4^{3-} f. CN^-

3.6B   Naming Ionic Compounds with Polyatomic Ions

Naming ionic compounds derived from polyatomic anions follows the same procedures outlined in Sections 3.4C and 3.4D. There is no easy trick for remembering the names and structures of the anions listed in Table 3.5. The names of the anions in boldface type are especially common and should be committed to memory.

SAMPLE PROBLEM 3.13 NAMING AN IONIC COMPOUND THAT CONTAINS A POLYATOMIC ION

Name each ionic compound: (a) $NaHCO_3$, the active ingredient in baking soda; (b) $Al_2(SO_4)_3$, an ingredient once used in antiperspirants but no longer considered effective.

Analysis

First determine if the cation has a fixed or variable charge. To name an ionic compound that contains a cation that always has the same charge, name the cation and then the anion. When the metal has a variable charge, use the overall anion charge to determine the charge on the cation. Then name the cation (using a Roman numeral or the suffix -ous or -ic), followed by the anion.

Solution

a. $NaHCO_3$: Sodium cations have a fixed charge of +1. The anion HCO_3^- is called bicarbonate or hydrogen carbonate.

   Answer: sodium bicarbonate or sodium hydrogen carbonate

b. $Al_2(SO_4)_3$: Aluminum cations have a fixed charge of +3. The anion SO_4^{2-} is called sulfate.

   Answer: aluminum sulfate

PRACTICE PROBLEM 3.13

Name each compound.

a. Na_2CO_3 b. $Ca(OH)_2$ c. $Mg(NO_3)_2$ d. $Mn(CH_3CO_2)_2$ e. $Fe(HSO_3)_3$ f. $Mg_3(PO_4)_2$

More Practice: Try Problems 3.67, 3.68, 3.73, 3.74.

The shells of oysters and other mollusks are composed largely of calcium carbonate, CaCO₃. ©Image Source/Getty Images RF

3.6C FOCUS ON HEALTH & MEDICINE
Useful Ionic Compounds

Ionic compounds are the active ingredients in several over-the-counter drugs. Examples include **calcium carbonate (CaCO₃),** the antacid in Tums; **magnesium hydroxide [Mg(OH)₂],** one of the active components in the antacids Maalox and milk of magnesia; and **iron(II) sulfate (FeSO₄),** an iron supplement used to treat anemia.

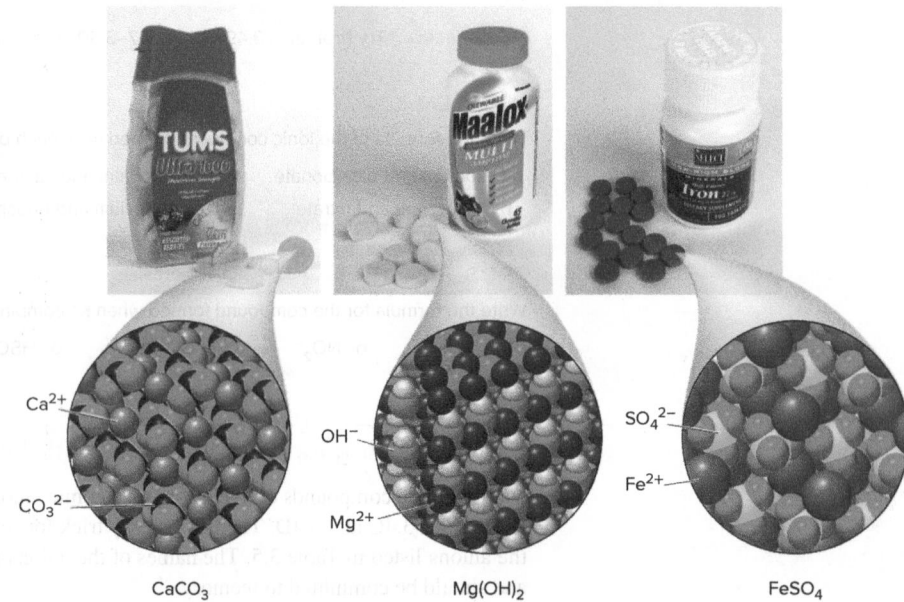

CaCO₃   Mg(OH)₂   FeSO₄

©McGraw-Hill Education/Jill Braaten, photographer

Some ionic compounds are given as intravenous drugs. Bicarbonate (HCO₃⁻) is an important polyatomic anion that controls the acid–base balance in the blood. When the blood becomes too acidic, sodium bicarbonate (NaHCO₃) is administered intravenously to decrease the acidity. Magnesium sulfate (MgSO₄), an over-the-counter laxative, is also given intravenously to prevent seizures caused by extremely high blood pressure associated with some pregnancies.

HEALTH NOTE

(top) Normal bone; (bottom) brittle bone due to osteoporosis. Osteoporosis results in a decrease in bone density, making bones brittle and easily fractured. ©Steve Gschmeissner/Science Source

3.6D FOCUS ON HEALTH & MEDICINE
Treating Osteoporosis

Although much of the body is composed of compounds held together by covalent bonds, about 70% of bone is composed largely of a complex ionic solid with the formula Ca₁₀(PO₄)₆(OH)₂ called **hydroxyapatite.** Throughout an individual's life, hydroxyapatite is constantly broken down and rebuilt. In postmenopausal women, however, the rate of bone loss often becomes greater than bone synthesis, and bones get brittle and easily broken. This condition is called **osteoporosis.**

In recent years, some prescription drugs have proven effective in combating osteoporosis. Sodium alendronate, trade name Fosamax, increases bone density by decreasing the rate of bone loss. Fosamax is an ionic compound with the formula Na(C₄H₁₂NO₇P₂). This compound contains a sodium cation, Na⁺, and a polyatomic anion, (C₄H₁₂NO₇P₂)⁻.

PROBLEM 3.16

Using the charges on the ions that compose hydroxyapatite, show that it has zero overall charge.

CHAPTER HIGHLIGHTS

KEY TERMS

Ammonium ion (3.6)
Anion (3.2)
Bonding (3.1)
Carbonate (3.6)
Cation (3.2)
Covalent bond (3.1)

Hydronium ion (3.6)
Hydroxide (3.6)
Ion (3.2)
Ionic bond (3.1)
Molecule (3.1)
Nomenclature (3.4)

Octet rule (3.2)
Phosphate (3.6)
Polyatomic ion (3.6)
Sulfate (3.6)

KEY CONCEPTS

① What are the basic features of ionic and covalent bonds? (3.1)

- Both ionic bonding and covalent bonding follow one general rule: Elements gain, lose, or share electrons to attain the electronic configuration of the noble gas closest to them in the periodic table.
- Ionic bonds result from the transfer of electrons from one element to another. Ionic bonds form between a metal and a nonmetal. Ionic compounds consist of oppositely charged ions that feel a strong electrostatic attraction for each other.
- Covalent bonds result from the sharing of electrons between two atoms. Covalent bonds occur between two nonmetals, or when a metalloid combines with a nonmetal. Covalent bonding forms discrete molecules.

② How can the periodic table be used to determine whether an atom forms a cation or an anion, and its resulting ionic charge? (3.2)

- Metals form cations and nonmetals form anions.
- By gaining or losing one, two, or three electrons, an atom forms an ion with a completely filled outer shell of electrons.
- The charge on main group ions can be predicted from the position in the periodic table. For metals in groups 1A, 2A, and 3A, the group number = the charge on the cation. For nonmetals in groups 5A, 6A, and 7A, the anion charge = 8 − (the group number).

③ What is the octet rule? (3.2)

- Main group elements are especially stable when they possess an octet of electrons. Main group elements gain or lose one, two, or three electrons to form ions with eight outer shell electrons.

④ What determines the formula of an ionic compound? (3.3)

- Cations and anions always form ionic compounds that have zero overall charge.
- Ionic compounds are written with the cation first, and then the anion, with subscripts to show how many of each are needed to have zero net charge.

⑤ How are ionic compounds named? (3.4)

- Ionic compounds are always named with the name of the cation first.
- With cations having a fixed charge, the cation has the same name as its neutral element. The name of the anion usually

ends in the suffix -ide if it is derived from a single atom or -ate (or -ite) if it is polyatomic.

- When the metal has a variable charge, use the overall anion charge to determine the charge on the cation. Then name the cation using a Roman numeral or the suffix -ous (for the ion with the lesser charge) or -ic (for the ion with the larger charge).

⑥ Describe the properties of ionic compounds. (3.5)

- Ionic compounds are crystalline solids with the ions arranged to maximize the interactions of the oppositely charged ions.
- Ionic compounds have high melting points and boiling points.
- Most ionic compounds are soluble in water and their aqueous solutions conduct an electric current.

⑦ What are polyatomic ions and how are they named? (3.6)

- Polyatomic ions are charged species that are composed of more than one element.
- The names for polyatomic cations end in the suffix -onium.
- Many polyatomic anions have names that end in the suffix -ate. The suffix -ite is used for an anion that has one fewer oxygen atom than a similar anion named with the -ate ending. When two anions differ in the presence of a hydrogen, the word hydrogen or the prefix bi- is added to the name of the anion.

⑧ List useful consumer products and drugs that are composed of ionic compounds.

- Useful ionic compounds that contain alkali metal cations and halogen anions include KI (iodine supplement), NaF (source of fluoride in toothpaste), and KCl (potassium supplement). (3.3)
- Other products contain SnF_2 (fluoride source in toothpaste), Al_2O_3 (abrasive in toothpaste), and ZnO (sunblock agent). (3.4)
- Useful ionic compounds with polyatomic anions include $CaCO_3$ (antacid and calcium supplement), magnesium hydroxide (antacid), and $FeSO_4$ (iron supplement). (3.6)

102   **Chapter 3** Ionic Compounds

PROBLEMS

Selected in-chapter and odd-numbered end-of-chapter problems have brief answers in Appendix B. The *Student Study Guide and Solutions Manual* contains detailed solutions to all in-chapter and odd-numbered end-of-chapter problems, as well as additional worked examples and a chapter self-test.

Ionic and Covalent Bonding

3.17 Which formulas represent ionic compounds and which represent covalent compounds?

  a. CO_2 b. H_2SO_4 c. KF   d. CH_5N

3.18 Which formulas represent ionic compounds and which represent covalent compounds?

  a. C_3H_8 b. ClBr   c. CuO   d. CH_4O

3.19 Which pairs of elements are likely to form ionic bonds and which pairs are likely to form covalent bonds?

  a. potassium and oxygen

  b. sulfur and carbon

  c. two bromine atoms

  d. carbon and oxygen

3.20 Which pairs of elements are likely to form ionic bonds and which pairs are likely to form covalent bonds?

  a. carbon and hydrogen

  b. sodium and sulfur

  c. hydrogen and oxygen

  d. magnesium and bromine

Ions

3.21 Give the ion symbol for the ion shown in the molecular art.

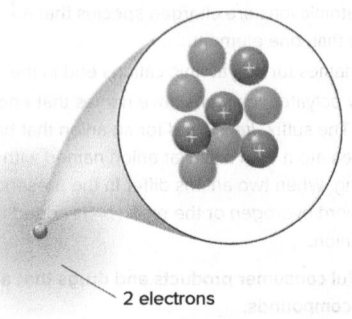

2 electrons

3.22 Give the ion symbol for the ion shown in the molecular art.

18 electrons

3.23 Write the ion symbol for an atom with the given number of protons and electrons.

  a. 22 protons and 20 electrons

  b. 16 protons and 18 electrons

  c. 13 protons and 10 electrons

  d. 17 protons and 18 electrons

  e. 20 protons and 18 electrons

3.24 How many protons and electrons are present in each ion?

  a. K^+ b. S^{2-} c. Mn^{2+} d. Fe^{2+} e. Cs^+ f. I^-

3.25 Identify each atom or ion.

a.   56 protons / 81 neutrons / 54 electrons   b.   15 protons / 16 neutrons / 18 electrons

3.26 Identify each atom or ion.

a.   37 protons / 48 neutrons / 37 electrons   b.   79 protons / 118 neutrons, / 76 electrons

3.27 What species fits each description?

  a. a period 2 element that forms a +2 cation

  b. an ion from group 7A with 18 electrons

  c. a cation from group 1A with 36 electrons

3.28 What species fits each description?

  a. a period 3 element that forms an ion with a −1 charge

  b. an ion from group 2A with 36 electrons

  c. an ion from group 6A with 18 electrons

3.29 Give the ion symbol for each ion.

  a. sodium ion   c. manganese ion   e. stannic

  b. selenide   d. gold(III)   f. mercurous

3.30 Give the ion symbol for each ion.

  a. barium ion   c. oxide   e. lead(IV)

  b. iron(II)   d. ferrous   f. cobalt(III)

3.31 What noble gas has the same electronic configuration as each ion?

  a. O^{2-} b. Mg^{2+} c. Al^{3+} d. S^{2-} e. F^- f. Be^{2+}

3.32 Give two cations and two anions that have the same electronic configuration as each noble gas: (a) neon; (b) argon.

3.33 How many electrons must be gained or lost by each element to achieve a noble gas configuration of electrons?

  a. lithium   b. iodine   c. sulfur   d. strontium

3.34 How many electrons must be gained or lost by each element to achieve a noble gas configuration of electrons?

  a. cesium   b. barium   c. selenium   d. aluminum

3.35 For each of the general electron-dot formulas for elements, give the following information: [1] the number of valence electrons; [2] the group number of the element; [3] how many electrons would be gained or lost to achieve a noble gas configuration; [4] the charge on the resulting ion; [5] an example of the element.

a. X·   b. :Ä·

3.36 Label each of the following elements or regions in the periodic table.

a. a group that forms cations with a +2 charge
b. a group that forms anions with a −2 charge
c. a group that forms cations with a +1 charge
d. a group that forms anions with a −1 charge
e. elements that form ions with the same electronic configuration as Ne
f. elements that form ions with the same electronic configuration as He

3.37 Consider the given electron-dot symbol for the following element:

·Q·

a. What is the group number of Q?
b. What is the charge on the ion formed from Q?
c. What is the formula of an ionic compound formed from Q and fluorine?
d. What is the formula of an ionic compound formed from Q and oxygen?

3.38 Consider the given electron-dot symbol for the following element:

:Ż·

a. What is the group number of Z?
b. What is the charge on the ion formed from Z?
c. What is the formula of an ionic compound formed from Z and sodium?
d. What is the formula of an ionic compound formed from Z and magnesium?

3.39 Use the element colors in Figure 2.3 (also shown on the inside back cover) and the information in Table 3.5 to identify each polyatomic ion. Give the name and proper formula, including charge.

a.   b.

3.40 Use the element colors in Figure 2.3 (also shown on the inside back cover) and the information in Table 3.5 to identify each polyatomic ion. Give the name and proper formula, including charge.

a.   b.

3.41 Use the element colors in Figure 2.3 (also shown on the inside back cover) and the information in Table 3.5 to identify each of the following anions. Give the name and proper formula, including the charge.

a.   b. ●●   c. ○

3.42 Use the element colors in Figure 2.3 (also shown on the inside back cover) and the information in Table 3.5 to identify each of the following anions. Give the name and proper formula, including the charge.

a. ●   b. ●   c. ●

3.43 How many protons and electrons are contained in each polyatomic ion?

a. OH^- b. H_3O^+ c. PO_4^{3-}

3.44 How many protons and electrons are contained in each polyatomic ion?

a. NH_4^+ b. CN^- c. CO_3^{2-}

3.45 Identify the polyatomic anion (including its proper charge) in each of the following ionic compounds. How many protons and electrons are present in each polyatomic anion?

a. $NaClO_2$ b. $Al(OCN)_3$

3.46 Identify the polyatomic anion (including its proper charge) in each of the following ionic compounds. How many protons and electrons are present in each polyatomic anion?

a. $KBrO_3$ b. $CaHPO_3$

Ionic Compounds

3.47 Write the formula for the ionic compound formed from each pair of elements.

a. calcium and sulfur
b. aluminum and bromine
c. lithium and iodine
d. nickel and chlorine
e. sodium and selenium

3.48 Write the formula for the ionic compound formed from each pair of elements.

a. barium and bromine
b. aluminum and sulfur
c. manganese and chlorine
d. zinc and sulfur
e. magnesium and fluorine

3.49 Write the formula for the ionic compound formed from each cation and anion.

a. lithium and nitrite
b. calcium and acetate
c. sodium and bisulfite
d. manganese and phosphate
e. magnesium and hydrogen sulfite

104   **Chapter 3**   Ionic Compounds

3.50 Write the formula for the ionic compound formed from each cation and anion.

    a. potassium and bicarbonate

    b. magnesium and nitrate

    c. lithium and carbonate

    d. potassium and cyanide

    e. ammonium and phosphate

3.51 Considering the indicated charges on the cation **X** and the anion **Y,** fill in the table with the formula of the ionic compound that results in zero overall charge. One entry is filled in.

	Y^-	Y^{2-}	Y^{3-}
X^+			
X^{2+}	XY_2		
X^{3+}			

3.52 What is the charge on the cation **M** in each of the following ionic compounds?

    a. MCl_2 b. MO c. M_2O_3 d. M_3N

3.53 What is the charge on the cation **M** in each of the following ionic compounds?

    a. M_2S b. MBr_3 c. $M(NO_3)_2$ d. $M(SO_4)_2$

3.54 What is the charge on the anion **Z** in each of the following ionic compounds?

    a. BaZ b. Al_2Z_3 c. Li_3Z d. Hg_2Z

3.55 Complete the following table by filling in the formula of the ionic compound derived from the cations on the left and each of the anions across the top.

	Br^-	OH^-	HCO_3^-	SO_3^{2-}	PO_4^{3-}
Na^+					
Co^{2+}					
Al^{3+}					

3.56 Complete the following table by filling in the formula of the ionic compound derived from the cations on the left and each of the anions across the top.

	I^-	CN^-	NO_3^-	SO_4^{2-}	HPO_4^{2-}
K^+					
Mg^{2+}					
Cr^{3+}					

3.57 Write the formula for the ionic compound formed from the bisulfate anion (HSO_4^-) and each cation: (a) K^+; (b) Ba^{2+}; (c) Al^{3+}; (d) Zn^{2+}.

3.58 Write the formula for the ionic compound formed from the sulfite anion (SO_3^{2-}) and each cation: (a) K^+; (b) Ba^{2+}; (c) Al^{3+}; (d) Zn^{2+}.

3.59 Write the formula for the ionic compound formed from the barium cation (Ba^{2+}) and each anion: (a) CN^-; (b) PO_4^{3-}; (c) HPO_4^{2-}; (d) $H_2PO_4^-$.

3.60 Write the formula for the ionic compound formed from the iron(III) cation (Fe^{3+}) and each anion: (a) CN^-; (b) PO_4^{3-}; (c) HPO_4^{2-}; (d) $H_2PO_4^-$.

Naming Ionic Compounds

3.61 Name each ionic compound.

    a. Na_2O d. $AgCl$ f. $RbBr$

    b. BaS e. $CoBr_2$ g. $PbBr_2$

    c. PbS_2

3.62 Name each ionic compound.

    a. KF d. SnO f. Li_2S

    b. $ZnCl_2$ e. $AuBr_3$ g. $SnBr_4$

    c. Cu_2S

3.63 Name each ionic compound.

    a. $FeCl_2$ b. $FeBr_3$ c. FeS d. Fe_2S_3

3.64 Name each ionic compound.

    a. $CrCl_2$ b. $CrBr_3$ c. CrO d. Cr_2O_3

3.65 Write formulas to illustrate the difference between each pair of compounds.

    a. sodium sulfide and sodium sulfate

    b. magnesium oxide and magnesium hydroxide

    c. magnesium sulfate and magnesium bisulfate

3.66 Write formulas to illustrate the difference between each pair of compounds.

    a. lithium sulfite and lithium sulfide

    b. sodium carbonate and sodium hydrogen carbonate

    c. calcium phosphate and calcium dihydrogen phosphate

3.67 Name each ionic compound.

    a. NH_4Cl c. $Cu(NO_3)_2$ e. $Fe(NO_3)_2$

    b. $PbSO_4$ d. $Ca(HCO_3)_2$

3.68 Name each ionic compound.

    a. $(NH_4)_2SO_4$ c. $Cr(CH_3CO_2)_3$ e. $Ni_3(PO_4)_2$

    b. NaH_2PO_4 d. $Sn(HPO_4)_2$

3.69 Liquid nutritional shakes that contain protein, vitamins, and minerals provide key dietary nutrients for children and adults who are recovering from illness or surgery. Write the formula for each of the following ionic compounds, which are ingredients in a widely used nutritional supplement: (a) calcium phosphate; (b) potassium hydroxide; (c) zinc sulfate; (d) ferrous sulfate; (e) manganese sulfate.

©Lenna Robinson/Shutterstock

3.70 Liquid dietary supplements with fewer grams of carbohydrates are made for individual who have diabetes. Write the formula for each of the following ionic compounds, which are ingredients in such a nutritional drink: (a) magnesium phosphate; (b) cupric sulfate; (c) potassium chloride; (d) calcium carbonate.

©Helen Sessions/Alamy

3.71 Write a formula from each name.
  a. magnesium carbonate
  b. nickel sulfate
  c. copper(II) hydroxide
  d. potassium hydrogen phosphate
  e. gold(III) nitrate
  f. lithium phosphate
  g. aluminum bicarbonate
  h. chromous cyanide

3.72 Write a formula from each name.
  a. copper(I) sulfite
  b. aluminum nitrate
  c. tin(II) acetate
  d. lead(IV) carbonate
  e. zinc hydrogen phosphate
  f. manganese dihydrogen phosphate
  g. ammonium cyanide
  h. iron(II) nitrate

3.73 Write the formula for the ionic compound formed from Pb^{4+} and each anion. Then name each compound.
  a. OH^- c. HCO_3^- e. PO_4^{3-}
  b. SO_4^{2-} d. NO_3^- f. $CH_3CO_2^-$

3.74 Write the formula for the ionic compound formed from Fe^{3+} and each anion. Then name each compound.
  a. OH^- c. HPO_4^{2-} e. PO_4^{3-}
  b. CO_3^{2-} d. NO_2^- f. $CH_3CO_2^-$

Properties of Ionic Compounds

3.75 Label each statement as "true" or "false." Correct any false statement to make it true.
  a. Ionic compounds have high melting points.
  b. Ionic compounds can be solid, liquid, or gas at room temperature.
  c. Most ionic compounds are insoluble in water.
  d. An ionic solid like sodium chloride consists of discrete pairs of sodium cations and chloride anions.

3.76 Label each statement as "true" or "false." Correct any false statement to make it true.
  a. Ionic compounds have high boiling points.
  b. The ions in a crystal lattice are arranged randomly and the overall charge is zero.
  c. When an ionic compound dissolves in water, the solution conducts electricity.
  d. In an ionic crystal, ions having like charges are arranged close to each other.

3.77 Which compound has the highest melting point: $NaCl$, CH_4, or H_2SO_4?

3.78 Which compound or element has the lowest boiling point: Cl_2, KI, or LiF?

Applications

3.79 Zinc is an essential nutrient needed by many enzymes to maintain proper cellular function. Zinc is obtained in many dietary sources, including oysters, beans, nuts, whole grains, and sunflower seeds. (a) How many protons and electrons are found in a neutral zinc atom? (b) How many electrons and protons are found in the Zn^{2+} cation? (c) Write the electronic configuration of the element zinc, and suggest which electrons are lost to form the Zn^{2+} cation.

3.80 Wilson's disease is an inherited defect in copper metabolism in which copper accumulates in tissues, causing neurological problems and liver disease. The disease can be treated with compounds that bind to copper and thus remove it from the tissues. (a) How many protons and electrons are found in a neutral copper atom? (b) How many electrons and protons are found in the Cu^+ cation? (c) How many electrons and protons are found in the Cu^{2+} cation? (d) Zinc acetate inhibits copper absorption, so it is used to treat Wilson's disease. What is the chemical formula of zinc acetate?

3.81 Na^+, K^+, Ca^{2+}, and Mg^{2+} are the four major cations in the body. For each cation, give the following information: (a) the number of protons; (b) the number of electrons; (c) the noble gas that has the same electronic configuration; (d) its role in the body.

3.82 Unlike many ionic compounds, calcium carbonate is insoluble in water. What information contained in this chapter suggested that calcium carbonate is water insoluble?

3.83 Write the formula for silver nitrate, an antiseptic and germ killing agent.

3.84 $CaSO_3$ is used to preserve cider and fruit juices. Name this ionic compound.

3.85 Ammonium nitrate is the most common source of the element nitrogen in fertilizers. When it is mixed with water, the solution gets cold, so it is used in instant cold packs. When mixed with diesel fuel, it forms an explosive mixture that can be used as a bomb. Write the formula of ammonium nitrate.

3.86 Write the formula for sodium phosphate, a key ingredient in many commercial detergents.

CHALLENGE PROBLEMS

3.87 Energy bars contain ionic compounds that serve as a source of the trace elements that the body needs each day for proper cellular function. Answer the following questions about some of the ingredients in one commercial product.

    a. Write the formulas for magnesium oxide and potassium iodide.

    b. The ingredient $CaHPO_4$ is called dicalcium phosphate on the label. What name would you give to this ionic compound?

    c. Give two different names for the ingredient $FePO_4$.

    d. Sodium selenite is one ingredient. Selenite is a polyatomic anion that contains a selenium atom in place of the sulfur atom in sulfite. With this in mind, suggest a formula for sodium selenite.

    e. Another ingredient is listed as chromium chloride. What is wrong with this name?

3.88 Some polyatomic anions contain a metal as part of the anion. For example, the anion dichromate has the formula $Cr_2O_7^{2-}$ and the anion permanganate has the formula MnO_4^-. Write the formula of the ionic compound formed from each of these anions and a potassium cation. Name each compound.

Like many drugs, acetaminophen, the active ingredient in the pain reliever Tylenol, is composed of covalent bonds.
©McGraw-Hill Education/Elite Images

Covalent Compounds

CHAPTER OUTLINE

4.1 Introduction to Covalent Bonding

4.2 Lewis Structures

4.3 Exceptions to the Octet Rule

4.4 Resonance

4.5 Naming Covalent Compounds

4.6 Molecular Shape

4.7 Electronegativity and Bond Polarity

4.8 Polarity of Molecules

4.9 FOCUS ON HEALTH & MEDICINE: Covalent Drugs and Medical Products

CHAPTER GOALS

In this chapter you will learn how to:

1. Recognize the bonding characteristics of covalent compounds
2. Draw Lewis structures for covalent compounds
3. Draw resonance structures for some ions and molecules
4. Name covalent compounds that contain two types of elements
5. Predict the shape around an atom in a molecule
6. Use electronegativity to determine whether a bond is polar or nonpolar
7. Determine whether a molecule is polar or nonpolar

Why Study
Covalent Compounds?

lthough all of Chapter 3 was devoted to ionic compounds, in truth, most compounds that we come in contact with in our daily lives are **covalent compounds,** formed by sharing electrons between atoms. The air we breathe is composed largely of the gases nitrogen and oxygen, two covalent molecules. The body is mostly water, which contains two covalent hydrogen–oxygen bonds. Most of the drugs routinely used—aspirin, acetaminophen, ibuprofen, and all antibiotics—are covalent compounds. Virtually all products of the chemical industry—polyethylene, nylon, synthetic dyes, gasoline, and pesticides, to name a few—are covalent compounds. In Chapter 4, we learn about the important features of covalent compounds.

4.1   Introduction to Covalent Bonding

In Section 3.1 we learned that **covalent bonds result from the *sharing* of electrons between two atoms.** For example, when two hydrogen atoms with one electron each (H·) combine, they form a covalent bond that contains two electrons. The two negatively charged electrons are now attracted to both positively charged hydrogen nuclei, forming the hydrogen **molecule, H_2.** This is an especially stable arrangement, because the shared electrons give each hydrogen atom the noble gas configuration of helium.

- A covalent bond is a two-electron bond in which the bonding atoms share valence electrons.
- A *molecule* is a compound held together by covalent bonds.

We use a **solid line between two element symbols to represent a two-electron bond.** Thus, the H_2 molecule can be drawn as:

$$H_2 \;=\; H\!:\!H \;=\; H\!\!-\!\!H \quad \text{two-electron bond}$$

Hydrogen is called a **diatomic molecule** because it contains just two atoms. In addition to hydrogen, six other elements exist as diatomic molecules: nitrogen (N_2), oxygen (O_2), fluorine (F_2), chlorine (Cl_2), bromine (Br_2), and iodine (I_2).

Hydrogen fluoride, HF, is an example of a diatomic molecule formed between two different atoms, hydrogen and fluorine. Hydrogen has one valence electron and fluorine has seven. H and F each donate one electron to form a single two-electron bond.

The resulting molecule gives both H and F a filled valence shell: H is surrounded by two electrons, giving it the noble gas configuration of helium, and F is surrounded by eight electrons, giving it the noble gas configuration of neon. The F atom shares two electrons in one covalent bond, and it also contains three pairs of electrons that it does not share with hydrogen. These unshared electron pairs are called **nonbonded electron pairs** or **lone pairs.**

Nonbonded electron pair = lone pair.

- In covalent bonding, atoms share electrons to attain the electronic configuration of the noble gas closest to them in the periodic table.

As a result, hydrogen shares two electrons. Other main group elements are especially stable when they possess an *octet* **of electrons in their outer shell.**

PROBLEM 4.1

Use electron-dot symbols to show how a hydrogen atom and a chlorine atom form the diatomic molecule HCl. Explain how each atom has the electronic configuration of the noble gas closest to it in the periodic table.

PROBLEM 4.2

Use electron-dot symbols to show how two chlorine atoms form the diatomic molecule Cl_2. Explain how each atom has the electronic configuration of the noble gas closest to it in the periodic table.

4.1A Covalent Bonding and the Periodic Table

When do two atoms form covalent bonds rather than ionic bonds? **Covalent bonds are formed when two nonmetals combine.** Nonmetals do not easily lose electrons, and as a result, one nonmetal does not readily transfer an electron to another nonmetal. **Covalent bonds are also formed when a metalloid bonds to a nonmetal.** Covalent bonding is preferred with elements that would otherwise have to gain or lose several electrons to form an ion with a complete outer shell of electrons.

Methane (CH_4), ammonia (NH_3), and water (H_2O) are three examples of covalent molecules in which each main group element is surrounded by eight electrons. Methane, a gas released by the decomposition of organic material in flooded rice fields, contains four covalent carbon–hydrogen bonds, each having two electrons. The nitrogen atom in NH_3, an agricultural fertilizer, is surrounded by an octet because it has three bonds and one lone pair. The oxygen atom in H_2O is also surrounded by an octet because it has two bonds and two lone pairs.

(top): ©Daniel C. Smith; (middle): ©Rick Dalton-Ag/Alamy; (bottom): Source: Photo by Tim McCabe, USDA Natural Resources Conservation Service

These electron-dot structures for molecules are called Lewis structures. Lewis structures show the location of all valence electrons in a molecule, both the shared electrons in bonds, and the nonbonded electron pairs. In Section 4.2, we will learn a general procedure for drawing Lewis structures.

How many covalent bonds will a particular atom typically form? As you might expect, it depends on the location of the atom in the periodic table. In the first row, hydrogen forms one covalent bond with its one valence electron. Other main group elements generally have no more than eight electrons around them. For neutral molecules, two consequences result.

- Atoms with one, two, or three valence electrons generally form one, two, or three bonds, respectively.
- Atoms with four or more valence electrons form enough bonds to give an octet. Thus, for atoms with four or more valence electrons:

$$\text{Predicted number of bonds} = 8 - \text{number of valence electrons}$$

These guidelines are used in Figure 4.1 to summarize the usual number of covalent bonds formed by some common atoms. Except for hydrogen, these common elements generally follow one rule in bonding:

$$\text{Number of bonds} + \text{Number of lone pairs} = 4$$

SAMPLE PROBLEM 4.1 PREDICTING THE NUMBER OF COVALENT BONDS

Without referring to Figure 4.1, how many covalent bonds are predicted for each atom: (a) B; (b) N?

Analysis

- Atoms with one, two, or three valence electrons form one, two, or three bonds, respectively.
- Atoms with four or more valence electrons form enough bonds to give an octet.

Solution

a. B has three valence electrons. Thus, it is expected to form three bonds.

b. N has five valence electrons. Since it contains more than four valence electrons, it is expected to form $8 - 5 = 3$ bonds.

PRACTICE PROBLEM 4.1

How many covalent bonds are predicted for each atom: (a) F; (b) Si; (c) Br; (d) O; (e) P; (f) S?

More Practice: Try Problems 4.17, 4.18.

PROBLEM 4.3

Fill in the lone pairs on each atom to give every main group element except hydrogen an octet.

a. H—C—Cl (with H above and below C)

b. H—N—O—H (with H below N)

c. H—C—O—H (with H above and below C)

d. Br—C—Br (with H above and below C)

Figure 4.1

Bonding Patterns for Common Main Group Elements

	hydrogen	carbon	nitrogen	oxygen	halogen
Number of bonds	1	4	3	2	1
Number of nonbonded electron pairs	0	0	1	2	3

X = F, Cl, Br, I

A nonmetal like oxygen forms both ionic and covalent bonds, depending on the identity of the element to which it bonds. What type of bonding is observed in CaO and CO_2? Explain why two different types of bonding are observed.

4.1B   FOCUS ON THE HUMAN BODY
Covalent Molecules and the Cardiovascular System

Living organisms are a sea of covalent molecules. The major component in the body, water, is a covalent molecule. In addition, the proteins that compose muscle, the carbohydrates that are metabolized for energy, stored fat, and DNA, the carrier of genetic information, are all covalent molecules. Some of these molecules are very large, and are composed of hundreds or thousands of covalent bonds.

Figure 4.2 contains a schematic of a blood vessel inside the heart, and it illustrates a few covalent molecules—water, hemoglobin, oxygen, glycine, and nitroglycerin—that play a role in the cardiovascular system. Blood is composed of water and red blood cells that contain the protein hemoglobin. Hemoglobin is a large covalent compound that complexes oxygen molecules and carries oxygen to tissues throughout the body. Heart muscle is composed of complex covalent protein molecules, which are synthesized from smaller molecules. The three-dimensional

Figure 4.2

Covalent Molecules and the Human Heart

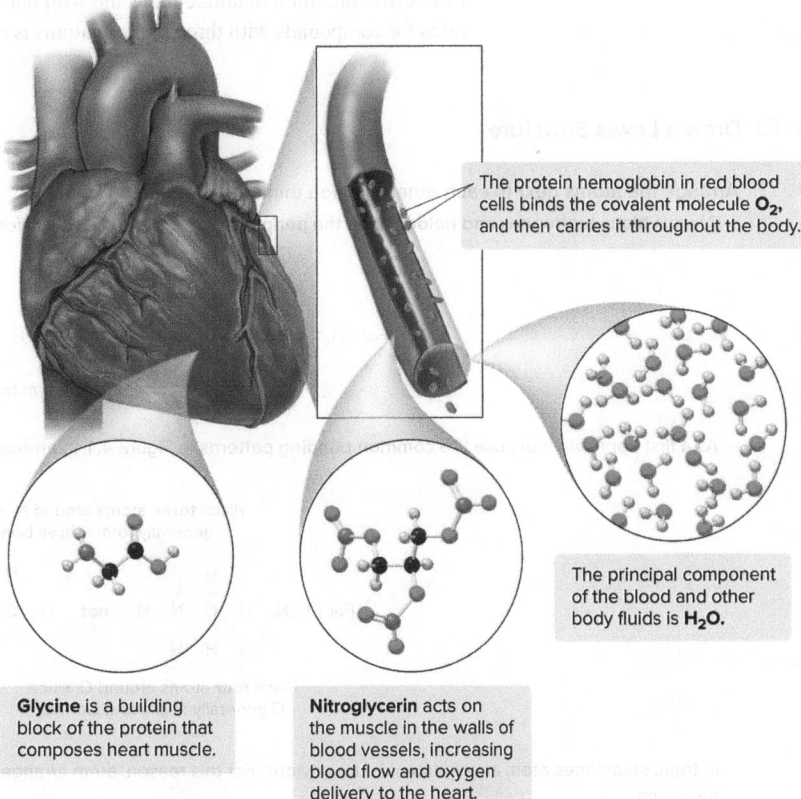

The protein hemoglobin in red blood cells binds the covalent molecule O_2, and then carries it throughout the body.

The principal component of the blood and other body fluids is H_2O.

Glycine is a building block of the protein that composes heart muscle.

Nitroglycerin acts on the muscle in the walls of blood vessels, increasing blood flow and oxygen delivery to the heart.

Some covalent compounds related to the chemistry of the heart include **water,** the most prevalent covalent compound in the body; **oxygen,** which is carried by the protein **hemoglobin** to the tissues; **glycine,** a building block of the proteins that compose heart muscle; and **nitroglycerin,** a drug used to treat some forms of heart disease.

structure of one of those molecules, glycine, is pictured. Finally, covalent compounds are used to treat heart disease. For example, nitroglycerin, a drug used when blood vessels have become narrow, increases blood flow and thereby oxygen delivery to the heart.

4.2   Lewis Structures

A molecular formula shows the number and identity of all of the atoms in a covalent compound, but it does not tell us what atoms are bonded to each other. Thus, the molecular formula NH_3 for ammonia shows that ammonia contains one nitrogen atom and three hydrogen atoms, but it does not tell us that ammonia has three covalent nitrogen–hydrogen bonds and that the N atom has a lone pair. **A Lewis structure, in contrast, shows the connectivity between the atoms, as well as where all the bonding and nonbonding valence electrons reside.**

4.2A   Drawing Lewis Structures

There are three general rules for drawing Lewis structures.

1. Draw only the *valence electrons*.
2. Give every main group element (except hydrogen) an *octet* of electrons.
3. Give each hydrogen two electrons.

In Section 4.1, Lewis structures were drawn for several covalent molecules. While drawing a Lewis structure for a diatomic molecule with one bond is straightforward, drawing Lewis structures for compounds with three or more atoms is easier if you follow a general procedure.

How To **Draw a Lewis Structure**

Step [1] **Arrange the atoms next to each other that you think are bonded together.**
- **Always place hydrogens and halogens on the periphery,** because these atoms form only one bond.

- As a first approximation, **use the common bonding patterns** in Figure 4.1 to arrange the atoms.

In truth, sometimes atom arrangement is not obvious. For this reason, atom arrangement will be specified for you in some problems.

Step [2] **Count the valence electrons.**
- **Use the group number of a main group element to give the number of valence electrons.**
- This sum gives the total number of electrons that must be used in drawing the Lewis structure.

—Continued

Step [3] **Arrange the electrons around the atoms.**
- **Place one bond between every two atoms,** giving two electrons to each H and no more than eight to all other main group atoms.
- Use all remaining electrons to **fill octets with lone pairs,** beginning with atoms on the periphery.
- If all valence electrons are used and an atom does not have an octet, proceed to Step [4].

Step [4] **Use multiple bonds to fill octets when needed.**
- **Convert one lone pair to one bonding pair of electrons for each two electrons needed to complete an octet.** This forms double or triple bonds in some molecules, as shown in Section 4.2B. While a single covalent bond contains **two** electrons, a double bond consists of **four** electrons, and a triple bond consists of **six** electrons.

Sample Problems 4.2 and 4.3 illustrate how to draw Lewis structures in two molecules that contain only single bonds.

SAMPLE PROBLEM 4.2 DRAWING A LEWIS STRUCTURE

Draw a Lewis structure for chloromethane, CH_3Cl, a compound produced by giant kelp and a component of volcanic emissions.

Analysis and Solution

[1] Arrange the atoms.

```
    H
H   C   Cl
    H
```

- Place C in the center and 3 H's and 1 Cl on the periphery.
- In this arrangement, C is surrounded by four atoms, its usual number.

The covalent molecule CH_3Cl is one of many gases released into the air from an erupting volcano.
©Ingram Publishing RF

[2] Count the electrons.
- Use the group number to determine the number of valence electrons.

Element	Group Number	Valence Electrons		Number of Atoms		Total Electrons
C	4A (14)	4	×	1	=	4 e⁻
H	1A (1)	1	×	3	=	3 e⁻
Cl	7A (17)	7	×	1	=	7 e⁻
				Total number of valence electrons =		**14 e⁻**

[3] Add the bonds and lone pairs.

```
    H                                    H  ← eight electrons around C                    H  ← eight electrons around Cl
H   C   Cl   - - - - - - - - →     H—C—Cl    - - - - - - - →    H—C—Cl:
    H         Add a bond between         H      Add three lone pairs        H
              the C and each atom.              to Cl to form an octet.
```

two electrons around H   14 e⁻ used altogether

First add four single bonds, three C—H bonds, and one C—Cl bond. This uses eight valence electrons and gives carbon an octet (four two-electron bonds) and each hydrogen two electrons. Next, give Cl an octet by adding three lone pairs. This uses all 14 valence electrons. To check if a Lewis structure is valid, we must answer YES to three questions.
- Have all the electrons been used?
- Is each H surrounded by two electrons?
- Is every other main group element surrounded by eight electrons?

Since the answer to all three questions is YES, we have drawn a valid Lewis structure for CH_3Cl.

PRACTICE PROBLEM 4.2

Draw a Lewis structure for each covalent molecule.

a. HBr   b. CH_3F c. H_2O_2 d. N_2H_4 e. C_2H_6 f. CH_2Cl_2

More Practice: Try Problems 4.23, 4.24a–c.

SAMPLE PROBLEM 4.3 DRAWING A LEWIS STRUCTURE

Draw a Lewis structure for methanol, a compound with molecular formula CH_4O. Methanol is a toxic compound that can cause blindness and even death when ingested in small quantities (Section 14.4).

Analysis and Solution

[1] Arrange the atoms.

$$
\begin{array}{c}
\text{H}\\
\text{H} \quad \text{C} \quad \text{O} \quad \text{H}\\
\text{H}
\end{array}
$$

- four atoms around C
- two atoms around O

[2] Count the electrons.

- Use the group number to determine the number of valence electrons.

Element	Group Number	Valence Electrons		Number of Atoms		Total Electrons
C	4A (14)	4	×	1	=	4 e⁻
O	6A (16)	6	×	1	=	6 e⁻
H	1A (1)	1	×	4	=	4 e⁻
			Total number of valence electrons =			14 e⁻

[3] Add the bonds and lone pairs.

Add bonds first...   ...then lone pairs.

$$
\begin{array}{ccc}
& \text{H} & \\
\text{H}-\text{C}-\text{O}-\text{H} & \dashrightarrow & \text{H}-\text{C}-\overset{..}{\underset{..}{\text{O}}}-\text{H}\\
& \text{H} & \\
& \text{no octet} &
\end{array}
$$

only 10 e⁻ used   14 e⁻ used

In step [3], placing bonds between all atoms uses only 10 electrons, and the O atom, with only four electrons, does not yet have a complete octet. To complete the structure, give the O atom two lone pairs. This uses all 14 electrons, giving every H two electrons and every main group element eight. We have now drawn a valid Lewis structure.

PRACTICE PROBLEM 4.3

Draw a Lewis structure for dimethyl ether (C_2H_6O) with the given arrangement of atoms.

$$
\begin{array}{ccccc}
\text{H} & & & \text{H} & \\
\text{H} & \text{C} & \text{O} & \text{C} & \text{H}\\
\text{H} & & & \text{H} &
\end{array}
$$

More Practice: Try Problem 4.25a.

4.2B Multiple Bonds

Sometimes it is not possible to give every main group element (except hydrogen) an octet of electrons by placing only single bonds in a molecule. For example, in drawing a Lewis structure for N_2, each N has five valence electrons, so there are 10 electrons to place. If there is only one N—N bond, adding lone pairs gives one or both N's fewer than eight electrons.

Add one bond.

For N_2:   N—N ⤑ $\ddot{\text{N}}-\ddot{\text{N}}$ or $\text{N}-\overset{..}{\ddot{\text{N}}}:$

Each N has five   Add lone pairs.

valence electrons.

total 10 e⁻   Each N has only 6 e⁻.

N has only 4 e⁻.

N has 8 e⁻.

In this case, we must convert a lone pair to a bonding pair of electrons to form a multiple bond. Since we have four fewer electrons than needed, **we must convert *two* lone pairs to *two* bonding pairs of electrons and form a *triple* bond.**

For example: [N–N diagram] Move 2 e⁻ to form a double bond. → [N=N] Move 2 e⁻ to form a triple bond. → [N≡N triple bond]

Each N has only 6 e⁻.   One N has only 6 e⁻.   Each N now has 8 e⁻.

- A triple bond contains *six* electrons in three two-electron bonds.

Sample Problem 4.4 illustrates another example of a Lewis structure that contains a double bond.

- A double bond contains four electrons in *two* two-electron bonds.

- After placing all electrons in bonds and lone pairs, use a lone pair to form a multiple bond if an atom does not have an octet.

SAMPLE PROBLEM 4.4 DRAWING A LEWIS STRUCTURE FOR A COMPOUND WITH A MULTIPLE BOND

Draw a Lewis structure for ethylene, a compound of molecular formula C_2H_4 in which each carbon is bonded to two hydrogens.

Analysis and Solution

Follow steps [1]–[3] to draw a Lewis structure.

[1] Arrange the atoms.

H C C H
H H
- Each C gets 2 H's.

[2] Count the electrons using the group number.

Element	Group Number	Valence Electrons		Number of Atoms		Total Electrons
C	4A (14)	4	×	2	=	8 e⁻
H	1A (1)	1	×	4	=	4 e⁻
		Total number of valence electrons =				12 e⁻

[3] Add the bonds and lone pairs.

Add bonds first...   ...then lone pairs.

H—C—C—H ---> H—C—C—H
   H H   H H
                  no octet

After placing five bonds between the atoms and adding the two remaining electrons as a lone pair, one C still has no octet.

[4] To give both C's an octet, change *one* lone pair into *one* bonding pair of electrons between the two C atoms, forming a *double* bond.

H—C—C—H Move a lone pair. ------> H—C=C—H
   H H   H H
                                     ethylene
double bond

- Each C now has four bonds.
- Each C is now surrounded by eight electrons.

This uses all 12 electrons, each C has an octet, and each H has two electrons. The Lewis structure is valid. **Ethylene contains a carbon–carbon double bond.**

Formic acid (CH₂O₂, Problem 4.5) is responsible for the sting of some types of ants. ©*Ted Nelson/Dembinsky Photo Associates*

PRACTICE PROBLEM 4.4

Draw a valid Lewis structure for each compound, using the given arrangement of atoms.

a.   HCN   H C N   b.   CH₂O   H C O
     hydrogen cyanide   formaldehyde   H

More Practice: Try Problems 4.24d; 4.25b, c; 4.26–4.28.

PROBLEM 4.5

Draw a Lewis structure for formic acid with the given arrangement of atoms.

O

H C O H

PROBLEM 4.6

(a) Use the element colors in Figure 2.3 (and shown on the inside back cover) to determine the molecular formula for dimethyl fumarate, a drug used to treat some forms of multiple sclerosis. (b) Draw a Lewis structure for dimethyl fumarate and include all nonbonded electron pairs on atoms that contain them.

dimethyl fumarate

4.3   Exceptions to the Octet Rule

Most of the common elements in covalent compounds—carbon, nitrogen, oxygen, and the halogens—generally follow the octet rule. **Hydrogen is a notable exception, because it accommodates only two electrons in bonding.** Additional exceptions include elements such as **boron** in group 3A, and elements in the third row and later in the periodic table, particularly **phosphorus** and **sulfur.**

4.3A   Elements in Group 3A

Elements in group 3A of the periodic table, such as boron, do not have enough valence electrons to form an octet in a neutral molecule. A Lewis structure for BF₃ illustrates that the boron atom has only six electrons around it. There is nothing we can do about this! There simply aren't enough electrons to form an octet.

:F̈:
|
:F̈—B—F̈:   only six electrons around B

4.3B   Elements in the Third Row

Another exception to the octet rule occurs with some elements located in the third row and later in the periodic table. These elements have empty *d* orbitals available to accept electrons, and thus they may have ***more than eight*** electrons around them. The two most common elements in this category are phosphorus and sulfur, which can have 10 or even 12 electrons around them.

Compounds with eight electrons around P and S		Exceptions to the octet rule	
8 electrons	8 electrons	10 electrons	12 electrons
:C̈l—P—C̈l: | :C̈l:	H—S̈—H	:O: ‖ HÖ—P—ÖH | :ÖH	:O: ‖ HÖ—S—ÖH ‖ :O:
phosphorus trichloride	hydrogen sulfide	phosphoric acid	sulfuric acid

While PCl_3 and H_2S contain phosphorus and sulfur atoms that follow the octet rule, H_3PO_4 (phosphoric acid) and H_2SO_4 (sulfuric acid) do not. The phosphorus atom in H_3PO_4 is surrounded by 10 electrons, and the sulfur atom in H_2SO_4 is surrounded by 12 electrons.

PROBLEM 4.7

Draw a Lewis structure for BBr_3, and explain why it does not follow the octet rule.

PROBLEM 4.8

Glyphosate is the most widely used weed killer and the active ingredient in Roundup and other lawn products. (a) Add lone pairs around all N and O atoms to complete octets. (b) How many electrons surround phosphorus in the given structure? (c) Which atoms in glyphosate do not follow the octet rule?

$$
\begin{array}{c}
\text{O} \quad \text{H} \qquad \text{H} \quad \text{O} \\
\| \quad | \qquad\qquad | \quad \| \\
\text{H—O—P—C—N—C—C—O—H} \\
| \quad | \quad | \quad | \quad | \\
\text{H—O} \quad \text{H} \quad \text{H} \quad \text{H} \quad \text{H}
\end{array}
$$

glyphosate

Glyphosate (Problem 4.8) is an effective herbicide because it interferes with the synthesis of key compounds needed for weed growth. ©Jill Braaten RF

4.4   Resonance

We sometimes must draw Lewis structures for ions that contain covalent bonds—that is, polyatomic ions. In this case, the charge on the ion must be taken into account when counting the number of valence electrons that must be placed around the atoms. In counting valence electrons:

- Add one electron for each negative charge.
- Subtract one electron for each positive charge.

For example, in drawing a Lewis structure for the cyanide anion, CN^-, there are 10 valence electrons—four from carbon, five from nitrogen, and one additional electron from the negative charge. In order to give each atom an octet, the two atoms must be joined by a triple bond, and both carbon and nitrogen have a lone pair.

Number of valence electrons   Lewis structure

$$
1\,e^- \quad \overset{}{\underset{4\,e^-\quad 5\,e^-}{CN^-}}
$$

10 valence electrons

$$
[:C\equiv N:]^-
$$

Each atom has an octet.

4.4A   Drawing Resonance Structures

Sometimes two or more valid Lewis structures are possible for a given arrangement of atoms. Sample Problem 4.5 illustrates that two Lewis structures are possible for the bicarbonate anion (HCO_3^-). The two different Lewis structures are called **resonance structures.**

- **Resonance structures are two or more Lewis structures having the same arrangement of atoms but a different arrangement of electrons.**

SAMPLE PROBLEM 4.5 DRAWING RESONANCE STRUCTURES

Draw a Lewis structure for HCO_3^- with the following arrangement of atoms:

$$
\begin{array}{c}
\text{O} \\
\text{H   O   C   O}
\end{array}
$$

Analysis and Solution

Follow steps [1]–[3] to draw a Lewis structure.

[1] Arrange the atoms.

$$
\begin{array}{c}
\text{O} \\
\text{H O C O}
\end{array}
$$

[2] Count the electrons using the group number.

Element	Group Number	Valence Electrons		Number of Atoms		Total Electrons
C	4A (14)	4	×	1	=	4 e⁻
O	6A (16)	6	×	3	=	18 e⁻
H	1A (1)	1	×	1	=	1 e⁻
(−)						1 e⁻
		Total number of valence electrons =				**24 e⁻**

[3] Add the bonds and lone pairs.

Add bonds first...   ...then lone pairs.

$$
\underset{\text{no octet}}{
\begin{array}{c}
\text{O} \\
\text{H—O—C—O}
\end{array}
\qquad
\begin{array}{c}
:\!\ddot{\text{O}}\!: \\
\text{H—}\ddot{\text{O}}\text{—C—}\ddot{\text{O}}:
\end{array}}
$$

After placing four bonds and adding the remaining 16 electrons as lone pairs, the carbon atom does not have an octet.

[4] Convert one lone pair on O into one bonding pair to form a double bond. There are two ways to do this.

$$
\text{H—}\ddot{\text{O}}\text{—C—}\ddot{\text{O}}: \;\dashrightarrow\; \left[\text{H—}\ddot{\text{O}}\text{—C—}\ddot{\text{O}}:\right]^{-} \quad \textbf{A} \quad \text{or} \quad \text{H—}\ddot{\text{O}}\text{—C—}\ddot{\text{O}}: \;\dashrightarrow\; \left[\text{H—}\ddot{\text{O}}\text{—C=}\ddot{\text{O}}:\right]^{-} \quad \textbf{B}
$$

Thus, there are two different Lewis structures, **A** and **B**, for the bicarbonate anion. **A** and **B** are resonance structures.

PRACTICE PROBLEM 4.5

Draw a second resonance structure for each ion.

a.
$$
\left[
\begin{array}{c}
\text{H} \quad :\!\ddot{\text{O}}: \\
\text{H—C—C—}\ddot{\text{O}}: \\
\text{H}
\end{array}
\right]^{-}
$$

b.
$$
\left[
\begin{array}{c}
:\!\ddot{\text{O}}: \\
\text{H—C—}\ddot{\text{N}}\text{—H}
\end{array}
\right]^{-}
$$

More Practice: Try Problems 4.35–4.40.

Two resonance structures differ in the location of multiple bonds and the position of lone pairs. In Lewis structures **A** and **B,** the location of one C=O and one lone pair is different. We often use a **double-headed arrow** (⟷) to show that two Lewis structures are resonance structures.

The position of the double bond is different.

$$
\textbf{A} = \left[
\begin{array}{c}
\ddot{\text{O}}: \\
\text{H—}\ddot{\text{O}}\text{—C—}\ddot{\text{O}}:
\end{array}
\right]^{-} \;\longleftrightarrow\; \left[
\begin{array}{c}
:\!\ddot{\text{O}}: \\
\text{H—}\ddot{\text{O}}\text{—C=}\ddot{\text{O}}:
\end{array}
\right]^{-} = \textbf{B}
$$

The position of a lone pair is different.

Which structure, **A** or **B,** is an accurate representation for HCO_3^-? The answer is ***neither of them.*** The true structure is a composite of both resonance forms and is called a **hybrid.** Experimentally it is shown that the carbon–oxygen bonds that appear as a double bond in one resonance structure and a single bond in the other, are really somewhere in between a C—O and a C=O. **Resonance stabilizes a molecule** by spreading out lone pairs and electron pairs in multiple bonds over a larger region of space. We say a molecule or ion that has two or more resonance structures is **resonance-stabilized.**

PROBLEM 4.9

Draw resonance structures for each polyatomic anion.

   a. NO_2^- (two resonance structures, central N atom)

   b. HCO_2^- (two resonance structures, central C atom)

4.4B FOCUS ON THE ENVIRONMENT
Ozone

In addition to polyatomic ions, resonance structures can be drawn for neutral molecules. For example, the molecule **ozone, O_3,** can be drawn as two resonance structures that differ in the placement of a double bond and a lone pair.

$$O_3: \quad \ddot{:}\overset{..}{O}=\overset{..}{O}-\overset{..}{\underset{..}{O}}: \quad \longleftrightarrow \quad :\overset{..}{\underset{..}{O}}-\overset{..}{O}=\overset{..}{O}:$$

Bonds and lone pairs that differ in the two resonance structures are drawn in red.

Ozone is formed in the upper atmosphere (the stratosphere) by the reaction of oxygen molecules (O_2) with oxygen atoms (O). Stratospheric ozone is vital to life: it acts as a shield, protecting the earth's surface from destructive ultraviolet radiation (Figure 4.3). A decrease in ozone concentration in this protective layer would have some immediate consequences, including an increase in the incidence of skin cancer and eye cataracts. We will learn about the interaction of ozone with covalent molecules that contain carbon–chlorine bonds in Chapter 14.

PROBLEM 4.10

Nitrous oxide, N_2O, is a sweet-smelling gas sometimes used as an anesthetic in dentistry. Draw three resonance structures for N_2O that contain a central nitrogen atom.

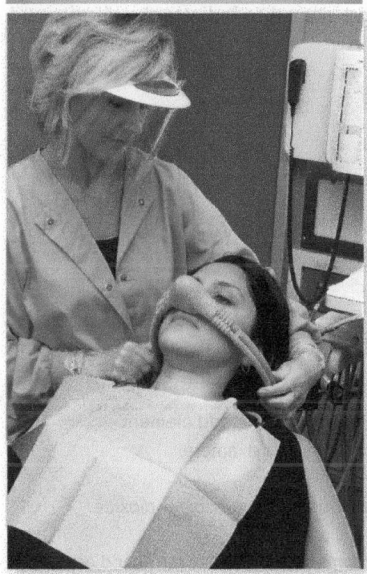

Nitrous oxide (N_2O, Problem 4.10) is a weak general anesthetic used for some dental procedures. Nitrous oxide is sometimes called laughing gas because it induces euphoria and mild hallucinations. ©*Jill Braaten RF*

Figure 4.3

Ozone in the Upper Atmosphere

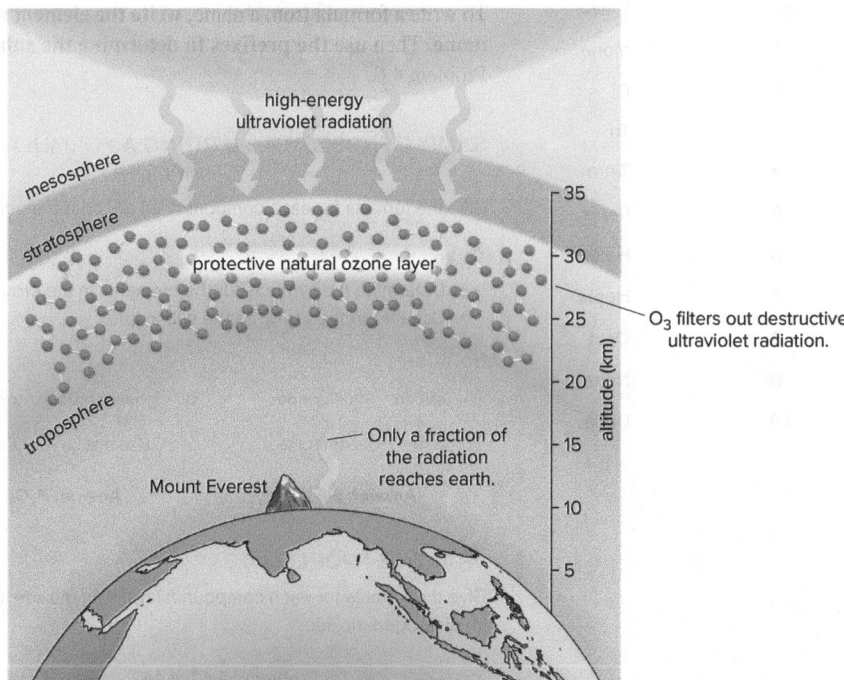

120   **Chapter 4**   Covalent Compounds

4.5   Naming Covalent Compounds

Although some covalent compounds are always referred to by their common names—
H_2O (water) and NH_3 (ammonia)—these names tell us nothing about the atoms that the molecule
contains. Other covalent compounds with two elements are named to indicate the identity and
number of elements they contain.

How To   Name a Covalent Molecule with Two Elements

Example: Name each covalent molecule: (a) NO_2; (b) N_2O_4.

Step [1]   Name the first nonmetal by its element name and the second using the suffix *-ide*.
  • In both compounds the first nonmetal is nitrogen.
  • To name the second element, change the name oxygen to **oxide**.

Step [2]   Add prefixes to show the number of atoms of each element.
  • Use a prefix from Table 4.1 for each element.
  • The prefix *mono-* is omitted when only one atom of the first element is present, but it is retained for the second element.
  • When the prefix and element name would place two vowels next to each other, omit the first vowel. For example,
    mono- + oxide = monoxide (*not* monooxide).
  a. NO_2 contains one N atom, so the prefix *mono-* is understood. Since NO_2 contains two O atoms, use the prefix *di-* → *di*oxide.
     Thus, NO_2 is **nitrogen dioxide.**
  b. N_2O_4 contains two N atoms, so use the prefix *di-* → *di*nitrogen. Since N_2O_4 contains four O atoms, use the prefix *tetra-* and omit
     the *a* → *tetr*oxide (*not* tetraoxide). Thus, N_2O_4 is **dinitrogen tetroxide.**

Table 4.1   Common Prefixes in Nomenclature

Number of Atoms	Prefix
1	Mono
2	Di
3	Tri
4	Tetra
5	Penta
6	Hexa
7	Hepta
8	Octa
9	Nona
10	Deca

PROBLEM 4.11

Name each compound: (a) CS_2; (b) SO_2; (c) PCl_5; (d) BF_3.

To write a formula from a name, **write the element symbols in the order of the elements in the
name.** Then **use the prefixes to determine the subscripts** of the formula, as shown in Sample
Problem 4.6.

**SAMPLE PROBLEM 4.6 WRITING A FORMULA FROM THE NAME OF A COVALENT
COMPOUND**

Give the formula for each compound: (a) silicon tetrafluoride; (b) diphosphorus pentoxide.

Analysis

  • Determine the symbols for the elements in the order given in the name.
  • Use the prefixes to write the subscripts.

Solution

a. silicon   tetrafluoride   b. diphosphorus pentoxide
     Si   4 F atoms   2 P atoms   5 O atoms

         Answer: SiF₄   **Answer: P₂O₅**

PRACTICE PROBLEM 4.6

Give the formula for each compound: (a) silicon dioxide; (b) phosphorus trichloride; (c) sulfur trioxide;
(d) dinitrogen trioxide.

More Practice: Try Problems 4.43, 4.44.

4.6   Molecular Shape

We can now use Lewis structures to determine the shape around a particular atom in a molecule. Consider the H_2O molecule. The Lewis structure tells us only which atoms are connected to each other, but it implies nothing about the geometry. Is H_2O a bent or linear molecule?

What is the bond angle?

$$H-\overset{..}{\underset{..}{O}}-H$$

To determine the shape around a given atom, we must first determine how many groups surround the atom. **A group is either an atom or a lone pair of electrons.** Then we use the **valence shell electron pair repulsion (VSEPR) theory** to determine the shape. VSEPR is based on the fact that electron pairs repel each other; thus:

- The most stable arrangement keeps these groups as far away from each other as possible.

In general, an atom has three possible arrangements of the groups that surround it.

linear   trigonal planar   tetrahedral

- An atom surrounded by two groups is linear and has a bond angle of 180°.
- An atom surrounded by three groups is trigonal planar and has bond angles of 120°.
- An atom surrounded by four groups is tetrahedral and has bond angles of 109.5°.

Let's examine several molecules. In each case we use the number of groups around a given atom in a Lewis structure to predict its geometry.

4.6A   Two Groups Around an Atom

> To determine geometry:
> [1] Draw a valid Lewis structure.
> [2] Count groups around a given atom.

Any atom surrounded by only two groups is linear and has a bond angle of 180°. Two examples illustrating this geometry are **CO_2** (carbon dioxide) and **HCN** (hydrogen cyanide). To determine the shape around the central atom in both molecules, **we draw the Lewis structure and count the number of groups—atoms and lone pairs—**that surround the central atom.

The Lewis structure for CO_2 contains a central carbon atom surrounded by two oxygen atoms. To give every atom an octet and the usual number of bonds requires two carbon–oxygen double bonds. The carbon atom is surrounded by two oxygen atoms and no lone pairs; that is, it is surrounded by two groups, making the molecule linear and the O—C—O bond angle 180°.

Carbon dioxide illustrates another important feature of VSEPR theory: *ignore multiple bonds in predicting geometry.* **Count only atoms and lone pairs.**

Similarly, the Lewis structure for HCN contains a central carbon atom surrounded by one hydrogen and one nitrogen. To give carbon and nitrogen an octet and the usual number of bonds requires a carbon–nitrogen triple bond. The carbon atom is surrounded by two atoms and no lone pairs; that is, it is surrounded by two groups, making the molecule linear and the H—C—N bond angle 180°.

122   Chapter 4   Covalent Compounds

Cassava is a widely grown root crop, first introduced to Africa by Portuguese traders from Brazil in the sixteenth century. The root must be boiled or roasted to remove linamarin before ingestion. Eating the root without processing affords high levels of HCN, a cellular poison with a characteristic almond odor. ©*Daniel C. Smith*

Trigonal = three-sided.

Over time, some adhesives and insulation made from formaldehyde can decompose back to formaldehyde, a reactive and potentially hazardous substance. Spider plants act as natural air purifiers by removing formaldehyde (H_2CO) from the air. ©*Image Source Black/ Alamy RF*

HCN, an extremely toxic gas, is produced by some naturally occurring molecules. For example, cassava, a woody shrub grown as a root crop in South America and Africa, contains the compound linamarin. Linamarin is not toxic itself, but it forms HCN in the presence of water and some enzymes. Cassava is safe to eat after the root has been peeled and boiled to remove the linamarin. If the root is eaten without processing, illness and even death can result from high levels of HCN formed from linamarin.

4.6B   Three Groups Around an Atom

Any atom surrounded by three groups is trigonal planar and has bond angles of 120°. Two examples illustrating this geometry are **BF_3** (boron trifluoride) and **$H_2C{=}O$** (formaldehyde).

| three atoms around B **three groups** | **trigonal planar** molecule | three atoms around C **three groups** | **trigonal planar** molecule |

In BF_3, the boron atom is surrounded by three fluorines and no lone pairs; that is, the boron is surrounded by three groups. A similar situation occurs with the carbon atom in $H_2C{=}O$. The carbon atom is surrounded by three atoms (two H's and one O) and no lone pairs—that is, three groups. To keep the three groups as far from each other as possible, they are arranged in a trigonal planar fashion, with bond angles of 120°.

4.6C   Four Groups Around an Atom

Any atom surrounded by four groups is tetrahedral and has bond angles of (approximately) 109.5°. For example, the simple organic compound methane, **CH_4**, has a central carbon atom with four bonds to hydrogen, each pointing to the corners of a tetrahedron.

tetrahedral carbon

How can we represent the three-dimensional geometry of a tetrahedron on a two-dimensional piece of paper? **Place two of the bonds in the plane of the paper, one bond in front, and one bond behind,** using the following conventions:

- A solid line is used for bonds in the plane.
- A wedge is used for a bond in front of the plane.
- A dashed wedge is used for a bond behind the plane.

bonds **in the plane**   bond **behind**

bond **in front**   **tetrahedral** molecule

Up to now, each of the groups around the central atom has been another atom. **A group can also be a lone pair of electrons.** NH_3 and H_2O represent two examples of molecules with atoms surrounded by four groups, some of which are lone pairs.

The Lewis structure for ammonia, **NH_3,** has an N atom surrounded by three hydrogen atoms and one lone pair of electrons—four groups. To keep four groups as far apart as possible, the three H atoms and the one lone pair around N point to the corners of a tetrahedron. The

H—N—H bond angle of 107° is close to the tetrahedral bond angle of 109.5°. This shape is referred to as **trigonal pyramidal,** because one of the groups around the N is a nonbonded electron pair, not another atom.

One corner of the tetrahedron has an **electron pair,** not a bond.

=

107°

trigonal pyramidal molecule

four groups around N
• three atoms
• one lone pair

The Lewis structure for water, **H_2O,** has an O atom surrounded by two hydrogen atoms and two lone pairs of electrons—four groups. In **H_2O,** the two H atoms and the two lone pairs around O point to the corners of a tetrahedron. The H—O—H bond angle of 105° is close to the tetrahedral bond angle of 109.5°. Water has a **bent** shape, because two of the groups around oxygen are lone pairs of electrons.

Two corners of the tetrahedron have **electron pairs,** not bonds.

=

105°

bent molecule

four groups around O
• two atoms
• two lone pairs

Common molecular shapes are summarized in Table 4.2. The three-dimensional shape determines the polarity of a molecule, which is discussed in Section 4.8. All of Chapter 15 is devoted to the importance of the three-dimensional shapes of molecules.

Table 4.2 Common Molecular Shapes Around Atoms

Total Number of Groups	Number of Atoms	Number of Lone Pairs	Shape Around an Atom (A)	Approximate Bond Angle (°)	Example
2	2	0	A—A linear	180	CO_2, HCN
3	3	0	trigonal planar	120	BF_3, H_2CO
4	4	0	tetrahedral	109.5	CH_4
4	3	1	trigonal pyramidal	~109.5[a]	NH_3
4	2	2	bent	~109.5[a]	H_2O

[a]The symbol "~" means approximately.

SAMPLE PROBLEM 4.7 DETERMINING SHAPE AROUND AN ATOM

Using the given Lewis structure, determine the shape around the second-row elements in each compound.

a. H—C≡C—H

acetylene

b. $\left[\text{H—N—H} \right]^{+}$ (with H above and below N)

ammonium ion

Analysis

To predict the shape around an atom, we need a **valid Lewis structure,** which is given in this problem. Then **count groups** around the atom to determine molecular shape using the information in Table 4.2.

Solution

a. Each C in H—C≡C—H is surrounded by two atoms (one C and one H) and no lone pairs—that is, **two groups.** An atom surrounded by two groups is **linear** with a 180° bond angle.

$$180°$$
$$\text{H}\overset{}{-}\text{C}\equiv\text{C}\overset{}{-}\text{H}$$
$$180°$$

b. The N atom in NH_4^+ is surrounded by four H atoms—that is, **four groups.** An atom surrounded by four groups is **tetrahedral,** with 109.5° bond angles.

109.5° N⁺ with four H atoms
tetrahedral

PRACTICE PROBLEM 4.7

What is the shape around the indicated atom in each molecule? Don't forget to draw in all needed lone pairs before determining molecular shape.

a. H_2S b. CH_2Cl_2 c. NCl_3 d. $H_2C=CH_2$

More Practice: Try Problems 4.45–4.54, 4.57, 4.58.

PROBLEM 4.12

$NaNH_2$, sodium amide, is a salt that contains a sodium cation, Na^+, and the polyatomic anion NH_2^-. Draw a Lewis structure for NH_2^-. Use the Lewis structure to determine which of the following ball-and-stick models represents the geometry of NH_2^-.

a.   b.

PROBLEM 4.13

(a) How many tetrahedral carbons does dihydroxyacetone contain? (b) How many trigonal planar carbons does it contain?

$$\text{H—O—C—C—C—O—H}$$

dihydroxyacetone

4.7   Electronegativity and Bond Polarity

When two atoms share electrons in a covalent bond, are the electrons in the bond attracted to both nuclei to the same extent? That depends on the **electronegativity** of the atoms in the bond.

- *Electronegativity* is a measure of an atom's attraction for electrons in a bond. Electronegativity tells us how much a particular atom "wants" electrons.

Figure 4.4 Electronegativity Values for Main Group Elements

The electronegativity of an atom is assigned a value from 0 to 4; **the *higher* the value, the *more electronegative* an atom is and the *more it is attracted* to the electrons in a bond.** The electronegativity values for main group elements are shown in Figure 4.4. The noble gases are not assigned values, because they do not typically form bonds.

Electronegativity values exhibit periodic trends.

- Electronegativity *increases* across a row of the periodic table as the nuclear charge increases (excluding the noble gases).
- Electronegativity *decreases* down a column of the periodic table as the atomic radius increases, pushing the valence electrons farther from the nucleus.

Thus, nonmetals have high electronegativity values compared to metals, because nonmetals have a strong tendency to hold on to and attract electrons. As a result, the most electronegative elements—fluorine and oxygen—are located at the **upper right-hand corner** of the periodic table, and the least electronegative elements are located in the lower left-hand corner.

PROBLEM 4.14

Using the trends in the periodic table, rank the following atoms in order of increasing electronegativity.

a. Li, Na, H   b. O, C, Be   c. Cl, I, F   d. B, O, N

Electronegativity values are used as a guideline to indicate whether the electrons in a bond are *equally* shared or *unequally* shared between two atoms. For example, whenever two *identical* atoms are bonded together, each atom attracts the electrons in the bond to the same extent. The electrons are equally shared, and the bond is said to be **nonpolar.** Thus, a **carbon–carbon bond is nonpolar,** as is the fluorine–fluorine bond in F_2. The same is true whenever two different atoms having *similar* electronegativities are bonded together. **C—H bonds are considered to be nonpolar,** because the electronegativity difference between C (2.5) and H (2.1) is small.

2.5 — C—C — 2.5   2.5 — C—H — 2.1

nonpolar bond   **nonpolar bond**

The small electronegativity difference
between C and H is ignored.

In contrast, bonding between atoms of *different* electronegativity results in the *unequal* sharing of electrons. For example, in a C—O bond, the electrons are pulled away from C (2.5) towards the element of higher electronegativity, O (3.5). **The bond is *polar*, or *polar covalent*.** The bond is said to have a **dipole**—that is, **a partial separation of charge.**

$$\overset{\delta+}{\underset{\underset{\text{a dipole}}{\longrightarrow}}{\overset{|}{\underset{|}{C}}}}\overset{\delta-}{\overset{}{O}}$$

A C–O bond is a *polar* bond.

The direction of polarity in a bond is often indicated by an arrow, with the head of the arrow pointing toward the more electronegative element. The tail of the arrow, with a perpendicular line drawn through it, is drawn at the less electronegative element. Alternatively, the lowercase Greek letter **delta (δ)** with a positive or negative charge is used, resulting in the symbols $\delta+$ and $\delta-$ to indicate this unequal sharing of electron density.

- The symbol $\delta+$ is given to the less electronegative atom.
- The symbol $\delta-$ is given to the more electronegative atom.

Students often wonder how large an electronegativity difference must be to consider a bond polar. That's hard to say. We will set an arbitrary value for this difference and use it as an approximation. **Usually, a polar bond will be one in which the electronegativity difference between two atoms is 0.5 unit or greater.**

As the electronegativity difference between the two atoms in a bond increases, the shared electrons are pulled more and more toward the more electronegative element. When the electronegativity difference is larger than 1.9 units, the electrons are essentially transferred from the less electronegative element to the more electronegative element and the bond is considered ionic. Table 4.3 summarizes the relationship between the electronegativity difference of the atoms in a bond and the type of bond formed.

Table 4.3 Electronegativity Difference and Bond Type

Electronegativity Difference	Bond Type	Electron Sharing
Less than 0.5 unit	Nonpolar	Electrons are equally shared.
0.5–1.9 units	Polar covalent	Electrons are unequally shared; they are pulled toward the more electronegative element.
Greater than 1.9 units	Ionic	Electrons are transferred from the less electronegative element to the more electronegative element.

SAMPLE PROBLEM 4.8 CLASSIFYING A BOND AS NONPOLAR, POLAR COVALENT, OR IONIC

Use electronegativity values to classify each bond as nonpolar, polar covalent, or ionic: (a) Cl_2; (b) HCl; (c) NaCl.

Analysis

Calculate the electronegativity difference between the two atoms and use the following rules: less than 0.5 (nonpolar); 0.5–1.9 (polar covalent); and greater than 1.9 (ionic).

Solution

	Electronegativity Difference	Bond Type
a. Cl_2	3.0 (Cl) − 3.0 (Cl) = 0	Nonpolar
b. HCl	3.0 (Cl) − 2.1 (H) = 0.9	Polar covalent
c. NaCl	3.0 (Cl) − 0.9 (Na) = 2.1	Ionic

PRACTICE PROBLEM 4.8

Use electronegativity values to classify the bond(s) in each compound as nonpolar, polar covalent, or ionic.

a. HF   b. MgO   c. F_2 d. ClF   e. H_2O f. NH_3

More Practice: Try Problems 4.63–4.66.

4.8 Polarity of Molecules

Thus far, we have been concerned with the polarity of a single bond. Is an entire covalent molecule polar or nonpolar? That depends on two factors: the **polarity of the individual bonds** and the **overall shape.** When a molecule contains zero or one polar bond, the following can be said:

- **A molecule with no polar bonds is a nonpolar molecule.**
- **A molecule with one polar bond is a polar molecule.**

Thus, CH_4 is a nonpolar molecule because all of the C—H bonds are nonpolar. In contrast, CH_3Cl contains only one polar bond, so it is a polar molecule. The dipole is in the same direction as the dipole of the only polar bond.

CH₄
no polar bonds
nonpolar molecule

polar bond
net dipole of the molecule

CH₃Cl
one polar bond
polar molecule

With covalent compounds that have more than one polar bond, the shape of the molecule determines the overall polarity.

- **If the individual bond dipoles do *not* cancel, the molecule is polar.**
- **If the individual bond dipoles *cancel*, the molecule is nonpolar.**

To determine the polarity of a molecule that has two or more polar bonds:

1. Identify all polar bonds based on electronegativity differences.
2. Determine the shape around individual atoms by counting groups.
3. Decide if individual dipoles cancel or reinforce.

Figure 4.5 illustrates several examples of polar and nonpolar molecules that contain polar bonds. The net dipole is the sum of all the bond dipoles in a molecule.

Figure 4.5   Examples of Polar and Nonpolar Molecules

one polar bond

three polar bonds
All dipoles cancel.
NO net dipole

net dipole

three polar bonds
All dipoles reinforce.

net dipole

two polar bonds
Two dipoles reinforce.

polar molecule   **nonpolar** molecule   **polar** molecule   **polar** molecule

SAMPLE PROBLEM 4.9 DETERMINING THE POLARITY OF A MOLECULE

Determine whether each molecule is polar or nonpolar: (a) H_2O; (b) CO_2.

Analysis

To determine the overall polarity of a molecule:

- Identify the polar bonds.
- Determine the shape around individual atoms.
- Decide if the individual bond dipoles cancel or reinforce.

Solution

a. **H_2O:** Each O—H bond is polar because the electronegativity difference between O (3.5) and H (2.1) is 1.4. Because the O atom of H_2O has two atoms and two lone pairs around it, H_2O is a **bent** molecule around the O atom. The two dipoles *reinforce* (both point *up*), so **H_2O has a net dipole**; that is, **H_2O is a polar molecule.**

> The two individual dipoles reinforce.

<table>
<tr><td>

$\delta-$

↖ O ↗
H   H
$\delta+$ $\delta+$

↑ net dipole

</td><td>

Do NOT draw H_2O as:

H—Ö—H

</td></tr>
</table>

The net dipole bisects the H—O—H bond angle.
The bent representation shows that the dipoles reinforce.

Note: **We must know the geometry to determine if two dipoles cancel or reinforce.** For example, do **not** draw H_2O as a linear molecule, because you might think that the two dipoles cancel, when in reality, they reinforce.

b. **CO_2:** Each C—O bond is polar because the electronegativity difference between O (3.5) and C (2.5) is 1.0. The Lewis structure of CO_2 (Section 4.6A) shows that the C atom is surrounded by two groups (two O atoms), making it **linear.** In this case, the two dipoles are equal and opposite in direction, so they *cancel*. Thus, CO_2 is a **nonpolar molecule** with **no net dipole.**

> The two dipoles cancel.

←   →
:Ö=C=Ö:
$\delta-$ $\delta+$ $\delta-$
NO net dipole

PRACTICE PROBLEM 4.9

Label the polar bonds in each molecule, and then decide if the molecule is polar or nonpolar.

  a. HCl   b. C_2H_6 c. CH_2F_2 d. HCN   e. CCl_4

More Practice: Try Problems 4.71–4.74.

4.9 FOCUS ON HEALTH & MEDICINE
Covalent Drugs and Medical Products

Most drugs and products used in medicine are made up of covalent molecules. Some are simple molecules containing only a few atoms, while others are very complex. The principles learned in this chapter apply to all molecules regardless of size. Two examples are shown.

Hydrogen peroxide, H_2O_2, is a simple covalent molecule used to disinfect wounds. We now know a great deal about the structure of H_2O_2. The Lewis structure for H_2O_2 contains an O—O bond, and each O atom has two lone pairs to give it an octet of electrons. Since each O atom is

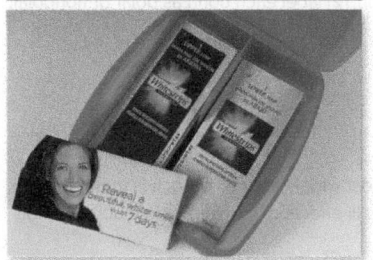

Many consumer products used to whiten teeth contain hydrogen peroxide.
©McGraw-Hill Education/Jill Braaten, photographer

surrounded by two atoms and two lone pairs, it has a **bent** structure. While the O—O bond is nonpolar, **both O—H bonds are polar,** because the electronegativity difference between oxygen (3.5) and hydrogen (2.1) is large (1.4).

©McGraw-Hill Education/Jill Braaten, photographer

Acetaminophen, a pain-reliever and antipyretic (an agent that reduces fever), is more complex, but we still know much about its structure. Each O atom has two lone pairs, and the N atom has one lone pair. Acetaminophen has six polar bonds, labeled in red. The number of groups around each atom determines its shape. One tetrahedral C surrounded by four groups and two trigonal planar C's are labeled.

©Jill Braaten RF

SAMPLE PROBLEM 4.10 DETERMINING STRUCTURAL FEATURES IN A MORE COMPLEX MOLECULE

Glycolic acid is a starting material used to manufacture dissolving sutures. (a) Place lone pairs where needed in the Lewis structure. (b) Give the shape around each atom in red. (c) Label all polar bonds.

glycolic acid

Analysis and Solution

a. Each O atom needs two lone pairs to make an octet.
b. Count groups to determine shape.

c. Because O is much more electronegative (3.5) than hydrogen (2.1) and carbon (2.5), all C—O and O—H bonds are polar and are labeled in red.

PRACTICE PROBLEM 4.10

In each compound: [1] determine the shape around each carbon; [2] label each bond as polar or nonpolar.

a. ethanol   b. acetaldehyde

Ethanol, the "alcohol" in alcoholic beverages, is the world's most widely abused drug. It is metabolized to acetaldehyde, a toxic compound that produces some of the ill effects of ingesting too much ethanol. Ethanol is discussed in greater detail in Chapter 14.

More Practice: Try Problems 4.77–4.80, 4.82.

SAMPLE PROBLEM 4.11 DETERMINING STRUCTURAL FEATURES USING A BALL-AND-STICK MODEL

Use the ball-and-stick model of vitamin B$_6$ to answer the questions.

a. Convert the ball-and-stick model to a Lewis structure by adding all needed lone pairs.
b. Determine the shape around atoms [1]–[3].
c. Label bonds **A–D** as polar or nonpolar.

vitamin B$_6$

Analysis

- Add lone pairs around the oxygen and nitrogen atoms to give octets. Each O atom has two lone pairs, and the N atom has one.
- To determine molecular shape, count groups around an atom and use the information in Table 4.2.
- A bond is polar if the electronegativity difference between the two atoms in a bond is between 0.5 and 1.9.

Solution

a. Lewis structure:

b. Shape:

[1] O is surrounded by two atoms and two lone pairs: bent shape.

[2] C is surrounded by four atoms: tetrahedral shape.

[3] C is surrounded by three atoms and no lone pairs: trigonal planar shape.

c. Because O (3.5) and N (3.0) are more electronegative than C (2.5) and H (2.1), bonds **A, B,** and **C** are polar. Bond **D** is between two C's, making it nonpolar.

PRACTICE PROBLEM 4.11

Use the ball-and-stick model of dihydrocapsaicin to answer the questions.

a. How many lone pairs of electrons does dihydrocapsaicin contain?
b. How many trigonal planar carbons are present?
c. Classify bonds **A–D** as polar or nonpolar.

Dihydrocapsaicin is one of the compounds responsible for the spiciness of hot peppers. ©*Daniel C. Smith*

More Practice: Try Problems 4.75, 4.76, 4.81, 4.85, 4.86.

CHAPTER HIGHLIGHTS

KEY TERMS

Covalent bond (4.1)
Diatomic molecule (4.1)
Dipole (4.7)
Double bond (4.2)
Double-headed arrow (4.4)
Electronegativity (4.7)
Hybrid (4.4)

Lewis structure (4.1)
Lone pair (4.1)
Molecular formula (4.2)
Molecule (4.1)
Multiple bond (4.2)
Nonbonded electron pair (4.1)

Nonpolar bond (4.7)
Polar bond (4.7)
Resonance structure (4.4)
Triple bond (4.2)
Valence shell electron pair repulsion (VSEPR) theory (4.6)

KEY CONCEPTS

① What are the characteristic bonding features of covalent compounds? (4.1)

- Covalent bonds result from the sharing of electrons between two atoms, forming molecules. Atoms share electrons to attain the electronic configuration of the noble gas nearest them in the periodic table. For many main group elements, this results in an octet of electrons.
- Covalent bonds are formed when two nonmetals combine or when a metalloid bonds to a nonmetal. Covalent bonds are preferred with elements that would have to gain or lose too many electrons to form an ion.
- Except for hydrogen, the common elements—C, N, O, and the halogens—follow one rule: **the number of bonds + the number of lone pairs = four.**

② What are Lewis structures and how are they drawn? (4.2)

- Lewis structures are electron-dot representations of molecules. Two-electron bonds are drawn with a solid line and nonbonded electrons are drawn with dots (:).
- Lewis structures contain only valence electrons. **Each H gets two electrons, and main group elements generally get eight.**

- After placing all electrons in bonds and lone pairs in a Lewis structure, it may be necessary to use lone pairs to form double or triple bonds if an atom does not have an octet.

③ What are resonance structures? (4.4)

- Resonance structures are two Lewis structures having the same arrangement of atoms but a different arrangement of electrons.
- The hybrid is a composite of all resonance structures that spreads out electron pairs in multiple bonds and lone pairs.

④ How are covalent compounds with two elements named? (4.5)

- Name the first nonmetal by its element name and the second using the suffix *-ide*. Add prefixes to indicate the number of atoms of each element.

⑤ How is the molecular shape around an atom determined? (4.6)

- **To determine the shape around an atom, count groups— atoms and lone pairs—and keep the groups as far away from each other as possible.**
- Two groups = linear, 180° bond angle; three groups = trigonal planar, 120° bond angle; four groups = tetrahedral, 109.5° bond angle.

6 **How does electronegativity determine bond polarity? (4.7)**
- Electronegativity is a measure of an atom's attraction for electrons in a bond.
- When two atoms have the same electronegativity value, or the difference is less than 0.5 unit, the electrons are equally shared and the bond is nonpolar.
- When two atoms have very different electronegativity values—a difference of 0.5–1.9 units—the electrons are unequally shared and the bond is polar.

7 **When is a molecule polar or nonpolar? (4.8)**
- A polar molecule has either one polar bond, or two or more bond dipoles that do not cancel.
- A nonpolar molecule has either all nonpolar bonds, or two or more bond dipoles that cancel.

PROBLEMS

Selected in-chapter and odd-numbered end-of-chapter problems have brief answers in Appendix B. The *Student Study Guide and Solutions Manual* contains detailed solutions to all in-chapter and odd-numbered end-of-chapter problems, as well as additional worked examples and a chapter self-test.

Covalent Bonding

4.15 For each pair of compounds, classify the bonding as ionic or covalent and explain your choice.
   a. LiCl and HCl   b. KBr and HBr

4.16 For each pair of compounds, classify the bonding as ionic or covalent and explain your choice.
   a. BeH_2 and $BeCl_2$ b. Na_3N and NH_3

4.17 How many bonds and lone pairs are typically observed with each element: (a) C; (b) Se; (c) I; (d) P?

4.18 How many bonds and lone pairs are typically observed with each element: (a) O; (b) Si; (c) Ge; (d) B?

4.19 Fill in the lone pairs needed to give the main group elements (except hydrogen) an octet. Acrylonitrile is a starting material used to manufacture synthetic Orlon and Acrilan fibers. Cysteine is an amino acid used to synthesize proteins.

   a.
   ```
        H  H
        |  |
   H—C=C—C≡N
   ```
   acrylonitrile

   b.
   ```
        H  H  O
        |  |  ||
   H—S—C—C—C—O—H
        |  |
        H  N—H
           |
           H
   ```
   cysteine

4.20 Fill in the lone pairs needed to give the main group elements (except hydrogen) an octet. Glycerol is a product of the metabolism of fats. Acrylamide is used to make polyacrylamide, which is used in some cosmetics and food packaging.

   a.
   ```
        H  H  H
        |  |  |
   H—O—C—C—C—O—H
        |  |  |
        H  O  H
           |
           H
   ```
   glycerol

   b.
   ```
              O
              ||
   H—C=C—C—N—H
        |  |  |  |
        H  H  H  H
   ```
   acrylamide

Lewis Structures

4.21 Convert the 3-D model of oxalic acid into a Lewis structure and include all nonbonded electron pairs on atoms that contain them. Oxalic acid occurs naturally in spinach and rhubarb. Although oxalic acid is toxic, you would have to eat about nine pounds of spinach at one time to ingest a fatal dose.

oxalic acid

4.22 Convert the 3-D model of the general anesthetic methoxyflurane into a Lewis structure and include all nonbonded electron pairs on atoms that contain them.

methoxyflurane

4.23 Draw a valid Lewis structure for each molecule.
   a. HI   b. CH_2F_2 c. H_2Se d. C_2Cl_6

4.24 Draw a valid Lewis structure for each molecule.
   a. CH_3Br b. PH_3 c. SiF_4 d. C_2HCl

4.25 Draw a valid Lewis structure for each compound using the given arrangement of atoms.

   a. CH_5N
   ```
         H
         
   H  C  N  H
   
         H
   ```

   b. HNO_2
   ```
      H  H
      
   H  O  N  O
      
         H
   ```

   c. C_3H_4
   ```
   H  C  C  C  H
   
            H
   ```

4.26 Draw a valid Lewis structure for each compound using the given arrangement of atoms.

a. C_2H_3N H C C N (with H above and H below first C)

b. HNO_3 H O N O (with O below N)

c. C_3H_6 H C C C H (with H H below and H H H)

4.27 Draw a valid Lewis structure for tetrafluoroethylene, C_2F_4, the industrial starting material used to prepare Teflon. Teflon is most widely used as a nonstick surface on pots and pans, but it has also found application in tape used by plumbers to seal joints, nail polish, and coatings on eyeglasses. Assume that each carbon is bonded to two fluorine atoms.

4.28 Draw a valid Lewis structure for phosgene, CCl_2O, which contains a central carbon atom. Phosgene is an extremely toxic gas used as a chemical weapon during World War I. It is now an important industrial starting material for the synthesis of Lexan, a lightweight transparent material used in bike helmets, goggles, and catcher's masks.

4.29 Draw a valid Lewis structure for each ion: (a) OH^-; (b) H_3O^+.

4.30 Draw a valid Lewis structure for each ion: (a) OCl^-; (b) CH_3O^-.

4.31 Keeping in mind that some elements violate the octet rule, convert the 3-D model of saccharin, the oldest known artificial sweetener, to a Lewis structure, including all lone pairs on atoms that contain them.

saccharin

©LunaseeStudios/Shutterstock RF

4.32 Keeping in mind that some elements violate the octet rule, draw a Lewis structure for each compound: (a) BeH_2; (b) PCl_5.

Resonance Structures

4.33 What is the difference between a resonance structure and a resonance hybrid?

4.34 Briefly explain why having two resonance structures for a molecule stabilizes it.

4.35 Draw a second resonance structure for the following anion:

4.36 Draw a second resonance structure for nitromethane, a compound used in drag racing fuels and in the manufacture of pharmaceuticals, pesticides, and fibers.

nitromethane

4.37 Label each pair of compounds as resonance structures or not resonance structures.

4.38 Label each pair of compounds as resonance structures or not resonance structures.

4.39 Draw three resonance structures for the carbonate anion (CO_3^{2-}) that contain a central carbon atom.

4.40 Draw three resonance structures for the nitrate anion (NO_3^-) that contain a central N atom.

Naming Covalent Compounds

4.41 Name each covalent compound.
a. PBr_3 b. SO_3 c. NCl_3 d. P_2S_5

4.42 Name each covalent compound.
a. SF_6 b. CBr_4 c. N_2O d. P_4O_{10}

4.43 Write a formula that corresponds to each name.
a. selenium dioxide   c. dinitrogen pentoxide
b. carbon tetrachloride

4.44 Write a formula that corresponds to each name.
a. silicon tetrafluoride   c. phosphorus triiodide
b. nitrogen monoxide

Molecular Shape

4.45 Add lone pairs where needed to give octets and then determine the shape around each indicated atom.

4.46 Add lone pairs where needed to give octets and then determine the shape around each indicated atom.

4.47 Match each compound with one of the molecular shapes shown below (**A** or **B**): (a) $BeCl_2$; (b) OF_2; (c) SCl_2.

A   **B**

4.48 Match each compound with one of the molecular shapes shown below (**C** or **D**): (a) BBr_3; (b) NBr_3; (c) PBr_3.

C   **D**

4.49 Add lone pairs where needed to give octets and then determine the shape around each indicated atom.

4.50 Add lone pairs where needed to give octets and then determine the shape around each indicated atom.

a.   c.

b.

4.51 Considering each of the given ball-and-stick models: [1] Does the dark red atom have one or more lone pairs of electrons on it? Explain your choice. [2] Give an example of a molecule that has the indicated geometry.

a.   b.

4.52 Considering each of the given ball-and-stick models: [1] Does the dark red atom have one or more lone pairs of electrons on it? Explain your choice. [2] Give an example of a molecule that has the indicated geometry.

a.   b.

4.53 The tartness of rhubarb is primarily due to malic acid.

rhubarb   malic acid
©mikeledray/Shutterstock RF

a. Draw a Lewis structure for malic acid with all bonds and lone pairs drawn in.

b. Determine the molecular shape around atoms **A–C**.

4.54 Give the molecular shape for the oxygen atom in H_2O and H_3O^+ and explain why they are different.

4.55 Predict the bond angles around the indicated atoms in each compound. Don't forget to draw in lone pairs where needed to give octets.

a. H—C—F   c. H—C≡C═O

b. H—C≡C—C—O—H

4.56 Predict the bond angles around the indicated atoms in each compound. Don't forget to draw in lone pairs where needed to give octets.

a. H—C—C—Cl   c. H—C═C—C—H

b. H—C≡C—C—N—H

4.57 Draw Lewis structures for CCl_4 and C_2Cl_4. Give the molecular shape around each carbon atom. Explain why the carbon atoms in the two molecules have different shapes.

4.58 Draw a Lewis structure for N_2H_4 and explain why the shape around each N atom should be described as trigonal pyramidal.

Electronegativity and Polarity

4.59 Rank the atoms in each group in order of increasing electronegativity.

a. Se, O, S   c. Li, Be, Na

b. P, Na, Cl

4.60 Rank the atoms in each group in order of increasing electronegativity.

a. Si, P, S   c. Se, Cl, Br

b. Be, Mg, Ca

4.61 Identify elements **A**, **B**, and **C** and rank them in order of increasing electronegativity.

4.62 Identify elements **D**, **E**, and **F** and rank them in order of increasing electronegativity.

4.63 Using electronegativity values, classify the bond formed between each pair of elements as polar covalent or ionic.
- a. hydrogen and bromine
- c. sodium and sulfur
- b. nitrogen and carbon
- d. lithium and oxygen

4.64 Using electronegativity values, classify the bond formed between each pair of elements as polar covalent or ionic.
- a. nitrogen and oxygen
- c. sulfur and chlorine
- b. oxygen and hydrogen
- d. sodium and chlorine

4.65 Label the bond formed between carbon and each of the following elements as nonpolar, polar, or ionic.
- a. carbon
- c. lithium
- e. hydrogen
- b. oxygen
- d. chlorine

4.66 Label the bond formed between fluorine and each of the following elements as nonpolar, polar, or ionic.
- a. hydrogen
- c. carbon
- e. sulfur
- b. fluorine
- d. lithium

4.67 Which bond in each pair is more polar—that is, has the larger electronegativity difference between atoms?
- a. C—O or C—N
- c. Si—C or P—H
- b. C—F or C—Cl

4.68 Which bond in each pair is more polar—that is, has the larger electronegativity difference between atoms?
- a. Si—O or Si—S
- c. C—B or C—Li
- b. H—F or H—Br

4.69 Label each bond in Problem 4.67 with δ+ and δ− to show the direction of polarity.

4.70 Label each bond in Problem 4.68 with δ+ and δ− to show the direction of polarity.

4.71 Label the polar bonds and then decide if each molecule is polar or nonpolar.

a.   b.

4.72 Label the polar bonds and then decide if each molecule is polar or nonpolar.

a.   b.

4.73 Explain why $CHCl_3$ is a polar molecule but CCl_4 is not.

4.74 Explain why H_2O is a polar molecule but H_2S is not.

General Questions

4.75 (a) Convert each ball-and-stick model to a Lewis structure and include all nonbonded electron pairs. (b) Label all polar bonds. (c) Is the molecule polar or nonpolar?

vinyl chloride   dichloroacetylene

A   **B**

4.76 (a) Convert each ball-and-stick model to a Lewis structure and include all nonbonded electron pairs. (b) Label all polar bonds. (c) Is the molecule polar or nonpolar?

1,1-dichloroethylene   tetrafluoroethylene

A   **B**

4.77 Answer the following questions about the molecule Cl_2O.
- a. How many valence electrons does Cl_2O contain?
- b. Draw a valid Lewis structure.
- c. Label all polar bonds.
- d. What is the shape around the O atom?
- e. Is Cl_2O a polar molecule? Explain.

4.78 Answer the following questions about the molecule OCS.
- a. How many valence electrons does OCS contain?
- b. Draw a valid Lewis structure.
- c. Label all polar bonds.
- d. What is the shape around the C atom?
- e. Is OCS a polar molecule? Explain.

Applications

4.79 Glycine is a building block used to make proteins, such as those in heart muscle (Figure 4.2).

glycine

- a. Add lone pairs where needed, and then count the total number of valence electrons in glycine.
- b. Determine the shape around the four indicated atoms.
- c. Label all of the polar bonds.
- d. Is glycine a polar or nonpolar molecule? Explain.

4.80 Lactic acid gives sour milk its distinctive taste. Lactic acid is also an ingredient in several skin care products that purportedly smooth fine lines and improve skin texture.

lactic acid

- a. Add lone pairs where needed, and then count the total number of valence electrons in lactic acid.
- b. Determine the shape around the four indicated atoms.
- c. Label all of the polar bonds.
- d. Is lactic acid a polar or nonpolar molecule? Explain.

136   **Chapter 4**   Covalent Compounds

4.81 Use the ball-and-stick model of zingerone, a pungent-tasting compound in ginger, to answer the questions.

zingerone

a. Convert the ball-and-stick model to a Lewis structure by adding all needed lone pairs. How many lone pairs does zingerone possess?

b. How many trigonal planar carbons are present?

c. Classify bonds **A–D** as polar or nonpolar.

4.82 CF_2Cl_2 belongs to a class of compounds called the chlorofluorocarbons (CFCs), once widely used as refrigerants and aerosol propellants. Draw a Lewis structure for CF_2Cl_2 and label the polar bonds. Is CF_2Cl_2 a polar or nonpolar molecule?

4.83 Serotonin ($C_{10}H_{12}N_2O$) is a neurotransmitter that is important in mood, sleep, perception, and temperature regulation. Fill in all lone pairs and double bonds to give every atom its usual bonding pattern.

serotonin

4.84 Phenylephrine ($C_9H_{13}NO_2$) is the decongestant in Sudafed PE. Phenylephrine replaced the decongestant pseudoephedrine, which was readily converted to the illegal stimulant

methamphetamine. Fill in all lone pairs and double bonds to give every atom its usual bonding pattern.

phenylephrine

4.85 Isobutyl cyanoacrylate is used in medical glues to close wounds, thus avoiding the need for sutures.

isobutyl cyanoacrylate

a. Convert the ball-and-stick model to a Lewis structure with all bonds and lone pairs drawn in.

b. Determine the shape around each carbon atom.

c. Label all polar bonds.

4.86 3-Methyl-2-hexenoic acid is one of the compounds that give human sweat its characteristic odor.

3-methyl-2-hexenoic acid

a. Convert the ball-and-stick model to a Lewis structure with all bonds and lone pairs drawn in.

b. Determine the shape around each carbon atom.

c. Label all polar bonds.

CHALLENGE PROBLEMS

4.87 Cyclopropane is a stable compound that contains three carbon atoms in a three-membered ring.

$$\begin{array}{c} \text{H} \quad \text{H} \\ \backslash \quad / \\ \text{C} \\ / \quad \backslash \\ \text{H—C——C—H} \\ | \qquad | \\ \text{H} \qquad \text{H} \end{array}$$

cyclopropane

a. What is the predicted shape around each carbon atom in the ring, given the number of groups around carbon?

b. What is the predicted C—C—C bond angle, given the shape and size of the ring?

c. Explain why cyclopropane is less stable than similar three-carbon compounds that do not contain a ring.

4.88 Although carbon has four bonds in stable molecules, sometimes reactive carbon intermediates that contain carbon atoms without

four bonds are formed for very short time periods. Examples of these unstable intermediates include the methyl carbocation $(CH_3)^+$ and the methyl carbanion $(CH_3)^-$. Draw Lewis structures for both unstable ions and predict the shape around carbon.

4.89 When fossil fuels containing sulfur are burned in power plants, large amounts of sulfur dioxide (SO_2) are released into the atmosphere, where some of it eventually forms the acid in acid rain. Draw three different Lewis structures for sulfur dioxide. Two Lewis structures must follow the octet rule, and one should illustrate that elements in the third row of the periodic table are often exceptions to the octet rule. Use the Lewis structures to explain why the O—S—O bond angle is 119°.

4.90 Draw five resonance structures for phosphate, PO_4^{3-}. Only one of these resonance structures follows the octet rule, and the remaining four illustrate that third-row elements are often exceptions to the octet rule.

5

Aspirin, a widely used over-the-counter pain reliever, is one of the countless products synthesized by the chemical industry using chemical reactions.
©Jill Braaten RF

Chemical Reactions

CHAPTER OUTLINE

5.1 Introduction to Chemical Reactions
5.2 Balancing Chemical Equations
5.3 Types of Reactions
5.4 Oxidation and Reduction
5.5 The Mole and Avogadro's Number
5.6 Mass to Mole Conversions
5.7 Mole Calculations in Chemical Equations
5.8 Mass Calculations in Chemical Equations
5.9 Percent Yield
5.10 Limiting Reactants

CHAPTER GOALS

In this chapter you will learn how to:

1 Write and balance chemical equations

2 Classify chemical reactions as combination, decomposition, single replacement, or double replacement

3 Define oxidation and reduction and recognize the components of a redox reaction

4 Define a mole and use Avogadro's number in calculations

5 Calculate formula weight and molar mass

6 Relate the mass of a substance to its number of moles

7 Carry out mole and mass calculations in chemical equations

8 Calculate percent yield

9 Determine the limiting reactant in a reaction

Why Study Chemical Reactions?

Having learned about atoms, ionic compounds, and covalent molecules in Chapters 2–4, we now turn our attention to chemical reactions. Reactions are at the heart of chemistry. An understanding of chemical processes has made possible the conversion of natural substances into new compounds with different and sometimes superior properties. Aspirin, ibuprofen, and nylon are all products of chemical reactions utilizing substances derived from petroleum. Chemical reactions are not limited to industrial processes. The metabolism of food involves a series of reactions that forms new compounds and also provides energy for the body's maintenance and growth. Burning gasoline, baking a cake, and photosynthesis involve chemical reactions. In Chapter 5 we learn the basic principles about chemical reactions.

5.1 Introduction to Chemical Reactions

Now that we have learned about compounds and the atoms that compose them, we can better understand the difference between the physical and chemical changes that were first discussed in Section 1.2.

5.1A General Features of Physical and Chemical Changes

- A physical change is a process that alters the physical state of a substance without changing its composition.

Changes in state—such as melting and boiling—are familiar examples of physical changes. When ice (solid water) melts to form liquid water, the highly organized water molecules in the solid phase become more disorganized in the liquid phase, but no bonds are broken or formed. Each water molecule (H_2O) is composed of two O—H bonds in both the solid and liquid phases.

©Daniel C. Smith

2 O—H bonds

solid H_2O

physical change   melting H_2O molecules are unchanged before and after melting.

2 O—H bonds

liquid H_2O

- A chemical change—chemical reaction—converts one substance into another.

Chemical reactions involve breaking bonds in the starting materials, called *reactants*, and forming new bonds in the *products*. The combustion of methane (CH_4), the main constituent of natural gas, in the presence of oxygen (O_2) to form carbon dioxide (CO_2) and water (H_2O) is an example of a chemical reaction. The carbon–hydrogen bonds in methane and the oxygen–oxygen bond in elemental oxygen are broken, and new carbon–oxygen and hydrogen–oxygen bonds are formed in the products.

SAMPLE PROBLEM 5.1 IDENTIFYING A CHEMICAL REACTION AND A PHYSICAL CHANGE

Identify each process as a chemical reaction or a physical change.

a.   b.

Analysis

- A chemical reaction occurs when the bonds in the reactants are broken and new bonds are formed in the products.
- A physical change occurs when the bonds in the reactants are the *same* as the bonds in the products.

Solution

Part (a) represents a chemical reaction—the reactants contain two N_2 molecules (with blue spheres joined) and two O_2 molecules (two red spheres joined), whereas the product contains four NO molecules (a red sphere joined to a blue sphere). Part (b) represents a physical change—boiling—because liquid H_2O molecules are converted to gaseous H_2O molecules and the bonds do not change.

PRACTICE PROBLEM 5.1

Use the molecular art to identify the process as a chemical reaction or a physical change, and explain your choice.

Chemical rxn.

$H_2 + O_2 \longrightarrow H_2O$

More Practice: Try Problems 5.23, 5.24.

(handwritten:) $CH_4 \; O_2 \rightarrow CO_2 \; H_2O$

PROBLEM 5.1

Use the molecular art to identify the process as a chemical reaction or a physical change, and explain your choice.

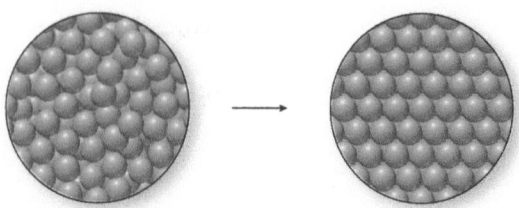

A chemical reaction may be accompanied by a visible change: two colorless reactants can form a colored product; a gas may be given off; two liquid reactants may yield a solid product. Sometimes heat is produced so that a reaction flask feels hot. A reaction having a characteristic visible change occurs when hydrogen peroxide (H_2O_2) is used to clean a bloody wound. An enzyme in the blood called catalase converts the H_2O_2 to water (H_2O) and oxygen (O_2), and bubbles of oxygen appear as a foam, as shown in Figure 5.1.

Figure 5.1   Treating Wounds with Hydrogen Peroxide—A Visible Chemical Reaction

H_2O

H_2O_2

$H_2O_2(aq)$

O_2

H_2O

The enzyme catalase in red blood converts hydrogen peroxide (H_2O_2) to water and oxygen gas, which appears as a visible white foam on the bloody surface. *(Left) ©McGraw-Hill Education/Jill Braaten, photographer, and Anthony Arena, Chemistry Consultant; (right) ©Daniel C. Smith*

5.1B   Writing Chemical Equations

- A *chemical equation* is an expression that uses chemical formulas and other symbols to illustrate what reactants constitute the starting materials in a reaction and what products are formed.

Chemical equations are written with the **reactants on the left** and the **products on the right,** separated by a horizontal arrow—a **reaction arrow**—that points from the reactants to the products. In the combustion of methane, methane (CH_4) and oxygen (O_2) are the reactants on the left side of the arrow, and carbon dioxide (CO_2) and water (H_2O) are the products on the right side.

coefficient   coefficient

Chemical equation CH_4 + $2\,O_2$ ⟶ CO_2 + $2\,H_2O$

reactants   products

The numbers written in front of any formula are called **coefficients. Coefficients show the number of molecules of a given element or compound that react or are formed.** When no number precedes a formula, the coefficient is assumed to be "1." In the combustion of methane, the coefficients tell us that one molecule of CH_4 reacts with two molecules of O_2 to form one molecule of CO_2 and two molecules of H_2O.

When a formula contains a subscript, **multiply its coefficient by the subscript** to give the total number of atoms of a given type in that formula.

2 O_2 molecules = 4 O atoms   2 H_2O molecules = 2 O atoms + 4 H atoms

Coefficients are used because all chemical reactions follow a fundamental principle of nature, the **law of conservation of matter,** which states:

  • **Atoms cannot be created or destroyed in a chemical reaction.**

Although bonds are broken and formed in reactions, the number of atoms of each element in the reactants must be the same as the number of atoms of each type in the products. **Coefficients are used to *balance* an equation,** making the number of atoms of each element the same on both sides of the equation.

$$CH_4 \quad + \quad 2\,O_2 \quad \longrightarrow \quad CO_2 \quad + \quad 2\,H_2O$$

Atoms in the reactants:
- 1 C atom
- 4 H atoms
- 4 O atoms

Atoms in the products:
- 1 C atom
- 4 H atoms
- 4 O atoms

Two other features are worthy of note. If heat is needed for a reaction to occur, the Greek letter delta (Δ) may be written over the arrow. The physical states of the reactants and products are sometimes indicated next to each formula—solid (s), liquid (l), or gas (g). If an aqueous solution is used—that is, if a reactant is dissolved in water—the symbol (aq) is used next to the reactant. When these features are added, the equation for the combustion of methane becomes:

Combustion of methane $$CH_4(g) \quad + \quad 2\,O_2(g) \quad \xrightarrow{\Delta} \quad CO_2(g) \quad + \quad 2\,H_2O(g)$$

The symbols used for chemical equations are summarized in Table 5.1.

Table 5.1   Symbols Used in Chemical Equations

Symbol	Meaning
$\longrightarrow$	Reaction arrow
Δ	Heat
(s)	Solid
(l)	Liquid
(g)	Gas
(aq)	Aqueous solution

SAMPLE PROBLEM 5.2 DETERMINING THE NUMBER OF ATOMS USING A COEFFICIENT AND SUBSCRIPT

Label the reactants and products, and indicate how many atoms of each type of element are present on each side of the equation.

$$C_2H_6O(l) + 3\,O_2(g) \longrightarrow 2\,CO_2(g) + 3\,H_2O(g)$$

Analysis

Reactants are on the left side of the arrow and products are on the right side in a chemical equation. When a formula contains a subscript, **multiply its coefficient by the subscript** to give the total number of atoms of a given type in the formula.

Solution

In this equation, the reactants are C_2H_6O and O_2, while the products are CO_2 and H_2O. If no coefficient is written, it is assumed to be "1." To determine the number of each type of atom when a formula has both a coefficient and a subscript, multiply the coefficient by the subscript.

1 C_2H_6O = 2 C's + 6 H's + 1 O

3 O_2 = 6 O's   Multiply the coefficient 3 by the subscript 2.

2 CO_2 = 2 C's + 4 O's   Multiply the coefficient 2 by each subscript;
                                  2×1 C = 2 C's; 2×2 O's = 4 O's.

3 H_2O = 6 H's + 3 O's   Multiply the coefficient 3 by each subscript;
                                  3×2 H's = 6 H's; 3×1 O = 3 O's.

Add up the atoms on each side to determine the total number for each type of element.

$$C_2H_6O(l) \;+\; 3\,O_2(g) \longrightarrow 2\,CO_2(g) \;+\; 3\,H_2O(g)$$

Atoms in the reactants:
• 2 C's   6 H's   7 O's

Atoms in the products:
• 2 C's   6 H's   7 O's

PRACTICE PROBLEM 5.2

Label the reactants and products, and indicate how many atoms of each type of element are present on each side of the following equations.

a. $2\,H_2O_2(aq) \longrightarrow 2\,H_2O(l) + O_2(g)$ (4 H, 4O)

b. $2\,C_8H_{18} + 25\,O_2 \longrightarrow 16\,CO_2 + 18\,H_2O$ (16 C, 36 H, 50 Ox)

c. $2\,Na_3PO_4(aq) + 3\,MgCl_2(aq) \longrightarrow Mg_3(PO_4)_2(s) + 6\,NaCl(aq)$ (6 Na, 2 P, 8 O, 3 mg, 6Cl)

More Practice: Try Problems 5.25, 5.26.

PROBLEM 5.2

One term in a balanced chemical equation contained the coefficient 3 in front of the formula $Al_2(SO_4)_3$. How many atoms of each type of element does this represent?

5.2   Balancing Chemical Equations

In order to carry out a reaction in the laboratory, we must know how much of each reactant we must combine to give the desired product. For example, if we wanted to synthesize aspirin ($C_9H_8O_4$) from a given amount of salicylic acid ($C_7H_6O_3$), say 100 g, we would have to determine how much acetic acid would be needed to carry out the reaction. A calculation of this sort begins with a **balanced chemical equation.**

salicylic acid   acetic acid   aspirin
$C_7H_6O_3$ $C_2H_4O_2$ $C_9H_8O_4$

In this example, the equation is balanced as written and the coefficient in front of each formula is "1." Thus, one molecule of salicylic acid reacts with one molecule of acetic acid to form one

ENVIRONMENTAL NOTE

The reaction of propane with oxygen forms carbon dioxide, water, and a great deal of energy that can be used for cooking, heating homes, drying clothes, and powering generators and vehicles. The combustion of propane and other fossil fuels adds a tremendous amount of CO_2 to the atmosphere each year, with clear environmental consequences (Section 12.8). *©Andrew Bret Wallis/ Stockbyte/Getty Images RF* molecule of aspirin and one molecule of water. More often, however, an equation must be balanced by adding coefficients in front of some formulas so that the **number of atoms of each element is equal on both sides of the equation.**

How To   Balance a Chemical Equation

Example: Write a balanced chemical equation for the reaction of propane (C_3H_8) with oxygen (O_2) to form carbon dioxide (CO_2) and water (H_2O).

Step [1]   Write the equation with the correct formulas.

- Write the reactants on the left side and the products on the right side of the reaction arrow, and check if the equation is balanced without adding any coefficients.

$$C_3H_8 \quad + \quad O_2 \quad \longrightarrow \quad CO_2 \quad + \quad H_2O$$

- This equation is not balanced as written because none of the elements—carbon, hydrogen, and oxygen—has the same number of atoms on both sides of the equation. For example, there are 3 C's on the left and only 1 C on the right.
- **The subscripts in a formula can *never* be changed to balance an equation.** Changing a subscript changes the identity of the compound. For example, changing CO_2 to CO would balance oxygen (there would be 2 O's on both sides of the equation), but that would change CO_2 (carbon dioxide) into CO (carbon monoxide).

Step [2]   Balance the equation with coefficients one element at a time.

- Begin with the most complex formula, and **start with an element that appears in only one formula on both sides of the equation.** Save the element found in multiple reactants or products for last. In this example, begin with either the C's or H's in C_3H_8. Since there are 3 C's on the left, place the coefficient 3 before CO_2 on the right.

$$C_3H_8 \; + \; O_2 \; \longrightarrow \; 3\,CO_2 \; + \; H_2O.$$

  └─ 3 C's on the left   └─ Place a 3 to balance C's.

- To balance the 8 H's in C_3H_8, place the coefficient 4 before H_2O on the right.

$$C_3H_8 \; + \; O_2 \; \longrightarrow \; 3\,CO_2 \; + \; 4\,H_2O$$

  └─ 8 H's on the left   └─ Place a 4 to balance H's.
                                  (4×2 H's in $H_2O = 8$ H's)

- The only element not balanced is oxygen, and at this point there are 10 O's on the right—six from three CO_2 molecules and four from four H_2O molecules. To balance the 10 O's on the right, place the coefficient 5 before O_2 on the left.

$$C_3H_8 \; + \; 5\,O_2 \; \longrightarrow \; 3\,CO_2 \; + \; 4\,H_2O$$

  Place a 5 to balance O's.   └─ 10 O's on the right

Step [3]   Check to make sure that the smallest set of whole numbers is used.

$$C_3H_8 \quad + \quad 5\,O_2 \quad \longrightarrow \quad 3\,CO_2 \quad + \quad 4\,H_2O$$

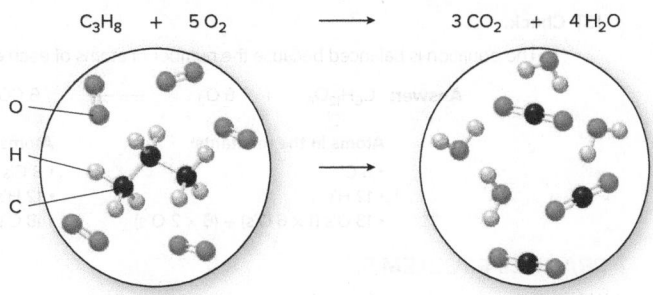

O
H
C

Atoms in the reactants:
- 3 C's   8 H's   10 O's (5×2 O's)

Atoms in the products:
- 3 C's   8 H's   10 O's [(3×2 O's) + (4×1 O)]

—Continued

How To, continued . . .

- This equation is balanced because the same number of C's, O's, and H's is present on both sides of the equation.
- Sometimes an equation is balanced but the lowest set of whole numbers is not used as coefficients. Say, for example, that balancing yielded the following equation:

$$2\ C_3H_8 + 10\ O_2 \longrightarrow 6\ CO_2 + 8\ H_2O$$

- This equation has the same number of C's, O's, and H's on both sides, but *each coefficient must be divided by two* to give the lowest set of whole numbers for the balanced equation, as drawn in the first equation in step [3].

Sample Problems 5.3–5.5 illustrate additional examples of balancing chemical equations. Sample Problem 5.4 shows how to balance an equation when there is an odd–even relationship of atoms in the reactants and products. Sample Problem 5.5 illustrates how to balance an equation that contains several polyatomic anions.

SAMPLE PROBLEM 5.3 BALANCING A CHEMICAL EQUATION

Write a balanced equation for the reaction of glucose ($C_6H_{12}O_6$) with oxygen (O_2) to form carbon dioxide (CO_2) and water (H_2O).

Analysis

Balance an equation with coefficients, one element at a time, beginning with the most complex formula and starting with an element that appears in only one formula on both sides of the equation. Continue placing coefficients until the **number of atoms of each element is equal on both sides of the equation.**

Solution

[1] **Write the equation with correct formulas.**

$$\underset{\text{glucose}}{C_6H_{12}O_6} + O_2 \longrightarrow CO_2 + H_2O$$

- None of the elements is balanced in this equation. As an example, there are 6 C's on the left side, but only 1 C on the right side.

[2] **Balance the equation with coefficients one element at a time.**

- Begin with glucose, because its formula is most complex. Balance the 6 C's of glucose by placing the coefficient 6 before CO_2. Balance the 12 H's of glucose by placing the coefficient 6 before H_2O.

Place a 6 to balance C's.

$$C_6H_{12}O_6 + O_2 \longrightarrow 6\ CO_2 + 6\ H_2O$$

Place a 6 to balance H's.

- The right side of the equation now has 18 O's. Since glucose already has 6 O's on the left side, 12 additional O's are needed on the left side. The equation will be balanced if the coefficient 6 is placed before O_2.

$$C_6H_{12}O_6 + 6\ O_2 \longrightarrow 6\ CO_2 + 6\ H_2O$$

Place a 6 to balance O's.

[3] **Check.**

- The equation is balanced because the number of atoms of each element is the same on both sides.

Answer: $C_6H_{12}O_6 + 6\ O_2 \longrightarrow 6\ CO_2 + 6\ H_2O$

Atoms in the reactants:	Atoms in the products:
• 6 C's	• 6 C's (6 × 1 C)
• 12 H's	• 12 H's (6 × 2 H's)
• 18 O's (1 × 6 O's) + (6 × 2 O's)	• 18 O's (6 × 2 O's) + (6 × 1 O)

PRACTICE PROBLEM 5.3

Write a balanced equation for each reaction.

a. $H_2 + O_2 \longrightarrow H_2O$ b. $NO + O_2 \longrightarrow NO_2$ c. $CH_4 + Cl_2 \longrightarrow CH_2Cl_2 + HCl$

More Practice: Try Problems 5.27; 5.28; 5.31a, b, d; 5.32a; 5.33–5.36.

Bagels, pasta, bread, and rice are high in starch, which is hydrolyzed to the simple carbohydrate glucose after ingestion. The metabolism of glucose forms CO_2 and H_2O and provides energy for bodily functions.
Source: Scott Bauer/USDA

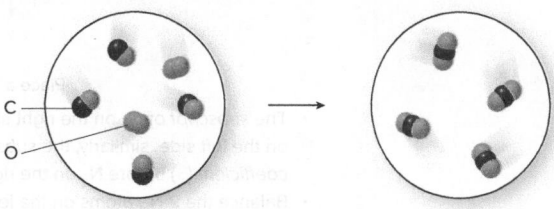

PROBLEM 5.3

Write a balanced equation for the following reaction, shown with molecular art.

C
O

Figure 5.2 Chemistry of an Automobile Airbag

a. The chemical reaction that inflates an airbag

inflated airbag

inflator

crash sensor

NaN_3
sodium azide

Na
N_2

b. An airbag deployed in a head-on collision

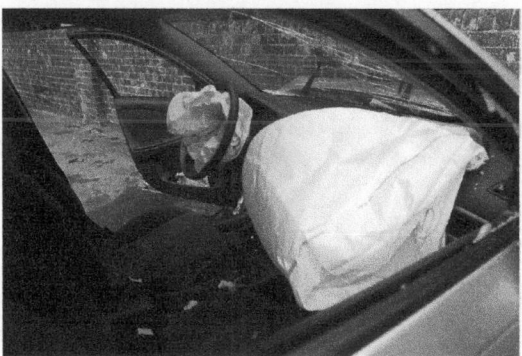

A severe car crash triggers an airbag to deploy when an electric sensor causes sodium azide (NaN_3) to ignite, converting it to sodium (Na) and nitrogen gas (N_2). The nitrogen gas causes the bag to inflate fully in 40 milliseconds, helping to protect passengers from serious injury. The sodium atoms formed in this first reaction are hazardous and subsequently converted to a safe sodium salt. It took 30 years to develop a reliable airbag system for automobiles. ©Jack Sullivan/Alamy

SAMPLE PROBLEM 5.4 BALANCING A CHEMICAL EQUATION WITH AN ODD–EVEN RELATIONSHIP OF ATOMS IN THE REACTANTS AND PRODUCTS

The airbag in an automobile inflates when ionic sodium azide (NaN_3), which is composed of Na^+ cations and the polyatomic anion, N_3^- (azide), rapidly decomposes to sodium (Na) and gaseous N_2 (Figure 5.2). Write a balanced equation for this reaction.

Analysis

Balance an equation with coefficients, one element at a time, beginning with the most complex formula and starting with an element that appears in only one formula on both sides of the equation. Continue placing coefficients until the **number of atoms of each element is equal on both sides of the equation.**

Solution

[1] Write the equation with correct formulas.

$$NaN_3 \longrightarrow Na + N_2$$
sodium azide

- The N atoms are not balanced because there are 3 N's on the left side and only 2 N's on the right.

[2] Balance the equation with coefficients.

- To balance the odd number of N atoms (3 N's) on the reactant side with the even number of N atoms on the product side (2 N's) requires the placement of two coefficients. Place the coefficient 2 on the left side (for a total of 6 N's in the reactants). Then place the coefficient 3 before N_2 (for

---

(handwritten margin notes, top left)

$2H_2 + O_2 \rightarrow 2H_2O$?
$8O + ONg \rightarrow H_4$

(handwritten margin notes, middle left)

$CH_4 + Cl_2 \rightarrow CH_2Cl_2 + 2HCl$
$C = 1$ $C = 1$
$H = 4$ $H = 4$
$Cl = 6 \checkmark$ $Cl = 6$

(handwritten margin notes, bottom left)

$2NO + O_2 \rightarrow 2NO_2$
$N = 1 \rightarrow N = 1$
$O = 3 \rightarrow O = 2$

a total of 6 N's in the product). Placing two coefficients is necessary whenever there is an odd–even relationship of atoms in the reactants and products (for any odd number other than one).

Place a 2 to give 6 N's on the left.

$$2\ NaN_3 \longrightarrow Na\ +\ 3\ N_2$$

Place a 3 to give 6 N's on the right.

- The *subscript* of N_2 on the right side is numerically equal to the *coefficient* (2) before NaN_3 on the left side; similarly, the *subscript* of NaN_3 on the left side is numerically equal to the *coefficient* (3) before N_2 on the right side.
- Balance the 2 Na atoms on the left side by placing a 2 before the Na atoms on the right.

$$2\ NaN_3 \longrightarrow 2\ Na\ +\ 3\ N_2$$

Place a 2 to balance Na's.

[3] Check and simplify.

- The equation is balanced because the number of atoms of each element is the same on both sides.

$$2\ NaN_3 \longrightarrow 2\ Na\ +\ 3\ N_2$$

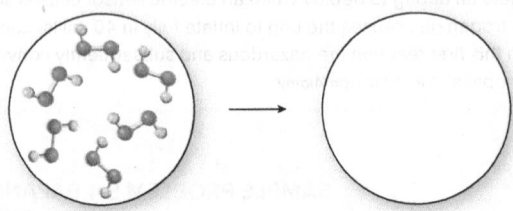

Atoms in the reactants:	**Atoms in the products:**
• 2 Na atoms	• 2 Na atoms
• 6 N atoms	• 6 N atoms
(2×3 N's)	(3×2 N's)

PRACTICE PROBLEM 5.4

Write a balanced equation for the reaction of ethane (C_2H_6) with O_2 to form CO_2 and H_2O.

More Practice: Try Problems 5.31c; 5.32b, c; 5.30.

PROBLEM 5.4

Consider the decomposition of hydrogen peroxide (H_2O_2) to form H_2O and O_2. (a) Write a balanced equation for this reaction. (b) Molecular art is used to show the molecules of starting material. Fill in the molecules of products using the balanced equation and following the law of conservation of matter.

SAMPLE PROBLEM 5.5 BALANCING AN EQUATION WITH POLYATOMIC IONS

Balance the following equation.

$$Ca_3(PO_4)_2\ +\ H_2SO_4 \longrightarrow CaSO_4\ +\ H_3PO_4$$

calcium phosphate   sulfuric acid   calcium sulfate   phosphoric acid

Analysis

Balance an equation with coefficients, one element at a time, beginning with the most complex formula and starting with an element that appears in only one formula on both sides of the equation. Continue placing coefficients until the **number of atoms of each element is equal on both sides of the equation.**

Solution

[1] Write the equation with correct formulas.

- The correct formula for each compound is given in the problem statement. When the reactants and products contain polyatomic ions, PO_4^{3-} and SO_4^{2-} in this case, **balance each ion as a *unit*** rather than balancing the individual atoms. Thus, phosphate is not balanced in the equation as written, because the left side has two PO_4^{3-} anions while the right side has only one.

[2] Balance the equation with coefficients.

- Begin with $Ca_3(PO_4)_2$. Balance the 3 Ca's by placing the coefficient 3 before $CaSO_4$. Balance the 2 PO_4^{3-} anions by placing the coefficient 2 before H_3PO_4.

$$\underset{\text{Place a 3 to balance Ca's.}}{Ca_3(PO_4)_2} \quad + \quad H_2SO_4 \quad \longrightarrow \quad 3\,CaSO_4 \quad + \quad 2\,H_3PO_4$$

Place a 2 to balance PO_4^{3-}.

- Two components are still not balanced—H atoms and sulfate anions (SO_4^{2-}). Both can be balanced by placing the coefficient 3 before H_2SO_4 on the left.

$$Ca_3(PO_4)_2 \quad + \quad \overset{\text{6 H's}}{3\,H_2SO_4} \quad \longrightarrow \quad 3\,CaSO_4 \quad + \quad \overset{\text{6 H's}}{2\,H_3PO_4}$$

3 SO_4^{2-} in both

Place a 3 to balance H and SO_4^{2-}.

[3] Check.

- The equation is balanced because the number of atoms and polyatomic anions is the same on both sides.

Answer: $Ca_3(PO_4)_2 \quad + \quad 3\,H_2SO_4 \quad \longrightarrow \quad 3\,CaSO_4 \quad + \quad 2\,H_3PO_4$

Atoms or ions in the reactants:	Atoms or ions in the products:
• 3 Ca's	• 3 Ca's
• 6 H's	• 6 H's
• 2 PO_4^{3-}	• 2 PO_4^{3-}
• 3 SO_4^{2-}	• 3 SO_4^{2-}

Ammonium hydrogen phosphate [$(NH_4)_2HPO_4$], the major phosphorus fertilizer, is formed from phosphoric acid, H_3PO_4, which is synthesized industrially by the chemical reaction in Sample Problem 5.5.

PRACTICE PROBLEM 5.5

Balance each chemical equation.

a. $Al + H_2SO_4 \longrightarrow Al_2(SO_4)_3 + H_2$ b. $Na_2SO_3 + H_3PO_4 \longrightarrow H_2SO_3 + Na_3PO_4$

More Practice: Try Problems 5.31e; 5.32d, e.

5.3 Types of Reactions

Although there is a great variety of known chemical reactions, many reactions fall into a few major categories. In this section we consider **combination, decomposition, single replacement, and double replacement reactions.** In Section 5.4, we will learn about reactions involving oxidation and reduction, and all of Chapter 9 is devoted to acid–base reactions.

5.3A   Combination and Decomposition Reactions

- A *combination reaction* is the joining of two or more reactants to form a single product.

In a general combination reaction, reactant **A** combines with reactant **B** to form the product **AB.**

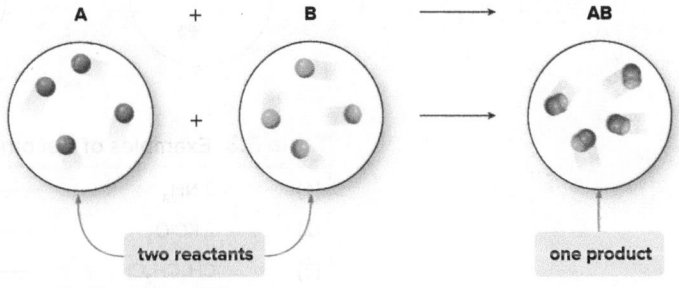

The reaction of hydrogen (H_2) with oxygen (O_2) to form water (H_2O) is an example of a combination reaction. **The reactants may be either elements or compounds, but the product is** *always* **a compound.** Other examples are shown in Table 5.2.

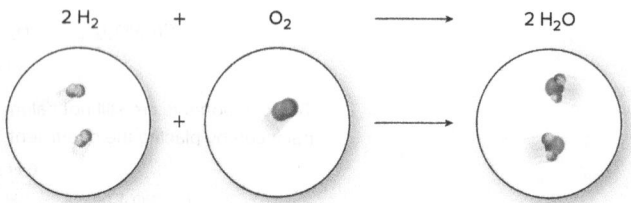

Table 5.2 Examples of Combination Reactions

[1]	N_2	+	$3 H_2$	$\longrightarrow$	$2 NH_3$
[2]	Ca	+	Br_2	$\longrightarrow$	$CaBr_2$
[3]	$H_2C{=}CH_2$	+	Cl_2	$\longrightarrow$	$ClCH_2CH_2Cl$

- A *decomposition reaction* is the conversion of a single reactant to two or more products.

In a general decomposition reaction, reactant **AB** forms product **A** and product **B.**

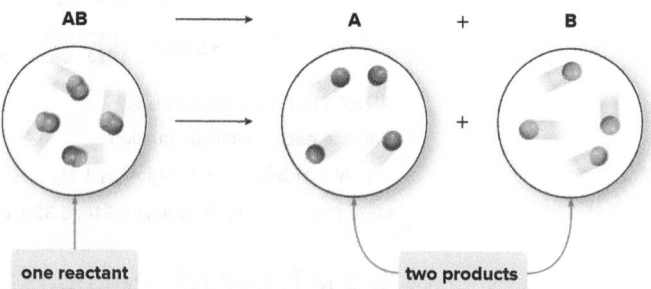

The conversion of hydrogen bromide (HBr) to hydrogen (H_2) and bromine (Br_2) is an example of a decomposition reaction. The conversion of NaN_3 to Na and N_2 in an automobile airbag (Sample Problem 5.4) is also a decomposition. **The products may be elements or compounds, but the reactant is** *always* **a compound.** Other examples are shown in Table 5.3.

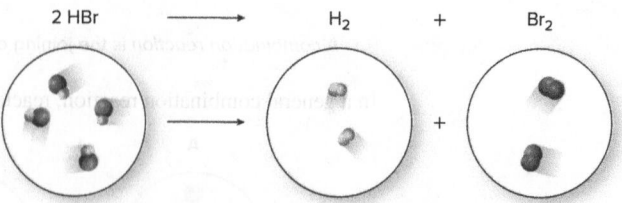

Table 5.3 Examples of Decomposition Reactions

[1]	$2 NH_3$	$\longrightarrow$	N_2	+	$3 H_2$
[2]	$2 KClO_3$	$\longrightarrow$	$2 KCl$	+	$3 O_2$
[3]	CH_3CH_2Cl	$\longrightarrow$	$H_2C{=}CH_2$	+	HCl

In comparing combination and decomposition:

- **Combination reactions form only *one product*, whereas decomposition reactions begin with only *one reactant*.**

The reddish brown color of polluted air is due to nitrogen dioxide (NO_2), an irritant formed by the reaction depicted in Sample Problem 5.6. ©Ed Pritchard/The Image Bank/Getty Images

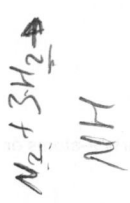

SAMPLE PROBLEM 5.6 CLASSIFYING A REACTION AS A COMBINATION OR DECOMPOSITION

Write a balanced equation for the reaction depicted in the molecular art, and classify the reaction as a combination or decomposition.

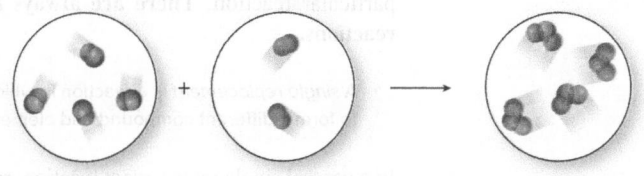

Analysis

- Use the common element colors on the inside back cover to write an equation for the reaction, making sure that the smallest set of whole numbers is used when balanced.
- A combination reaction joins two reactants together to form a single product, whereas a decomposition reaction converts a single reactant to two products.

Solution

Since a red sphere represents oxygen and a blue sphere represents nitrogen, the molecular art depicts the reaction of four NO molecules with two O_2 molecules to form four NO_2 molecules. The coefficients must be divided by two to obtain the smallest set of whole numbers.

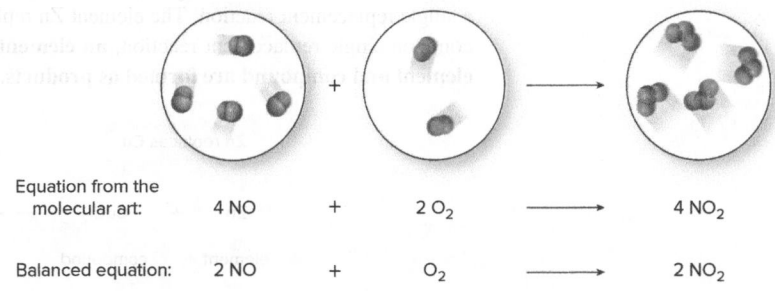

Equation from the molecular art:	4 NO	+	2 O_2	⟶	4 NO_2
Balanced equation:	2 NO	+	O_2	⟶	2 NO_2

The reaction is a **combination** because two reactants join to form a single product.

PRACTICE PROBLEM 5.6

Write a balanced equation for the reaction depicted in the molecular art, and classify the reaction as a combination or decomposition.

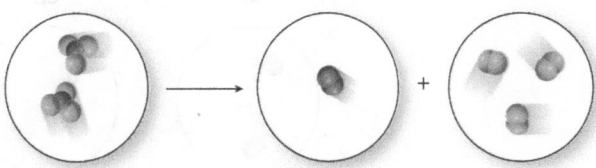

More Practice: Try Problems 5.37–5.40; 5.43a, c; 5.44b, d.

PROBLEM 5.5

Classify each reaction as a combination or decomposition.

a. $Cu(s) + S(s) \longrightarrow CuS(s)$

b. $CuCO_3(s) \longrightarrow CuO(s) + CO_2(g)$

c. $H_2(g) + Cl_2(g) \longrightarrow 2\ HCl(g)$

d. $C_6H_{12}O_6(aq) \longrightarrow 2\ C_2H_6O(aq) + 2\ CO_2(g)$

5.3B Replacement Reactions

In a **replacement reaction,** an element in a reactant is replaced by another element. Replacement reactions are characterized as **single replacement** or **double replacement,** depending on the particular reaction. **There are always** *two* **reactants and** *two* **products in replacement reactions.**

- A *single replacement* is a reaction in which one element replaces another element in a compound to form a different compound and element as products.

In a general single replacement reaction, reactants **A** and **BC** form products **B** and **AC.**

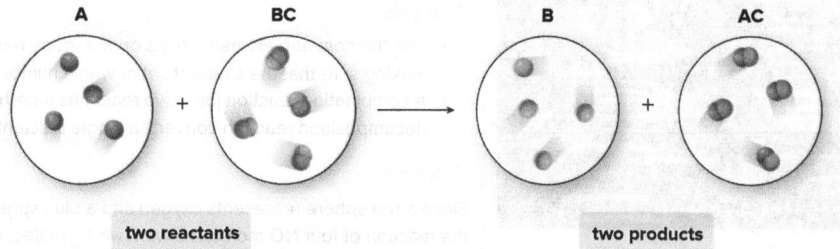

two reactants   two products

The reaction of zinc with $CuCl_2$ [copper(II) chloride] to form $ZnCl_2$ (zinc chloride) and copper is a single replacement reaction. The element Zn replaces Cu in the compound $CuCl_2$. In the most common single replacement reaction, **an element and compound are the reactants, and an element and compound are formed as products.**

Zn replaces Cu.

Zn + $CuCl_2$ $\longrightarrow$ $ZnCl_2$ + Cu

element   compound   compound   element

- A *double replacement* is a reaction in which two compounds exchange "parts"—atoms or ions—to form two new compounds.

In a general double replacement reaction, reactants **AB** and **CD** form products **AD** and **CB** by the exchange of **A** for **C** in the reactants.

two reactants   two products

The reaction of $BaCl_2$ (barium chloride) with K_2CO_3 (potassium carbonate) to form $BaCO_3$ (barium carbonate) and KCl (potassium chloride) is a double replacement reaction. The cations Ba^{2+} and K^+ exchange places to form two new ionic compounds. In double replacement, **two compounds are reactants and two compounds are products.**

Ba^{2+} and K^+ exchange places.

$$BaCl_2 \ + \ K_2CO_3 \longrightarrow BaCO_3 \ + \ 2\ KCl$$

compound   compound   compound   compound

Table 5.4 contains additional examples of single and double replacement reactions.

Table 5.4 Examples of Single and Double Replacement Reactions

Type of Reaction	Examples	Comment
Single replacement		
	[1] $2\ NaCl + Br_2 \longrightarrow 2\ NaBr + Cl_2$	The element Br replaces Cl in the compound NaCl.
	[2] $Fe + CuSO_4 \longrightarrow FeSO_4 + Cu$	The element Fe replaces Cu in the compound $CuSO_4$.
Double replacement		
	[1] $AgNO_3 + NaCl \longrightarrow AgCl + NaNO_3$	The ions Ag^+ and Na^+ exchange.
	[2] $HCl + NaOH \longrightarrow H_2O + NaCl$	The species H and Na^+ exchange.

SAMPLE PROBLEM 5.7 CLASSIFYING A REACTION AS A SINGLE OR DOUBLE REPLACEMENT

Classify each reaction as a single replacement or double replacement reaction.

a. $CuO + 2\ HCl \longrightarrow CuCl_2 + H_2O$ b. $Zn + 2\ HCl \longrightarrow ZnCl_2 + H_2$

Analysis

- In a single replacement reaction, one element replaces another element in a compound to form a new compound and new element.
- In a double replacement reaction, two compounds exchange atoms or ions to form two new compounds.

Solution

a. The reaction is a double replacement because the Cu^{2+} (in $CuSO_4$) and H (in HCl) exchange to form two new compounds.

Cu^{2+} and H exchange.

$$CuO \ + \ 2\ HCl \longrightarrow CuCl_2 \ + \ H_2O$$

compound   compound   compound   compound

b. The reaction is a single replacement because the element Zn replaces the H atom in HCl to form a new compound and new element.

Zn replaces H.

$$Zn \ + \ 2\ HCl \longrightarrow ZnCl_2 \ + \ H_2$$

element   compound   compound   element

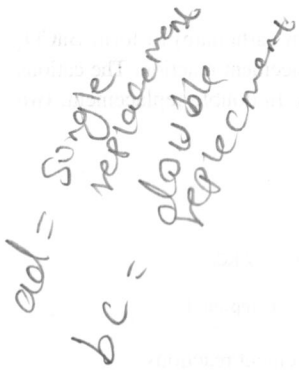

(handwritten margin notes) ad = single replacement bc = double replacement

PRACTICE PROBLEM 5.7

Classify each reaction as a single replacement or double replacement reaction.

a. $Ni(NO_3)_2 + Mg \longrightarrow Ni + Mg(NO_3)_2$

b. $2 KI + Sn(NO_3)_2 \longrightarrow SnI_2 + 2 KNO_3$

c. $KCN + HCl \longrightarrow KCl + HCN$

d. $6 Na + Al_2(SO_4)_3 \longrightarrow 3 Na_2SO_4 + 2 Al$

More Practice: Try Problems 5.41; 5.42; 5.43b, d; 5.44a, c.

PROBLEM 5.6

Classify each reaction as a combination, decomposition, single replacement, or double replacement reaction.

a. $2 HgO \longrightarrow 2 Hg + O_2$

b. $Mg + ZnCl_2 \longrightarrow MgCl_2 + Zn$

c. $H_2C{=}CH_2 + HBr \longrightarrow CH_3CH_2Br$

d. $KNO_3 + HBr \longrightarrow KBr + HNO_3$

PROBLEM 5.7

Fill in the needed reactants or products for each of the following reaction types, and balance the equation.

a. combination: $C + O_2 \longrightarrow \boxed{}$

b. decomposition: $MgCO_3 \longrightarrow MgO + \boxed{}$

c. single replacement: $Ag + \boxed{} \longrightarrow Li + Ag_2CO_3$

d. double replacement: $Na_2CO_3 + BaBr_2 \longrightarrow \boxed{} + \boxed{}$

5.4 Oxidation and Reduction

Oxidation and reduction reactions constitute a class of chemical reactions that involves electron transfer.

5.4A General Features of Oxidation–Reduction Reactions

A common type of chemical reaction involves the transfer of electrons from one element to another. When iron rusts, methane and wood burn, and a battery generates electricity, one element gains electrons and another loses them. These reactions involve **oxidation** and **reduction.**

- Oxidation is the loss of electrons from an atom.
- Reduction is the gain of electrons by an atom.

Oxidation and reduction are opposite processes, and both occur together in a single reaction called an **oxidation–reduction** or **redox reaction.** A redox reaction always has two components— one that is oxidized and one that is reduced.

- A redox reaction involves the transfer of electrons from one element to another.

An example of an oxidation–reduction reaction occurs when Zn metal reacts with Cu^{2+} cations, as shown in Figure 5.3.

Cu²⁺ gains two electrons.

$$Zn + Cu^{2+} \longrightarrow Zn^{2+} + Cu$$

Zn loses two electrons.

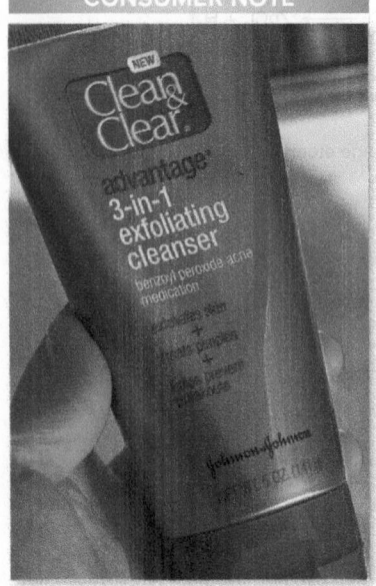

Benzoyl peroxide ($C_{14}H_{10}O_4$) is the active ingredient in several acne medications. Benzoyl peroxide kills bacteria by oxidation reactions. ©Jill Braaten RF

Figure 5.3　A Redox Reaction—The Transfer of Electrons from Zn to Cu^{2+}

A redox reaction occurs when a strip of Zn metal is placed in a solution of Cu^{2+} ions. In this reaction, Zn loses two electrons to form Zn^{2+}, which goes into solution. Cu^{2+} gains two electrons to form Cu metal, which precipitates out of solution, forming a coating on the zinc strip.

- Zn loses two electrons to form Zn^{2+}, so Zn is oxidized.
- Cu^{2+} gains two electrons to form Cu metal, so Cu^{2+} is reduced.

Each of these processes can be written as individual reactions, called **half reactions,** to emphasize which electrons are gained and lost.

- A compound that oxidizes another compound is called an *oxidizing agent*. An oxidizing agent gains electrons, so it is reduced.
- A compound that reduces another compound is called a *reducing agent*. A reducing agent loses electrons, so it is oxidized.

In this example, Zn loses electrons to Cu^{2+}. Zn is a **reducing agent** because it causes Cu^{2+} to gain electrons and become reduced. Cu^{2+} is an **oxidizing agent** because it causes Zn to lose electrons and become oxidized.

To draw the products of an oxidation–reduction reaction, we must decide which element or ion gains electrons and which element or ion loses electrons. Use the following guidelines.

- When considering neutral atoms, metals lose electrons and nonmetals gain electrons.
- When considering ions, cations tend to gain electrons and anions tend to lose electrons.

154   **Chapter 5**   Chemical Reactions

Figure 5.4   Examples of Oxidation and Reduction Reactions

Oxidation Reactions

$Na \longrightarrow Na^+ + e^-$

$Mg \longrightarrow Mg^{2+} + 2 e^-$

$2 Cl^- \longrightarrow Cl_2 + 2 e^-$

$2 O^{2-} \longrightarrow O_2 + 4 e^-$

Electrons are **lost.**

Reduction Reactions

$Cl_2 + 2 e^- \longrightarrow 2 Cl^-$

$O_2 + 4 e^- \longrightarrow 2 O^{2-}$

$Cu^{2+} + 2 e^- \longrightarrow Cu$

$Ag^+ + e^- \longrightarrow Ag$

Electrons are **gained.**

Thus, the metals sodium (Na) and magnesium (Mg) readily lose electrons to form the cations Na^+ and Mg^{2+}, respectively; that is, they are oxidized. The nonmetals O_2 and Cl_2 readily gain electrons to form $2 O^{2-}$ and $2 Cl^-$, respectively; that is, they are reduced. A positively charged ion like Cu^{2+} is reduced to Cu by gaining two electrons, whereas two negatively charged Cl^- anions are oxidized to Cl_2 by losing two electrons. These reactions and additional examples are shown in Figure 5.4.

SAMPLE PROBLEM 5.8 IDENTIFYING THE COMPONENTS OF A REDOX REACTION

Identify the species that is oxidized and the species that is reduced in the following reaction. Write out half reactions to show how many electrons are gained or lost by each species.

$$Mg(s) + 2 H^+(aq) \longrightarrow Mg^{2+}(aq) + H_2(g)$$

Analysis

- **Metals and anions tend to lose electrons** and thus undergo oxidation.
- **Nonmetals and cations tend to gain electrons** and thus undergo reduction.

Solution

The metal Mg is oxidized to Mg^{2+}, thus losing two electrons. Two H^+ cations gain a total of two electrons, and so are reduced to the nonmetal H_2.

$Mg(s) \longrightarrow Mg^{2+}(aq) + 2 e^-$

Mg is oxidized.

$2 H^+(aq) + 2 e^- \longrightarrow H_2(g)$

H^+ is reduced.   Two electrons are needed to balance charge.

We need enough electrons so that **the total charge is the same on both sides of the equation.** Since $2 H^+$ cations have a +2 overall charge, this means that $2 e^-$ must be gained, so that the total charge on both sides of the equation is zero.

PRACTICE PROBLEM 5.8

Identify the species that is oxidized and the species that is reduced in each reaction. Write out half reactions to show how many electrons are gained or lost by each species.

a. $Zn(s) + 2 H^+(aq) \longrightarrow Zn^{2+}(aq) + H_2(g)$

b. $Fe^{3+}(aq) + Al(s) \longrightarrow Al^{3+}(aq) + Fe(s)$

c. $2 I^- + Br_2 \longrightarrow I_2 + 2 Br^-$

d. $2 AgBr \longrightarrow 2 Ag + Br_2$

More Practice: Try Problems 5.47–5.50, 5.52.

5.4B   Examples of Oxidation–Reduction Reactions

Many common processes involve oxidation and reduction. For example, common antiseptics like iodine (I_2) and hydrogen peroxide (H_2O_2) are oxidizing agents that clean wounds by oxidizing, thereby killing bacteria that might cause infection.

When iron (Fe) rusts, it is oxidized by the oxygen in air to form iron(III) oxide, Fe_2O_3. In this redox reaction, neutral iron atoms are oxidized to Fe^{3+} cations, and elemental O_2 is reduced to O^{2-} anions.

Fe atom

Fe^{3+}

O^{2-}

$$4\ Fe(s)\ +\ 3\ O_2(g)\ \longrightarrow\ 2\ Fe_2O_3(s)$$

neutral elements

Each Fe ion has a +3 charge.

Each O ion has a −2 charge.

©Tony Cordoza/Alamy RF   ©Clair Dunn/Alamy

Batteries consist of a metal and a cation that undergo a redox reaction. When the electrons are transferred from the metal to the cation, an electric current results, which can supply power for a lightbulb, radio, computer, or watch. For example, an alkaline battery usually contains zinc powder and Mn^{4+} cations, together with sodium or potassium hydroxide (NaOH or KOH), as shown in Figure 5.5.

$$Zn\ +\ 2\ MnO_2\ \longrightarrow\ ZnO\ +\ Mn_2O_3$$

Mn^{4+} \quad Zn^{2+} \quad Mn^{3+}

In this redox reaction, neutral Zn atoms are oxidized to Zn^{2+} cations. Mn^{4+} cations are reduced to Mn^{3+} cations. The oxygen anions (O^{2-}) just balance the charge of the metal cations and are neither oxidized nor reduced.

In some reactions it is much less apparent which reactant is oxidized and which is reduced. For example, in the combustion of methane (CH_4) with oxygen to form CO_2 and H_2O, there are no

Figure 5.5   A Flashlight Battery—An Example of a Redox Reaction

Zn is oxidized. MnO_2 is reduced.

brass pin   Zn MnO_2

Redox Reaction

Oxidation: $Zn \longrightarrow Zn^{2+} + 2\ e^-$

Reduction: $2\ Mn^{4+} + 2\ e^- \longrightarrow 2\ Mn^{3+}$

Alkaline batteries consist of zinc powder (Zn) and manganese dioxide (MnO_2), along with a paste of sodium hydroxide (NaOH) or potassium hydroxide (KOH). When electrical contact is made, Zn atoms lose electrons, which flow toward the Mn^{4+} cations in MnO_2. The resulting electric current can be used to power a lightbulb, radio, or other electrical device. ©Keith Eng, 2008 metals or cations that obviously lose or gain electrons, yet this is a redox reaction. In these instances, it is often best to count oxygen and hydrogen atoms.

- Oxidation results in the gain of oxygen atoms or the loss of hydrogen atoms.
- Reduction results in the loss of oxygen atoms or the gain of hydrogen atoms.

CH_4 is oxidized because it gains two oxygen atoms to form CO_2. O_2 is reduced because it gains two hydrogen atoms to form H_2O.

PROBLEM 5.8

Identify the species that is oxidized and the species that is reduced in the following reaction. The oxide anion (O^{2-}) is unchanged in the reaction.

$$Zn + HgO \longrightarrow ZnO + Hg$$

PROBLEM 5.9

a. Write a balanced equation for the reaction depicted in the molecular art.
b. Identify the species that is oxidized and the species that is reduced.

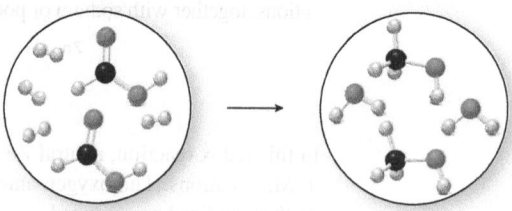

5.4C   FOCUS ON HEALTH & MEDICINE
Pacemakers

A pacemaker is a small electrical device implanted in an individual's chest and used to maintain an adequate heart rate (Figure 5.6). A pacemaker contains a small, long-lasting battery that generates an electrical impulse by a redox reaction.

Most pacemakers used today contain a lithium–iodine battery. Each neutral lithium atom is oxidized to Li^+ by losing one electron. Each I_2 molecule is reduced by gaining two electrons and forming $2\ I^-$. Since the balanced equation contains two Li atoms for each I_2 molecule, the number of electrons lost by Li atoms equals the number of electrons gained by I_2.

Figure 5.6 The Lithium–Iodine Battery in a Pacemaker

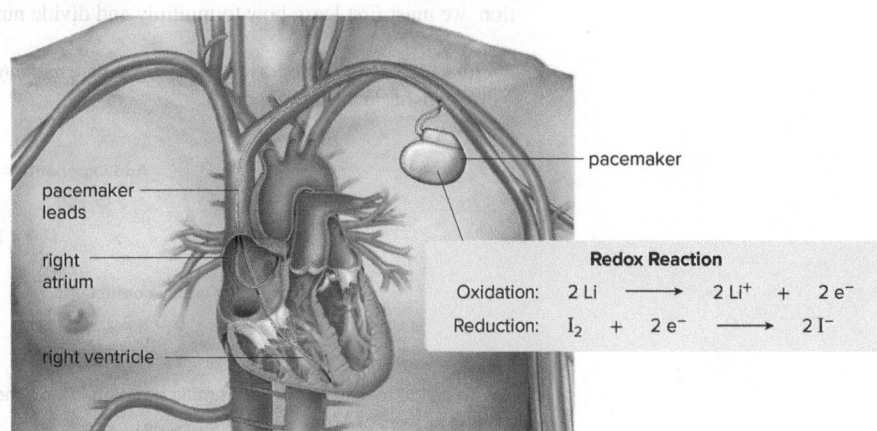

pacemaker

pacemaker
leads

right
atrium

right ventricle

Redox Reaction

Oxidation: $2\,Li \longrightarrow 2\,Li^+ + 2\,e^-$

Reduction: $I_2 + 2\,e^- \longrightarrow 2\,I^-$

A pacemaker generates a small electrical impulse that triggers the heart to beat. Today's pacemakers sense when the heart beats normally and provide an electrical signal only when the heart rate slows. Such devices are called "demand" pacemakers, and they quickly replaced earlier "fixed" rate models that continuously produced impulses to set the heart rate at a fixed value.

PROBLEM 5.10

Early pacemakers generated an electrical impulse by the following reaction. What species is the oxidizing agent and what species is the reducing agent in this reaction?

$$Zn + Hg^{2+} \longrightarrow Zn^{2+} + Hg$$

5.5 The Mole and Avogadro's Number

Although the chemical equations in Section 5.2 were discussed in terms of individual atoms and molecules, atoms are exceedingly small. It is more convenient to talk about larger quantities of atoms, and for this reason, scientists use the **mole.** A mole defines a quantity, much like a dozen items means 12, and a case of soda means 24 cans. The only difference is that a mole is much larger.

- A *mole* is a quantity that contains 6.02×10^{23} items—usually atoms, molecules, or ions.

The definition of a mole is based on the number of atoms contained in exactly 12 g of the carbon-12 isotope. This number is called **Avogadro's number,** after the Italian scientist Amadeo Avogadro, who first proposed the concept of a mole in the nineteenth century. One mole, abbreviated as **mol,** always contains an Avogadro's number of particles.

1 mole of C atoms = 6.02×10^{23} C atoms

1 mole of H_2O molecules = 6.02×10^{23} H_2O molecules

1 mole of vitamin C molecules = 6.02×10^{23} vitamin C molecules

Each sample contains one mole of the substance—water (H_2O molecules), salt (NaCl, one mole of Na^+ and one mole of Cl^-), and aspirin ($C_9H_8O_4$ molecules). Pictured is a mole of aspirin *molecules,* not a mole of aspirin *tablets,* which is a quantity too large to easily represent.
©McGraw-Hill Education/Jill Braaten, photographer, and Anthony Arena, Chemistry Consultant

PROBLEM 5.11

How many items are contained in one mole of (a) baseballs; (b) bicycles; (c) Cheerios; (d) CH_4 molecules?

We can use Avogadro's number as a conversion factor to relate the number of moles of a substance to the number of atoms or molecules it contains.

Two possible conversion factors: $\dfrac{1\ mol}{6.02 \times 10^{23}\ atoms}$ or $\dfrac{6.02 \times 10^{23}\ atoms}{1\ mol}$

These conversion factors allow us to determine how many atoms or molecules are contained in a given number of moles. To carry out calculations that contain numbers written in scientific notation, we must first learn how to multiply and divide numbers written in this form.

- To multiply two numbers in scientific notation, *multiply* the coefficients together **and** *add* the exponents in the powers of 10.

Add exponents.
(5 + 2)

(3.0×10^5) × (2.0×10^2) = 6.0×10^7

Multiply coefficients.
(3.0×2.0)

- To divide two numbers in scientific notation, *divide* the coefficients and *subtract* the exponents in the powers of 10.

Divide coefficients. $\dfrac{6.0 \times 10^2}{2.0 \times 10^{20}}$ **Subtract exponents.**   = 3.0×10^{-18}
$(6.0 \div 2.0)$ $(2 - 20)$

For a number written in scientific notation as $y \times 10^x$, y is the **coefficient** and x is the **exponent** in the power of 10 (Section 1.6).

Sample Problems 5.9 and 5.10 illustrate how to interconvert moles and molecules. In both problems we follow the stepwise procedure for problem solving using conversion factors outlined in Section 1.7B.

SAMPLE PROBLEM 5.9 CONVERTING MOLES TO THE NUMBER OF MOLECULES

How many molecules are contained in 5.0 mol of carbon dioxide (CO_2)?

Analysis and Solution

[1] Identify the original quantity and the desired quantity.

5.0 mol of CO_2 ? number of molecules of CO_2
original quantity   desired quantity

[2] Write out the conversion factors.

- Choose the conversion factor that places the unwanted unit, mol, in the denominator so that the units cancel.

$\dfrac{1 \text{ mol}}{6.02 \times 10^{23} \text{ molecules}}$ or $\dfrac{6.02 \times 10^{23} \text{ molecules}}{1 \text{ mol}}$

Choose this conversion factor to cancel mol.

[3] Set up and solve the problem.

- Multiply the original quantity by the conversion factor to obtain the desired quantity.

Convert to a number between 1 and 10.

5.0 mol   × $\dfrac{6.02 \times 10^{23} \text{ molecules}}{1 \text{ mol}}$ = $30. \times 10^{23}$ molecules

Moles cancel.   = 3.0×10^{24} molecules of CO_2

Answer

- Multiplication first gives an answer that is not written in scientific notation because the coefficient (30.) is greater than 10. Moving the decimal point one place to the *left* and *increasing* the exponent by one gives the answer written in the proper form.

PRACTICE PROBLEM 5.9

How many carbon atoms are contained in each of the following number of moles: (a) 2.00 mol; (b) 6.00 mol; (c) 0.500 mol; (d) 25.0 mol?

More Practice: Try Problem 5.67.

1.20×10^{24}
3.61×10^{24}
3.01×10^{23}
1.50×10^{25}

PROBLEM 5.12

How many molecules are contained in each of the following number of moles?

a. 2.5 mol of penicillin molecules

b. 0.25 mol of NH_3 molecules

c. 0.40 mol of sugar molecules

d. 55.3 mol of acetaminophen molecules

SAMPLE PROBLEM 5.10 CONVERTING THE NUMBER OF MOLECULES TO MOLES

How many moles of aspirin contain 8.62×10^{25} molecules?

Analysis and Solution

[1] Identify the original quantity and the desired quantity.

$$8.62 \times 10^{25} \text{ molecules of aspirin} \qquad \text{? moles of aspirin}$$
$$\text{original quantity} \qquad\qquad \text{desired quantity}$$

[2] Write out the conversion factors.

- Choose the conversion factor that places the unwanted unit, number of molecules, in the denominator so that the units cancel.

$$\frac{6.02 \times 10^{23} \text{ molecules}}{1 \text{ mol}} \qquad \text{or} \qquad \frac{1 \text{ mol}}{6.02 \times 10^{23} \text{ molecules}}$$

Choose this conversion factor to cancel molecules.

[3] Set up and solve the problem.

- Multiply the original quantity by the conversion factor to obtain the desired quantity.
- To divide numbers using scientific notation, divide the coefficients (8.62 ÷ 6.02) and subtract the exponents (25 − 23).

$$8.62 \times 10^{25} \text{ molecules} \quad \times \quad \frac{1 \text{ mol}}{6.02 \times 10^{23} \text{ molecules}} \quad = \quad 1.43 \times 10^2 \text{ mol}$$

Molecules cancel.

$$= 143 \text{ mol of aspirin}$$

Answer

PRACTICE PROBLEM 5.10

How many moles of water contain each of the following number of molecules?

a. 6.02×10^{25} molecules

b. 3.01×10^{22} molecules

c. 9.0×10^{24} molecules

More Practice: Try Problem 5.68.

5.6 Mass to Mole Conversions

In Section 2.3, we learned that the *atomic weight* **is the average mass of an element,** reported in atomic mass units (amu), and that the atomic weight of each element appears just below its chemical symbol in the periodic table. Thus, carbon has an atomic weight of 12.01 amu. We use atomic weights to calculate the mass of a compound.

> • The *formula weight* is the sum of the atomic weights of all the atoms in a compound, reported in atomic mass units (amu).

The term "formula weight" is used for both ionic and covalent compounds. Often the term **"molecular weight"** is used in place of formula weight for covalent compounds, because they are composed of molecules, not ions. The formula weight of ionic sodium chloride (NaCl) is 58.44 amu, which is determined by adding up the atomic weights of Na (22.99 amu) and Cl (35.45 amu). The stepwise procedure for calculating the formula weight of compounds whose chemical formulas contain subscripts is shown in the accompanying *How To*.

Formula weight of NaCl:	
Atomic weight of 1 Na	= 22.99 amu
Atomic weight of 1 Cl	= 35.45 amu
Formula weight of NaCl	= 58.44 amu

How To   Calculate the Formula Weight of a Compound

Example: Calculate the formula weight for iron(II) sulfate, $FeSO_4$, an iron supplement used to treat anemia.

Step [1]   Write the correct formula and determine the number of atoms of each element from the subscripts.

• $FeSO_4$ contains 1 Fe atom, 1 S atom, and 4 O atoms.

Step [2]   Multiply the number of atoms of each element by the atomic weight and add the results.

$$1 \text{ Fe atom} \times 55.85 \text{ amu} = 55.85 \text{ amu}$$
$$1 \text{ S atom} \times 32.07 \text{ amu} = 32.07 \text{ amu}$$
$$4 \text{ O atoms} \times 16.00 \text{ amu} = 64.00 \text{ amu}$$
$$\text{Formula weight of } FeSO_4 = 151.92 \text{ amu} \qquad \textbf{Answer}$$

Cucumber aldehyde is a powerful odorant that can be detected in very low concentrations when a cucumber is cut.
©McGraw-Hill Education/Jill Braaten, photographer

PROBLEM 5.13

Calculate the formula weight of each ionic compound.

a. $CaCO_3$, a common calcium supplement
b. KI, the essential nutrient added to NaCl to make iodized salt

PROBLEM 5.14

The unmistakable odor of a freshly cut cucumber is due to cucumber aldehyde. (a) What is the chemical formula of cucumber aldehyde? (b) Calculate its molecular weight.

cucumber aldehyde

5.6A   Molar Mass

When reactions are carried out in the laboratory, single atoms and molecules are much too small to measure out. Instead, substances are weighed on a balance and amounts are typically reported

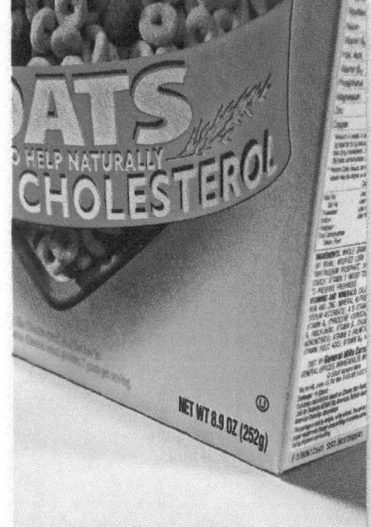

When a consumer product contains a great many lightweight small objects—for example, Cheerios—it is typically sold by weight, not by the number of objects. We buy Cheerios in an 8.9-oz box, not a box that contains 2,554 Cheerios.
©McGraw-Hill Education/Jill Braaten, photographer

in grams, not atomic mass units. To determine how many atoms or molecules are contained in a given mass, we use its **molar mass.**

- The *molar mass* is the mass of one mole of any substance, reported in grams per mole.

The value of the molar mass of an element in the periodic table (in grams per mole) is the same as the value of its atomic weight (in amu). Thus, the molar mass of carbon is 12.01 g/mol, because its atomic weight is 12.01 amu; that is, one mole of carbon atoms weighs 12.01 g.

| 6 |
| C |
| 12.01 |

- Carbon's **atomic weight** is 12.01 amu.
- Carbon's **molar mass** is 12.01 g/mol.
- **One mole of carbon atoms weighs 12.01 g.**

- The value of the molar mass of a compound in grams equals the value of its formula weight in amu.

Since the formula weight of NaCl is 58.44 amu, its molar mass is 58.44 g/mol. One mole of NaCl weighs 58.44 g. We use a compound's formula weight to calculate its molar mass, as shown in Sample Problem 5.11.

SAMPLE PROBLEM 5.11 CALCULATING MOLAR MASS

What is the molar mass of nicotine ($C_{10}H_{14}N_2$), the toxic and addictive stimulant in tobacco?

Analysis

Determine the number of atoms of each element from the subscripts in the chemical formula, multiply the number of atoms of each element by the atomic weight, and add up the results.

Solution

$$10 \text{ C atoms} \times 12.01 \text{ amu} = 120.1 \text{ amu}$$
$$14 \text{ H atoms} \times 1.008 \text{ amu} = 14.11 \text{ amu}$$
$$2 \text{ N atoms} \times 14.01 \text{ amu} = 28.02 \text{ amu}$$
$$\text{Formula weight of nicotine} = 162.23 \text{ amu rounded to } 162.2 \text{ amu}$$

Answer: The formula weight of nicotine is 162.2 amu, so the molar mass of nicotine is 162.2 g/mol.

PRACTICE PROBLEM 5.11

What is the molar mass of ginkgolide B ($C_{20}H_{24}O_{10}$), a complex compound isolated from the ginkgo tree? Extracts of the roots, bark, and seeds of the ginkgo tree comprise the most widely taken herbal supplements used today.

More Practice: Try Problems 5.53–5.56.

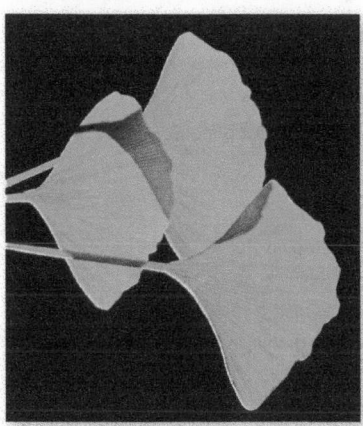

Ginkgo extracts from the tree *Ginkgo biloba* contain ginkgolide B (Practice Problem 5.11), a complex compound that was synthesized by a series of chemical reactions in the laboratory of Nobel Laureate E. J. Corey at Harvard University in 1988. ©Science Photo Library/ Getty Images RF

5.6B Relating Grams to Moles

The molar mass is a very useful quantity because it relates the number of *moles* to the number of *grams* of a substance. In this way, the molar mass can be used as a conversion factor. For example, since the molar mass of H_2O is 18.02 g/mol, two conversion factors can be written.

$$\frac{18.02 \text{ g } H_2O}{1 \text{ mol}} \quad \text{or} \quad \frac{1 \text{ mol}}{18.02 \text{ g } H_2O}$$

Using these conversion factors, we can convert a given number of moles of water to grams, or a specific number of grams of water to moles.

SAMPLE PROBLEM 5.12 CONVERTING MOLES TO MASS

What is the mass of 0.25 mol of water?

Analysis and Solution

[1] Identify the original quantity and the desired quantity.

$$0.25 \text{ mol of } H_2O \qquad ? \text{ g of } H_2O$$
original quantity desired quantity

[2] Write out the conversion factors.

- Choose the conversion factor that places the unwanted unit, moles, in the denominator so that the units cancel.

$$\frac{1 \text{ mol}}{18.02 \text{ g } H_2O} \quad \text{or} \quad \boxed{\frac{18.02 \text{ g } H_2O}{1 \text{ mol}}} \quad \text{Choose this conversion factor to cancel mol.}$$

[3] Set up and solve the problem.

- Multiply the original quantity by the conversion factor to obtain the desired quantity.

$$0.25 \text{ mol} \quad \times \quad \frac{18.02 \text{ g } H_2O}{1 \text{ mol}} \quad = \quad 4.5 \text{ g of } H_2O$$

Moles cancel. **Answer**

PRACTICE PROBLEM 5.12

Calculate the number of grams contained in each of the following number of moles.

a. 0.500 mol of NaCl
b. 2.00 mol of KI

c. 3.60 mol of C_2H_4 (ethylene)
d. 0.820 mol of CH_4O (methanol)

More Practice: Try Problems 5.61; 5.62; 5.71a, b; 5.72a, b.

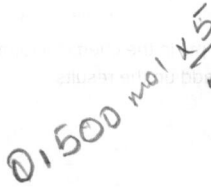

SAMPLE PROBLEM 5.13 CONVERTING MASS TO MOLES

How many moles are present in 100. g of aspirin ($C_9H_8O_4$, molar mass 180.2 g/mol)?

Analysis and Solution

[1] Identify the original quantity and the desired quantity.

$$100. \text{ g of aspirin} \qquad ? \text{ mol of aspirin}$$
original quantity desired quantity

[2] Write out the conversion factors.

- Choose the conversion factor that places the unwanted unit, grams, in the denominator so that the units cancel.

$$\frac{180.2 \text{ g aspirin}}{1 \text{ mol}} \quad \text{or} \quad \boxed{\frac{1 \text{ mol}}{180.2 \text{ g aspirin}}} \quad \text{Choose this conversion factor to cancel g.}$$

[3] Set up and solve the problem.

- Multiply the original quantity by the conversion factor to obtain the desired quantity.

$$100. \text{ g} \quad \times \quad \frac{1 \text{ mol}}{180.2 \text{ g aspirin}} \quad = \quad 0.555 \text{ mol of aspirin}$$

Grams cancel. **Answer**

PRACTICE PROBLEM 5.13

How many moles are contained in each of the following?

a. 100. g of NaCl   b. 25.5 g of CH_4 c. 0.250 g of aspirin ($C_9H_8O_4$)   d. 25.0 g of H_2O

More Practice: Try Problems 5.65, 5.66.

Vitamin C, the molecule depicted on the front cover of this text, is needed in the formation of the protein collagen, which forms the connective tissue in blood vessels and muscle. We will learn more about the properties of vitamin C in Section 11.7. ©Denise Bush/iStock/Getty Images RF

PROBLEM 5.15

How many moles are contained in a 1,000.-mg dose of a vitamin C supplement (molar mass of vitamin C 176.1 g/mol)?

5.6C Relating Grams to Number of Atoms or Molecules

Since the molar mass of a substance gives the number of grams in a mole and a mole contains 6.02×10^{23} molecules (or atoms), **we can use molar mass to show the relationship between** *grams* **and** *number of molecules* **(or atoms).** For example, since the molar mass of aspirin is 180.2 g/mol, the following relationships exist:

$$\frac{180.2 \text{ g aspirin}}{1 \text{ mol}} = \frac{180.2 \text{ g aspirin}}{6.02 \times 10^{23} \text{ molecules}}$$

$$1 \text{ mol} = 6.02 \times 10^{23} \text{ molecules}$$

SAMPLE PROBLEM 5.14 CONVERTING MASS TO THE NUMBER OF MOLECULES

How many molecules are contained in a 325-mg tablet of aspirin ($C_9H_8O_4$, molar mass 180.2 g/mol)?

Analysis and Solution

[1] Identify the original quantity and the desired quantity.

325 mg of aspirin	? molecules of aspirin
original quantity	desired quantity

[2] Write out the conversion factors.

• We have no conversion factor that directly relates milligrams to number of molecules. We do know, however, how to relate milligrams to grams, and grams to number of molecules. In other words, we need two conversion factors to solve this problem.
• Choose the conversion factors that place the unwanted units, grams and milligrams, in the denominator so that the units cancel.

g–mg conversion factors

$$\frac{1000 \text{ mg}}{1 \text{ g}} \quad \text{or} \quad \frac{1 \text{ g}}{1000 \text{ mg}}$$

gram–number of molecules conversion factors

$$\frac{180.2 \text{ g aspirin}}{6.02 \times 10^{23} \text{ molecules}} \quad \text{or} \quad \frac{6.02 \times 10^{23} \text{ molecules}}{180.2 \text{ g aspirin}}$$

Choose the conversion factors with the unwanted units—mg and g—in the denominator.

[3] Set up and solve the problem.

• Arrange each term so that the units in the numerator of one term cancel the units in the denominator of the adjacent term. The single desired unit, number of molecules, must be located in the numerator of one term.

$$325 \text{ mg aspirin} \times \frac{1 \text{ g}}{1000 \text{ mg}} \times \frac{6.02 \times 10^{23} \text{ molecules}}{180.2 \text{ g aspirin}} = 1.09 \times 10^{21} \text{ molecules of aspirin}$$

Answer

Milligrams cancel.   Grams cancel.

PRACTICE PROBLEM 5.14

How many molecules are contained in two 500.-mg tablets of penicillin ($C_{16}H_{18}N_2O_4S$, molar mass 334.4 g/mol)?

More Practice: Try Problems 5.71c, d; 5.72c, d.

325 mg × $\frac{}{g}$ $\frac{}{g}$ molecule

164   **Chapter 5** Chemical Reactions

NO, nitrogen monoxide, is formed from N_2 and O_2 at very high temperature in automobile engines and coal-burning furnaces. NO is a reactive air pollutant that goes on to form other air pollutants, such as ozone (O_3) and nitric acid (HNO_3). HNO_3 is one component of acid rain that can devastate forests and acidify streams, making them unfit for fish and other wildlife. ©Hisham F. Ibrahim/ Getty Images RF

5.7   Mole Calculations in Chemical Equations

Having learned about moles and molar mass, we can now return to balanced chemical equations. As we learned in Section 5.2, the coefficients in a balanced chemical equation tell us the number of *molecules* of each compound that react or are formed in a given reaction.

- A balanced chemical equation also tells us the number of *moles* of each reactant that combine and the number of *moles* of each product formed.

$$1\,N_2(g) \quad + \quad 1\,O_2(g) \quad \xrightarrow{\Delta} \quad 2\,NO(g)$$

one molecule of N_2 one molecule of O_2 two molecules of NO
one mole of N_2 one mole of O_2 two moles of NO

[The coefficient "1" has been written for emphasis.]

For example, the balanced chemical equation for the high temperature reaction of N_2 and O_2 to form nitrogen monoxide, NO, shows that one *molecule* of N_2 combines with one *molecule* of O_2 to form two *molecules* of NO. It also shows that one *mole* of N_2 combines with one *mole* of O_2 to form two *moles* of NO.

Coefficients are used to form mole ratios, which can serve as conversion factors. These ratios tell us the relative number of moles of reactants that combine in a reaction, as well as the relative number of moles of product formed from a given reactant, as shown in Sample Problem 5.15.

Mole ratios: $\dfrac{1\text{ mol }N_2}{1\text{ mol }O_2}$ $\dfrac{1\text{ mol }N_2}{2\text{ mol }NO}$ $\dfrac{1\text{ mol }O_2}{2\text{ mol }NO}$

two reactants   reactant–product   reactant–product
N_2 and O_2 N_2 and NO O_2 and NO

- Use the mole ratio from the coefficients in the balanced equation to convert the number of moles of one compound (A) into the number of moles of another compound (B).

Moles of **A** ───────────→ Moles of **B**

mole–mole
conversion factor

Meters that measure CO levels in homes are sold commercially. CO, a colorless, odorless gas, is a minor product formed whenever fossil fuels and wood are burned. In poorly ventilated rooms, such as those found in modern, well-insulated homes, CO levels can reach unhealthy levels. ©Keith Eng, 2008

SAMPLE PROBLEM 5.15 DETERMINING MOLES OF PRODUCT USING A BALANCED EQUATION

Carbon monoxide (CO) is a poisonous gas that combines with hemoglobin in the blood, thus reducing the amount of oxygen that can be delivered to tissues. Under certain conditions, CO is formed when ethane (C_2H_6) in natural gas is burned in the presence of oxygen. Using the balanced equation, how many moles of CO are produced from 3.5 mol of C_2H_6?

$$2\,C_2H_6(g) \quad + \quad 5\,O_2(g) \quad \xrightarrow{\Delta} \quad 4\,CO(g) \quad + \quad 6\,H_2O(g)$$

Analysis and Solution

[1] **Identify the original quantity and the desired quantity.**

3.5 mol of C_2H_6 ? mol of CO
original quantity   desired quantity

[2] **Write out the conversion factors.**

- Use the coefficients in the balanced equation to write mole–mole conversion factors for the two compounds, C_2H_6 and CO. Choose the conversion factor that places the unwanted unit, moles of C_2H_6, in the denominator so that the units cancel.

$\dfrac{2\text{ mol }C_2H_6}{4\text{ mol }CO}$ or $\boxed{\dfrac{4\text{ mol }CO}{2\text{ mol }C_2H_6}}$ Choose this conversion factor to cancel mol C_2H_6.

[3] Set up and solve the problem.

- Multiply the original quantity by the conversion factor to obtain the desired quantity.

$$3.5 \text{ mol } C_2H_6 \quad \times \quad \frac{4 \text{ mol CO}}{2 \text{ mol } C_2H_6} \quad = \quad 7.0 \text{ mol CO}$$

Moles C_2H_6 cancel.   **Answer**

PRACTICE PROBLEM 5.15

Use the balanced equation for the reaction of N_2 and O_2 to form NO at the beginning of Section 5.7 to answer each question.

a. How many moles of NO are formed from 3.3 mol of N_2?

b. How many moles of NO are formed from 0.50 mol of O_2?

c. How many moles of O_2 are needed to completely react with 1.2 mol of N_2?

More Practice: Try Problems 5.73, 5.74.

PROBLEM 5.16

Use the balanced equation in Sample Problem 5.15 to answer each question.

a. How many moles of O_2 are needed to react completely with 3.0 mol of C_2H_6?

b. How many moles of H_2O are formed from 0.50 mol of C_2H_6?

c. How many moles of C_2H_6 are needed to form 3.0 mol of CO?

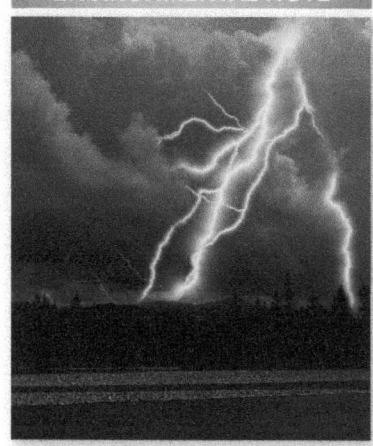

ENVIRONMENTAL NOTE

Lightning produces O_3 from O_2 during an electrical storm. O_3 at the ground level is an unwanted pollutant. In the stratosphere, however, it protects us from harmful radiation from the sun (Section 4.4B). ©Comstock/Stockbyte/Getty Images RF

5.8 Mass Calculations in Chemical Equations

Since a mole represents an enormously large number of very small molecules, there is no way to directly count the number of moles or molecules used in a chemical reaction. Instead, we utilize a balance to measure the number of grams of a compound used and the number of grams of product formed. The number of grams of a substance and the number of moles it contains are related by the molar mass (Section 5.6).

5.8A Converting Moles of Reactant to Grams of Product

To determine how many grams of product are expected from a given number of moles of reactant, two operations are necessary. First, we must determine how many moles of product to expect using the coefficients of the balanced chemical equation (Section 5.7). Then, we convert the number of moles of product to the number of grams using the molar mass (Section 5.6). Each step needs a conversion factor. The stepwise procedure is outlined in the accompanying *How To,* and then illustrated with an example in Sample Problem 5.16.

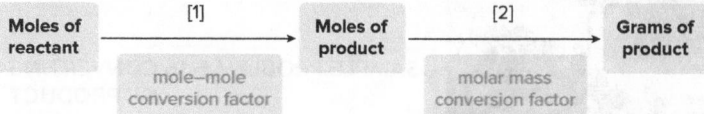

Moles of reactant	[1] mole–mole conversion factor	Moles of product	[2] molar mass conversion factor	Grams of product

How To Convert Moles of Reactant to Grams of Product

Example: In the upper atmosphere, high-energy radiation from the sun converts oxygen (O_2) to ozone (O_3). Using the balanced equation, how many grams of O_3 are formed from 9.0 mol of O_2?

$$3 O_2(g) \xrightarrow{\text{sunlight}} 2 O_3(g)$$

Step [1] Convert the number of moles of reactant to the number of moles of product using a mole–mole conversion factor.

- Use the coefficients in the balanced chemical equation to write mole–mole conversion factors.

$$\frac{3 \text{ mol } O_2}{2 \text{ mol } O_3} \quad \text{or} \quad \frac{2 \text{ mol } O_3}{3 \text{ mol } O_2}$$

Choose this conversion factor to cancel mol O_2.

—Continued

How To, continued . . .

- Multiply the number of moles of starting material (9.0 mol) by the conversion factor to give the number of moles of product. In this example, 6.0 mol of O_3 are formed.

Moles of reactant		Moles of product

$$9.0 \text{ mol } O_2 \quad \times \quad \frac{2 \text{ mol } O_3}{3 \text{ mol } O_2} \quad = \quad 6.0 \text{ mol } O_3$$

Moles O_2 cancel.

Step [2] **Convert the number of moles of product to the number of grams of product using the product's molar mass.**

- Use the molar mass of the product (O_3) to write a conversion factor. The molar mass of O_3 is 48.00 g/mol (3 O atoms × 16.00 g/mol for each O atom = 48.00 g/mol).

$$\frac{1 \text{ mol } O_3}{48.00 \text{ g } O_3} \quad \text{or} \quad \frac{48.00 \text{ g } O_3}{1 \text{ mol } O_3}$$

Choose this conversion factor to cancel mol.

- Multiply the number of moles of product (from step [1]) by the conversion factor to give the number of grams of product.

Moles of product		Grams of product

$$6.0 \text{ mol } O_3 \quad \times \quad \frac{48.00 \text{ g } O_3}{1 \text{ mol } O_3} \quad = \quad 288 \text{ g, rounded to } 290 \text{ g of } O_3$$

Moles cancel.

Answer

It is also possible to combine the multiplication operations from steps [1] and [2] into a single operation using both conversion factors. This converts the moles of starting material to grams of product all at once. Both the one-step and stepwise approaches give the same overall result.

Moles of reactant		mole–mole conversion factor		molar mass conversion factor		Grams of product

$$9.0 \text{ mol } O_2 \quad \times \quad \frac{2 \text{ mol } O_3}{3 \text{ mol } O_2} \quad \times \quad \frac{48.00 \text{ g } O_3}{1 \text{ mol } O_3} \quad = \quad 290 \text{ g of } O_3$$

Moles O_2 cancel. Moles O_3 cancel.

Answer

Ethanol (C_2H_6O) is the alcohol in red wine, formed by the fermentation of grapes. Ethanol depresses the central nervous system, increases the production of stomach acid, and dilates blood vessels. Excessive alcohol consumption is a major health problem in the United States. ©*Image Source RF*

SAMPLE PROBLEM 5.16 CONVERTING MOLES OF REACTANT TO GRAMS OF PRODUCT

Wine is produced by the fermentation of grapes. In fermentation, the carbohydrate glucose ($C_6H_{12}O_6$) is converted to ethanol and carbon dioxide according to the given balanced equation. How many grams of ethanol (C_2H_6O, molar mass 46.07 g/mol) are produced from 5.00 mol of glucose?

$$C_6H_{12}O_6(aq) \longrightarrow 2\ C_2H_6O(aq) + 2\ CO_2(g)$$
glucose   ethanol

Analysis and Solution

[1] **Convert the number of moles of reactant to the number of moles of product using a mole–mole conversion factor.**

- Use the coefficients in the balanced chemical equation to write mole–mole conversion factors for the two compounds—one mole of glucose ($C_6H_{12}O_6$) forms two moles of ethanol (C_2H_6O).

- Multiply the number of moles of reactant (glucose) by the conversion factor to give the number of moles of product (ethanol).

Moles of reactant		mole–mole conversion factor		Moles of product

$$5.00 \text{ mol } C_6H_{12}O_6 \quad \times \quad \frac{2 \text{ mol } C_2H_6O}{1 \text{ mol } C_6H_{12}O_6} \quad = \quad 10.0 \text{ mol } C_2H_6O$$

Moles $C_6H_{12}O_6$ cancel.

[2] Convert the number of moles of product to the number of grams of product using the product's molar mass.

- Use the molar mass of the product (C_2H_6O, molar mass 46.07 g/mol) to write a conversion factor.
- Multiply the number of moles of product (from step [1]) by the conversion factor to give the number of grams of product.

Moles of product		molar mass conversion factor		Grams of product

$$10.0 \text{ mol } C_2H_6O \quad \times \quad \frac{46.07 \text{ g } C_2H_6O}{1 \text{ mol } C_2H_6O} \quad = \quad 461 \text{ g } C_2H_6O$$

Moles cancel.   **Answer**

PRACTICE PROBLEM 5.16

Using the balanced equation for fermentation written in Sample Problem 5.16, answer the following questions.

  a. How many grams of ethanol are formed from 0.55 mol of glucose?

  b. How many grams of CO_2 are formed from 0.25 mol of glucose?

  c. How many grams of glucose are needed to form 1.0 mol of ethanol?

More Practice: Try Problems 5.75, 5.76.

PROBLEM 5.17

Using the balanced equation for the combustion of ethanol, answer the following questions.

$$C_2H_6O(l) + 3 O_2(g) \longrightarrow 2 CO_2(g) + 3 H_2O(g)$$
$$\text{ethanol}$$

  a. How many grams of CO_2 are formed from 0.50 mol of ethanol?

  b. How many grams of H_2O are formed from 2.4 mol of ethanol?

  c. How many grams of O_2 are needed to react with 0.25 mol of ethanol?

5.8B   Converting Grams of Reactant to Grams of Product

The coefficients in chemical equations tell us the ratio of the number of *molecules* or *moles* that are involved in a chemical reaction. The coefficients do *not*, however, tell us directly about the number of grams. That's because the molar mass—the number of grams in one mole—of a substance depends on the identity of the elements that compose it. One mole of H_2O molecules weighs 18.02 g, one mole of NaCl weighs 58.44 g, and one mole of sugar molecules weighs 342.3 g (Figure 5.7).

In the laboratory, we measure out the number of grams of a reactant on a balance. This does not tell us directly the number of grams of a particular product that will form, because in all likelihood, the molar masses of the reactant and product are different. To carry out this type of calculation—grams of one compound (reactant) to grams of another compound (product)—three operations are necessary.

First, we must determine how many moles of reactant are contained in the given number of grams using the molar mass. Then, we can determine the number of moles of product expected

Figure 5.7 One Mole of Water, Table Salt, and Table Sugar

one mole of table sugar
C₁₂H₂₂O₁₁
342.3 g/mol

one mole of table salt
NaCl
58.44 g/mol

one mole of water molecules
H₂O
18.02 g/mol

One mole of each substance has the same number of units—6.02 × 10²³ H₂O molecules, 6.02 × 10²³ Na⁺ and Cl⁻ ions, and 6.02 × 10²³ sugar molecules. The molar mass of each substance is *different*, however, because they are each composed of *different* elements. ©McGraw-Hill Education/Jill Braaten, photographer, and Anthony Arena, Chemistry Consultant

using the coefficients of the balanced chemical equation. Finally, we convert the number of moles of product to the number of grams of product using its molar mass. Now there are three steps and three conversion factors. The stepwise procedure is outlined in the accompanying *How To*, and then illustrated with an example in Sample Problem 5.17.

| **Grams of reactant** | →[1] molar mass conversion factor | **Moles of reactant** | →[2] mole–mole conversion factor | **Moles of product** | →[3] molar mass conversion factor | **Grams of product** |

How To Convert Grams of Reactant to Grams of Product

Example: Ethanol (C₂H₆O, molar mass 46.07 g/mol) is synthesized by reacting ethylene (C₂H₄, molar mass 28.05 g/mol) with water. How many grams of ethanol are formed from 14 g of ethylene?

ethylene   ethanol

Step [1] Convert the number of grams of reactant to the number of moles of reactant using the reactant's molar mass.

• Use the molar mass of the reactant (C₂H₄) to write a conversion factor.

$$\frac{28.05 \text{ g } C_2H_4}{1 \text{ mol } C_2H_4} \quad \text{or} \quad \frac{1 \text{ mol } C_2H_4}{28.05 \text{ g } C_2H_4}$$ Choose this conversion factor to cancel g.

—Continued

How To, continued . . .

- Multiply the number of grams of reactant by the conversion factor to give the number of moles of reactant.

Grams of reactant		Moles of reactant

$$14 \text{ g } C_2H_4 \quad \times \quad \frac{1 \text{ mol } C_2H_4}{28.05 \text{ g } C_2H_4} \quad = \quad 0.50 \text{ mol } C_2H_4$$

Grams cancel.

Step [2] Convert the number of moles of reactant to the number of moles of product using a mole–mole conversion factor.

- Use the coefficients in the balanced chemical equation to write mole–mole conversion factors.

$$\frac{1 \text{ mol } C_2H_4}{1 \text{ mol } C_2H_6O} \quad \text{or} \quad \frac{1 \text{ mol } C_2H_6O}{1 \text{ mol } C_2H_4}$$

Choose this conversion factor to cancel mol C_2H_4.

- Multiply the number of moles of reactant by the conversion factor to give the number of moles of product. In this example, 0.50 mol of C_2H_6O is formed.

Moles of reactant		Moles of product

$$0.50 \text{ mol } C_2H_4 \quad \times \quad \frac{1 \text{ mol } C_2H_6O}{1 \text{ mol } C_2H_4} \quad = \quad 0.50 \text{ mol } C_2H_6O$$

Moles C_2H_4 cancel.

Step [3] Convert the number of moles of product to the number of grams of product using the product's molar mass.

- Use the molar mass of the product (C_2H_6O) to write a conversion factor.

$$\frac{1 \text{ mol } C_2H_6O}{46.07 \text{ g } C_2H_6O} \quad \text{or} \quad \frac{46.07 \text{ g } C_2H_6O}{1 \text{ mol } C_2H_6O}$$

Choose this conversion factor to cancel mol C_2H_6O.

- Multiply the number of moles of product (from step [2]) by the conversion factor to give the number of grams of product.

Moles of product		Grams of product

$$0.50 \text{ mol } C_2H_6O \quad \times \quad \frac{46.07 \text{ g } C_2H_6O}{1 \text{ mol } C_2H_6O} \quad = \quad 23 \text{ g } C_2H_6O$$

Moles C_2H_6O cancel. **Answer**

It is also possible to combine the multiplication operations from steps [1], [2], and [3] into a single operation using all three conversion factors. This converts grams of starting material to grams of product all at once. Both the one-step and stepwise approaches give the same overall result.

Grams of reactant		molar mass conversion factor		mole–mole conversion factor		molar mass conversion factor		Grams of product

$$14 \text{ g } C_2H_4 \quad \times \quad \frac{1 \text{ mol } C_2H_4}{28.05 \text{ g } C_2H_4} \quad \times \quad \frac{1 \text{ mol } C_2H_6O}{1 \text{ mol } C_2H_4} \quad \times \quad \frac{46.07 \text{ g } C_2H_6O}{1 \text{ mol } C_2H_6O} \quad = \quad 23 \text{ g } C_2H_6O$$

Grams cancel. Moles C_2H_4 cancel. Moles C_2H_6O cancel. **Answer**

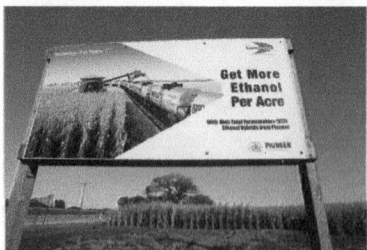

Ethanol is used as a gasoline additive. Although some of the ethanol used for this purpose comes from corn and other grains, much of it is still produced by the reaction of ethylene with water (*How To*, p. 168). Ethanol produced from grains is a renewable resource, whereas ethanol produced from ethylene is not, because ethylene is made from crude oil. Thus, running your car on gasohol (gasoline mixed with ethanol) reduces our reliance on fossil fuels only if the ethanol is produced from renewable sources such as grains or sugarcane. ©Scott Olson/Getty Images News/Getty Images

SAMPLE PROBLEM 5.17 CONVERTING GRAMS OF REACTANT TO GRAMS OF PRODUCT

How many grams of aspirin are formed from 10.0 g of salicylic acid using the given balanced equation?

$$C_7H_6O_3(s) \;+\; C_2H_4O_2(l) \longrightarrow C_9H_8O_4(s) \;+\; H_2O(l)$$

salicylic acid   acetic acid   aspirin

Analysis and Solution

[1] Convert the number of grams of reactant to the number of moles of reactant using the reactant's molar mass.

- Use the molar mass of the reactant ($C_7H_6O_3$, molar mass 138.1 g/mol) to write a conversion factor. Multiply the number of grams of reactant by the conversion factor to give the number of moles of reactant.

Grams of reactant		molar mass conversion factor		Moles of reactant

$$10.0 \; \text{g} \; C_7H_6O_3 \quad \times \quad \frac{1 \; \text{mol} \; C_7H_6O_3}{138.1 \; \text{g} \; C_7H_6O_3} \quad = \quad 0.0724 \; \text{mol} \; C_7H_6O_3$$

Grams cancel.

[2] Convert the number of moles of reactant to the number of moles of product using a mole–mole conversion factor.

- Use the coefficients in the balanced chemical equation to write mole–mole conversion factors for the two compounds—one mole of salicylic acid ($C_7H_6O_3$) forms one mole of aspirin ($C_9H_8O_4$).
- Multiply the number of moles of reactant (salicylic acid) by the conversion factor to give the number of moles of product (aspirin).

Moles of reactant		mole–mole conversion factor		Moles of product

$$0.0724 \; \text{mol} \; C_7H_6O_3 \quad \times \quad \frac{1 \; \text{mol} \; C_9H_8O_4}{1 \; \text{mol} \; C_7H_6O_3} \quad = \quad 0.0724 \; \text{mol} \; C_9H_8O_4$$

Moles $C_7H_6O_3$ cancel.

[3] Convert the number of moles of product to the number of grams of product using the product's molar mass.

- Use the molar mass of the product ($C_9H_8O_4$, molar mass 180.2 g/mol) to write a conversion factor. Multiply the number of moles of product (from step [2]) by the conversion factor to give the number of grams of product.

Moles of product		molar mass conversion factor		Grams of product

$$0.0724 \; \text{mol} \; C_9H_8O_4 \quad \times \quad \frac{180.2 \; \text{g} \; C_9H_8O_4}{1 \; \text{mol} \; C_9H_8O_4} \quad = \quad 13.0 \; \text{g} \; C_9H_8O_4$$

Moles cancel.

Answer

PRACTICE PROBLEM 5.17

Use the balanced equation in Sample Problem 5.17 for the conversion of salicylic acid and acetic acid to aspirin to answer the following questions.

  a. How many grams of aspirin are formed from 55.5 g of salicylic acid?

  b. How many grams of acetic acid are needed to react with 55.5 g of salicylic acid?

  c. How many grams of water are formed from 55.5 g of salicylic acid?

More Practice: Try Problems 5.91f, 5.92f.

PROBLEM 5.18

Use the balanced equation, $N_2 + O_2 \longrightarrow 2\ NO$, to answer the following questions.

a. How many grams of NO are formed from 10.0 g of N_2?

b. How many grams of NO are formed from 10.0 g of O_2?

c. How many grams of O_2 are needed to react completely with 10.0 g of N_2?

5.9 Percent Yield

In determining the number of moles or grams of product in Sections 5.7 and 5.8, we assumed that each reaction gives the maximum amount of product from a given amount of reactant. This value is called the **theoretical yield** of a reaction.

- The *theoretical yield* is the amount of product expected from a given amount of reactant based on the coefficients in the balanced chemical equation.

Usually, however, the amount of product formed is *less* than the maximum amount predicted. Sometimes other undesired reactions, called **side reactions,** occur between the reactants. At other times the desired product is formed, but it goes on to react further to form another product. Moreover, each time material is weighed and transferred to a reaction vessel, or anytime a separation or purification step is carried out, material is inadvertently lost.

- The *actual yield* is the amount of product isolated from a reaction.

5.9A Calculating Percent Yield

The theoretical and actual yields are typically reported in grams. The amount of product actually formed in a particular reaction is reported as a **percent yield.**

$$\text{Percent yield} = \frac{\text{actual yield (g)}}{\text{theoretical yield (g)}} \times 100\%$$

For example, if a reaction forms 25.0 g of product and the theoretical yield is 40.0 g, the percent yield is calculated as follows.

$$\textbf{Percent yield} = \frac{25.0\ g}{40.0\ g} \times 100\% = 62.5\%$$

The actual yield is an experimental value determined by weighing the product obtained on a balance. The theoretical yield, on the other hand, is calculated from the coefficients of the balanced equation. ©*McGraw-Hill Education/Jill Braaten, photographer, and Anthony Arena, Chemistry Consultant*

SAMPLE PROBLEM 5.18 CALCULATING PERCENT YIELD

Consider the reaction of ethylene (C_2H_4) and water to form ethanol (C_2H_6O), which was mentioned in Section 5.8B. If the theoretical yield of ethanol is 23 g in a reaction, what is the percent yield of ethanol if only 15 g of ethanol are actually formed?

Analysis

Use the formula, percent yield = (actual yield/theoretical yield) × 100% to calculate the percent yield.

Solution

$$\text{Percent yield} = \frac{\text{actual yield (g)}}{\text{theoretical yield (g)}} \times 100\%$$

$$= \frac{15\ g}{23\ g} \times 100\% = 65\%$$

Answer

PRACTICE PROBLEM 5.18

What is the percent yield of **X** in a reaction that uses 12.0 g of **Y**, has a theoretical yield of 25.0 g of **X**, and an actual yield of 22.0 g of **X**?

More Practice: Try Problems 5.77, 5.78.

SAMPLE PROBLEM 5.19 CALCULATING THEORETICAL YIELD AND PERCENT YIELD

When charcoal is burned, the carbon (C) it contains reacts with oxygen (O_2) to form carbon dioxide (CO_2). (a) What is the theoretical yield of CO_2 in grams from 0.50 mol of C? (b) What is the percent yield if 10.0 g of CO_2 are formed?

$$C(s) \ + \ O_2(g) \longrightarrow CO_2(g)$$

Analysis

To answer part (a), convert the number of moles of reactant to the number of moles of product, as in Section 5.8A. Then, convert the number of moles of product to the number of grams of product using the product's molar mass. This is the theoretical yield. To answer part (b), use the formula, percent yield = (actual yield/theoretical yield) × 100%.

Solution

a. Calculate the theoretical yield using the procedure outlined in Sample Problem 5.16.

[1] **Convert the number of moles of reactant to the number of moles of product using a mole–mole conversion factor.**

- Use the coefficients in the balanced equation to write a mole–mole conversion factor for the two compounds—one mole of carbon forms one mole of CO_2. Multiply the number of moles of reactant (carbon) by the conversion factor to give the number of moles of product (CO_2).

Moles of reactant	mole–mole conversion factor	Moles of product
0.50 mol C	× $\dfrac{1 \text{ mol CO}_2}{1 \text{ mol C}}$ =	0.50 mol CO_2

[2] **Convert the number of moles of product to the number of grams of product—the theoretical yield—using the product's molar mass.**

- Use the molar mass of the product (CO_2, molar mass 44.01 g/mol) to write a conversion factor. Multiply the number of moles of product (from step [1]) by the conversion factor to give the number of grams of product.

Moles of product	molar mass conversion factor	Grams of product
0.50 mol CO_2	× $\dfrac{44.01 \text{ g CO}_2}{1 \text{ mol CO}_2}$ =	22 g CO_2

Theoretical yield
Answer: part (a)

b. Use the theoretical yield from part (a) and the given actual yield to calculate the percent yield.

$$\text{Percent yield} = \frac{\text{actual yield (g)}}{\text{theoretical yield (g)}} \times 100\%$$

$$= \frac{10.0 \text{ g}}{22 \text{ g}} \times 100\% = 45\%$$

Answer: part (b)

PRACTICE PROBLEM 5.19

Using the chemical equation in Sample Problem 5.19, answer each question. (a) What is the theoretical yield of CO_2 in grams from 3.50 mol of charcoal? (b) What is the percent yield if the reaction gives 53.5 g of CO_2?

More Practice: Try Problems 5.91e, 5.92e, 5.95b.

5.9B Calculating Percent Yield from Grams of Reactant

Since we weigh the amount of reactants and products on a balance, we must be able to calculate a percent yield from the number of grams of reactant used and the number of grams of product formed. This latter quantity is the **actual yield,** and it is always experimentally determined; that

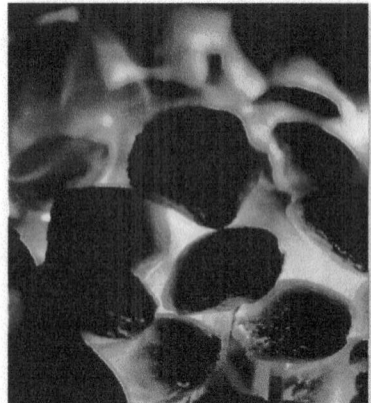

Charcoal is composed of a network of covalently bonded carbon atoms. When charcoal is burned in a grill or coal is burned in a furnace, carbon atoms combine with O_2 from the air to form carbon dioxide (CO_2). ©Ryan McVay/Getty Images RF

is, it is *not* a calculated value. We can carry out this lengthy calculation by putting together the steps in Sample Problems 5.17 and 5.18. Sample Problem 5.20 illustrates the steps used to calculate a percent yield when the number of grams of reactant used and the actual yield of product formed are both known.

SAMPLE PROBLEM 5.20 CALCULATING PERCENT YIELD FROM GRAMS OF REACTANT

Acetaminophen, the active ingredient in Tylenol, can be prepared by the chemical reaction given below. What is the percent yield when 60.0 g of 4-aminophenol reacts with acetyl chloride to form 70.0 g of acetaminophen?

4-aminophenol	acetyl	acetaminophen
molar mass 109.1 g/mol	chloride	molar mass 151.2 g/mol

$$HO-C_6H_4-NH_2 \ + \ C_2H_3ClO \ \longrightarrow \ HO-C_6H_4-NH-C(=O)-CH_3 \ + \ HCl$$

Analysis

To find the theoretical yield, convert grams of reactant to grams of product, following the three steps in Sample Problem 5.17. Then, use the formula, percent yield = (actual yield/theoretical yield) × 100%.

Solution

[1] Convert the number of grams of reactant to the number of moles of reactant using the reactant's molar mass.

- Use the molar mass of the reactant, 4-aminophenol, to write a conversion factor. Multiply the number of grams of reactant by the conversion factor to give the number of moles of reactant.

Grams of reactant		molar mass conversion factor		**Moles of reactant**
60.0 g 4-aminophenol	×	$\dfrac{\text{1 mol 4-aminophenol}}{\text{109.1 g 4-aminophenol}}$	=	0.550 mol 4-aminophenol

[2] Convert the number of moles of reactant to the number of moles of product using a mole–mole conversion factor.

- Use the coefficients in the balanced chemical equation to write a mole–mole conversion factor—one mole of 4-aminophenol forms one mole of acetaminophen. Multiply the number of moles of reactant by the conversion factor to give the number of moles of product.

Moles of reactant		mole–mole conversion factor		**Moles of product**
0.550 mol 4-aminophenol	×	$\dfrac{\text{1 mol acetaminophen}}{\text{1 mol 4-aminophenol}}$	=	0.550 mol acetaminophen

[3] Convert the number of moles of product to the number of grams of product using the product's molar mass.

- Use the molar mass of the product to write a conversion factor. Multiply the number of moles of product (from step [2]) by the conversion factor to give the number of grams of product.

Moles of product		molar mass conversion factor		**Grams of product**
0.550 mol acetaminophen	×	$\dfrac{\text{151.2 g acetaminophen}}{\text{1 mol acetaminophen}}$	=	83.2 g acetaminophen

Theoretical yield

[4] Use the theoretical yield and the given actual yield to calculate the percent yield.

$$\text{Percent yield} = \frac{\text{actual yield (g)}}{\text{theoretical yield (g)}} \times 100\%$$

$$= \frac{70.0 \text{ g}}{83.2 \text{ g}} \times 100\% = 84.1\%$$

Answer

PRACTICE PROBLEM 5.20

Using the equation in Sample Problem 5.20, answer each question. (a) What is the theoretical yield of acetaminophen in grams from 80.0 g of 4-aminophenol? (b) What is the percent yield if the reaction gives 65.5 g of acetaminophen?

More Practice: Try Problems 5.79; 5.80; 5.91g, h; 5.92g, h.

PROBLEM 5.19

Consider the conversion of oxygen (O_2) to ozone (O_3) described in Section 5.8A; that is, $3 O_2 \longrightarrow 2 O_3$. (a) What is the theoretical yield of O_3 in grams from 324 g of O_2? (b) What is the percent yield if the reaction actually gives 122 g of O_3?

5.9C   FOCUS ON HEALTH & MEDICINE
The Importance of Percent Yield
in the Pharmaceutical Industry

Although some drugs, like the cardiac drug digoxin (used to treat congestive heart failure, Section 1.1), are isolated directly from a natural source, most widely used drugs are synthesized in the laboratory. All common pain relievers—aspirin, acetaminophen, and ibuprofen—are synthetic. The same is true for the bronchodilator albuterol (trade names Proventil or Ventolin), the antidepressant fluoxetine (trade name Prozac), and the cholesterol-lowering medication atorvastatin (trade name Lipitor), whose three-dimensional structures are shown in Figure 5.8.

Figure 5.8

Three Widely Used Synthetic Drugs—
Albuterol, Fluoxetine, and Atorvastatin

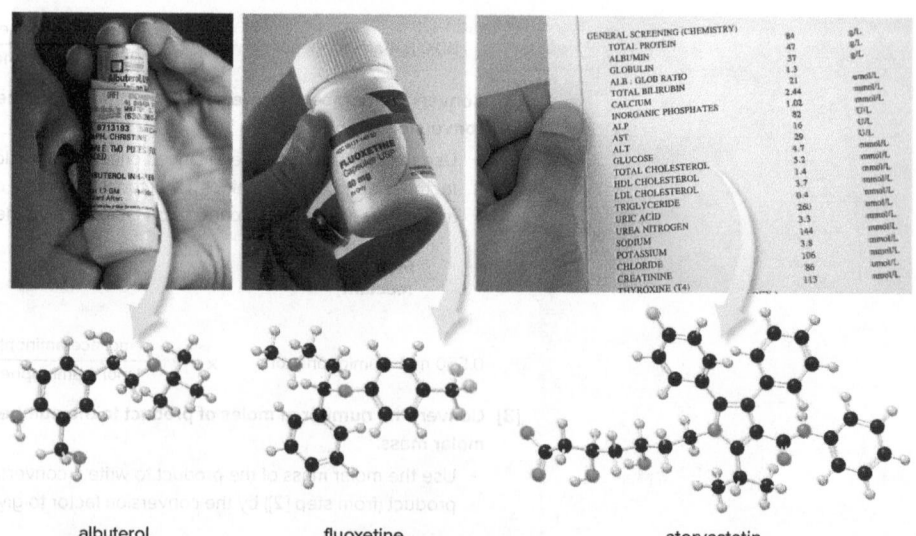

albuterol   fluoxetine   atorvastatin

Most commonly prescribed drugs are synthesized in the laboratory. Albuterol (Proventil, Ventolin) is a bronchodilator—that is, it widens airways—so it is used to treat asthma. Fluoxetine (Prozac) is one of the most common antidepressants currently on the market, used by over 40 million individuals since 1986. Atorvastatin (Lipitor) lowers cholesterol levels and in this way decreases the risk of heart attack and stroke. *(left & middle): ©McGraw-Hill Education/Jill Braaten, photographer; (right): ©Beaconstox/Alamy*

Once it has been determined that a drug is safe and effective, a pharmaceutical company must be able to prepare large quantities of the material cost-efficiently. This means that cheap and readily available starting materials must be used. It also means that the reactions used to synthesize a drug must proceed in high yield. Rarely is a drug prepared in a single step, and typically, five or more steps may be required in a synthesis.

- **To determine the overall percent yield in a synthesis that has more than one step, multiply the percent yield for each step.**

For example, if a synthesis has five steps and each step has a 90.% yield (0.90 written as a decimal), the overall yield is

$$0.90 \times 0.90 \times 0.90 \times 0.90 \times 0.90 = 0.59 = 59\%$$

    yield for each step,   **overall yield**
    written as a decimal   **for five steps**

Thus, even if all steps proceed in high yield, the overall yield is considerably lower—59% in this example. If only one step has a lower yield, say 50.%, the overall yield drops even more, from 59% to 33%.

$$0.50 \times 0.90 \times 0.90 \times 0.90 \times 0.90 = 0.33 = 33\%$$

    one low-yield reaction   **overall yield**
                   for five steps

Moreover, many drugs are synthesized by routes that require 10 or more steps, resulting in a low overall yield. Thus, pharmaceutical companies are faced with the task of developing drugs that have the desired physiological effects, which are prepared by reactions that give high yields of the desired compounds.

PROBLEM 5.20

The synthetic antiviral drug Tamiflu, currently the most effective agent against avian influenza, is prepared by a 10-step synthesis. What is the overall yield of Tamiflu in each of the following 10-step syntheses?

 a. Each step proceeds in 90.% yield.

 b. Each step proceeds in 80.% yield.

 c. One step proceeds in 50.% yield, while the rest occur in 90.% yield.

 d. The following yields are recorded: 20.% (one reaction), 50.% (two reactions), 80.% (all remaining reactions).

5.10 Limiting Reactants

Up to now we have assumed that we have the exact ratio of the reactants needed to carry out a reaction. In the following reaction, the mole ratio of **A** to **B** is 1:1, so one molecule of **A** is needed to react with one molecule of **B** to form one molecule of the product, **AB.**

One molecule of **A** reacts with one molecule of **B.**

1 **A**   +   1 **B** ⟶ 1 **A—B**

One mole of each reactant is needed.

Suppose, instead, that the reaction contains an *excess* of **B**, as shown in the molecular art, where the reaction mixture contains six molecules of **A** and eight molecules of **B**. In this case, all six **A** molecules react with six **B** molecules, and two **B** molecules are left over. Reactant **A** is all used up, so the amount of **A** *limits* how much product **AB** can be formed.

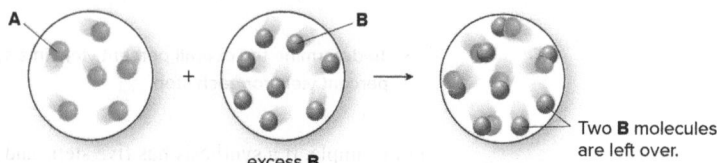

• The *limiting reactant* is the reactant that is completely used up in a reaction.

In this example, **A** is the limiting reactant since **B** is present in excess.

5.10A   Determining the Limiting Reactant

We deal with the concept of limiting reactants often in everyday life. To make turkey sandwiches, we may use two pieces of bread for each slice of turkey. If we had eight slices of bread and three slices of turkey, we could make three sandwiches using six slices of bread and three pieces of turkey, leaving two pieces of bread left over. In this case, the turkey is the limiting reactant and the bread is present in excess.

excess reactant   limiting reactant   product   leftovers

Sample Problem 5.21 illustrates how to determine which reactant is limiting using the mole ratios in a balanced equation.

SAMPLE PROBLEM 5.21 DETERMINING THE LIMITING REACTANT

Consider the reaction of hydrogen and oxygen to form water, according to the balanced equation: $2\,H_2(g) + O_2(g) \longrightarrow 2\,H_2O(l)$. Identify the limiting reactant in the molecular art, and draw a representation showing how much product is formed and what reactant molecules are left over.

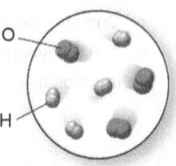

Analysis

Use the amount of each reactant and the mole ratio from the balanced equation to determine the limiting reactant. Use the amount of limiting reactant to determine the amount of product formed.

Solution

[1] **To determine how much of one reactant is needed to react with a second reactant, label one reactant as the original quantity and the second reactant as the unknown quantity.**

• These labels are completely arbitrary. In this example we identify the number of molecules of H_2 as the original quantity.

4 molecules of H_2 ? molecules of O_2
original quantity   unknown quantity

[2] Write out the conversion factors that relate the number of moles (or molecules) of reactants.

- Use the coefficients in the balanced equation to write a mole–mole (or molecule–molecule) conversion factor for H_2 and O_2.

$$\frac{2 \text{ molecules } H_2}{1 \text{ molecule } O_2} \quad \text{or} \quad \frac{1 \text{ molecule } O_2}{2 \text{ molecules } H_2}$$

Choose this conversion factor to cancel molecules of H_2.

[3] Calculate the number of moles (or molecules) of the second reactant needed for complete reaction.

$$4 \text{ molecules } H_2 \times \frac{1 \text{ molecule } O_2}{2 \text{ molecules } H_2} = 2 \text{ molecules of } O_2 \text{ needed}$$

[4] Analyze the two possible outcomes.

- If the amount present of the second reactant is *less than* what is needed, the *second reactant is the limiting reactant.*
- If the amount present of the second reactant is *greater than* what is needed, the *second reactant is in excess.*

In this reaction only two molecules of O_2 are needed but three molecules of O_2 are present, so O_2 is present in excess and **H_2 is the limiting reactant.** To draw the molecular art representing the product, we must know what happens to each reactant and how much product is formed.

4 molecules of H_2O

1 O_2 left over

- Since H_2 is the limiting reactant, all of the H_2 is consumed and none is left.
- Since two molecules of O_2 react and three were present at the outset, one molecule of O_2 is left over.
- Using the balanced equation, the number of molecules of product formed equals the number of molecules of the limiting reactant consumed. Thus, four molecules of H_2 yield four molecules of H_2O.

Summary	Reactants		Product
Equation	2 H_2 +	O_2 ⟶	2 H_2O
Initial quantities	4 molecules	3 molecules	0 molecules
Used or formed	−4 molecules	−2 molecules	+4 molecules
Molecules remaining	0 molecules	1 molecule	4 molecules
	Limiting reactant	Excess reactant	

PRACTICE PROBLEM 5.21

Consider the reaction of hydrogen and nitrogen to form ammonia, according to the balanced equation: $3 H_2(g) + N_2(g) \longrightarrow 2 NH_3(g)$. Identify the limiting reactant in the molecular art, and draw a representation showing how much product is formed and what reactant molecules are left over.

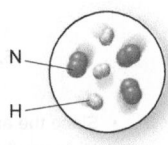

More Practice: Try Problems 5.81, 5.82.

PROBLEM 5.21

Using the balanced equation for the reaction of H_2 with O_2 to form H_2O in Sample Problem 5.21, determine the limiting reactant under each of the following conditions.

a. 5.0 mol H_2 and 5.0 mol O_2

b. 5.0 mol H_2 and 8.0 mol O_2

c. 8.0 mol H_2 and 2.0 mol O_2

d. 2.0 mol H_2 and 5.0 mol O_2

5.10B Using the Limiting Reactant to Determine How Much Product Is Formed

When a reaction has a limiting reactant,

> • The number of moles of limiting reactant determines the number of moles of product that can form.

For example, the molecular art shows the reaction of **A₂** with **B₂** to form **AB**, with **B₂** present in excess. The amount of **A₂**, the limiting reactant, determines how much **AB** can form. Since the balanced equation shows that each **A₂** molecule forms two **AB** molecules, three **A₂** molecules form six **AB** molecules.

Three **A₂** molecules form six **AB** molecules.

Sample Problem 5.22 illustrates how to determine the amount of product formed from a limiting reactant using mole ratios in a balanced equation. **Keep in mind that the number of moles (*not* grams) of the limiting reactant determines the number of moles (*not* grams) of product.**

SAMPLE PROBLEM 5.22 USING THE LIMITING REACTANT TO DETERMINE MOLES OF PRODUCT FORMED

Using the balanced equation, $3\,H_2(g) + N_2(g) \longrightarrow 2\,NH_3(g)$, calculate the number of moles of product formed from 5.0 moles of H_2 and 3.0 moles of N_2.

Analysis and Solution

[1] **Determine the limiting reactant as in Sample Problem 5.21.**
   • Identify H_2 as the original quantity and use the mole ratio from the balanced equation as a conversion factor to calculate how much N_2 is needed for complete reaction.

$$5.0\ \text{mol } H_2 \quad \times \quad \frac{1\ \text{mol } N_2}{3\ \text{mol } H_2} \quad = \quad 1.7\ \text{mol } N_2 \text{ needed}$$

mole–mole conversion factor

   • Since the amount of N_2 present is greater than what is needed, N_2 is present in excess and **H_2 is the limiting reactant.**

[2] **Convert the number of moles of limiting reactant to the number of moles of product using a mole–mole conversion factor.**

mole–mole conversion factor

$$5.0\ \text{mol } H_2 \quad \times \quad \frac{2\ \text{mol } NH_3}{3\ \text{mol } H_2} \quad = \quad 3.3\ \text{mol } NH_3 \text{ formed}$$

Answer

PRACTICE PROBLEM 5.22

Using the balanced equation, $3\,H_2(g) + N_2(g) \longrightarrow 2\,NH_3(g)$, calculate the number of moles of product formed under each of the following reaction conditions.

a. 1.5 mol H_2 and 1.0 mol N_2 c. 2.0 mol H_2 and 3.0 mol N_2

b. 1.0 mol H_2 and 2.0 mol N_2 d. 7.5 mol H_2 and 2.0 mol N_2

More Practice: Try Problems 5.83, 5.84, 5.85a, b, 5.87, 5.88.

PROBLEM 5.22

Using Sample Problem 5.21 as a guide, complete the following table using the given balanced equation and the initial quantities of reactants. Label the limiting reactant and the reactant used in excess.

	Reactants			Products
Equation	$2\,H_2$	+	O_2 $\longrightarrow$	$2\,H_2O$
Initial quantities	8 molecules		3 molecules	0 molecules
Molecules used or formed				
Molecules remaining				

5.10C   Determining the Limiting Reactant Using the Number of Grams

In the laboratory, we measure out the number of grams (not the number of moles) of each reactant on a balance. To determine the limiting reactant from the number of grams, we must first determine the number of moles of each reactant using the molar mass, as shown in Sample Problem 5.23.

SAMPLE PROBLEM 5.23 DETERMINING THE LIMITING REACTANT FROM GRAMS OF REACTANTS

Using the balanced equation, $N_2(g) + O_2(g) \longrightarrow 2\,NO(g)$, determine the limiting reactant when 10.0 g of N_2 (molar mass 28.02 g/mol) react with 10.0 g of O_2 (molar mass 32.00 g/mol).

Analysis

Convert the number of grams to the number of moles for each reactant, and then use the steps in Sample Problem 5.21 to determine the limiting reactant.

Solution

[1] Convert the number of grams of each reactant to the number of moles using the molar masses.

$$\text{Moles of } N_2: \quad 10.0 \text{ g } N_2 \times \frac{1 \text{ mol } N_2}{28.02 \text{ g } N_2} = 0.357 \text{ mol } N_2$$

$$\text{Moles of } O_2: \quad 10.0 \text{ g } O_2 \times \frac{1 \text{ mol } O_2}{32.00 \text{ g } O_2} = 0.313 \text{ mol } O_2$$

[2] Determine the limiting reactant as in Sample Problem 5.21.

- Identify N_2 as the original quantity and use the mole ratio from the balanced equation as a conversion factor to calculate how much O_2 is needed for complete reaction.

mole–mole
conversion factor

$$0.357 \text{ mol } N_2 \quad \times \quad \frac{1 \text{ mol } O_2}{1 \text{ mol } N_2} \quad = \quad 0.357 \text{ mol } O_2 \text{ needed}$$

- Since the amount of O_2 present is less than what is needed, **O_2 is the limiting reactant.**

PRACTICE PROBLEM 5.23

Using the balanced equation, $N_2(g) + O_2(g) \longrightarrow 2\,NO(g)$, determine the limiting reactant under the following conditions (N_2, molar mass 28.02 g/mol; O_2, molar mass 32.00 g/mol).

a. 12.5 g N_2 and 15.0 g O_2 b. 14.0 g N_2 and 13.0 g O_2

More Practice: Try Problems 5.85c, d.

SAMPLE PROBLEM 5.24 USING THE LIMITING REACTANT TO DETERMINE GRAMS OF PRODUCT FORMED

Using the balanced equation, $N_2(g) + O_2(g) \longrightarrow 2\,NO(g)$, calculate the number of grams of NO (molar mass 30.01 g/mol) formed when 10.0 g of N_2 (molar mass 28.02 g/mol) react with 10.0 g of O_2 (molar mass 32.00 g/mol).

Analysis

Three steps are required:

- Determine the limiting reactant.
- Use the mole ratio from the balanced equation to calculate the number of moles of product formed.
- Convert the moles of product to grams using the molar mass.

Solution

[1] Determine the limiting reactant.

- Convert the number of grams of each reactant to the number of moles using the molar masses.
- Use a mole–mole conversion factor to determine which reactant is present in excess.
- As shown in Sample Problem 5.23, when 10.0 g of N_2 (0.357 mol) react with 10.0 g (0.313 mol) of O_2, O_2 is the limiting reactant.

[2] Convert the number of moles of limiting reactant to the number of moles of product using a mole–mole conversion factor.

$$0.313 \text{ mol } O_2 \quad \times \quad \frac{2 \text{ mol NO}}{1 \text{ mol } O_2} \quad = \quad 0.626 \text{ mol NO formed}$$

mole–mole conversion factor

[3] Convert the number of moles of product to the number of grams using the molar mass.

$$0.626 \text{ mol NO} \times \frac{30.01 \text{ g NO}}{1 \text{ mol NO}} = 18.8 \text{ g NO formed}$$
Answer

PRACTICE PROBLEM 5.24

For each set of reaction conditions in Practice Problem 5.23, calculate the number of grams of product formed.

More Practice: Try Problem 5.86.

CHAPTER HIGHLIGHTS

KEY TERMS

Actual yield (5.9)	Half reaction (5.4)	Percent yield (5.9)
Avogadro's number (5.5)	Law of conservation of matter (5.1)	Product (5.1)
Balanced chemical equation (5.2)	Limiting reactant (5.10)	Reactant (5.1)
Chemical equation (5.1)	Molar mass (5.6)	Redox reaction (5.4)
Combination reaction (5.3)	Mole (5.5)	Reducing agent (5.4)
Decomposition reaction (5.3)	Molecular weight (5.6)	Reduction (5.4)
Double replacement reaction (5.3)	Oxidation (5.4)	Single replacement reaction (5.3)
Formula weight (5.6)	Oxidizing agent (5.4)	Theoretical yield (5.9)

KEY CONCEPTS

❶ What do the terms in a chemical equation mean and how is an equation balanced? (5.1, 5.2)

- A chemical equation contains the reactants on the left side of an arrow and the products on the right. The coefficients tell

how many molecules or moles of a substance react or are formed.

- A chemical equation is balanced by placing coefficients in front of chemical formulas one at a time, beginning with the most complex formula, so that the number of atoms of each element is the same on both sides. You must *not* balance the chemical equation by changing the subscripts in the chemical formulas of the reactants or products.

2 **List four common types of reactions. (5.3)**

- In a combination reaction, two or more reactants join to form one product.
- In a decomposition reaction, one reactant is converted to two or more products.
- In a single replacement reaction, an element replaces another element in a compound to form a new element and a new compound.
- In a double replacement reaction, two compounds exchange atoms or ions to form two new compounds.

3 **What are oxidation and reduction reactions? (5.4)**

- Oxidation–reduction or redox reactions are electron transfer reactions.
- Oxidation results in the loss of electrons. Metals and anions tend to undergo oxidation. In some reactions, oxidation results in the gain of O atoms or the loss of H atoms.
- Reduction results in the gain of electrons. Nonmetals and cations tend to undergo reduction. In some reactions, reduction results in the loss of O atoms or the gain of H atoms.

4 **Define the terms mole and Avogadro's number. (5.5)**

- A mole is a quantity that contains 6.02×10^{23} atoms, molecules, or ions.
- Avogadro's number is the number of particles in a mole—6.02×10^{23}.
- The number of molecules in a given number of moles is calculated using Avogadro's number.

5 **How are formula weight and molar mass calculated? (5.6)**

- The formula weight is the sum of the atomic weights of all the atoms in a compound, reported in atomic mass units.

- The molar mass is the mass of one mole of a substance, reported in grams. The molar mass is numerically equal to the formula weight, but the units are different (g/mol not amu).

6 **How are the mass of a substance and its number of moles related? (5.6)**

- The molar mass is used as a conversion factor to determine how many grams are contained in a given number of moles of a substance. Similarly, the molar mass is used to determine how many moles of a substance are contained in a given number of grams.

7 **How can a balanced equation and molar mass be used to calculate the number of moles and mass of a reaction product? (5.7, 5.8)**

- The coefficients in a balanced chemical equation tell us the number of moles of each reactant that combine and the number of moles of each product formed. Coefficients are used to form mole ratios that serve as conversion factors relating the number of moles of reactants and products.
- When the mass of a substance in a reaction must be calculated, first its number of moles is determined using mole ratios, and then the molar mass is used to convert moles to grams.

8 **What is percent yield? (5.9)**

- Percent yield = (actual yield/theoretical yield) × 100%.
- The actual yield is the amount of product formed in a reaction, determined by weighing a product on a balance. The theoretical yield is a quantity calculated from a balanced chemical equation, using mole ratios and molar masses. The theoretical yield is the maximum amount of product that can form in a chemical reaction from the amount of reactants used.

9 **What is the limiting reactant in a reaction? (5.10)**

- The limiting reactant is the reactant that is completely used up in a reaction. The number of moles of limiting reactant determines the number of moles of product formed using mole ratios in the balanced equation.

PROBLEMS

Selected in-chapter and odd-numbered end-of-chapter problems have brief answers in Appendix B. The *Student Study Guide and Solutions Manual* contains detailed solutions to all in-chapter and odd-numbered end-of-chapter problems, as well as additional worked examples and a chapter self-test.

Chemical Reactions and Chemical Equations

5.23 Use the molecular art to identify the process as a chemical reaction or a physical change. If a chemical reaction occurs, write the equation from the molecular art. If a physical change occurs, identify the phase change.

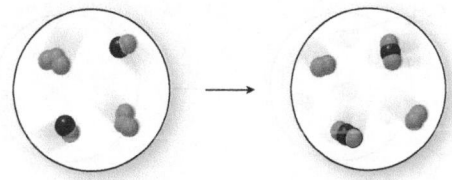

5.24 Diagram [1] represents the compound **AB,** which contains two elements, **A** shown with red spheres, and **B** shown with blue spheres. Label each transformation as a physical change or a chemical reaction: (a) [1] ⟶ [2]; (b) [1] ⟶ [3].

[1]　　　　[2]　　　　[3]

5.25 How many atoms of each element are drawn on each side of the following equations? Label the equations as balanced or not balanced.

a. $2\,HCl(aq) + Ca(s) \longrightarrow CaCl_2(aq) + H_2(g)$

b. $TiCl_4 + 2\,H_2O \longrightarrow TiO_2 + HCl$

c. $Al(OH)_3 + H_3PO_4 \longrightarrow AlPO_4 + 3\,H_2O$

182   Chapter 5   Chemical Reactions

5.26 How many atoms of each element are drawn on each side of the following equations? Label the equations as balanced or not balanced.

a. $3 NO_2 + H_2O \longrightarrow HNO_3 + 2 NO$

b. $2 H_2S + 3 O_2 \longrightarrow H_2O + 2 SO_2$

c. $Ca(OH)_2 + 2 HNO_3 \longrightarrow 2 H_2O + Ca(NO_3)_2$

5.27 Use the molecular art to write a balanced equation for the given reaction.

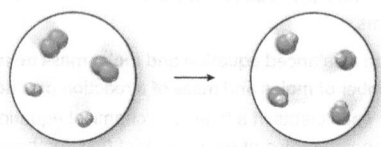

5.28 Use the molecular art to write a balanced equation for the given reaction.

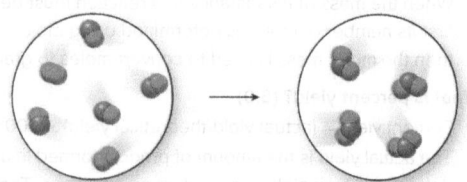

5.29 Use the molecular art to write a balanced equation for the given reaction.

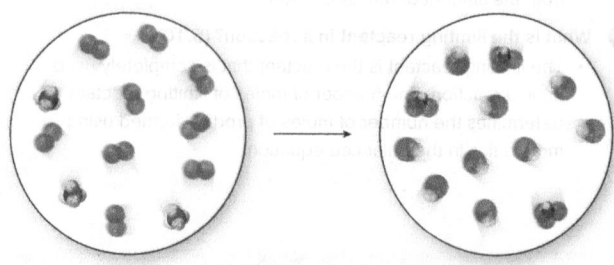

5.30 Some coal is high in sulfur (S) content, and when it burns, it forms sulfuric acid (H_2SO_4), a major component of acid rain, by a series of reactions. Balance the equation for the overall conversion drawn below.

$$S(s) + O_2(g) + H_2O(l) \longrightarrow H_2SO_4(l)$$

5.31 Balance each equation.

a. $Ni(s) + HCl(aq) \longrightarrow NiCl_2(aq) + H_2(g)$

b. $CH_4(g) + Cl_2(g) \longrightarrow CCl_4(g) + HCl(g)$

c. $KClO_3 \longrightarrow KCl + O_2$

d. $Al_2O_3 + HCl \longrightarrow AlCl_3 + H_2O$

e. $Al(OH)_3 + H_2SO_4 \longrightarrow Al_2(SO_4)_3 + H_2O$

5.32 Balance each equation.

a. $Mg(s) + HBr(aq) \longrightarrow MgBr_2(s) + H_2(g)$

b. $CO(g) + O_2(g) \longrightarrow CO_2(g)$

c. $PbS(s) + O_2(g) \longrightarrow PbO(s) + SO_2(g)$

d. $H_2SO_4 + NaOH \longrightarrow Na_2SO_4 + H_2O$

e. $H_3PO_4 + Ca(OH)_2 \longrightarrow Ca_3(PO_4)_2 + H_2O$

5.33 Consider the reaction, $O_3 + CO \longrightarrow O_2 + CO_2$. Molecular art is used to show the starting materials for this reaction. Fill in the molecules of the products using the balanced equation and following the law of conservation of matter.

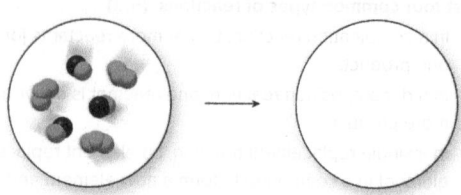

5.34 Consider the reaction, $2 NO + 2 CO \longrightarrow N_2 + 2 CO_2$. Molecular art is used to show the starting materials for this reaction. Fill in the molecules of the products using the balanced equation and following the law of conservation of matter.

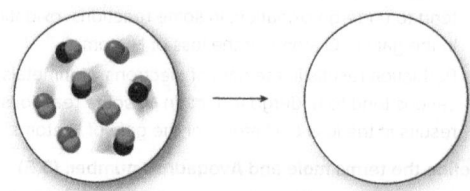

5.35 Consider the combustion of benzene (C_6H_6) with O_2 to form CO_2 and H_2O. (a) Write a balanced equation for this reaction. (b) Molecular art is used to show the molecules of starting material. Fill in the molecules of products using the balanced equation. Be sure to follow the law of conservation of matter.

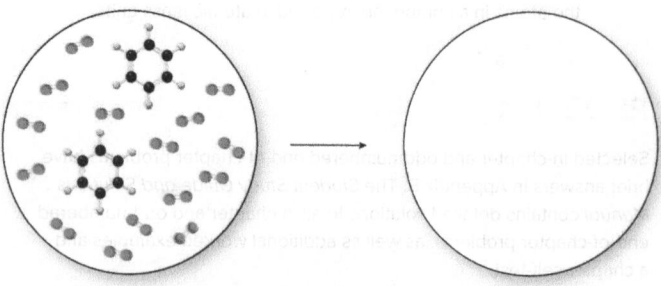

5.36 Consider the combustion of acetylene (C_2H_2) with O_2 to form CO_2 and H_2O. (a) Write a balanced equation for this reaction. (b) Molecular art is used to show the molecules of starting material. Fill in the molecules of products using the balanced equation.

C_2H_2

Types of Reactions

5.37 For the reaction depicted in the molecular art: (a) Use the common element colors on the inside back cover to give the formula for each reactant and product. (b) Write a balanced equation. (c) Classify the reaction as combination, decomposition, single replacement, or double replacement.

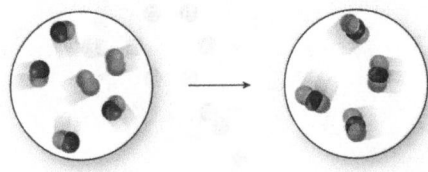

5.38 Answer the questions in Problem 5.37 for the reaction depicted in the molecular art.

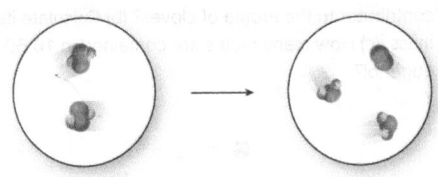

5.39 Answer the questions in Problem 5.37 for the reaction depicted in the molecular art.

5.40 Answer the questions in Problem 5.37 for the reaction depicted in the molecular art.

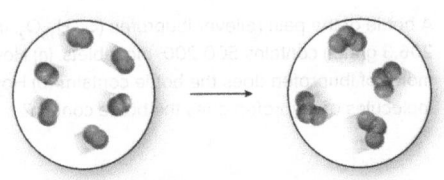

5.41 Classify the reaction depicted in the molecular art as combination, decomposition, single replacement, or double replacement.

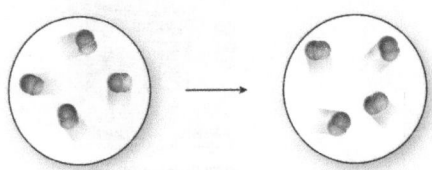

5.42 Classify the reaction depicted in the molecular art as combination, decomposition, single replacement, or double replacement.

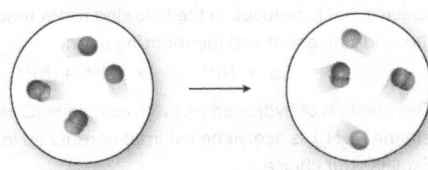

5.43 Classify each reaction as combination, decomposition, single replacement, or double replacement.
a. $2 Br-Cl \longrightarrow Br_2 + Cl_2$
b. $F_2 + 2 NaBr \longrightarrow 2 NaF + Br_2$
c. $4 Fe + 3 O_2 \longrightarrow 2 Fe_2O_3$
d. $HNO_3 + KOH \longrightarrow KNO_3 + H_2O$

5.44 Classify each reaction as combination, decomposition, single replacement, or double replacement.
a. $2 Al + 6 HCl \longrightarrow 2 AlCl_3 + 3 H_2$
b. $H_2SO_4 \longrightarrow SO_3 + H_2O$
c. $H_2SO_4 + 2 NaOH \longrightarrow Na_2SO_4 + 2 H_2O$
d. $2 Ca + O_2 \longrightarrow 2 CaO$

5.45 Fill in the needed reactant or product for each of the following reaction types, and balance the equation.
a. combination: $Na + \boxed{} \longrightarrow NaCl$
b. decomposition: $NI_3 \longrightarrow \boxed{} + \boxed{}$
c. single replacement: $Cl_2 + KI \longrightarrow \boxed{} + \boxed{}$
d. double replacement: $KOH + HI \longrightarrow \boxed{} + \boxed{}$

5.46 Fill in the needed reactant or product for each of the following reaction types, and balance the equation.
a. combination: $N_2 + \boxed{} \longrightarrow Mg_3N_2$
b. decomposition: $SO_3 \longrightarrow SO_2 + \boxed{}$
c. single replacement: $Ag + CuBr_2 \longrightarrow \boxed{} + \boxed{}$
d. double replacement: $NaOH + HBr \longrightarrow \boxed{} + \boxed{}$

Oxidation–Reduction Reactions

5.47 Identify the species that is oxidized and the species that is reduced in each reaction. Write out two half reactions to show how many electrons are gained or lost by each species.
a. $Fe + Cu^{2+} \longrightarrow Fe^{2+} + Cu$
b. $Cl_2 + 2 I^- \longrightarrow I_2 + 2 Cl^-$
c. $2 Na + Cl_2 \longrightarrow 2 NaCl$

5.48 Identify the species that is oxidized and the species that is reduced in each reaction. Write out two half reactions to show how many electrons are gained or lost by each species.
a. $Mg + Fe^{2+} \longrightarrow Mg^{2+} + Fe$
b. $Cu^{2+} + Sn \longrightarrow Sn^{2+} + Cu$
c. $4 Na + O_2 \longrightarrow 2 Na_2O$

5.49 Zinc–silver oxide batteries are used in cameras and hearing aids. Identify the species that is oxidized and the species that is reduced in the following redox reaction. Identify the oxidizing agent and the reducing agent.

$$Zn + Ag_2O \longrightarrow ZnO + 2 Ag$$

184   **Chapter 5**   Chemical Reactions

5.50 Rechargeable nickel–cadmium batteries are used in appliances and power tools. Identify the species that is oxidized and the species that is reduced in the following redox reaction. Identify the oxidizing agent and the reducing agent.

$$Cd + Ni^{4+} \longrightarrow Cd^{2+} + Ni^{2+}$$

5.51 The reaction of hydrogen (H_2) with acetylene (C_2H_2) forms ethane (C_2H_6). Is acetylene oxidized or reduced in this reaction? Explain your choice.

5.52 The reaction of magnesium metal (Mg) with oxygen (O_2) forms MgO. Write a balanced equation for this redox reaction. Write two half reactions to show how many electrons are gained or lost by each species.

Formula Weight and Molar Mass

5.53 Calculate the formula weight and molar mass of each compound.
   a. $NaNO_2$ (sodium nitrite), a preservative in hot dogs, ham, and other cured meats
   b. $Al_2(SO_4)_3$ (aluminum sulfate), once used as a common antiperspirant
   c. $C_6H_8O_6$ (vitamin C)

5.54 Calculate the formula weight and molar mass of each compound.
   a. $MgSO_4$ (magnesium sulfate), a laxative
   b. $Ca_3(PO_4)_2$ (calcium phosphate), a calcium supplement
   c. $C_{16}H_{16}ClNO_2S$ (Plavix), a drug used to treat coronary artery disease

5.55 L-Dopa is a drug used to treat Parkinson's disease.

L-dopa

   a. What is the molecular formula of L-dopa?
   b. What is the formula weight of L-dopa?
   c. What is the molar mass of L-dopa?

5.56 Niacin, vitamin B_3, is found in soybeans, which contain it naturally, and cereals, which are fortified with it.

niacin

   a. What is the molecular formula of niacin?
   b. What is the formula weight of niacin?
   c. What is the molar mass of niacin?

Moles, Mass, and Avogadro's Number

5.57 Which quantity has the greater mass?
   a. 1 mol of Fe atoms or 1 mol of Sn atoms
   b. 1 mol of C atoms or 6.02×10^{23} N atoms
   c. 1 mol of N atoms or 1 mol of N_2 molecules
   d. 1 mol of CO_2 molecules or 3.01×10^{23} N_2O molecules

5.58 Which quantity has the greater mass?
   a. 1 mol of Si atoms or 1 mol of Ar atoms
   b. 1 mol of He atoms or 6.02×10^{23} H atoms
   c. 1 mol of Cl atoms or 1 mol of Cl_2 molecules
   d. 1 mol of C_2H_4 molecules or 3.01×10^{23} C_2H_4 molecules

5.59 Mescaline is a hallucinogen in peyote, a cactus native to the southwestern United States and Mexico. (a) What is the chemical formula of mescaline? (b) Calculate its molar mass. (c) How many moles are contained in 7.50 g of mescaline?

mescaline

5.60 (a) What is the chemical formula of eugenol, the main contributor to the aroma of cloves? (b) Calculate its molar mass. (c) How many moles are contained in 10.50 g of eugenol?

eugenol

5.61 How many grams are contained in 5.00 mol of each compound?
   a. HCl   b. Na_2SO_4 c. C_2H_2 d. $Al(OH)_3$

5.62 How many grams are contained in 0.50 mol of each compound?
   a. NaOH   b. $CaSO_4$ c. C_3H_6 d. $Mg(OH)_2$

5.63 A bottle of the pain reliever ibuprofen ($C_{13}H_{18}O_2$, molar mass 206.3 g/mol) contains 500 200.-mg tablets. (a) How many moles of ibuprofen does the bottle contain? (b) How many molecules of ibuprofen does the bottle contain?

©Jill Braaten RF

5.64 One dose of Maalox contains 500. mg each of $Mg(OH)_2$ and $Al(OH)_3$. How many moles of each compound are contained in a single dose?

©McGraw-Hill Education/Jill
Braaten, photographer

5.65 How many moles are contained in each number of grams of table sugar ($C_{12}H_{22}O_{11}$, molar mass 342.3 g/mol)?

    a. 0.500 g   b. 5.00 g   c. 25.0 g   d. 0.0250 g

5.66 How many moles are contained in each number of grams of fructose ($C_6H_{12}O_6$, molar mass 180.2 g/mol), a carbohydrate that is about twice as sweet as table sugar? "Lite" food products use half as much fructose as table sugar to achieve the same sweet taste but with fewer calories.

    a. 0.500 g   b. 5.00 g   c. 25.0 g   d. 0.0250 g

5.67 How many molecules of butane (C_4H_{10}) are contained in the following number of moles: (a) 2.00 mol; (b) 0.250 mol; (c) 26.5 mol; (d) 222 mol; (e) 5.00×10^5 mol?

5.68 How many moles of pentane (C_5H_{12}) are contained in the following number of molecules?

    a. 5.00×10^{19} molecules   c. 8.32×10^{21} molecules
    b. 6.51×10^{28} molecules   d. 3.10×10^{20} molecules

5.69 The average nicotine ($C_{10}H_{14}N_2$, molar mass 162.3 g/mol) content of a Camel cigarette is 1.93 mg. Suppose an individual smokes one pack of 20 cigarettes a day.

    a. How many moles of nicotine are smoked in a day?
    b. How many molecules of nicotine are smoked in a day?

©Joel Saget/AFP/Getty Images

5.70 How many moles of sucrose (table sugar, $C_{12}H_{22}O_{11}$, molar mass 342.3 g/mol) are contained in a 5-lb bag of sugar?

©Rachel Esptein/PhotoEdit

5.71 What is the mass in grams of each quantity of lactic acid ($C_3H_6O_3$, molar mass 90.08 g/mol), the compound responsible for the aching feeling of tired muscles during vigorous exercise?

    a. 3.60 mol   c. 7.3×10^{24} molecules
    b. 0.580 mol   d. 6.56×10^{22} molecules

5.72 What is the mass in grams of each quantity of vitamin D (molar mass 384.7 g/mol), which is needed for forming and maintaining healthy bones?

    a. 3.6 mol   c. 7.3×10^{24} molecules
    b. 0.58 mol   d. 6.56×10^{22} molecules

Mass and Mole Calculations in Chemical Equations

5.73 Using the balanced equation for the combustion of acetylene, answer the following questions.

$$2 \text{ H–C}\equiv\text{C–H} + 5 \text{ O}_2 \longrightarrow 4 \text{ CO}_2 + 2 \text{ H}_2\text{O}$$
    acetylene

    a. How many moles of O_2 are needed to react completely with 5.00 mol of C_2H_2?
    b. How many moles of CO_2 are formed from 6.0 mol of C_2H_2?
    c. How many moles of H_2O are formed from 0.50 mol of C_2H_2?
    d. How many moles of C_2H_2 are needed to form 0.80 mol of CO_2?

5.74 Sodium metal (Na) reacts violently when added to water according to the following balanced equation.

$$2 \text{ Na}(s) + 2 \text{ H}_2\text{O}(l) \longrightarrow 2 \text{ NaOH}(aq) + \text{H}_2(g)$$

    a. How many moles of H_2O are needed to react completely with 3.0 mol of Na?
    b. How many moles of H_2 are formed from 0.38 mol of Na?
    c. How many moles of H_2 are formed from 3.64 mol of H_2O?

5.75 Using the balanced equation for the combustion of acetylene in Problem 5.73, answer the following questions.

    a. How many grams of CO_2 are formed from 2.5 mol of C_2H_2?
    b. How many grams of CO_2 are formed from 0.50 mol of C_2H_2?
    c. How many grams of H_2O are formed from 0.25 mol of C_2H_2?
    d. How many grams of O_2 are needed to react with 3.0 mol of C_2H_2?

5.76 Using the balanced equation for the reaction of Na with H_2O in Problem 5.74, answer the following questions.

  a. How many grams of NaOH are formed from 3.0 mol of Na?

  b. How many grams of H_2 are formed from 0.30 mol of Na?

  c. How many grams of H_2O are needed to react completely with 0.20 mol of Na?

Theoretical Yield and Percent Yield

5.77 What is the percent yield of **B** in a reaction that uses 10.0 g of starting material **A**, has a theoretical yield of 12.0 g of **B**, and an actual yield of 9.0 g of **B**?

5.78 What is the percent yield of **B** in a reaction that uses 25.0 g of starting material **A**, has a theoretical yield of 20.0 g of **B**, and an actual yield of 17.0 g of **B**?

5.79 The reaction of methane (CH_4) with Cl_2 forms chloroform ($CHCl_3$) and HCl. Although $CHCl_3$ is a general anesthetic, it is no longer used for this purpose because it is also carcinogenic. The molar masses for all substances are given under the balanced equation.

$$CH_4(g) \ + \ 3\,Cl_2(g) \longrightarrow CHCl_3(l) \ + \ 3\,HCl(g)$$
16.04 g/mol 70.90 g/mol   119.4 g/mol   36.46 g/mol

  a. What is the theoretical yield of $CHCl_3$ in grams from 3.20 g of CH_4?

  b. What is the percent yield if 15.0 g of $CHCl_3$ are actually formed in this reaction?

5.80 Methanol (CH_4O), which is used as a fuel in high-performance racing cars, burns in the presence of O_2 to form CO_2 and H_2O. The molar masses for all substances are given under the balanced equation.

$$2\,CH_4O(l) \ + \ 3\,O_2(g) \longrightarrow 2\,CO_2(g) \ + \ 4\,H_2O(g)$$
32.04 g/mol 32.00 g/mol   44.01 g/mol 18.02 g/mol

  a. What is the theoretical yield of CO_2 from 48.0 g of methanol?

  b. What is the percent yield of CO_2 if 48.0 g of CO_2 are formed?

Limiting Reactants

5.81 Consider the given reaction mixture that contains **A** and **B** molecules, represented by red and blue spheres, respectively. Given each of the following chemical equations, which reactant, **A** or **B**, is present in excess? Which reactant is the limiting reactant?

  a. $A + B \longrightarrow C$

  b. $2\,A + B \longrightarrow C$

  c. $A + 2\,B \longrightarrow C$

5.82 Consider the reaction of A_2 and B_2 to form A_2B, according to the balanced equation: $2\,A_2 + B_2 \longrightarrow 2\,A_2B$. Identify the limiting reactant in the molecular art, and draw a representation showing how much product is formed and what reactant molecules are left over.

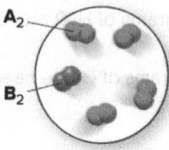

5.83 Consider the reaction with the balanced equation, $N_2 + 2\,O_2 \longrightarrow 2\,NO_2$. (a) Identify the limiting reactant under the reaction conditions shown in the molecular art. (b) What reactant molecules are left over? (c) Draw a representation showing what the product mixture looks like when the reaction is complete.

5.84 Consider the reaction with the balanced equation, $N_2 + 3\,H_2 \longrightarrow 2\,NH_3$. (a) Identify the limiting reactant under the reaction conditions shown in the molecular art. (b) What reactant molecules are left over in this reaction? (c) Draw a representation showing what the product mixture looks like when the reaction is complete.

5.85 Using the balanced equation, $2\,NO + O_2 \longrightarrow 2\,NO_2$, determine the limiting reactant under each of the following conditions.

  a. 1.0 mol NO and 1.0 mol O_2

  b. 2.0 mol NO and 0.50 mol O_2

  c. 10.0 g NO and 10.0 g O_2

  d. 28.0 g NO and 16.0 g O_2

5.86 For each set of reaction conditions in Problem 5.85, calculate how many moles of the product NO_2 form. Then, calculate the number of grams of product that forms.

5.87 Complete the following table using the given balanced equation and the initial quantities of reactants. Label the limiting reactant and the reactant used in excess.

	Reactants		**Products**	
Equation	C_2H_4 +	$3\,O_2 \longrightarrow$	$2\,CO_2$ +	$2\,H_2O$
Initial quantities	8 molecules	15 molecules	0 molecules	0 molecules
Molecules used or formed				
Molecules remaining				

5.88 Complete the following table using the given balanced equation and the initial quantities of reactants. Label the limiting reactant and the reactant used in excess.

	Reactants		Products	
Equation	$2 C_4H_{10}$ +	$13 O_2$ $\longrightarrow$	$8 CO_2$ +	$10 H_2O$
Initial quantities	4.20 mol	6.50 mol	0.00 mol	0.00 mol
Moles used or formed				
Moles remaining				

5.89 The local anesthetic ethyl chloride (C_2H_5Cl, molar mass 64.51 g/mol) can be prepared by reaction of ethylene (C_2H_4, molar mass 28.05 g/mol) with HCl (molar mass 36.46 g/mol), according to the balanced equation, $C_2H_4 + HCl \longrightarrow C_2H_5Cl$.
   a. If 8.00 g of ethylene and 12.0 g of HCl are used, how many moles of each reactant are used?
   b. What is the limiting reactant?
   c. How many moles of product are formed?
   d. How many grams of product are formed?
   e. If 10.6 g of product are formed, what is the percent yield of the reaction?

5.90 The solvent dichloromethane (CH_2Cl_2, molar mass 84.93 g/mol) can be prepared by reaction of methane (CH_4, molar mass 16.04 g/mol) with Cl_2 (molar mass 70.90 g/mol), according to the balanced equation, $CH_4 + 2 Cl_2 \longrightarrow CH_2Cl_2 + 2 HCl$.
   a. If 5.00 g of methane and 15.0 g of Cl_2 are used, how many moles of each reactant are used?
   b. What is the limiting reactant?
   c. How many moles of product are formed?
   d. How many grams of product are formed?
   e. If 5.6 g of product are formed, what is the percent yield of the reaction?

General Questions and Applications

5.91 Answer the following questions about the conversion of the sucrose ($C_{12}H_{22}O_{11}$) in sugarcane to ethanol (C_2H_6O) and CO_2 according to the following unbalanced equation. In this way sugarcane is a renewable source of ethanol, which is used as a fuel additive in gasoline.

$$C_{12}H_{22}O_{11}(s) + H_2O(l) \longrightarrow C_2H_6O(l) + CO_2(g)$$
$$\text{sucrose} \qquad\qquad\qquad \text{ethanol}$$

   a. What is the molar mass of sucrose?
   b. Balance the given equation.
   c. How many moles of ethanol are formed from 2 mol of sucrose?
   d. How many moles of water are needed to react with 10 mol of sucrose?
   e. How many grams of ethanol are formed from 0.550 mol of sucrose?
   f. How many grams of ethanol are formed from 34.2 g of sucrose?
   g. What is the theoretical yield of ethanol in grams from 17.1 g of sucrose?
   h. If 1.25 g of ethanol are formed in the reaction in part (g), what is the percent yield of ethanol?

5.92 Answer the following questions about diethyl ether ($C_4H_{10}O$), the first widely used general anesthetic. Diethyl ether can be prepared from ethanol according to the following unbalanced equation.

$$C_2H_6O(l) \longrightarrow C_4H_{10}O(l) + H_2O(l)$$
$$\text{ethanol} \qquad\qquad \text{diethyl ether}$$

   a. What is the molar mass of diethyl ether?
   b. Balance the given equation.
   c. How many moles of diethyl ether are formed from 2 mol of ethanol?
   d. How many moles of water are formed from 10 mol of ethanol?
   e. How many grams of diethyl ether are formed from 0.55 mol of ethanol?
   f. How many grams of diethyl ether are formed from 4.60 g of ethanol?
   g. What is the theoretical yield of diethyl ether in grams from 2.30 g of ethanol?
   h. If 1.80 g of diethyl ether are formed in the reaction in part (g), what is the percent yield of diethyl ether?

5.93 If the daily recommended intake of sodium ions is 2,400 mg, how many Na^+ ions does this correspond to?

5.94 How many molecules are contained in a glass that holds 250 g of water? How many moles does this correspond to?

5.95 DDT, a pesticide that kills disease-carrying mosquitoes, is synthesized by the given equation. DDT is now banned in the United States because it is a persistent environmental pollutant that only slowly degrades.

$$2 C_6H_5Cl + C_2HCl_3O \longrightarrow C_{14}H_9Cl_5 + H_2O$$
$$\text{chlorobenzene} \qquad\qquad\qquad \text{DDT}$$
$$\text{112.6 g/mol}$$

   a. What is the molar mass of DDT?
   b. How many grams of DDT would be formed from 0.10 mol of chlorobenzene?
   c. What is the theoretical yield of DDT in grams from 11.3 g of chlorobenzene?
   d. If 15.0 g of DDT are formed in the reaction in part (c), what is the percent yield of DDT?

5.96 Fats, such as butter, and oils, such as corn oil, are formed from compounds called fatty acids, one of which is linolenic acid ($C_{18}H_{30}O_2$). Linolenic acid undergoes reactions with hydrogen and oxygen to form the products shown in each equation.

[1] $C_{18}H_{30}O_2 + H_2 \longrightarrow C_{18}H_{36}O_2$
    linolenic acid

[2] $C_{18}H_{30}O_2 + O_2 \longrightarrow CO_2 + H_2O$
    linolenic acid

   a. Calculate the molar mass of linolenic acid.
   b. Balance Equation [1], which shows the reaction with hydrogen.
   c. Balance Equation [2], which shows the reaction with oxygen.
   d. How many grams of product are formed from 10.0 g of linolenic acid in Equation [1]?

CHALLENGE PROBLEMS

5.97   TCDD, also called dioxin ($C_{12}H_4Cl_4O_2$, molar mass 322.0 g/mol), is a potent poison. The average lethal dose in humans is estimated to be 3.0×10^{-2} mg per kg of body weight. (a) How many grams constitute a lethal dose for a 70.-kg individual? (b) How many molecules of TCDD does this correspond to?

5.98   A 12-oz can of diet soda contains 180 mg of the artificial sweetener aspartame (trade names NutraSweet and Equal). When aspartame is ingested, it is metabolized to phenylalanine, aspartic acid, and methanol, according to the balanced equation:

$$C_{14}H_{18}N_2O_5 \ + \ 2\,H_2O \ \longrightarrow \ C_9H_{11}NO_2 \ + \ C_4H_7NO_4 \ + \ CH_3OH$$

aspartame   phenylalanine   aspartic   methanol
                                          acid

a. Using this equation, determine how much methanol (in mg) is formed on metabolism of the aspartame in each 12-oz can. The molar mass of aspartame is 294.2 g/mol, and the molar mass of methanol is 32.04 g/mol.

b. Methanol is a toxic compound, with the average lethal dose in humans estimated at 428 mg/kg of body weight. How many cans of soda would a 52-kg individual have to ingest to obtain a lethal dose of methanol?

203

Ethanol produced from corn and grain is a renewable fuel source that releases energy when it burns in the presence of oxygen, forming carbon dioxide and water. ©smereka/Shutterstock RF

Energy Changes, Reaction Rates, and Equilibrium

CHAPTER OUTLINE

6.1 Energy

6.2 Energy Changes in Reactions

6.3 Energy Diagrams

6.4 Reaction Rates

6.5 Equilibrium

6.6 Le Châtelier's Principle

6.7 FOCUS ON THE HUMAN BODY: Body Temperature

CHAPTER GOALS

In this chapter you will learn how to:

1 Define energy and become familiar with the units of energy

2 Use bond dissociation energies to predict bond strength

3 Describe energy changes in a reaction, and classify reactions as endothermic or exothermic

4 Draw energy diagrams

5 Predict the effect of concentration, temperature, and the presence of a catalyst on the rate of a reaction

6 Describe the basic features of chemical equilibrium and write an expression for an equilibrium constant

7 Use Le Châtelier's principle to predict what happens when equilibrium is disturbed

8 Use Le Châtelier's principle and reaction rates to explain the regulation of body temperature

<table>
<tr><td>

Why Study
**Energy Changes and
Reaction Rates?**

</td><td>

I n Chapter 6 we turn our attention to two facets of chemical reactions: energy changes and reaction rates. Why do some reactions—like the combustion of fossil fuels or the metabolism of carbohydrates—release a great deal of energy that can be used for powering a car or running a marathon, whereas other reactions absorb energy from the environment? What factors affect how fast a reaction proceeds? To answer these and related questions, we must learn about what happens when molecules come together in a reaction, as well as what energy changes are observed when bonds are broken and formed.

</td></tr>
</table>

6.1   Energy

Energy **is the capacity to do work.** Whenever you throw a ball, ride a bike, or read a newspaper, you use energy to do work. There are two types of energy.

- Potential energy is stored energy.
- Kinetic energy is the energy of motion.

The water at the top of a waterfall has potential energy because of its position. This potential energy becomes kinetic energy as the water falls. ©*Daniel C. Smith*

A ball at the top of a hill or the water in a reservoir behind a dam are examples of potential energy. When the ball rolls down the hill or the water flows over the dam, the stored potential energy is converted to the kinetic energy of motion. Although energy can be converted from one form to another, one rule, the **law of conservation of energy,** governs the process.

- The total energy in the universe does not change. Energy cannot be created or destroyed.

The energy stored in chemical bonds—both ionic and covalent—is a form of potential energy. In chemical reactions, potential energy may be released and converted to heat, the kinetic energy of the moving particles of the product. **Reactions that form products having *lower* potential energy than the reactants are favored.**

- A compound with lower potential energy is more stable than a compound with higher potential energy.

6.1A   The Units of Energy

The joule, named after the nineteenth-century English physicist James Prescott Joule, is pronounced *jewel.*

Energy can be measured using two different units, **calories (cal)** and **joules (J).** A **calorie** is the amount of energy needed to raise the temperature of 1 g of water 1 °C. Joules and calories are related in the following way.

$$1 \text{ cal} = 4.184 \text{ J}$$

Since both the calorie and the joule are small units of measurement, more often energies in reactions are reported with kilocalories (kcal) and kilojoules (kJ). Recall from Table 1.2 that the prefix *kilo* means 1,000.

$$1 \text{ kcal} = 1{,}000 \text{ cal}$$
$$1 \text{ kJ} = 1{,}000 \text{ J}$$
$$1 \text{ kcal} = 4.184 \text{ kJ}$$

To convert a quantity from one unit of measurement to another, set up conversion factors and use the method first shown in Section 1.7B and illustrated in Sample Problem 6.1.

SAMPLE PROBLEM 6.1 CONVERTING KILOJOULES TO KILOCALORIES

A reaction releases 421 kJ of energy. How many kilocalories does this correspond to?

Analysis and Solution

[1] Identify the original quantity and the desired quantity.

$$421 \text{ kJ} \qquad\qquad ? \text{ kcal}$$

original quantity   desired quantity

[2] Write out the conversion factors.

- Choose the conversion factor that places the unwanted unit, kilojoules, in the denominator so that the units cancel.

kJ–kcal conversion factors

$$\frac{4.184 \text{ kJ}}{1 \text{ kcal}} \quad \text{or} \quad \boxed{\frac{1 \text{ kcal}}{4.184 \text{ kJ}}}$$ ← Choose this conversion factor to cancel kJ.

[3] Set up and solve the problem.

- Multiply the original quantity by the conversion factor to obtain the desired quantity.

$$421 \text{ kJ} \quad \times \quad \frac{1 \text{ kcal}}{4.184 \text{ kJ}} \quad = \quad 100.6 \text{ kcal, rounded to 101 kcal}$$

Kilojoules cancel.   **Answer**

PRACTICE PROBLEM 6.1

Carry out each of the following conversions.

  a. 42 J to cal   b. 55.6 kcal to cal   c. 326 kcal to kJ   d. 25.6 kcal to J

More Practice: Try Problems 6.13–6.16.

PROBLEM 6.1

Combustion of 1 g of gasoline releases 11.5 kcal of energy. How many kilojoules of energy are released? How many joules does this correspond to?

WHEATS

Nutrition Facts
Serving Size 1 cup (55 g)
Servings Per Container about 13

Amount Per Serving

Calories 200   Calories from Fat 10

	% Daily Value*
Total Fat 1g	2%
Saturated Fat 0g	0%
Trans Fat 0g	
Cholesterol 0mg	0%
Sodium 0mg	0%
Potassium 180mg	5%
Total Carbohydrate 42g	14%
Dietary Fiber 5g	20%
Sugars 12g	
Protein 5g	

Vitamin A 0%	•	Vitamin C 0%
Calcium 0%	•	Iron 90%
Thiamine 25%	•	Riboflavin 25%
Niacin 25%	•	Vitamin B6 25%

©McGraw-Hill Education/Jill Braaten,
photographer

6.1B FOCUS ON THE HUMAN BODY
Energy and Nutrition

When we eat food, the protein, carbohydrates, and fat (lipid) in the food are metabolized to form simpler molecules that in turn are used to prepare new molecules that cells need for maintenance and growth. This process also generates the energy needed for the organs to function, allowing the heart to beat, the lungs to breathe, and the brain to think.

The amount of stored energy in food is measured using nutritional Calories (uppercase C), where 1 Cal = 1,000 cal. Since 1,000 cal = 1 kcal, the following relationships exist.

Nutritional Calorie

$$1 \text{ Cal} = 1 \text{ kcal}$$
$$1 \text{ Cal} = 1,000 \text{ cal}$$

Table 6.1   Caloric Value for Three Classes of Compounds

	Cal/g	cal/g
Protein	4	4,000
Carbohydrate	4	4,000
Fat	9	9,000

One nutritional Calorie (1 Cal) = 1,000 cal = 1 kcal.

Upon metabolism, protein, carbohydrates, and fat each release a predictable amount of energy, the **caloric value** of the substance. For example, one gram of protein or one gram of carbohydrate typically releases about 4 Cal/g, whereas fat releases 9 Cal/g (Table 6.1). If we know the amount of each of these substances contained in a food product, we can make a first approximation of the number of Calories it contains by using caloric values as conversion factors, as illustrated in Sample Problem 6.2.

When an individual eats more Calories than are needed for normal bodily maintenance, the body stores the excess as fat. The average body fat content for men and women is about 20% and 25%, respectively. This stored fat can fill the body's energy needs for two or three months. Frequent ingestion of a large excess of Calories results in a great deal of stored fat, causing an individual to be overweight.

SAMPLE PROBLEM 6.2 CALCULATING NUTRITIONAL CALORIES

If a baked potato contains 3 g of protein, a trace of fat, and 23 g of carbohydrates, estimate its number of Calories.

Analysis

Use the caloric value (Cal/g) of each class of molecule to form a conversion factor to convert the number of grams to Calories and add up the results.

Solution

[1] Identify the original quantity and the desired quantity.

3 g protein

23 g carbohydrates   ? Cal

original quantities   desired quantity

[2] Write out the conversion factors.

- Write out conversion factors that relate the number of grams to the number of Calories for each substance. Each conversion factor must place the unwanted unit, grams, in the denominator so that the units cancel.

Cal–g conversion factor for protein   Cal–g conversion factor for carbohydrates

$$\frac{4\text{ Cal}}{1\text{ g protein}} \qquad \frac{4\text{ Cal}}{1\text{ g carbohydrate}}$$

[3] Set up and solve the problem.

- Multiply the original quantity by the conversion factor for both protein and carbohydrates and add up the results to obtain the desired quantity.

Calories due to protein   Calories due to carbohydrate

Total Calories $= \quad 3\text{ g} \times \dfrac{4\text{ Cal}}{1\text{ g protein}} \quad + \quad 23\text{ g carbohydrate} \times \dfrac{4\text{ Cal}}{1\text{ g carbohydrate}}$

Grams cancel.   Grams cancel.

$= \quad\quad 12\text{ Cal} \quad\quad + \quad\quad 92\text{ Cal}$

Total Calories $= \quad$ 104 Cal, rounded to 100 Cal

Answer

PRACTICE PROBLEM 6.2

How many Calories are contained in one tablespoon of olive oil, which has 14 g of fat?

More Practice: Try Problems 6.17–6.22.

PROBLEM 6.2

Use the number of grams of protein, carbohydrates, and fat in the accompanying container of yogurt to estimate the number of Calories in a serving.

6.2   Energy Changes in Reactions

When molecules come together and react, bonds are broken in the reactants and new bonds are formed in the products. **Breaking a bond requires energy.** For example, 58 kcal of energy is needed to break the chlorine–chlorine bond in a mole of chlorine molecules (Cl_2).

To cleave this bond...

...58 kcal/mol of energy must be added.

Knowing the number of grams of protein, carbohydrates, and fat allows you to estimate how many Calories a food product contains. A quarter-pound burger with cheese with 29 g of protein, 40 g of carbohydrates, and 26 g of fat contains 510 Calories.
©FoodCollection/StockFood RF

©The Photo Works/Alamy

In contrast, when the chlorine–chlorine bond is formed, 58 kcal of energy is *released*. **The amount of energy needed to break a bond is the same amount that is released when that bond is formed.**

When this bond is formed...

$$:\ddot{C}l\cdot \ + \ \cdot\ddot{C}l: \ \longrightarrow \ :\ddot{C}l-\ddot{C}l:$$

...58 kcal/mol of energy is released.

- Bond breaking always requires an input of energy and bond formation always releases energy.

The energy absorbed or released in any reaction is called the **heat of reaction** or the **enthalpy change,** symbolized by **ΔH.** The heat of reaction is given a positive ($+$) or negative ($-$) sign depending on whether energy is absorbed or released.

- When energy is absorbed, the reaction is said to be *endothermic* and ΔH is positive ($+$).
- When energy is released, the reaction is said to be *exothermic* and ΔH is negative ($-$).

Thus, $\Delta H = +58$ kcal/mol for cleaving the Cl—Cl bond and the reaction is endothermic; on the other hand, $\Delta H = -58$ kcal/mol for forming the Cl—Cl bond and the reaction is exothermic. The heat of reaction is reported as the number of kilocalories *per mole*. The cleavage of two moles of chlorine–chlorine bonds requires twice as much energy; that is, (2 mol)($+58$ kcal/mol) $= +116$ kcal.

6.2A Bond Dissociation Energy

The heat of reaction (ΔH) for breaking a covalent bond by equally dividing the electrons between the two atoms in the bond is called the **bond dissociation energy.** Because bond breaking requires energy, **bond dissociation energies are always *positive* numbers,** and breaking a covalent bond into the atoms that compose it is always **endothermic.** Since **bond formation always *releases* energy,** forming a bond is **exothermic and ΔH is a *negative* number.** The H—H bond requires $+104$ kcal/mol to cleave and releases -104 kcal/mol when formed. Table 6.2 lists bond dissociation energies for some simple molecules.

Bond breaking is **endothermic.**
Energy must be added.

$$H-H \ \longrightarrow \ H\cdot \ + \ \cdot H \qquad \Delta H = +104 \text{ kcal/mol}$$

$$H\cdot \ + \ \cdot H \ \longrightarrow \ H-H \qquad \Delta H = -104 \text{ kcal/mol}$$

Bond making is **exothermic.**
Energy is released.

Table 6.2 Bond Dissociation Energies (ΔH) for Some Common Bonds ($A–B \rightarrow A\cdot + \cdot B$)	
Bond	ΔH (kcal/mol)
H—H	$+104$
F—F	$+38$
Cl—Cl	$+58$
Br—Br	$+46$
I—I	$+36$
H—OH	$+119$
H—F	$+136$
H—Cl	$+103$
H—Br	$+88$
H—I	$+71$

SAMPLE PROBLEM 6.3 CLASSIFYING A REACTION AS ENDOTHERMIC OR EXOTHERMIC

Write the equation for the formation of HCl from H and Cl atoms. Classify the reaction as endothermic or exothermic, and give the ΔH using the values in Table 6.2.

Analysis

Bond formation is exothermic and ΔH is ($-$). The energy released in forming a bond is ($-$) the bond dissociation energy.

Solution

Energy is released.

$$H\cdot \ + \ \cdot\ddot{C}l: \ \longrightarrow \ H-\ddot{C}l: \qquad \Delta H = -103 \text{ kcal/mol}$$

Bond formation is **exothermic.**

PRACTICE PROBLEM 6.3

Using the values in Table 6.2, give ΔH for each reaction, and classify the reaction as endothermic or exothermic.

a. H—B̈r: ⟶ H· + ·B̈r: c. H—ÖH ⟶ H· + ·ÖH

b. H· + ·F̈: ⟶ H—F̈:

More Practice: Try Problems 6.25, 6.26.

Bond dissociation energies tell us about bond strength.

- **The *stronger* the bond, the *higher* its bond dissociation energy.**

For example, since the bond dissociation energy for the H—H bond (+104 kcal/mol) is *higher* than the bond dissociation energy for the Cl—Cl bond (+58 kcal/mol), the H—H bond is *stronger*.

Bond dissociation energies exhibit periodic trends, much like atomic radius (Section 2.8A) and electronegativity (Section 4.7). In the series, HF, HCl, HBr, and HI, hydrogen is bonded to the first four elements of group 7A (the halogens). According to Table 6.2, the bond dissociation energies of these compounds *decrease* down the column from HF → HCl → HBr → HI. HI has the *weakest* of these four bonds because the valence electrons used by I to form the H—I bond are farther from the nucleus than the valence electrons in Br, Cl, or F. Similarly, HF has the *strongest* of these four bonds because the valence electrons in F are closer to the nucleus than those in Cl, Br, or I. This is a specific example of a general periodic trend.

highest bond dissociation energy strongest bond			lowest bond dissociation energy weakest bond	
H—F̈:	H—C̈l:		H—B̈r:	H—Ï:
ΔH = +136 kcal/mol	+103 kcal/mol		+88 kcal/mol	+71 kcal/mol

- **In comparing bonds formed from atoms in the same group of the periodic table, bond dissociation energies generally *decrease* going down the column.**

SAMPLE PROBLEM 6.4 DETERMINING THE RELATIVE BOND DISSOCIATION ENERGY

Considering the indicated carbon–halogen bonds, which bond is predicted to have the higher bond dissociation energy? Which bond is stronger?

Analysis

The higher the bond dissociation energy, the stronger the bond. In comparing bonds to atoms in the same group of the periodic table, bond dissociation energies and bond strength *decrease* down a column.

Solution

Since Cl is below F in the same group of the periodic table, the C—Cl bond is predicted to have the *lower* bond dissociation energy, thus making it *weaker*. The actual values for the bond dissociation energies are given and illustrate that the prediction is indeed true.

lower bond dissociation energy
weaker bond

ΔH = +109 kcal/mol   ΔH = +84 kcal/mol

PRACTICE PROBLEM 6.4

Which indicated bond in each pair of compounds has the higher bond dissociation energy? Which is the stronger bond?

More Practice: Try Problems 6.23, 6.24.

6.2B   Calculations Involving ΔH Values

Most reactions involve breaking and forming more than one bond. In these instances, the heat of reaction measures the difference between the energy needed to break bonds in the reactants and the energy released from the bonds formed in the products. In other words, **ΔH indicates the relative strength of bonds broken and formed in a reaction.**

- When ΔH is negative, more energy is released in forming bonds than is needed to break bonds. The bonds formed in the products are *stronger* than the bonds broken in the reactants. The reaction is *exothermic*.

For example, when methane (CH_4) burns in the presence of oxygen (O_2) to form CO_2 and H_2O, 213 kcal of energy is released in the form of heat.

The methane produced by decomposing waste material in large landfills is burned to produce energy for heating and generating electricity.
©Stockbyte/Getty Images RF

Heat is released.

$$CH_4(g) + 2\,O_2(g) \longrightarrow CO_2(g) + 2\,H_2O(l) \quad \Delta H = -213\text{ kcal}$$

In this reaction energy is released, ΔH is negative (−), and the reaction is exothermic. The bonds formed are stronger than the bonds broken, because more energy is released in forming the bonds in CO_2 and H_2O than is absorbed in breaking the bonds in CH_4 and O_2. **Since energy is released, the products are *lower* in energy than the reactants.**

When the values for ΔH are reported in kilocalories per mole (kcal/mol), this means that the given amount of energy is released (or absorbed) for the molar quantities shown by the coefficients in the balanced chemical equation. Thus, 213 kcal of energy is released when 1 mol of CH_4 reacts with 2 mol of O_2 to form 1 mol of CO_2 and 2 mol of H_2O.

- When ΔH is positive, more energy is needed to break bonds than is released in forming bonds. The bonds broken in the reactants are *stronger* than the bonds formed in the product. The reaction is *endothermic*.

For example, in the process of photosynthesis, green plants use chlorophyll to convert CO_2 and H_2O to glucose ($C_6H_{12}O_6$, a simple carbohydrate) and O_2 and 678 kcal of energy is absorbed.

$$6\,CO_2(g) + 6\,H_2O(l) \longrightarrow C_6H_{12}O_6(aq) + 6\,O_2(g) \quad \Delta H = +678\text{ kcal}$$

In this reaction energy is absorbed, ΔH is positive (+), and the reaction is endothermic. The bonds broken are stronger than the bonds formed, because more energy is needed to break the bonds in CO_2 and H_2O than is released in forming the bonds in $C_6H_{12}O_6$ and O_2. **Since energy is absorbed, the products are *higher* in energy than the reactants.**

Table 6.3 summarizes the characteristics of energy changes in reactions.

Photosynthesis is an endothermic reaction. Energy from sunlight is absorbed in the reaction and stored in the bonds of the products.
©Comstock/Stockbyte/Getty Images RF

PROBLEM 6.3

Answer the following questions using the given equation and ΔH. (a) Is heat absorbed or released? (b) Which bonds are stronger, those in the reactants or those in the products? (c) Are the reactants or products lower in energy? (d) Is the reaction endothermic or exothermic?

$$2\,NH_3(g) \longrightarrow 3\,H_2(g) + N_2(g) \quad \Delta H = +22.0\text{ kcal}$$

Table 6.3 Endothermic and Exothermic Reactions

Endothermic Reaction	Exothermic Reaction
• Heat is absorbed.	• Heat is released.
• ΔH is positive.	• ΔH is negative.
• The bonds broken in the reactants are *stronger* than the bonds formed in the products.	• The bonds formed in the products are *stronger* than the bonds broken in the reactants.
• The products are *higher* in energy than the reactants.	• The products are *lower* in energy than the reactants.

Once we know the ΔH for a balanced chemical reaction, we can use this information to calculate how much energy is absorbed or released for any given amount of reactant or product. A value for ΔH and the coefficients of the balanced equation are used to set up conversion factors, as shown in Sample Problem 6.5. To convert the number of grams of a reactant to the number of kilocalories released, we must use the molar mass, as shown in Sample Problem 6.6.

SAMPLE PROBLEM 6.5 CALCULATING THE ENERGY CHANGE USING A BALANCED EQUATION

The combustion of propane (C_3H_8) with O_2 according to the given balanced chemical equation releases 531 kcal. How many kilocalories of energy are released when 0.750 mol of propane is burned?

$$C_3H_8(g) + 5\ O_2(g) \longrightarrow 3\ CO_2(g) + 4\ H_2O(l) \qquad \Delta H = -531\ \text{kcal}$$
propane

Analysis

Use the given value of ΔH to set up a conversion factor that relates the kcal of energy released to the number of moles of C_3H_8.

Solution

The given ΔH value is the amount of energy released when 1 mol of C_3H_8 reacts with 5 mol of O_2. Set up a conversion factor that relates kilocalories to moles of C_3H_8, with moles in the denominator to cancel this unwanted unit.

kcal–mol
conversion factor

$$0.750\ \text{mol}\ C_3H_8 \times \frac{531\ \text{kcal}}{1\ \text{mol}\ C_3H_8} = 398\ \text{kcal of energy released}$$

Moles cancel.

Answer

PRACTICE PROBLEM 6.5

Given the ΔH and balanced equation in Sample Problem 6.5, how many kilocalories of energy are released when 1.00 mol of O_2 reacts with propane?

More Practice: Try Problems 6.27, 6.28.

SAMPLE PROBLEM 6.6 CALCULATING THE ENERGY CHANGE OF A REACTION FROM GRAMS OF REACTANT

Using the given value of ΔH and the balanced equation for the reaction of Mg with H_2O (in the presence of a small amount of Fe and NaCl), how many kilocalories of energy are released when 4.00 g of Mg are used in this reaction?

$$Mg(s) + 2\ H_2O(l) \longrightarrow Mg(OH)_2(s) + H_2(g) \qquad \Delta H = -83.9\ \text{kcal}$$

Analysis

To relate the number of grams of Mg to the number of kilocalories of energy released, two operations are needed: [1] Convert the number of grams to the number of moles using the molar mass. [2] Convert

The energy released from the reaction of magnesium and water (Sample Problem 6.6) provides a flameless method for heating the food rations of military personnel. *Source: Tech. Sgt. David McLeod/Defenseimagery.MIL Department of Defense (DoD)*

the number of moles to the number of kilocalories using ΔH (kcal/mol) and the coefficients of the balanced chemical equation.

Solution

[1] Convert the number of grams of magnesium to the number of moles of magnesium.

- Use the molar mass of the reactant (Mg, molar mass 24.31 g/mol) to write a conversion factor. Multiply the number of grams of magnesium by the conversion factor to give the number of moles of magnesium.

molar mass conversion factor

$$4.00 \text{ g Mg} \quad \times \quad \frac{1 \text{ mol Mg}}{24.31 \text{ g Mg}} \quad = \quad 0.165 \text{ mol Mg}$$

Grams cancel.

[2] Convert the number of moles of magnesium to the number of kilocalories using a kcal–mole conversion factor.

- Use the ΔH and the number of moles of magnesium in the balanced chemical equation to write a kcal–mole conversion factor—one mole of magnesium (Mg) releases 83.9 kcal of energy. Multiply the number of moles of magnesium by the conversion factor to give the number of kilocalories of energy released. This process was illustrated in Sample Problem 6.5.

kcal–mol conversion factor

$$0.165 \text{ mol Mg} \quad \times \quad \frac{83.9 \text{ kcal}}{1 \text{ mol Mg}} \quad = \quad 13.8 \text{ kcal of energy released}$$

Moles cancel.

Answer

PRACTICE PROBLEM 6.6

Answer the following questions about the fermentation of glucose ($C_6H_{12}O_6$, molar mass 180.2 g/mol) to ethanol (C_2H_6O) and CO_2.

$$C_6H_{12}O_6(s) \longrightarrow 2\,C_2H_6O(l) + 2\,CO_2(g) \qquad \Delta H = -16 \text{ kcal}$$
glucose   ethanol

a. How many kilocalories of energy are released from 6.0 mol of glucose?

b. How many kilocalories of energy are released when 1.0 mol of ethanol is formed?

c. How many kilocalories of energy are released from 20.0 g of glucose?

More Practice: Try Problems 6.29, 6.30.

6.3 Energy Diagrams

On a molecular level, what happens when a reaction occurs? In order for two molecules to react, they must collide, and in the collision, the kinetic energy they possess is used to break bonds. Not every collision between two molecules, however, leads to a reaction. **Collisions must have the proper orientation and enough energy for the reaction to occur.**

How does the orientation of a collision affect a reaction? Consider a general reaction between two starting materials, **A—B** and **C** in which the **A—B** bond is broken and a new **B—C** bond is formed.

This bond breaks.   This bond forms.

Since **C** forms a new bond with **B,** a reaction occurs only when **C** collides with **B.** If **C** collides with **A,** no bond breaking or bond making can occur, and a reaction does not take place. Since molecular collisions are random events, many collisions are ineffective because they do not place the reacting atoms close to each other.

proper orientation	improper orientation
C collides with **B**, so a new **B–C** bond can form.	**C** collides with **A**, so a new **B–C** bond cannot form.

The energy of the reacting molecules also determines whether a particular collision will lead to a reaction. In any given sample, molecules possess a wide range of kinetic energies. Some are fast moving and possess more kinetic energy than others that are slow moving. Since the kinetic energy of the reacting molecules **A—B** and **C** provides the energy to break the **A—B** bond, **reaction occurs only when the reactants possess sufficient energy.**

- Thus, only collisions that have sufficient energy and proper orientation lead to a reaction.

The energy changes in a reaction are often illustrated on an **energy diagram,** which plots energy on the vertical axis, and the progress of the reaction—the **reaction coordinate**—on the horizontal axis. The reactants are written on the left side and the products on the right side, and a smooth curve that illustrates how energy changes with time connects them. Let's assume that the products, **A** and **B—C,** are lower in energy than the reactants, **A—B** and **C.**

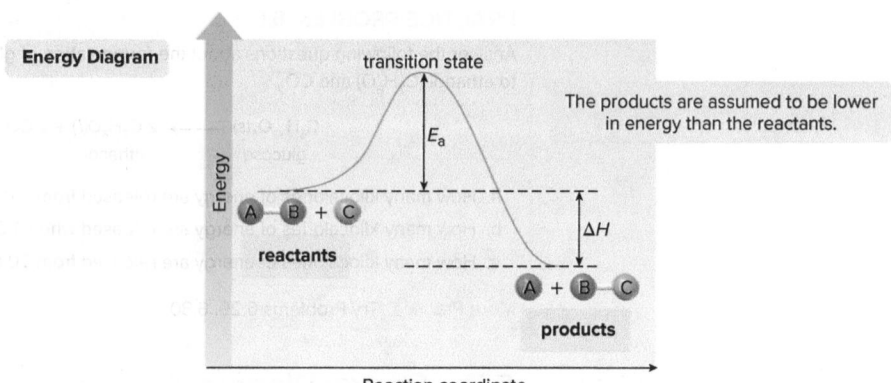

Reaction coordinate

When the reactants **A—B** and **C** approach each other, their electron clouds feel some repulsion, causing an increase in energy until a maximum value is reached. This point is called the **transition state.** In the transition state, the bond between **A** and **B** is partially broken and the bond between **B** and **C** is partially formed. The transition state is located at the top of the energy hill that separates reactants from products. To draw a transition state, we use **dashed lines** for any bond that is broken or formed.

This bond is partially broken. ⌐   This bond is partially formed.

At the transition state, the bond between **A** and **B** can re-form to regenerate reactants, or the bond between **B** and **C** can form to generate products. As the bond forms between **B** and **C**, the energy decreases until some stable energy minimum is reached. The products are drawn lower in energy than the reactants to reflect the initial assumption about their relative energies.

- The difference in energy between the reactants and the transition state is called the *energy of activation*, symbolized by E_a.

The energy of activation is the minimum amount of energy needed for a reaction to occur. It represents the amount of energy that the reactants must possess for the reaction to take place. The energy of activation is often called the **energy barrier** that must be crossed. The height of the energy barrier—the magnitude of the energy of activation—determines the **reaction rate, how fast the reaction occurs.**

- When the energy of activation is *high,* few molecules have enough energy to cross the energy barrier and the reaction is *slow.*
- When the energy of activation is *low,* many molecules have enough energy to cross the energy barrier and the reaction is *fast.*

The difference in energy between the reactants and products is the ΔH, which is also labeled on the energy diagram. When the products are *lower* in energy than the reactants, as is the case here, the bonds in the product are *stronger* than the bonds in the reactants. ΔH is *negative* (−), and the reaction is *exothermic.*

Energy diagrams can be drawn for any reaction. In the endothermic reaction shown in Figure 6.1, the products are higher in energy than the reactants.

An energy diagram is a visual tool that helps to illustrate both the rate of a reaction (by the height of the energy barrier), and the energy difference between the reactants and the products. Keep in mind that these two quantities are independent. **A large E_a does not tell us anything about the relative energies of the reactants and products.**

- The size of E_a determines the rate of a reaction.
- The sign of ΔH determines whether the products or reactants are lower in energy. Reactions are favored in which ΔH is negative and the products are lower in energy, making them more stable than the reactants.

Figure 6.1

Energy Diagram for
an Endothermic Reaction

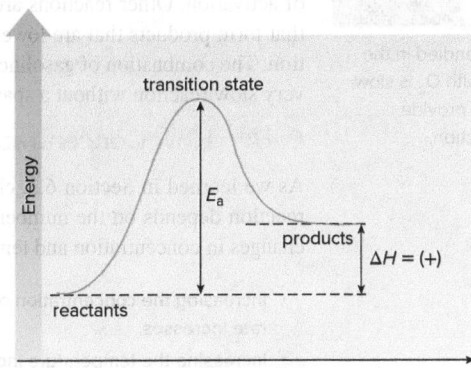

- E_a is the energy difference between the reactants and the transition state.
- ΔH is the difference in energy between the reactants and products.
- Because the products are *higher* in energy than the reactants, ΔH is *positive* (+) and the reaction is *endothermic.*

SAMPLE PROBLEM 6.7 DRAWING AN ENERGY DIAGRAM

Draw an energy diagram for a reaction with a low energy of activation and a ΔH of -10 kcal/mol. Label the axes, reactants, products, transition state, E_a, and ΔH.

Analysis

A low energy of activation means a low energy barrier and a small hill that separates reactants and products. When ΔH is $(-)$, the products are lower in energy than the reactants.

Solution

PRACTICE PROBLEM 6.7

Draw an energy diagram for a reaction with a high E_a and a $\Delta H = +20$ kcal/mol.

More Practice: Try Problems 6.31–6.36.

6.4 Reaction Rates

Even though we may not realize it, the rate of chemical processes affects many facets of our lives. Aspirin is an effective pain reliever because it rapidly blocks the synthesis of pain-causing molecules. Butter turns rancid with time because its fat molecules are slowly oxidized by oxygen in the air to undesirable by-products. DDT is a persistent environmental pollutant because it does not react appreciably with water, oxygen, or any other chemical with which it comes into contact. All of these processes occur at different rates, resulting in beneficial or harmful effects.

The energy of activation, the minimum amount of energy needed for a reaction to occur, is a fundamental characteristic of a reaction. Some reactions are fast because they have low energies of activation. Other reactions are slow because the energy of activation is high. Even reactions that form products that are lower in energy than the reactants can have high energies of activation. The combustion of gasoline to form CO_2 and H_2O releases a great deal of energy, but it is a very slow reaction without a spark or flame to initiate the reaction.

6.4A How Concentration and Temperature Affect Reaction Rate

As we learned in Section 6.3, chemical reactions occur when molecules collide. The rate of a reaction depends on the number of collisions and the effectiveness of each collision. How do changes in concentration and temperature affect the reaction rate?

- Increasing the concentration of the reactants increases the number of collisions, so the reaction rate increases.
- Increasing the temperature increases the reaction rate.

Increasing the temperature increases the reaction rate for two reasons. First, increasing the temperature increases the kinetic energy, which increases the number of collisions. Second, increasing the temperature increases the *average* kinetic energy of the reactants. Because the kinetic energy of colliding molecules is used for bond cleavage, more molecules have sufficient energy

ENVIRONMENTAL NOTE

Gasoline can be safely handled in the air because its reaction with O_2 is slow unless there is a spark to provide energy to initiate the reaction.
©Creatas/PunchStock RF

to cause bond breaking, and the reaction rate increases. As a general rule, a reaction rate *doubles* for each 10 °C the temperature is *raised*. Similarly, a reaction rate is generally *halved* for each 10 °C the temperature is *lowered*.

PROBLEM 6.4

Consider the reaction of ozone (O_3) with nitrogen monoxide (NO), which occurs in smog. What effect would each of the following changes have on the rate of this reaction?

$$O_3(g) + NO(g) \longrightarrow O_2(g) + NO_2(g)$$

a. increasing the concentration of O_3

b. decreasing the concentration of NO

c. increasing the temperature

d. decreasing the temperature

6.4B Catalysts

Some reactions do not occur in a reasonable period of time unless a **catalyst** is added.

- A *catalyst* is a substance that speeds up the rate of a reaction. A catalyst is recovered unchanged in a reaction, and it does not appear in the product.

Catalysts accelerate a reaction by lowering the energy of activation (Figure 6.2). They have no effect on the energies of the reactants and products. Thus, the addition of a catalyst lowers E_a but does not affect ΔH.

Metals are often used as catalysts in reactions. For example, ethylene ($CH_2=CH_2$) does not react appreciably with hydrogen (H_2), but in the presence of palladium (Pd) a rapid reaction occurs and ethane (C_2H_6) is formed as the product. The metal serves as a surface that brings together both reactants, facilitating the reaction. This reaction, called **hydrogenation,** is used in the food industry to prepare margarine, peanut butter, and many other consumer products that contain vegetable oils (Section 13.7).

H₂C=CH₂ (ethylene)   + H_2 $\xrightarrow{\text{Pd}}$ C_2H_6 (ethane)

catalyst

PROBLEM 6.5

Draw an energy diagram for an uncatalyzed exothermic reaction. Then draw an energy diagram for the same reaction when a catalyst is added. Label the axes, reactants, products, and energy of activation for both reactions.

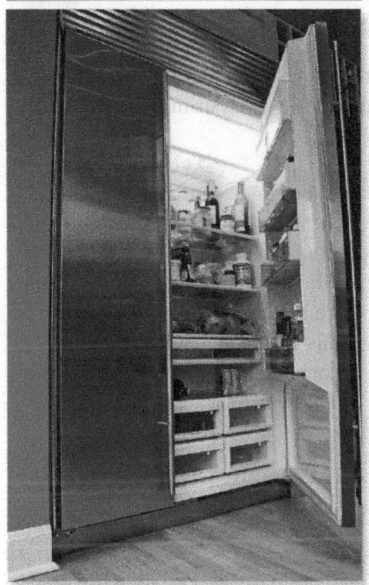

We store food in a cold refrigerator to slow the reactions that cause food to spoil.
©McGraw-Hill Education/Jill Braaten, photographer

Figure 6.2   The Effect of a Catalyst on a Reaction

uncatalyzed reaction: **higher** E_a ----➤ **slower** reaction

catalyzed reaction: **lower** E_a ----➤ **faster** reaction

A catalyst lowers the energy of activation, thus increasing the rate of the catalyzed reaction. The energy of the reactants and products is the same in both the uncatalyzed and catalyzed reactions.

6.4C   FOCUS ON THE HUMAN BODY
Lactase, a Biological Catalyst

The catalysts that synthesize and break down biological molecules in living organisms are governed by the same principles as the metals in organic reactions. The catalysts in living organisms, however, are protein molecules called **enzymes.**

Enzymes are discussed in greater detail in Sections 21.9 and 21.10.

• *Enzymes* are biological catalysts held together in a very specific three-dimensional shape.

An enzyme contains a region called its **active site** that binds a reactant, which then undergoes a very specific reaction with an enhanced rate. For example, **lactase** is the enzyme that binds **lactose,** the principal carbohydrate in milk (Figure 6.3). Once bound, lactose is converted into two simpler sugars, glucose and galactose. When individuals lack adequate amounts of this enzyme, they are unable to digest lactose, and this causes abdominal cramping and diarrhea.

Figure 6.3   Lactase, an Example of a Biological Catalyst

lactose
$C_{12}H_{22}O_{11}$

enzyme

active site

lactase

[1]

The enzyme catalyzes the breaking of this bond.

enzyme

lactase

The enzyme is the catalyst. It is recovered unchanged in the reaction.

[2] H_2O

+

galactose
$C_6H_{12}O_6$

+

glucose
$C_6H_{12}O_6$

The enzyme lactase binds the carbohydrate lactose ($C_{12}H_{22}O_{11}$) in its active site in step [1]. Lactose then reacts with water to break a bond and form two simpler sugars, galactose and glucose, in step [2]. This process is the first step in digesting lactose, the principal carbohydrate in milk. Without the enzyme, individuals are unable to convert lactose to galactose and glucose, lactose cannot be metabolized, and digestive problems result. ©*McGraw-Hill Education/Jill Braaten, photographer*

6.4D FOCUS ON THE ENVIRONMENT
Catalytic Converters

There is a direct link between the poor air quality in large metropolitan areas like Los Angeles and an increase in respiratory diseases. ©Ingram Publishing/SuperStock RF

The combustion of gasoline with oxygen provides a great deal of energy, much like the oxidation reactions of methane and propane discussed in Section 6.2B, and this energy is used to power vehicles. As the number of automobiles increased in the twentieth century, the air pollution they were responsible for became a major problem, especially in congested urban areas.

One problem with the auto engines of the 1970s centered on the carbon- and nitrogen-containing by-products emitted in engine exhaust. In addition to CO_2 and H_2O formed during combustion, auto exhaust also contained unreacted gasoline molecules (general formula C_xH_y), the toxic gas carbon monoxide (CO, Section 5.7), and nitrogen monoxide (NO, Section 5.7, a contributing component of acid rain). **Catalytic converters** were devised to clean up these polluting automobile emissions.

The newest catalytic converters, called three-way catalytic converters, use a metal as a surface to catalyze three reactions, as shown in Figure 6.4. Both the unreacted gasoline molecules and carbon monoxide (CO) are oxidized to CO_2 and H_2O. Nitrogen monoxide is also converted to oxygen and nitrogen. In this way, three molecules that contribute to unhealthy smog levels are removed, and the only materials in the engine exhaust are CO_2, H_2O, N_2, and O_2.

Figure 6.4 How a Catalytic Converter Works

$$C_xH_y + O_2 \longrightarrow CO_2 + H_2O \text{ (unbalanced)}$$
$$2\,CO + O_2 \longrightarrow 2\,CO_2$$
$$2\,NO \longrightarrow N_2 + O_2$$

A catalytic converter uses a metal catalyst—rhodium, platinum, or palladium—to catalyze three reactions that clean up the exhaust from an auto engine.

6.5 Equilibrium

Thus far in discussing reactions we have assumed that the reactants are completely converted to products. A reaction of this sort is said to **go to completion.** Sometimes, however, a reaction is **reversible;** that is, reactants can come together and form products, and products can come together to re-form reactants.

• A *reversible reaction* can occur in either direction, from reactants to products or from products to reactants.

Consider the reversible reaction of carbon monoxide (CO) with water to form carbon dioxide (CO_2) and hydrogen. Two full-headed arrows ($\rightleftarrows$) are used to show that the reaction can proceed from left to right and right to left as written.

The **forward** reaction proceeds to the ***right***.

$$CO(g) \;+\; H_2O(g) \;\rightleftarrows\; CO_2(g) \;+\; H_2(g)$$

The **reverse** reaction proceeds to the ***left***.

• The *forward* reaction proceeds from left to right as drawn.
• The *reverse* reaction proceeds from right to left as drawn.

When CO and H_2O are mixed together, they react to form CO_2 and H_2 by the forward reaction. Once CO_2 and H_2 are formed, they can react together to form CO and H_2O by the reverse reaction. The rate of the forward reaction is rapid at first, and then decreases as the concentration of reactants decreases. The rate of the reverse reaction is slow at first, but speeds up as the concentration of the products increases.

• When the rate of the forward reaction equals the rate of the reverse reaction, the net concentrations of all species do not change and the system is at *equilibrium*.

The forward and reverse reactions do not stop once equilibrium has been reached. The reactants and products continue to react. Since the rates of the forward and reverse reactions are equal, however, the **net concentrations of all reactants and products do *not* change.** Molecular art in Figure 6.5 shows how the reversible reaction A $\rightleftarrows$ B reaches equilibrium.

PROBLEM 6.6

Identify the forward and reverse reactions in each of the following reversible reactions.

a. $2\,SO_2(g) + O_2(g) \rightleftarrows 2\,SO_3(g)$
b. $N_2(g) + O_2(g) \rightleftarrows 2\,NO(g)$
c. $C_2H_4O_2 + CH_4O \rightleftarrows C_3H_6O_2 + H_2O$

Figure 6.5

Attaining Equilibrium in a Reaction, A $\rightleftarrows$ B

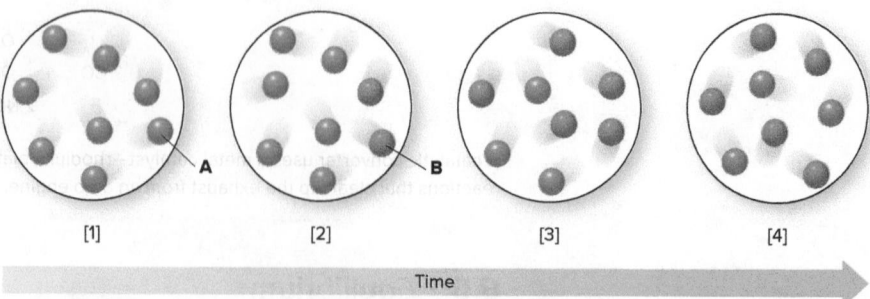

The conversion of **A** (shown in blue spheres) to **B** (shown in red spheres) is a reversible reaction. Initially, the reaction contains only **A** (diagram [1]). As **A** reacts to form **B**, the amount of **B** increases (diagram [2]). As **B** is formed, it can be re-converted to **A**. At equilibrium (diagrams [3] and [4]), the amounts of **A** and **B** do not change, but the conversion of **A** to **B** and the conversion of **B** to **A** still occur.

6.5A The Equilibrium Constant

Because the net concentrations of the reactants and products do not change at equilibrium, they are used to define an expression, the **equilibrium constant, K,** which has a characteristic value for a reaction at a given temperature. When discussing equilibrium it is not the absolute number of moles that is the important quantity, but rather it is the *concentration,* **the number of moles in a given volume.** Brackets, [ ], are used to symbolize concentration, which is reported in moles per liter (mol/L).

Consider the following general reaction, where **A** and **B** represent reactants, **C** and **D** represent products, and *a, b, c,* and *d* represent the coefficients in the balanced chemical equation.

$$a\mathbf{A} \ + \ b\mathbf{B} \ \rightleftharpoons \ c\mathbf{C} \ + \ d\mathbf{D}$$

The equilibrium constant K is the ratio of the concentrations of the products (**C** and **D**) multiplied together, to the concentrations of the reactants (**A** and **B**) multiplied together. Each concentration term is raised to a power equal to the coefficient in the balanced chemical equation.

concentration of each product (mol/L)

$$\text{Equilibrium constant} \ = \ K \ = \ \frac{[\text{products}]}{[\text{reactants}]}$$

concentration of each reactant (mol/L)

$$K \ = \ \frac{[\mathbf{C}]^c[\mathbf{D}]^d}{[\mathbf{A}]^a[\mathbf{B}]^b}$$

The expression for the equilibrium constant for any reaction can be written from a balanced equation, as shown for the reaction of N_2 and O_2 to form NO.

above the division line

Balanced equation: $N_2(g) \ + \ O_2(g) \ \rightleftharpoons \ 2\,NO(g)$

below the division line

The coefficient becomes the exponent.

$$\text{Equilibrium constant} \ = \ K \ = \ \frac{[NO]^2}{[N_2][O_2]}$$

SAMPLE PROBLEM 6.8 WRITING THE EXPRESSION FOR AN EQUILIBRIUM CONSTANT

Write the expression for the equilibrium constant for the following balanced equation.

$$2\,CO(g) \ + \ O_2(g) \ \rightleftharpoons \ 2\,CO_2(g)$$

Analysis

To write an expression for the equilibrium constant, multiply the concentration of the products together and divide this number by the product of the concentrations of the reactants. Each concentration term must be raised to a power equal to the coefficient in the balanced chemical equation.

Solution

The concentration of the sole product, CO_2, is placed in the numerator and raised to the second power because this term has the coefficient "2." The denominator contains concentration terms for the two reactants, CO and O_2, multiplied together. Because the coefficient preceding CO in the balanced equation is "2," this concentration term has an exponent of "2."

$$\text{Equilibrium constant} = K = \frac{[CO_2]^2}{[CO]^2[O_2]}$$

PRACTICE PROBLEM 6.8

Write the expression for the equilibrium constant for each equation.

a. $PCl_3(g) + Cl_2(g) \rightleftharpoons PCl_5(g)$

b. $2\,SO_2(g) + O_2(g) \rightleftharpoons 2\,SO_3(g)$

c. $H_2(g) + Br_2(g) \rightleftharpoons 2\,HBr(g)$

d. $CH_4(g) + 3\,Cl_2(g) \rightleftharpoons CHCl_3(g) + 3\,HCl(g)$

More Practice: Try Problems 6.53–6.56, 6.57a, 6.58a, 6.61a, 6.62a.

6.5B   The Magnitude of the Equilibrium Constant

The magnitude of the equilibrium constant tells us whether the products or reactants are favored once equilibrium is reached.

- When the equilibrium constant is much greater than one ($K > 1$), the concentration of the products is larger than the concentration of the reactants. We say equilibrium lies to the *right* and favors the *products*.

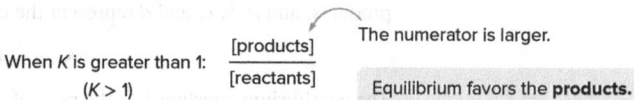

- When the equilibrium constant is much less than one ($K < 1$), the concentration of the reactants is larger than the concentration of the products. We say equilibrium lies to the *left* and favors the *reactants*.

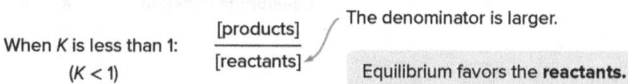

- When the equilibrium constant is around 1, anywhere in the range of 0.01–100, both reactants and products are present at equilibrium.

When K is approximately equal to 1: $\dfrac{[\text{products}]}{[\text{reactants}]}$ Both reactants and products are present.
($K \approx 1$)

For example, the equilibrium constant for the reaction of H_2 and O_2 to form water is much greater than one, so the product, H_2O, is highly favored at equilibrium. A reaction with such a large K essentially goes to completion, with little or no reactants left.

$$2\,H_2(g) \;+\; O_2(g) \;\rightleftharpoons\; 2\,H_2O(g) \qquad K \;=\; 2.9 \times 10^{82}$$

- The product is highly favored since $K > 1$.
- Equilibrium lies to the right.

In contrast, the equilibrium constant for the conversion of O_2 to O_3 is much less than one, so the reactant, O_2, is highly favored at equilibrium, and almost no product, O_3, is formed. The relationship between the equilibrium constant and the direction of equilibrium is summarized in Table 6.4. Molecular art in Figure 6.6 also illustrates the three possibilities.

$$3\,O_2(g) \;\rightleftharpoons\; 2\,O_3(g) \qquad K \;=\; 2.7 \times 10^{-29}$$

- The reactant is highly favored since $K < 1$.
- Equilibrium lies to the left.

Table 6.4 How the Magnitude of K Relates to the Direction of Equilibrium

Value of K	Position of Equilibrium
$K > 1$	Equilibrium favors the products. Equilibrium lies to the right.
$K < 1$	Equilibrium favors the reactants. Equilibrium lies to the left.
$K \approx 1$	Both the reactants and products are present at equilibrium.

Figure 6.6

The Relationship Between the Size of *K* and the Amount of **A** and **B** in a Reaction, **A** ⇌ **B**

a. *K* > 1

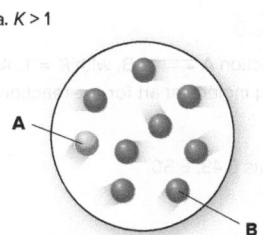

• **[B]** > **[A]**, so equilibrium favors the products.

b. *K* < 1

• **[A]** > **[B]**, so equilibrium favors the reactants.

c. *K* ≈ 1

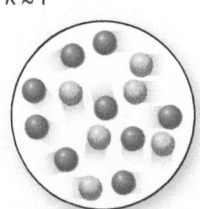

• **[A]** ≈ **[B]**, so both reactants and products are present.

Generally there is a relationship between the equilibrium constant *K* and the ΔH of a reaction.

- The products of a reaction are favored when *K* is much greater than one (*K* > 1), and ΔH is negative. In other words, equilibrium favors the products when they are lower in energy than the reactants.

There is, however, no relationship between *K* and the reaction rate. Some reactions with very large equilibrium constants are still very slow. Moreover, a catalyst may speed up a reaction, but it does not affect the size of *K*. With a catalyst, equilibrium is reached more quickly, but the relative concentrations of reactants and products do not change.

SAMPLE PROBLEM 6.9 USING THE EQUILIBRIUM CONSTANT TO DETERMINE THE AMOUNT OF PRODUCT

Consider the reversible reaction **A** ⇌ **B**, with *K* = 10. Assume the reaction begins with only **A**, and draw a representation for the reaction mixture at equilibrium.

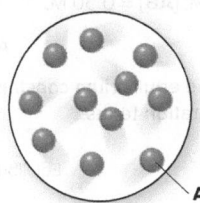

Analysis

Write the expression for the equilibrium constant, and use the value of *K* to determine the relative amounts of product (**B**) and reactant (**A**).

Solution

In this reaction, *K* = [**B**]/[**A**] = 10. Since the concentration of the product is in the numerator, this means that there is 10 times as much product (**B**) as reactant (**A**) at equilibrium.

For *K* = 10: $K = \dfrac{[\mathbf{B}]}{[\mathbf{A}]} = \dfrac{10}{1}$ 10 times as much **B** as **A**

To represent equilibrium in this reaction using molecular art, draw 10 times as many **B** spheres (in red) as **A** spheres (in blue).

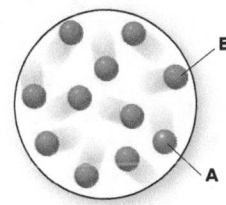

PRACTICE PROBLEM 6.9

Consider the reversible reaction **A** ⇌ **B**, with $K = 1$. Assuming the reaction begins with only **A**, draw a representation using molecular art for the reaction mixture at equilibrium. Use blue spheres for **A** and red spheres for **B**.

More Practice: Try Problems 6.49, 6.50.

PROBLEM 6.7

Given each equilibrium constant, state whether the reactants are favored, the products are favored, or both the reactants and products are present at equilibrium.

   a. 5.0×10^{-4} b. 4.4×10^{5} c. 350   d. 0.35

PROBLEM 6.8

Consider the following reaction: $2\,H_2(g) + S_2(g) \rightleftharpoons 2\,H_2S(g)$ with $K = 1.1 \times 10^7$. (a) Write the expression for the equilibrium constant for this reaction. (b) Are the reactants or products favored at equilibrium? (c) Would you predict ΔH to be positive or negative? (d) Are the reactants or products lower in energy? (e) Would you predict this reaction to be fast or slow? Explain your choice.

6.5C   Calculating the Equilibrium Constant

The equilibrium constant for a reaction is an experimentally determined value, and thus it can be calculated if the concentrations of all substances involved in a reaction are measured at equilibrium. Concentrations are reported in moles per liter (mol/L), symbolized as M.

How To Calculate the Equilibrium Constant for a Reaction

Example: Calculate K for the reaction between the general reactants A_2 and B_2. The equilibrium concentrations are as follows: $[A_2] = 0.25$ M; $[B_2] = 0.25$ M; $[AB] = 0.50$ M.

$$A_2 + B_2 \rightleftharpoons 2\,AB$$

Step [1] **Write the expression for the equilibrium constant from the balanced chemical equation, using the coefficients as exponents for the concentration terms.**

$$\text{Equilibrium constant} = K = \frac{[AB]^2}{[A_2][B_2]}$$

Step [2] **Substitute the given concentrations in the equilibrium expression and calculate K.**
   • Since the concentration is always reported in mol/L (M), these units are omitted during the calculation.

$$K = \frac{[AB]^2}{[A_2][B_2]} = \frac{[0.50]^2}{[0.25][0.25]} = \frac{(0.50) \times (0.50)}{0.0625}$$

$$= \frac{0.25}{0.0625} = 4.0$$
Answer

SAMPLE PROBLEM 6.10 CALCULATING THE EQUILIBRIUM CONSTANT USING MOLECULAR ART

Using the equilibrium mixture of reactants and products, calculate K for the reaction with the balanced equation, $A_2 + B_2 \longrightarrow 2\,AB$.

Analysis and Solution

[1] Write the expression for K using the balanced equation.

- Write the concentration of the only product, **AB**, in the numerator, and use an exponent of "2" because the balanced equation has the coefficient of "2" for this term.
- Write the concentration terms for the two reactants in the denominator, multiplied together.

$$K = \frac{[\textbf{AB}]^2}{[\textbf{A}_2][\textbf{B}_2]}$$

[2] Substitute the number of molecules of reactants and products in the expression for K.

$$K = \frac{[\textbf{AB}]^2}{[\textbf{A}_2][\textbf{B}_2]} = \frac{(3 \text{ molecules } \textbf{AB})^2}{(1 \text{ molecule } \textbf{A}_2)(1 \text{ molecule } \textbf{B}_2)} = \frac{9}{1} = 9$$

PRACTICE PROBLEM 6.10

Using the equilibrium mixture of reactants and products, calculate K for the reaction with the balanced equation, $2\,\textbf{AB} \longrightarrow \textbf{A}_2 + \textbf{B}_2$.

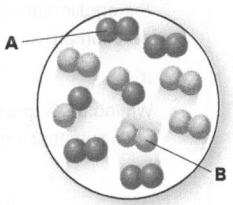

More Practice: Try Problems 6.51, 6.52, 6.59, 6.60.

SAMPLE PROBLEM 6.11 CALCULATING THE EQUILIBRIUM CONSTANT

Calculate K for the reaction of N_2 and H_2 to form NH_3 with the given balanced equation and the following equilibrium concentrations: $[N_2] = 0.12$ M; $[H_2] = 0.36$ M; $[NH_3] = 1.1$ M.

$$N_2(g) + 3\,H_2(g) \rightleftharpoons 2\,NH_3(g)$$

Analysis

Write an expression for K using the balanced equation and substitute the equilibrium concentrations of all substances in the expression.

Solution

$$K = \frac{[NH_3]^2}{[N_2][H_2]^3} = \frac{(1.1)^2}{(0.12)(0.36)^3} = \frac{1.1 \times 1.1}{0.12 \times 0.36 \times 0.36 \times 0.36}$$

$$= \frac{1.21}{0.0056} = 216 \text{ rounded to } 220$$

Answer

PRACTICE PROBLEM 6.11

Calculate the equilibrium constant for each reaction using the balanced chemical equations and the concentrations of the substances at equilibrium.

a. $CO(g) + H_2O(g) \rightleftharpoons CO_2(g) + H_2(g)$ $[CO] = 0.0236$ M; $[H_2O] = 0.00240$ M; $[CO_2] = 0.0164$ M; $[H_2] = 0.0164$ M

b. $2\,NO_2(g) \rightleftharpoons N_2O_4(g)$ $[NO_2] = 0.0760$ M; $[N_2O_4] = 1.26$ M

More Practice: Try Problems 6.61, 6.62.

The conversion of nitrogen and hydrogen to ammonia (Sample Problem 6.11) is an exceedingly important reaction, because it converts molecular nitrogen from the air to a nitrogen compound (NH_3) that can be used as a fertilizer for plants. In the early twentieth century, German chemist Fritz Haber developed a catalyst that enabled this reaction to proceed quickly to afford favorable yields of NH_3. This process paved the way for large-scale agriculture, which provides food for the world's growing population.
©Comstock/PunchStock RF

SAMPLE PROBLEM 6.12 DETERMINING WHETHER A SYSTEM IS AT EQUILIBRIUM

Consider the representation depicted in the molecular art for the reaction $A_2 + B_2 \rightleftharpoons 2\,AB$ with an equilibrium constant $K = 4$. (a) Determine whether the system is at equilibrium. (b) If not, in which direction will the reaction proceed to achieve equilibrium?

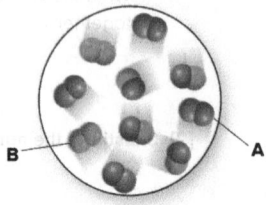

Analysis

- Write the expression for the equilibrium constant for the reaction and substitute the number of molecules of reactants and products to see if the system is at equilibrium.
- If the value is *smaller* than the equilibrium constant, there is less product than would be present at equilibrium, so the reaction proceeds to the *right* to form more product. If the value is *larger* than the equilibrium constant, there is more product than would be present at equilibrium, so the reaction proceeds to the *left* to form more reactants.

Solution

a. Writing the expression for the equilibrium constant and substituting the number of molecules of each substance gives the following result:

$$K = \frac{[AB]^2}{[A_2][B_2]} = \frac{(4 \text{ molecules } AB)^2}{(4 \text{ molecules } A_2)(2 \text{ molecules } B_2)} = \frac{16}{8} = 2$$

Since this value is *less* than the equilibrium constant ($K = 4$), the system is *not* at equilibrium.

b. Since the value is smaller than the equilibrium constant, there is less product than would be present at equilibrium, so the reaction proceeds to the right to form more product **AB.**

PRACTICE PROBLEM 6.12

Consider the representation depicted in the molecular art for the reaction $A + B \rightleftharpoons C + D$ with an equilibrium constant $K = 8$. (a) Determine whether the system is at equilibrium. (b) If not, in which direction will the reaction proceed to achieve equilibrium?

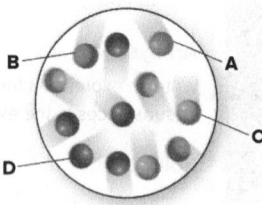

More Practice: Try Problems 6.45, 6.46.

6.6   Le Châtelier's Principle

What happens when a reaction is at equilibrium and something changes? For example, what happens when the temperature is increased or some additional reactant is added? **Le Châtelier's principle** is a general rule used to explain the effect of a change in reaction conditions on equilibrium. Le Châtelier's principle states:

- **If a chemical system at equilibrium is disturbed or stressed, the system will react in the direction that counteracts the disturbance or relieves the stress.**

Let's examine the effect of changes in concentration, temperature, and pressure on equilibrium.

6.6A Concentration Changes

Consider the reaction of carbon monoxide (CO) with oxygen (O_2) to form carbon dioxide (CO_2).

$$2\ CO(g) + O_2(g) \rightleftharpoons 2\ CO_2(g)$$

If the reactants and products are at equilibrium, what happens if the concentration of CO is increased? Now the equilibrium is disturbed and, as a result, the rate of the forward reaction increases to produce more CO_2. We can think of **added reactant as driving the equilibrium to the** *right*.

When the system reaches equilibrium once again, the concentrations of CO_2 and CO are both higher. Since O_2 reacted with the additional CO, its new value at equilibrium is lower. Even though the concentrations of reactants and products are different, the value of K is the same.

Figure 6.7 uses molecular art to illustrate the effect of added reactant in another reaction.

What happens, instead, if the concentration of CO_2 is increased? Now the equilibrium is disturbed but there is more product than there should be. As a result, the rate of the reverse reaction

---

Figure 6.7   The Effect of Added Reactant on Equilibrium for the Reaction, $N_2 + 3\ H_2 \rightleftharpoons 2\ NH_3$

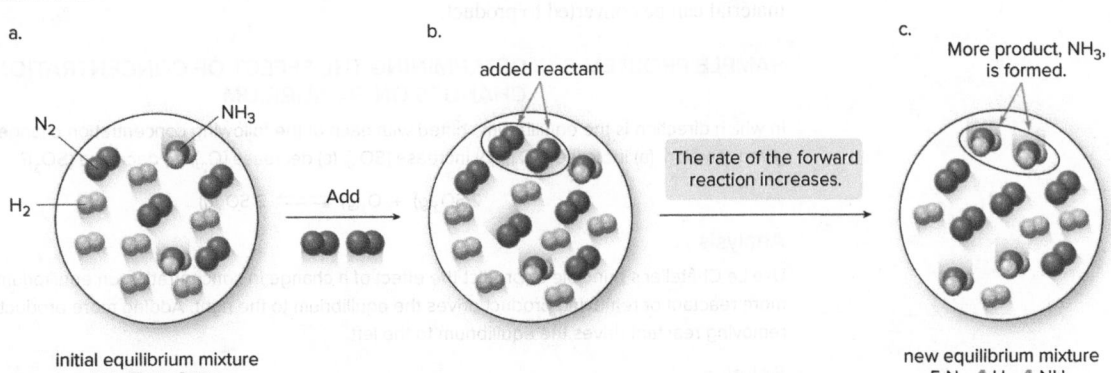

(a) The initial equilibrium mixture shows four molecules of N_2, seven molecules of H_2, and two molecules of the product NH_3. (b) When more N_2, a reactant, is added the equilibrium is disturbed, and the rate of the forward reaction increases to form more product, NH_3. (c) In the new equilibrium mixture, the amount of NH_3 has increased (four molecules). Because H_2, a reactant, is used to form NH_3, the amount of H_2 has decreased (four molecules).

increases to produce more of both reactants, CO and O_2. We can think of **added product as driving the equilibrium to the *left*.**

Adding more product...

$$2\ CO(g)\ +\ O_2(g)\ \rightleftharpoons\ 2\ CO_2(g)$$

...drives the reaction to the left.

When the system reaches equilibrium once again, the concentrations of CO, O_2, and CO_2 are all higher. Even though the concentrations of reactants and products are different, the value of K is the same.

If CO_2 is added...

$$2\ CO(g)\ +\ O_2(g)\ \rightleftharpoons\ 2\ CO_2(g)$$

...this increases...   ...and this increases.

Similar arguments can be made about the effect of decreasing the concentration of a reactant or product. Sometimes, when $K < 1$ and the amount of product at equilibrium is not high, a product is removed from the reaction mixture as it is formed. For example, ethanol (C_2H_6O) can be converted to ethylene ($CH_2{=}CH_2$) and water in the presence of a small amount of acid, but equilibrium does not favor the products.

Removing a product...

...drives the reaction to the right.

In this case, water can be removed from the reaction as it is formed. A decrease in concentration of one product results in more of the forward reaction to form more product. **This process drives the equilibrium to the right.** If water is continuously removed, essentially all of the starting material can be converted to product.

SAMPLE PROBLEM 6.13 DETERMINING THE EFFECT OF CONCENTRATION
CHANGES ON EQUILIBRIUM

In which direction is the equilibrium shifted with each of the following concentration changes for the given reaction: (a) increase $[SO_2]$; (b) increase $[SO_3]$; (c) decrease $[O_2]$; (d) decrease $[SO_3]$?

$$2\ SO_2(g)\ +\ O_2(g)\ \rightleftharpoons\ 2\ SO_3(g)$$

Analysis

Use Le Châtelier's principle to predict the effect of a change in concentration on equilibrium. Adding more reactant or removing product drives the equilibrium to the right. Adding more product or removing reactant drives the equilibrium to the left.

Solution

a. Increasing $[SO_2]$, a reactant, drives the equilibrium to the right to form more product.

b. Increasing $[SO_3]$, a product, drives the equilibrium to the left to form more reactants.

c. Decreasing $[O_2]$, a reactant, drives the equilibrium to the left to form more reactants.

d. Decreasing $[SO_3]$, a product, drives the equilibrium to the right to form more product.

PRACTICE PROBLEM 6.13

In which direction is the equilibrium shifted with each of the following concentration changes for the given reaction: (a) increase $[H_2]$; (b) increase $[HCl]$; (c) decrease $[Cl_2]$; (d) decrease $[HCl]$?

$$H_2(g) + Cl_2(g) \rightleftharpoons 2\ HCl(g)$$

More Practice: Try Problems 6.63–6.66, 6.69a–c, 6.70a–c, 6.71a–c, 6.72a–c.

6.6B   Temperature Changes

In order to predict what effect a change of temperature has on a reaction, we must know if a reaction is endothermic or exothermic.

- When temperature is increased, the reaction that absorbs heat is favored.
- When temperature is decreased, the reaction that releases heat is favored.

For example, the reaction of N_2 and O_2 to form NO is an endothermic reaction ($\Delta H = +43$ kcal/mol). **Since an endothermic reaction absorbs heat, increasing the temperature increases the rate of the *forward* reaction to form more product.** The equilibrium shifts to the right.

In the exothermic reaction of N_2 and H_2 to form NH_3 ($\Delta H = -22$ kcal/mol), **increasing the temperature increases the rate of the *reverse* reaction to form more reactants.** When temperature is increased, the reaction that absorbs heat, in this case the reverse reaction, predominates and the equilibrium shifts to the left.

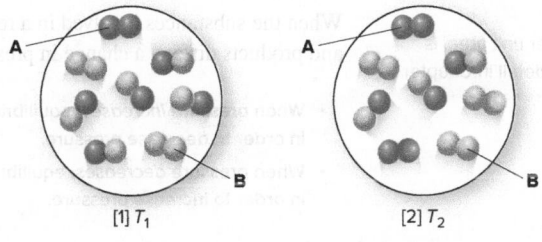

SAMPLE PROBLEM 6.14 DETERMINING THE EFFECT OF TEMPERATURE CHANGE ON EQUILIBRIUM

Consider the reaction with the balanced chemical equation, $A_2 + B_2 \rightleftharpoons 2\ AB$. If representations [1] and [2] show equilibrium mixtures at two different temperatures ($T_2 > T_1$), is the reaction endothermic or exothermic?

Analysis

Look at the number of molecules of reactants and products at each temperature and apply Le Châtelier's principle:

- When the temperature of an *endothermic* reaction is increased, equilibrium favors the *products.*
- When the temperature of an *exothermic* reaction is increased, equilibrium favors the *reactants.*

Solution

At T_1, there are five molecules of the product **AB** and three molecules of reactants (1 **A$_2$** and 2 **B$_2$**), whereas at T_2, there are only three molecules of the product **AB** and five molecules of reactants (2 **A$_2$** and 3 **B$_2$**). Because there is more product at T_1, the lower temperature, the reaction is exothermic.

PRACTICE PROBLEM 6.14

Consider the reaction with the balanced chemical equation, 2 **AB** $\rightleftharpoons$ **A$_2$** + **B$_2$**. If representations [1] and [2] in Sample Problem 6.14 show equilibrium mixtures at two different temperatures ($T_2 > T_1$), is the reaction endothermic or exothermic?

More Practice: Try Problems 6.67, 6.68.

SAMPLE PROBLEM 6.15 DETERMINING THE EFFECT OF TEMPERATURE CHANGE ON EQUILIBRIUM

The reaction of SO_2 with O_2 to form SO_3 is an exothermic reaction. In which direction is the equilibrium shifted when the temperature is (a) increased; (b) decreased?

Analysis

When temperature is increased, the reaction that removes heat is favored. When temperature is decreased, the reaction that adds heat is favored.

Solution

In an exothermic reaction, the forward reaction releases heat and the reverse reaction absorbs heat. (a) When the temperature is increased, the reverse reaction is favored because it removes heat, so the equilibrium shifts to the reactants (to the left). (b) When the temperature is decreased, the forward reaction is favored because it adds heat, so the equilibrium shifts to the products (to the right).

PRACTICE PROBLEM 6.15

The conversion of H_2O to H_2 and O_2 is an endothermic reaction. In which direction is the equilibrium shifted when the temperature is (a) increased; (b) decreased?

More Practice: Try Problems 6.69d; 6.70d; 6.71e, f; 6.72d, e.

PROBLEM 6.9

The reaction of O_3 with NO to form NO_2 and O_2 is an exothermic reaction. In which direction is the equilibrium shifted when the temperature is (a) increased; (b) decreased?

6.6C   Pressure Changes

Pressure, the force per unit area, is discussed in greater detail in Chapter 7.

When the substances involved in a reaction are gases and the total number of moles of reactants and products differs, a change in pressure has an effect on equilibrium.

- When pressure *increases*, equilibrium shifts in the direction that *decreases* the number of moles in order to decrease pressure.
- When pressure *decreases*, equilibrium shifts in the direction that *increases* the number of moles in order to increase pressure.

In the reaction of N_2 and H_2 to form NH_3, there are four moles of reactants but only two moles of product. When the pressure of the system is increased, the equilibrium shifts to the right because there are fewer moles of product.

Increasing pressure...

$$N_2(g) \quad + \quad 3\,H_2(g) \rightleftharpoons 2\,NH_3(g)$$

4 moles   2 moles

This side has fewer moles.

...drives the reaction to the right.

In contrast, when the pressure of the system is decreased, the equilibrium shifts to the left because there are more moles of reactants.

$$N_2(g) \quad + \quad 3\,H_2(g) \rightleftharpoons 2\,NH_3(g)$$

This side has more moles.   4 moles   2 moles

Decreasing pressure...

...drives the reaction to the left.

Table 6.5 summarizes the effects of changes in reaction conditions on the direction of an equilibrium.

Table 6.5 The Effects of Changes in Conditions on Equilibrium

Change	Effect on Equilibrium
Concentration	
• Adding reactant	Equilibrium favors the products.
• Removing reactant	Equilibrium favors the reactants.
• Adding product	Equilibrium favors the reactants.
• Removing product	Equilibrium favors the products.
Temperature	
• Increasing temperature	In an endothermic reaction, equilibrium favors the products. In an exothermic reaction, equilibrium favors the reactants.
• Decreasing temperature	In an endothermic reaction, equilibrium favors the reactants. In an exothermic reaction, equilibrium favors the products.
Pressure	
• Increasing pressure	Equilibrium favors the side that has fewer moles.
• Decreasing pressure	Equilibrium favors the side that has more moles.

SAMPLE PROBLEM 6.16 DETERMINING THE EFFECT OF PRESSURE CHANGES ON EQUILIBRIUM

In which direction is the equilibrium shifted in the following reaction when the pressure is (a) increased; (b) decreased?

$$H{-}C{\equiv}C{-}H(g) + 2\,H_2(g) \rightleftharpoons C_2H_6(g)$$

Analysis

• When pressure is *increased*, the equilibrium shifts in the direction that *decreases* the number of moles.
• When pressure is *decreased*, the equilibrium shifts in the direction that *increases* the number of moles.

216   **Chapter 6** Energy Changes, Reaction Rates, and Equilibrium

Solution

In this reaction, there are three moles of reactants and only one mole of product. (a) Increasing the pressure shifts the equilibrium to the right, to the side of fewer moles. (b) Decreasing the pressure shifts the equilibrium to the left, to the side of more moles.

PRACTICE PROBLEM 6.16

In which direction is the equilibrium shifted in the following reaction when the pressure is (a) increased; (b) decreased?

$$C_2H_4(g) + Cl_2(g) \rightleftharpoons C_2H_4Cl_2(g)$$

More Practice: Try Problems 6.69f, 6.70f, 6.71d, 6.72f.

PROBLEM 6.10

Label each statement about the following exothermic reaction as True or False.

$$4\ NH_3(g) + 3\ O_2(g) \rightleftharpoons 2\ N_2(g) + 6\ H_2O(g)$$

a. Increasing the temperature drives the equilibrium to the right.
b. Doubling the concentration of N_2 drives the reaction to the left.
c. Increasing the pressure by adding an inert gas like helium has no effect on the direction of equilibrium.
d. Removing H_2O drives the reaction to the right.

6.7 FOCUS ON THE HUMAN BODY
Body Temperature

The human body is an enormously complex organism that illustrates important features of energy and reaction rates. At any moment, millions of reactions occur in the body, when nutrients are metabolized and new cell materials are synthesized.

Normal body temperature, 37 °C, reflects a delicate balance between the amount of heat absorbed and released in all of the reactions and other processes. Since reaction rate increases with increasing temperature, it is crucial to maintain the right temperature for proper body function. When temperature increases, reactions proceed at a faster rate. An individual must breathe more rapidly and the heart must pump harder to supply oxygen for the faster metabolic processes. When temperature decreases, reactions slow down, less heat is generated in exothermic reactions, and it becomes harder and harder to maintain an adequate body temperature.

Thermoregulation—regulating temperature—is a complex mechanism that involves the brain, the circulatory system, and the skin (Figure 6.8). Temperature sensors in the skin and body core signal when there is a temperature change. The hypothalamus region of the brain, in turn, responds to changes in its environment in a process that is reminiscent of Le Châtelier's principle.

When the temperature increases, the body must somehow rid itself of excess heat. Blood vessels near the surface of the skin are dilated to release more heat. Sweat glands are stimulated so the body can be cooled by the evaporation of water from the skin's surface.

When the temperature decreases, the body must generate more heat as well as slow down the loss of heat to the surroundings. Blood vessels constrict to reduce heat loss from the skin, and muscles shiver to generate more heat.

An infection in the body is often accompanied by a fever; that is, the temperature in the body increases. A fever is part of the body's response to increase the rates of defensive reactions that kill bacteria. The respiratory rate and heart rate increase to supply more oxygen needed for faster reactions.

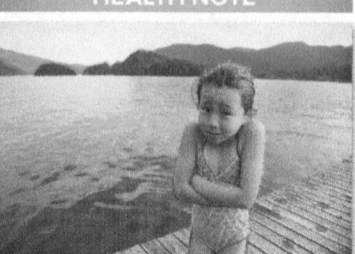

HEALTH NOTE

Shivering, a reflex that occurs when someone is cold, generates warmth from the small, rapid movements of muscles.
©Blend Images-Don Mason/Brand X Pictures/ Getty Images RF

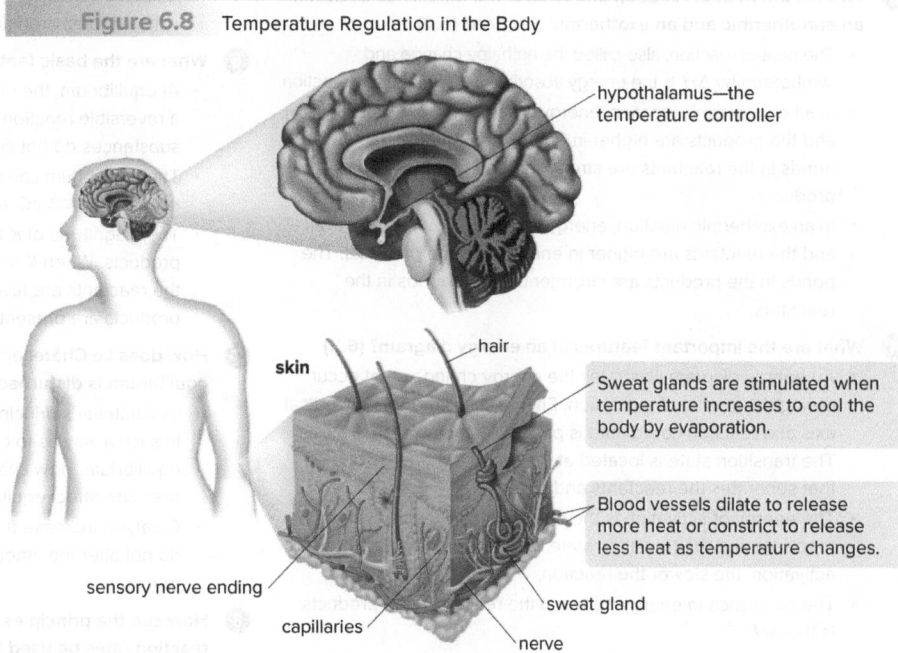

Figure 6.8   Temperature Regulation in the Body

hypothalamus—the
temperature controller

skin

hair

Sweat glands are stimulated when
temperature increases to cool the
body by evaporation.

Blood vessels dilate to release
more heat or constrict to release
less heat as temperature changes.

sensory nerve ending

capillaries

sweat gland

nerve

When the temperature in the environment around the body changes, the body works to counteract the change, in a method similar to Le Châtelier's principle. The hypothalamus acts as a thermostat, which signals the body to respond to temperature changes. When the temperature increases, the body must dissipate excess heat by dilating blood vessels and sweating. When the temperature decreases, blood vessels constrict and the body shivers.

CHAPTER HIGHLIGHTS

KEY TERMS

Active site (6.4)

Bond dissociation energy (6.2)

Calorie (6.1)

Catalyst (6.4)

Endothermic reaction (6.2)

Energy (6.1)

Energy diagram (6.3)

Energy of activation (6.3)

Enthalpy change (6.2)

Enzyme (6.4)

Equilibrium (6.5)

Equilibrium constant (6.5)

Exothermic reaction (6.2)

Forward reaction (6.5)

Heat of reaction (6.2)

Joule (6.1)

Kinetic energy (6.1)

Law of conservation of energy (6.1)

Le Châtelier's principle (6.6)

Potential energy (6.1)

Reaction rate (6.3)

Reverse reaction (6.5)

Reversible reaction (6.5)

Transition state (6.3)

KEY CONCEPTS

❶ What is energy and what units are used to measure energy? (6.1)

- Energy is the capacity to do work. Kinetic energy is the energy of motion, whereas potential energy is stored energy.
- Energy is measured in calories (cal) or joules (J), where 1 cal = 4.184 J.
- One nutritional calorie (Cal) = 1 kcal = 1,000 cal.

❷ Define bond dissociation energy and describe its relationship to bond strength. (6.2)

- The bond dissociation energy is the energy needed to break a covalent bond by equally dividing the electrons between the two atoms in the bond.
- The *higher* the bond dissociation energy, the *stronger* the bond.

③ What is the heat of reaction and what is the difference between an endothermic and an exothermic reaction? (6.2)

- The heat of reaction, also called the enthalpy change and symbolized by ΔH, is the energy absorbed or released in a reaction.
- In an endothermic reaction, energy is absorbed, ΔH is positive (+), and the products are higher in energy than the reactants. The bonds in the reactants are stronger than the bonds in the products.
- In an exothermic reaction, energy is released, ΔH is negative (−), and the reactants are higher in energy than the products. The bonds in the products are stronger than the bonds in the reactants.

④ What are the important features of an energy diagram? (6.3)

- An energy diagram illustrates the energy changes that occur during the course of a reaction. Energy is plotted on the vertical axis and reaction coordinate is plotted on the horizontal axis. The transition state is located at the top of the energy barrier that separates the reactants and products.
- The energy of activation is the energy difference between the reactants and the transition state. The higher the energy of activation, the slower the reaction.
- The difference in energy between the reactants and products is the ΔH.

⑤ How do temperature, concentration, and catalysts affect the rate of a reaction? (6.4)

- Increasing the temperature and concentration increases the reaction rate.
- A catalyst speeds up the rate of a reaction without affecting the energies of the reactants and products. Enzymes are biological catalysts that increase the rate of reactions in living organisms.

Catalytic converters use a catalyst to convert automobile engine exhaust to environmentally cleaner products.

⑥ What are the basic features of equilibrium? (6.5)

- At equilibrium, the rates of the forward and reverse reactions in a reversible reaction are equal and the net concentrations of all substances do not change.
- The equilibrium constant for a reaction $a\text{A} + b\text{B} \rightleftharpoons c\text{C} + d\text{D}$ is written as $K = ([\text{C}]^c[\text{D}]^d)/([\text{A}]^a[\text{B}]^b)$.
- The magnitude of K tells the relative amount of reactants and products. When $K > 1$, the products are favored; when $K < 1$, the reactants are favored; when $K \approx 1$, both reactants and products are present at equilibrium.

⑦ How does Le Châtelier's principle predict what happens when equilibrium is disturbed? (6.6)

- Le Châtelier's principle states that a system at equilibrium reacts in such a way as to counteract any disturbance to the equilibrium. How changes in concentration, temperature, and pressure affect equilibrium are summarized in Table 6.5.
- Catalysts increase the rate at which equilibrium is reached but do not alter the amount of any substance involved in the reaction.

⑧ How can the principles that describe equilibrium and reaction rates be used to understand the regulation of body temperature? (6.7)

- Increasing temperature increases the rates of the reactions in the body.
- When temperature is increased, the body dissipates excess heat by dilating blood vessels and sweating. When temperature is decreased, blood vessels constrict to conserve heat, and the body shivers to generate more heat.

PROBLEMS

Selected in-chapter and odd-numbered end-of-chapter problems have brief answers in Appendix B. The *Student Study Guide and Solutions Manual* contains detailed solutions to all in-chapter and odd-numbered end-of-chapter problems, as well as additional worked examples and a chapter self-test.

Energy

6.11 What is the difference between kinetic energy and potential energy? Give an example of each type.

6.12 What is the difference between a calorie and a Calorie?

6.13 Riding a bicycle at 12–13 miles per hour uses 563 Calories in an hour. Convert this value to (a) calories; (b) kilocalories; (c) joules; (d) kilojoules.

6.14 Running at a rate of 6 mi/h uses 704 Calories in an hour. Convert this value to (a) calories; (b) kilocalories; (c) joules; (d) kilojoules.

6.15 Carry out each of the following conversions.
  a. 50 cal to kcal
  b. 56 cal to kJ
  c. 0.96 kJ to cal
  d. 4,230 kJ to cal

6.16 Carry out each of the following conversions.
  a. 5 kcal to cal
  b. 2,560 cal to kJ
  c. 1.22 kJ to cal
  d. 4,230 J to kcal

6.17 Estimate the number of Calories in two tablespoons of peanut butter, which contains 16 g of protein, 7 g of carbohydrates, and 16 g of fat.

6.18 A can of soda contains 120 Calories and no protein or fat. How many grams of carbohydrates are present in each can?

6.19 Which product has more Calories in a half-cup serving: Ben and Jerry's Cherry Garcia ice cream (13 g of fat, 23 g of carbohydrates, 4 g of protein) or Ben and Jerry's Cherry Garcia frozen yogurt (3 g of fat, 32 g of carbohydrates, 5 g of protein), which is lower in fat, but considerably higher in carbohydrate content?

©McGraw-Hill Education

6.20 Using the nutrition labels for two different types of Caesar salad dressing (**A** and **B**), calculate the total Calories in one tablespoon of each product, and determine which label is for the "lite" variety of salad dressing.

A	% Daily Values*		B	% Daily Values*
Total Fat 8.48g	13%		**Total Fat** 0.66g	1%
Saturated Fat 1.292g	6%		Saturated Fat 0.105g	1%
Polyunsaturated Fat 4.83g			Polyunsaturated Fat 0.355g	
Monounsaturated Fat 1.985g			Monounsaturated Fat 0.169g	
Cholesterol 0mg	0%		**Cholesterol** 0mg	0%
Sodium 158mg	7%		**Sodium** 162mg	7%
Potassium 4mg			**Potassium** 4mg	
Total Carbohydrate 0.46g	0%		**Total Carbohydrate** 2.79g	1%
Dietary Fiber 0g	0%		Dietary Fiber 0g	0%
Sugars 0.19g			Sugars 2.45g	
Protein 0.18g			**Protein** 0.04g	
Vitamin A 0% Vitamin C 0%			Vitamin A 0% Vitamin C 0%	
Calcium 0% Iron 0%			Calcium 0% Iron 0%	
*Percent Daily Values are based on a 2000 Calorie diet. Your daily values may be higher or lower depending on your Calorie needs.			*Percent Daily Values are based on a 2000 Calorie diet. Your daily values may be higher or lower depending on your Calorie needs.	

6.21 Use the number of grams of protein, carbohydrate, and fat in the accompanying label to estimate the number of Calories in a serving of whole milk.

©McGraw-Hill Education/Mark Dierker, photographer

6.22 Use the number of grams of protein, carbohydrate, and fat in the accompanying label to estimate the number of Calories in a serving of pizza.

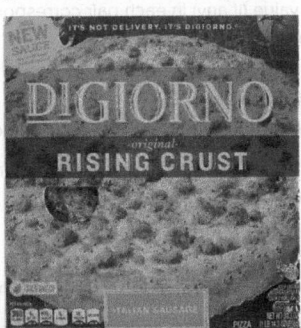

©McGraw-Hill Education/Mark Dierker, photographer

Bond Dissociation Energy and ΔH

6.23 Based on the location of the elements in the periodic table, which species in each pair has the stronger bond?

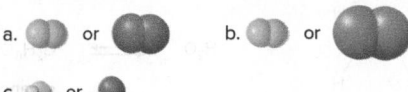

6.24 Using the given bond dissociation energies, rank the indicated bonds in order of increasing strength.

$\Delta H = +104$ kcal/mol　　$\Delta H = +98$ kcal/mol　　$\Delta H = +125$ kcal/mol

6.25 Do each of the following statements describe an endothermic or exothermic reaction?
   a. ΔH is a negative value.
   b. The energy of the reactants is lower than the energy of the products.
   c. Energy is absorbed in the reaction.
   d. The bonds in the products are stronger than the bonds in the reactants.

6.26 Do each of the following statements describe an endothermic or exothermic reaction?
   a. ΔH is a positive value.
   b. The energy of the products is lower than the energy of the reactants.
   c. Energy is released in the reaction.
   d. The bonds in the reactants are stronger than the bonds in the products.

6.27 The combustion of coal with oxygen forms CO_2 and releases 94 kcal of energy.
$$C(s) + O_2(g) \longrightarrow CO_2(g)$$
   a. How much energy is released when 2.5 mol of C reacts?
   b. How much energy is released when 3.0 mol of O_2 reacts?
   c. How much energy is released when 25.0 g of C reacts?

6.28 Ammonia (NH_3) decomposes to hydrogen and nitrogen and 22.0 kcal of energy is absorbed.
$$2\,NH_3(g) \longrightarrow 3\,H_2(g) + N_2(g)$$
   a. How much energy is absorbed when 1.0 mol of N_2 is formed?
   b. How much energy is absorbed when 1.0 mol of NH_3 reacts?
   c. How much energy is absorbed when 3.50 g of NH_3 reacts?

6.29 The metabolism of glucose (molar mass 180.2 g/mol) with oxygen forms CO_2 and H_2O and releases 678 kcal of energy.
$$\underset{\text{glucose}}{C_6H_{12}O_6(aq)} + 6\,O_2(g) \rightleftharpoons 6\,CO_2(g) + 6\,H_2O(l)$$
   a. Are the bonds formed in the products stronger or weaker than the bonds broken in the reactants?
   b. How much energy is released when 4.00 mol of glucose is metabolized?
   c. How much energy is released when 3.00 mol of O_2 reacts?
   d. How much energy is released when 10.0 g of glucose reacts?

220   **Chapter 6**   Energy Changes, Reaction Rates, and Equilibrium

6.30 Ethanol (C_2H_6O), a gasoline additive, is formed by the reaction of ethylene (CH_2=CH_2) with water. The ΔH for this reaction is −9.0 kcal.

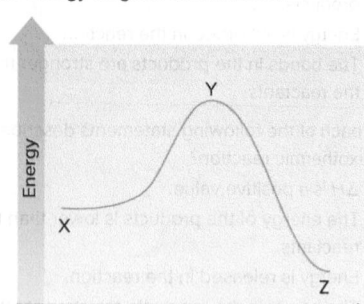

ethylene   + H_2O ⇌ C_2H_6O
                                      ethanol

a. How much energy is released when 3.5 mol of ethylene reacts?

b. How much energy is released when 0.50 mol of H_2O reacts?

c. How much energy is released when 15.0 g of ethylene reacts?

d. How much energy is released when 2.5 g of ethanol is formed?

Energy Diagrams

6.31 Consider the energy diagram drawn below.

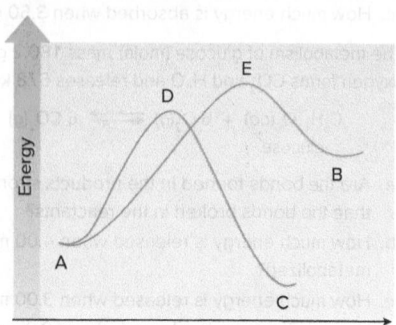

a. Which point on the graph corresponds to reactants?

b. Which point on the graph corresponds to products?

c. Which point on the graph corresponds to the transition state?

d. The difference in energy between which two points equals the energy of activation?

e. The difference in energy between which two points equals the ΔH?

f. Which point is highest in energy?

g. Which point is lowest in energy?

6.32 Compound **A** can be converted to either **B** or **C.** The energy diagrams for both processes are drawn on the graph below.

a. Label each reaction as endothermic or exothermic.

b. Which reaction is faster?

c. Which reaction generates the product lower in energy?

d. Which points on the graphs correspond to transition states?

e. Label the energy of activation for each reaction.

f. Label the ΔH for each reaction.

6.33 Draw an energy diagram that fits each description.

a. an endothermic reaction with a high E_a

b. a reaction that has a low E_a and ΔH is negative

c. a slow reaction in which the products are at a lower energy than the reactants

6.34 Draw an energy diagram that fits each description.

a. an exothermic reaction with a high E_a

b. a reaction with a low E_a and a positive value of ΔH

c. a fast reaction in which the products are at a lower energy than the reactants

6.35 Draw an energy diagram for the following reaction in which $\Delta H = -12$ kcal/mol and $E_a = 5$ kcal: $A_2 + B_2 \longrightarrow 2\ AB.$ Label the axes, reactants, products, transition state, E_a, and ΔH. Is the reaction endothermic or exothermic?

6.36 Draw an energy diagram for the following reaction in which $\Delta H = +13$ kcal/mol and $E_a = 21$ kcal: $A + B \longrightarrow C.$ Label the axes, reactants, products, transition state, E_a, and ΔH. Are the products or reactants higher in energy?

Reaction Rates

6.37 State two reasons why increasing temperature increases reaction rate.

6.38 Why does decreasing concentration decrease the rate of a chemical reaction?

6.39 Which value (if any) in each pair corresponds to a faster reaction? Explain your choice.

a. $E_a = 10$ kcal or $E_a = 1$ kcal

b. $K = 10$ or $K = 100$

c. $\Delta H = -2$ kcal/mol or $\Delta H = +2$ kcal/mol

6.40 Which value (if any) in each pair corresponds to a faster reaction? Explain your choice.

a. $E_a = 0.10$ kcal or $E_a = 1$ kcal

b. $K = 10$ or $K = 0.001$

c. $\Delta H = -25$ kcal/mol or $\Delta H = -2$ kcal/mol

6.41 Which of the following affect the rate of a reaction: (a) K; (b) E_a; (c) temperature?

6.42 Which of the following affect the rate of a reaction: (a) concentration; (b) ΔH; (c) energy difference between the reactants and the transition state?

6.43 How does a catalyst affect each of the following: (a) reaction rate; (b) ΔH; (c) E_a; (d) K; (e) relative energy of the reactants and products?

6.44 What is the difference between a catalyst and an enzyme?

Equilibrium

6.45 Consider the representation depicted in the molecular art for the reaction **A** + **B** ⇌ **C** + **D** with an equilibrium constant $K = 4$. (a) Determine whether the system is at equilibrium. (b) If not, in which direction will the reaction proceed to achieve equilibrium?

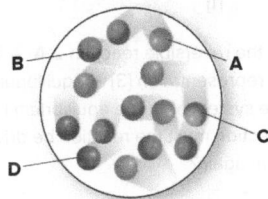

6.46 Consider the representation depicted in the molecular art for the reaction **A₂** + **B₂** ⇌ 2 **AB** with an equilibrium constant $K = 6$. (a) Determine whether the system is at equilibrium. (b) If not, in which direction will the reaction proceed to achieve equilibrium?

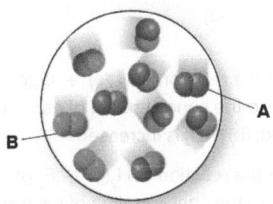

6.47 For each value, are the reactants or products favored at equilibrium?
  a. $K = 5.2 \times 10^3$
  b. $\Delta H = -27$ kcal/mol
  c. $K = 0.002$
  d. $\Delta H = +2$ kcal/mol

6.48 For each value, are the reactants or products favored at equilibrium?
  a. $K = 5.2 \times 10^{-6}$
  b. $\Delta H = +16$ kcal/mol
  c. $K = 10,000$
  d. $\Delta H = -21$ kcal/mol

6.49 Consider the reversible reaction **A** ⇌ **B**, and assume the reaction begins with pure **A**. Using red spheres for **A** and blue spheres for **B**, match each representation to one of the following equilibrium constants: [1] $K = 5$; [2] $K = 1$; [3] $K = 0.5$.

a.   b.   c.

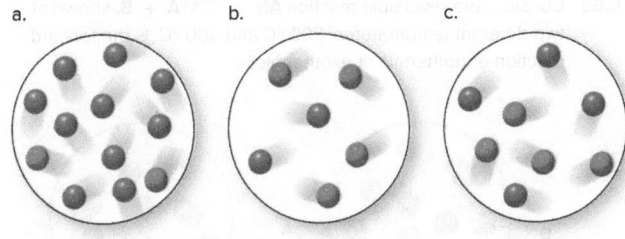

6.50 Consider the reversible reaction **A** ⇌ **B**, with $K = 0.1$. Assume the reaction begins with only **A**, and draw a representation using molecular art for the reaction mixture at equilibrium. Use red spheres for **A** and blue spheres for **B**.

6.51 Consider three different equilibrium mixtures shown in representations [1]–[3]. (a) Which reaction has the largest equilibrium constant? (b) Which reaction has the smallest equilibrium constant?

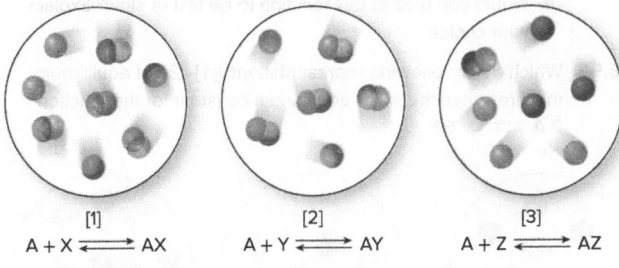

[1]   [2]   [3]
A + X ⇌ AX   A + Y ⇌ AY   A + Z ⇌ AZ

6.52 Consider three different equilibrium mixtures shown in representations [1]–[3] for the reaction **A₂** + **B₂** ⇌ 2 **AB**. Which diagram represents a reaction that has an equilibrium constant of 16?

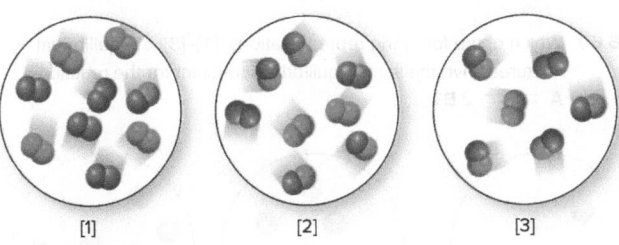

[1]   [2]   [3]

6.53 Write an expression for the equilibrium constant for each reaction.
  a. $2\,NO(g) + O_2(g) \rightleftharpoons 2\,NO_2(g)$
  b. $CH_4(g) + 2\,Br_2(g) \rightleftharpoons CH_2Br_2(g) + 2\,HBr(g)$

6.54 Write an expression for the equilibrium constant for each reaction.
  a. $HBr + H_2O \rightleftharpoons H_3O^+ + Br^-$
  b. $2\,HCl(g) \rightleftharpoons H_2(g) + Cl_2(g)$

6.55 Use each expression for the equilibrium constant to write a chemical equation.
  a. $K = \dfrac{[A_2]}{[A]^2}$
  b. $K = \dfrac{[AB_3]^2}{[A_2][B_2]^3}$

6.56 Use each expression for the equilibrium constant to write a chemical equation.
  a. $K = \dfrac{[AB_2]^2}{[A_2][B_2]^2}$
  b. $K = \dfrac{[A_2B_3]}{[A]^2[B]^3}$

6.57 Consider the following reaction: $2\,HBr(g) \rightleftharpoons H_2(g) + Br_2(g)$ with $K = 5.3 \times 10^{-20}$.
  a. Write the expression for the equilibrium constant for this reaction.
  b. Are the reactants or products favored at equilibrium?
  c. Would you predict ΔH to be positive or negative?
  d. Are the reactants or products lower in energy?
  e. Would you predict this reaction to be fast or slow? Explain your choice.

222　**Chapter 6**　Energy Changes, Reaction Rates, and Equilibrium

6.58 Consider the following reaction: $CO(g) + Cl_2(g) \rightleftharpoons COCl_2(g)$ with $K = 6.6 \times 10^{11}$.

    a. Write the expression for the equilibrium constant for this reaction.

    b. Are the reactants or products favored at equilibrium?

    c. Would you predict ΔH to be positive or negative?

    d. Are the reactants or products lower in energy?

    e. Would you predict this reaction to be fast or slow? Explain your choice.

6.59 Which of the following representations ([1]–[3]) of equilibrium mixtures have the same equilibrium constant for the reaction $2\,A \rightleftharpoons B$?

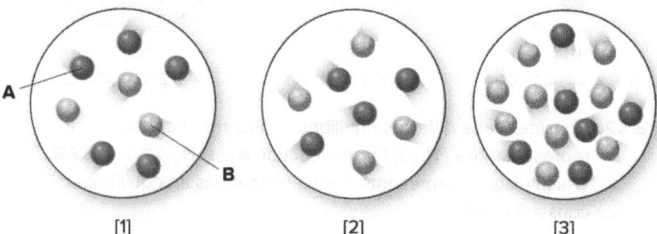

[1]　　　　　　[2]　　　　　　[3]

6.60 Which of the following representations ([1]–[3]) of equilibrium mixtures have the same equilibrium constant for the reaction $A \rightleftharpoons 2\,B$?

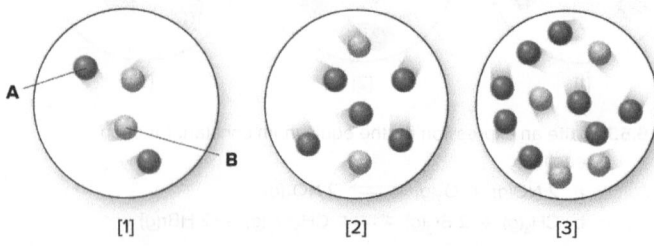

[1]　　　　　　[2]　　　　　　[3]

6.61 Consider the following reaction.

$$CO(g) + H_2O(g) \rightleftharpoons CO_2(g) + H_2(g)$$

    a. Write the expression for the equilibrium constant.

    b. Calculate K using the following concentrations of each substance at equilibrium: $[CO] = 0.090$ M; $[H_2O] = 0.12$ M; $[CO_2] = 0.15$ M; $[H_2] = 0.30$ M.

6.62 Consider the following reaction.

$$H_2(g) + I_2(g) \rightleftharpoons 2\,HI(g)$$

    a. Write the expression for the equilibrium constant.

    b. Calculate K using the following concentrations of each substance at equilibrium: $[H_2] = 0.95$ M; $[I_2] = 0.78$ M; $[HI] = 0.27$ M.

Le Châtelier's Principle

6.63 Consider the reversible reaction $A + B \rightleftharpoons AB$, shown in representation [1] at equilibrium. If representation [2] shows the system after the equilibrium has been disturbed, in which direction must the reaction be driven to achieve equilibrium again?

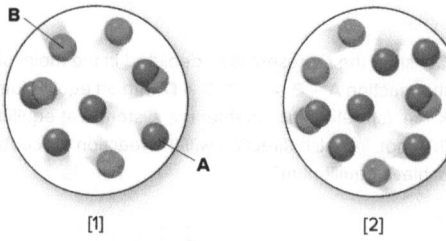

[1]　　　　　　　　[2]

6.64 Consider the reversible reaction $2\,A + B_2 \rightleftharpoons 2\,AB$, shown in representation [3] at equilibrium. If representation [4] shows the system after the equilibrium has been disturbed, in which direction must the reaction be driven to achieve equilibrium again?

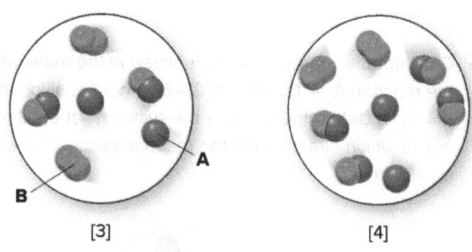

[3]　　　　　　　　[4]

6.65 Consider the reaction of $N_2(g) + O_2(g) \rightleftharpoons 2\,NO(g)$. What happens to the concentration of each substance when (a) $[O_2]$ is increased; (b) $[NO]$ is increased?

6.66 Consider the reaction of $H_2(g) + F_2(g) \rightleftharpoons 2\,HF(g)$. What happens to the concentration of each substance when (a) $[H_2]$ is decreased; (b) $[HF]$ is increased?

6.67 Consider the reversible endothermic reaction $A + B \rightleftharpoons AB$, shown in diagrams [1] and [2] at two different temperatures, 100 °C and 200 °C. Which diagram corresponds to each temperature?

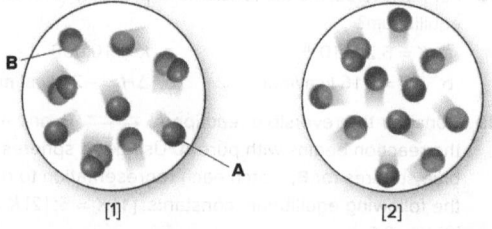

[1]　　　　　　　　[2]

6.68 Consider the reversible reaction $AB \rightleftharpoons A + B$, shown at two different temperatures, 200 °C and 400 °C. Is the forward reaction endothermic or exothermic?

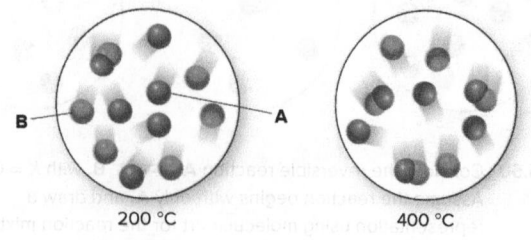

200 °C　　　　　　400 °C

6.69 Consider the endothermic conversion of oxygen to ozone:
$3 O_2(g) \rightleftharpoons 2 O_3(g)$. What effect does each of the following changes have on the direction of equilibrium?

a. decrease $[O_3]$
b. decrease $[O_2]$
c. increase $[O_3]$
d. decrease temperature
e. add a catalyst
f. increase pressure

6.70 Consider the exothermic reaction: $H_2(g) + I_2(g) \rightleftharpoons 2 HI(g)$. What effect does each of the following changes have on the direction of equilibrium?

a. decrease $[HI]$
b. increase $[H_2]$
c. decrease $[I_2]$
d. increase temperature
e. decrease temperature
f. increase pressure

6.71 Consider the exothermic reaction:
$C_2H_4(g) + Cl_2(g) \rightleftharpoons C_2H_4Cl_2(g)$. What effect does each of the following changes have on the direction of equilibrium?

a. increase $[C_2H_4]$
b. decrease $[Cl_2]$
c. decrease $[C_2H_4Cl_2]$
d. decrease pressure
e. increase temperature
f. decrease temperature

6.72 Consider the endothermic reaction:
$2 NH_3(g) \rightleftharpoons 3 H_2(g) + N_2(g)$. What effect does each of the following changes have on the direction of equilibrium?

a. increase $[NH_3]$
b. decrease $[N_2]$
c. increase $[H_2]$
d. increase temperature
e. decrease temperature
f. increase pressure

General Problems

6.73 Consider the gas-phase reaction of ethylene (CH_2=CH_2) with hydrogen to form ethane (C_2H_6), which occurs in the presence of a palladium catalyst (Section 6.4B).

a. Write the expression for the equilibrium constant for this reaction.
b. If $\Delta H = -28$ kcal, are the products or reactants higher in energy?
c. Which is likely to be true about the equilibrium constant for the reaction: $K > 1$ or $K < 1$?
d. How much energy is released when 20.0 g of ethylene reacts?
e. What happens to the rate of the reaction if the concentration of ethylene is increased?
f. What happens to the equilibrium when each of the following changes occurs: [1] an increase in $[H_2]$; [2] a decrease in $[C_2H_6]$; [3] an increase in temperature; [4] an increase in pressure; [5] removal of the palladium catalyst?

6.74 Methanol (CH_4O), which is used as a fuel in race cars, burns in oxygen (O_2) to form CO_2 and H_2O.

a. Write a balanced equation for this reaction.

b. Write the expression for the equilibrium constant for this reaction.
c. If $\Delta H = -174$ kcal per mole of methanol, are the products or reactants higher in energy?
d. How much energy is released when 10.0 g of methanol is burned?
e. Although this reaction is exothermic, the reaction is very slow unless a spark or flame initiates the reaction. Explain how this can be possible.

Applications

6.75 What is the role of lactase and why is it important in the human body?

6.76 How does a catalytic converter clean up automobile emissions?

6.77 A patient receives 2,000 mL of a glucose solution that contains 5 g of glucose in 100 mL. How many Calories does the glucose, a simple carbohydrate, contain?

6.78 The reaction of salicylic acid with acetic acid yields aspirin and water according to the given balanced equation. Since the equilibrium constant for this reaction is close to one, both reactants and products are present at equilibrium. If the reaction has a small negative value of ΔH, suggest ways that this equilibrium could be driven to the right to favor products.

$$C_7H_6O_3 + C_2H_4O_2 \rightleftharpoons C_9H_8O_4 + H_2O$$
salicylic acid   acetic acid   aspirin

6.79 Walking at a brisk pace burns off about 280 Cal/h. How long would you have to walk to burn off the Calories obtained from eating a cheeseburger that contained 32 g of protein, 29 g of fat, and 34 g of carbohydrates?

6.80 How many kilocalories does a runner expend when he runs for 4.5 h and uses 710 Cal/h? How many pieces of pizza that each contain 12 g of protein, 11 g of fat, and 30 g of carbohydrates could be eaten after the race to replenish these Calories?

6.81 Bicycling 10 miles per hour expends 290 Cal/h. How many chocolate chip cookies that contain 50. Cal each can you eat to equal the number of Calories used during a 1.5-h ride?

6.82 One mole of ethanol (C_2H_6O) releases 327 kcal when burned, whereas one mole of hydrogen (H_2) releases only 68.4 kcal/mol. How many kcal/g are released when each of these fuels is burned? On a per gram basis, which substance would be a better source of energy?

CHALLENGE PROBLEMS

6.83 Let's assume that a gallon of gasoline contains pure octane (C_8H_{18}) and has a density of 0.700 g/mL. When gasoline is burned, it releases 1,303 kcal of energy per mole of octane. How many kilocalories of energy are released from burning one gallon of gasoline?

6.84 An energy bar contains 4 g of fat, 12 g of protein, and 24 g of carbohydrates. How many kilojoules of energy are obtained from eating two bars per day for a month? Write the answer in scientific notation.

7

Scuba divers must carefully plan the depth and duration of their dives to avoid "the bends," a dangerous condition caused by the formation of nitrogen gas bubbles in the bloodstream.
©Daniel C. Smith

Gases, Liquids, and Solids

CHAPTER OUTLINE

7.1   The Three States of Matter
7.2   Gases and Pressure
7.3   Gas Laws That Relate Pressure, Volume, and Temperature
7.4   Avogadro's Law—How Volume and Moles Are Related
7.5   The Ideal Gas Law
7.6   Dalton's Law and Partial Pressures
7.7   Intermolecular Forces, Boiling Point, and Melting Point
7.8   The Liquid State
7.9   The Solid State
7.10 Specific Heat
7.11 Energy and Phase Changes
7.12 Heating and Cooling Curves

CHAPTER GOALS

In this chapter you will learn how to:

1. Measure pressure and convert one unit of pressure to another
2. Describe the relationship between the pressure, volume, and temperature of a gas using gas laws
3. Describe the relationship between the volume and number of moles of a gas
4. Write the equation for the ideal gas law and use it in calculations
5. Use Dalton's law to determine the partial pressure and total pressure of a gas mixture
6. Determine the types of intermolecular forces in a compound and how these forces determine a compound's boiling point and melting point
7. Describe the properties of a liquid, including vapor pressure, viscosity, and surface tension
8. Describe the features of different types of solids
9. Define specific heat and use specific heat to determine the amount of heat gained or lost by a substance
10. Describe the energy changes that accompany changes of state
11. Interpret the changes depicted in heating and cooling curves

In Chapter 7 we study the properties of gases, liquids, and solids. Why is air pulled into the lungs when we expand our rib cage and diaphragm? Why does a lid pop off a container of food when it is heated in the microwave? Why does sweating cool down the body? To answer questions of this sort, we must understand the properties of the three states of matter, as well as the energy changes involved when one state is converted to another.

7.1   The Three States of Matter

As we first learned in Section 1.2, matter exists in three common states—**gas, liquid,** and **solid.**

- A gas consists of particles that are far apart and move rapidly and independently from each other.
- A liquid consists of particles that are much closer together but are still somewhat disorganized since they can move about. The particles in a liquid are close enough that they exert a force of attraction on each other.
- A solid consists of particles—atoms, molecules, or ions—that are close to each other and are often highly organized. The particles in a solid have little freedom of motion and are held together by attractive forces.

As shown in Figure 7.1, air is composed largely of N_2 and O_2 molecules, along with small amounts of argon (Ar), carbon dioxide (CO_2), and water molecules that move about rapidly. Liquid water is composed of H_2O molecules that have no particular organization. Sand is a solid composed of SiO_2, which contains a network of covalent silicon–oxygen bonds.

Whether a substance exists as a gas, liquid, or solid depends on the balance between the kinetic energy of its particles and the strength of the interactions between the particles. In a gas, the kinetic energy of motion is high and the particles are far apart from each other. As a

Figure 7.1   The Three States of Matter—Solid, Liquid, and Gas

solid SiO_2 liquid H_2O N_2 and O_2 gases

Most sand is composed of silicon dioxide (SiO_2), which forms a three-dimensional network of covalent bonds. Liquid water is composed of H_2O molecules, which can move past each other but are held close together by a force of attraction (Section 7.7). Air contains primarily N_2 and O_2 molecules that move rapidly with no force of attraction for each other. ©*Daniel C. Smith* result, the attractive forces between the particles are negligible and gas particles move freely. In a liquid, attractive forces hold the particles much closer together, so the distance between particles and the kinetic energy is much less than in the gas. In a solid, the attractive forces between particles are even stronger, so the distance between individual particles is small and there is little freedom of motion. The properties of gases, liquids, and solids are summarized in Table 7.1.

Table 7.1 Properties of Gases, Liquids, and Solids

Property	Gas	Liquid	Solid
Shape and Volume	Expands to fill its container	A fixed volume that takes the shape of the container it occupies	A definite shape and volume
Arrangement of Particles	Randomly arranged, disorganized, and far apart	Randomly arranged but close	Fixed arrangement of very close particles
Density	Low (< 0.01 g/mL)	High (~1 g/mL)[a]	High (1–10 g/mL)
Particle Movement	Very fast	Moderate	Slow
Interaction Between Particles	None	Strong	Very strong

[a]The symbol "~" means approximately.

PROBLEM 7.1

How do gaseous, liquid, and solid methanol (CH_4O) compare in each of the following features:
(a) density; (b) the space between the molecules; (c) the attractive force between the molecules?

7.2 Gases and Pressure

Anyone who has ridden a bike against the wind knows that even though we can't see the gas molecules of the air, we can feel them as we move through them.

Simple gases in the atmosphere—oxygen (O_2), carbon dioxide (CO_2), and ozone (O_3)—are vital to life. Oxygen, which constitutes 21% of the earth's atmosphere, is needed for metabolic processes that convert carbohydrates to energy. Green plants use carbon dioxide, a minor component of the atmosphere, to store the energy of the sun in the bonds of carbohydrate molecules during photosynthesis. Ozone forms a protective shield in the upper atmosphere to filter out harmful radiation from the sun, thus keeping it from the surface of the earth.

7.2A Properties of Gases

Helium, a noble gas composed of He atoms, and oxygen, a gas composed of diatomic O_2 molecules, behave differently in chemical reactions. Many of their physical properties, however, and the properties of all gases, can be explained by the **kinetic–molecular theory of gases,** a set of principles based on the following assumptions:

- A gas consists of particles—atoms or molecules—that move randomly and rapidly.
- The size of gas particles is negligible compared to the space between the particles.
- Because the space between gas particles is large, gas particles exert no attractive forces on each other.
- The kinetic energy of gas particles increases with increasing temperature.
- When gas particles collide with each other, they rebound and travel in new directions. When gas particles collide with the walls of a container, they exert a pressure.

Because gas particles move rapidly, two gases mix together quickly. Moreover, when a gas is added to a container, the particles rapidly move to fill the entire container.

7.2B Gas Pressure

When many gas molecules strike a surface, they exert a measurable pressure. **Pressure (P) is the force (F) exerted per unit area (A) when gas particles hit a surface.**

$$\text{Pressure} = \frac{\text{Force}}{\text{Area}} = \frac{F}{A}$$

Gas pressure depends on the number of collisions of gas particles. Factors that *increase* the number of collisions *increase* the pressure. All of the gases in the atmosphere collectively exert **atmospheric pressure** on the surface of the earth. The value of the atmospheric pressure varies with location, decreasing with increasing altitude. Atmospheric pressure also varies slightly from day to day, depending on the weather.

Atmospheric pressure is measured with a **barometer** (Figure 7.2). A barometer consists of a column of mercury (Hg) sealed at one end and inverted in a dish of mercury. The downward pressure exerted by the mercury in the column equals the atmospheric pressure on the mercury in the dish. Thus, the height of the mercury in the column measures the atmospheric pressure. Atmospheric pressure at sea level corresponds to a column of mercury 760. mm in height.

Many different units are used for pressure. The two most common units are the **atmosphere (atm)** and **millimeters of mercury (mm Hg)**, where **1 atm = 760. mm Hg.** One millimeter of mercury is also called one **torr.** In the United States, the common pressure unit is **pounds per square inch (psi)**, where **1 atm = 14.7 psi.** Pressure can also be measured in pascals (Pa), where 1 mm Hg = 133.32 Pa.

$$\begin{aligned}
1 \text{ atm} &= 760. \text{ mm Hg} \\
&= 760. \text{ torr} \\
&= 14.7 \text{ psi} \\
&= 101{,}325 \text{ Pa}
\end{aligned}$$

To convert a value from one pressure unit to another, set up conversion factors and use the method in Sample Problem 7.1.

Figure 7.2

A Barometer—A Device for Measuring Atmospheric Pressure

vacuum

atmospheric pressure

760 mm

mercury-filled dish

A barometer measures atmospheric pressure. Air pressure on the Hg in the dish pushes Hg up a sealed glass tube to a height that equals the atmospheric pressure.

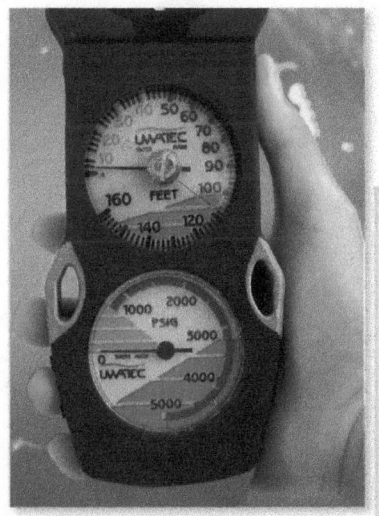

A scuba diver's pressure gauge shows the amount of air (usually measured in psi) in his tank before and during a dive.
©Daniel C. Smith

SAMPLE PROBLEM 7.1 CONVERTING ONE UNIT OF PRESSURE TO ANOTHER

A scuba diver typically begins a dive with a compressed air tank at 3,000. psi. Convert this value to (a) atmospheres; (b) mm Hg.

Analysis

To solve each part, set up conversion factors that relate the two units under consideration. Use conversion factors that place the unwanted unit, psi, in the denominator to cancel.

In part (a), the conversion factor must relate psi and atm:	In part (b), the conversion factor must relate psi and mm Hg:
psi–atm conversion factor	psi–mm Hg conversion factor
$\dfrac{1 \text{ atm}}{14.7 \text{ psi}}$	$\dfrac{760. \text{ mm Hg}}{14.7 \text{ psi}}$
unwanted unit	unwanted unit

Solution

a. Convert the original unit (3,000. psi) to the desired unit (atm) using the conversion factor:

$$3000. \text{ psi} \times \frac{1 \text{ atm}}{14.7 \text{ psi}} = 204 \text{ atm}$$

Psi cancels.   **Answer**

b. Convert the original unit (3,000. psi) to the desired unit (mm Hg) using the conversion factor:

$$3000. \text{ psi} \times \frac{760. \text{ mm Hg}}{14.7 \text{ psi}} = 155,000 \text{ mm Hg}$$

Psi cancels.   **Answer**

PRACTICE PROBLEM 7.1

Convert each pressure unit to the indicated unit.

a. 3.0 atm to mm Hg   b. 720 mm Hg to psi   c. 424 mm Hg to atm

More Practice: Try Problems 7.19–7.22.

7.2C   FOCUS ON HEALTH & MEDICINE
Blood Pressure

Taking a patient's blood pressure is an important part of most physical examinations. Blood pressure measures the pressure in an artery of the upper arm using a device called a **sphygmomanometer.** A blood pressure reading consists of two numbers such as 120/80, where both values represent pressures in mm Hg. The higher number is the systolic pressure and refers to the maximum pressure in the artery right after the heart contracts. The lower number is the diastolic pressure and represents the minimum pressure when the heart muscle relaxes. A desirable systolic pressure is in the range of 100–120 mm Hg. A desirable diastolic pressure is in the range of 60–80 mm Hg. Figure 7.3 illustrates how a sphygmomanometer records pressure in a blood vessel.

Figure 7.3   Measuring Blood Pressure

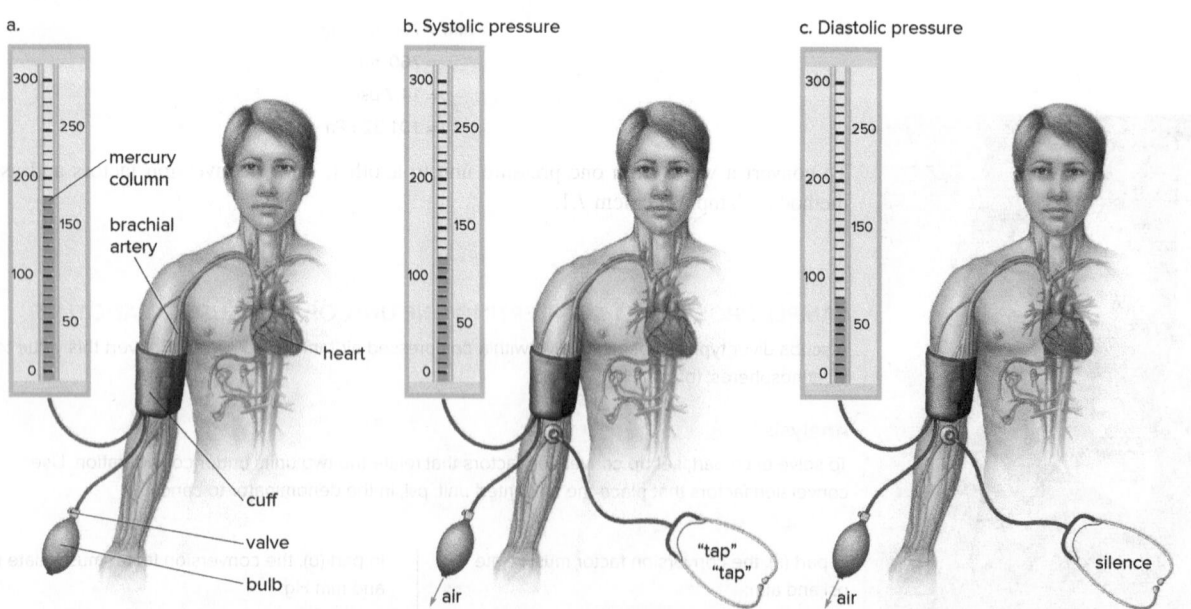

(a) To measure blood pressure, a cuff is inflated around the upper arm and a stethoscope is used to listen to the sound of blood flowing through the brachial artery. When the pressure in the cuff is high, it constricts the artery, so that no blood can flow to the lower arm. (b) Slowly the pressure in the cuff is decreased, and when it gets to the point that blood begins to spurt into the artery, a tapping sound is heard in the stethoscope. This value corresponds to the systolic blood pressure. (c) When the pressure in the cuff is further decreased, so that blood once again flows freely in the artery, the tapping sound disappears and the diastolic pressure is recorded.

When a patient's systolic pressure is routinely 140 mm Hg or greater or diastolic pressure is 90 mm Hg or greater, an individual is said to have **hypertension**—that is, high blood pressure. Consistently high blood pressure leads to increased risk of stroke and heart attacks. Many forms of hypertension can be controlled with medications such as propranolol (trade name Inderal, Problem 15.13).

7.3 Gas Laws That Relate Pressure, Volume, and Temperature

Four variables are important in discussing the behavior of gases—pressure (P), volume (V), temperature (T), and number of moles (n). The relationship of these variables is described by equations called **gas laws** that predict the behavior of all gases as conditions change. Three gas laws illustrate the interrelationship of pressure, volume, and temperature.

- Boyle's law relates pressure and volume.
- Charles's law relates volume and temperature.
- Gay–Lussac's law relates pressure and temperature.

7.3A Boyle's Law—How the Pressure and Volume of a Gas Are Related

Boyle's law describes how the volume of a gas changes as the pressure is changed.

- Boyle's law: For a fixed amount of gas at constant temperature, the pressure and volume of a gas are inversely related.

When two quantities are *inversely* related, one quantity *increases* as the other *decreases*. **The product of the two quantities, however, is a *constant*,** symbolized by k.

When pressure increases...

Pressure × Volume = constant

...volume decreases.

$$PV = k$$

If the volume of a cylinder is decreased, the particles of a gas are more crowded, more collisions occur, and the pressure increases. Thus, if the volume of a cylinder of gas is halved, the pressure of the gas inside the cylinder doubles. The same number of gas particles occupies *half* the volume and exerts *two* times the pressure.

$P = 1$ atm   Decrease volume. $P = 2$ atm

Pressure increases.

$V = 2$ L $V = 1$ L

If we know the pressure and volume under an initial set of conditions (P_1 and V_1), we can calculate the pressure or volume under a different set of conditions (P_2 and V_2), because the product of pressure and volume is a constant.

$$P_1V_1 = P_2V_2$$

initial conditions   new conditions

How To   **Use Boyle's Law to Calculate a New Gas Volume or Pressure**

Example: If a 4.0-L container of helium gas has a pressure of 10.0 atm, what pressure does the gas exert if the volume is increased to 6.0 L?

Step [1]   **Identify the known quantities and the desired quantity.**

- To solve an equation using Boyle's law, we must know three quantities and solve for one quantity. In this case P_1, V_1, and V_2 are known and the final pressure, P_2, must be determined.

$$P_1 = 10.0 \text{ atm}$$
$$V_1 = 4.0 \text{ L} \qquad V_2 = 6.0 \text{ L} \qquad\qquad P_2 = ?$$

known quantities   desired quantity

Step [2]   **Write the equation and rearrange it to isolate the desired quantity on one side.**

- Rearrange the equation for Boyle's law so that the unknown quantity, P_2, is present alone on one side.

$$P_1V_1 \quad = \quad P_2V_2 \qquad \text{Solve for } P_2 \text{ by dividing both sides by } V_2.$$

$$\frac{P_1V_1}{V_2} \quad = \quad P_2$$

Step [3]   **Solve the problem.**

- Substitute the known quantities into the equation and solve for P_2. Identical units must be used for two similar quantities (liters in this case), so that the units cancel.

$$P_2 \quad = \quad \frac{P_1V_1}{V_2} \quad = \quad \frac{(10.0 \text{ atm})(4.0 \text{ L})}{6.0 \text{ L}} \quad = \quad 6.7 \text{ atm}$$

Liters cancel. **Answer**

- In this example, the *volume increased* so the *pressure decreased.*

SAMPLE PROBLEM 7.2 DETERMINING GAS VOLUME USING BOYLE'S LAW

A tank of compressed air for scuba diving contains 8.5 L of gas at 204 atm pressure. What volume of air does this gas occupy at 1.0 atm?

Analysis

Boyle's law can be used to solve this problem because an initial pressure and volume (P_1 and V_1) and a final pressure (P_2) are known, and a final volume (V_2) must be determined.

Solution

[1] Identify the known quantities and the desired quantity.

$$P_1 = 204 \text{ atm} \qquad P_2 = 1.0 \text{ atm}$$
$$V_1 = 8.5 \text{ L} \qquad\qquad\qquad\qquad V_2 = ?$$

known quantities   desired quantity

[2] Write the equation and rearrange it to isolate the desired quantity, V_2, on one side.

$$P_1V_1 \quad = \quad P_2V_2 \qquad \text{Solve for } V_2 \text{ by dividing both sides by } P_2.$$

$$\frac{P_1V_1}{P_2} \quad = \quad V_2$$

[3] Solve the problem.

- Substitute the three known quantities into the equation and solve for V_2.

$$V_2 \quad = \quad \frac{P_1V_1}{P_2} \quad = \quad \frac{(204 \text{ atm})(8.5 \text{ L})}{1.0 \text{ atm}} \quad = \quad 1,734 \text{ rounded to } 1,700 \text{ L}$$

Answer

Atm cancels.

- Thus, the *volume increased* because the *pressure decreased.*

PRACTICE PROBLEM 7.2

A sample of helium gas has a volume of 2.0 L at a pressure of 4.0 atm. What is the volume of gas (in L) at each of the following pressures?

a. 5.0 atm   b. 2.5 atm   c. 10.0 atm   d. 380 mm Hg

More Practice: Try Problems 7.31–7.34.

PROBLEM 7.2

A sample of nitrogen gas has a volume of 15.0 mL at a pressure of 0.50 atm. What is the pressure exerted by the gas (in atm) if the volume is changed to each of the following values?

a. 30.0 mL   b. 5.0 mL   c. 100. mL   d. 1.0 L

Boyle's law explains how air is brought into or expelled from the lungs as the rib cage and diaphragm expand and contract when we breathe (Figure 7.4).

Figure 7.4   Focus on the Human Body: Boyle's Law and Breathing

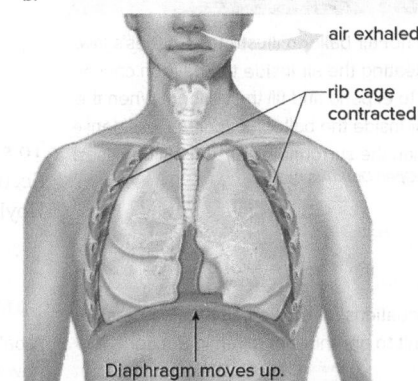

a.   air inhaled   b.   air exhaled

rib cage expanded   rib cage contracted

Diaphragm moves down.   Diaphragm moves up.

a. When an individual inhales, the rib cage expands and the diaphragm is lowered, thus increasing the volume of the lungs. According to Boyle's law, increasing the volume of the lungs decreases the pressure inside the lungs. The decrease in pressure draws air into the lungs.

b. When an individual exhales, the rib cage contracts and the diaphragm is raised, thus decreasing the volume of the lungs. Since the volume is now decreased, the pressure inside the lungs increases, causing air to be expelled into the surroundings.

7.3B   Charles's Law—How the Volume and Temperature of a Gas Are Related

All gases expand when they are heated and contract when they are cooled. Charles's law describes how the volume of a gas changes as the Kelvin temperature is changed.

- **Charles's law: For a fixed amount of gas at constant pressure, the volume of a gas is proportional to its Kelvin temperature.**

Volume and temperature are *proportional;* that is, as one quantity *increases,* the other *increases* as well. Thus, **dividing volume by temperature is a constant (*k*).**

$$\frac{V}{T} = k$$

A hot air balloon illustrates Charles's law. Heating the air inside the balloon causes it to expand and fill the balloon. When the air inside the balloon becomes less dense than the surrounding air, the balloon rises.
©Open Door/Alamy RF

Increasing the temperature increases the kinetic energy of the gas particles, and they move faster and spread out, thus occupying a larger volume. Note that **Kelvin temperature** must be used in calculations involving gas laws. Any temperature reported in °C or °F must be converted to kelvins (K) prior to carrying out the calculation.

Since dividing the volume of a gas by the temperature gives a constant, knowing the volume and temperature under an initial set of conditions (V_1 and T_1) means we can calculate the volume or temperature under another set of conditions (V_2 and T_2) when either volume or temperature is changed.

$$\frac{V_1}{T_1} = \frac{V_2}{T_2}$$

initial conditions   new conditions

To solve a problem of this sort, we follow the same three steps listed in the *How To* outlined in Section 7.3A, except we use the equation for Charles's law in step [2] in place of the equation for Boyle's law. This procedure is illustrated in Sample Problem 7.3.

Equations for converting one temperature unit to another are given in Section 1.9.

SAMPLE PROBLEM 7.3 DETERMINING GAS VOLUME USING CHARLES'S LAW

A balloon that contains 0.50 L of air at 25 °C is cooled to −196 °C. What volume does the balloon now occupy?

Analysis

Since this question deals with volume and temperature, Charles's law is used to determine a final volume because three quantities are known—the initial volume and temperature (V_1 and T_1), and the final temperature (T_2).

Solution

[1] Identify the known quantities and the desired quantity.

$$V_1 = 0.50 \text{ L}$$
$$T_1 = 25 \text{ °C} \qquad\qquad T_2 = -196 \text{ °C} \qquad\qquad V_2 = ?$$
known quantities   desired quantity

- Both temperatures must be converted to Kelvin temperatures using the equation $T_K = T_C + 273$.
- $T_1 = 25 \text{ °C} + 273 = 298 \text{ K}$
- $T_2 = -196 \text{ °C} + 273 = 77 \text{ K}$

[2] Write the equation and rearrange it to isolate the desired quantity, V_2, on one side.

- Use Charles's law.

$$\frac{V_1}{T_1} = \frac{V_2}{T_2} \qquad \text{Solve for } V_2 \text{ by multiplying both sides by } T_2.$$

$$\frac{V_1 T_2}{T_1} = V_2$$

[3] Solve the problem.

- Substitute the three known quantities into the equation and solve for V_2.

$$V_2 = \frac{V_1 T_2}{T_1} = \frac{(0.50 \text{ L})(77 \text{ K})}{298 \text{ K}} = 0.13 \text{ L}$$

Kelvins cancel.   **Answer**

- Since the *temperature has decreased*, the *volume of gas must decrease* as well.

PRACTICE PROBLEM 7.3

A volume of 0.50 L of air at 37 °C is expelled from the lungs into cold surroundings at 0.0 °C. What volume (in L) does the expelled air occupy at this temperature?

More Practice: Try Problems 7.35–7.38.

PROBLEM 7.3

(a) A volume (25.0 L) of gas at 45 K is heated to 450 K. What volume (in L) does the gas now occupy?

(b) A volume (50.0 mL) of gas at 400. °C is cooled to 50. °C. What volume (in mL) does the gas now occupy?

Charles's law can be used to explain how wind currents form at the beach (Figure 7.5). The air above land heats up faster than the air above water. As the temperature of the air above the land increases, the volume that it occupies increases; that is, the air expands and, as a result, its density decreases. This warmer, less dense air then rises, and the cooler, denser air above the water moves toward the land as wind, filling the space left vacant by the warm, rising air.

Figure 7.5   Focus on the Environment: How Charles's Law Explains Wind Currents

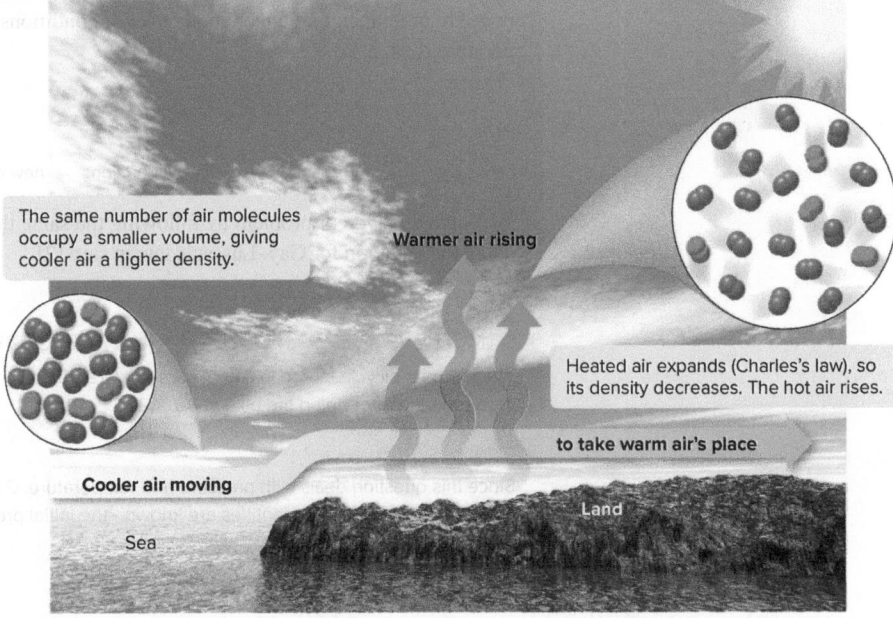

The same number of air molecules occupy a smaller volume, giving cooler air a higher density.

Warmer air rising

Heated air expands (Charles's law), so its density decreases. The hot air rises.

to take warm air's place

Cooler air moving

Land

Sea

7.3C   Gay–Lussac's Law—How the Pressure and Temperature of a Gas Are Related

Gay–Lussac's law describes how the pressure of a gas changes as the Kelvin temperature is changed.

- **Gay–Lussac's law:** For a fixed amount of gas at constant volume, the pressure of a gas is proportional to its Kelvin temperature.

Pressure and temperature are _proportional;_ that is, as one quantity _increases,_ the other _increases._ Thus, **dividing the pressure by the temperature is a constant (k).**

$$\frac{P}{T} = k$$

Increasing the temperature increases the kinetic energy of the gas particles, thus increasing the number of collisions and the force they exert. If the volume is kept constant, the pressure exerted by the particles increases.

Gay–Lussac's law explains why a lid pops off a closed container when it is heated in a microwave. Increasing the temperature increases the gas pressure inside the container, so the lid pops off to release the faster-moving gas particles.

Since dividing the pressure of a gas by the temperature gives a constant, knowing the pressure and Kelvin temperature under an initial set of conditions (P_1 and T_1) means we can calculate the pressure or temperature under another set of conditions (P_2 and T_2) when either pressure or temperature is changed.

$$\frac{P_1}{T_1} = \frac{P_2}{T_2}$$

initial conditions   new conditions

We solve this type of problem by following the same three steps in the _How To_ in Section 7.3A, using the equation for Gay–Lussac's law in step [2].

SAMPLE PROBLEM 7.4 DETERMINING PRESSURE USING GAY–LUSSAC'S LAW

The tire on a bicycle stored in a cool garage at 18 °C had a pressure of 80. psi. What is the pressure inside the tire after riding the bike at 43 °C?

Analysis

Since this question deals with pressure and temperature, Gay–Lussac's law is used to determine a final pressure because three quantities are known—the initial pressure and temperature (P_1 and T_1), and the final temperature (T_2).

Solution

[1] Identify the known quantities and the desired quantity.

$$P_1 = 80.\ \text{psi}$$

$$T_1 = 18\ °\text{C} \qquad\qquad T_2 = 43\ °\text{C} \qquad\qquad P_2 = ?$$

          known quantities   desired quantity

- Both temperatures must be converted to Kelvin temperatures.
- $T_1 = T_C + 273 = 18\ °\text{C} + 273 = 291\ \text{K}$
- $T_2 = T_C + 273 = 43\ °\text{C} + 273 = 316\ \text{K}$

[2] Write the equation and rearrange it to isolate the desired quantity, P_2, on one side.

- Use Gay–Lussac's law. Since the initial pressure is reported in psi, the final pressure will be calculated in psi.

$$\frac{P_1}{T_1} = \frac{P_2}{T_2} \quad \text{Solve for } P_2 \text{ by multiplying both sides by } T_2.$$

$$\frac{P_1 T_2}{T_1} = P_2$$

[3] Solve the problem.

- Substitute the three known quantities into the equation and solve for P_2.

$$P_2 = \frac{P_1 T_2}{T_1} = \frac{(80.\text{ psi})(316\text{ K})}{291\text{ K}} = 87\text{ psi}$$

Kelvins cancel. **Answer**

- Since the *temperature has increased,* the *pressure of the gas must increase* as well.

PRACTICE PROBLEM 7.4

A pressure cooker is used to cook food in a closed pot. By heating the contents of a pressure cooker at constant volume, the pressure increases. If the steam inside the pressure cooker is initially at 100. °C and 1.00 atm, what is the final temperature of the steam if the pressure is increased to 1.05 atm?

More Practice: Try Problems 7.39–7.42.

Food cooks faster in a pressure cooker because the reactions involved in cooking occur at a faster rate at a higher temperature. ©Bill Aron/PhotoEdit

PROBLEM 7.4

The temperature of a 0.50-L gas sample at 25 °C and 1.00 atm is changed to each of the following temperatures. What is the final pressure of the system?

a. 310. K   b. 150. K   c. 50. °C   d. 200. °C

7.3D The Combined Gas Law

All three gas laws—Boyle's, Charles's, and Gay–Lussac's laws—can be combined in a single equation, the **combined gas law,** that relates pressure, volume, and temperature.

$$\frac{P_2 V_2}{T_2} = \frac{P_1 V_1}{T_1}$$

initial conditions   new conditions

The combined gas law contains six terms that relate the pressure, volume, and temperature of an initial and final state of a gas. It can be used to calculate one quantity when the other five are known, as long as the number of moles of gas (n) is constant. The combined gas law is used for determining the effect of changing two factors—such as pressure and temperature—on the third factor, volume.

We solve this type of problem by following the same three steps in the *How To* in Section 7.3A, using the equation for the combined gas law in step [2]. Sample Problem 7.5 shows how this is done. Table 7.2 summarizes the equations for the gas laws presented in Section 7.3.

SAMPLE PROBLEM 7.5 USING THE COMBINED GAS LAW IN A CALCULATION

A weather balloon contains 222 L of helium at 20. °C and 760 mm Hg. What is the volume of the balloon when it ascends to an altitude where the temperature is −40. °C and the pressure is 540 mm Hg?

Analysis

Since this question deals with pressure, volume, and temperature, the combined gas law is used to determine a final volume (V_2) because five quantities are known—the initial pressure, volume, and temperature (P_1, V_1, and T_1), and the final pressure and temperature (P_2 and T_2).

Solution

[1] Identify the known quantities and the desired quantity.

$$P_1 = 760 \text{ mm Hg} \qquad P_2 = 540 \text{ mm Hg}$$
$$T_1 = 20.\,°C \qquad T_2 = -40.\,°C$$
$$V_1 = 222 \text{ L} \qquad\qquad\qquad V_2 = \,?$$

known quantities   desired quantity

- Both temperatures must be converted to Kelvin temperatures.
- $T_1 = T_C + 273 = 20.\,°C + 273 = 293 \text{ K}$
- $T_2 = T_C + 273 = -40.\,°C + 273 = 233 \text{ K}$

[2] Write the equation and rearrange it to isolate the desired quantity, V_2, on one side.

- Use the combined gas law.

$$\frac{P_1 V_1}{T_1} = \frac{P_2 V_2}{T_2} \qquad \text{Solve for } V_2 \text{ by multiplying both sides by } \frac{T_2}{P_2}.$$

$$\frac{P_1 V_1 T_2}{T_1 P_2} = V_2$$

[3] Solve the problem.

- Substitute the five known quantities into the equation and solve for V_2.

$$V_2 = \frac{P_1 V_1 T_2}{T_1 P_2} = \frac{(760 \text{ mm Hg})(222 \text{ L})(233 \text{ K})}{(293 \text{ K})(540 \text{ mm Hg})} = 248.5 \text{ L rounded to 250 L}$$

Answer

Kelvins and mm Hg cancel.

PRACTICE PROBLEM 7.5

The pressure inside a 1.0-L balloon at 25 °C was 750 mm Hg. What is the pressure inside the balloon when it is cooled to −40. °C and expands to 2.0 L in volume?

More Practice: Try Problems 7.43, 7.44.

Table 7.2 Summary of the Gas Laws That Relate Pressure, Volume, and Temperature

Law	Equation	Relationship
Boyle's law	$P_1 V_1 = P_2 V_2$	As P increases, V decreases for constant T and n.
Charles's law	$\dfrac{V_1}{T_1} = \dfrac{V_2}{T_2}$	As T increases, V increases for constant P and n.
Gay–Lussac's law	$\dfrac{P_1}{T_1} = \dfrac{P_2}{T_2}$	As T increases, P increases for constant V and n.
Combined gas law	$\dfrac{P_1 V_1}{T_1} = \dfrac{P_2 V_2}{T_2}$	The combined gas law shows the relationship of P, V, and T when two quantities are changed and the number of moles (n) is constant.

7.4   Avogadro's Law—How Volume and Moles Are Related

Each equation in Section 7.3 was written for a constant amount of gas; that is, the number of moles (n) did not change. **Avogadro's law** describes the relationship between the number of moles of a gas and its volume.

- Avogadro's law: When the pressure and temperature are held constant, the volume of a gas is proportional to the number of moles present.

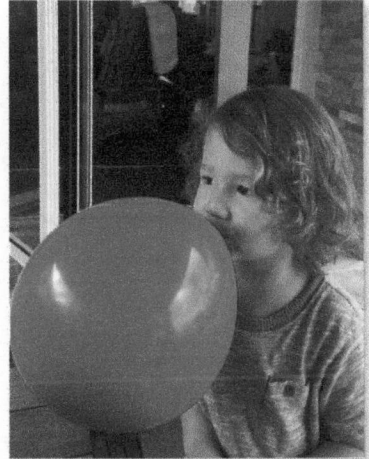

A balloon inflates when someone blows into it because the volume increases with an increased number of moles of air.
©Daniel C. Smith

As the number of moles of a gas *increases,* its volume *increases* as well. Thus, dividing the volume by the number of moles is a constant (k). **The value of k is the same regardless of the identity of the gas.**

$$\frac{V}{n} = k$$

Thus, if the pressure and temperature of a system are held constant, **increasing the number of moles increases the volume of a gas.**

$V = 1\,L$ Increase the number of moles. $V = 2\,L$

Volume increases.

$n = 1$ mol $n = 2$ mol

Since dividing the volume of a gas by the number of moles is a constant, knowing the volume and number of moles initially (V_1 and n_1) means we can calculate a new volume or number of moles (V_2 and n_2) when one of these quantities is changed.

$$\frac{V_1}{n_1} = \frac{V_2}{n_2}$$

initial conditions   new conditions

To solve a problem of this sort, we follow the same three steps listed in the *How To* outlined in Section 7.3A, using Avogadro's law in step [2].

SAMPLE PROBLEM 7.6 DETERMINING MOLES USING AVOGADRO'S LAW

The lungs of an average male hold 0.25 mol of air in a volume of 5.8 L. How many moles of air do the lungs of an average female hold if the volume is 4.6 L?

Analysis

This question deals with volume and number of moles, so Avogadro's law is used to determine a final number of moles when three quantities are known—the initial volume and number of moles (V_1 and n_1), and the final volume (V_2).

Solution

[1] Identify the known quantities and the desired quantity.

$V_1 = 5.8$ L $V_2 = 4.6$ L
$n_1 = 0.25$ mol $n_2 = ?$

known quantities   desired quantity

[2] Write the equation and rearrange it to isolate the desired quantity, n_2, on one side.
- Use Avogadro's law. To solve for n_2, we must invert the numerator and denominator on *both* sides of the equation, and then multiply by V_2.

$$\frac{V_1}{n_1} = \frac{V_2}{n_2} \xrightarrow[\text{on both sides.}]{\text{Switch } V \text{ and } n} \frac{n_1}{V_1} = \frac{n_2}{V_2} \quad \text{Solve for } n_2 \text{ by multiplying both sides by } V_2.$$

$$\frac{n_1 V_2}{V_1} = n_2$$

[3] Solve the problem.
- Substitute the three known quantities into the equation and solve for n_2.

$$n_2 = \frac{n_1 V_2}{V_1} = \frac{(0.25 \text{ mol})(4.6 \text{ L})}{(5.8 \text{ L})} = 0.20 \text{ mol}$$

Liters cancel. **Answer**

PRACTICE PROBLEM 7.6

A sample of nitrogen gas contains 5.0 mol in a volume of 3.5 L. Calculate the new volume of the container if the pressure and temperature are kept constant but the number of moles of nitrogen is changed to each of the following values: (a) 2.5 mol; (b) 3.65 mol; (c) 21.5 mol.

More Practice: Try Problems 7.45, 7.46.

Avogadro's law allows us to compare the amounts of any two gases by comparing their volumes. Often amounts of gas are compared at a set of **standard conditions of temperature and pressure,** abbreviated as **STP.**

- **STP conditions are:**   1 atm (760 mm Hg) for pressure
                                                  273 K (0 °C) for temperature
- **At STP, one mole of any gas has the same volume, 22.4 L, called the** *standard molar volume.*

Under STP conditions, one mole of nitrogen gas and one mole of helium gas each contain 6.02×10^{23} particles of gas and occupy a volume of 22.4 L at 0 °C and 1 atm pressure. Since the molar masses of nitrogen and helium are different (28.02 g for N_2 compared to 4.003 g for He), one mole of each substance has a *different* mass.

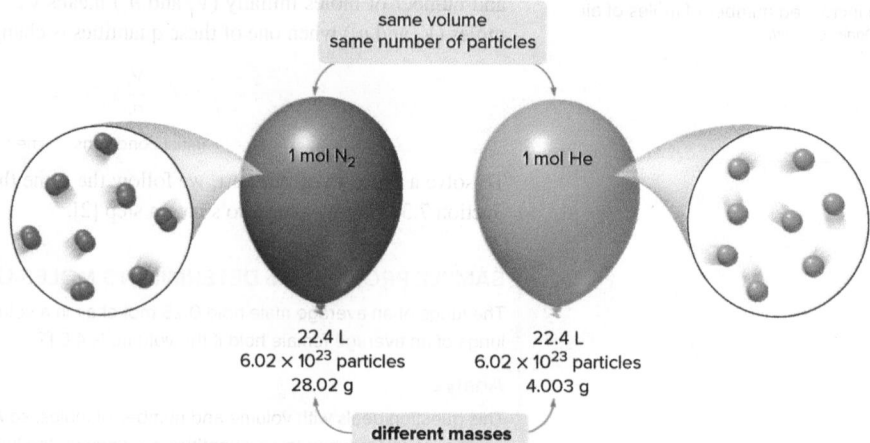

The standard molar volume can be used to set up conversion factors that relate the volume and number of moles of a gas at STP, as shown in the following stepwise procedure.

How To   **Convert Moles of Gas to Volume at STP**

Example: How many moles are contained in 2.0 L of N_2 at standard temperature and pressure?

 Step [1]   **Identify the known quantities and the desired quantity.**

2.0 L of N_2 ? moles of N_2
original quantity   desired quantity

 Step [2]   **Write out the conversion factors.**
- Set up conversion factors that relate the number of moles of a gas to volume at STP. Choose the conversion factor that places the unwanted unit, liters, in the denominator so that the units cancel.

$$\frac{22.4\ \text{L}}{1\ \text{mol}} \quad \text{or} \quad \frac{1\ \text{mol}}{22.4\ \text{L}}$$

Choose this conversion factor to cancel L.

 Step [3]   **Solve the problem.**
- Multiply the original quantity by the conversion factor to obtain the desired quantity.

$$2.0\ \cancel{\text{L}} \quad \times \quad \frac{1\ \text{mol}}{22.4\ \cancel{\text{L}}} \quad = \quad 0.089\ \text{mol of } N_2$$

Liters cancel.   **Answer**

By using the molar mass of a gas, we can determine the volume of a gas from a given number of grams, as shown in Sample Problem 7.7.

SAMPLE PROBLEM 7.7 CONVERTING GRAMS OF GAS TO VOLUME AT STP

Burning one mole of propane in a gas grill adds 132 g of carbon dioxide (CO_2) to the atmosphere. What volume of CO_2 does this correspond to at STP?

Analysis

To solve this problem, we must convert the number of grams of CO_2 to moles using the molar mass. The number of moles of CO_2 can then be converted to its volume using a mole–volume conversion factor (1 mol/22.4 L).

Solution

[1] Identify the known quantities and the desired quantity.

$$132 \text{ g } CO_2 \qquad\qquad ? \text{ L } CO_2$$

known quantity   desired quantity

[2] Convert the number of grams of CO_2 to the number of moles of CO_2 using the molar mass.

molar mass
conversion factor

$$132 \text{ g } CO_2 \quad \times \quad \frac{1 \text{ mol } CO_2}{44.01 \text{ g } CO_2} \quad = \quad 3.00 \text{ mol } CO_2$$

Grams cancel.

[3] Convert the number of moles of CO_2 to the volume of CO_2 using a mole–volume conversion factor.

mole–volume
conversion factor

$$3.00 \text{ mol } CO_2 \quad \times \quad \frac{22.4 \text{ L}}{1 \text{ mol}} \quad = \quad 67.2 \text{ L } CO_2$$

Moles cancel.   **Answer**

PRACTICE PROBLEM 7.7

How many liters does each of the following quantities of O_2 occupy at STP: (a) 4.5 mol; (b) 0.35 mol; (c) 18.0 g?

More Practice: Try Problems 7.47, 7.48.

PROBLEM 7.5

How many moles are contained in the following volumes of air at STP: (a) 1.5 L; (b) 8.5 L; (c) 25 mL?

7.5   The Ideal Gas Law

All four properties of gases—pressure, volume, temperature, and number of moles—can be combined into a single equation called the **ideal gas law.** The product of pressure and volume divided by the product of moles and Kelvin temperature is a constant, called the **universal gas constant** and symbolized by **R.**

$$\frac{PV}{nT} \quad = \quad R \qquad \text{universal gas constant}$$

More often the equation is rearranged and written in the following way:

$$PV = nRT$$

Ideal gas law

For atm: $R = 0.0821 \dfrac{L \cdot atm}{mol \cdot K}$

For mm Hg: $R = 62.4 \dfrac{L \cdot mm\,Hg}{mol \cdot K}$

The value of the universal gas constant R depends on its units. The two most common values of R are given using atmospheres or mm Hg for pressure, liters for volume, and kelvins for temperature. **Be careful to use the correct value of R for the pressure units in the problem you are solving.**

The ideal gas law can be used to find any value—*P, V, n,* or *T*—as long as three of the quantities are known. Solving a problem using the ideal gas law is shown in the stepwise *How To* procedure and in Sample Problem 7.8. Although the ideal gas law gives exact answers only for a perfectly "ideal" gas, it gives a good approximation for most real gases, such as the oxygen and carbon dioxide in breathing, as well (Figure 7.6).

Figure 7.6   Focus on the Human Body: The Lungs

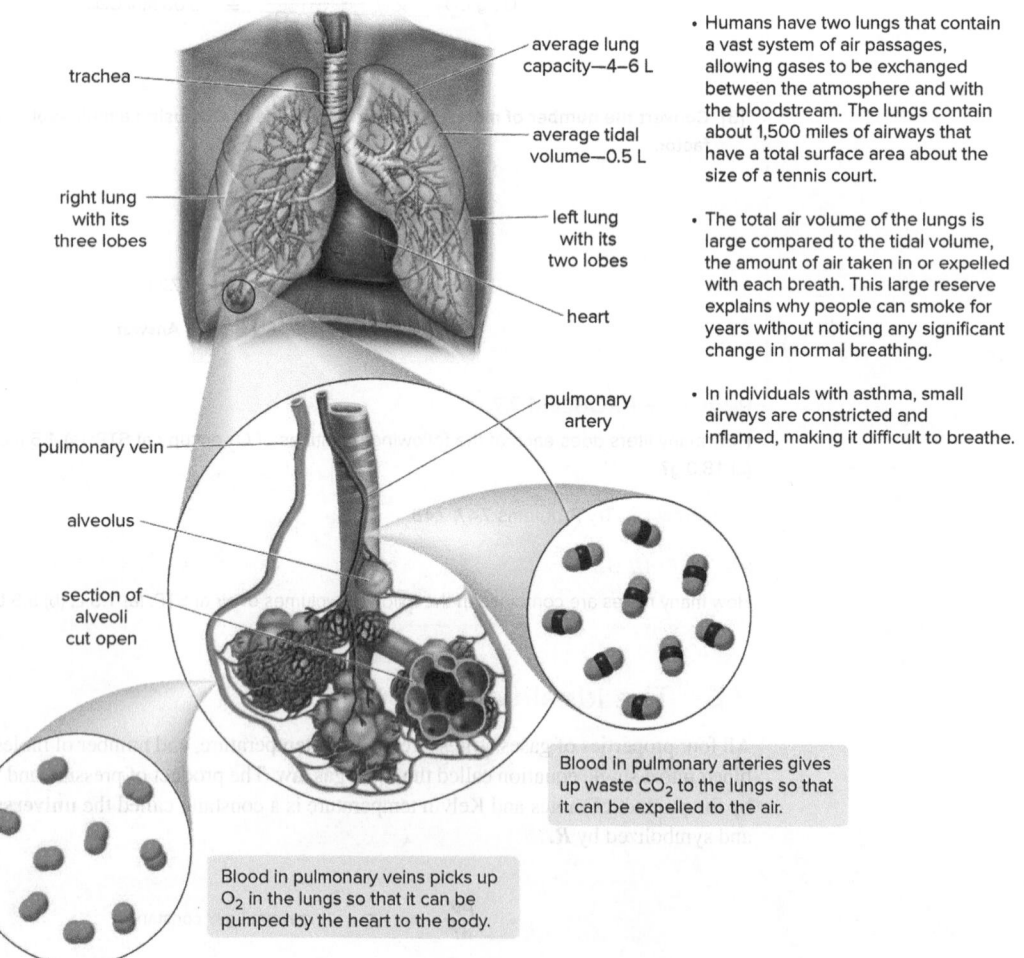

trachea

right lung with its three lobes

average lung capacity—4–6 L

average tidal volume—0.5 L

left lung with its two lobes

heart

pulmonary vein

alveolus

section of alveoli cut open

pulmonary artery

- Humans have two lungs that contain a vast system of air passages, allowing gases to be exchanged between the atmosphere and with the bloodstream. The lungs contain about 1,500 miles of airways that have a total surface area about the size of a tennis court.

- The total air volume of the lungs is large compared to the tidal volume, the amount of air taken in or expelled with each breath. This large reserve explains why people can smoke for years without noticing any significant change in normal breathing.

- In individuals with asthma, small airways are constricted and inflamed, making it difficult to breathe.

Blood in pulmonary arteries gives up waste CO_2 to the lungs so that it can be expelled to the air.

Blood in pulmonary veins picks up O_2 in the lungs so that it can be pumped by the heart to the body.

How To Carry Out Calculations with the Ideal Gas Law

Example: How many moles of gas are contained in a typical human breath that takes in 0.50 L of air at 1.0 atm pressure and 37 °C?

Step [1] Identify the known quantities and the desired quantity.

$$P = 1.0 \text{ atm}$$
$$V = 0.50 \text{ L}$$
$$T = 37 \text{ °C} \qquad n = ? \text{ mol}$$

known quantities   desired quantity

Step [2] Convert all values to proper units and choose the value of *R* that contains these units.
- Convert T_C to T_K. $T_K = T_C + 273 = 37 \text{ °C} + 273 = 310.\text{ K}$
- Use the value of *R* in atm because the pressure is given in atm; that is, $R = 0.0821 \text{ L} \cdot \text{atm/(mol} \cdot \text{K)}$.

Step [3] Write the equation and rearrange it to isolate the desired quantity on one side.
- Use the ideal gas law and solve for *n* by dividing both sides by *RT*.

$$PV = nRT \qquad \text{Solve for } n \text{ by dividing both sides by } RT.$$

$$\frac{PV}{RT} = n$$

Step [4] Solve the problem.
- Substitute the known quantities into the equation and solve for *n*.

$$n = \frac{PV}{RT} = \frac{(1.0 \text{ atm})(0.50 \text{ L})}{\left(0.0821 \dfrac{\text{L} \cdot \text{atm}}{\text{mol} \cdot \text{K}}\right)(310.\text{ K})} = 0.0196 \text{ rounded to } 0.020 \text{ mol}$$

Answer

SAMPLE PROBLEM 7.8 USING THE IDEAL GAS LAW IN A CALCULATION

If a person exhales 25.0 g of CO_2 in an hour, what volume does this amount occupy at 1.00 atm and 37 °C?

Analysis

Use the ideal gas law to calculate *V*, because *P* and *T* are known and *n* can be determined by using the molar mass of CO_2 (44.01 g/mol).

Solution

[1] Identify the known quantities and the desired quantity.

$$P = 1.00 \text{ atm}$$
$$T = 37 \text{ °C} \qquad 25.0 \text{ g } CO_2 \qquad V = ? \text{ L}$$

known quantities   desired quantity

[2] Convert all values to proper units and choose the value of *R* that contains these units.
- Convert T_C to T_K. $T_K = T_C + 273 = 37 \text{ °C} + 273 = 310.\text{ K}$
- Use the value of *R* with atm because the pressure is given in atm; that is, $R = 0.0821 \text{ L} \cdot \text{atm/(mol} \cdot \text{K)}$.
- Convert the number of grams of CO_2 to the number of moles of CO_2 using the molar mass (44.01 g/mol).

molar mass conversion factor

$$25.0 \text{ g } CO_2 \times \frac{1 \text{ mol } CO_2}{44.01 \text{ g } CO_2} = 0.568 \text{ mol } CO_2$$

Grams cancel.

[3] Write the equation and rearrange it to isolate the desired quantity, V, on one side.

- Use the ideal gas law and solve for V by dividing both sides by P.

$$PV = nRT \qquad \text{Solve for } V \text{ by dividing both sides by } P.$$

$$V = \frac{nRT}{P}$$

[4] Solve the problem.

- Substitute the three known quantities into the equation and solve for V.

$$V = \frac{nRT}{P} = \frac{(0.568 \text{ mol})\left(0.0821 \dfrac{\text{L} \cdot \text{atm}}{\text{mol} \cdot \text{K}}\right)(310. \text{ K})}{1.0 \text{ atm}} = 14.5 \text{ L}$$

Answer

PRACTICE PROBLEM 7.8

How many moles of oxygen (O_2) are contained in a 5.0-L cylinder that has a pressure of 175 atm and a temperature of 20. °C?

More Practice: Try Problems 7.49–7.54.

PROBLEM 7.6

Determine the pressure of N_2 (in atm) under each of the following conditions.

   a. 0.45 mol at 25 °C in 10.0 L   b. 10.0 g at 20. °C in 5.0 L

7.6   Dalton's Law and Partial Pressures

Since gas particles are very far apart compared to the size of an individual particle, gas particles behave independently. As a result, the identity of the components of a gas mixture does not matter, and **a mixture of gases behaves like a pure gas.** Each component of a gas mixture is said to exert a pressure called its **partial pressure. Dalton's law** describes the relationship between the partial pressures of the components and the total pressure of a gas mixture.

- **Dalton's law: The** *total pressure* **(P_{total}) of a gas mixture is the sum of the partial pressures of its component gases.**

Thus, if a mixture has two gases (**A** and **B**) with partial pressures P_A and P_B, respectively, the total pressure of the system (P_{total}) is the sum of the two partial pressures. The partial pressure of a component of a mixture is the same pressure that the gas would exert if it were a pure gas.

$$
\begin{array}{ccccc}
P_A = 5 \text{ atm} & & P_B = 3 \text{ atm} & & P_{total} = 8 \text{ atm} \\
P_A & + & P_B & = & P_{total} \\
\text{partial pressure of } \mathbf{A} & & \text{partial pressure of } \mathbf{B} & & \text{total pressure}
\end{array}
$$

SAMPLE PROBLEM 7.9 CALCULATING PRESSURE USING DALTON'S LAW

A sample of exhaled air from the lungs contains four gases with the following partial pressures: N_2 (563 mm Hg), O_2 (118 mm Hg), CO_2 (30. mm Hg), and H_2O (50. mm Hg). What is the total pressure of the sample?

Since the partial pressure of O_2 is low at very high altitudes, most mountain climbers use supplemental O_2 tanks above about 24,000 ft. ©Barry C. Bishop/National Geographic/Getty Images

Analysis

Using Dalton's law, the total pressure is the sum of the partial pressures.

Solution

Adding up the four partial pressures gives the total:

$$563 + 118 + 30. + 50. = 761 \text{ mm Hg (total pressure)}$$

PRACTICE PROBLEM 7.9

CO_2 was added to a cylinder containing 2.5 atm of O_2 to give a total pressure of 4.0 atm of gas. What is the partial pressure of O_2 and CO_2 in the final mixture?

More Practice: Try Problems 7.55, 7.56.

We can also calculate the partial pressure of each gas in a mixture if two quantities are known—[1] the total pressure and [2] the percent of each component—as shown in Sample Problem 7.10.

SAMPLE PROBLEM 7.10 DETERMINING PARTIAL PRESSURE USING DALTON'S LAW

Air is a mixture of 21% O_2, 78% N_2, and 1% argon by volume. What is the partial pressure of each gas at sea level, where the total pressure is 760 mm Hg?

Analysis

Convert each percent to a decimal by moving the decimal point two places to the left. Multiply each decimal by the total pressure to obtain the partial pressure for each component.

Solution

		Partial pressure
Fraction O_2:	21% = 0.21	0.21×760 mm Hg = 160 mm Hg (O_2)
Fraction N_2:	78% = 0.78	0.78×760 mm Hg = 590 mm Hg (N_2)
Fraction Ar:	1% = 0.01	0.01×760 mm Hg = $\underline{\quad 8 \text{ mm Hg (Ar)}}$
		758 rounded to 760 mm Hg

PRACTICE PROBLEM 7.10

Nitrox is a gas mixture used in scuba diving that contains a higher-than-normal level of oxygen and a lower-than-normal level of nitrogen. A lower amount of nitrogen reduces the risk of "the bends."

   a. What percent of N_2 and O_2 is present in the given nitrox tank?

   b. What is the partial pressure of each gas (in psi) in the tank?

More Practice: Try Problems 7.57–7.60.

---

nitrox tank
3,500 psi

The high pressures of a hyperbaric chamber can be used to treat patients fighting infections and scuba divers suffering from the bends.
©Spencer Grant/PhotoEdit

The composition of the atmosphere does not change with location, even though the total atmospheric pressure decreases with increasing altitude. At high altitudes, therefore, the partial pressure of oxygen is much lower than it is at sea level, making breathing difficult. This is why mountain climbers use supplemental oxygen at altitudes above 8,000 m.

In contrast, a hyperbaric chamber is a device that maintains air pressure two to three times higher than normal. Hyperbaric chambers have many uses. At this higher pressure the partial pressure of O_2 is higher. For burn patients, the higher pressure of O_2 increases the amount of O_2 in the blood, where it can be used by the body for reactions that fight infections.

When a scuba diver surfaces too quickly, the N_2 dissolved in the blood can form microscopic bubbles that cause pain in joints and can occlude small blood vessels, causing organ injury. This condition, called the bends, is treated by placing a diver in a hyperbaric chamber, where the elevated pressure decreases the size of the N_2 bubbles, which are then eliminated as N_2 gas from the lungs as the pressure is slowly decreased.

PROBLEM 7.7

At the summit of Kilimanjaro, the highest mountain in Africa with an elevation of 5,895 m, the partial pressure of oxygen is 78.5 mm Hg. What is the atmospheric pressure at the top of Mount Kilimanjaro?

7.7 Intermolecular Forces, Boiling Point, and Melting Point

Unlike gases, the behavior of liquids and solids cannot be described by a set of laws that can be applied regardless of the identity of the substance. Since liquids and solids are composed of particles that are much closer together, **a force of attraction exists between them.**

Ionic compounds are composed of extensive arrays of oppositely charged ions that are held together by strong electrostatic interactions. These ionic interactions are much stronger than the forces between covalent molecules, so it takes a great deal of energy to separate ions from each other (Section 3.5).

In covalent compounds, the nature and strength of the attraction between individual molecules depend on the identity of the atoms.

> • Intermolecular forces are the attractive forces that exist *between* molecules.

There are three different types of intermolecular forces in covalent molecules, presented in order of *increasing strength:*

> • London dispersion forces
> • Dipole–dipole interactions
> • Hydrogen bonding

Thus, a compound that exhibits hydrogen bonding has stronger intermolecular forces than a compound of similar size that has dipole–dipole interactions. Likewise, a compound that has dipole–dipole interactions has stronger intermolecular forces than a compound of similar size that has only London dispersion forces. The strength of the intermolecular forces determines whether a compound has a high or low melting point and boiling point, and thus if the compound is a solid, liquid, or gas at a given temperature.

7.7A London Dispersion Forces

London dispersion forces can also be called **van der Waals forces.**

> • London dispersion forces are very weak interactions due to the momentary changes in electron density in a molecule.

For example, although a nonpolar methane molecule (CH_4) has no net dipole, at any one instant its electron density may not be completely symmetrical. If more electron density is present in one region of the molecule, less electron density must be present some place else, and this creates a *temporary* dipole. A temporary dipole in one CH_4 molecule induces a temporary dipole in another CH_4 molecule, with the partial positive and negative charges arranged close to each other. **The weak interaction between these temporary dipoles constitutes London dispersion forces.**

Although any single interaction is weak, a large number of London dispersion forces creates a strong force. For example, geckos stick to walls and ceilings by London dispersion forces between the surfaces and the 500,000 tiny hairs on each foot. ©Kuttelvaserova Stuchelova/ Shutterstock RF; ©Andrew Syred/Science Source

London dispersion force between two CH_4 molecules

More electron density in one region creates a partial negative charge (δ−).

Less electron density in one region creates a partial positive charge (δ+).

All **covalent compounds exhibit London dispersion forces.** These intermolecular forces are the only intermolecular forces present in nonpolar compounds. The strength of these forces is related to the size of the molecule.

- **The larger the molecule, the larger the attractive force between two molecules, and the stronger the intermolecular forces.**

Atoms like the noble gases helium and argon exhibit London dispersion forces, too. The attractive forces between argon atoms are stronger than the attractive forces between helium atoms, because argon atoms are considerably larger in size.

PROBLEM 7.8

Which of the following compounds exhibit London dispersion forces: (a) NH_3; (b) H_2O; (c) HCl; (d) ethane (C_2H_6)?

7.7B Dipole–Dipole Interactions

How to determine whether a molecule is polar is shown in Section 4.8.

- **Dipole–dipole interactions are the attractive forces between the permanent dipoles of two polar molecules.**

For example, the carbon–oxygen bond in formaldehyde, $H_2C=O$, is polar because oxygen is more electronegative than carbon. This polar bond gives formaldehyde a permanent dipole, making it a polar molecule. The dipoles in adjacent formaldehyde molecules can align so that the partial positive and partial negative charges are close to each other. These attractive forces due to permanent dipoles are much stronger than London dispersion forces.

formaldehyde

PROBLEM 7.9

Draw the individual dipoles of two H—Cl molecules and show how the dipoles are aligned in a dipole–dipole interaction.

7.7C Hydrogen Bonding

- **Hydrogen bonding occurs when a hydrogen atom bonded to O, N, or F is electrostatically attracted to an O, N, or F atom in another molecule.**

hydrogen bond between two H_2O molecules

covalent O—H bond

Hydrogen bonding can occur only when molecules contain a hydrogen atom bonded to a very electronegative atom—that is, oxygen, nitrogen, or fluorine. For example, two H_2O molecules can hydrogen bond to each other: a hydrogen atom is covalently bonded to oxygen in one water

Figure 7.7

Hydrogen Bonding and DNA

DNA double helix

Hydrogen-bonding interactions are shown as dashed red lines.

DNA is composed of two long strands of atoms that wind around each other in an arrangement called a double helix. The two strands are held together by an extensive network of hydrogen bonds. In each hydrogen bond, a hydrogen atom of an N—H bond on one chain is intermolecularly hydrogen bonded to an oxygen or nitrogen atom on an adjacent chain. Five hydrogen bonds are indicated.

molecule, and hydrogen bonded to an oxygen atom in another water molecule. **Hydrogen bonds are the strongest of the three types of intermolecular forces.** Table 7.3 summarizes the three types of intermolecular forces.

Table 7.3 **Summary of the Types of Intermolecular Forces**

Type of Force	Relative Strength	Exhibited by	Example
London dispersion	Weak	All molecules	CH_4, H_2CO, H_2O
Dipole–dipole	Moderate	Molecules with a net dipole	H_2CO, H_2O
Hydrogen bonding	Strong	Molecules with an O—H, N—H, or H—F bond	H_2O

Hydrogen bonding is important in many biological molecules, including proteins and DNA. DNA, which is contained in the chromosomes of the nucleus of a cell, is responsible for the storage of all genetic information. DNA is composed of two long strands of atoms that are held together by hydrogen bonding as shown in Figure 7.7. A detailed discussion of DNA appears in Chapter 22.

SAMPLE PROBLEM 7.11 DETERMINING THE TYPES OF INTERMOLECULAR FORCES IN A COMPOUND

What types of intermolecular forces are present in each compound: (a) HCl; (b) C_2H_6 (ethane); (c) NH_3?

Analysis

- London dispersion forces are present in all covalent compounds.
- Dipole–dipole interactions are present only in polar compounds with a permanent dipole.
- Hydrogen bonding occurs only in compounds that contain an O—H, N—H, or H—F bond.

Solution

a.

- HCl has London forces like all covalent compounds.
- HCl has a polar bond, so it exhibits dipole–dipole interactions.
- HCl has no H atom on an O, N, or F, so it has no intermolecular hydrogen bonding.

b.

$$\text{H}-\underset{\underset{\text{H}}{|}}{\overset{\overset{\text{H}}{|}}{\text{C}}}-\underset{\underset{\text{H}}{|}}{\overset{\overset{\text{H}}{|}}{\text{C}}}-\text{H}$$

nonpolar molecule

- C_2H_6 is a nonpolar molecule because it has only nonpolar C—C and C—H bonds. Thus, it exhibits only London forces.

c.

net dipole

- NH_3 has London forces like all covalent compounds.
- NH_3 has a net dipole from its three polar bonds (Section 4.8), so it exhibits dipole–dipole interactions.
- NH_3 has a H atom bonded to N, so it exhibits intermolecular hydrogen bonding.

PRACTICE PROBLEM 7.11

What types of intermolecular forces are present in each molecule?

a. Cl_2 b. HCN   c. HF   d. CH_3Cl e. H_2

More Practice: Try Problems 7.61–7.67.

PROBLEM 7.10

Which species in each pair has stronger intermolecular forces?

a. CO_2 or H_2O b. CO_2 or HBr   c. HBr or H_2O d. He atoms or Ne atoms

7.7D   Boiling Point and Melting Point

The **boiling point (bp)** of a compound is the temperature at which a liquid is converted to the gas phase, while the **melting point (mp)** is the temperature at which a solid is converted to the liquid phase. The strength of the intermolecular forces determines the boiling point and melting point of compounds.

- The *stronger* the intermolecular forces, the *higher* the boiling point and melting point.

In boiling, energy must be supplied to overcome the attractive forces of the liquid state and separate the molecules to the gas phase. Similarly, in melting, energy must be supplied to overcome the highly ordered solid state and convert it to the less ordered liquid phase. A stronger force of attraction between molecules means that more energy must be supplied to overcome those intermolecular forces, increasing the boiling point and melting point.

In comparing compounds of similar size, the following trend is observed:

Compounds with London dispersion forces only	Compounds with dipole–dipole interactions	Compounds that can hydrogen bond

Increasing strength of intermolecular forces
Increasing boiling point
Increasing melting point

Methane (CH_4) and water (H_2O) are both small molecules with hydrogen atoms bonded to a second-row element, so you might expect them to have similar melting points and boiling points. Methane, however, is a nonpolar molecule that exhibits only London dispersion forces, whereas water is a polar molecule that can form intermolecular hydrogen bonds. As a result, the melting point and boiling point of water are *much higher* than those of methane. In fact, the hydrogen bonds in water are so strong that it is a liquid at room temperature, whereas methane is a gas.

methane	water
London forces only	hydrogen bonding
bp = −162 °C	bp = 100 °C ← stronger forces
mp = −183 °C	mp = 0 °C ← higher bp and mp

In comparing two compounds with similar types of intermolecular forces, the higher molecular weight compound generally has more surface area and therefore a larger force of attraction, giving it the higher boiling point and melting point. Thus, propane (C_3H_8) and butane (C_4H_{10}) have only nonpolar bonds and London forces, but butane is larger and therefore has the higher boiling point and melting point.

propane	butane
bp = −42 °C	bp = −0.5 °C
mp = −190 °C	mp = −138 °C

larger molecule
stronger forces
higher bp and mp

SAMPLE PROBLEM 7.12 PREDICTING THE RELATIVE BOILING POINT AND MELTING POINT OF TWO COMPOUNDS

(a) Which compound, **A** or **B**, has the higher boiling point? (b) Which compound, **C** or **D**, has the higher melting point?

NH₃	CH₄	H—C—O—H	H—C—Cl
ammonia	methane	methanol	chloromethane
A	**B**	**C**	**D**

Analysis

Determine the types of intermolecular forces in each compound. The compound with the stronger forces has the higher boiling point or melting point.

Solution

a. NH_3 (**A**) has an N—H bond, so it exhibits intermolecular hydrogen bonding. CH_4 (**B**) has only London forces because it has only nonpolar C—H bonds. NH_3 has stronger forces and the higher boiling point.

b. Methanol (**C**) has an O—H bond, so it can intermolecularly hydrogen bond. Chloromethane (**D**) has a polar C—Cl bond, so it has dipole–dipole interactions, but it cannot hydrogen bond. **C** has stronger forces, so **C** has the higher melting point.

PRACTICE PROBLEM 7.12

Which compound in each pair has the higher boiling point?

a. CH_4 or C_2H_6 b. C_2H_6 or CH_3OH c. HBr or HCl   d. C_2H_6 or CH_3Br

More Practice: Try Problems 7.68–7.70.

PROBLEM 7.11

Which compound in each pair has the higher melting point?

a.   b.

A   **B**   **C**   **D**

7.8   The Liquid State

Since liquid molecules are much closer together than gas molecules, many properties of a liquid are determined by the strength of its intermolecular forces. The molecules in a liquid are still much more mobile than those of a solid, though, making liquids fluid and giving them no definite shape. Some liquid molecules move fast enough that they escape the liquid phase altogether and become gas molecules that are very far apart from each other.

7.8A   Vapor Pressure

When a liquid is placed in an open container, liquid molecules near the surface that have enough kinetic energy to overcome the intermolecular forces escape to the gas phase. This process, **evaporation,** will continue until all of the liquid has become gas. A puddle of water formed after a rainstorm evaporates as all of the liquid water is converted to gas molecules called water **vapor.** **Evaporation is an** *endothermic* **process**—it absorbs heat from the surroundings. This explains why the skin is cooled as sweat evaporates.

Chloroethane (CH_3CH_2Cl), commonly called ethyl chloride, is a local anesthetic. When chloroethane is sprayed on a wound it quickly evaporates, causing a cooling sensation that numbs the site of an injury. *Source: Courtesy of Gebauer Company, Cleveland, Ohio*

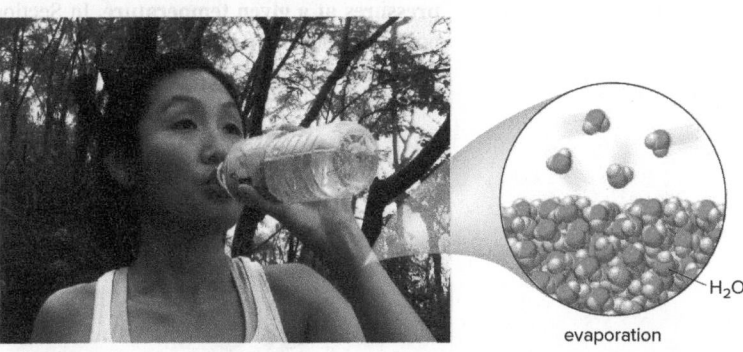

©Daniel C. Smith

evaporation H_2O

In a closed container, some liquid molecules evaporate from the surface and enter the gas phase. As more molecules accumulate in the gas phase, some molecules re-enter the liquid phase in the process of **condensation. Condensation is an** *exothermic* **process**—it gives off heat to the surroundings. At equilibrium, the rate of evaporation and the rate of condensation are equal.

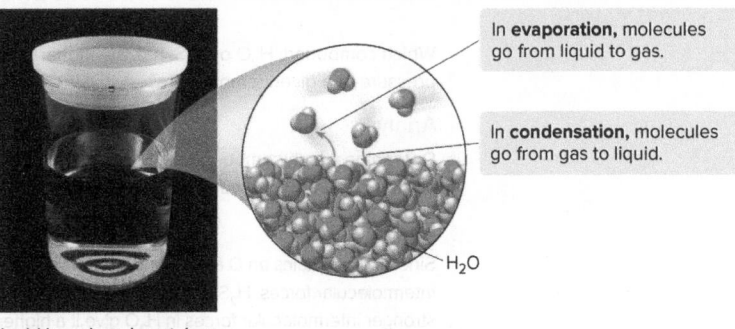

In **evaporation,** molecules go from liquid to gas.

In **condensation,** molecules go from gas to liquid.

H_2O

liquid in a closed container
©McGraw-Hill Education/Jill Braaten, photographer

The gas laws we have already learned can describe the behavior of the gas molecules above a liquid. In particular, these gas molecules exert pressure, called **vapor pressure.**

- Vapor pressure is the pressure exerted by gas molecules in equilibrium with the liquid phase.

The vapor pressure exerted by a particular liquid depends on the identity of the liquid and the temperature. As the temperature is increased, the kinetic energy of the molecules increases and more molecules escape into the gas phase.

- Vapor pressure increases with increasing temperature.

When the temperature is high enough that the vapor pressure above the liquid equals the atmospheric pressure, even molecules below the surface of the liquid have enough kinetic energy to enter the gas phase and the liquid boils. The *normal boiling point* of a liquid is the temperature at which its vapor pressure equals 760 mm Hg.

The boiling point depends on the atmospheric pressure. At the lower atmospheric pressure of higher altitudes, a liquid has a lower boiling point because the vapor pressure above the liquid equals the atmospheric pressure at a lower temperature. In Denver, Colorado (elevation 1,609 m, or 5,280 ft), where atmospheric pressure is typically 630 mm Hg, water boils at 93 °C.

How is the strength of the intermolecular forces related to the vapor pressure? The stronger the intermolecular forces, the less readily a compound escapes from the liquid to the gas phase. Thus,

- The stronger the intermolecular forces, the lower the vapor pressure at a given temperature.

Compounds with strong intermolecular forces have high boiling points and low vapor pressures at a given temperature. In Section 7.7 we learned that water has a *higher* boiling point than methane (CH_4) because water can hydrogen bond while methane cannot. At any given temperature, water has a *lower* vapor pressure because its molecules are held more tightly and remain in the liquid phase.

more gas molecules
higher vapor pressure

fewer gas molecules
lower vapor pressure

H_2O

Stronger intermolecular forces
keep the H_2O molecules as a liquid.

CH_4

Weaker intermolecular forces allow more
CH_4 molecules to escape to the gas phase.

SAMPLE PROBLEM 7.13 USING THE STRENGTH OF INTERMOLECULAR FORCES TO DETERMINE VAPOR PRESSURE AND BOILING POINT

Which compound, H_2O or H_2S, has the higher boiling point? Which compound has the higher vapor pressure at a given temperature?

Analysis

Determine which compound has the stronger intermolecular forces. **Stronger forces mean a higher boiling point and a lower vapor pressure.**

Solution

Since H_2O contains an O atom bonded to H, H_2O exhibits hydrogen bonding, the strongest of the intermolecular forces. H_2S has no hydrogen bonding because it has no hydrogen bonded to O, N, or F. The stronger intermolecular forces in H_2O give it a higher boiling point. The weaker intermolecular forces in H_2S mean that the molecules escape into the gas phase more readily, giving H_2S the higher vapor pressure.

PRACTICE PROBLEM 7.13

Which molecule in each pair has the higher vapor pressure at a given temperature?

a. CH_4 or NH_3 b. CH_4 or C_2H_6 c. C_2H_6 or CH_3OH

More Practice: Try Problems 7.71–7.74.

7.8B   Viscosity and Surface Tension

Viscosity and surface tension are two more properties of liquids that can be explained at least in part by the strength of the intermolecular forces.

Viscosity **is a measure of a fluid's resistance to flow freely.** A viscous liquid is one that feels "thicker." **Compounds with stronger intermolecular forces tend to be more viscous** than compounds with weaker forces. Thus water is more viscous than gasoline, which is composed of nonpolar molecules with weak intermolecular forces. The size of molecules also plays a role. Large molecules do not slide past each other as freely, so substances composed of large molecules tend to be more viscous. Olive oil, for example, is more viscous than water because olive oil is composed of compounds with three long floppy chains that contain more than 50 atoms in each chain.

Surface tension **is a measure of the resistance of a liquid to spread out.** Molecules in the interior of a liquid are surrounded by intermolecular forces on all sides, making them more stable than surface molecules that experience intermolecular forces only from neighbors on the side and below (Figure 7.8a). This makes surface molecules less stable. **The** *stronger* **the intermolecular forces, the stronger surface molecules are pulled down toward the interior of a liquid and the** *higher* **the surface tension.** Because water has strong intermolecular hydrogen bonding, its surface tension is high. This explains why water striders can walk across the surface (Figure 7.8b), and why a paper clip can "float" on water.

PROBLEM 7.12

Would you predict the surface tension of gasoline, composed of molecules containing only carbon and hydrogen atoms, to be higher or lower than the surface tension of water?

Figure 7.8   Surface Tension

H_2O on the surface

a.   b.

H_2O in the interior

(a) Interior molecules experience intermolecular forces (shown with double-headed arrows) evenly in all directions, whereas surface molecules experience uneven interactions and are pulled downward toward the interior. (b) Water's high surface tension allows a water strider to walk on the surface.
©McGraw-Hill Education/Jill Braaten, photographer; ©blickwinkel/Alamy

7.9   The Solid State

When a liquid is cooled so that the intermolecular forces are stronger than the kinetic energy of the particles, a solid is formed. Solids can be either **crystalline** or **amorphous.**

- A crystalline solid has a regular arrangement of particles—atoms, molecules, or ions—with a repeating structure.
- An amorphous solid has no regular arrangement of its closely packed particles.

There are four different types of crystalline solids—**ionic, molecular, network,** and **metallic**—as shown in Figure 7.9.

Figure 7.9   Four Examples of Crystalline Solids

a. Table salt (NaCl)   b. Ice (H_2O molecules)   c. Sand (SiO_2)   d. Copper (Cu)

Na⁺
Cl⁻
H_2O molecule
O
Si
Cu atom

(a) Sodium chloride, NaCl, an ionic solid; (b) ice, a molecular solid composed of H_2O molecules arranged in a hexagonal pattern; (c) silicon dioxide, SiO_2, a network solid that comprises sand; (d) metallic copper. ©*McGraw-Hill Education/Jill Braaten, photographer*

An **ionic solid** is composed of oppositely charged ions. For example, sodium chloride, NaCl, is composed of Na⁺ cations and Cl⁻ anions, arranged so that each Na⁺ cation is surrounded by six Cl⁻ anions and each Cl⁻ anion is surrounded by six Na⁺ cations.

A **molecular solid** is composed of individual molecules arranged regularly. Ice, for example, contains a hexagonal arrangement of water molecules that are extensively hydrogen bonded to each other. In fact, the crystalline structure of water accounts for one of its unique properties. Water is one of the few substances whose solid phase is *less* dense than its liquid phase. As a result, solid ice floats on liquid water. A sheet of ice freezes on top of a lake, allowing plant and animal life to survive beneath the surface.

A **network solid** is composed of a vast number of atoms covalently bonded together, forming sheets or three-dimensional arrays. Quartz sand, SiO_2, contains an infinite network of silicon and oxygen atoms. Each silicon atom is bonded to four oxygen atoms and each oxygen is bonded to two silicon atoms, so that there are twice as many oxygen atoms as silicon. Other examples include diamond and graphite, two elemental forms of carbon, whose structures appeared in Figure 2.6.

Since metals are atoms that readily give up their electrons, a **metallic solid** such as copper or silver can be thought of as a lattice of metal cations surrounded by a cloud of electrons that move freely. Because of their loosely held, delocalized electrons, metals conduct electricity and heat.

In contrast to crystalline solids, **amorphous solids have no regular arrangement of particles.** Amorphous solids can be formed when a liquid cools too quickly to allow the regular crystalline pattern to form. Substances composed of very large strands of covalent molecules also tend to form amorphous solids, because the chains can become folded and intertwined, making an organized regular arrangement impossible. Examples of amorphous solids include rubber, glass, and most plastics.

PROBLEM 7.13
Which type of crystalline solid is formed by each substance: (a) $CaCl_2$; (b) Fe (iron); (c) sugar ($C_{12}H_{22}O_{11}$); (d) $NH_3(s)$?

A polycarbonate helmet, polyethylene water bottle, and rubber tires are all examples of amorphous solids.
©Karl Weatherly/Getty Images RF

7.10 Specific Heat

In addition to melting point and boiling point (Section 7.7D), several other physical properties are determined by the strength of intermolecular forces. For example, **specific heat (SH)** is a physical property that reflects the ability of a substance to absorb heat. Some substances—solids, liquids, or gases—are capable of absorbing a great deal of heat as temperature increases, whereas other substances are not.

- The specific heat is the amount of heat energy (in calories or joules) needed to raise the temperature of 1 g of a substance by 1 °C.

$$\text{specific heat} = \frac{\text{heat}}{\text{mass} \times \Delta T} = \frac{\text{cal (or J)}}{\text{g} \cdot \text{°C}}$$

The specific heat of water is 1.00 cal/(g · °C), meaning that 1.00 cal of heat must be added to increase the temperature of 1.00 g of water by 1.00 °C. The amount of heat that must be added for a particular temperature increase depends on the amount of sample present. To increase the temperature of 2.00 g of water by 1 °C requires 2.00 cal of heat. Table 7.4 lists the specific heat values for a variety of substances.

- The *larger* the specific heat of a substance, the *less* its temperature will change when it absorbs a particular amount of heat energy.

The specific heat of graphite is about twice that of copper. Adding 1.00 cal of heat will raise the temperature of 1.00 g of graphite by 5.9 °C but raise the temperature of 1.00 g of copper by 11.1 °C. Because metals like copper have low specific heats, they absorb and transfer heat readily. We use copper, iron, or aluminum cookware because the metals readily transfer heat from the stove to the food in the pan.

The specific heat of water is very high compared to other liquids. As a result, **water absorbs a large amount of heat with only a small change in temperature.** Water has a high specific heat because of its strong intermolecular forces. Since water molecules are held together with an

Table 7.4 Specific Heats of Some Substances

Substance	cal/(g · °C)	J/(g · °C)	Substance	cal/(g · °C)	J/(g · °C)
Aluminum	0.214	0.895	2-Propanol	0.612	2.56
Carbon (graphite)	0.169	0.707	Rock	0.200	0.837
Copper	0.0900	0.377	Sand	0.200	0.837
Ethanol	0.583	2.44	Silver	0.0560	0.234
Gold	0.0310	0.130	Water(*l*)	1.00	4.18
Iron	0.107	0.448	Water(*g*)	0.481	2.01
Mercury	0.0335	0.140	Water(*s*)	0.486	2.03

extensive array of hydrogen bonds, it takes a great deal of energy to break these bonds and increase the disorder of the water molecules.

Moreover, since the amount of heat absorbed for a given temperature increase equals the amount of heat released upon cooling, water releases a great deal of energy when its temperature drops even a few degrees. A large body of water thus acts as a reservoir to absorb or release heat as temperature increases or decreases, and, in this way, it moderates the climate of the land nearby.

SAMPLE PROBLEM 7.14 USING SPECIFIC HEAT WHEN A SUBSTANCE ABSORBS OR RELEASES HEAT

Consider the elements aluminum, copper, gold, and iron in Table 7.4. (a) If 10 kcal of heat is added to 10 g of each element, which element will have the highest temperature? (b) Which element would require the largest amount of heat to raise the temperature of a 5-g sample by 5 °C?

Analysis

- The *larger* the specific heat, the *less* the temperature of a substance will change when it absorbs heat energy.
- The *larger* the specific heat, the *more* heat that must be added to *increase* the temperature of a substance a given number of degrees.

Solution

The specific heats of the metals in Table 7.4 increase in the following order: gold < copper < iron < aluminum. In part (a), gold has the lowest specific heat, so its temperature will be the highest if the same amount of heat is added to the same mass of all four elements. In part (b), aluminum has the largest specific heat, so it will require the largest amount of heat to raise its temperature the same number of degrees as the same mass of the other elements.

PRACTICE PROBLEM 7.14

A student has two containers—one with 10 g of sand and one with 10 g of ethanol. (a) Which substance has the higher temperature after 10.0 cal of heat is added to each container? (b) Which substance requires the larger amount of heat to raise its temperature by 10 °C?

More Practice: Try Problems 7.79, 7.80.

PROBLEM 7.14

The human body is composed of about 70% water. How does this help the body to maintain a steady internal temperature?

We can use the specific heat as a conversion factor to calculate how much heat is absorbed or lost from a substance as long as its mass and change in temperature are known, using the equation:

heat absorbed or released

$$\text{heat} = \text{mass} \times \underset{\Delta T}{\text{temperature change}} \times \text{specific heat}$$

$$\text{cal} = \text{g} \times \text{°C} \times \frac{\text{cal}}{\text{g} \cdot \text{°C}}$$

Sample Problem 7.15 shows how to use specific heat to calculate the amount of heat absorbed by a substance when the mass and temperature change are known.

SAMPLE PROBLEM 7.15 USING SPECIFIC HEAT IN CALCULATIONS

How many calories are needed to heat a pot of 1,600 g of water from 25 °C to 100. °C?

Analysis

Use specific heat as a conversion factor to calculate the amount of heat absorbed using the known mass and temperature change.

Solution

[1] Identify the known quantities and the desired quantity.

$$\text{mass} = 1{,}600 \text{ g}$$
$$T_1 = 25\ °C$$
$$T_2 = 100.\ °C \qquad \text{? calories}$$

known quantities   desired quantity

- Subtract the initial temperature (T_1) from the final temperature (T_2) to determine the temperature change: $T_2 - T_1 = \Delta T = 100. - 25 = 75\ °C$.
- The specific heat of water is 1.00 cal/(g · °C).

[2] Write the equation.

- The specific heat is a conversion factor that relates the heat absorbed to the temperature change (ΔT) and mass.

$$\text{heat} \quad = \quad \text{mass} \quad \times \quad \Delta T \quad \times \quad \text{specific heat}$$
$$\text{cal} \quad = \quad \text{g} \quad \times \quad °C \quad \times \quad \frac{\text{cal}}{\text{g} \cdot °C}$$

[3] Solve the equation.

- Substitute the known quantities into the equation and solve for heat in calories.

$$\text{cal} \quad = \quad 1600\ \cancel{g} \quad \times \quad 75\ \cancel{°C} \quad \times \quad \frac{1.00\ \text{cal}}{1\ \cancel{g} \cdot 1\ \cancel{°C}} \quad = \quad 1.2 \ \times \ 10^5\ \text{cal}$$

Answer

PRACTICE PROBLEM 7.15

How much energy is required to heat 28.0 g of iron from 19 °C to 150. °C? Report your answer in calories and joules.

More Practice: Try Problems 7.81, 7.82.

PROBLEM 7.15

How much energy is released when 200. g of water is cooled from 55 °C to 12 °C? Report your answer in calories and kilocalories.

Building on what you have learned in Sample Problem 7.15, Sample Problem 7.16 shows how to determine the temperature change of a given mass of a substance when the amount of heat absorbed is known.

SAMPLE PROBLEM 7.16 USING SPECIFIC HEAT TO CALCULATE A FINAL TEMPERATURE

If 400. cal of heat is added to 25.0 g of 2-propanol at 21 °C, what is the final temperature?

Analysis

Use specific heat as a conversion factor to determine the temperature change (ΔT) given the known mass of the substance and the amount of heat absorbed. Add the temperature change to the initial temperature (T_1) to obtain the final temperature (T_2).

Solution

[1] Identify the known quantities and the desired quantity.

$$\text{mass} = 25.0 \text{ g}$$
$$\text{heat added} = 400.\ \text{cal}$$
$$T_1 = 21\ °C \qquad \qquad T_2 = ?$$

known quantities   desired quantity

- According to Table 7.4, the specific heat of 2-propanol is 0.612 cal/(g · °C).

[2] Write the equation and rearrange it to isolate ΔT on one side.

• Divide both sides of the equation by mass (in g) and specific heat [in cal/(g · °C)] to place ΔT (in °C) on one side.

$$\text{heat} \quad = \quad \text{mass} \quad \times \quad \Delta T \quad \times \quad \text{specific heat}$$

$$\frac{\text{heat}}{\text{mass} \cdot \text{specific heat}} \quad = \quad \Delta T$$

$$\frac{\text{cal}}{\text{g} \cdot \text{cal}/(\text{g} \cdot {}^\circ\text{C})} \quad = \quad \Delta T$$

[3] Solve the equation to determine the change in temperature.

$$\Delta T \quad = \quad \frac{\text{cal}}{\text{g} \cdot \text{cal}/(\text{g} \cdot {}^\circ\text{C})} \quad = \quad \frac{400. \text{ cal}}{25.0 \text{ g} \cdot 0.612 \text{ cal}/(\text{g} \cdot {}^\circ\text{C})} \quad = \quad 26.1 \,{}^\circ\text{C}$$

temperature change

[4] Add the change in temperature (ΔT) to T_1 to obtain the final temperature T_2.

$$21 \quad + \quad 26.1 \quad = \quad 47 \,{}^\circ\text{C} \quad = \quad T_2$$

final temperature

PRACTICE PROBLEM 7.16

If 20. cal of heat is added to 10.0 g each of copper and mercury at 15 °C, what is the final temperature of each element?

More Practice: Try Problems 7.83, 7.84.

PROBLEM 7.16

If the initial temperature of 120. g of ethanol is 20. °C, what will be the final temperature after 950. cal of heat is added?

7.11   Energy and Phase Changes

In Section 7.7 we learned how the strength of intermolecular forces in a liquid and solid affect a compound's boiling point and melting point. Let's now look in more detail at the energy changes that occur during phase changes.

7.11A   Converting a Solid to a Liquid

Converting a solid to a liquid is called *melting*. Melting is an *endothermic* process. Energy must be absorbed to overcome some of the attractive intermolecular forces that hold the organized solid molecules together to form the more random liquid phase. The amount of energy needed to melt 1 g of a substance is called its **heat of fusion.**

ice

H_2O

liquid water

(left & right): ©McGraw-Hill Education/Jill Braaten, photographer

When an ice cube is added to a liquid at room temperature, the ice cube melts. The energy needed for melting is "pulled" from the warmer liquid molecules and the liquid cools down. ©McGraw-Hill Education/ Suzie Ross, photographer

Freezing is the opposite of melting; that is, *freezing* **converts a liquid to a solid.** Freezing is an *exothermic* process because energy is released as the faster moving liquid molecules form an organized solid in which particles have little freedom of motion. For a given mass of a particular substance, the amount of energy released in freezing is the same as the amount of energy absorbed during melting.

Heats of fusion are reported in calories per gram (cal/g). A heat of fusion can be used as a conversion factor to determine how much energy is absorbed when a particular amount of a substance melts, as shown in Sample Problem 7.17.

SAMPLE PROBLEM 7.17   USING THE HEAT OF FUSION TO DETERMINE ENERGY CHANGES

How much energy in calories is absorbed when 50.0 g of ice cubes melt? The heat of fusion of H_2O is 79.7 cal/g.

Analysis

Use the heat of fusion as a conversion factor to determine the amount of energy absorbed in melting.

Solution

[1]   Identify the original quantity and the desired quantity.

$$\underset{\text{original quantity}}{50.0 \text{ g}} \qquad \underset{\text{desired quantity}}{? \text{ calories}}$$

[2]   Write out the conversion factors.

- Use the heat of fusion as a conversion factor to convert grams to calories.

g–cal conversion factors

$$\frac{1 \text{ g}}{79.7 \text{ cal}} \quad \text{or} \quad \boxed{\frac{79.7 \text{ cal}}{1 \text{ g}}}$$

Choose this conversion factor to cancel the unwanted unit, g.

[3]   Solve the problem.

$$50.0 \text{ g} \times \frac{79.7 \text{ cal}}{1 \text{ g}} = 3{,}985 \text{ cal rounded to 3,990 cal}$$

Answer

Grams cancel.

PRACTICE PROBLEM 7.17

Use the heat of fusion of water from Sample Problem 7.17 to answer each question.

a. How much energy in calories is released when 50.0 g of water freezes?

b. How much energy in calories is absorbed when 35.0 g of water melts?

c. How much energy in kilocalories is absorbed when 35.0 g of water melts?

d. How much energy in calories is absorbed when 1.00 mol of water melts?

More Practice: Try Problems 7.87a, b; 7.88.

7.11B   Converting a Liquid to a Gas

Converting a liquid to a gas is called *vaporization*. Vaporization is an *endothermic* process. Energy must be absorbed to overcome the attractive intermolecular forces of the liquid phase to form gas molecules. The amount of energy needed to vaporize 1 g of a substance is called its **heat of vaporization.**

liquid water   steam

(left & right): ©McGraw-Hill Education/Jill Braaten, photographer

Condensation is the opposite of vaporization; that is, **condensation converts a gas to a liquid.** Condensation is an *exothermic* process because energy is released as the faster-moving gas molecules form the more organized liquid phase. For a given mass of a particular substance, the amount of energy released in condensation equals the amount of energy absorbed during vaporization.

Heats of vaporization are reported in calories per gram (cal/g). A high heat of vaporization means that a substance absorbs a great deal of energy as it is converted from a liquid to a gas. **Water has a high heat of vaporization.** As a result, the evaporation of sweat from the skin is a very effective cooling mechanism for the body. The heat of vaporization can be used as a conversion factor to determine how much energy is absorbed when a particular amount of a substance vaporizes, as shown in Sample Problem 7.18.

SAMPLE PROBLEM 7.18 USING THE HEAT OF VAPORIZATION TO DETERMINE ENERGY CHANGES

How much heat in kilocalories is absorbed when 22.0 g of 2-propanol evaporates after being rubbed on the skin? The heat of vaporization of 2-propanol is 159 cal/g.

Analysis

Use the heat of vaporization to convert grams to an energy unit, calories. Calories must also be converted to kilocalories using a cal–kcal conversion factor.

Solution

[1] Identify the original quantity and the desired quantity.

22.0 g   ? kilocalories

original quantity   desired quantity

[2] Write out the conversion factors.

- We have no conversion factor that relates grams and kilocalories directly. We do know, however, how to relate grams to calories using the heat of vaporization, and calories to kilocalories.

g–cal conversion factors   cal–kcal conversion factors

$\dfrac{1\text{ g}}{159\text{ cal}}$ or $\dfrac{159\text{ cal}}{1\text{ g}}$ $\dfrac{1000\text{ cal}}{1\text{ kcal}}$ or $\dfrac{1\text{ kcal}}{1000\text{ cal}}$

Choose the conversion factors with the unwanted units—g and cal—in the denominator.

[3] Solve the problem.

$22.0\ \cancel{g} \ \times \ \dfrac{159\ \text{cal}}{1\ \cancel{g}} \ \times \ \dfrac{1\ \text{kcal}}{1000\ \cancel{cal}} \ = \ 3.50\ \text{kcal}$

Grams cancel.   Calories cancel.   **Answer**

PRACTICE PROBLEM 7.18

Answer the following questions about water, which has a heat of vaporization of 540 cal/g.

  a. How much energy in calories is absorbed when 42 g of water is vaporized?

  b. How much energy in calories is released when 42 g of water is condensed?

  c. How much energy in kilocalories is absorbed when 1.00 mol of water is vaporized?

  d. How much energy in kilocalories is absorbed when 3.5 mol of water is vaporized?

More Practice: Try Problems 7.87c, d; 7.88.

7.11C   Converting a Solid to a Gas

Occasionally a solid phase forms a gas phase without passing through the liquid state. This process is called **sublimation.** The reverse process, conversion of a gas directly to a solid, is called **deposition.** Carbon dioxide is called *dry ice* because solid carbon dioxide (CO_2) sublimes to gaseous CO_2 without forming liquid CO_2.

$CO_2(s)$ $CO_2(g)$

(left & right): ©McGraw-Hill Education/Jill Braaten, photographer

Carbon dioxide is a good example of a solid that undergoes this process at atmospheric pressure. At reduced pressure other substances sublime. For example, freeze-dried foods are prepared by subliming water from a food product at low pressure.

Table 7.5 summarizes the phase changes in Section 7.11.

Table 7.5 Summary of Energy and Phase Changes

Process	Phases	Energy Change
Melting	Solid ⟶ liquid	Endothermic process—Energy is absorbed.
Freezing	Liquid ⟶ solid	Exothermic process—Energy is released.
Vaporization	Liquid ⟶ gas	Endothermic process—Energy is absorbed.
Condensation	Gas ⟶ liquid	Exothermic process—Energy is released.
Sublimation	Solid ⟶ gas	Endothermic process—Energy is absorbed.
Deposition	Gas ⟶ solid	Exothermic process—Energy is released.

SAMPLE PROBLEM 7.19 DETERMINING ENERGY CHANGES DURING CHANGES OF STATE

Is the process depicted in the molecular art endothermic or exothermic?

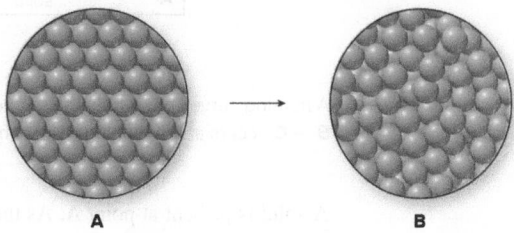

A   B

Analysis

- Identify the phase by the distance between the spheres and their level of organization. A solid has closely packed spheres that are well organized; a liquid has closely packed but randomly arranged spheres; a gas has randomly arranged spheres that are far apart.
- Classify the transformation as melting, freezing, vaporization, condensation, sublimation, or deposition, depending on the phases depicted.

Solution

A represents a solid and **B** represents a liquid, so the molecular art represents melting. Melting is an endothermic process because energy must be absorbed to convert the more ordered solid state to the less ordered liquid state.

PRACTICE PROBLEM 7.19

Is the process depicted in the molecular art endothermic or exothermic?

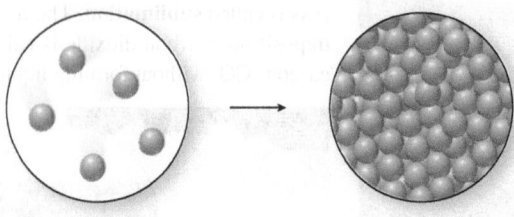

More Practice: Try Problems 7.85, 7.86.

7.12 Heating and Cooling Curves

The changes of state described in Section 7.11 can be illustrated on a single graph called a **heating curve** when heat is added and a **cooling curve** when heat is removed.

7.12A Heating Curves

A **heating curve** shows how the temperature of a substance (plotted on the vertical axis) changes as heat is *added*. A general heating curve is shown in Figure 7.10.

Figure 7.10

Heating Curve

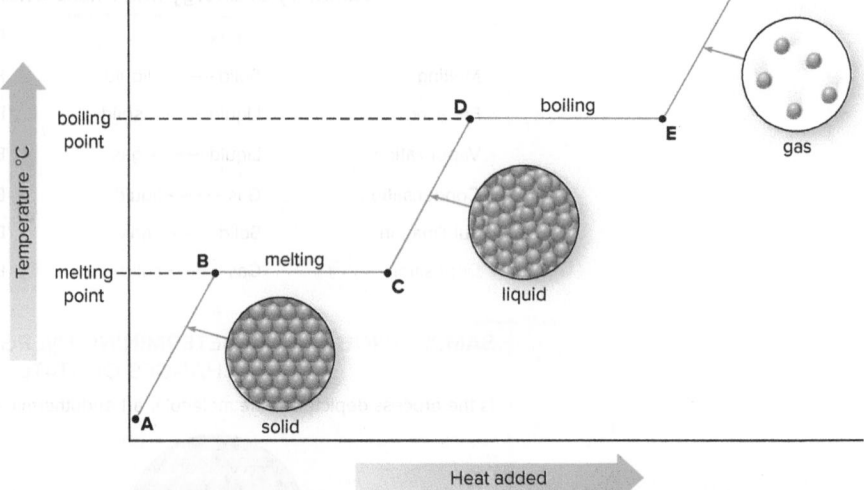

A heating curve shows how the temperature of a substance changes as heat is added. The plateau **B → C** occurs at the melting point, whereas the plateau **D → E** occurs at the boiling point.

A solid is present at point **A.** As the solid is heated, it increases in temperature until its melting point is reached at **B.** More heat causes the solid to melt to a liquid, without increasing its temperature (the plateau **B → C**). Added heat increases the temperature of the liquid until its boiling point is reached at **D.** More heat causes the liquid to boil to form a gas, without increasing its temperature (the plateau **D → E**). Additional heat then increases the temperature of the gas. Each diagonal line corresponds to the presence of a single phase—solid, liquid, or gas—whereas horizontal lines correspond to phase changes—solid to liquid or liquid to gas.

7.12B Cooling Curves

A **cooling curve** illustrates how the temperature of a substance (plotted on the vertical axis) changes as heat is *removed*. A cooling curve for water is shown in Figure 7.11.

Figure 7.11

Cooling Curve for Water

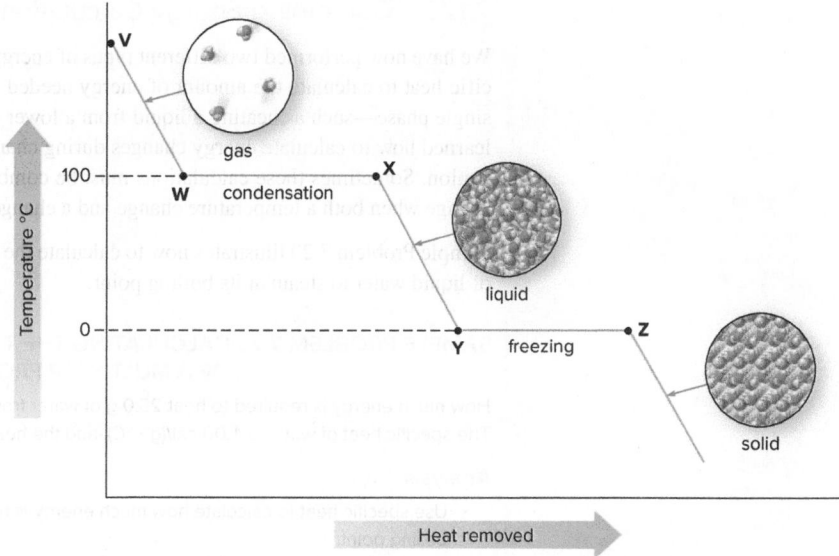

The cooling curve shows how the temperature of water changes as heat is removed. The plateau **W → X** occurs at the boiling point, whereas the plateau **Y → Z** occurs at the freezing point.

Gaseous water is present at point **V.** As the gas is cooled, it decreases in temperature until its boiling point is reached at **W.** Condensation at 100 °C forms liquid water, represented by the plateau **W → X.** Further cooling of the liquid water takes place until its freezing point (melting point) is reached at **Y.** Freezing water forms ice at 0 °C, represented by the plateau **Y → Z.** Cooling the ice further decreases its temperature below its freezing point.

PROBLEM 7.17

Answer the following questions about the graph.

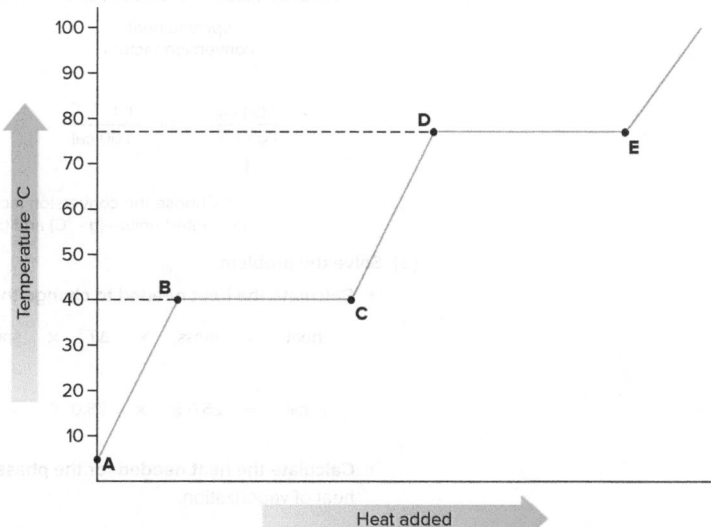

a. Does the graph illustrate a heating curve or a cooling curve?

b. What is the melting point of the substance?

c. What is the boiling point of the substance?

d. What phase(s) are present at plateau **B → C?**

e. What phase(s) are present along the diagonal **C → D?**

7.12C   Combining Energy Calculations

We have now performed two different types of energy calculations. In Section 7.10 we used specific heat to calculate the amount of energy needed to raise the temperature of a substance in a single phase—such as heating a liquid from a lower to a higher temperature. In Section 7.11 we learned how to calculate energy changes during changes of state using heats of fusion or vaporization. Sometimes these calculations must be combined together to determine the total energy change when both a temperature change and a change of state occur.

Sample Problem 7.20 illustrates how to calculate the total energy needed to convert a given mass of liquid water to steam at its boiling point.

SAMPLE PROBLEM 7.20 CALCULATING THE TOTAL ENERGY CHANGE
OF A MULTISTEP PROCESS

How much energy is required to heat 25.0 g of water from 25 °C to a gas at its boiling point of 100. °C? The specific heat of water is 1.00 cal/(g · °C), and the heat of vaporization of water is 540 cal/g.

Analysis

- Use specific heat to calculate how much energy is required to heat the given mass of water to its boiling point.
- Use the heat of vaporization to calculate how much energy is required to convert liquid water to a gas.

Solution

[1] Identify the original quantities and the desired quantity.

$$\text{mass} = 25.0 \text{ g}$$
$$T_1 = 25 \text{ °C}$$
$$T_2 = 100. \text{ °C} \qquad \text{? calories}$$

known quantities   desired quantity

- Subtract the initial temperature (T_1) from the final temperature (T_2) to determine the temperature change: $T_2 - T_1 = \Delta T = 100. - 25 = 75$ °C.

[2] Write out the conversion factors.

- Conversion factors are needed for both the specific heat and the heat of vaporization.

specific heat
conversion factors

$$\frac{1.00 \text{ cal}}{1 \text{ g} \cdot 1 \text{ °C}} \quad \text{or} \quad \frac{1 \text{ g} \cdot 1 \text{ °C}}{1.00 \text{ cal}}$$

heat of vaporization
conversion factors

$$\frac{540 \text{ cal}}{1 \text{ g}} \quad \text{or} \quad \frac{1 \text{ g}}{540 \text{ cal}}$$

Choose the conversion factors that place the unwanted units—(g · °C) and g—in the denominator.

[3] Solve the problem.

- **Calculate the heat needed to change the temperature** of water 75 °C using specific heat.

$$\text{heat} = \text{mass} \times \Delta T \times \text{specific heat}$$

$$\text{cal} = 25.0 \text{ g} \times 75.0 \text{ °C} \times \frac{1.00 \text{ cal}}{1 \text{ g} \cdot 1 \text{ °C}} = 1{,}875 \text{ cal rounded to } 1{,}900 \text{ cal}$$

- **Calculate the heat needed for the phase change** (liquid water ⟶ gaseous water) using the heat of vaporization.

$$\text{cal} = 25.0 \text{ g} \times \frac{540 \text{ cal}}{1 \text{ g}} = 13{,}500 \text{ cal rounded to } 14{,}000 \text{ cal}$$

- Add the two values together to obtain the total energy required.

$$\text{Total energy} = 1{,}900 \text{ cal} + 14{,}000 \text{ cal} = 15{,}900 \text{ cal rounded to } 16{,}000 \text{ cal}$$

Answer

PRACTICE PROBLEM 7.20

How much energy (in calories) is released when 50.0 g of water is cooled from 25 °C to solid ice at 0.0 °C? The specific heat of water is 1.00 cal/(g · °C), and the heat of fusion of water is 79.7 cal/g.

More Practice: Try Problems 7.93, 7.94.

PROBLEM 7.18

How much energy (in calories) is required to melt 25.0 g of ice to water at 0.0 °C, heat the liquid water to 100. °C, and vaporize the water to steam at 100. °C? The specific heat of water is 1.00 cal/(g · °C), the heat of fusion of water is 79.7 cal/g, and the heat of vaporization of water is 540 cal/g.

CHAPTER HIGHLIGHTS

KEY TERMS

Amorphous solid (7.9)
Atmosphere (7.2)
Avogadro's law (7.4)
Barometer (7.2)
Boiling point (bp, 7.7)
Boyle's law (7.3)
Charles's law (7.3)
Combined gas law (7.3)
Condensation (7.8, 7.11)
Cooling curve (7.12)
Crystalline solid (7.9)
Dalton's law (7.6)
Deposition (7.11)
Dipole–dipole interactions (7.7)
Evaporation (7.8)
Freezing (7.11)

Gas laws (7.3)
Gay–Lussac's law (7.3)
Heating curve (7.12)
Heat of fusion (7.11)
Heat of vaporization (7.11)
Hydrogen bonding (7.7)
Ideal gas law (7.5)
Intermolecular forces (7.7)
Ionic solid (7.9)
Kinetic–molecular theory (7.2)
London dispersion forces (7.7)
Melting (7.11)
Melting point (mp, 7.7)
Metallic solid (7.9)
Millimeters of mercury (7.2)
Molecular solid (7.9)

Network solid (7.9)
Normal boiling point (7.8)
Partial pressure (7.6)
Pressure (7.2)
Specific heat (7.10)
Standard molar volume (7.4)
STP (7.4)
Sublimation (7.11)
Surface tension (7.8)
Universal gas constant (7.5)
Vapor (7.8)
Vapor pressure (7.8)
Vaporization (7.11)
Viscosity (7.8)

KEY CONCEPTS

1 What is pressure and what units are used to measure it? (7.2)
- Pressure is the force per unit area. The pressure of a gas is the force exerted when gas particles strike a surface. Pressure is measured by a barometer and recorded in atmospheres (atm), millimeters of mercury (mm Hg), or pounds per square inch (psi).
- 1 atm = 760 mm Hg = 14.7 psi.

2 What are gas laws and how are they used to describe the relationship between the pressure, volume, and temperature of a gas? (7.3)
- Because gas particles are far apart and behave independently, a set of gas laws describes the behavior of all gases regardless of their identity. Three gas laws—Boyle's law, Charles's law, and Gay–Lussac's law—describe the relationship between the pressure, volume, and temperature of a gas. These gas laws are summarized in "Key Equations—The Gas Laws" on page 264.

- For a constant amount of gas, the following relationships exist.
  - The pressure and volume of a gas are inversely related, so increasing the pressure decreases the volume at constant temperature.
  - The volume of a gas is proportional to its Kelvin temperature, so increasing the temperature increases the volume at constant pressure.
  - The pressure of a gas is proportional to its Kelvin temperature, so increasing the temperature increases the pressure at constant volume.

3 Describe the relationship between the volume and number of moles of a gas. (7.4)
- Avogadro's law states that when temperature and pressure are held constant, the volume of a gas is proportional to its number of moles.
- One mole of any gas has the same volume, the standard molar volume of 22.4 L, at 1 atm and 273 K (STP).

4 What is the ideal gas law? (7.5)

- The ideal gas law is an equation that relates the pressure (P), volume (V), temperature (T), and number of moles (n) of a gas; $PV = nRT$, where R is the universal gas constant. The ideal gas law can be used to calculate any one of the four variables, as long as the other three variables are known.

5 What is Dalton's law and how is it used to relate partial pressures and the total pressure of a gas mixture? (7.6)

- Dalton's law states that the total pressure of a gas mixture is the sum of the partial pressures of its component gases. The partial pressure is the pressure exerted by each component of a mixture.

6 What types of intermolecular forces exist and how do they determine a compound's boiling point and melting point? (7.7)

- Intermolecular forces are the forces of attraction between molecules. Three types of intermolecular forces exist in covalent compounds. London dispersion forces are due to momentary changes in electron density in a molecule. Dipole–dipole interactions are due to permanent dipoles. Hydrogen bonding, the strongest intermolecular force, results when a H atom bonded to an O, N, or F is attracted to an O, N, or F atom in another molecule.
- The stronger the intermolecular forces, the higher the boiling point and melting point of a compound.

7 Describe three features of the liquid state—vapor pressure, viscosity, and surface tension. (7.8)

- Vapor pressure is the pressure exerted by gas molecules in equilibrium with the liquid phase. Vapor pressure increases with increasing temperature. The higher the vapor pressure at a given temperature, the lower the boiling point of a compound.
- Viscosity measures a liquid's resistance to flow. More viscous compounds tend to have stronger intermolecular forces or they have high molecular weights.
- Surface tension measures a liquid's resistance to spreading out. The stronger the intermolecular forces, the higher the surface tension.

8 Describe the features of different types of solids. (7.9)

- Solids can be amorphous or crystalline. An amorphous solid has no regular arrangement of particles. A crystalline solid has a regular arrangement of particles in a repeating pattern. There are four types of crystalline solids. Ionic solids are composed of ions. Molecular solids are composed of individual molecules. Network solids are composed of vast repeating arrays of covalently bonded atoms in a regular three-dimensional arrangement. Metallic solids are composed of metal cations with a cloud of delocalized electrons.

9 What is specific heat? (7.10)

- Specific heat is the amount of energy needed to raise the temperature of 1 g of a substance by 1 °C.
- Specific heat is used as a conversion factor to calculate how much heat a known mass of a substance absorbs or how much its temperature changes.

10 Describe the energy changes that accompany changes of state. (7.11)

- A phase change converts one state to another. Energy is absorbed when a more organized state is converted to a less organized state. Thus, energy is absorbed when a solid melts to form a liquid, or when a liquid vaporizes to form a gas.
- Energy is released when a less organized state is converted to a more organized state. Thus, energy is released when a gas condenses to form a liquid, or a liquid freezes to form a solid.
- The heat of fusion is the energy needed to melt 1 g of a substance, whereas the heat of vaporization is the energy needed to vaporize 1 g of a substance.

11 What changes are depicted on heating and cooling curves? (7.12)

- A heating curve shows how the temperature of a substance changes as heat is added. Diagonal lines show the temperature increase of a single phase. Horizontal lines correspond to phase changes—solid to liquid or liquid to gas.
- A cooling curve shows how the temperature of a substance changes as heat is removed. Diagonal lines show the temperature decrease of a single phase. Horizontal lines correspond to phase changes—gas to liquid or liquid to solid.

KEY EQUATIONS—THE GAS LAWS

Name	Equation	Variables Related	Constant Terms
Boyle's law	$P_1 V_1 = P_2 V_2$	P, V	T, n
Charles's law	$\dfrac{V_1}{T_1} = \dfrac{V_2}{T_2}$	V, T	P, n
Gay–Lussac's law	$\dfrac{P_1}{T_1} = \dfrac{P_2}{T_2}$	P, T	V, n
Combined gas law	$\dfrac{P_1 V_1}{T_1} = \dfrac{P_2 V_2}{T_2}$	P, V, T	n
Avogadro's law	$\dfrac{V_1}{n_1} = \dfrac{V_2}{n_2}$	V, n	P, T
Ideal gas law	$PV = nRT$	P, V, T, n	R

PROBLEMS

Selected in-chapter and odd-numbered end-of-chapter problems have brief answers in Appendix B. The *Student Study Guide and Solutions Manual* contains detailed solutions to all in-chapter and odd-numbered end-of-chapter problems, as well as additional worked examples and a chapter self-test.

Pressure

7.19 (a) What is the pressure in psi (pounds per square inch) on the given pressure gauge used for scuba diving? (b) How many mm Hg does this correspond to?

7.20 (a) What is the pressure in psi (pounds per square inch) on the given pressure gauge used for scuba diving? (b) How many pascals (Pa) does this correspond to?

7.21 Convert each quantity to the indicated unit.
    a. 2.8 atm to psi   c. 20.0 atm to torr
    b. 520 mm Hg to atm   d. 100. mm Hg to Pa

7.22 The compressed air tank of a scuba diver reads 3,200 psi at the beginning of a dive and 825 psi at the end of a dive. Convert each of these values to atm and mm Hg.

General Gas Law Problems

7.23 Assume that each of the following samples is at the same temperature. (a) Which diagram represents the sample at the highest pressure? (b) Which diagram represents the sample at the lowest pressure?

        [1]   [2]   [3]

7.24 Use the diagrams in Problem 7.23 to answer the following questions.
    a. What happens to the pressure when sample [1] is heated and the volume is kept constant?
    b. What happens to the pressure of sample [2] when the volume is halved and the temperature is kept constant?
    c. What happens to the pressure of sample [3] when its volume is halved and its Kelvin temperature is doubled?

7.25 **X** consists of a flexible container with eight particles of a gas as shown. What happens to the pressure of the system when **X** is converted to the representations in parts (a), (b), and (c)?

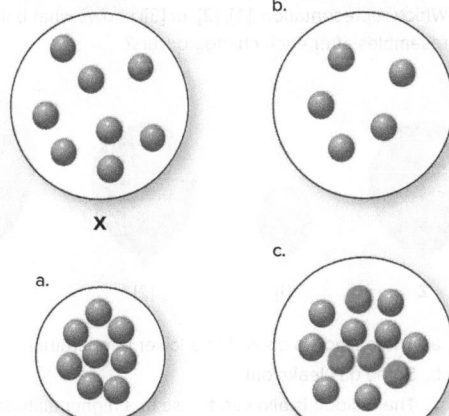

7.26 Suppose **A** represents a balloon that can expand or contract. **A** contains 10 particles of a gas as shown. Draw a diagram that shows the volume of **A** when each change occurs.

    a. The volume is halved and the temperature and number of particles remain the same.
    b. The pressure is doubled and the temperature and number of particles remain the same.
    c. The temperature is increased and the pressure and number of particles remain the same.
    d. The number of particles is doubled and the pressure and temperature remain the same.

7.27 Draw a picture that represents the given balloon when each of the following changes occurs.

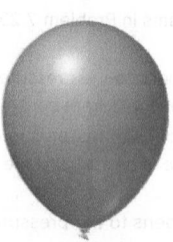

a. The balloon is inflated outside on a cold winter day and then taken inside a building at 75 °F.

b. The balloon is taken to the top of Mauna Kea, Hawaii (elevation 13,796 ft). Assume the temperature is constant.

c. The balloon is taken inside an airplane pressurized at 0.8 atm.

7.28 Which representation ([1], [2], or [3]) shows what balloon **Z** resembles after each change occurs?

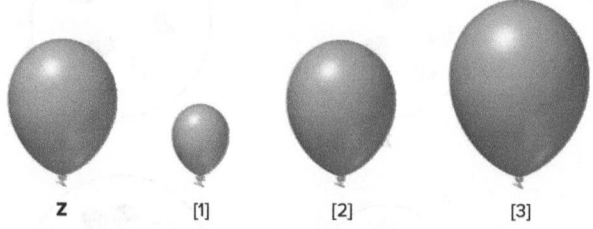

Z	[1]	[2]	[3]

a. The balloon is cooled to a lower temperature.

b. Some gas leaks out.

c. The balloon is allowed to rise to a higher altitude.

7.29 A balloon is filled with helium at sea level. What happens to the volume of the balloon in each instance? Explain each answer.

a. The balloon floats to a higher altitude.

b. The balloon is placed in a bath of liquid nitrogen at −196 °C.

c. The balloon is placed inside a hyperbaric chamber at a pressure of 2.5 atm.

d. The balloon is heated inside a microwave.

7.30 Suppose you have a fixed amount of gas in a container with a movable piston, as drawn. Re-draw the container and piston to illustrate what it looks like after each of the following changes takes place.

piston

a. The temperature is held constant and the pressure is doubled.

b. The pressure is held constant and the Kelvin temperature is doubled.

c. The pressure is halved and the Kelvin temperature is halved.

Boyle's Law

7.31 Assuming a fixed amount of gas at constant temperature, complete the following table.

	P_1	V_1	P_2	V_2
a.	2.0 atm	3.0 L	8.0 atm	?
b.	55 mm Hg	0.35 L	18 mm Hg	?
c.	705 mm Hg	215 mL	?	1.52 L

7.32 Assuming a fixed amount of gas at constant temperature, complete the following table.

	P_1	V_1	P_2	V_2
a.	2.5 atm	1.5 L	3.8 atm	?
b.	2.0 atm	350 mL	750 mm Hg	?
c.	75 mm Hg	9.1 mL	?	890 mL

7.33 If a scuba diver releases a 10.-mL air bubble below the surface where the pressure is 3.5 atm, what is the volume (in mL) of the bubble when it rises to the surface and the pressure is 1.0 atm?

©Daniel C. Smith

7.34 If you pack a bag of potato chips for a snack on a plane ride, the bag appears to have inflated when you take it out to open. If the initial volume of air in the bag was 250 mL at 760 mm Hg, and the plane is pressurized at 650 mm Hg, what is the final volume of the bag?

©Martin Shields/Alamy

Charles's Law

7.35 Assuming a fixed amount of gas at constant pressure, complete the following table.

	V_1	T_1	V_2	T_2
a.	5.0 L	310 K	?	250 K
b.	150 mL	45 K	?	45 °C
c.	60.0 L	0.0 °C	180 L	?

7.36 Assuming a fixed amount of gas at constant pressure, complete the following table.

	V_1	T_1	V_2	T_2
a.	10.0 mL	210 K	?	450 K
b.	255 mL	55 °C	?	150 K
c.	13 L	−150 °C	52 L	?

7.37 If a balloon containing 2.2 L of gas at 25 °C is cooled to −78 °C, what is its new volume?

7.38 How hot must the air in a balloon be heated if initially it has a volume of 750. L at 20 °C and the final volume must be 1,000. L?

Gay–Lussac's Law

7.39 Assuming a fixed amount of gas at constant volume, complete the following table.

	P_1	T_1	P_2	T_2
a.	3.25 atm	298 K	?	398 K
b.	550 mm Hg	273 K	?	−100. °C
c.	0.50 atm	250 °C	955 mm Hg	?

7.40 Assuming a fixed amount of gas at constant volume, complete the following table.

	P_1	T_1	P_2	T_2
a.	1.74 atm	120 °C	?	20. °C
b.	220 mm Hg	150 °C	?	300. K
c.	0.75 atm	198 °C	220 mm Hg	?

7.41 An autoclave is a pressurized container used to sterilize medical equipment by heating it to a high temperature under pressure. If an autoclave containing steam at 100. °C and 1.0 atm pressure is then heated to 150. °C, what is the pressure inside it?

7.42 If a plastic container at 1.0 °C and 750. mm Hg is heated in a microwave oven to 80. °C, what is the pressure inside the container?

Combined Gas Law

7.43 Assuming a fixed amount of gas, complete the following table.

	P_1	V_1	T_1	P_2	V_2	T_2
a.	0.90 atm	4.0 L	265 K	?	3.0 L	310 K
b.	1.2 atm	75 L	5.0 °C	700. mm Hg	?	50 °C
c.	200. mm Hg	125 mL	298 K	100. mm Hg	0.62 L	?

7.44 Assuming a fixed amount of gas, complete the following table.

	P_1	V_1	T_1	P_2	V_2	T_2
a.	0.55 atm	1.1 L	340 K	?	3.0 L	298 K
b.	735 mm Hg	1.2 L	298 K	1.1 atm	?	0.0 °C
c.	7.5 atm	230 mL	−120 °C	15 atm	0.45 L	?

Avogadro's Law

7.45 How many moles of helium are contained in each volume at STP: (a) 5.0 L; (b) 11.2 L; (c) 50.0 mL?

7.46 How many moles of argon are contained in each volume at STP: (a) 4.0 L; (b) 31.2 L; (c) 120 mL?

7.47 Calculate the volume of each substance at STP.
   a. 4.2 mol Ar   b. 3.5 g CO_2 c. 2.1 g N_2

7.48 Consider balloons **A** and **B**, which contain CH_4 and C_2H_6, respectively, at the same temperature and volume. (a) How does the pressure exerted by the gases in **A** and **B** compare? (b) How do the masses of the gases inside balloons **A** and **B** compare? (c) How do the densities of the gases inside balloons **A** and **B** compare?

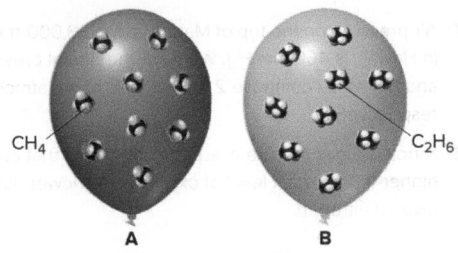

Ideal Gas Law

7.49 How many moles of gas are contained in a human breath that occupies 0.45 L and has a pressure of 747 mm Hg at 37 °C?

7.50 How many moles of gas are contained in a compressed air tank for scuba diving that has a volume of 7.0 L and a pressure of 210 atm at 25 °C?

7.51 How many moles of air are present in the lungs if they occupy a volume of 5.0 L at 37 °C and 740 mm Hg? How many molecules of air does this correspond to?

7.52 If a cylinder contains 10.0 g of CO_2 in 10.0 L at 325 K, what is the pressure?

7.53 Which sample contains more moles: 2.0 L of O_2 at 273 K and 500. mm Hg, or 1.5 L of N_2 at 298 K and 650 mm Hg? Which sample has more mass?

7.54 An unknown amount of gas occupies 30.0 L at 2.1 atm and 298 K. How many moles does the sample contain? What is the mass if the gas is helium? What is the mass if the gas is argon?

Dalton's Law and Partial Pressure

7.55 The molecular art shows a closed container with two gases, **A** (red spheres) and **B** (blue spheres) at a pressure of 630 mm Hg. What is the partial pressure of **A** and **B**?

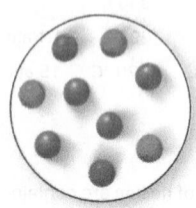

7.56 If the pressure due to the red spheres in the molecular art is 480 mm Hg, what is the pressure due to the blue spheres? What is the total pressure of the system?

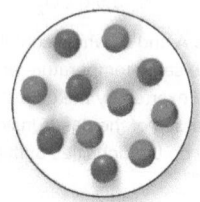

7.57 Air pressure on the top of Mauna Loa, a 13,000-ft mountain in Hawaii, is 460 mm Hg. What are the partial pressures of O_2 and N_2, which compose 21% and 78% of the atmosphere, respectively?

7.58 Nitrox is a gas mixture used in scuba diving that contains a higher-than-normal level of oxygen and a lower-than-normal level of nitrogen.

3,200 psi

  a. What percent of N_2 and O_2 is present in the given nitrox tank?

  b. What is the partial pressure of each gas (in psi) in the tank?

7.59 The partial pressure of N_2 in the air is 593 mm Hg at 1 atm. What is the partial pressure of N_2 in a bubble of air a scuba diver breathes when he is 66 ft below the surface of the water where the pressure is 3.00 atm?

7.60 If N_2 is added to a balloon that contains O_2 (partial pressure 450 mm Hg) and CO_2 (partial pressure 150 mm Hg) to give a total pressure of 850 mm Hg, what is the partial pressure of each gas in the final mixture?

Intermolecular Forces

7.61 Why is H_2O a liquid at room temperature, but H_2S, which has a higher molecular weight and a larger surface area, is a gas at room temperature?

7.62 Why is Cl_2 a gas, Br_2 a liquid, and I_2 a solid at room temperature?

7.63 What types of intermolecular forces are present in each compound?

a.   b.

7.64 What types of intermolecular forces are exhibited by each compound? Acetaldehyde is formed when ethanol, the alcohol in alcoholic beverages, is metabolized, and acetic acid gives vinegar its biting odor and taste.

a.   b.

    acetaldehyde   acetic acid

7.65 Which molecules are capable of intermolecular hydrogen bonding?

  a. H—C≡C—H   b. CO_2 c. Br_2 d. $H-\overset{\displaystyle H}{\underset{\displaystyle H}{C}}-\overset{\displaystyle H}{N}-H$

7.66 Which molecules are capable of intermolecular hydrogen bonding?

  a. N_2 b. $H-\overset{\displaystyle H}{\underset{\displaystyle H}{C}}-F$ c. HI   d. $H-\overset{\displaystyle H}{\underset{\displaystyle H}{C}}-O-H$

7.67 Can two molecules of formaldehyde ($H_2C{=}O$) intermolecularly hydrogen bond to each other? Explain why or why not.

7.68 Explain why the boiling point of **A** is higher than the boiling point of **B** despite the fact that **A** and **B** have the same chemical formula (C_3H_9N).

     A   B

7.69 Which compound, undecane or pentane, has the higher melting point? Explain.

undecane

pentane

7.70 Ethanol and dimethyl ether have the same molecular formula.

ethanol   dimethyl ether

a. What types of intermolecular forces are present in each compound?
b. Which compound has the higher boiling point?
c. Which compound has the higher vapor pressure at a given temperature?

7.71 Given the following vapor pressures at 20 °C, arrange the compounds in order of increasing boiling point: butane, 1,650 mm Hg; acetaldehyde, 740 mm Hg; Freon-113, 284 mm Hg.

7.72 Using the given boiling points, predict which compound has the higher vapor pressure at a given temperature.
a. ethanol (C_2H_6O, bp 78 °C) or 1-propanol (C_3H_8O, bp 97 °C)
b. hexane (C_6H_{14}, bp 69 °C) or octane (C_8H_{18}, bp 125 °C)

7.73 Consider the two liquids **A** and **B** shown in closed containers. (a) Which liquid has the higher vapor pressure? (b) Which liquid exhibits the stronger intermolecular forces? (c) Which liquid has the higher boiling point?

A   B

7.74 Consider the two liquids **A** and **B** in closed containers shown in Problem 7.73. Which liquid corresponds to

acetone and which liquid corresponds to acetic acid? Explain your choice.

acetone   acetic acid

Liquids and Solids

7.75 Explain why glycerol is *more* viscous than water, but acetone is *less* viscous than water. Glycerol is a component of skin lotions and creams. Acetone is the main ingredient in nail polish remover.

glycerol   acetone

7.76 Explain the following observation. When a needle is carefully placed on the surface of water, it floats, yet when its tip is pushed below the surface, it sinks to the bottom.

7.77 Classify each solid as amorphous, ionic, molecular, network, or metallic.
a. KI
b. CO_2
c. bronze, an alloy of Cu and Sn
d. diamond
e. the plastic polyethylene

7.78 Classify each solid as amorphous, ionic, molecular, network, or metallic.
a. $CaCO_3$
b. CH_3COOH (acetic acid)
c. Ag
d. graphite
e. the plastic polypropylene

Specific Heat

7.79 Consider the two beakers containing the same mass of **X** and **Y** that were at the same initial temperature. Which compound, **X** or **Y**, has the higher specific heat if the same amount of heat was added to both substances?

75 °C   63 °C

X   Y

7.80 Consider the following three containers (**A–C**) drawn below. (a) If the same amount of heat is added to all three samples, which sample has the highest temperature? (b) Which sample has the lowest temperature?

ethanol   ethanol   2-propanol

A   **B**   **C**

7.81 How much energy is absorbed or lost in each of the following? Calculate your answer in both calories and joules.
   a. the energy needed to heat 50. g of water from 15 °C to 50. °C
   b. the energy lost when 250 g of aluminium is cooled from 125 °C to 50. °C

7.82 How many calories of heat are needed to increase the temperature of 55 g of ethanol from 18 °C to 48 °C?

7.83 Which of the following samples has the higher temperature?
   a. 100. g of liquid water at 16.0 °C that absorbs 200. cal of heat
   b. 50.0 g of liquid water at 16.0 °C that absorbs 350. J of heat

7.84 If it takes 37.0 cal of heat to raise the temperature of 12.0 g of a substance by 8.5 °C, what is its specific heat?

Energy and Phase Changes

7.85 What phase change is shown in the accompanying molecular art? Is energy absorbed or released during the process?

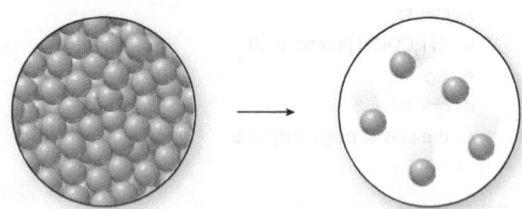

7.86 What phase change is shown in the accompanying molecular art? Is energy absorbed or released during the process?

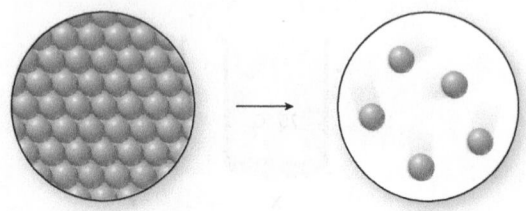

7.87 Indicate whether heat is absorbed or released in each process.
   a. melting 100 g of ice
   b. freezing 25 g of water
   c. condensing 20 g of steam
   d. vaporizing 30 g of water

7.88 Which process requires more energy, melting 250 g of ice or vaporizing 50.0 g of water? The heat of fusion of water is 79.7 cal/g and the heat of vaporization is 540 cal/g.

Heating and Cooling Curves

7.89 Consider the cooling curve drawn below.

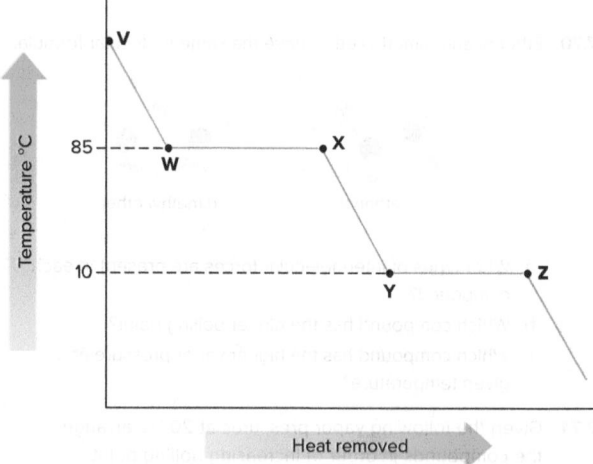

a. Which line segment corresponds to the following changes of state?

[1]

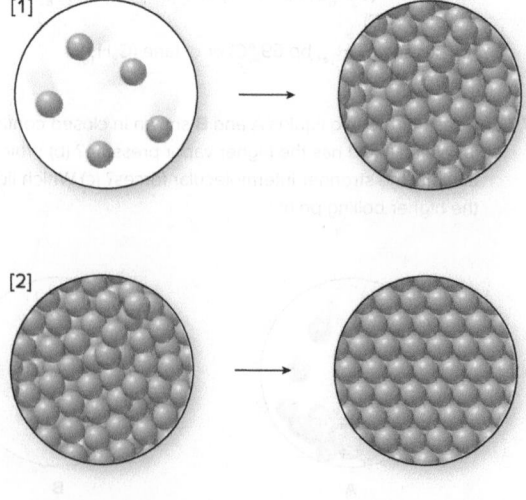

[2]

b. What is the melting point of the substance?
c. What is the boiling point of the substance?

7.90 Which line segments on the cooling curve in Problem 7.89 correspond to each of the following physical states?

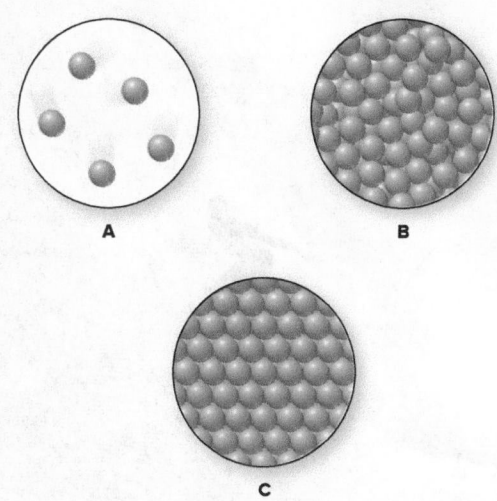

A   **B**

C

7.91 Draw the heating curve that is observed when octane is warmed from −70 °C to 130 °C. Octane, a component of gasoline, has a melting point of −57 °C and a boiling point of 126 °C.

7.92 Draw the heating curve that is observed when ice is warmed from −20 °C to 120 °C. Which sections of the curve correspond to the molecular art in **A**, **B**, and **C**?

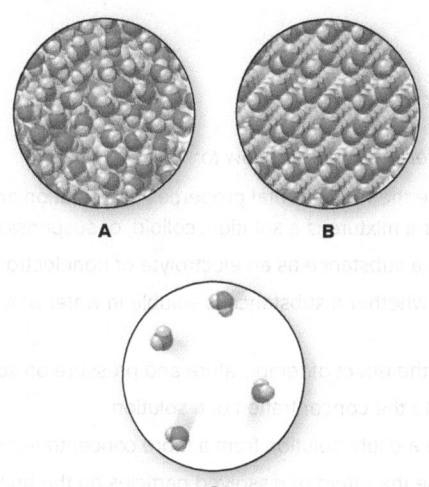

A   **B**

C

Combined Energy Calculations

7.93 Use the following values to answer each part. The specific heat of water is 1.00 cal/(g · °C); the heat of fusion of water is 79.7 cal/g; and the heat of vaporization of water is 540 cal/g.
   a. How much energy (in calories) is needed to melt 45 g of ice at 0.0 °C and warm it to 55 °C?
   b. How much energy (in calories) is released when 45 g of water at 55 °C is cooled to 0.0 °C, and frozen to solid ice at 0.0 °C?
   c. How much energy (in kilocalories) is released when 35 g of steam at 100. °C is condensed to water, the water is cooled to 0.0 °C, and the water is frozen to solid ice at 0.0 °C?

7.94 Use the values in Problem 7.93 to solve each part.
   a. How much energy (in calories) is needed to heat 150 g of water from 35 °C to 100. °C and vaporize the water to steam at 100. °C?
   b. How much energy (in kilocalories) is released when 42 g of steam is condensed to water at 100. °C, the water is cooled to 0.0 °C, and the water is frozen to solid ice at 0.0 °C?

Applications

7.95 Explain why cooling a full glass water bottle to −10 °C causes the bottle to crack.

7.96 Why does a bubble at the bottom of a glass of a soft drink get larger as it rises to the surface?

7.97 A common laboratory test for a patient is to measure blood gases—that is, the partial pressures of O_2 and CO_2 in oxygenated blood. Normal values are 100 mm Hg for O_2 and 40 mm Hg for CO_2. A high or low level of one or both readings has some underlying cause. Offer an explanation for each of the following situations.
   a. If a patient comes in agitated and hyperventilating— breathing very rapidly—the partial pressure of O_2 is normal but the partial pressure of CO_2 is 22 mm Hg.
   b. A patient with chronic lung disease has a partial pressure of O_2 of 60 mm Hg and a partial pressure of CO_2 of 60 mm Hg.

7.98 Explain why you feel cool when you get out of a swimming pool, even when the air temperature is quite warm. Then explain why the water feels warmer when you get back into the swimming pool.

CHALLENGE PROBLEMS

7.99 A gas (4.0 g) occupies 11.2 L at 2 atm and 273 K. What is the molar mass of the gas? What is the identity of the gas?

7.100 As we learned in Chapter 5, an automobile airbag inflates when NaN_3 is converted to Na and N_2 according to the equation, $2\ NaN_3 \longrightarrow 2\ Na + 3\ N_2$. What volume of N_2 would be produced if 100. g of NaN_3 completely reacted at STP?

Seawater in the world's oceans is an aqueous solution of dissolved salts, mainly sodium chloride.
©EpicStockMedia/Alamy RF

Solutions

CHAPTER OUTLINE

8.1 Mixtures

8.2 Electrolytes and Nonelectrolytes

8.3 Solubility—General Features

8.4 Solubility—Effects of Temperature and Pressure

8.5 Concentration Units—Percent Concentration

8.6 Concentration Units—Molarity

8.7 Dilution

8.8 Colligative Properties

8.9 Osmosis and Dialysis

CHAPTER GOALS

In this chapter you will learn how to:

1. Describe the fundamental properties of a solution and determine whether a mixture is a solution, colloid, or suspension
2. Classify a substance as an electrolyte or nonelectrolyte
3. Predict whether a substance is soluble in water or a nonpolar solvent
4. Predict the effect of temperature and pressure on solubility
5. Calculate the concentration of a solution
6. Prepare a dilute solution from a more concentrated solution
7. Describe the effect of dissolved particles on the boiling point and melting point of a solution
8. Describe the process of osmosis and how it relates to biological membranes and dialysis

I n Chapter 8 we study **solutions**—homogeneous mixtures of two or more substances. Why are table salt (NaCl) and sugar (sucrose) soluble in water but vegetable oil and gasoline are not? How does a healthcare professional take a drug as supplied by the manufacturer and prepare a dilute solution to administer a proper dose to a patient? An understanding of solubility and concentration is needed to explain each of these phenomena.

8.1 Mixtures

Thus far we have concentrated primarily on **pure substances**—elements, covalent compounds, and ionic compounds. Most matter with which we come into contact, however, is a **mixture** composed of two or more pure substances. The air we breathe is composed of nitrogen and oxygen, together with small amounts of argon, water vapor, carbon dioxide, and other gases. Seawater is composed largely of sodium chloride and water. A mixture may be **heterogeneous** or **homogeneous.**

- A *heterogeneous* mixture does not have a uniform composition throughout a sample.
- A *homogeneous* mixture has a uniform composition throughout a sample.

8.1A Solutions

The most common type of homogeneous mixture is a solution.

- A *solution* is a homogeneous mixture that contains small particles. Liquid solutions are transparent.

A cup of hot coffee, vinegar, and gasoline are transparent solutions. Any phase of matter can form a solution (Figure 8.1). Air is a solution of gases. An intravenous saline solution contains solid sodium chloride (NaCl) in liquid water. A dental filling contains liquid mercury (Hg) in solid silver.

A pepperoni pizza is a heterogeneous mixture, whereas a soft drink is a homogeneous solution. ©Jill Braaten RF

Figure 8.1 Three Different Types of Solutions

a. Air: Two (or more) gases   b. Saline solution: A solid in a liquid   c. Dental filling: A liquid in a solid

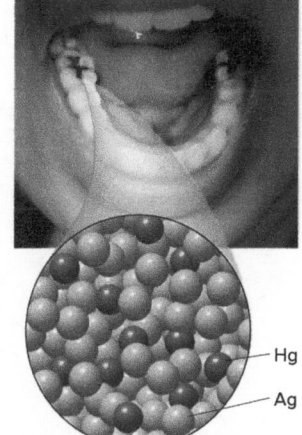

O_2
CO_2
N_2
H_2O
Cl^-
Na^+
Hg
Ag

a. Air is a solution of gases, primarily N_2 and O_2. The lungs contain significant amounts of H_2O and CO_2 as well.

b. An IV saline solution contains solid sodium chloride (NaCl) dissolved in liquid water.

c. A dental filling contains a liquid, mercury (Hg), dissolved in solid silver (Ag).

(b): ©Digital Vision/Alamy RF; (c): ©Keith Eng, 2008

When two substances form a solution, the substance present in the lesser amount is called the **solute,** and the substance present in the larger amount is the **solvent.** A solution with water as the solvent is called an **aqueous solution.**

Although a solution can be separated into its pure components, **one component of a solution cannot be filtered away from the other component,** because the particles of the solute are similar in size to the particles of the solvent. For a particular solute and solvent, solutions having different compositions are possible. For example, 1.0 g of NaCl can be mixed with 50.0 g of water or 10.0 g of NaCl can be mixed with 50.0 g of water.

8.1B Colloids and Suspensions

Colloids and suspensions are mixtures that contain larger particles than the particles in a solution.

- A *colloid* is a homogeneous mixture with larger particles, often having an opaque appearance.
- A *suspension* is a heterogeneous mixture that contains large particles suspended in a liquid.

Like solutions, the particles in a colloid generally cannot be filtered from its other components, and they do not settle out on standing. By definition, **a colloid contains particles that are 1 nm–1 μm in diameter.** Milk is a colloid. Homogenized milk is an opaque homogeneous mixture that contains large protein and fat molecules that do not dissolve in water. Homogenized milk does not have to be shaken before drinking because the particles of fat and protein do not settle out.

A suspension is a heterogeneous mixture that contains particles greater than 1 μm in diameter. The particles are so large that they do not dissolve in a liquid, and they can be either filtered away from the liquid or separated using a centrifuge. The particles in a suspension settle out on standing, and the suspension must be shaken to disperse the particles. Milk of magnesia, a common antacid, is a suspension that must be shaken before using because the active ingredients settle out.

Table 8.1 summarizes the properties of solutions, colloids, and suspensions.

Blood is a suspension containing blood cells that can be separated from liquid blood plasma by centrifugation.
©iStockphoto/Getty Images RF

Table 8.1 **Solutions, Colloids, and Suspensions**

Mixture	Particle Size	Settling	Separation
Solution	Small, < 1 nm	No	The components cannot be separated by filtration.
Colloid	Larger, 1 nm–1 μm	No	The components cannot be separated by common filtration techniques.
Suspension	Large, > 1 μm	Yes	The components can be separated by filtration or centrifugation.

PROBLEM 8.1

Classify each substance as a heterogeneous mixture, solution, or colloid: (a) Cherry Garcia ice cream (cherry ice cream + chocolate bits + cherries); (b) mayonnaise; (c) seltzer water; (d) nail polish remover; (e) brass (an alloy of Cu and Zn).

PROBLEM 8.2

Use the appearance of each product to classify it as a solution, colloid, or suspension: (a) orange juice (with the label shown); (b) apple juice; (c) passion orange guava (POG) drink.

a.

b.

c.
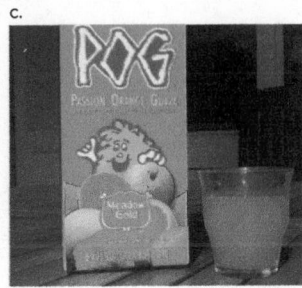

©McGraw-Hill Education   ©iStockphoto/Getty Images RF   ©Daniel C. Smith

8.2 Electrolytes and Nonelectrolytes

A solute that dissolves in water to form ions conducts an electric current, whereas a solute that contains only neutral molecules does not.

- A substance that conducts an electric current in water is called an *electrolyte*.
- A substance that does not conduct an electric current in water is called a *nonelectrolyte*.

8.2A Classification

Consider the difference between an aqueous solution of sodium chloride, NaCl, and an aqueous solution of hydrogen peroxide, H_2O_2. A solution of sodium chloride contains Na^+ cations and Cl^- anions and conducts electricity. A solution of hydrogen peroxide contains only uncharged H_2O_2 molecules in H_2O, so it does not conduct electricity.

(left & right): ©McGraw-Hill Education/Jill Braaten, photographer

Electrolytes can be classified as strong or weak, depending on the extent that the compound dissociates (forms ions).

A **strong electrolyte** dissociates completely to form ions when it dissolves in water. NaCl is a strong electrolyte because all of the species present in solution are Na^+ cations and Cl^- anions.

A **weak electrolyte** dissolves in water to yield largely uncharged molecules, but a small fraction of the molecules form ions. When ammonia (NH_3) dissolves in water, the predominant species is uncharged NH_3 molecules, but some NH_3 molecules react with water to form NH_4^+ cations and OH^- anions. Since a weak electrolyte contains some ions, it conducts an electric current, but not as well as a strong electrolyte. Common weak electrolytes are the weak acids and bases that we will learn about in Chapter 9.

NH_3 is a weak electrolyte because it exists in H_2O largely as uncharged NH_3 molecules, together with a small number of ions (NH_4^+ and OH^-).

NH_3 dissolved in H_2O

NH_4^+
OH^-
NH_3

©McGraw-Hill Education/Jill Braaten, photographer

Table 8.2 summarizes the characteristics of strong electrolytes, weak electrolytes, and non-electrolytes, and lists examples of each.

Table 8.2 Strong Electrolytes, Weak Electrolytes, and Nonelectrolytes

Solute	Species in Solution	Conductivity	Examples
Strong electrolyte	Ions	Conducts an electric current	NaCl, KOH, HCl, KBr
Weak electrolyte	Molecules with a few ions	Conducts an electric current	NH_3, CH_3CO_2H, HF
Nonelectrolyte	Molecules	Does not conduct an electric current	CH_3CH_2OH, H_2O_2

PROBLEM 8.3

Consider the following diagrams for an aqueous solution of a compound **AB** (with **A** represented by red spheres and **B** represented by blue spheres). Label each diagram as a strong electrolyte, weak electrolyte, or nonelectrolyte.

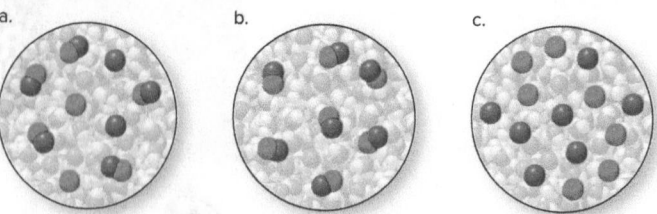

a.

b.

c.

PROBLEM 8.4

Classify each solution as an electrolyte or nonelectrolyte: (a) KCl in H_2O; (b) sucrose ($C_{12}H_{22}O_{11}$) in H_2O; (c) KI in H_2O.

8.2B Equivalents

Blood plasma contains electrolytes with dissolved ions such as Na^+, K^+, Cl^-, and HCO_3^-. An **equivalent (Eq)** is a unit used to express the amount of each ion in solution. An equivalent relates the amount of an ion to its charge.

- An *equivalent* is the number of moles of charge that a mole of ions contributes to a solution.

Thus, one mole of K^+ equals one equivalent of K^+ ions because potassium bears a +1 charge. One mole of Ca^{2+} equals two equivalents of Ca^{2+} ions because calcium bears a +2 charge. **The number of equivalents per mole of an ion equals the charge on the ion,** as shown in Table 8.3.

Table 8.3 Moles and Equivalents

Ion	Equivalents
1 mol Na^+	1 Eq Na^+
1 mol Ca^{2+}	2 Eq Ca^{2+}
1 mol HCO_3^-	1 Eq HCO_3^-
1 mol PO_4^{3-}	3 Eq PO_4^{3-}

SAMPLE PROBLEM 8.1 CALCULATING THE NUMBER OF EQUIVALENTS OF AN ION

How many equivalents of sulfate (SO_4^{2-}) are present in a solution that contains 3.2 moles of SO_4^{2-}?

Analysis

Use a conversion factor that relates the number of moles of the ion to its number of equivalents.

Solution

Since sulfate has a -2 charge, there are 2 Eq of SO_4^{2-} ions per mole of SO_4^{2-}.

$$3.2 \text{ mol } SO_4^{2-} \times \frac{2 \text{ Eq } SO_4^{2-}}{1 \text{ mol } SO_4^{2-}} = 6.4 \text{ Eq } SO_4^{2-}$$
Answer

PRACTICE PROBLEM 8.1

Using the given number of moles, determine how many equivalents of each ion are present.

a. 1 mol Na^+ b. 1 mol Mg^{2+} c. 0.5 mol K^+ d. 0.5 mol PO_4^{3-}

More Practice: Try Problem 8.29.

The amount of an electrolyte in blood plasma and IV solutions is often reported in the number of milliequivalents per liter of solution (mEq/L), where 1,000 mEq = 1 Eq. In solutions that contain ions, **there must be a balance between the total positive charge and total negative charge of all the ions present.** Thus, if a solution of KCl contains 40 mEq/L of K^+ ions, it must also contain 40 mEq/L of Cl^- ions.

SAMPLE PROBLEM 8.2 CALCULATING MILLIEQUIVALENTS OF AN ION

If an intravenous aqueous NaCl solution contains 154 mEq/L of Na^+ ions, how many milliequivalents of Na^+ is a patient given in 800. mL of solution?

Analysis and Solution

[1] Identify the known quantities and the desired quantity.

154 mEq/L Na^+ in solution
800. mL of solution
known quantities

? mEq Na^+
desired quantity

[2] Write out the conversion factors.

- Set up a conversion factor that relates milliequivalents to volume. Since the volume of the solution is given in mL, a mL–L conversion factor is needed as well.

mEq–L conversion factors

$$\frac{154 \text{ mEq } Na^+}{1 \text{ L}} \quad or \quad \frac{1 \text{ L}}{154 \text{ mEq } Na^+}$$

L–mL conversion factors

$$\frac{1 \text{ L}}{1000 \text{ mL}} \quad or \quad \frac{1000 \text{ mL}}{1 \text{ L}}$$

Use the conversion factors with the unwanted units—L and mL—in the denominator.

[3] Solve the problem.

- Multiply the original quantity by the conversion factors to obtain the desired quantity.

$$800. \text{ mL} \times \frac{1 \text{ L}}{1000 \text{ mL}} \times \frac{154 \text{ mEq } Na^+}{1 \text{ L}} = 123 \text{ mEq } Na^+$$
Answer

PRACTICE PROBLEM 8.2

If a KCl solution given intravenously to a patient that has a low potassium level contains 40. mEq of K⁺ per liter, how many milliequivalents of K⁺ are present in 550 mL of the solution?

More Practice: Try Problems 8.30–8.32.

PROBLEM 8.5

A solution contains the following ions: Na^+ (15 mEq/L), K^+ (10. mEq/L), and Ca^{2+} (4 mEq/L). If Cl^- is the only anion present in the solution, what is its concentration in mEq/L?

PROBLEM 8.6

If a solution contains 125 mEq of Na^+ per liter, how many milliliters of solution contain 25 mEq of Na^+?

8.3   Solubility—General Features

Solubility is the amount of solute that dissolves in a given amount of solvent, usually reported in grams of solute per 100 mL of solution (g/100 mL). A solution that has less than the maximum number of grams of solute is said to be **unsaturated.** A solution that has the maximum number of grams of solute that can dissolve is said to be **saturated.** If we added more solute to a saturated solution, the additional solute would remain undissolved in the flask.

8.3A   Basic Principles

What determines if a compound dissolves in a particular solvent? Whether a compound is soluble in a given solvent depends on the strength of the interactions between the compound and the solvent. As a result, compounds are soluble in solvents to which they are strongly attracted; that is, compounds are soluble in solvents with similar intermolecular forces. Solubility is often summed up in three words: **"Like dissolves like."**

- Most ionic and polar covalent compounds are soluble in water, a polar solvent.
- Nonpolar compounds are soluble in nonpolar solvents.

Water-soluble compounds are ionic or are small polar molecules that can hydrogen bond with the water solvent. For example, solid sodium chloride (NaCl) is held together by very strong electrostatic interactions of the oppositely charged ions. When it is mixed with water, the Na^+ and Cl^- ions are separated from each other and surrounded by polar water molecules (Figure 8.2).

Figure 8.2   Dissolving Sodium Chloride in Water

When ionic NaCl dissolves in water, the Na^+ and Cl^- interactions of the crystal are replaced by new interactions of Na^+ and Cl^- ions with the solvent. Each ion is surrounded by a loose shell of water molecules arranged so that oppositely charged species are close to each other.
(left & right): ©McGraw-Hill Education/Jill Braaten, photographer

Each Na^+ is surrounded by water molecules arranged with their O atoms (which bear a partial negative charge) in close proximity to the positive charge of the cation. Each Cl^- is surrounded by water molecules arranged with their H atoms (which bear a partial positive charge) in close proximity to the negative charge of the anion.

- **The attraction of an ion with a dipole in a molecule is called an ion–dipole interaction.**

The ion–dipole interactions between Na^+, Cl^-, and water provide the energy needed to break apart the ions from the crystal lattice. The water molecules form a loose shell of solvent around each ion. The process of surrounding particles of a solute with solvent molecules is called **solvation.**

Small uncharged molecules that can hydrogen bond with water are also soluble. Thus, ethanol (C_2H_5OH), which is present in alcoholic beverages, dissolves in water because hydrogen bonding occurs between the OH group in ethanol and the OH group of water.

CH₃CH₂OH
ethanol

hydrogen bond

H_2O

Ethanol can hydrogen bond with water.

©FoodCollection/StockFood RF

The basic principles of solubility explain why some vitamins are fat soluble while others are water soluble, as discussed in Chapter 11.

Water solubility for uncharged molecules occurs only with small polar molecules or those with many O or N atoms that can hydrogen bond to water. Thus, stearic acid ($C_{18}H_{36}O_2$), a component of animal fats, is *insoluble* in water because its nonpolar part (C—C and C—H bonds) is large compared to its polar part (C—O and O—H bonds). On the other hand, glucose ($C_6H_{12}O_6$), a simple carbohydrate, is *soluble* in water because it has many OH groups and thus many opportunities for hydrogen bonding with water.

Stearic acid–Water insoluble

many nonpolar C–C and C–H bonds

polar C–O and
O–H bonds

Most of the molecule is nonpolar, so it is
not attracted to a polar solvent like H_2O.

Glucose–Water soluble

many O–H bonds for
hydrogen bonding to H_2O

Figure 8.3   Solubility—A Nonpolar Compound in a Nonpolar Solvent

CCl$_4$

octane

octane in CCl$_4$

Octane (C$_8$H$_{18}$) dissolves in CCl$_4$ because both are nonpolar liquids that exhibit only London dispersion forces. ©*Tom Pantages*

Nonpolar compounds are soluble in nonpolar solvents. As a result, octane (C$_8$H$_{18}$), a component of gasoline, dissolves in the nonpolar solvent carbon tetrachloride (CCl$_4$), as shown in Figure 8.3. Animal fat and vegetable oils, which are composed largely of nonpolar C—C and C—H bonds, are soluble in CCl$_4$, but are insoluble in a polar solvent like water. These solubility properties explain why "oil and water don't mix."

Dissolving a solute in a solvent is a physical process that is accompanied by an energy change. Breaking up the particles of the solute requires energy, and forming new attractive forces between the solute and the solvent releases energy.

- When solvation releases more energy than that required to separate particles, the overall process is exothermic (heat is released).
- When the separation of particles requires more energy than is released during solvation, the process is endothermic (heat is absorbed).

These energy changes are used to an advantage in commercially available hot packs and cold packs. A hot pack, sometimes used for pain relief of sore muscles, contains calcium chloride (CaCl$_2$) or magnesium sulfate (MgSO$_4$) and water. Breaking the seal that separates them allows the salt to dissolve in the water, releasing heat, and the pouch gets warm. In contrast, ammonium nitrate (NH$_4$NO$_3$) absorbs heat on mixing with water, so this salt is found in instant cold packs used to reduce swelling.

©*Keith Eng, 2008*

SAMPLE PROBLEM 8.3 PREDICTING WATER SOLUBILITY

Predict the water solubility of each compound: (a) KCl; (b) methanol (CH$_3$OH); (c) hexane (C$_6$H$_{14}$).

Analysis

Use the general solubility rule—"like dissolves like."

- Generally, ionic and small polar compounds that can hydrogen bond are soluble in water.
- Nonpolar compounds are soluble in nonpolar solvents.

Solution

a. KCl is an ionic compound, so it dissolves in water, a polar solvent.

b. CH_3OH is a small polar molecule that contains an OH group. As a result, it can hydrogen bond to water, making it soluble.

c. Hexane (C_6H_{14}) has only nonpolar C—C and C—H bonds, making it a nonpolar molecule that is therefore water insoluble.

PRACTICE PROBLEM 8.3

Which compounds are water soluble?

a. $NaNO_3$ b. CH_4 c. HO—C—C—OH (with H H above and H H below each C)   d. KBr   e. NH_2OH

More Practice: Try Problems 8.33, 8.37, 8.38.

PROBLEM 8.7

Which pairs of compounds will form a solution?

a. benzene (C_6H_6) and hexane (C_6H_{14})   c. NaCl and hexane (C_6H_{14})
b. Na_2SO_4 and H_2O d. H_2O and CCl_4

8.3B Ionic Compounds—Additional Principles

Although ionic compounds are generally water soluble, some are not. If the attraction between the ions in a crystalline solid is stronger than the forces of attraction between the ions and water, the ionic compound does not dissolve. The identity of the cation and anion in the ionic compound determines its water solubility. Two rules can be used to predict water solubility.

General Rules for the Solubility of Ionic Compounds

Rule [1] A compound is soluble if it contains one of the following cations:
- Group 1A cations: Li^+, Na^+, K^+, Rb^+, Cs^+
- Ammonium, NH_4^+

Rule [2] A compound is soluble if it contains one of the following anions:
- Halide: Cl^-, Br^-, I^-, except for salts with Ag^+, Hg_2^{2+}, and Pb^{2+}
- Nitrate, NO_3^-
- Acetate, $CH_3CO_2^-$
- Sulfate, SO_4^{2-}, except for salts with Ba^{2+}, Hg_2^{2+}, and Pb^{2+}

Thus, Na_2CO_3 is water soluble because it contains a Na^+ cation (rule [1]), but $CaCO_3$ is water insoluble because it contains none of the ions listed in rules [1] and [2]. In dealing with the solubility of ionic compounds in this text, we will assume the compound to be water soluble unless specifically asked to consider the solubility rules just mentioned.

SAMPLE PROBLEM 8.4 USING THE SOLUBILITY RULES FOR IONIC COMPOUNDS

Use the solubility rules to predict whether the following ionic compounds are soluble in water:
(a) Na_3PO_4; (b) $Mg_3(PO_4)_2$; (c) KOH.

Analysis

Identify the cation and anion and use the solubility rules to predict if the ionic compound is water soluble.

Solution

a. Na_3PO_4 contains a Na^+ cation, and all Na^+ salts are soluble regardless of the anion.

b. $Mg_3(PO_4)_2$ contains none of the cations or anions listed under the solubility rules, so it is water insoluble.

c. KOH contains a K^+ cation, and all K^+ salts are soluble regardless of the anion.

PRACTICE PROBLEM 8.4

Use the solubility rules to predict whether the following ionic compounds are soluble in water:
(a) Li_2CO_3; (b) $MgCO_3$; (c) KBr; (d) $PbSO_4$; (e) $CaCl_2$; (f) $MgCl_2$.

More Practice: Try Problems 8.34, 8.49, 8.50.

PROBLEM 8.8

Use the solubility rules for ionic compounds to explain why milk of magnesia, which contains $Mg(OH)_2$ and water, is a heterogeneous mixture rather than a solution.

8.4   Solubility—Effects of Temperature and Pressure

Both temperature and pressure can affect solubility.

8.4A   Temperature Effects

For most ionic and molecular solids, solubility generally *increases* as temperature *increases*. Thus, sugar is much more soluble in a cup of hot coffee than in a glass of iced tea. If a solid is dissolved in a solvent at high temperature and then the solution is slowly cooled, the solubility of the solute decreases and it precipitates from the solution. Sometimes, however, if cooling is very slow, the solution becomes **supersaturated** with solute; that is, the solution contains more than the predicted maximum amount of solute at a given temperature. Such a solution is unstable, and when it is disturbed, the solute precipitates rapidly.

In contrast, **the solubility of gases *decreases* with increasing temperature.** Because increasing temperature increases the kinetic energy, more gas particles escape into the gas phase and fewer remain in solution. Increasing temperature decreases the solubility of oxygen in lakes and streams. In cases where industrial plants operating near lakes or streams have raised water temperature, marine life dies from lack of sufficient oxygen in solution.

PROBLEM 8.9

Why does a soft drink become "flat" faster when it is left open at room temperature compared to when it is left open in the refrigerator?

8.4B   Pressure Effects

Pressure changes do not affect the solubility of liquids and solids, but pressure affects the solubility of gases a great deal. **Henry's law** describes the effect of pressure on gas solubility.

> • Henry's law: The solubility of a gas in a liquid is proportional to the partial pressure of the gas above the liquid.

Thus, the **higher the pressure, the higher the solubility of a gas in a solvent.** A practical demonstration of Henry's law occurs whenever we open a carbonated soft drink. Soft drinks containing dissolved CO_2 are sealed under greater than 1 atm pressure. When a can is opened, the pressure above the liquid decreases to 1 atm, so the solubility of the CO_2 in the soda decreases as well and some of the dissolved CO_2 fizzes out of solution (Figure 8.4).

Scuba divers often hold on to a rope so that they ascend to the surface slowly after a dive, in order to avoid forming bubbles of nitrogen gas in joints and blood vessels. ©Stephen Frink/Getty Images RF

As we learned in Section 7.6, increasing gas solubility affects scuba divers because more N_2 is dissolved in the blood under the higher pressures experienced under water. Divers must ascend slowly to avoid forming bubbles of N_2 in joints and small blood vessels. If a diver ascends slowly, the external pressure around the diver slowly decreases and, by Henry's law, the solubility of the gas in the diver's blood slowly decreases as well.

Figure 8.4 Henry's Law and Carbonated Beverages

The air pressure in a closed can of soda is approximately 2 atm. When the can is opened, the pressure above the liquid in the can decreases to 1 atm, so the CO_2 concentration in the soda decreases as well, and the gas fizzes from the soda. *(left & right): ©McGraw-Hill Education/Jill Braaten, photographer*

PROBLEM 8.10

Predict the effect each change has on the solubility of [1] $Na_2CO_3(s)$; [2] $N_2(g)$.

  a. increasing the temperature   c. increasing the pressure

  b. decreasing the temperature   d. decreasing the pressure

8.5 Concentration Units—Percent Concentration

In using a solution in the laboratory or in administering the proper dose of a liquid medication, we must know its *concentration*—**how much solute is dissolved in a given amount of solution.** Concentration can be measured in several different ways that use mass, volume, or moles. Two useful measures of concentration are reported as percentages—that is, the number of grams or milliliters of solute per 100 mL of solution.

8.5A Weight/Volume Percent

One of the most common measures of concentration is **weight/volume percent concentration, (w/v)%—that is, the number of grams of solute dissolved in 100 mL of solution.** Mathematically, weight/volume percent is calculated by dividing the number of grams of solute in a given number of milliliters of solution, and multiplying by 100%.

> **Weight/volume percent concentration**
>
> $$(w/v)\% = \frac{\text{mass of solute (g)}}{\text{volume of solution (mL)}} \times 100\%$$

For example, vinegar contains 5 g of acetic acid dissolved in 100 mL of solution, so the acetic acid concentration is 5% (w/v).

$$(w/v)\% = \frac{5 \text{ g acetic acid}}{100 \text{ mL vinegar solution}} \times 100\% = 5\% \text{ (w/v) acetic acid}$$

Note that the volume used to calculate concentration is the *final* volume of the solution, not the volume of solvent added to make the solution. A special flask called a **volumetric flask** is used

Figure 8.5   Making a Solution with a Particular Concentration

a. Add the solute.

b. Add the solvent.

To make a solution of a given concentration, (a) add a measured number of grams of solute to a volumetric flask; (b) then add solvent to dissolve the solid, bringing the level of the solvent to the calibrated mark on the neck of the flask. *(a & b): ©McGraw-Hill Education/Jill Braaten, photographer*

to make a solution of a given concentration (Figure 8.5). The solute is placed in the flask and then enough solvent is added to dissolve the solute by mixing. Next, additional solvent is added until it reaches a calibrated line that measures the final volume of the solution.

SAMPLE PROBLEM 8.5 CALCULATING WEIGHT/VOLUME PERCENT CONCENTRATION

Chloraseptic sore throat spray contains 0.35 g of the antiseptic phenol dissolved in 25 mL of solution. What is the weight/volume percent concentration of phenol?

Analysis

Use the formula (w/v)% = (grams of solute)/(mL of solution) × 100%.

Solution

$$(w/v)\% = \frac{0.35 \text{ g phenol}}{25 \text{ mL solution}} \times 100\% = 1.4\% \text{ (w/v) phenol}$$

Answer

PRACTICE PROBLEM 8.5

A commercial mouthwash contains 4.3 g of ethanol and 0.021 g of antiseptic in each 30.-mL portion. Calculate the weight/volume percent concentration of each component.

More Practice: Try Problems 8.51a, 8.52a, 8.53, 8.54, 8.99.

PROBLEM 8.11

What is the weight/volume percent concentration of sodium chloride in seawater if one liter contains 35 g of NaCl?

8.5B Volume/Volume Percent

The alcohol (ethanol) content of wine, beer, and other alcoholic beverages is reported using volume/volume percent concentration. Wines typically contain 10–13% (v/v) ethanol, whereas beer usually contains 3–5%. ©Christian Delbert/ Shutterstock RF

When the solute in a solution is a liquid, its concentration is often reported using **volume/volume percent concentration, (v/v)%—that is, the number of milliliters of solute dissolved in 100 mL of solution.** Mathematically, volume/volume percent is calculated by dividing the number of milliliters of solute in a given number of milliliters of solution, and multiplying by 100%.

Volume/volume percent concentration

$$(v/v)\% = \frac{\text{volume of solute (mL)}}{\text{volume of solution (mL)}} \times 100\%$$

For example, a bottle of rubbing alcohol that contains 70 mL of 2-propanol in 100 mL of solution has a 70% (v/v) concentration of 2-propanol.

$$(v/v)\% = \frac{70 \text{ mL 2-propanol}}{100 \text{ mL rubbing alcohol}} \times 100\% = 70\% \text{ (v/v) 2-propanol}$$

SAMPLE PROBLEM 8.6 CALCULATING VOLUME/VOLUME PERCENT CONCENTRATION

A 750-mL bottle of wine contains 101 mL of ethanol. What is the volume/volume percent concentration of ethanol?

Analysis

Use the formula (v/v)% = (mL of solute)/(mL of solution) × 100%.

Solution

$$(v/v)\% = \frac{101 \text{ mL ethanol}}{750 \text{ mL wine}} \times 100\% = 14\% \text{ (v/v) ethanol}$$

Answer

PRACTICE PROBLEM 8.6

A 1.0-oz bottle of lemon extract contains 24 mL of ethanol. What is the volume/volume percent concentration of ethanol?

More Practice: Try Problems 8.55, 8.56.

CONSUMER NOTE

Lemon extract (Practice Problem 8.6) used in cooking is prepared from lemon rind, ethanol, and water. ©Sheila Fitzgerald/ Shutterstock RF

8.5C Using a Percent Concentration as a Conversion Factor

Percent concentration can be used as a conversion factor to relate the amount of solute (either grams or milliliters) to the amount of solution. For example, ketamine, an anesthetic especially useful for children, is supplied as a 5.0% (w/v) solution, meaning that 5.0 g of ketamine are present in 100 mL of solution. Two conversion factors derived from the percent concentration can be written.

$$5.0\% \text{ (w/v) ketamine} \qquad \frac{5.0 \text{ g ketamine}}{100 \text{ mL solution}} \quad \text{or} \quad \frac{100 \text{ mL solution}}{5.0 \text{ g ketamine}}$$

weight/volume
percent concentration

We can use these conversion factors to determine the amount of solute contained in a given volume of solution (Sample Problem 8.7), or to determine how much solution contains a given number of grams of solute (Sample Problem 8.8).

HEALTH NOTE

Ketamine is a widely used anesthetic in both human and veterinary medicine. It has been illegally used as a recreational drug because it can produce hallucinations. ©David Hoffman Photo Library/Alamy

SAMPLE PROBLEM 8.7 USING PERCENT CONCENTRATION TO DETERMINE GRAMS OF SOLUTE

A saline solution used in intravenous drips for patients who cannot take oral fluids contains 0.92% (w/v) NaCl in water. How many grams of NaCl are contained in 250 mL of this solution?

Analysis and Solution

[1] Identify the known quantities and the desired quantity.

0.92% (w/v) NaCl solution	
250 mL	? g NaCl
known quantities	desired quantity

©McGraw-Hill Education/Mark Dierker, photographer

[2] Write out the conversion factors.

- Set up conversion factors that relate grams of NaCl to the volume of the solution using the weight/volume percent concentration.

$$\frac{100 \text{ mL solution}}{0.92 \text{ g NaCl}} \quad \text{or} \quad \frac{0.92 \text{ g NaCl}}{100 \text{ mL solution}} \quad \text{Choose this conversion factor to cancel mL.}$$

[3] Solve the problem.

- Multiply the original quantity by the conversion factor to obtain the desired quantity.

$$250 \text{ mL} \times \frac{0.92 \text{ g NaCl}}{100 \text{ mL solution}} = 2.3 \text{ g NaCl}$$

Answer

PRACTICE PROBLEM 8.7

The pain reliever ibuprofen is sold as an oral suspension for children 2–11 years of age. (a) What is the weight/volume percent concentration in the suspension of ibuprofen shown in the given label? (b) How many milligrams would you obtain in a 2.5-tsp dose? (1 tsp = 5 mL) (c) Why do the directions on the medicine bottle say, "Shake well before using"?

More Practice: Try Problem 8.51b.

SAMPLE PROBLEM 8.8 USING PERCENT CONCENTRATION TO DETERMINE THE VOLUME OF SOLUTION

What volume of a 5.0% (w/v) solution of ketamine contains 75 mg?

Analysis and Solution

[1] Identify the known quantities and the desired quantity.

$$\underset{\text{known quantities}}{\underbrace{\begin{array}{c} 5.0\% \text{ (w/v) ketamine solution} \\ 75 \text{ mg} \end{array}}} \qquad \underset{\text{desired quantity}}{\underbrace{? \text{ mL ketamine}}}$$

[2] Write out the conversion factors.

- Use the weight/volume percent concentration to set up conversion factors that relate grams of ketamine to mL of solution. Since percent concentration is expressed in grams, a mg–g conversion factor is needed as well.

mg–g conversion factors   g–mL solution conversion factors

$$\frac{1000 \text{ mg}}{1 \text{ g}} \quad \text{or} \quad \frac{1 \text{ g}}{1000 \text{ mg}} \qquad\qquad \frac{5.0 \text{ g ketamine}}{100 \text{ mL solution}} \quad \text{or} \quad \frac{100 \text{ mL solution}}{5.0 \text{ g ketamine}}$$

Choose the conversion factors with the unwanted units—mg and g—in the denominator.

[3] Solve the problem.

- Multiply the original quantity by the conversion factors to obtain the desired quantity.

$$75 \text{ mg ketamine} \times \frac{1 \text{ g}}{1000 \text{ mg}} \times \frac{100 \text{ mL solution}}{5.0 \text{ g ketamine}} = 1.5 \text{ mL solution}$$

Answer

PRACTICE PROBLEM 8.8

A drink sold in a health food store contains 0.50% (w/v) of vitamin C. What volume would you have to ingest to obtain 1,000. mg of vitamin C?

More Practice: Try Problems 8.52b, 8.65.

Alcohol-based hand sanitizers clean hands by killing many types of disease-causing bacteria and viruses. ©McGraw-Hill Education/Mark Dierker, photographer

PROBLEM 8.12

How many mL of ethanol are contained in an 8.0-oz bottle of hand sanitizer that has a concentration of 62% (v/v) of ethanol? (1 fl oz = 29.6 mL)

8.5D   Parts Per Million

When a solution contains a very small concentration of solute, concentration is often expressed in **parts per million (ppm).** Whereas percent concentration is the number of "parts"—grams or milliliters—in 100 parts (100 mL) of solution, parts per million is the number of "parts" in 1,000,000 parts of solution. The "parts" may be expressed in either mass or volume units as long as the *same* unit is used for both the numerator and denominator.

Parts per million

$$ppm = \frac{mass\ of\ solute\ (g)}{mass\ of\ solution\ (g)} \times 10^6$$

or

$$ppm = \frac{volume\ of\ solute\ (mL)}{volume\ of\ solution\ (mL)} \times 10^6$$

A sample of seawater that contains 1.3 g of magnesium ions in 10^6 g of solution contains 1.3 ppm of magnesium.

$$ppm = \frac{1.3\ g\ magnesium}{10^6\ g\ seawater} \times 10^6 = 1.3\ ppm\ magnesium$$

Parts per million is used as a concentration unit for very dilute solutions. When water is the solvent, the density of the solution is close to the density of pure water, which is 1.0 g/mL at room temperature. In this case, the numerical value of the denominator is the same no matter if the unit is grams or milliliters. Thus, an aqueous solution that contains 2 ppm of MTBE, a gasoline additive and environmental pollutant, can be written in the following ways:

$$\frac{2\ g\ MTBE}{10^6\ g\ solution} \times 10^6 = \frac{2\ g\ MTBE}{10^6\ mL\ solution} \times 10^6 = 2\ ppm\ MTBE$$

10^6 mL has a mass of 10^6 g.

ENVIRONMENTAL NOTE

Seabirds such as osprey that feed on fish contaminated with the pesticide DDT accumulate an average of 25 parts per million of DDT in their fatty tissues. When DDT concentration is high, mother osprey produce eggs with very thin shells that are easily crushed, so fewer osprey chicks hatch. ©Comstock/Getty Images RF

SAMPLE PROBLEM 8.9 CALCULATING PARTS PER MILLION

What is the concentration in parts per million of DDT in the tissues of a seabird that contains 50. mg of DDT in 1,900 g of tissue? DDT, a nonbiodegradable pesticide that is a persistent environmental pollutant, has been banned from use in the United States since 1973.

Analysis

Use the formula ppm = (g of solute)/(g of solution) × 10^6.

Solution

[1] Convert milligrams of DDT to grams of DDT so that both the solute and solution have the same unit.

$$50.\ mg\ DDT \times \frac{1\ g}{1000\ mg} = 0.050\ g\ DDT$$

[2] Use the formula to calculate parts per million.

$$\frac{0.050\ g\ DDT}{1900\ g\ tissue} \times 10^6 = 26\ ppm\ DDT$$

Answer

PRACTICE PROBLEM 8.9

What is the concentration in parts per million of DDT in each of the following?

a. 0.042 mg in 1,400 g plankton

b. 5 × 10^{-4} g in 1.0 kg minnow tissue

c. 2.0 mg in 1.0 kg needlefish tissue

d. 225 µg in 1.0 kg breast milk

More Practice: Try Problems 8.67, 8.68, 8.100.

8.6   Concentration Units—Molarity

The most common measure of concentration in the laboratory is *molarity*—**the number of moles of solute per liter of solution,** abbreviated as M.

$$\text{Molarity} = M = \frac{\text{moles of solute (mol)}}{\text{liter of solution (L)}}$$

A solution that is formed from 1.00 mol (58.4 g) of NaCl in enough water to give 1.00 L of solution has a molarity of 1.00 M. A solution that is formed from 2.50 mol (146 g) of NaCl in enough water to give 2.50 L of solution is also a 1.00 M solution. Both solutions contain the *same number of moles per unit volume.*

$$M = \frac{\text{moles of solute (mol)}}{V\ (\text{L})} = \frac{1.00\ \text{mol NaCl}}{1.00\ \text{L solution}} = 1.00\ \text{M}$$

$$M = \frac{\text{moles of solute (mol)}}{V\ (\text{L})} = \frac{2.50\ \text{mol NaCl}}{2.50\ \text{L solution}} = 1.00\ \text{M}$$

same concentration
same number of moles per unit volume (*V*)

Since quantities in the laboratory are weighed on a balance, we must learn how to determine molarity beginning with a particular number of grams of a substance, as shown in the accompanying stepwise procedure.

How To **Calculate Molarity from a Given Number of Grams of Solute**

Example: Calculate the molarity of a solution made from 20.0 g of NaOH in 250 mL of solution.

Step [1] Identify the known quantities and the desired quantity.

20.0 g NaOH

250 mL solution   ? M (mol/L)

known quantities   desired quantity

Step [2] Convert the number of grams of solute to the number of moles. Convert the volume of the solution to liters, if necessary.

• Use the molar mass to convert grams of NaOH to moles of NaOH (molar mass 40.00 g/mol).

molar mass
conversion factor

$$20.0\ \cancel{\text{g}}\ \text{NaOH}\ \times\ \frac{1\ \text{mol}}{40.00\ \cancel{\text{g}}\ \text{NaOH}} = 0.500\ \text{mol NaOH}$$

Grams cancel.

• Convert milliliters of solution to liters of solution using a mL–L conversion factor.

mL–L
conversion factor

$$250\ \cancel{\text{mL}}\ \text{solution}\ \times\ \frac{1\ \text{L}}{1000\ \cancel{\text{mL}}} = 0.25\ \text{L solution}$$

Milliliters cancel.

Step [3] Divide the number of moles of solute by the number of liters of solution to obtain the molarity.

$$M = \frac{\text{moles of solute (mol)}}{V\ (\text{L})} = \frac{0.500\ \text{mol NaOH}}{0.25\ \text{L solution}} = 2.0\ \text{M}$$

molarity   **Answer**

SAMPLE PROBLEM 8.10 CALCULATING THE MOLARITY OF A SOLUTION

What is the molarity of an intravenous glucose solution prepared from 108 g of glucose in 2.0 L of solution?

Analysis and Solution

[1] Identify the known quantities and the desired quantity.

108 g glucose
2.0 L solution   ? M (mol/L)
known quantities   desired quantity

[2] Convert the number of grams of glucose to the number of moles using the molar mass (180.2 g/mol).

$$108 \text{ g glucose} \times \frac{1 \text{ mol}}{180.2 \text{ g}} = 0.599 \text{ mol glucose}$$

Grams cancel.

- Since the volume of the solution is given in liters, no conversion is necessary for volume.

[3] Divide the number of moles of solute by the number of liters of solution to obtain the molarity.

$$M = \frac{\text{moles of solute (mol)}}{V(L)} = \frac{0.599 \text{ mol glucose}}{2.0 \text{ L solution}} = 0.30 \text{ M}$$

molarity   **Answer**

PRACTICE PROBLEM 8.10

Calculate the molarity of each aqueous solution with the given amount of NaCl (molar mass 58.44 g/mol) and final volume.

a. 1.0 mol in 0.50 L   c. 0.050 mol in 5.0 mL   e. 24.4 g in 350 mL

b. 2.0 mol in 250 mL   d. 12.0 g in 2.0 L   f. 60.0 g in 750 mL

More Practice: Try Problems 8.57, 8.58.

PROBLEM 8.13

What is the molarity of acetic acid in vinegar that contains 5.00 g of acetic acid (molar mass 60.05 g/mol) in 100. mL of solution?

Molarity is a conversion factor that relates the number of moles of solute to the volume of solution it occupies. Thus, if we know the molarity and volume of a solution, we can calculate the number of moles it contains. If we know the molarity and number of moles, we can calculate the volume in liters.

To calculate the **moles** of solute...   ...rearrange the equation for molarity (M):

$$\frac{\text{moles of solute (mol)}}{V(L)} = M \qquad\qquad \text{moles of solute (mol)} = M \times V(L)$$

To calculate the **volume** of solution...   ...rearrange the equation for molarity (M):

$$\frac{\text{moles of solute (mol)}}{V(L)} = M \qquad\qquad V(L) = \frac{\text{moles of solute (mol)}}{M}$$

The main component of vinegar is acetic acid ($C_2H_4O_2$, Problem 8.13).
©McGraw-Hill Education/ Mark Dierker, photographer

SAMPLE PROBLEM 8.11 CALCULATING VOLUME FROM MOLARITY AND MOLES

What volume in milliliters of a 0.30 M solution of glucose contains 0.025 mol of glucose?

Analysis

Use the equation, $V = $ (moles of solute)/M, to find the volume in liters, and then convert the liters to milliliters.

Solution

[1] Identify the known quantities and the desired quantity.

$$\begin{array}{cc} 0.30\ M & ?\ V\ (mL)\ solution \\ 0.025\ mol\ glucose & \\ \text{known quantities} & \text{desired quantity} \end{array}$$

[2] Divide the number of moles by molarity to obtain the volume in liters.

$$V(L) = \frac{\text{moles of solute (mol)}}{M}$$

$$= \frac{0.025\ \text{mol glucose}}{0.30\ \text{mol/L}} = 0.083\ \text{L solution}$$

[3] Use a mL–L conversion factor to convert liters to milliliters.

mL–L conversion factor

$$0.083\ \cancel{L}\ \text{solution} \quad \times \quad \frac{1000\ mL}{1\ \cancel{L}} \quad = \quad 83\ mL\ \text{glucose solution}$$

Liters cancel.

Answer

PRACTICE PROBLEM 8.11

How many milliliters of a 1.5 M glucose solution contain each of the following number of moles?

   a. 0.15 mol   b. 0.020 mol   c. 0.0030 mol   d. 3.0 mol

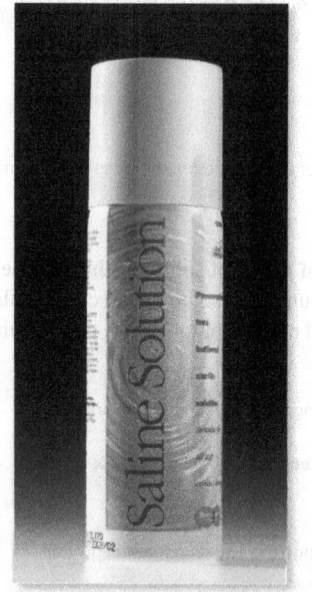

Saline solutions are used for intravenous infusion, wound flushing, contact lens storage, and many other purposes.
©SSPL/Getty Images

SAMPLE PROBLEM 8.12 DETERMINING THE NUMBER OF MOLES IN A SOLUTION

How many moles of NaCl are contained in 710 mL of a 0.15 M NaCl solution used for rinsing and storing contact lenses?

Analysis

Convert milliliters to liters and then use the equation, moles of solute (mol) = M × V, to find the number of moles.

Solution

[1] Identify the known quantities and the desired quantity.

$$\begin{array}{cc} 0.15\ M\ NaCl\ solution & ?\ mol\ NaCl \\ 710\ mL\ solution & \\ \text{known quantities} & \text{desired quantity} \end{array}$$

[2] Use a mL–L conversion factor to convert milliliters to liters.

mL–L conversion factor

$$710\ \cancel{mL}\ \text{solution} \quad \times \quad \frac{1\ L}{1000\ \cancel{mL}} \quad = \quad 0.71\ \text{L solution}$$

[3] Multiply the molarity by the volume in liters to obtain the number of moles.

$$\text{moles of NaCl (mol)} \quad = \quad M \quad \times \quad V$$

$$= \quad \frac{0.15\ mol\ NaCl}{1\ \cancel{L}} \quad \times \quad 0.71\ \cancel{L} \quad = \quad 0.11\ mol\ NaCl$$

Answer

PRACTICE PROBLEM 8.12

How many moles of NaCl are contained in each volume of aqueous NaCl solution?

   a. 2.0 L of a 2.0 M solution   c. 25 mL of a 2.0 M solution

   b. 2.5 L of a 0.25 M solution   d. 250 mL of a 0.25 M solution

More Practice: Try Problems 8.61, 8.62.

Since the number of grams and moles of a substance is related by the molar mass, we can convert a given volume of solution to the number of grams of solute it contains by carrying out the step-wise calculation shown in Sample Problem 8.13.

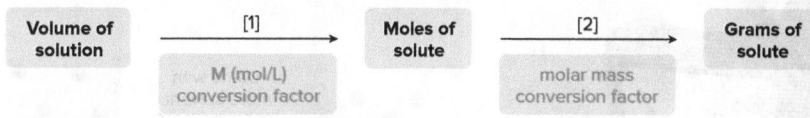

SAMPLE PROBLEM 8.13 DETERMINING THE NUMBER OF GRAMS IN A SOLUTION

How many grams of aspirin are contained in 50.0 mL of a 0.050 M solution?

Analysis

Use the molarity to convert the volume of the solution to moles of solute. Then use the molar mass to convert moles to grams.

Solution

[1] Identify the known quantities and the desired quantity.

$$0.050 \text{ M}$$
$$50.0 \text{ mL solution} \qquad\qquad ? \text{ g aspirin}$$
$$\text{known quantities} \qquad\qquad \text{desired quantity}$$

[2] Determine the number of moles of aspirin using the molarity.

$$\boxed{\text{volume}} \qquad \boxed{\text{molarity}} \qquad \boxed{\text{mL–L conversion factor}}$$

$$50.0 \text{ mL solution} \quad\times\quad \frac{0.050 \text{ mol aspirin}}{1 \text{ L}} \quad\times\quad \frac{1 \text{ L}}{1000 \text{ mL}} \quad=\quad 0.0025 \text{ mol aspirin}$$

[3] Convert the number of moles of aspirin to grams using the molar mass (180.2 g/mol).

$$\boxed{\text{molar mass conversion factor}}$$

$$0.0025 \text{ mol aspirin} \quad\times\quad \frac{180.2 \text{ g aspirin}}{1 \text{ mol aspirin}} \quad=\quad 0.45 \text{ g aspirin}$$
$$\underset{\text{Moles cancel.}}{} \qquad\qquad\qquad \textbf{Answer}$$

PRACTICE PROBLEM 8.13

How many grams of NaCl are contained in each of the following volumes of a 1.25 M solution?

  a. 0.10 L   b. 2.0 L   c. 0.55 L   d. 50. mL

More Practice: Try Problems 8.63, 8.64.

PROBLEM 8.14

How many milliliters of a 0.25 M sucrose solution contain each of the following number of grams? The molar mass of sucrose ($C_{12}H_{22}O_{11}$) is 342.3 g/mol.

  a. 0.500 g   b. 2.0 g   c. 1.25 g   d. 50.0 mg

8.7 Dilution

Sometimes a solution has a higher concentration than is needed. **Dilution is the addition of solvent to decrease the concentration of the solution.** For example, a stock solution of a drug is often supplied in a concentrated form to take up less space on a pharmacy shelf, and then it is diluted so that it can be administered in a reasonable volume and lower concentration that allows for more accurate dosing.

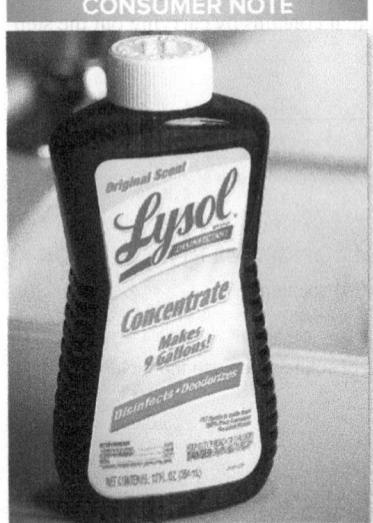

Some cleaning products are sold as concentrated solutions, which are then diluted prior to use. ©Jill Braaten RF

A key fact to keep in mind is that the **amount of solute is** *constant.* Only the volume of the solution is changed by adding solvent.

Dilute with more solvent.

The diluted solution contains the *same* number of molecules in a *larger* volume.

initial solution   diluted solution

In using molarity as a measure of concentration in Section 8.6, we learned that the number of moles of solute can be calculated from the molarity and volume of a solution.

$$\text{moles of solute} = \text{molarity} \times \text{volume}$$

$$\text{mol} = \text{MV}$$

Thus, if we have initial values for the molarity and volume (M_1 and V_1), we can calculate a new value for the molarity or volume (M_2 or V_2), because the product of the molarity and volume equals the number of moles, a constant.

$$\underset{\text{initial values}}{M_1 V_1} = \underset{\text{final values}}{M_2 V_2}$$

Although molarity is the most common concentration measure in the laboratory, the same facts hold in diluting solutions reported in other concentration units—percent concentration and parts per million—as well. In general, therefore, if we have initial values for the concentration and volume (C_1 and V_1), we can calculate a new value for the concentration or volume (C_2 or V_2), because the product of the concentration and volume is a constant.

$$\underset{\text{initial values}}{C_1 V_1} = \underset{\text{final values}}{C_2 V_2}$$

SAMPLE PROBLEM 8.14 CALCULATING CONCENTRATION AFTER DILUTION

What is the concentration of a solution formed by diluting 5.0 mL of a 3.2 M glucose solution to 40.0 mL?

Analysis

Since we know an initial molarity and volume (M_1 and V_1) and a final volume (V_2), we can calculate a new molarity (M_2) using the equation $M_1 V_1 = M_2 V_2$.

Solution

[1] Identify the known quantities and the desired quantity.

$$M_1 = 3.2 \text{ M} \qquad\qquad\qquad M_2 = ?$$
$$V_1 = 5.0 \text{ mL} \quad V_2 = 40.0 \text{ mL}$$
$$\underset{\text{known quantities}}{\qquad} \qquad \underset{\text{desired quantity}}{\qquad}$$

[2] Write the equation and rearrange it to isolate the desired quantity, M_2, on one side.

$$M_1 V_1 = M_2 V_2 \quad \text{Solve for } M_2 \text{ by dividing both sides by } V_2.$$

$$\frac{M_1 V_1}{V_2} = M_2$$

[3] Solve the problem.

• Substitute the three known quantities into the equation and solve for M_2.

$$M_2 = \frac{M_1 V_1}{V_2} = \frac{(3.2 \text{ M})(5.0 \text{ mL})}{(40.0 \text{ mL})} = 0.40 \text{ M glucose solution}$$
$$\textbf{Answer}$$

PRACTICE PROBLEM 8.14

What is the concentration of a solution formed by diluting 25.0 mL of a 3.8 M glucose solution to 275 mL?

More Practice: Try Problems 8.71a, 8.72a, 8.73, 8.74b.

PROBLEM 8.15

If the solution of A^+B^- in **X** is diluted, which representation (**D–F**) represents the final solution?

| X | D | E | F |

SAMPLE PROBLEM 8.15 DETERMINING THE VOLUME USED FOR DILUTION

Dopamine is a potent drug administered intravenously to increase blood pressure in seriously ill patients. How many milliliters of a 4.0% (w/v) solution must be used to prepare 250 mL of a 0.080% (w/v) solution?

Analysis

Since we know an initial concentration (C_1), a final concentration (C_2), and a final volume (V_2), we can calculate the volume (V_1) of the initial solution that must be used with the equation, $C_1V_1 = C_2V_2$.

Solution

[1] Identify the known quantities and the desired quantity.

$$C_1 = 4.0\% \text{ (w/v)} \qquad C_2 = 0.080\% \text{ (w/v)}$$
$$V_2 = 250 \text{ mL} \qquad\qquad V_1 = ?$$

known quantities   desired quantity

[2] Write the equation and rearrange it to isolate the desired quantity, V_1, on one side.

$$C_1V_1 = C_2V_2 \qquad \text{Solve for } V_1 \text{ by dividing both sides by } C_1.$$

$$V_1 = \frac{C_2V_2}{C_1}$$

[3] Solve the problem.

- Substitute the three known quantities into the equation and solve for V_1.

$$V_1 = \frac{(0.080\%)(250 \text{ mL})}{4.0\%} = 5.0 \text{ mL dopamine solution}$$

Answer

PRACTICE PROBLEM 8.15

How many milliliters of a 6.0 M NaOH solution would be needed to prepare each solution?

  a. 525 mL of a 2.5 M solution   c. 450 mL of a 0.10 M solution

  b. 750 mL of a 4.0 M solution   d. 25 mL of a 3.5 M solution

More Practice: Try Problems 8.71b, 8.72b, 8.75, 8.76.

PROBLEM 8.16

Ketamine (Section 8.5C) is supplied in a solution of 100. mg/mL. If 2.0 mL of this solution is diluted to a volume of 10.0 mL, how much of the diluted solution should be administered to supply a dose of 75 mg?

8.8   Colligative Properties

Although many properties of a solution are similar to those of a pure solvent, the boiling point and melting point of a solution differ from the boiling point and melting point of the solvent used to make it.

> • *Colligative properties* are properties of a solution that depend on the concentration of the solute but not its identity.

Thus, the *number* of dissolved particles of solute affects the properties of the solution, but the identity of the solute does not. In this section we examine how a dissolved solute increases the boiling point and decreases the melting point of a solution. In Section 8.9 we look at **osmosis,** a process that involves the diffusion of solvent across a semipermeable membrane.

8.8A   Boiling Point Elevation

A solute in a solution can be **volatile** or **nonvolatile.**

> • A volatile solute readily escapes into the vapor phase.
> • A nonvolatile solute does not readily escape into the vapor phase, and thus it has a negligible vapor pressure at a given temperature.

Figure 8.6 compares the vapor pressure above a pure liquid (water) with the vapor pressure above a solution made by dissolving a nonvolatile solute in water. The vapor pressure of a solution composed of a nonvolatile solute and a liquid solvent consists solely of gas molecules derived from the solvent. Since there are fewer solvent molecules in the solution than there are in the pure liquid, there are fewer molecules in the gas phase as well. **As a result, the vapor pressure above the solution is *lower* than the vapor pressure of the pure solvent.**

What effect does this lower vapor pressure have on the boiling point of the solution? The boiling point is the temperature at which the vapor pressure equals the atmospheric pressure. A lower vapor pressure means that the solution must be heated to a higher temperature to get the vapor pressure to equal the atmospheric pressure. This results in **boiling point elevation.**

> • A liquid solution that contains a nonvolatile solute has a *higher* boiling point than the solvent alone.

Figure 8.6   Vapor Pressure Above a Liquid Solution

H_2O pure liquid   solution   solute H_2O

When a nonvolatile solute is added to a solvent, there are fewer molecules of solvent in the gas phase, so the vapor pressure of the solution above the solvent is lower. *(left & right): ©McGraw-Hill Education/Jill Braaten, photographer*

The amount that the boiling point increases depends only on the number of dissolved particles. For example,

> • One mole of any nonvolatile solute raises the boiling point of one kilogram of water by 0.51 °C.

Thus, one mole of glucose molecules raises the boiling point of 1 kg of water by 0.51 °C, to 100.51 °C. Since NaCl contains two particles—Na⁺ cations and Cl⁻ anions—per mole, one mole of NaCl raises the boiling point of 1 kg of water by 2 × 0.51 °C or 1.02 °C, to 101.02 °C, rounded to 101.0 °C.

SAMPLE PROBLEM 8.16 CALCULATING THE BOILING POINT ELEVATION OF A SOLUTION

What is the boiling point of a solution that contains 0.45 mol of KCl in 1.00 kg of water?

Analysis

Determine the number of "particles" contained in the solute. Use 0.51 °C/mol as a conversion factor to relate the temperature change to the number of moles of solute particles.

Solution

Each KCl provides two "particles," K⁺ and Cl⁻.

$$\text{temperature increase} = \frac{0.51\ °C}{\text{mol particles}} \times 0.45\ \text{mol KCl} \times \frac{2\ \text{mol particles}}{\text{mol KCl}} = 0.46\ °C$$

The boiling point of the solution is 100.0 °C + 0.46 °C = 100.46 °C, rounded to 100.5 °C.

PRACTICE PROBLEM 8.16

What is the boiling point of a solution prepared from the given quantity of solute in 1.00 kg of water?

  a. 2.0 mol of sucrose molecules   c. 2.0 mol of $CaCl_2$

  b. 2.0 mol of KNO_3 d. 20.0 g of NaCl

More Practice: Try Problems 8.77a, 8.78a, 8.79, 8.83a, 8.84a, 8.86.

8.8B   Freezing Point Depression

In a similar manner, a dissolved solute lowers the freezing point of a solvent. The presence of solute molecules makes it harder for solvent molecules to form an organized crystalline solid, thus lowering the temperature at which the liquid phase becomes solid. This results in **freezing point depression.**

> • A liquid solution that contains a nonvolatile solute has a *lower* freezing point than the solvent alone.

The amount of freezing point depression depends only on the number of dissolved particles. For example,

> • One mole of any nonvolatile solute lowers the freezing point of one kilogram of water by 1.86 °C.

Thus, one mole of glucose molecules lowers the freezing point of 1 kg of water to −1.86 °C. Since NaCl contains two particles—Na⁺ cations and Cl⁻ anions—per mole, one mole of NaCl lowers the freezing point of 1 kg of water by 2 × (−1.86 °C) or −3.72 °C.

Several practical applications exploit freezing point depression. Antifreeze, which contains nonvolatile ethylene glycol, is added to automobile radiators to lower the freezing point of the water

Airplane wings are de-iced with a solution that contains ethylene glycol, which lowers the freezing point, so the ice melts.
©Traverse City Record-Eagle, John L. Russell/AP Wide World Photos

in the cooling system, so it does not freeze in cold climates. Fish that inhabit cold environments produce large amounts of glycerol, $C_3H_8O_3$, which lowers the freezing point of their blood, thus allowing it to remain fluid in very cold water.

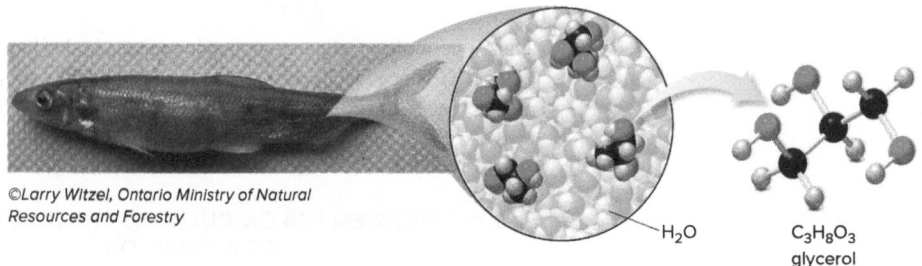

©Larry Witzel, Ontario Ministry of Natural
Resources and Forestry

SAMPLE PROBLEM 8.17 COMPARING MELTING POINTS BY COUNTING PARTICLES

Consider two solutions, 1.0 mol of NaCl and 2.0 mol of sucrose (table sugar), each dissolved in 1 kg of water, shown in representations **A** and **B** in molecular art. How do the melting points of these solutions compare?

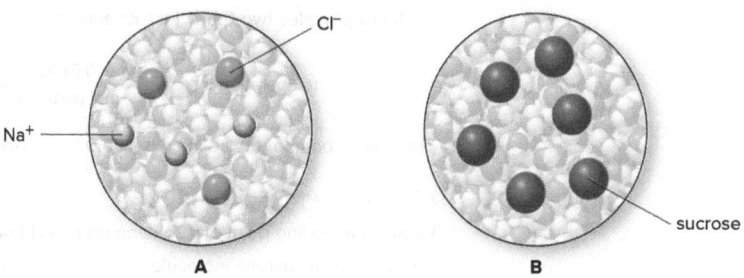

Analysis

The amount of freezing point depression depends only on the number of dissolved particles, so determine the number of particles of each solute.

Solution

One mole of NaCl contains two particles—Na^+ cations and Cl^- anions—so 2.0 mol of particles are present. Two moles of sucrose molecules contain 2.0 mol of particles, as well. Because both solutions have the same number of dissolved particles, the freezing point is lowered to the same extent, and the melting points are the same.

PRACTICE PROBLEM 8.17

Representations **A, B,** and **C** each show an aqueous solution formed from 1.0 mol of solute dissolved in 1 kg of water. (a) Which solution has the highest melting point? (b) Which solution has the lowest melting point?

| 1.0 mol **X** | 1.0 mol **YZ** | 1.0 mol **UV$_2$** |
| **A** | **B** | **C** |

More Practice: Try Problems 8.77b, 8.78b, 8.83b, 8.84b.

SAMPLE PROBLEM 8.18 CALCULATING THE FREEZING POINT DEPRESSION OF A SOLUTION

What is the melting point of a solution that contains 3.00 mol of $CaCl_2$ dissolved in 1.00 kg of water? $CaCl_2$ is used in rock salt to melt ice and snow on highways and sidewalks in the winter.

Analysis

Determine the number of "particles" contained in the solute. Use 1.86 °C/mol as a conversion factor to relate the temperature change to the number of moles of solute particles.

Solution

Each $CaCl_2$ provides three "particles," Ca^+ and 2 Cl^-.

$$\text{temperature decrease} = \frac{1.86\ °C}{\text{mol particles}} \times 3.00\ \text{mol } CaCl_2 \times \frac{3\ \text{mol particles}}{\text{mol } CaCl_2} = 16.7\ °C$$

The melting point of the solution is 0.0 °C + (−16.7 °C) = −16.7 °C.

PRACTICE PROBLEM 8.18

What is the melting point of a solution prepared from the given quantity of solute in 1.00 kg of water?

a. 2.0 mol of sucrose molecules
b. 2.0 mol of KNO_3
c. 2.0 mol of $CaCl_2$
d. 20.0 g of NaCl

More Practice: Try Problems 8.80–8.82, 8.85.

PROBLEM 8.17

What is the melting point of a solution that is formed when 250 g of ethylene glycol ($C_2H_6O_2$) is dissolved in 1.00 kg of water?

8.9   Osmosis and Dialysis

The membrane that surrounds living cells is an example of a **semipermeable membrane**—a membrane that allows water and small molecules to pass across, but ions and large molecules cannot.

semipermeable membrane

H_2O —

— H_2O

solute

solute + solvent   solvent only

• *Osmosis* is the passage of solvent, usually water, across a semipermeable membrane from a solution of low solute concentration to a solution of higher solute concentration.

8.9A   Osmotic Pressure

What happens when water and an aqueous glucose solution are separated by a semipermeable membrane? Water flows back and forth across the membrane, but more water flows from the side that has pure solvent toward the side that has dissolved glucose. This decreases the volume of pure solvent on one side of the membrane and increases the volume of the glucose solution on the other side.

semipermeable membrane

H₂O

glucose + H₂O solution

time

osmotic pressure

H₂O

glucose + H₂O solution

More H₂O molecules diffuse into the glucose solution, where the concentration of H₂O is lower.

H₂O

glucose

The increased volume of the glucose solution creates increased pressure on one side of the membrane. When the increased pressure gets to a certain point, it prevents more water movement to further dilute the glucose solution. Water continues to diffuse back and forth across the membrane, but the level of the two liquids does not change any further.

- **Osmotic pressure** is the pressure that prevents the flow of additional solvent into a solution on one side of a semipermeable membrane.

Osmotic pressure is a colligative property, so it depends only on the number of particles in a solution. **The *greater* the number of dissolved particles, the *greater* the osmotic pressure.** A 0.1 M NaCl solution has twice the osmotic pressure as a 0.1 M glucose solution, because each NaCl is composed of two particles, Na⁺ cations and Cl⁻ anions.

If, instead of having pure water on one side of the membrane, there were two solutions of different concentrations, water would flow from the side of the *less* concentrated solution to dilute the *more* concentrated solution.

SAMPLE PROBLEM 8.19 PREDICTING THE RESULT OF OSMOSIS

A 0.1 M glucose solution is separated from a 0.2 M glucose solution by a semipermeable membrane. (a) Which solution exerts the greater osmotic pressure? (b) In which direction will water flow between the two solutions? (c) Describe the level of the two solutions when equilibrium is reached.

Analysis

The solvent (water) flows from the less concentrated solution to the more concentrated solution.

Solution

a. The *greater* the number of dissolved particles, the *higher* the osmotic pressure, so the 0.2 M glucose solution exerts the greater pressure.

b. Water will flow from the less concentrated solution (0.1 M) to the more concentrated solution (0.2 M).

c. Since water flows into the 0.2 M solution, its height will increase, and the height of the 0.1 M glucose solution will decrease.

PRACTICE PROBLEM 8.19

Which solution in each pair exerts the greater osmotic pressure?

a. 1.0% sugar solution or 5.0% sugar solution
b. 3.0 M NaCl solution or a 4.0 M NaCl solution
c. 1.0 M glucose solution or a 0.75 M NaCl solution

More Practice: Try Problems 8.77c, 8.78c, 8.83c, 8.84c, 8.87, 8.88.

PROBLEM 8.18

Consider the two aqueous solutions separated by a semipermeable membrane, shown in representation **A**. Which diagram (**B–D**) represents the final appearance of the liquids and dissolved solute?

8.9B FOCUS ON THE HUMAN BODY
Osmosis and Biological Membranes

Since cell membranes are semipermeable and biological fluids contain dissolved ions and molecules, osmosis is an ongoing phenomenon in living cells. Fluids on both sides of a cell membrane must have the same osmotic pressure to avoid pressure buildup inside or outside the cell. Any intravenous solution given to a patient, therefore, must have the same osmotic pressure as the fluids in the body.

• **Two solutions with the same osmotic pressure are said to be *isotonic*.**

Isotonic solutions used in hospitals include 0.92% (w/v) NaCl solution (or 0.15 M NaCl solution) and 5.0% (w/v) glucose solution. Although these solutions do not contain exactly the same ions or molecules present in body fluids, they exert the same osmotic pressure. *Remember:* **With a colligative property the concentration of particles is important, but not the identity of those particles.**

If a red blood cell is placed in an isotonic NaCl solution, called physiological saline solution, the red blood cells retain their same size and shape because the osmotic pressure inside and outside the cell is the same (Figure 8.7a). What happens if a red blood cell is placed in a solution having a different osmotic pressure?

• **A *hypotonic* solution has a lower osmotic pressure than body fluids.**
• **A *hypertonic* solution has a higher osmotic pressure than body fluids.**

In a hypotonic solution, the concentration of particles outside the cell is lower than the concentration of particles inside the cell. In other words, the concentration of water outside the cell is *higher* than the concentration of water inside the cell, so water diffuses inside (Figure 8.7b). As a result, the cell swells and eventually bursts. This swelling and rupture of red blood cells is called **hemolysis.**

In a hypertonic solution, the concentration of particles outside the cell is higher than the concentration of particles inside the cell. In other words, the concentration of

300   **Chapter 8** Solutions

Figure 8.7

The Effect of Osmotic Pressure
Differences on Red Blood Cells

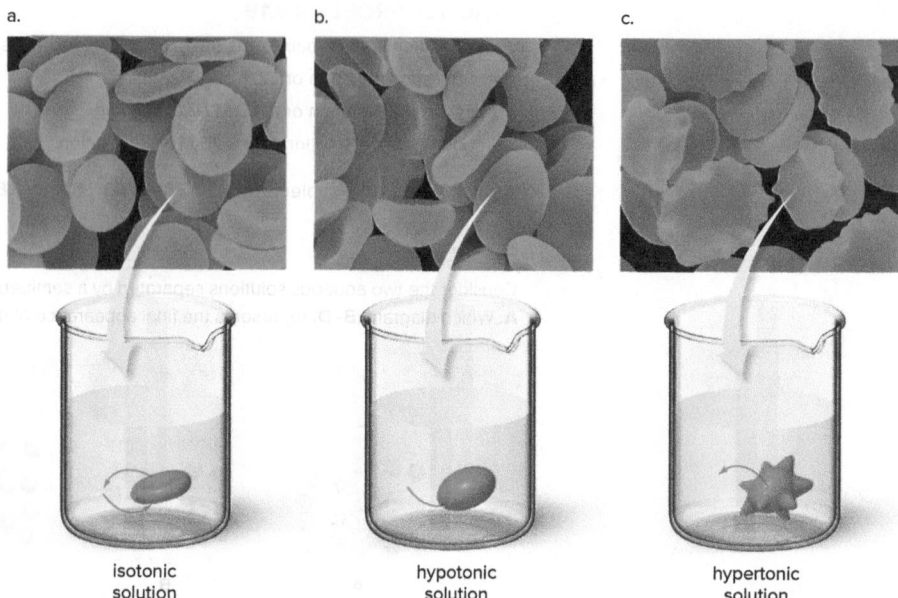

isotonic
solution

hypotonic
solution

hypertonic
solution

(a) In an **isotonic** solution, the movement of water into and out of the red blood cell occurs to an equal
extent and the red blood cell keeps its normal volume. (b) In a **hypotonic** solution, more water moves
into the cell than diffuses out, so the cell swells and eventually it can rupture (hemolysis). (c) In a
hypertonic solution, more water moves out of the cell than diffuses in, so the cell shrivels (crenation).
(a–c): ©Dennis Kunkel Microscopy/Science Source

water inside the cell is *higher* than the concentration of water outside the cell, so water
diffuses out of the cell (Figure 7.7c). As a result, the cell shrinks. This process is called
crenation.

PROBLEM 8.19

Which aqueous solution (**B–D**) is isotonic with solution **A?**

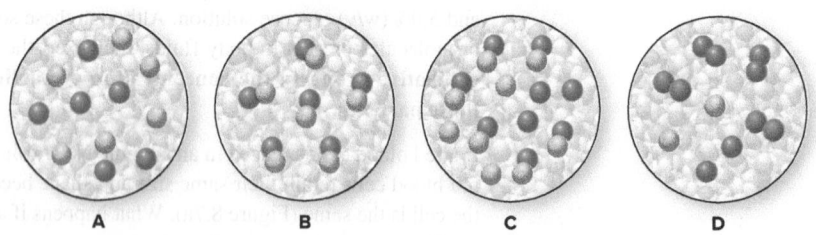

A   B   C   D

PROBLEM 8.20

What happens to a red blood cell when it is placed in each of the following solutions:
(a) 3% (w/v) glucose solution; (b) 0.15 M KCl solution; (c) 0.15 M Na_2CO_3 solution?

8.9C   FOCUS ON HEALTH & MEDICINE
Dialysis

Dialysis is also a process that involves the selective passage of substances across a semipermeable
membrane, called a dialyzing membrane. In dialysis, however, water, small molecules, and ions
can travel across the membrane; only large biological molecules like proteins and starch cannot.

Figure 8.8   Dialysis of Body Fluids by the Kidneys

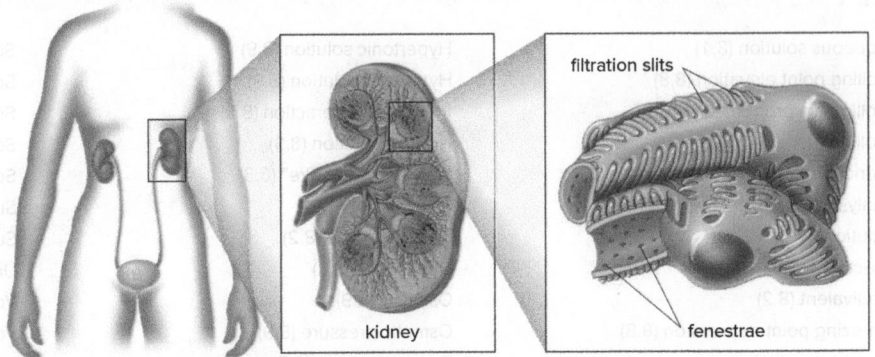

Body fluids are dialyzed by passage through the kidneys, which contain more than a million nephrons that filter out small molecules and ions from the blood. Useful materials are then reabsorbed, while urea and other waste products are eliminated in urine.

In the human body, blood is filtered through the kidneys by the process of dialysis (Figure 8.8). Each kidney contains over a million nephrons, tubelike structures with filtration membranes. These membranes filter small molecules—glucose, amino acids, urea, ions, and water—from the blood. Useful materials are then reabsorbed, but urea and other waste products are eliminated in urine.

When an individual's kidneys are incapable of removing waste products from the blood, **hemodialysis** is used (Figure 8.9). A patient's blood flows through a long tube connected to a cellophane membrane suspended in an isotonic solution that contains NaCl, KCl, NaHCO$_3$, and glucose. Small molecules like urea cross the membrane into the solution, thus removing them from the blood. Red blood cells and large molecules are not removed from the blood because they are too big to cross the dialyzing membrane.

Figure 8.9   Hemodialysis

When a patient's kidneys no longer function properly, periodic dialysis treatments are used to remove waste products from the blood. Blood is passed through a dialyzer, which contains a membrane that allows small molecules to pass through, thus acting as an artificial kidney. Each treatment takes several hours. Patients usually require two to three treatments per week.

CHAPTER HIGHLIGHTS

KEY TERMS

Aqueous solution (8.1)	Hypertonic solution (8.9)	Solubility (8.3)
Boiling point elevation (8.8)	Hypotonic solution (8.9)	Solute (8.1)
Colligative properties (8.8)	Ion–dipole interaction (8.3)	Solution (8.1)
Colloid (8.1)	Isotonic solution (8.9)	Solvation (8.3)
Concentration (8.5)	"Like dissolves like" (8.3)	Solvent (8.1)
Dialysis (8.9)	Molarity (8.6)	Supersaturated solution (8.4)
Dilution (8.7)	Nonelectrolyte (8.2)	Suspension (8.1)
Electrolyte (8.2)	Nonvolatile (8.8)	Unsaturated solution (8.3)
Equivalent (8.2)	Osmosis (8.9)	Volatile (8.8)
Freezing point depression (8.8)	Osmotic pressure (8.9)	Volume/volume percent concentration (8.5)
Henry's law (8.4)	Parts per million (8.5)	Weight/volume percent concentration (8.5)
Heterogeneous mixture (8.1)	Saturated solution (8.3)	
Homogeneous mixture (8.1)	Semipermeable membrane (8.9)	

KEY CONCEPTS

① What are the characteristics of solutions, colloids, and suspensions? (8.1)

- A solution is a homogeneous mixture that contains small dissolved particles. Any phase of matter can form solutions. The substance present in the lesser amount is called the solute, and the substance present in the larger amount is the solvent.
- A colloid is a homogeneous mixture with larger particles (1 nm–1 μm), often having an opaque appearance.
- A suspension is a heterogeneous mixture that contains large particles (> 1 μm) suspended in a liquid.

② What is the difference between an electrolyte and a nonelectrolyte? (8.2)

- An electrolyte dissolves in water to form ions, so it conducts an electric current. A strong electrolyte dissociates completely to form ions, whereas a weak electrolyte contains mostly uncharged molecules in water, together with a small number of ions.
- A nonelectrolyte dissolves in water to form uncharged molecules that do not conduct an electric current.

③ What determines whether a substance is soluble in water or a nonpolar solvent? (8.3)

- One rule summarizes solubility: "Like dissolves like."
- Most ionic compounds are soluble in water. If the attractive forces between the ions and water are stronger than the attraction between the ions in the crystal, an ionic compound dissolves in water.
- Small polar compounds that can hydrogen bond are soluble in water.
- Nonpolar compounds are soluble in nonpolar solvents. Compounds with many nonpolar C—C and C—H bonds are soluble in nonpolar solvents.

④ What effect do temperature and pressure have on solubility? (8.4)

- The solubility of solids in a liquid solvent generally increases with increasing temperature. The solubility of gases decreases with increasing temperature.
- Increasing pressure increases the solubility of a gas in a solvent. Pressure changes do not affect the solubility of liquids and solids.

⑤ How is the concentration of a solution expressed? (8.5, 8.6)

- Concentration is a measure of how much solute is dissolved in a given amount of solution, and can be measured using mass, volume, or moles.
- Weight/volume (w/v) percent concentration is the number of grams of solute dissolved in 100 mL of solution.
- Volume/volume (v/v) percent concentration is the number of milliliters of solute dissolved in 100 mL of solution.
- Parts per million (ppm) is the number of parts of solute in 1,000,000 parts of solution, where the units for both the solute and the solution are the same.
- Molarity (M) is the number of moles of solute per liter of solution.

⑥ How are dilutions performed? (8.7)

- Dilution is the addition of solvent to decrease the concentration of a solute. Since the number of moles of solute is constant in carrying out a dilution, a new molarity or volume (M_2 and V_2) can be calculated from a given molarity and volume (M_1 and V_1) using the equation $M_1V_1 = M_2V_2$, as long as three of the four quantities are known.

⑦ How do dissolved particles affect the boiling point and melting point of a solution? (8.8)

- A nonvolatile solute lowers the vapor pressure above a solution, thus increasing its boiling point.

- A nonvolatile solute makes it harder for solvent molecules to form a crystalline solid, thus decreasing its melting point.

⑧ What is osmosis? (8.9)
- Osmosis is the passage of solvent, usually water, across a semipermeable membrane. Solvent always moves from the less concentrated solution to the more concentrated solution, until the osmotic pressure prevents additional flow of solvent.

- Since living cells contain and are surrounded by biological solutions separated by a semipermeable membrane, the osmotic pressure must be the same on both sides of the membrane. Dialysis is similar to osmosis in that it involves the selective passage of several substances—water, small molecules, and ions—across a dialyzing membrane.

KEY EQUATIONS—CONCENTRATION

Weight/volume percent concentration

$$(\text{w/v})\% = \frac{\text{mass of solute (g)}}{\text{volume of solution (mL)}} \times 100\%$$

Volume/volume percent concentration

$$(\text{v/v})\% = \frac{\text{volume of solute (mL)}}{\text{volume of solution (mL)}} \times 100\%$$

Parts per million

$$\text{ppm} = \frac{\text{parts of solute (g or mL)}}{\text{parts of solution (g or mL)}} \times 10^6$$

Molarity

$$M = \frac{\text{moles of solute (mol)}}{\text{liter of solution (L)}}$$

PROBLEMS

Selected in-chapter and odd-numbered end-of-chapter problems have brief answers in Appendix B. The *Student Study Guide and Solutions Manual* contains detailed solutions to all in-chapter and odd-numbered end-of-chapter problems, as well as additional worked examples and a chapter self-test.

Solutions, Colloids, and Suspensions

8.21 Considering the size of the particles, classify each mixture as a solution, colloid, or suspension.

1.5 × 10⁻⁷ m

2.0 × 10⁻⁵ m

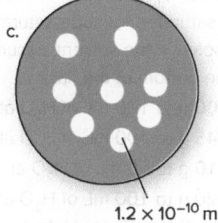
1.2 × 10⁻¹⁰ m

8.22 Based on physical appearance alone, classify each product as a solution, colloid, or heterogeneous mixture.

a.

b.

(a & b): ©McGraw-Hill Education/Mark Dierker, photographer

8.23 Which representation of molecular art better shows a solution of KI dissolved in water? Explain your choice. Will this solution conduct an electric current?

A

B

8.24 Which representation of molecular art better shows a solution of NaF dissolved in water? Explain your choice. Will this solution conduct an electric current?

 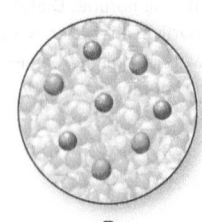

A   B

8.25 Classify each of the following as a solution, colloid, or suspension.

   a. bronze (an alloy of Sn and Cu)   e. gasoline

   b. diet soda   f. fog

   c. orange juice with pulp   g. shaving cream

   d. household ammonia   h. Gatorade sports drink

8.26 Classify each of the following as a solution, colloid, or suspension.

   a. soft drink   e. bleach

   b. cream   f. grape juice

   c. wine   g. liquid soap

   d. muddy water

Electrolytes and Equivalents

8.27 Label each diagram as a strong electrolyte, weak electrolyte, or nonelectrolyte.

a.   b.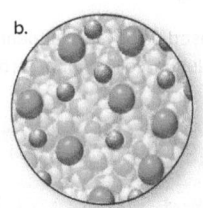

8.28 Label each diagram as a strong electrolyte, weak electrolyte, or nonelectrolyte.

a.   b.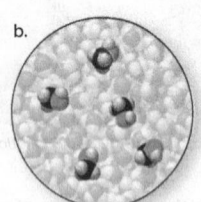

8.29 A solution contains 2.5 mol KCl and 2.5 mol $CaSO_4$. How many equivalents of each ion are present?

8.30 A dextrose solution contains 40. mEq/L Na^+ and 15 mEq/L of $HPO_4{}^{2-}$, in addition to other ions. How many milliequivalents of each ion are present in 320 mL of solution?

8.31 If a solution contains 132 mEq/L of Na^+, how many milliequivalents of Na^+ are present in each of the following volumes of solution: (a) 1.0 L; (b) 2.0 L; (c) 440 mL?

8.32 Ringer's solution is an intravenous solution used for the replacement of electrolytes when an individual is dehydrated. Ringer's solution contains the following cations: Na^+ (147 mEq/L),

K^+ (4 mEq/L), and Ca^{2+} (4 mEq/L). (a) How many milliequivalents of Na^+ are present in 125 mL of Ringer's solution? (b) If the only anion in Ringer's solution is Cl^-, what is the concentration of Cl^- in mEq/L?

Solubility

8.33 Consider a mixture of two substances shown in blue and red spheres in diagrams **A** and **B**. Which diagram best represents each type of mixture: (a) a polar solute and polar solvent; (b) a nonpolar solute and nonpolar solvent; (c) a nonpolar solute and a polar solvent; (d) a polar solute and nonpolar solvent?

A   B

8.34 Which diagram (**C** or **D**) best represents what occurs when each of the following ionic compounds dissolves in water: (a) RbBr; (b) $ZnCO_3$; (c) AgCl; (d) NH_4OH; (e) $MgSO_4$?

ionic compound

 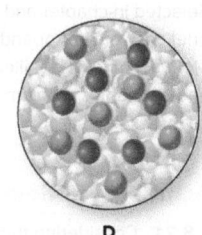

C   D

8.35 If the solubility of KCl in 100 mL of H_2O is 34 g at 20 °C and 43 g at 50 °C, label each of the following solutions as unsaturated, saturated, or supersaturated. If more solid is added than can dissolve in the solvent, assume that undissolved solid remains at the bottom of the flask.

   a. adding 30 g to 100 mL of H_2O at 20 °C

   b. adding 65 g to 100 mL of H_2O at 50 °C

   c. adding 20 g to 50 mL of H_2O at 20 °C

   d. adding 42 g to 100 mL of H_2O at 50 °C and slowly cooling to 20 °C to give a clear solution with no precipitate

8.36 If the solubility of sucrose in 100 mL of H_2O is 204 g at 20 °C and 260 g at 50 °C, label each of the following solutions as unsaturated, saturated, or supersaturated. If more solid is added than can dissolve in the solvent, assume that undissolved solid remains at the bottom of the flask.

   a. adding 200 g to 100 mL of H_2O at 20 °C

   b. adding 245 g to 100 mL of H_2O at 50 °C

   c. adding 110 g to 50 mL of H_2O at 20 °C

   d. adding 220 g to 100 mL of H_2O at 50 °C and slowly cooling to 20 °C to give a clear solution with no precipitate

8.37 Which compounds are soluble in water?
   a. LiCl   b. C_7H_8 c. Na_3PO_4

8.38 Which compounds are soluble in water?
   a. C_5H_{12} b. $CaCl_2$ c. CH_3Br

8.39 Using the ball-and-stick model for methanol (CH_3OH), draw a representation for the solution that results when methanol is dissolved in water.

8.40 Using the ball-and-stick model for dimethyl ether [$(CH_3)_2O$], draw a representation for the solution that results when dimethyl ether is dissolved in water.

8.41 Explain the statement "Oil and water don't mix."

8.42 Explain why a bottle of salad dressing that contains oil and vinegar has two layers.

8.43 Explain why cholesterol, a compound with molecular formula $C_{27}H_{46}O$ and one OH group, is soluble in CCl_4 but insoluble in water.

8.44 Which of the following pairs of compounds form a solution?
   a. KCl and CCl_4
   b. 1-propanol (C_3H_8O) and H_2O
   c. cyclodecanone ($C_{10}H_{18}O$) and H_2O
   d. pentane (C_5H_{12}) and hexane (C_6H_{14})

8.45 The molecular art represents O_2 molecules dissolved in water at 25 °C. Draw a representation for the solution that results (a) after heating to 50 °C; (b) after cooling to 10 °C.

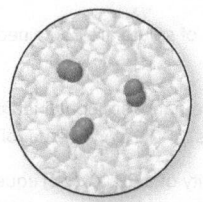

8.46 The molecular art represents NaCl dissolved in water at 25 °C. Assume that this solution is saturated in NaCl and that solid NaCl remains at the bottom of the flask in which the solution is stored. Draw a representation for the solution that results (a) after heating to 50 °C; (b) after cooling to 10 °C.

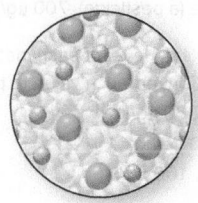

8.47 How is the solubility of solid NaCl in water affected by each of the following changes?
   a. increasing the temperature from 25 °C to 50 °C
   b. decreasing the temperature from 25 °C to 0 °C
   c. increasing the pressure from 1 atm to 2 atm
   d. decreasing the pressure from 5 atm to 1 atm

8.48 How is the solubility of helium gas in water affected by each of the following changes?
   a. increasing the temperature from 25 °C to 50 °C
   b. decreasing the temperature from 25 °C to 0 °C
   c. increasing the pressure from 1 atm to 2 atm
   d. decreasing the pressure from 5 atm to 1 atm

8.49 Use the solubility rules listed in Section 8.3B to predict whether each of the following ionic compounds is soluble in water.
   a. K_2SO_4 e. $Fe(NO_3)_3$
   b. $MgSO_4$ f. $PbCl_2$
   c. $ZnCO_3$ g. CsCl
   d. KI   h. $Ni(HCO_3)_2$

8.50 Use the solubility rules listed in Section 8.3B to predict whether each of the following ionic compounds is soluble in water.
   a. $Al(NO_3)_3$ e. $CuCO_3$
   b. $NaHCO_3$ f. $(NH_4)_2SO_4$
   c. $Cr(OH)_2$ g. $Fe(OH)_3$
   d. LiOH   h. $(NH_4)_3PO_4$

Concentration

8.51 The pain reliever acetaminophen is sold as an oral suspension for children 2–11 years of age.

   a. What is the weight/volume percent concentration of acetaminophen in the suspension shown (160 mg per 5.0 mL)?
   b. How many grams of acetaminophen are contained in a bottle that holds 4.0 fl oz?

8.52 Amoxil is an antibiotic used to treat infections of the ear, nose, and throat. It is sold as a suspension in water.

    a. What is the weight/volume percent concentration in a suspension of Amoxil that contains 50 mg/mL?

    b. If the typical pediatric dose is 25 mg/kg per day, what volume of drug is given for a 15-kg child?

8.53 What is the weight/volume percent concentration using the given amount of solute and total volume of solution?

    a. 10.0 g of LiCl in 750 mL of solution

    b. 25 g of $NaNO_3$ in 150 mL of solution

    c. 40.0 g of NaOH in 500. mL of solution

8.54 What is the weight/volume percent concentration using the given amount of solute and total volume of solution?

    a. 5.5 g of LiCl in 550 mL of solution

    b. 12.5 g of $NaNO_3$ in 250 mL of solution

    c. 20.0 g of NaOH in 400. mL of solution

8.55 Cinnamon sticks, powdered cinnamon, or cinnamon extract can be used for cinnamon flavoring in baking. How many milliliters of ethanol are contained in a 2.0-oz bottle of cinnamon extract that has a volume/volume percentage concentration of 40.% ethanol?

©McGraw-Hill Education

8.56 A 1.0-oz bottle of orange extract contains 23 mL of ethanol. What is the volume/volume percent concentration of ethanol?

©McGraw-Hill Education

8.57 What is the molarity of a solution prepared using the given amount of solute and total volume of solution?

    a. 3.5 mol of KCl in 1.50 L of solution

    b. 0.44 mol of $NaNO_3$ in 855 mL of solution

    c. 25.0 g of NaCl in 650 mL of solution

    d. 10.0 g of $NaHCO_3$ in 3.3 L of solution

8.58 What is the molarity of a solution prepared using the given amount of solute and total volume of solution?

    a. 2.4 mol of NaOH in 1.50 L of solution

    b. 0.48 mol of KNO_3 in 750 mL of solution

    c. 25.0 g of KCl in 650 mL of solution

    d. 10.0 g of Na_2CO_3 in 3.8 L of solution

8.59 How would you use a 250-mL volumetric flask to prepare each of the following solutions?

    a. 4.8% (w/v) acetic acid in water

    b. 22% (v/v) ethyl acetate in water

    c. 2.5 M NaCl solution

8.60 How would you use a 250-mL volumetric flask to prepare each of the following solutions?

    a. 2.0% (w/v) KCl in water

    b. 34% (v/v) ethanol in water

    c. 4.0 M NaCl solution

8.61 How many moles of solute are contained in each solution?

    a. 150 mL of a 0.25 M $NaNO_3$ solution

    b. 45 mL of a 2.0 M HNO_3 solution

    c. 2.5 L of a 1.5 M HCl solution

8.62 How many moles of solute are contained in each solution?

    a. 250 mL of a 0.55 M $NaNO_3$ solution

    b. 145 mL of a 4.0 M HNO_3 solution

    c. 6.5 L of a 2.5 M HCl solution

8.63 How many grams of solute are contained in each solution in Problem 8.61?

8.64 How many grams of solute are contained in each solution in Problem 8.62?

8.65 How many mL of ethanol are contained in a 750-mL bottle of wine that contains 11.0% (v/v) of ethanol?

8.66 What is the molarity of a 20.0% (v/v) aqueous ethanol solution? The density of ethanol (C_2H_6O, molar mass 46.07 g/mol) is 0.790 g/mL.

8.67 The maximum safe level of each compound in drinking water is given below. Convert each value to parts per million.

    a. chloroform ($CHCl_3$, a solvent), 80 µg/kg

    b. glyphosate (a pesticide), 700 µg/kg

8.68 The maximum safe level of each metal in drinking water is given below. Convert each value to parts per million.

    a. copper, 1,300 µg/kg

    b. arsenic, 10 µg/kg

    c. chromium, 100 µg/kg

Dilution

8.69 If the solution in **X** is diluted, which representation (**A–C**) represents the final solution?

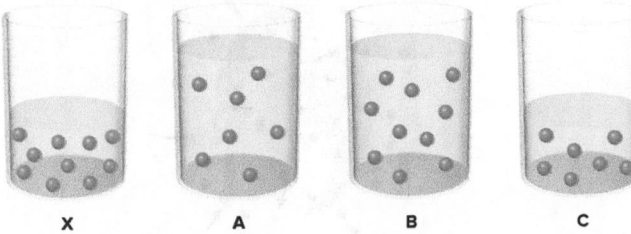

8.70 Consider solutions **A, B,** and **C** in Problem 8.69. If the volumes of **A** and **B** are twice the volume of **C**, which solution is most concentrated? Which solution is least concentrated?

8.71 (a) If **A** represents a 0.1 M aqueous NaCl solution, what is the concentration of **B**, a solution formed by dilution of **A** with water? (b) If the volume of **A** is 50.0 mL, how much water is added to form **B**?

8.72 (a) If **C** represents a 2.0 M aqueous NaCl solution, what is the concentration of **D**, a solution formed by dilution of **C** with water? (b) If the volume of **C** is 100. mL, how much water is added to form **D**?

8.73 What is the weight/volume percent concentration of a 30.0% (w/v) solution of vitamin C after each of the following dilutions?
a. 100. mL diluted to 200. mL
b. 100. mL diluted to 500. mL
c. 250 mL diluted to 1.5 L
d. 0.35 L diluted to 750 mL

8.74 One gram (1.00 g) of vitamin B_3 (niacin) is dissolved in water to give 10.0 mL of solution. (a) What is the weight/volume percent concentration of this solution? (b) What is the concentration of a solution formed by diluting 1.0 mL of this solution to each of the following volumes: [1] 10.0 mL; [2] 2.5 mL; [3] 50.0 mL; [4] 120 mL?

8.75 How many milliliters of a 2.5 M NaCl solution would be needed to prepare each solution?
a. 25 mL of a 1.0 M solution
b. 1.5 L of a 0.75 M solution
c. 15 mL of a 0.25 M solution
d. 250 mL of a 0.025 M solution

8.76 How many milliliters of a 5.0 M sucrose solution would be needed to prepare each solution?
a. 45 mL of a 4.0 M solution
b. 150 mL of a 0.5 M solution
c. 1.2 L of a 0.025 M solution
d. 750 mL of a 1.0 M solution

Colligative Properties

8.77 Representations **A** and **B** each show aqueous solutions formed from 1.0 mol of a solute dissolved in 1 kg of water. (a) Which solution has the higher boiling point? (b) Which solution has the higher melting point? (c) Which solution has the higher osmotic pressure?

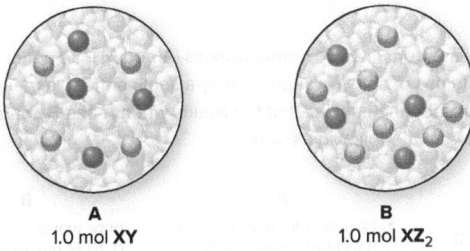

8.78 Representations **A** (containing 1.0 mol of NaCl) and **B** (containing 0.5 mol of Na_2SO_4) show aqueous solutions of solutes dissolved in 1 kg of water. (a) Which solution has the higher boiling point? (b) Which solution has the higher melting point? (c) Which solution has the higher osmotic pressure?

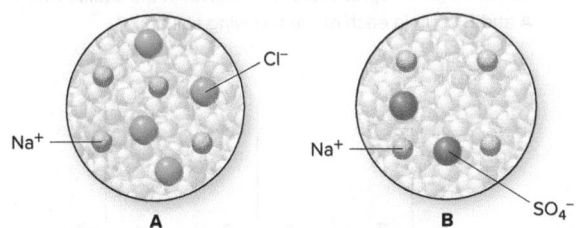

8.79 What is the boiling point of a solution that contains each of the following quantities of solute in 1.00 kg of water?
a. 3.0 mol of fructose molecules
b. 1.2 mol of KI
c. 1.5 mol of Na_3PO_4

8.80 What is the freezing point of each solution in Problem 8.79?

8.81 If 150 g of ethylene glycol ($C_2H_6O_2$) is added to 1,000. g of water, what is the freezing point?

8.82 How many grams of ethylene glycol must be added to 1,000. g of water to form a solution that has a freezing point of −10. °C?

8.83 In comparing a 1.0 M NaCl solution and a 1.0 M glucose solution, which solution has the higher: (a) boiling point; (b) melting point; (c) osmotic pressure; (d) vapor pressure at a given temperature?

8.84 In comparing a 1.0 M NaCl solution and a 1.0 M $CaCl_2$ solution, which solution has the higher: (a) boiling point; (b) melting point; (c) osmotic pressure; (d) vapor pressure at a given temperature?

8.85 Which solution in each pair has the higher melting point?
   a. 0.10 M NaOH or 0.10 M glucose
   b. 0.20 M NaCl or 0.15 M $CaCl_2$
   c. 0.10 M Na_2SO_4 or 0.10 M Na_3PO_4
   d. 0.10 M glucose or 0.20 M glucose

8.86 Which solution in each pair in Problem 8.85 has the higher boiling point?

Osmosis

8.87 A flask contains two compartments (**A** and **B**) with equal volumes of solution separated by a semipermeable membrane. Describe the final level of the liquids when **A** and **B** contain each of the following solutions.

	A	**B**
a.	1% (w/v) glucose solution	pure water
b.	0.10 M glucose solution	0.20 M glucose solution
c.	0.10 M NaCl solution	0.10 M NaI solution
d.	0.10 M $CaCl_2$ solution	0.10 M NaCl solution
e.	0.20 M glucose solution	0.10 M NaCl solution

8.88 A flask contains two compartments (**A** and **B**) with equal volumes of solution separated by a semipermeable membrane. Which diagram represents the final level of the liquids when **A** and **B** contain each of the following solutions?

	A	**B**
a.	10% (w/v) glucose	20% (w/v) glucose
b.	0.20 M NaCl	0.30 M glucose
c.	pure water	5% (w/v) glucose
d.	2.0 M NaCl	pure water
e.	3% (w/v) sucrose	1% (w/v) sucrose

8.89 The molecular art illustrates a red blood cell in an aqueous solution that contains dissolved solute particles shown in blue spheres. Black arrows show the direction of movement of water across the cell membrane. Is the red blood cell in a hypotonic, isotonic, or hypertonic solution?

8.90 Answer the question from Problem 8.89 for the following diagram.

Applications

8.91 Explain why opening a warm can of soda causes a louder "whoosh" and more fizzing than opening a cold can of soda.

8.92 Explain why more sugar dissolves in a cup of hot coffee than a glass of iced coffee.

8.93 If the concentration of glucose in the blood is 90 mg/100 mL, what is the weight/volume percent concentration of glucose? What is the molarity of glucose (molar mass 180.2 g/mol) in the blood?

8.94 If the human body contains 5.0 L of blood, how many grams of glucose are present in the blood if the concentration is 90. mg/100. mL?

8.95 Mannitol, a carbohydrate, is supplied as a 25% (w/v) solution. This hypertonic solution is given to patients who have sustained a head injury with associated brain swelling. (a) What volume should be given to provide a dose of 70. g? (b) How does the hypertonic mannitol benefit brain swelling?

8.96 A patient receives 750 mL of a 10.% (w/v) aqueous glucose solution. (a) How many grams of glucose does the patient receive? (b) How many moles of glucose (molar mass 180.2 g/mol) does the patient receive?

8.97 Explain why a cucumber placed in a concentrated salt solution shrivels.

8.98 Explain why a raisin placed in water swells.

8.99 A sports drink contains 15 g of soluble complex carbohydrates in 8.0 oz (1 fl oz = 29.6 mL). What weight/volume percent concentration does this represent?

8.100 A sports drink contains 25 mg of magnesium in an 8.0-oz portion (1 fl oz = 29.6 mL). How many parts per million does this represent? Assume that the mass of 1.0 mL of the solution is 1.0 g.

8.101 Each day, the stomach produces 2.0 L of gastric juice that contains 0.10 M HCl. How many grams of HCl does this correspond to?

8.102 An individual is legally intoxicated with a blood alcohol level of 0.08% (w/v) of ethanol. How many milligrams of ethanol are contained in 5.0 L of blood with this level?

CHALLENGE PROBLEMS

8.103 The therapeutic concentration—the concentration needed to be effective—of acetaminophen ($C_8H_9NO_2$, molar mass 151.2 g/mol) is 10–20 µg/mL. Assume that the density of blood is 1.0 g/mL.

    a. If the concentration of acetaminophen in the blood was measured at 15 ppm, is this concentration in the therapeutic range?

    b. How many moles of acetaminophen are present at this concentration in 5.0 L of blood?

8.104 One individual was told that his total blood cholesterol concentration should be less than 200. mg/dL and another individual was told that his total cholesterol should be less than 5.2×10^{-3} M. Are these two values equivalent? If the values differ, which number represents the higher value?

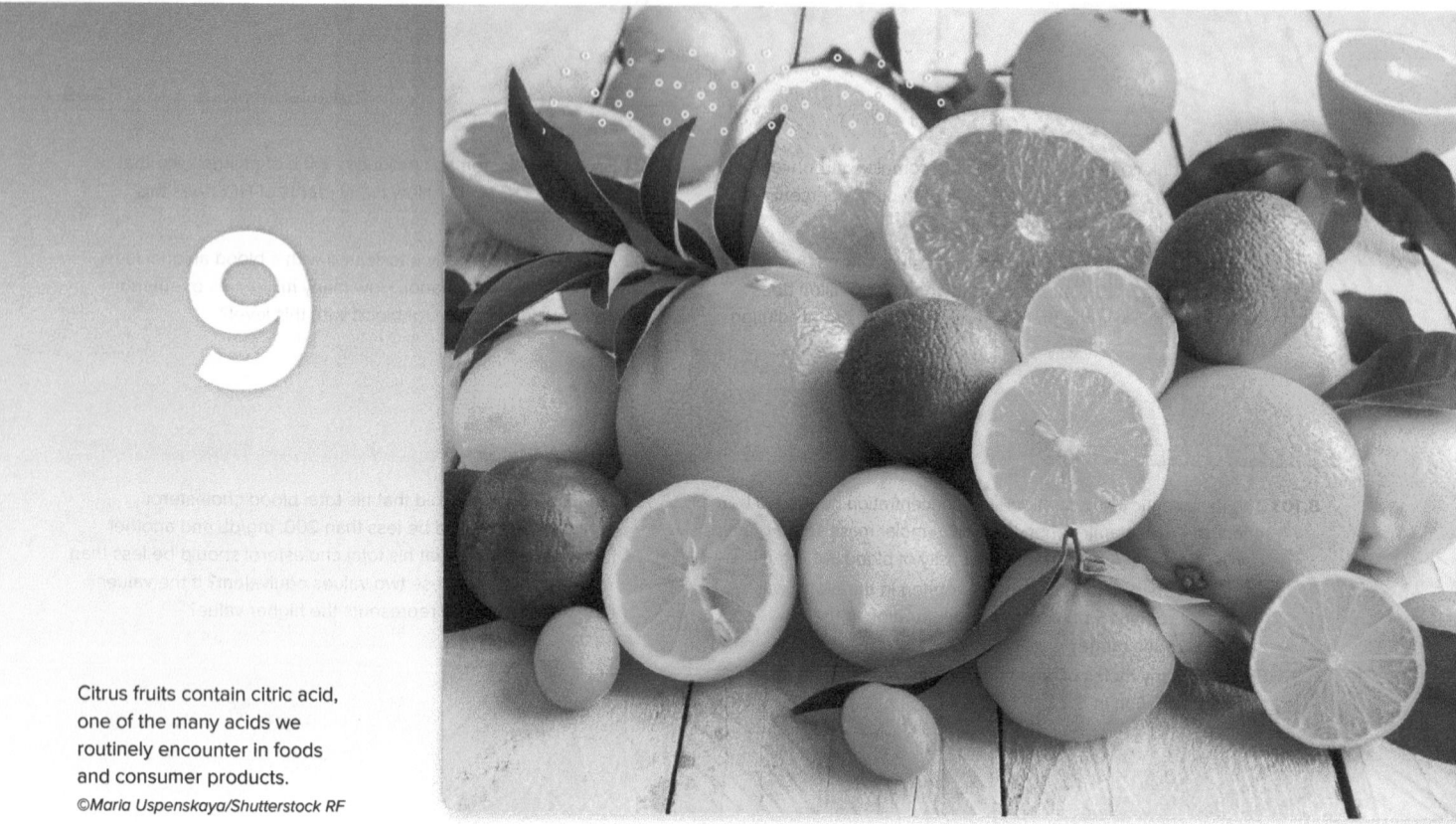

9

Citrus fruits contain citric acid, one of the many acids we routinely encounter in foods and consumer products.
©Maria Uspenskaya/Shutterstock RF

Acids and Bases

CHAPTER OUTLINE

9.1 Introduction to Acids and Bases

9.2 The Reaction of a Brønsted–Lowry Acid with a Brønsted–Lowry Base

9.3 Acid and Base Strength

9.4 Equilibrium and Acid Dissociation Constants

9.5 The Dissociation of Water

9.6 The pH Scale

9.7 Common Acid–Base Reactions

9.8 The Acidity and Basicity of Salt Solutions

9.9 Titration

9.10 Buffers

9.11 FOCUS ON THE HUMAN BODY: Buffers in the Blood

CHAPTER GOALS

In this chapter you will learn how to:

1. Identify acids and bases and describe their characteristics
2. Write equations for acid–base reactions
3. Relate acid strength to the direction of equilibrium of an acid–base reaction
4. Define the acid dissociation constant and relate its magnitude to acid strength
5. Define the ion–product of water and use it to calculate hydronium or hydroxide ion concentration
6. Calculate pH
7. Draw the products of common acid–base reactions
8. Determine whether a salt solution is acidic, basic, or neutral
9. Use a titration to determine the concentration of an acid or a base
10. Describe the fundamental features of a buffer
11. Understand the importance of buffers in maintaining pH in the body

Why Study Acids and Bases?

Chemical terms such as *anion* and *cation* may be unfamiliar to most nonscientists, but **acid** has found a place in everyday language. Commercials advertise the latest remedy for the heartburn caused by excess stomach *acid*. The nightly news may report the latest environmental impact of *acid* rain. Wine lovers often know that wine sours because its alcohol has turned to *acid*. *Acid* comes from the Latin word *acidus,* meaning sour, because when tasting compounds was a routine method of identification, these compounds were found to be sour. Acids commonly react with **bases,** and many products, including antacid tablets, glass cleaners, and drain cleaners, all contain bases. In Chapter 9 we learn about the characteristics of acids and bases and the reactions they undergo.

9.1   Introduction to Acids and Bases

The earliest definition of acids and bases was suggested by Swedish chemist Svante Arrhenius in the late nineteenth century. According to Arrhenius,

- An *acid* contains a hydrogen atom and dissolves in water to form a hydrogen ion, H^+.
- A *base* contains hydroxide and dissolves in water to form OH^-.

By this definition, hydrogen chloride (HCl) is an acid because it forms aqueous H^+ and Cl^- when it dissolves in water. Sodium hydroxide (NaOH) is a base because it contains OH^- and forms solvated Na^+ and OH^- ions when it dissolves in water.

$$HCl(g) \longrightarrow H^+(aq) + Cl^-(aq)$$

acid

H^+ is formed from HCl.

$$NaOH(s) \longrightarrow Na^+(aq) + OH^-(aq)$$

base

OH^- is formed from NaOH.

$H^+(aq)$ and $H_3O^+(aq)$ are sometimes used interchangeably by chemists. Keep in mind, however, that $H^+(aq)$ does not really exist in aqueous solution.

While the Arrhenius definition correctly predicts the behavior of many acids and bases, this definition is limited and sometimes inaccurate. We now know, for example, that the hydrogen ion, H^+, does *not* exist in water. H^+ is a naked proton with no electrons, and this concentrated positive charge reacts rapidly with a molecule of H_2O to form the **hydronium ion, H_3O^+.** Although $H^+(aq)$ will sometimes be written in an equation for emphasis, $H_3O^+(aq)$ is actually the reacting species.

$$H^+(aq) + H_2O(l) \longrightarrow H_3O^+(aq)$$

hydrogen ion

hydronium ion

actually present in aqueous solution

does not really exist
in aqueous solution

Moreover, several compounds contain no hydroxide anions, yet they still exhibit the characteristic properties of a base. Examples include the neutral molecule ammonia (NH_3) and the salt sodium carbonate (Na_2CO_3). As a result, a more general definition of acids and bases, proposed by Johannes **Brønsted** and Thomas **Lowry** in the early twentieth century, is widely used today.

In the Brønsted–Lowry definition, acids and bases are classified according to whether they can donate or accept a **proton**—a positively charged hydrogen ion, H^+.

- A Brønsted–Lowry acid is a *proton donor.*
- A Brønsted–Lowry base is a *proton acceptor.*

326

General, Organic, and Biochemisty

Consider what happens when HCl is dissolved in water.

This proton is donated.⌐   ⌐H₂O accepts a proton.

$$HCl(g) \quad + \quad H_2O(l) \quad \longrightarrow \quad H_3O^+(aq) \quad + \quad Cl^-(aq)$$

Brønsted–Lowry   **Brønsted–Lowry**
acid   **base**

- HCl is a Brønsted–Lowry *acid* because it *donates* a proton to the solvent water.
- H₂O is a Brønsted–Lowry *base* because it *accepts* a proton from HCl.

Before we learn more about the details of this process, we must first learn about the characteristics of Brønsted–Lowry acids and bases.

9.1A   Brønsted–Lowry Acids

A Brønsted–Lowry acid must contain a hydrogen atom. HCl is a Brønsted–Lowry acid because it *donates* a proton (H^+) to water when it dissolves, forming the hydronium ion (H_3O^+) and chloride (Cl^-).

$$HCl(g) \quad + \quad H_2O(l) \quad \longrightarrow \quad H_3O^+(aq) \quad + \quad Cl^-(aq)$$

This proton is donated to H₂O.
Brønsted–Lowry acid

Although hydrogen chloride, HCl, is a covalent molecule and a gas at room temperature, when it dissolves in water it reacts to form two ions, H_3O^+ and Cl^-. An aqueous solution of hydrogen chloride is called **hydrochloric acid.**

H₂O

HCl

Cl⁻

H₃O⁺

HCl gas   liquid H₂O   hydrochloric acid

(left & right): ©McGraw-Hill Education/Jill Braaten, photographer

Because a Brønsted–Lowry acid contains a hydrogen atom, a general Brønsted–Lowry acid is often written as **HA. A** can be a single atom such as Cl or Br. Thus, HCl and HBr are Brønsted–Lowry acids. **A** can also be a polyatomic ion. Sulfuric acid (H_2SO_4) and nitric acid (HNO_3) are Brønsted–Lowry acids, as well. **Carboxylic acids** are a group of Brønsted–Lowry acids that contain the atoms COOH arranged so that the carbon atom is doubly bonded to one O atom and singly bonded to another. Acetic acid, CH_3COOH, is a simple carboxylic acid. Although carboxylic acids may contain several hydrogen atoms, the **H atom of the OH group is the acidic proton that is donated.**

acidic H atom

acetic acid
a carboxylic acid

The names of common acids are derived from the anions formed when they dissolve in water.

- For acids derived from anions whose names end in the suffix *-ide*, add the prefix *hydro* and change the *-ide* ending to *-ic acid*.
- For acids derived from polyatomic anions whose names end in the suffix *-ate*, change the *-ate* ending to *-ic acid*.
- For acids derived from polyatomic anions whose names end in the suffix *-ite*, change the *-ite* ending to *-ous acid*.

Anion	Acid
Cl^-	HCl
chlor**ide** ------>	**hydro**chlor**ic acid**
SO_4^{2-}	H_2SO_4
sulf**ate** ------>	sulfur**ic acid**
SO_3^{2-}	H_2SO_3
sulf**ite** ------>	sulfur**ous acid**

Additional examples are listed in Table 9.1.

Table 9.1 Names of Common Acids

Anion	Name of Anion	Acid	Name of Acid
Br^-	Bromide	HBr	Hydrobromic acid
PO_4^{3-}	Phosphate	H_3PO_4	Phosphoric acid
CO_3^{2-}	Carbonate	H_2CO_3	Carbonic acid
$CH_3CO_2^-$	Acetate	CH_3CO_2H	Acetic acid
NO_2^-	Nitrite	HNO_2	Nitrous acid

PROBLEM 9.1

Name each acid: (a) HF; (b) HNO_3; (c) HCN.

PROBLEM 9.2

If the polyatomic anion ClO_2^- is called chlorite, what is the name for the acid $HClO_2$?

A Brønsted–Lowry acid may contain one or more protons that can be donated.

- A monoprotic acid contains *one* acidic proton. HCl is a monoprotic acid.
- A diprotic acid contains *two* acidic protons. H_2SO_4 is a diprotic acid.
- A triprotic acid contains *three* acidic protons. H_3PO_4 is a triprotic acid.

Although a Brønsted–Lowry acid must contain a hydrogen atom, **it may be a neutral molecule or contain a net positive or negative charge.** Thus, H_3O^+, HCl, and HSO_4^- are all Brønsted–Lowry acids even though their net charges are +1, 0, and −1, respectively. Vinegar, citrus fruits, and carbonated soft drinks all contain Brønsted–Lowry acids, as shown in Figure 9.1.

SAMPLE PROBLEM 9.1 IDENTIFYING BRØNSTED–LOWRY ACIDS

Which of the following species can be Brønsted–Lowry acids: (a) HF; (b) HSO_3^-; (c) Cl_2?

Analysis

A Brønsted–Lowry acid must contain a hydrogen atom, but it may be neutral or contain a net positive or negative charge.

Solution

a. HF is a Brønsted–Lowry acid because it contains a H.

b. HSO_3^- is a Brønsted–Lowry acid because it contains a H.

c. Cl_2 is not a Brønsted–Lowry acid because it does *not* contain a H.

PRACTICE PROBLEM 9.1

Which of the following species can be Brønsted–Lowry acids: (a) HI; (b) SO_4^{2-}; (c) $H_2PO_4^-$; (d) Cl^-?

More Practice: Try Problems 9.21, 9.22.

Figure 9.1   Examples of Brønsted–Lowry Acids in Food Products

a.   b.   c.

acetic acid   citric acid   carbonic acid
CH_3COOH $C_6H_8O_7$ H_2CO_3

a. Acetic acid is the sour-tasting component of vinegar. The air oxidation of ethanol to acetic acid is the process that makes "bad" wine taste sour.

b. Citric acid, mentioned in the chapter opener, imparts a sour taste to oranges, lemons, and other citrus fruits.

c. Carbonated beverages contain carbonic acid, H_2CO_3.

(a): ©Jill Braaten RF; (b): ©pikselstock/Shutterstock RF; (c): ©Andrew Bret Wallis/Stockbyte/Getty Images RF

9.1B   Brønsted–Lowry Bases

A Brønsted–Lowry base is a proton acceptor and as such, it must be able to form a bond to a proton. Because a proton has no electrons, **a base must contain a lone pair of electrons** that can be donated to form a new bond. Thus, ammonia (NH_3) is a Brønsted–Lowry base because it contains a nitrogen atom with a lone pair of electrons. When NH_3 is dissolved in water, its N atom accepts a proton from H_2O, forming ammonium (NH_4^+) and hydroxide (OH^-).

$$NH_3(g) \quad + \quad H_2O(l) \quad \longrightarrow \quad NH_4^+(aq) \quad + \quad OH^-(aq)$$

This electron pair forms a new
bond to the H from H_2O.
Brønsted–Lowry base

A general Brønsted–Lowry base is often written as **B:** to emphasize that the base must contain a lone pair of electrons to bond to a proton. A base may be neutral or, more commonly, have a net negative charge. Hydroxide (OH^-), which contains an oxygen atom with three lone pairs of electrons,

Figure 9.2   Examples of Brønsted–Lowry Bases in Consumer Products

a.

b.

c.

OH⁻
NH₄⁺
NH₃
H₂O
CO₃²⁻
Ca²⁺
OH⁻
Na⁺
H₂O
solid CaCO₃
solid NaOH

a. Calcium carbonate ($CaCO_3$), a base, is the active ingredient in the antacid Rolaids.

b. Windex and other household cleaners contain ammonia (NH_3) dissolved in water, forming NH_4^+ cations and OH^- anions.

c. Drain cleaners contain pellets of solid sodium hydroxide (NaOH), which form Na^+ cations and OH^- anions when mixed with water.

(a–c): ©McGraw-Hill Education/Jill Braaten, photographer

is the most common Brønsted–Lowry base. The source of hydroxide anions can be a variety of metal salts, including NaOH, KOH, $Mg(OH)_2$, and $Ca(OH)_2$. Ammonia (NH_3) and water (H_2O) are both Brønsted–Lowry bases because each contains an atom with a lone pair of electrons.

Common Brønsted–Lowry Bases		
NaOH sodium hydroxide	$Mg(OH)_2$ magnesium hydroxide	$\overset{..}{N}H_3$ ammonia
KOH potassium hydroxide	$Ca(OH)_2$ calcium hydroxide	$H_2\overset{..}{O}:$ water

OH^- is the base in each metal salt.

Lone pairs make these neutral compounds bases.

Many consumer products contain Brønsted–Lowry bases, as shown in Figure 9.2.

SAMPLE PROBLEM 9.2 IDENTIFYING BRØNSTED–LOWRY BASES

Which of the following species can be Brønsted–Lowry bases: (a) LiOH; (b) Cl^-; (c) CH_4?

Analysis

A Brønsted–Lowry base must contain a lone pair of electrons, but it may be neutral or have a net negative charge.

Solution

a. LiOH is a base because it contains hydroxide, OH^-, which has three lone pairs on its O atom.

b. Cl^- is a base because it has four lone pairs.

c. CH_4 is not a base because it has *no* lone pairs.

PRACTICE PROBLEM 9.2

Which of the following species can be Brønsted–Lowry bases: (a) $Al(OH)_3$; (b) Br^-; (c) NH_4^+; (d) CN^-?

More Practice: Try Problems 9.23, 9.24.

SAMPLE PROBLEM 9.3 IDENTIFYING BRØNSTED–LOWRY ACIDS AND BASES

Classify each reactant as a Brønsted–Lowry acid or base.

a. $HF(g) + H_2O(l) \longrightarrow F^-(aq) + H_3O^+(aq)$

b. $SO_4{}^{2-}(aq) + H_2O(l) \longrightarrow HSO_4{}^-(aq) + OH^-(aq)$

Analysis

In each equation, the Brønsted–Lowry acid *loses* a proton and the Brønsted–Lowry base *gains* a proton.

Solution

a. HF is the acid because it loses a proton (H^+) to form F^-, and H_2O is the base because it gains a proton to form H_3O^+.

$$\text{gain of } H^+$$

$$HF(g) \quad + \quad H_2O(l) \quad \longrightarrow \quad F^-(aq) \quad + \quad H_3O^+(aq)$$
$$\text{acid} \qquad\qquad \text{base}$$

$$\text{loss of } H^+$$

b. H_2O is the acid because it loses a proton (H^+) to form OH^-, and $SO_4{}^{2-}$ is the base because it gains a proton to form $HSO_4{}^-$.

$$\text{gain of } H^+$$

$$SO_4{}^{2-}(aq) \quad + \quad H_2O(l) \quad \longrightarrow \quad HSO_4{}^-(aq) \quad + \quad OH^-(aq)$$
$$\text{base} \qquad\qquad\qquad \text{acid}$$

$$\text{loss of } H^+$$

PRACTICE PROBLEM 9.3

Classify each reactant as a Brønsted–Lowry acid or base.

a. $HCl(g) + NH_3(g) \longrightarrow Cl^-(aq) + NH_4{}^+(aq)$

b. $CH_3COOH(l) + H_2O(l) \longrightarrow CH_3COO^-(aq) + H_3O^+(aq)$

c. $OH^-(aq) + HSO_4{}^-(aq) \longrightarrow H_2O(l) + SO_4{}^{2-}(aq)$

More Practice: Try Problems 9.31, 9.32.

9.2   The Reaction of a Brønsted–Lowry Acid with a Brønsted–Lowry Base

When a Brønsted–Lowry acid reacts with a Brønsted–Lowry base, a proton is *transferred* from the acid to the base. **The Brønsted–Lowry acid donates a proton to the Brønsted–Lowry base, which accepts it.**

Consider, for example, the reaction of the general acid H—A with the general base B:. **In an acid–base reaction, one bond is broken and one bond is formed.** The electron pair of the base B: forms a new bond to the proton of the acid, forming H—B$^+$. The acid H—A loses a proton, leaving the electron pair in the H—A bond on A, forming A:$^-$.

- The product formed by loss of a proton from an acid is called its *conjugate base.*
- The product formed by gain of a proton by a base is called its *conjugate acid.*

Thus, the conjugate base of the acid HA is A:⁻. The conjugate acid of the base B: is HB⁺.

- **Two species that differ by the presence of a proton are called a conjugate acid–base pair.**

Thus, in an acid–base reaction, the acid and the base on the left side of the equation (HA and B:) form two products that are also an acid and a base (HB⁺ and A:⁻). Equilibrium arrows ($\rightleftharpoons$) are often used to separate reactants and products because the reaction can proceed in either the forward or the reverse directions. In some reactions, the products are greatly favored, as discussed in Section 9.3.

When HBr is dissolved in water, for example, the acid HBr loses a proton to form its conjugate base Br^-, and the base H_2O gains a proton to form H_3O^+.

$$\text{H—Br} + \text{H}_2\text{O} \rightleftharpoons \text{Br}^- + \text{H}_3\text{O}^+$$

gain of H^+

acid   base   conjugate base   conjugate acid

loss of H^+

Thus, HBr and Br^- are a conjugate acid–base pair because these two species differ by the presence of a proton (H^+). H_2O and H_3O^+ are also a conjugate acid–base pair because these two species differ by the presence of a proton as well.

The net charge must be the same on both sides of the equation. In this example, the two reactants are neutral (zero net charge), and the sum of the −1 and +1 charges in the products is also zero.

Take particular note of what happens to the charges in each conjugate acid–base pair. **When a species gains a proton (H^+), it gains a +1 charge.** Thus, if a reactant is neutral to begin with, it ends up with a +1 charge. **When a species loses a proton (H^+), it effectively gains a −1 charge** because the product has one fewer proton (+1 charge) than it started with. Thus, if a reactant is neutral to begin with, it ends up with a −1 charge.

0 charge   add H^+ +1 charge
H_2O → H_3O^+
base

0 charge   lose H^+ −1 charge
H—Br → Br^-
acid   Take away +1 charge.

The reaction of ammonia (NH_3) with HCl is also a Brønsted–Lowry acid–base reaction. In this example, NH_3 is the base because it gains a proton to form its conjugate acid, NH_4^+. HCl is the acid because it donates a proton, forming its conjugate base, Cl^-.

gain of H^+

$$\text{H—}\overset{\text{H}}{\underset{\text{H}}{\text{N}}}\text{—H} + \text{HCl}(g) \rightleftharpoons \left[\text{H—}\overset{\text{H}}{\underset{\text{H}}{\text{N}}}\text{—H}\right]^+ + \text{Cl}^-(aq)$$

base   acid   conjugate acid   conjugate base

loss of H^+

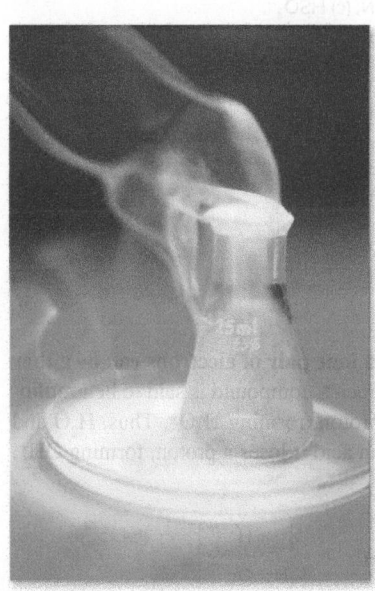

When HCl donates a proton to NH_3 in the absence of water, NH_4^+ and Cl^- are formed, which combine to form solid ammonium chloride, NH_4Cl.
©*Charles D. Winters/Science Source*

- **A Brønsted–Lowry acid–base reaction is a *proton transfer reaction* because it always results in the transfer of a proton from an acid to a base.**

The ability to identify and draw a conjugate acid or base from a given starting material is a necessary skill, illustrated in Sample Problems 9.4 and 9.5.

SAMPLE PROBLEM 9.4 DRAWING THE CONJUGATE ACID OF A BASE

Determine the conjugate acid of each base: (a) F^-; (b) NO_3^-.

Analysis

Conjugate acid–base pairs differ by the presence of a proton. To draw a conjugate acid from a base, *add* a proton, H^+. This adds +1 to the charge of the base to give the charge on the conjugate acid.

Solution

a. $F^- + H^+$ gives HF as the conjugate acid. HF has no charge because a proton with a +1 charge is added to an anion with a −1 charge.

b. $NO_3^- + H^+$ gives HNO_3 (nitric acid) as the conjugate acid. HNO_3 has no charge because a proton with a +1 charge is added to an anion with a −1 charge.

PRACTICE PROBLEM 9.4

Determine the conjugate acid of each species: (a) H_2O; (b) I^-; (c) HCO_3^-.

More Practice: Try Problems 9.25, 9.26, 9.35a, 9.36a.

SAMPLE PROBLEM 9.5 DRAWING THE CONJUGATE BASE OF AN ACID

Determine the conjugate base of each acid: (a) H_2O; (b) HCO_3^-.

Analysis

Conjugate acid–base pairs differ by the presence of a proton. To draw a conjugate base from an acid, *remove* a proton, H^+. This adds −1 to the charge of the acid to give the charge on the conjugate base.

Solution

a. Remove H^+ from H_2O to form OH^-, the conjugate base. OH^- has a −1 charge because −1 is added to a molecule that was neutral to begin with.

b. Remove H^+ from HCO_3^- to form CO_3^{2-}, the conjugate base. CO_3^{2-} has a −2 charge because −1 is added to an anion that had a −1 charge to begin with.

PRACTICE PROBLEM 9.5

Determine the conjugate base of each species: (a) H_2S; (b) HCN; (c) HSO_4^-.

More Practice: Try Problems 9.27–9.30, 9.35b, 9.36b.

PROBLEM 9.3

Draw the structure of the conjugate base of each acid.

a.   b.

A compound that contains both a hydrogen atom and a lone pair of electrons can be either an acid or a base, depending on the particular reaction. Such a compound is said to be **amphoteric.** For example, when H_2O acts as a base it gains a proton, forming H_3O^+. Thus, H_2O and H_3O^+ are a conjugate acid–base pair. When H_2O acts as an acid it loses a proton, forming OH^-. H_2O and OH^- are also a conjugate acid–base pair.

H_2O as a base	H—Ö—H	$\xrightarrow{\text{add } H^+}$	$\left[\text{H—O—H} \atop \text{H} \right]^+$
	base		conjugate acid

H_2O as an acid	H—Ö—H	$\xrightarrow{\text{remove } H^+}$	$[\text{H—Ö:}]^-$
	acid		conjugate base

SAMPLE PROBLEM 9.6 IDENTIFYING THE ACID, BASE, CONJUGATE ACID, AND CONJUGATE BASE IN A REACTION

Label the acid, the base, the conjugate acid, and the conjugate base in the following reaction.

$$NH_4^+(aq) + OH^-(aq) \rightleftharpoons NH_3(g) + H_2O(l)$$

Analysis

- The Brønsted–Lowry acid loses a proton to form its conjugate base.
- The Brønsted–Lowry base gains a proton to form its conjugate acid.

Solution

NH_4^+ is the acid because it loses a proton to form NH_3, its conjugate base. OH^- is the base because it gains a proton to form its conjugate acid, H_2O.

gain of H⁺

$NH_4^+(aq)$ + $OH^-(aq)$ $\rightleftharpoons$ $NH_3(g)$ + $H_2O(l)$

acid   base   conjugate base   conjugate acid

loss of H⁺

PRACTICE PROBLEM 9.6

Label the acid, the base, the conjugate acid, and the conjugate base in each reaction.

a. $H_2O(l) + HI(g) \longrightarrow I^-(aq) + H_3O^+(aq)$ b. $Br^-(aq) + HNO_3(aq) \longrightarrow HBr(aq) + NO_3^-(aq)$

More Practice: Try Problems 9.33, 9.34.

PROBLEM 9.4

Identify the acid, the base, the conjugate acid, and the conjugate base in the following reaction.

PROBLEM 9.5

Ammonia, NH_3, is amphoteric. (a) Draw the conjugate acid of NH_3. (b) Draw the conjugate base of NH_3.

PROBLEM 9.6

Fill in the missing product in each acid–base equation.

a. $HSO_4^- + H_2O \rightleftharpoons \boxed{} + OH^-$

b. $HSO_4^- + H_2O \rightleftharpoons \boxed{} + H_3O^+$

9.3 Acid and Base Strength

Although all Brønsted–Lowry acids contain protons, some acids readily donate protons whereas others do not. Similarly, some Brønsted–Lowry bases accept a proton much more readily than others. How readily proton transfer occurs is determined by the strength of the acid and base.

9.3A Relating Acid and Base Strength

When an acid dissolves in water, proton transfer forms H_3O^+ and an anion. **The splitting apart of a covalent molecule (or an ionic compound) into individual ions is called** *dissociation.* Acids differ in their tendency to donate a proton; that is, acids differ in the extent to which they *dissociate* in water.

- A strong acid readily donates a proton. When a strong acid dissolves in water, 100% of the acid dissociates into ions.
- A weak acid less readily donates a proton. When a weak acid dissolves in water, only a small fraction of the acid dissociates into ions.

Table 9.2 Relative Strength of Acids and Their Conjugate Bases

Acid		Conjugate Base	
Strong Acids			
Hydroiodic acid	HI	I⁻	Iodide ion
Hydrobromic acid	HBr	Br⁻	Bromide ion
Hydrochloric acid	HCl	Cl⁻	Chloride ion
Sulfuric acid	H_2SO_4	HSO_4^-	Hydrogen sulfate ion
Nitric acid	HNO_3	NO_3^-	Nitrate ion
Hydronium ion	H_3O^+	H_2O	**Water**
Weak Acids			
Phosphoric acid	H_3PO_4	$H_2PO_4^-$	Dihydrogen phosphate ion
Hydrofluoric acid	HF	F⁻	Fluoride ion
Acetic acid	CH_3COOH	CH_3COO^-	Acetate ion
Carbonic acid	H_2CO_3	HCO_3^-	Bicarbonate ion
Ammonium ion	NH_4^+	NH_3	Ammonia
Hydrocyanic acid	HCN	CN⁻	Cyanide ion
Water	H_2O	OH⁻	Hydroxide ion

Increasing acid strength (left); *Increasing base strength* (right)

Common strong acids include **HI, HBr, HCl, H₂SO₄,** and **HNO₃** (Table 9.2). When each acid is dissolved in water, 100% of the acid dissociates, forming H_3O^+ and the conjugate base, as shown for HCl and H_2SO_4.

- Use a *single* reaction arrow.
- The product is greatly favored at equilibrium.

$$HCl(g) + H_2O(l) \longrightarrow H_3O^+(aq) + Cl^-(aq)$$
strong acid   conjugate base

$$H_2SO_4(l) + H_2O(l) \longrightarrow H_3O^+(aq) + HSO_4^-(aq)$$
strong acid   conjugate base

HCl, hydrochloric acid, is secreted by the stomach to digest food (Figure 9.3), and **H₂SO₄,** sulfuric acid, is an important industrial starting material in the synthesis of phosphate fertilizers. A single reaction arrow (⟶) is drawn to show that essentially all of the reactants are converted to products.

Acetic acid, **CH₃COOH,** is a weak acid. When acetic acid dissolves in water, only a small fraction of acetic acid molecules donate a proton to water to form H_3O^+ and the conjugate base, CH_3COO^-. The major species at equilibrium is the undissociated acid, CH_3COOH. Equilibrium arrows that are unequal in length (⇌) are used to show that the equilibrium lies to the left. Other weak acids and their conjugate bases are listed in Table 9.2.

- Use *unequal* reaction arrows.
- The reactants are favored at equilibrium.

$$CH_3COOH(l) + H_2O(l) \rightleftharpoons H_3O^+(aq) + CH_3COO^-(aq)$$
weak acid   conjugate base

Figure 9.4 illustrates the difference between an aqueous solution of a strong acid that is completely dissociated and a weak acid that contains much undissociated acid. Sample Problems 9.7 and 9.8 illustrate how the extent of dissociation and acid strength are related.

Figure 9.3   Focus on the Human Body: Hydrochloric Acid in the Stomach

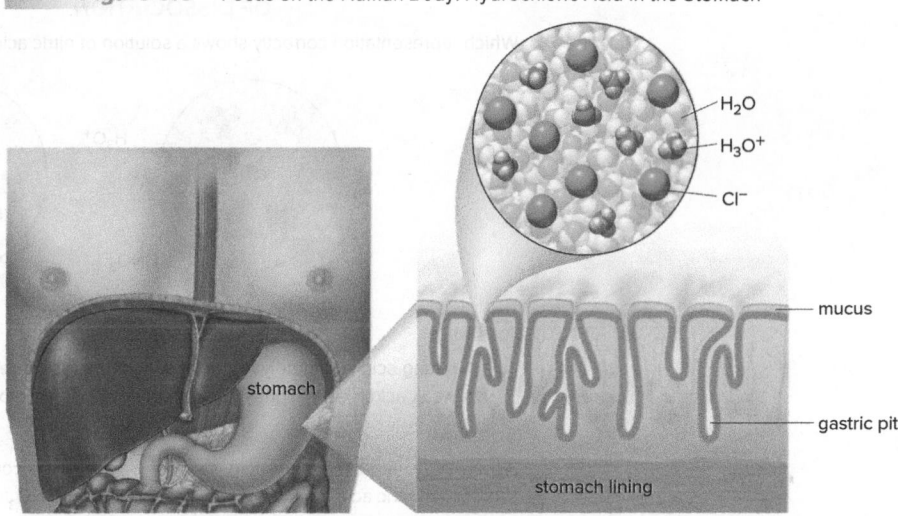

mucus

gastric pit

stomach lining

The thick mucous layer protects the stomach lining.

Although HCl is a corrosive acid secreted in the stomach, a thick layer of mucus covering the stomach wall protects it from damage by the strong acid. The strong acid HCl is completely dissociated to H_3O^+ and Cl^-.

Figure 9.4   A Strong and Weak Acid Dissolved in Water

hydrochloric acid

Cl^-

H_3O^+

A strong acid is completely dissociated.

vinegar

CH_3COO^-

H_3O^+

CH_3COOH

A weak acid contains mostly undissociated acid, CH_3COOH.

- The strong acid HCl completely dissociates into H_3O^+ and Cl^- in water.

- Vinegar contains CH_3COOH dissolved in H_2O. The weak acid CH_3COOH is only slightly dissociated into H_3O^+ and CH_3COO^-, so mostly CH_3COOH is present at equilibrium. The space-filling model for CH_3COOH shows a gray sphere (H) joined to a red sphere (O). CH_3COO^- has no H bonded to O, so it does not have a gray sphere joined to a red sphere.

(left & right): ©McGraw-Hill Education/Jill Braaten, photographer

SAMPLE PROBLEM 9.7 RELATING ACID STRENGTH TO THE EXTENT OF DISSOCIATION

Which representation correctly shows a solution of nitric acid (HNO_3) dissolved in water?

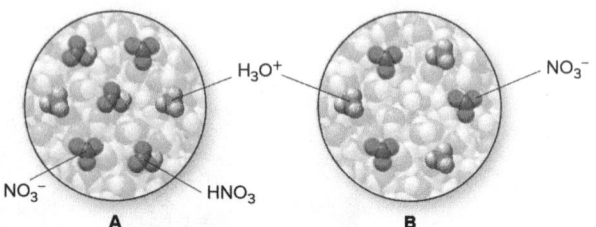

Analysis

- A strong acid completely dissociates into ions, so there is no neutral acid in water.
- A weak acid is only slightly dissociated into ions, so mostly neutral acid is present in water.

Solution

According to Table 9.2, nitric acid is a strong acid, so it is completely dissociated in water. Diagram **B** represents nitric acid because it shows only H_3O^+ and NO_3^- in solution, and no undissociated acid HNO_3 is present.

PRACTICE PROBLEM 9.7

Diagrams **A** and **B** represent two acids dissolved in water. Use the common element colors on the inside back cover to identify the species in each diagram, and label each acid as strong or weak.

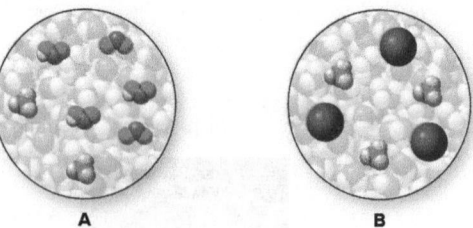

More Practice: Try Problems 9.41, 9.42.

SAMPLE PROBLEM 9.8 USING THE EXTENT OF DISSOCIATION TO DETERMINE RELATIVE ACID STRENGTH

Diagrams **A–C** represent three acids (HA) dissolved in water. Which representation shows the strongest acid? Which representation shows the weakest acid?

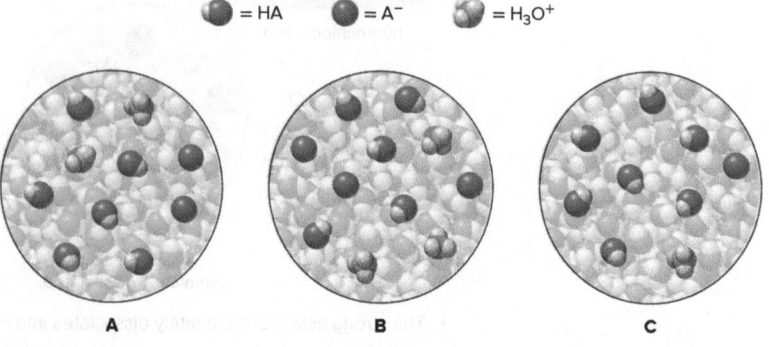

Analysis

The stronger the acid, the more readily it dissociates to form its conjugate base A^- and H_3O^+. In molecular art, the strongest acid has the most A^- and H_3O^+ ions, and the fewest molecules of undissociated HA.

Solution

B is the strongest acid because it contains the largest number of A^- and H_3O^+ ions (three each) and the smallest number (five) of undissociated HA molecules. **C** is the weakest acid because it contains the smallest number of A^- and H_3O^+ ions (one each) and the largest number (seven) of undissociated HA molecules.

PRACTICE PROBLEM 9.8

Diagrams **D–F** represent three acids (HA) dissolved in water. Rank the three acids (**D–F**) in order of increasing acidity.

More Practice: Try Problems 9.43, 9.44.

Bases also differ in their ability to accept a proton.

- **A strong base readily accepts a proton. When a strong base dissolves in water, 100% of the base dissociates into ions.**
- **A weak base less readily accepts a proton. When a weak base dissolves in water, only a small fraction of the base forms ions.**

The most common strong base is hydroxide, **OH⁻,** used as a variety of metal salts, including NaOH and KOH. Solid NaOH dissolves in water to form solvated Na^+ cations and OH^- anions. In contrast, when **NH₃,** a weak base, dissolves in water, only a small fraction of NH_3 molecules react to form NH_4^+ and OH^-. The major species at equilibrium is the undissociated molecule, NH_3.

Figure 9.5 illustrates the difference between aqueous solutions of strong and weak bases. Table 9.2 lists common bases.

An inverse relationship exists between acid and base strength.

- **A strong acid readily donates a proton, forming a *weak* conjugate base.**
- **A strong base readily accepts a proton, forming a *weak* conjugate acid.**

Why does this inverse relationship exist? Since a strong acid readily donates a proton, it forms a conjugate base that has little ability to accept a proton. Since a strong base readily accepts a proton, it forms a conjugate acid that tightly holds on to its proton, making it a weak acid.

Figure 9.5   A Strong and Weak Base Dissolved in Water

sodium hydroxide

Na⁺

OH⁻

A strong base is
completely dissociated.

ammonia

NH_3

NH_4^+

OH⁻

A weak base contains mostly
undissociated base, NH_3.

- The strong base NaOH completely dissociates into Na^+ and OH^- in water.
- The weak base NH_3 is only slightly dissociated into NH_4^+ and OH^-, so mostly NH_3 is present at equilibrium.

(left & right): ©McGraw-Hill Education/Jill Braaten, photographer

Thus, a *strong* acid like HCl forms a *weak* conjugate base (Cl^-), and a *strong* base like OH^- forms a *weak* conjugate acid (H_2O). The entries in Table 9.2 are arranged in order of *decreasing* acid strength. This means that Table 9.2 is also arranged in order of *increasing* strength of the resulting conjugate bases. Knowing the relative strength of two acids makes it possible to predict the relative strength of their conjugate bases.

SAMPLE PROBLEM 9.9 RELATING ACID AND BASE STRENGTH

Using Table 9.2: (a) Is H_3PO_4 or HF the stronger acid? (b) Draw the conjugate base of each acid and predict which base is stronger.

Analysis

The stronger the acid, the weaker the conjugate base.

Solution

a. H_3PO_4 is located above HF in Table 9.2, making it the stronger acid.

b. To draw each conjugate base, remove a proton (H^+). Since each acid is neutral, both conjugate bases have a −1 charge. Since HF is the weaker acid, F^- is the stronger conjugate base.

$$H_3PO_4 \xrightarrow{\text{lose } H^+} H_2PO_4^- \quad \boxed{\textbf{weaker} \text{ base}}$$

stronger acid

$$HF \xrightarrow{\text{lose } H^+} F^- \quad \boxed{\textbf{stronger} \text{ base}}$$

weaker acid

PRACTICE PROBLEM 9.9

Label the stronger acid in each pair. Which acid has the stronger conjugate base?

a. H_2SO_4 or H_3PO_4 b. HF or HCl   c. H_2CO_3 or NH_4^+ d. HCN or HF

More Practice: Try Problems 9.45, 9.46, 9.49, 9.50.

9.3B   Using Acid Strength to Predict the Direction of Equilibrium

A Brønsted–Lowry acid–base reaction represents an equilibrium. Since an acid donates a proton to a base, forming a conjugate acid and conjugate base, there are always two acids and two bases in the reaction mixture. Which pair of acids and bases is favored at equilibrium? **The position of the equilibrium depends upon the strength of the acids and bases.**

> • **The stronger acid reacts with the stronger base to form the weaker acid and weaker base.**

Since a strong acid readily donates a proton and a strong base readily accepts one, these two species react to form a weaker conjugate acid and base that do not donate or accept a proton as readily. Thus, **when the stronger acid and base are the reactants on the left side, the reaction readily occurs and the reaction proceeds to the** *right*.

On the other hand, **if an acid–base reaction would form the stronger acid and base, equilibrium favors the reactants and little product forms.**

Predicting the direction of equilibrium using the information in Table 9.2 is illustrated in the accompanying stepwise *How To* procedure.

How To   **Predict the Direction of Equilibrium in an Acid–Base Reaction**

Example: Are the reactants or products favored in the following acid–base reaction?

$$HCN(g) + OH^-(aq) \rightleftharpoons CN^-(aq) + H_2O(l)$$

Step [1] Identify the acid in the reactants and the conjugate acid in the products.

$$\underset{\text{acid}}{HCN(g)} + \underset{\text{base}}{OH^-(aq)} \rightleftharpoons \underset{\text{conjugate base}}{CN^-(aq)} + \underset{\text{conjugate acid}}{H_2O(l)}$$

gain of H⁺

loss of H⁺

- • HCN is the acid because it donates a proton.
- • H_2O is the conjugate acid formed from the hydroxide base.

Step [2] Determine the relative strength of the acid and the conjugate acid.

- • According to Table 9.2, HCN is a stronger acid than H_2O.

Step [3] Equilibrium favors the formation of the weaker acid.

- • Since the stronger acid HCN is a reactant, the reaction *proceeds to the right* as written, to form the weaker acid, H_2O. Unequal equilibrium arrows should be drawn with the larger arrow pointing toward the product side on the right.

$$\underset{\text{stronger acid}}{HCN(g)} + OH^-(aq) \rightleftharpoons CN^-(aq) + \underset{\text{weaker acid}}{H_2O(l)}$$

Products are favored.

HEALTH NOTE

Lactic acid accumulates in tissues during vigorous exercise, making muscles feel tired and sore. The formation of lactic acid is discussed in greater detail in Section 24.4. ©Digital Vision Ltd./ SuperStock RF

PROBLEM 9.7

Are the reactants or products favored at equilibrium in each reaction?

a. $HF(g) + OH^-(aq) \rightleftharpoons F^-(aq) + H_2O(l)$

b. $NH_4^+(aq) + Cl^-(aq) \rightleftharpoons NH_3(g) + HCl(aq)$

c. $HCO_3^-(aq) + H_3O^+(aq) \rightleftharpoons H_2CO_3(aq) + H_2O(l)$

PROBLEM 9.8

If lactic acid is similar in strength to acetic acid (Table 9.2), predict whether reactants or products are favored in each reaction.

CH₃—C—C structure with OH, OH, H, O
$C_3H_6O_3$
lactic acid

a. $C_3H_6O_3(aq) + H_2O(l) \rightleftharpoons C_3H_5O_3^-(aq) + H_3O^+(aq)$
lactic acid

b. $C_3H_6O_3(aq) + HCO_3^-(aq) \rightleftharpoons C_3H_5O_3^-(aq) + H_2CO_3(aq)$
lactic acid

9.4 Equilibrium and Acid Dissociation Constants

Like all equilibria, we can write an expression for the equilibrium constant for the acid–base reaction that takes place when an acid HA dissolves in water. The equilibrium constant (K) shows the ratio of the concentrations of the products to the concentrations of the reactants.

Reaction $HA(aq) + H_2O(l) \rightleftharpoons H_3O^+(aq) + A:^-$

Equilibrium constant $K = \dfrac{[H_3O^+][A:^-]}{[HA][H_2O]}$ concentrations of the products / concentrations of the reactants

Water serves as both the base and the solvent. Since water is a liquid and its concentration is essentially constant, the equation can be rearranged by multiplying both sides by [H₂O]. This forms a new constant called the **acid dissociation constant, K_a.**

$$K_a = K[H_2O] = \dfrac{[H_3O^+][A:^-]}{[HA]}$$

acid dissociation constant

How is K_a related to acid strength? The stronger the acid, the higher the concentration of the products of an acid–base reaction, and the larger the numerator in the expression for K_a. As a result:

- The stronger the acid, the larger the value of K_a.

The strong acids listed in Table 9.2 all have K_a values much greater than 1. Weak acids have K_a values less than 1. The K_a's for several weak acids are listed in Table 9.3.

SAMPLE PROBLEM 9.10 USING K_a TO DETERMINE ACID STRENGTH

Which acid in each pair is stronger: (a) HCN or HSO_4^-; (b) CH_3COOH or NH_4^+?

Analysis

Use Table 9.3 to find the K_a for each acid. **The acid with the larger K_a is the stronger acid.**

Solution

a.   HCN HSO_4^- b. CH_3COOH NH_4^+

$K_a = 4.9 \times 10^{-10}$ $K_a = 1.2 \times 10^{-2}$ 1.8×10^{-5} 5.6×10^{-10}

                              larger K_a larger K_a

                          stronger acid   **stronger acid**

PRACTICE PROBLEM 9.10

Rank the acids in each group in order of increasing acid strength.

a. H_3PO_4, $H_2PO_4^-$, HPO_4^{2-} b. HCN, HF, CH_3COOH

More Practice: Try Problems 9.51–9.54.

Table 9.3 Acid Dissociation Constants (K_a) for Common Weak Acids

Acid	Structure	K_a
Hydrogen sulfate ion	HSO_4^-	1.2×10^{-2}
Phosphoric acid	H_3PO_4	7.5×10^{-3}
Hydrofluoric acid	HF	7.2×10^{-4}
Acetic acid	CH_3COOH	1.8×10^{-5}
Carbonic acid	H_2CO_3	4.3×10^{-7}
Dihydrogen phosphate ion	$H_2PO_4^-$	6.2×10^{-8}
Ammonium ion	NH_4^+	5.6×10^{-10}
Hydrocyanic acid	HCN	4.9×10^{-10}
Bicarbonate ion	HCO_3^-	5.6×10^{-11}
Hydrogen phosphate ion	HPO_4^{2-}	2.2×10^{-13}

Increasing acidity ↑

vitamin C
ascorbic acid
$C_6H_8O_6$

Because K_a values tell us the relative strength of two acids, we can use K_a's to predict the direction of equilibrium in an acid–base reaction, as shown in Sample Problem 9.11.

• **Equilibrium favors the formation of the weaker acid—that is, the acid with the *smaller* K_a value.**

Citrus fruits (oranges, grapefruit, and lemons) are well-known sources of vitamin C (ascorbic acid, Sample Problem 9.11), but guava, kiwifruit, and rose hips are excellent sources, too.
©McGraw-Hill Education/Jill Braaten, photographer

SAMPLE PROBLEM 9.11 USING K_a TO DETERMINE THE DIRECTION OF EQUILIBRIUM

Ascorbic acid, vitamin C, is needed for the formation of collagen, a common protein in connective tissues in muscles and blood vessels. If vitamin C has a K_a of 7.9×10^{-5}, are the reactants or products favored in the following acid–base reaction?

$$C_6H_8O_6(aq) + NH_3(aq) \rightleftharpoons C_6H_7O_6^-(aq) + NH_4^+(aq)$$
vitamin C   conjugate base
                                         of vitamin C

Analysis

To determine the direction of equilibrium, we must identify the acid in the reactants and the conjugate acid in the products. Then compare their K_a's. **Equilibrium favors the formation of the acid with the smaller K_a value.**

Solution

Vitamin C is the acid and NH_3 is the base on the reactant side. NH_3 gains a proton to form its conjugate acid, NH_4^+, which has a K_a of 5.6×10^{-10} (Table 9.3). The conjugate acid, therefore, has a *smaller* K_a than vitamin C (7.9×10^{-5}), making it the *weaker acid*. Thus, the products are favored at equilibrium.

products favored

$$C_6H_8O_6(aq) + NH_3(aq) \longrightarrow C_6H_7O_6^-(aq) + NH_4^+(aq)$$
vitamin C   conjugate acid

$K_a = 7.9 \times 10^{-5}$ $K_a = 5.6 \times 10^{-10}$
larger K_a smaller K_a
stronger acid   **weaker acid**

PRACTICE PROBLEM 9.11

Use the acid dissociation constants in Table 9.3 to determine whether the reactants or products are favored in the following reaction.

$$HCO_3^-(aq) + NH_3(aq) \rightleftharpoons CO_3^{2-}(aq) + NH_4^+(aq)$$

More Practice: Try Problems 9.57, 9.58.

PROBLEM 9.9

Consider the weak acids, HCN and H_2CO_3.

a. Which acid has the larger K_a?
b. Which acid is stronger?
c. Which acid has the stronger conjugate base?
d. Which acid has the weaker conjugate base?
e. When each acid is dissolved in water, for which acid does the equilibrium lie further to the right?

9.5   The Dissociation of Water

In Section 9.2 we learned that water can behave as *both* a Brønsted–Lowry acid and a Brønsted–Lowry base. As a result, two molecules of water can react together in an acid–base reaction.

| acid | base | conjugate base | conjugate acid |

H_2O donates H^+. H_2O accepts H^+.

- One molecule of H_2O donates a proton (H^+), forming its conjugate base OH^-.
- One molecule of H_2O accepts a proton, forming its conjugate acid H_3O^+.

Equilibrium favors the starting materials in this reaction, because the reactant acid, H_2O, is much weaker than the conjugate acid, H_3O^+. Thus, pure water contains an exceedingly low concentration of ions, H_3O^+ and OH^-.

As usual, an expression for the equilibrium constant can be written that shows the ratio of the concentrations of the products, H_3O^+ and OH^-, to the concentration of the reactants, two molecules of H_2O. Since water is a liquid and its concentration is essentially constant, this equation can be rearranged by multiplying by $[H_2O]^2$ to afford a new equilibrium constant, K_w, **the ion–product constant** for water.

$$K = \frac{[H_3O^+][OH^-]}{[H_2O][H_2O]} = \frac{[H_3O^+][OH^-]}{[H_2O]^2}$$ — Multiply both sides by $[H_2O]^2$.

$$K_w = K[H_2O]^2 = [H_3O^+][OH^-]$$

ion–product constant

$$K_w = [H_3O^+][OH^-]$$

Since one H_3O^+ ion and one OH^- ion are formed in each reaction, the concentrations of H_3O^+ and OH^- are equal in pure water. Experimentally it can be shown that the $[H_3O^+] = [OH^-] = 1.0 \times 10^{-7}$ M at 25 °C. Thus,

$$K_w = [H_3O^+][OH^-]$$
$$K_w = (1.0 \times 10^{-7}) \times (1.0 \times 10^{-7})$$
$$K_w = 1.0 \times 10^{-14}$$

- The product, $[H_3O^+][OH^-]$, is a constant, 1.0×10^{-14}, for all aqueous solutions at 25 °C.

Thus, **the value of K_w applies to any aqueous solution,** not just pure water. If we know the concentration of one ion, H_3O^+ or OH^-, we can find the concentration of the other by rearranging the expression for K_w.

To calculate $[OH^-]$ when $[H_3O^+]$ is known:

$$K_w = [H_3O^+][OH^-]$$

$$[OH^-] = \frac{K_w}{[H_3O^+]}$$

$$[OH^-] = \frac{1.0 \times 10^{-14}}{[H_3O^+]}$$

To calculate $[H_3O^+]$ when $[OH^-]$ is known:

$$K_w = [H_3O^+][OH^-]$$

$$[H_3O^+] = \frac{K_w}{[OH^-]}$$

$$[H_3O^+] = \frac{1.0 \times 10^{-14}}{[OH^-]}$$

How to write numbers in scientific notation was presented in Section 1.6. Multiplying and dividing numbers written in scientific notation was described in Section 5.5.

Thus, if the concentration of H_3O^+ in a cup of coffee is 1.0×10^{-5} M, we can use this value to calculate $[OH^-]$.

$$[OH^-] = \frac{K_w}{[H_3O^+]} = \frac{1.0 \times 10^{-14}}{1.0 \times 10^{-5}}$$

$$[OH^-] = 1.0 \times 10^{-9} \text{ M}$$

hydroxide ion concentration
in a cup of coffee

In a cup of coffee, therefore, the concentration of H_3O^+ ions is greater than the concentration of OH^- ions, but the product of these concentrations, 1.0×10^{-14}, is a constant, K_w.

Pure water and any solution that has an equal concentration of H_3O^+ and OH^- ions (1.0×10^{-7}) is said to be *neutral.* Other solutions are classified as **acidic** or **basic,** depending on which ion is present in a higher concentration.

- In an *acidic* solution, $[H_3O^+] > [OH^-]$; thus, $[H_3O^+] > 10^{-7}$ M.
- In a *basic* solution, $[OH^-] > [H_3O^+]$; thus, $[OH^-] > 10^{-7}$ M.

Coffee is an *acidic* solution because the concentration of H_3O^+ is *greater* than the concentration of OH^-. ©Comstock/Stockbyte/ Getty Images RF

In an acidic solution, the concentration of the acid H_3O^+ is *greater* than the concentration of the base OH^-. In a basic solution, the concentration of the base OH^- is *greater* than the concentration of the acid H_3O^+. Table 9.4 summarizes information about neutral, acidic, and basic solutions.

Table 9.4 Neutral, Acidic, and Basic Solutions

Type	$[H_3O^+]$ and $[OH^-]$	$[H_3O^+]$	$[OH^-]$
Neutral	$[H_3O^+] = [OH^-]$	10^{-7} M	10^{-7} M
Acidic	$[H_3O^+] > [OH^-]$	$> 10^{-7}$ M	$< 10^{-7}$ M
Basic	$[H_3O^+] < [OH^-]$	$< 10^{-7}$ M	$> 10^{-7}$ M

SAMPLE PROBLEM 9.12 CALCULATING [OH⁻] WHEN [H₃O⁺] IS KNOWN

If $[H_3O^+]$ in blood is 4.0×10^{-8} M, what is the value of $[OH^-]$? Is blood acidic, basic, or neutral?

Analysis

Use the equation $[OH^-] = K_w/[H_3O^+]$ to calculate the hydroxide ion concentration.

Solution

Substitute the given value of $[H_3O^+]$ in the equation to find $[OH^-]$.

$$[OH^-] = \frac{K_w}{[H_3O^+]} = \frac{1.0 \times 10^{-14}}{4.0 \times 10^{-8}} = 2.5 \times 10^{-7} \text{ M}$$

hydroxide ion concentration
in the blood

Since $[OH^-] > [H_3O^+]$, blood is a basic solution.

PRACTICE PROBLEM 9.12

Calculate the value of $[OH^-]$ from the given $[H_3O^+]$ in each solution and label the solution as acidic or basic: (a) $[H_3O^+] = 10^{-3}$ M; (b) $[H_3O^+] = 10^{-11}$ M; (c) $[H_3O^+] = 2.8 \times 10^{-10}$ M; (d) $[H_3O^+] = 5.6 \times 10^{-4}$ M.

More Practice: Try Problems 9.61–9.66.

PROBLEM 9.10

Calculate the value of $[H_3O^+]$ from the given $[OH^-]$ in each solution and label the solution as acidic or basic: (a) $[OH^-] = 10^{-6}$ M; (b) $[OH^-] = 10^{-9}$ M; (c) $[OH^-] = 5.2 \times 10^{-11}$ M; (d) $[OH^-] = 7.3 \times 10^{-4}$ M.

Since a *strong* acid like HCl is completely dissociated in aqueous solution, the **concentration of the acid tells us the concentration of hydronium ions** present. Thus, a 0.1 M HCl solution completely dissociates, so the concentration of H_3O^+ is 0.1 M. This value can then be used to calculate the hydroxide ion concentration. Similarly, a *strong* base like NaOH completely dissociates, so the **concentration of the base gives the concentration of hydroxide ions** present. Thus, the concentration of OH^- in a 0.1 M NaOH solution is 0.1 M.

In **0.1 M** HCl solution:	$[H_3O^+] = $ **0.1 M** $= 1 \times 10^{-1}$ M
strong acid	
In **0.1 M** NaOH solution:	$[OH^-] = $ **0.1 M** $= 1 \times 10^{-1}$ M
strong base	

SAMPLE PROBLEM 9.13 CALCULATING [H₃O⁺] AND [OH⁻] IN A SOLUTION OF A STRONG BASE

Calculate the value of $[H_3O^+]$ and $[OH^-]$ in a 0.01 M NaOH solution.

Analysis

Since NaOH is a strong base that completely dissociates to form Na^+ and OH^-, the concentration of NaOH gives the concentration of OH^- ions. The $[OH^-]$ can then be used to calculate $[H_3O^+]$ from the expression for K_w.

Solution

The value of $[OH^-]$ in a 0.01 M NaOH solution is 0.01 M $= 1 \times 10^{-2}$ M.

$$[H_3O^+] = \frac{K_w}{[OH^-]} = \frac{1 \times 10^{-14}}{1 \times 10^{-2}} = 1 \times 10^{-12} \text{ M}$$

concentration of OH^- ⟵

concentration of H_3O^+

PRACTICE PROBLEM 9.13

Calculate the value of $[H_3O^+]$ and $[OH^-]$ in each solution: (a) 0.001 M NaOH; (b) 0.001 M HCl; (c) 1.5 M HCl; (d) 0.30 M NaOH.

9.6   The pH Scale

Knowing the hydronium ion concentration is necessary in many different instances. The blood must have an H_3O^+ concentration in a very narrow range for an individual's good health. Plants thrive in soil that is not too acidic or too basic. The H_3O^+ concentration in a swimming pool must be measured and adjusted to keep the water clean and free from bacteria and algae.

9.6A   Calculating pH

Since values for the hydronium ion concentration are very small, with negative powers of 10, the **pH scale** is used to more conveniently report $[H_3O^+]$. The pH of a solution is a number generally between 0 and 14, defined in terms of the *logarithm* (log) of the H_3O^+ concentration.

$$pH = -\log[H_3O^+]$$

A logarithm is an exponent of a power of 10.

The log is the exponent.

$$\log(10^5) = 5 \qquad \log(10^{-10}) = -10 \qquad \log(0.001) = \log(10^{-3}) = -3$$

The log is the exponent.   Convert to scientific notation.

In calculating pH, first consider an H_3O^+ concentration that has a coefficient of *one* when the number is written in scientific notation. For example, the value of $[H_3O^+]$ in apple juice is about 1×10^{-4}, or 10^{-4} written without the coefficient. The pH of this solution is calculated as follows:

$$pH = -\log[H_3O^+] = -\log(10^{-4})$$
$$= -(-4) = 4$$
pH of apple juice

Since pH is defined as the *negative* logarithm of $[H_3O^+]$ and these concentrations have *negative* exponents (10^{-x}), pH values are *positive* numbers.

Whether a solution is acidic, neutral, or basic can now be defined in terms of its pH.

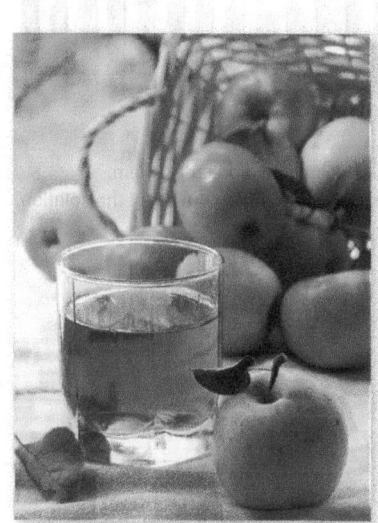

Apple juice has a pH of about 4, so it is an acidic solution. ©Wiktory/Shutterstock RF

- **Acidic solution:**   pH < 7 $\longrightarrow$ $[H_3O^+] > 1 \times 10^{-7}$
- **Neutral solution:** pH = 7 $\longrightarrow$ $[H_3O^+] = 1 \times 10^{-7}$
- **Basic solution:**   pH > 7 $\longrightarrow$ $[H_3O^+] < 1 \times 10^{-7}$

Note the relationship between $[H_3O^+]$ and pH.

- The *lower* the pH, the *higher* the concentration of H_3O^+.

Since pH is measured on a *logarithmic* scale, **a small difference in pH translates to a large change in H_3O^+ concentration.** For example, a difference of one pH unit means a ten-fold difference in H_3O^+ concentration. A difference of three pH units means a thousand-fold difference in H_3O^+ concentration.

A difference of one pH unit...

pH = 2 $[H_3O^+] = 1 \times 10^{-2}$
pH = 3 $[H_3O^+] = 1 \times 10^{-3}$

...means the $[H_3O^+]$ differs by a factor of 10.

A difference of three pH units...

pH = 2 $[H_3O^+] = 1 \times 10^{-2}$
pH = 5 $[H_3O^+] = 1 \times 10^{-5}$

...means the $[H_3O^+]$ differs by a factor of 1,000.

PROBLEM 9.11

(a) What is the difference in $[H_3O^+]$ for each pair of solutions with the given pH values? (b) Which pH value indicates the higher concentration of H_3O^+?

[1] pH = 4 and pH = 5   [2] pH = 4 and pH = 6   [3] pH = 6 and pH = 10

The pH of a solution can be measured using a pH meter as shown in Figure 9.6. Approximate pH values are determined using pH paper or indicators that turn different colors depending on the pH of the solution. The pH of various substances is shown in Figure 9.7.

Converting a given H_3O^+ concentration to a pH value is shown in Sample Problem 9.14. The reverse process, converting a pH value to an H_3O^+ concentration, is shown in Sample Problem 9.15.

Figure 9.6   Measuring pH

a.

b.

c.

a. A pH meter is a small electronic device that measures pH when an electrode is dipped into a solution.
b. Paper strips called pH paper change color corresponding to a particular pH, when a drop of an aqueous solution is applied to them.
c. An acid–base indicator can be used to give an approximate pH. The indicator is a dye that changes color depending on the pH of the solution.

(a): ©McGraw-Hill Education/Stephen Frisch, photographer; (b): ©sciencephotos/Alamy; (c): ©Leslie Garland Picture Library/Alamy

Figure 9.7   The pH of Some Common Substances

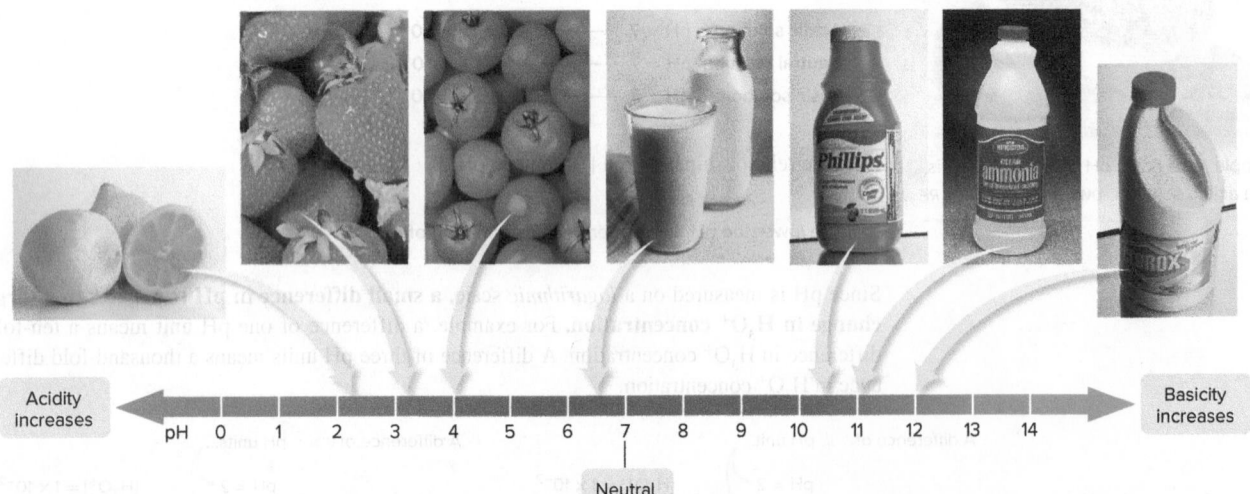

Acidity increases

pH 0 1 2 3 4 5 6 7 8 9 10 11 12 13 14

Basicity increases

Neutral

The pH of many fruits is less than 7, making them acidic. Many cleaning agents, such as household ammonia and bleach, are basic (pH > 7).
(left to right): ©Humberto Olarte Cupas/Alamy RF; ©Ken Welsh/age fotostock RF; ©Brand X Pictures/Stockbyte/Getty Images RF; ©Mitch Hrdlicka/Stockbyte/Getty Images RF; ©McGraw-Hill Education/Jill Braaten, photographer; ©McGraw-Hill Education/Terry Wild Studio; ©McGraw-Hill Education/Jill Braaten, photographer

SAMPLE PROBLEM 9.14 CALCULATING pH FROM [H₃O⁺]

What is the pH of a urine sample that has an H_3O^+ concentration of 1×10^{-5} M? Classify the solution as acidic, basic, or neutral.

Analysis

Use the formula **pH = −log [H₃O⁺]**. When the coefficient of a number written in scientific notation is one, the pH equals the value x in 10^{-x}.

Solution

$$pH = -\log[H_3O^+] = -\log(10^{-5})$$
$$= -(-5) = 5 \quad \text{pH of urine sample}$$

Answer

The urine sample is acidic because the pH < 7.

PRACTICE PROBLEM 9.14

Convert each H_3O^+ concentration to a pH value.

a. 1×10^{-6} M   b. 1×10^{-12} M   c. 0.000 01 M   d. 0.000 000 000 01 M

More Practice: Try Problems 9.67a, 9.68a.

SAMPLE PROBLEM 9.15 DETERMINING [H₃O⁺] FROM pH

What is the H_3O^+ concentration in lemon juice that has a pH of about 2? Classify the solution as acidic, basic, or neutral.

Analysis

To find [H₃O⁺] from a pH, which is a logarithm, we must determine what number corresponds to the given logarithm. When the pH is a whole number x, the value of x becomes the exponent in the expression $1 \times 10^{-x} = [H_3O^+]$.

Solution

If the pH of lemon juice is 2, $[H_3O^+] = 1 \times 10^{-2}$ M. The pH is less than 7, so the lemon juice is acidic.

PRACTICE PROBLEM 9.15

What H_3O^+ concentration corresponds to each pH value: (a) 13; (b) 7; (c) 3? Label each solution as acidic, basic, or neutral.

More Practice: Try Problems 9.71a, b; 9.72a, b.

Determining logarithms and anti-logarithms using an electronic calculator is shown in Appendix A.

Because seawater contains dissolved salts, its pH is 8.50, making it slightly basic, not neutral like pure water.
©Bogdan Bratosin/Getty Images RF

9.6B   Calculating pH Using a Calculator

To calculate the pH of a solution in which the hydronium ion concentration has a coefficient in scientific notation that is *not* equal to one—as in 2.0×10^{-3}—you need a calculator that has a log function. How the keys are labeled and the order of the steps depend on your particular calculator.

Enter this number on your calculator.

$$pH = -\log[H_3O^+] = -\log(2.0 \times 10^{-3})$$
$$= -(-2.70) = 2.70$$

Similarly, when a reported pH is *not* a whole number—as in the pH = 8.50 for a sample of seawater—you need a calculator to calculate an *antilogarithm*—that is, the number that has a logarithm of 8.50. To make sure your calculation is correct, note that since the pH of seawater is between 8 and 9, the H_3O^+ concentration must be between 10^{-8} and 10^{-9}.

$$[H_3O^+] = \text{antilog}(-pH) = \text{antilog}(-8.50)$$
$$= 3.2 \times 10^{-9} \text{ M}$$

Care must be taken in keeping track of significant figures when using logarithms.

- **A logarithm has the same number of digits to the right of the decimal point as are contained in the coefficient of the original number.**

$$[H_3O^+] \quad = \quad 3.2 \times 10^{-9} \text{ M} \qquad \text{pH} = 8.50 \qquad \text{two digits after the decimal point}$$

two **significant figures**

SAMPLE PROBLEM 9.16 DETERMINING pH FROM [H₃O⁺] USING A CALCULATOR

What is the pH of wine that has an H_3O^+ concentration of 3.2×10^{-4} M?

Analysis

Use a calculator to determine the logarithm of a number that contains a coefficient in scientific notation that is not a whole number; $\text{pH} = -\log [H_3O^+]$.

Solution

The order of the steps in using an electronic calculator, as well as the labels on the calculator buttons, vary. In some cases it is possible to calculate the pH by following three steps: enter the number (H_3O^+ concentration); press the *log* button; and press the change sign key. Consult your calculator manual if these steps do not give the desired value. Because the coefficient in the original number had two significant figures, the pH must have two digits to the right of the decimal point.

two **significant figures**

$$\text{pH} = -\log [H_3O^+] \quad = \quad -\log(3.2 \times 10^{-4})$$
$$= \quad -(-3.49) \quad = \quad 3.49 \quad \text{two digits to the right of the decimal point}$$

PRACTICE PROBLEM 9.16

Convert each H_3O^+ concentration to a pH value.

  a. 1.8×10^{-6} M   b. 9.21×10^{-12} M   c. 0.000 088 M   d. 0.000 000 000 076 2 M

More Problems: Try Problems 9.67b–d, 9.68b–d.

SAMPLE PROBLEM 9.17 DETERMINING [H₃O⁺] FROM pH USING A CALCULATOR

What is the H_3O^+ concentration in sweat that has a pH of 5.8?

Analysis

Use a calculator to determine the antilogarithm of the negative of the pH; $[H_3O^+] = \text{antilog}(-\text{pH})$.

Solution

The order of the steps in using an electronic calculator, as well as the labels on the calculator buttons, vary. In some cases it is possible to calculate $[H_3O^+]$ by the following steps: enter the pH value; press the change sign key; and press the *2nd + log* buttons. Since the pH has only one number to the right of the decimal point, the H_3O^+ concentration must have only one significant figure in its coefficient.

one **digit to the right of the decimal point**

$$[H_3O^+] \quad = \quad \text{antilog}(-\text{pH}) \quad = \quad \text{antilog}(-5.8)$$
$$[H_3O^+] \quad = \quad 2 \times 10^{-6} \text{ M}$$

one **significant figure**

PRACTICE PROBLEM 9.17

What H_3O^+ concentration corresponds to each pH value: (a) 10.2; (b) 7.8; (c) 4.3?

More Problems: Try Problems 9.71–9.76, 9.104, 9.106.

PROBLEM 9.12

What is the H_3O^+ concentration in a sports drink that has a pH of 3.30?

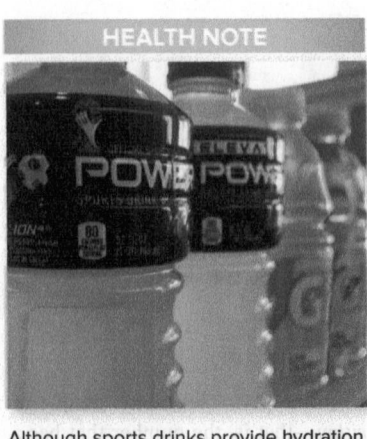

Although sports drinks provide hydration and electrolyte replacement for athletes, their low pH may lead to dental erosion if they are heavily consumed. ©McGraw-Hill Education/Mark Dierker, photographer

9.6C FOCUS ON THE HUMAN BODY
The pH of Body Fluids

The human body contains fluids that vary in pH as shown in Figure 9.8. While saliva is slightly acidic, the gastric juice in the stomach has the lowest pH found in the body. The strongly acidic environment of the stomach aids in the digestion of food. It also kills many types of bacteria that might be inadvertently consumed along with food and drink. When food leaves the stomach, it passes to the basic environment of the small intestines. Bases in the small intestines react with acid from the stomach.

Figure 9.8

Variation in pH Values in the Human Body

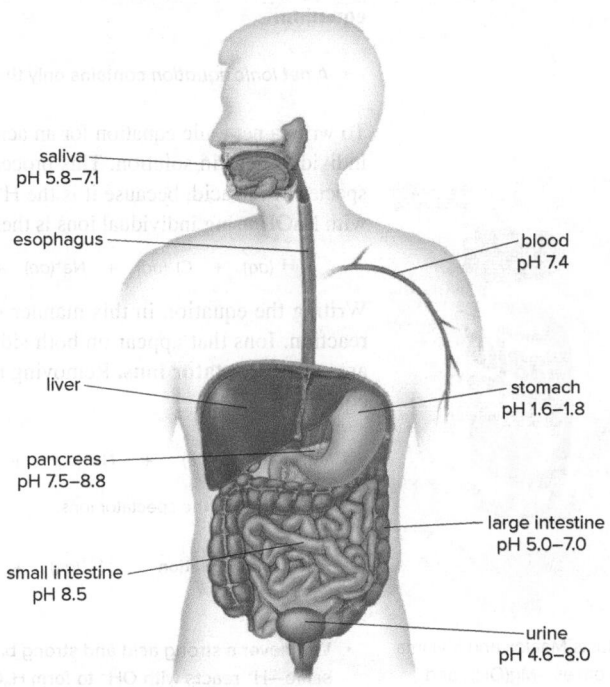

saliva
pH 5.8–7.1

esophagus

blood
pH 7.4

liver

stomach
pH 1.6–1.8

pancreas
pH 7.5–8.8

large intestine
pH 5.0–7.0

small intestine
pH 8.5

urine
pH 4.6–8.0

The pH of some body fluids must occupy a very narrow range. For example, a healthy individual has a blood pH in the range of 7.35–7.45. Maintaining this pH is accomplished by a complex mechanism described in Section 9.11. The pH of other fluids can be more variable. Urine has a pH anywhere from 4.6 to 8.0, depending on an individual's recent diet and exercise.

9.7 Common Acid–Base Reactions

Although we have already seen a variety of acid–base reactions in Sections 9.2–9.4, two common reactions deserve additional attention—reaction of acids with hydroxide bases (OH^-), and reaction of acids with bicarbonate (HCO_3^-) or carbonate (CO_3^{2-}).

9.7A Reaction of Acids with Hydroxide Bases

The reaction of a Brønsted–Lowry acid (HA) with the metal salt of a hydroxide base (MOH) is an example of a *neutralization* reaction—**an acid–base reaction that produces a salt and water as products.**

$$HA(aq) + MOH(aq) \longrightarrow H\text{—}OH(l) + MA(aq)$$

acid   base   water   salt

- The acid HA donates a proton (H^+) to the OH^- base to form H_2O.
- The anion A^- from the acid combines with the cation M^+ from the base to form the salt MA.

For example, hydrochloric acid, HCl, reacts with sodium hydroxide, NaOH, to form water and sodium chloride, NaCl. A single reaction arrow is drawn between reactants and products because equilibrium greatly favors the products.

$$HCl(aq) \ + \ NaOH(aq) \longrightarrow H{-}OH(l) \ + \ NaCl(aq)$$
$$\text{acid} \qquad\qquad \text{base} \qquad\qquad\qquad \text{water} \qquad\qquad \text{salt}$$

The important reacting species in this reaction are H^+ from the acid HCl and OH^- from the base NaOH. To more clearly see the acid–base reaction, we can write an equation that contains only the species that are actually involved in the reaction. Such an equation is called a **net ionic equation.**

- A *net ionic equation* contains only the species involved in a reaction.

To write a net ionic equation for an acid–base reaction, we first write the acid, base, and salt as individual ions in solution. This process is simplified if we use H^+ (not H_3O^+) as the reacting species of the acid, because it is the H^+ ion that is transferred to the base. The reaction of HCl with NaOH using individual ions is then drawn as:

$$H^+(aq) \ + \ Cl^-(aq) \ + \ Na^+(aq) \ + \ OH^-(aq) \longrightarrow H{-}OH(l) \ + \ Na^+(aq) \ + \ Cl^-(aq)$$

Writing the equation in this manner shows that the Na^+ and Cl^- ions are unchanged in the reaction. Ions that appear on both sides of an equation but undergo no change in a reaction are called **spectator ions.** Removing the spectator ions from the equation gives the net ionic equation.

$$H^+(aq) \ + \ \cancel{Cl^-}(aq) \ + \ \cancel{Na^+}(aq) \ + \ OH^-(aq) \longrightarrow H{-}OH(l) \ + \ \cancel{Na^+}(aq) \ + \ \cancel{Cl^-}(aq)$$

Omit the spectator ions. Omit the spectator ions.

| **Net ionic equation** | $H^+(aq) \ + \ OH^-(aq) \longrightarrow H{-}OH(l)$ |

- Whenever a strong acid and strong base react, the net ionic equation is always the same—H^+ reacts with OH^- to form H_2O.

To draw the products of these neutralization reactions, keep in mind that **two products are always formed—water and a metal salt.** Balancing an acid–base equation can be done with the stepwise procedure for balancing a general reaction outlined in Section 5.2. The coefficients in a balanced chemical equation illustrate that **one H^+ ion is always needed to react with each OH^- anion.**

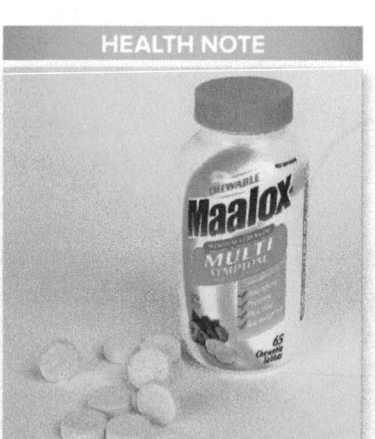

The antacid products Maalox and Mylanta both contain two bases—$Mg(OH)_2$ and $Al(OH)_3$—that react with excess stomach acid. A combination of bases is used so that the constipating effect of the aluminum salt is counteracted by the laxative effect of the magnesium salt.
©McGraw-Hill Education/Jill Braaten, photographer

How To **Draw a Balanced Equation for a Neutralization Reaction Between HA and MOH**

Example: Write a balanced equation for the reaction of $Mg(OH)_2$, an active ingredient in the antacid product Maalox, with the hydrochloric acid (HCl) in the stomach.

Step [1] **Identify the acid and base in the reactants and draw H_2O as one product.**

- HCl is the acid and $Mg(OH)_2$ is the base. H^+ from the acid reacts with OH^- from the base to form H_2O.

$$HCl(aq) \ + \ Mg(OH)_2(aq) \longrightarrow H_2O(l) \ + \ salt$$
$$\text{acid} \qquad\qquad \text{base}$$

Step [2] **Determine the structure of the salt formed as product.**

- The salt is formed from the elements of the acid and base that are *not* used to form H_2O. **The anion of the salt comes from the acid and the cation of the salt comes from the base.**
- In this case, Cl^- (from HCl) and Mg^{2+} [from $Mg(OH)_2$] combine to form the salt $MgCl_2$.

—Continued

Step [3] Balance the equation.

• Follow the procedure in Section 5.2 to balance an equation. The balanced equation shows that *two* moles of HCl are needed for *each* mole of $Mg(OH)_2$, because each mole of $Mg(OH)_2$ contains two moles of OH^-.

Place a **2** to balance H and O.

$$2\,HCl(aq) \;+\; Mg(OH)_2(aq) \longrightarrow 2\,H_2O(l) \;+\; MgCl_2$$

Place a **2** to balance Cl.

PROBLEM 9.13

Write a balanced equation for each acid–base reaction.

a. $HNO_3(aq) + NaOH(aq) \longrightarrow$

b. $H_2SO_4(aq) + KOH(aq) \longrightarrow$

PROBLEM 9.14

Write the net ionic equation for each reaction in Problem 9.13.

9.7B Reaction of Acids with Bicarbonate and Carbonate

Acids react with the bases bicarbonate (HCO_3^-) and carbonate (CO_3^{2-}). A bicarbonate base reacts with *one* proton to form carbonic acid, H_2CO_3. A carbonate base reacts with *two* protons. The carbonic acid formed in these reactions is unstable and decomposes to form CO_2 and H_2O. Thus, when an acid reacts with either base, bubbles of CO_2 gas are given off.

$$H^+(aq) \;+\; HCO_3^-(aq) \longrightarrow \left[H_2CO_3(aq) \right] \longrightarrow H_2O(l) \;+\; CO_2(g)$$

1 H^+ needed   bicarbonate   bubbles of CO_2

$$2\,H^+(aq) \;+\; CO_3^{2-}(aq) \longrightarrow \left[H_2CO_3(aq) \right] \longrightarrow H_2O(l) \;+\; CO_2(g)$$

2 H^+ needed   carbonate

Sodium bicarbonate ($NaHCO_3$), an ingredient in the over-the-counter antacid Alka-Seltzer, is the metal salt of a bicarbonate base that reacts with excess stomach acid, releasing CO_2. Like the neutralization reactions in Section 9.7A, a salt, NaCl, is formed in which the cation (Na^+) comes from the base and the anion (Cl^-) comes from the acid.

$$HCl(aq) \;+\; NaHCO_3(aq) \longrightarrow NaCl(aq) \;+\; H_2CO_3(aq)$$

acid   base   salt

$$\longrightarrow H_2O(l) \;+\; CO_2(g)$$

Calcium carbonate ($CaCO_3$), a calcium supplement and antacid in Tums, also reacts with excess stomach acid with release of CO_2. Since each carbonate ion reacts with two protons, the balanced equation shows a 2:1 ratio of HCl to $CaCO_3$.

$$2\,HCl(aq) \;+\; CaCO_3(aq) \longrightarrow CaCl_2(aq) \;+\; H_2CO_3(aq)$$

acid   base   salt

$$\longrightarrow H_2O(l) \;+\; CO_2(g)$$

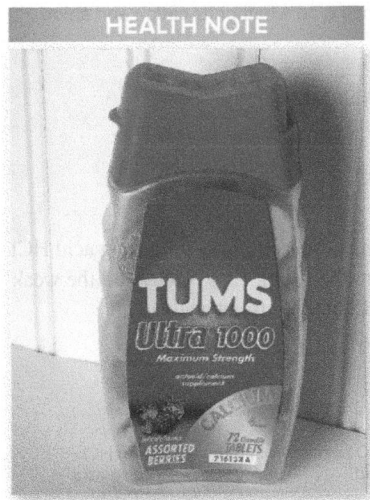

Like taking other over-the-counter medications, care must be exercised when using antacids. Ingestion of large amounts of $CaCO_3$ can increase the incidence of kidney stones. ©McGraw-Hill Education/Jill Braaten, photographer

SAMPLE PROBLEM 9.18 WRITING A BALANCED ACID–BASE EQUATION WITH THE BASE $NaHCO_3$

Write a balanced equation for the reaction of H_2SO_4 with $NaHCO_3$.

Analysis

The acid and base react to form a salt and carbonic acid (H_2CO_3), which decomposes to CO_2 and H_2O.

Solution

- H_2SO_4 is the acid and $NaHCO_3$ is the base.
- H^+ from the acid reacts with HCO_3^- from the base to give H_2CO_3, which decomposes to H_2O and CO_2.
- A salt (Na_2SO_4) is also formed from the cation of the base (Na^+) and the anion of the acid (SO_4^{2-}).

$$\underset{\text{acid}}{H_2SO_4(aq)} \;+\; \underset{\text{base}}{NaHCO_3(aq)} \longrightarrow \underset{\text{salt}}{Na_2SO_4(aq)} \;+\; \underset{\text{from } H_2CO_3}{H_2O(l) \;+\; CO_2(g)}$$

Unbalanced equation:

To balance the equation, place coefficients so the number of atoms on both sides of the arrow is the same.

Place a 2 to balance Na...

$$\underset{\text{acid}}{H_2SO_4(aq)} \;+\; \underset{\text{base}}{2\,NaHCO_3(aq)} \longrightarrow \underset{\text{salt}}{Na_2SO_4(aq)} \;+\; 2\,H_2O(l) \;+\; 2\,CO_2(g)$$

...then place 2's to balance C, H, and O.

PRACTICE PROBLEM 9.18

The acid in acid rain is generally sulfuric acid (H_2SO_4). When this rainwater falls on statues composed of marble ($CaCO_3$), the H_2SO_4 slowly dissolves the $CaCO_3$. Write a balanced equation for this acid–base reaction.

More Practice: Try Problems 9.81–9.84.

PROBLEM 9.15

Write a balanced equation for the reaction of nitric acid (HNO_3) with each base: (a) $NaHCO_3$; (b) $MgCO_3$.

9.8   The Acidity and Basicity of Salt Solutions

Thus far we have discussed what occurs when an acid or a base dissolves in water. What happens to the pH of water when a salt is dissolved? A salt is the product of a neutralization reaction (Section 9.7A). Does this mean that a salt dissolved in water forms a neutral solution with a pH of 7?

- A salt can form an acidic, basic, or neutral solution depending on whether its cation and anion are derived from a strong or weak acid and base.

Let's first examine what acid and base are used to form a salt M^+A^-.

- The cation M^+ comes from the base.
- The anion A^- comes from the acid HA.

Thus, we consider NaCl to be a salt formed when the strong base NaOH and the strong acid HCl react together. On the other hand, $NaHCO_3$ is formed from the strong base NaOH and the weak acid H_2CO_3, and NH_4Cl is formed from the weak base NH_3 and the strong acid HCl.

NaCl		NaHCO$_3$		NH$_4$Cl	
Na$^+$	Cl$^-$	Na$^+$	HCO$_3^-$	NH$_4^+$	Cl$^-$
from NaOH	from HCl	from NaOH	from H$_2$CO$_3$	from NH$_3$	from HCl
strong base	**strong** acid	**strong** base	**weak** acid	**weak** base	**strong** acid

A salt derived from a strong base and a strong acid forms a neutral solution (pH = 7). When one ion of a salt is derived from a weak acid or base, one principle is followed: **the ion derived from the *stronger* acid or base determines whether the solution is acidic or basic.**

- A salt derived from a *strong base* and a weak acid forms a *basic* solution (pH > 7).
- A salt derived from a weak base and a *strong acid* forms an *acidic* solution (pH < 7).

For example, when $NaHCO_3$ dissolves in water, it forms $Na^+(aq)$ and $HCO_3^-(aq)$. Alkali metal cations like Na^+ do not react with H_2O, but HCO_3^- reacts with H_2O to form OH^-. Thus, **$NaHCO_3$, a salt derived from a *strong* base and a weak acid, forms a *basic* solution.**

$$HCO_3^-(aq) \ + \ H_2O(l) \ \rightleftharpoons \ H_2CO_3(aq) \ + \ \boxed{OH^-(aq)}$$

Hydroxide makes the solution basic,
so the pH > 7.

When NH_4Cl dissolves in water it forms $NH_4^+(aq)$ and $Cl^-(aq)$. Halide anions like Cl^- do not react with H_2O, but NH_4^+ reacts with H_2O to form H_3O^+. Thus, **NH_4Cl, a salt derived from a *strong* acid and a weak base, forms an *acidic* solution.**

$$NH_4^+(aq) \ + \ H_2O(l) \ \rightleftharpoons \ NH_3(aq) \ + \ \boxed{H_3O^+(aq)}$$

H_3O^+ makes the solution acidic,
so the pH < 7.

When $NaCl$ dissolves in water it forms $Na^+(aq)$ and $Cl^-(aq)$. Neither ion reacts with water. Since no acid–base reaction occurs, the solution remains neutral. Thus, **$NaCl$, a salt derived from a strong acid and strong base, forms a neutral solution.** The acidity and basicity of salt solutions is summarized in Table 9.5.

Table 9.5 The Acidity and Basicity of Salt Solutions

Cation Derived from	Anion Derived from	Solution	pH	Examples
Strong base	**Strong acid**	**Neutral**	7	$NaCl$, KBr, $NaNO_3$
Strong base	Weak acid	**Basic**	> 7	$NaHCO_3$, KCN, CaF_2
Weak base	**Strong acid**	**Acidic**	< 7	NH_4Cl, NH_4NO_3

SAMPLE PROBLEM 9.19 DETERMINING WHETHER A SALT SOLUTION IS ACIDIC, BASIC, OR NEUTRAL

Determine whether each salt forms an acidic, basic, or neutral solution when dissolved in water:
(a) NaF; (b) KNO_3; (c) NH_4Br.

Analysis

Determine what type of acid and base (strong or weak) are used to form the salt.

- When the ions in the salt come from a strong acid and strong base, the solution is neutral.
- When the ions come from acids and bases of different strength, the ion derived from the *stronger* reactant determines the acidity.

Solution

a. NaF
  Na^+ F^-

from NaOH   from HF
strong base weak acid

basic solution

b. KNO_3
  K^+ NO_3^-

from KOH   from HNO_3
strong base **strong acid**

neutral solution

c. NH_4Br
  NH_4^+ Br^-

from NH_3 from HBr
weak base   **strong acid**

acidic solution

PRACTICE PROBLEM 9.19

Determine whether each salt forms an acidic, basic, or neutral solution when dissolved in water: (a) KI;
(b) K_2CO_3; (c) $Ca(NO_3)_2$; (d) NH_4I; (e) $BaCl_2$; (f) Na_3PO_4.

More Practice: Try Problems 9.85, 9.86.

PROBLEM 9.16

Which of the following salts forms an aqueous solution that has a pH > 7: (a) LiCl; (b) K_2CO_3; (c) NH_4Br; (d) $MgCO_3$?

9.9   Titration

Sometimes it is necessary to know the exact concentration of acid or base in a solution. To determine the molarity of a solution, we carry out a **titration.** A titration uses a *buret,* a calibrated tube with a stopcock at the bottom that allows a solution of known molarity to be added in small quantities to a solution of unknown molarity. The procedure for determining the total acid concentration of a solution of HCl is illustrated in Figure 9.9.

Figure 9.9   Titration of an Acid with a Base of Known Concentration

a.

b.

c.

Steps in determining the molarity of a solution of HCl:

a. Add a measured volume of HCl solution to a flask. Add an acid–base indicator, often phenolphthalein, which is colorless in acid but turns bright pink in base.
b. Fill a buret with an NaOH solution of known molarity and slowly add it to the HCl solution.
c. Add NaOH solution until the *end point* is reached, the point at which the indicator changes color. At the end point, the **number of moles of NaOH added equals the number of moles of HCl** in the flask. In other words, all of the HCl has reacted with NaOH and the solution is no longer acidic. Read the volume of NaOH solution added from the buret. Using the known volume and molarity of the NaOH solution and the known volume of HCl solution, the molarity of the HCl solution can be calculated.

(a–c): ©McGraw-Hill Education/Jill Braaten, photographer

How does a titration tell us the concentration of an HCl solution? A titration is based on the acid–base reaction that occurs between the acid in the flask (HCl) and the base that is added (NaOH). **When the number of moles of base added equals the number of moles of acid in the flask, the acid is *neutralized*, forming a salt and water.**

At the end point, the number of moles of
the acid (H^+) and the base (OH^-) are equal.

$$HCl(aq) \ + \ NaOH(aq) \ \rightleftharpoons \ NaCl(aq) \ + \ H_2O(l)$$

To determine an unknown molarity from titration data requires three operations.

First, we determine the number of moles of base added using its known molarity and volume. Then we use coefficients in the balanced acid–base equation to tell us the number of moles of acid that react with the base. Finally, we determine the molarity of the acid from the calculated number of moles and the known volume of the acid.

How To Determine the Molarity of an Acid Solution from a Titration

Example: What is the molarity of an HCl solution if 22.5 mL of a 0.100 M NaOH solution are needed to titrate a 25.0 mL sample of the acid?

Step [1] Determine the number of moles of base used to neutralize the acid.

- Convert milliliters to liters of base using a mL–L conversion factor. Use the molarity (M) and volume (V) of the base to calculate the number of moles (mol = MV).

$$22.5 \text{ mL NaOH} \times \frac{1 \text{ L}}{1000 \text{ mL}} \times \frac{0.100 \text{ mol NaOH}}{1 \text{ L}} = 0.002\ 25 \text{ mol NaOH}$$

Step [2] Determine the number of moles of acid that react from the balanced chemical equation.

- In this reaction, one mole of HCl reacts with one mole of NaOH, so the number of moles of NaOH equals the number of moles of HCl at the end point.

$$\text{HCl}(aq) + \text{NaOH}(aq) \longrightarrow \text{NaCl}(aq) + \text{H}_2\text{O}(l)$$
0.002 25 mol   0.002 25 mol

Step [3] Determine the molarity of the acid from the number of moles and known volume.

- Convert milliliters to liters of acid using a mL–L conversion factor. Use the number of moles and known volume of the acid to calculate the molarity (M = mol/L).

$$M = \frac{\text{mol}}{\text{L}} = \frac{0.002\ 25 \text{ mol HCl}}{25.0 \text{ mL solution}} \times \frac{1000 \text{ mL}}{1 \text{ L}} = 0.0900 \text{ M HCl}$$

Sample Problem 9.20 illustrates a calculation for a titration in which the ratio of acid to base in the balanced acid–base equation is something other than 1:1.

SAMPLE PROBLEM 9.20

Acid rain is rainwater with a lower-than-normal pH, caused by the presence of dissolved acids such as H_2SO_4. What is the molarity of H_2SO_4 in rainwater if 5.22 mL of a 0.20 M NaOH solution are needed to titrate 125 mL of the sample? The balanced equation for this acid–base reaction is given.

$$H_2SO_4(aq) + 2 \text{ NaOH}(aq) \longrightarrow Na_2SO_4(aq) + 2 H_2O(l)$$

342   Chapter 9   Acids and Bases

The sulfur oxides produced when sulfur-containing fuel is burned form H_2SO_4, which acidifies rainwater. This acid rain destroys forest vegetation and makes lakes and streams too acidic for fish and shellfish to survive. ©Piotr Zawisza/ Getty Images RF

Analysis and Solution

[1] Determine the number of moles of base used to neutralize the acid.

- Use the molarity (M) and volume (V) of the base to calculate the number of moles (mol = MV).

$$5.22 \ \cancel{mL} \ NaOH \times \frac{1 \ \cancel{L}}{1000 \ \cancel{mL}} \times \frac{0.20 \ mol \ NaOH}{1 \ \cancel{L}} = 0.0010 \ mol \ NaOH$$

[2] Determine the number of moles of acid that react from the balanced chemical equation.

- Since each H_2SO_4 molecule contains two protons, *one* mole of the acid H_2SO_4 reacts with *two* moles of the base NaOH in the neutralization reaction. The coefficients in the balanced equation form a mole ratio to calculate the number of moles of acid that react.

$$0.0010 \ \cancel{mol} \ NaOH \times \frac{1 \ mol \ H_2SO_4}{2 \ \cancel{mol} \ NaOH} = 0.000 \ 50 \ mol \ H_2SO_4$$

[3] Determine the molarity of the acid from the number of moles and known volume.

$$M = \frac{mol}{L} = \frac{0.000 \ 50 \ mol \ H_2SO_4}{125 \ \cancel{mL} \ solution} \times \frac{1000 \ \cancel{mL}}{1 \ L} = 0.0040 \ M \ H_2SO_4$$

molarity   **Answer**

PRACTICE PROBLEM 9.20

What is the molarity of an HCl solution if 25.5 mL of a 0.24 M NaOH solution are needed to neutralize 15.0 mL of the sample?

More Problems: Try Problems 9.87–9.92.

PROBLEM 9.17

How many milliliters of 2.0 M NaOH are needed to neutralize 5.0 mL of a 6.0 M H_2SO_4 solution?

9.10   Buffers

A *buffer* **is a solution whose pH changes very little when acid or base is added.** Most buffers are solutions composed of approximately equal amounts of a weak acid and the salt of its conjugate base.

- **The weak acid of the buffer reacts with added base, OH⁻.**
- **The conjugate base of the buffer reacts with added acid, H_3O^+.**

9.10A   General Characteristics of a Buffer

The effect of a buffer can be illustrated by comparing the pH change that occurs when a small amount of strong acid or strong base is added to water, compared to the pH change that occurs when the same amount of strong acid or strong base is added to a buffer, as shown in Figure 9.10. When 0.020 mol of HCl is added to 1.0 L of water, the pH changes from 7 to 1.7, and when 0.020 mol of NaOH is added to 1.0 L of water, the pH changes from 7 to 12.3. In this example, addition of a small quantity of a strong acid or strong base to neutral water changes the pH by over 5 pH units.

In contrast, a buffer prepared from 0.50 M acetic acid (CH_3COOH) and 0.50 M sodium acetate ($NaCH_3COO$) has a pH of 4.74. Addition of the same quantity of acid, 0.020 mol HCl, changes the pH to 4.70, and addition of the same quantity of base, 0.020 mol of NaOH, changes the pH to 4.77. In this example, the change of pH in the presence of the buffer is no more than 0.04 pH unit!

Why is a buffer able to absorb acid or base with very little pH change? Let's use as an example a buffer that contains equal concentrations of acetic acid (CH_3COOH), and the sodium salt of its conjugate base, sodium acetate ($NaCH_3COO$). CH_3COOH is a weak acid, so when it dissolves in

Figure 9.10

The Effect of a Buffer on pH Changes

a.

Add 0.020 mol HCl.

7.0 pH   1.7 pH   12.3 pH

H₂O

Add 0.020 mol NaOH.

b.

Add 0.020 mol HCl.

4.74 pH   4.70 pH   4.77 pH

buffer

Add 0.020 mol NaOH.

a. The pH of pure water changes drastically when a small amount of strong acid or strong base is added.

b. The pH of a buffer changes very little when the same amount of strong acid or strong base is added.

water, only a small fraction dissociates to form its conjugate base CH_3COO^-. In the buffer solution, however, the sodium acetate provides an equal amount of the conjugate base.

$$CH_3COOH(aq) + H_2O(l) \rightleftharpoons H_3O^+(aq) + CH_3COO^-(aq)$$

approximately equal amounts

In Section 9.4, we learned how to write the expression for the acid dissociation constant K_a for this reaction. Rearranging this expression to solve for $[H_3O^+]$ then illustrates why a buffer does not change pH much when acid or base is added.

Expression for K_a: $\quad K_a = \dfrac{[H_3O^+][CH_3COO^-]}{[CH_3COOH]}$

Rearranging the expression: $\quad [H_3O^+] = K_a \times \dfrac{[CH_3COOH]}{[CH_3COO^-]}$

If this ratio does not change much, then $[H_3O^+]$ does not change much.

The H_3O^+ concentration depends on two terms—K_a, which is a constant, and the ratio of the concentrations of the weak acid and its conjugate base. If these concentrations do not change much, then the concentration of H_3O^+ and therefore the pH do not change much.

344 **Chapter 9** Acids and Bases

Suppose a small amount of strong acid is added to the buffer. Added H_3O^+ reacts with CH_3COO^- to form CH_3COOH, so that $[CH_3COO^-]$ decreases slightly and $[CH_3COOH]$ increases slightly. However, the ratio of these two concentrations is not altered significantly, so the $[H_3O^+]$ and therefore the pH change only slightly.

On the other hand, if a small amount of strong base is added to the buffer, OH^- reacts with CH_3COOH to form CH_3COO^-, so that $[CH_3COOH]$ decreases slightly and $[CH_3COO^-]$ increases slightly. However, the ratio of these two concentrations is not altered significantly, so the $[H_3O^+]$ and therefore the pH change only slightly.

For a buffer to be effective, the amount of added acid or base must be small compared to the amount of buffer present. When a large amount of acid or base is added to a buffer, the concentrations of the weak acid and its conjugate base change a great deal, so the H_3O^+ concentration changes a great deal as well. Some common buffers are listed in Table 9.6.

Table 9.6 Common Buffers

Buffer	Weak Acid	Conjugate Base	K_a
Acetic acid/acetate	CH_3COOH	CH_3COO^-	1.8×10^{-5}
Bicarbonate/carbonate	HCO_3^-	CO_3^{2-}	5.6×10^{-11}
Dihydrogen phosphate/ hydrogen phosphate	$H_2PO_4^-$	HPO_4^{2-}	6.2×10^{-8}
Hydrogen phosphate/ phosphate	HPO_4^{2-}	PO_4^{3-}	2.2×10^{-13}

PROBLEM 9.18

Determine whether a solution containing each of the following substances is a buffer. Explain your reasoning.

a. HBr and NaBr   b. HF and KF   c. CH_3COOH alone

PROBLEM 9.19

Consider a buffer prepared from the weak acid HCO_3^- and its conjugate base CO_3^{2-}.

$$HCO_3^-(aq) + H_2O(l) \rightleftharpoons CO_3^{2-}(aq) + H_3O^+(aq)$$

a. Explain why both HCO_3^- and CO_3^{2-} are needed to prepare the buffer.

b. What happens to the concentrations of HCO_3^- and CO_3^{2-} when a small amount of acid is added to the buffer?

c. What happens to the concentrations of HCO_3^- and CO_3^{2-} when a small amount of base is added to the buffer?

9.10B Calculating the pH of a Buffer

The effective pH range of a buffer depends on its K_a. The pH of a buffer can be calculated from the K_a of the weak acid (HA), and the concentrations of the weak acid (HA) and conjugate base (A:$^-$) used to prepare it, as shown in Sample Problem 9.21.

Acid dissociation constant K_a for the general acid HA:

Rearranging the expression to solve for [H$_3$O$^+$]:

$$K_a = \frac{[H_3O^+][A:^-]}{[HA]} \qquad [H_3O^+] = K_a \times \frac{[HA]}{[A:^-]}$$

determines the buffer pH

SAMPLE PROBLEM 9.21 CALCULATING THE pH OF A BUFFER

What is the pH of a buffer that contains 0.20 M CH_3COOH and 0.20 M $NaCH_3COO$?

Analysis

Use the K_a of the weak acid of the buffer in Table 9.6 and the expression $[H_3O^+] = K_a([HA]/[A:^-])$ to calculate $[H_3O^+]$. Calculate the pH using the expression, pH = $-\log [H_3O^+]$.

Solution

[1] Substitute the given concentrations of CH_3COOH and CH_3COO^- for [HA] and [A:$^-$], respectively. K_a for CH_3COOH is 1.8×10^{-5}.

$$[H_3O^+] = K_a \times \frac{[CH_3COOH]}{[CH_3COO^-]} = (1.8 \times 10^{-5}) \times \frac{[0.20 \text{ M}]}{[0.20 \text{ M}]}$$

$$[H_3O^+] = 1.8 \times 10^{-5} \text{ M}$$

[2] Use an electronic calculator to convert the H_3O^+ concentration to pH, as in Sample Problem 9.16.

$$\text{pH} = -\log [H_3O^+] = -\log(1.8 \times 10^{-5})$$

$$\text{pH} = 4.74$$

PRACTICE PROBLEM 9.21

Calculate the pH of a dihydrogen phosphate/hydrogen phosphate buffer prepared with each of the following concentrations. What do you conclude about the pH of a buffer when equal concentrations of the weak acid and conjugate base are used to prepare it?

a. 0.10 M NaH_2PO_4 and 0.10 M Na_2HPO_4

b. 1.0 M NaH_2PO_4 and 1.0 M Na_2HPO_4

c. 0.50 M NaH_2PO_4 and 0.50 M Na_2HPO_4

More Practice: Try Problems 9.99–9.102.

PROBLEM 9.20

What is the pH of a buffer that contains 0.20 M CH_3COOH and 0.15 M $NaCH_3COO$?

General, Organic, and Biochemisty

9.10C FOCUS ON THE ENVIRONMENT

Acid Rain and a Naturally Buffered Lake

Unpolluted rainwater is not a neutral solution with a pH of 7; rather, because it contains dissolved carbon dioxide, it is slightly acidic with a pH of about 5.6.

$$CO_2(g) \;+\; 2\,H_2O(l) \;\rightleftharpoons\; H_3O^+(aq) \;+\; HCO_3^-(aq)$$

carbon dioxide
from the air

A low concentration of H_3O^+ gives rainwater a pH < 7.

Rainwater that contains dissolved H_2SO_4 (or HNO_3) from burning fossil fuels has a pH lower than 5.6. In some parts of the United States, rainwater often has a pH range of 4–5, and readings as low as pH = 1.8 have been recorded. When the rain in a region consistently has a lower-than-normal pH, this acid rain can have a devastating effect on plant and animal life.

The pH of some lakes changes drastically as the result of acid rain, whereas the pH of other lakes does not. In fact, the ability of some lakes to absorb acid rain without much pH change is entirely due to buffers (Figure 9.11). Lakes that are surrounded by limestone-rich soil are in contact with solid calcium carbonate, $CaCO_3$. As a result, the lake contains a natural carbonate/bicarbonate buffer. When acid precipitation falls on the lake, the dissolved carbonate (CO_3^{2-}) reacts with the acid to form bicarbonate (HCO_3^-).

The buffer reacts with added acid from rain.

$$CO_3^{2-}(aq) \;+\; H_3O^+(aq) \;\rightleftharpoons\; HCO_3^-(aq) \;+\; H_2O(l)$$

A lake surrounded by limestone contains a natural CO_3^{2-}/HCO_3^- buffer.

The carbonate/bicarbonate buffer thus allows the lake to resist large pH changes when acid is added. In some areas acidic lakes have been treated with limestone, thus adding calcium carbonate to neutralize the acid and restore the natural pH. This procedure is expensive and temporary because with time and more acid rain, the pH of the lakes decreases again.

Figure 9.11   Acid Rain and a Naturally Buffered Lake

Acid precipitation contains H_2SO_4 and HNO_3 dissolved in rain and snow.

CO_3^{2-}

HCO_3^-

lake surrounded by limestone ($CaCO_3$)

lake with no natural buffer

Acid rain adds H_3O^+ to the water, decreasing the pH.

The lake contains a natural buffer of CO_3^{2-} and HCO_3^-. H_3O^+ from rain reacts with dissolved CO_3^{2-}, forming more HCO_3^-. Since the concentrations of CO_3^{2-} and HCO_3^- do not change by much, the pH changes only slightly.

9.11 FOCUS ON THE HUMAN BODY
Buffers in the Blood

The normal blood pH of a healthy individual is in the range of 7.35 to 7.45. A pH above or below this range is generally indicative of an imbalance in respiratory or metabolic processes. The body is able to maintain a very stable pH because the blood and other tissues are buffered. The principal buffer in the blood is carbonic acid/bicarbonate (H_2CO_3/HCO_3^-).

In examining the carbonic acid/bicarbonate buffer system in the blood, two equilibria are important. First of all, carbonic acid (H_2CO_3) is in equilibrium with CO_2 dissolved in the bloodstream (Section 9.7). Second, since carbonic acid is a weak acid, it is also dissociated in water to form its conjugate base, bicarbonate (HCO_3^-). Bicarbonate is also generated in the kidneys.

HEALTH NOTE

$$CO_2(g) + H_2O(l) \rightleftharpoons \underset{\text{carbonic acid}}{H_2CO_3(aq)} \overset{H_2O}{\rightleftharpoons} H_3O^+(aq) + \underset{\text{bicarbonate}}{HCO_3^-(aq)}$$

principal buffer in the blood

Individuals with cystic fibrosis, the most common genetic disease in Caucasians, produce thick mucus in the lungs, resulting in a higher-than-normal level of CO_2 and respiratory acidosis.

CO_2 is constantly produced by metabolic processes in the body and then transported to the lungs to be eliminated. Thus, **the amount of CO_2 dissolved in the blood is directly related to the H_3O^+ concentration and therefore the pH of the blood.** If the pH of the blood is lower than 7.35, the blood is more acidic than normal, and the condition is called **acidosis.** If the pH of the blood is higher than 7.45, the blood is more basic than normal, and the condition is called **alkalosis.**

Le Châtelier's principle explains the effect of increasing or decreasing the level of dissolved CO_2 on the pH of the blood. A higher-than-normal CO_2 concentration shifts the equilibrium to the right, increasing the H_3O^+ concentration and lowering the pH. **Respiratory acidosis** results when the body fails to eliminate adequate amounts of CO_2 through the lungs. This may occur in patients with advanced lung disease or respiratory failure.

A lower respiratory rate increases [CO_2].

$$CO_2(g) + 2 H_2O(g) \rightleftharpoons H_3O^+(aq) + HCO_3^-(aq)$$

This drives the reaction to the right, increasing [H_3O^+].
Blood has a higher [H_3O^+] $\longrightarrow$ lower pH.

A lower-than-normal CO_2 concentration shifts the equilibria to the left, decreasing the H_3O^+ concentration and raising the pH. **Respiratory alkalosis** is caused by hyperventilation, very rapid breathing that occurs when an individual experiences excitement or panic.

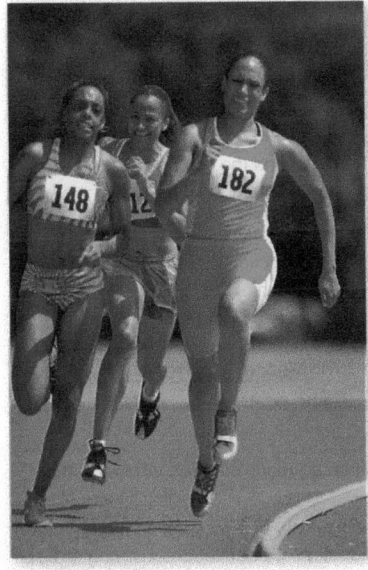

HEALTH NOTE

$$CO_2(g) + 2 H_2O(g) \rightleftharpoons H_3O^+(aq) + HCO_3^-(aq)$$

A faster respiratory rate decreases [CO_2].

During strenuous exercise, the lungs expel more CO_2 than usual and the pH of the blood increases.
©JupiterImages/Brand X/Alamy RF

This drives the reaction to the left, decreasing [H_3O^+].
Blood has a lower [H_3O^+] $\longrightarrow$ higher pH.

The pH of the blood may also be altered when the metabolic processes of the body are not in balance. **Metabolic acidosis** results when excessive amounts of acid are produced and the blood pH falls. This may be observed in patients with severe infections (sepsis) when a large amount of lactic acid accumulates. It may also occur in poorly controlled diabetes when keto acid levels rise (Chapter 24). **Metabolic alkalosis** may occur when recurrent vomiting decreases the amount of acid in the stomach, thus causing a rise in pH.

CHAPTER HIGHLIGHTS

KEY TERMS

Acid (9.1)

Acid dissociation constant (K_a, 9.4)

Acidic solution (9.5)

Amphoteric (9.2)

Base (9.1)

Basic solution (9.5)

Brønsted–Lowry acid (9.1)

Brønsted–Lowry base (9.1)

Buffer (9.10)

Conjugate acid (9.2)

Conjugate acid–base pair (9.2)

Conjugate base (9.2)

Diprotic acid (9.1)

Dissociation (9.3)

Ion–product constant (K_w, 9.5)

Monoprotic acid (9.1)

Net ionic equation (9.7)

Neutral solution (9.5)

Neutralization reaction (9.7)

pH scale (9.6)

Proton transfer reaction (9.2)

Spectator ion (9.7)

Titration (9.9)

Triprotic acid (9.1)

KEY CONCEPTS

① Describe the principal features of acids and bases. (9.1)

- A Brønsted–Lowry acid is a proton donor, often symbolized by HA. A Brønsted–Lowry acid must contain one or more hydrogen atoms.
- A Brønsted–Lowry base is a proton acceptor, often symbolized by B:. To form a bond to a proton, a Brønsted–Lowry base must contain a lone pair of electrons.

② What are the principal features of an acid–base reaction? (9.2)

- In a Brønsted–Lowry acid–base reaction, a proton is transferred from the acid (HA) to the base (B:). In this reaction, the acid loses a proton to form its conjugate base (A:⁻) and the base gains a proton to form its conjugate acid (HB⁺).

③ How is acid strength related to the direction of equilibrium in an acid–base reaction? (9.3)

- A strong acid readily donates a proton, and when dissolved in water, 100% of the acid dissociates into ions, forming H_3O^+. A strong base readily accepts a proton, and when dissolved in water, 100% of the base dissociates into ions, forming OH^-.
- An inverse relationship exists between acid and base strength. A strong acid forms a weak conjugate base, whereas a weak acid forms a strong conjugate base.
- In an acid–base reaction, the stronger acid reacts with the stronger base to form the weaker acid and the weaker base.

④ What is the acid dissociation constant and how is it related to acid strength? (9.4)

- For a general acid HA, the acid dissociation constant K_a is defined by the equation:

$$K_a = \frac{[H_3O^+][A:^-]}{[HA]}$$

- The stronger the acid, the larger the K_a. Equilibrium in an acid–base reaction favors formation of the acid with the smaller K_a value.

⑤ What is the ion–product of water and how is it used to calculate hydronium or hydroxide ion concentration? (9.5)

- The ion–product of water, K_w, is a constant for all aqueous solutions; $K_w = [H_3O^+][OH^-] = 1.0 \times 10^{-14}$ at 25 °C. If either $[H_3O^+]$ or $[OH^-]$ is known, the other value can be calculated from K_w.

⑥ What is pH? (9.6)

- The pH of a solution measures the concentration of H_3O^+; pH = −log $[H_3O^+]$.
- A pH = 7 means $[H_3O^+] = [OH^-]$ and the solution is neutral.
- A pH < 7 means $[H_3O^+] > [OH^-]$ and the solution is acidic.
- A pH > 7 means $[H_3O^+] < [OH^-]$ and the solution is basic.

⑦ Draw the products of some common acid–base reactions. (9.7)

- In a Brønsted–Lowry acid–base reaction with hydroxide bases (MOH), the acid HA donates a proton to OH^- to form H_2O. The anion from the acid HA combines with the cation M^+ of the base to form the salt MA. This reaction is called a neutralization reaction.
- In acid–base reactions with bicarbonate (HCO_3^-) or carbonate (CO_3^{2-}) bases, carbonic acid (H_2CO_3) is formed, which decomposes to form H_2O and CO_2.

⑧ What happens to the pH of an aqueous solution when a salt is dissolved? (9.8)

- A salt can form an acidic, basic, or neutral solution depending on whether its cation and anion are derived from strong or weak acids and bases. A salt derived from a strong acid and strong base forms a neutral solution with pH = 7. When one ion of a salt is derived from a weak acid or base, the ion derived from the stronger acid or base determines whether the solution is acidic or basic.

9 How is a titration used to determine the concentration of an acid or base? (9.9)

• A titration is a procedure that uses a base (or acid) of known volume and molarity to react with a known volume of acid (or base) of unknown molarity. The volume and molarity of the base are used to calculate the number of moles of base that react, and from this value, the molarity of the acid can be determined.

10 What is a buffer? (9.10)

• A buffer is a solution whose pH changes very little when acid or base is added. Most buffers are composed of approximately equal amounts of a weak acid and the salt of its conjugate base.

11 What is the principal buffer present in the blood? (9.11)

• The principal buffer in the blood is carbonic acid/bicarbonate. Since carbonic acid (H_2CO_3) is in equilibrium with dissolved CO_2, the amount of CO_2 in the blood affects its pH, which is normally maintained in the range of 7.35–7.45. When the CO_2 concentration in the blood is higher than normal, the acid–base equilibrium shifts to form more H_3O^+ and the pH decreases. When the CO_2 concentration in the blood is lower than normal, the acid–base equilibrium shifts to consume $[H_3O^+]$, so $[H_3O^+]$ decreases, and the pH increases.

PROBLEMS

Selected in-chapter and odd-numbered end-of-chapter problems have brief answers in Appendix B. The *Student Study Guide and Solutions Manual* contains detailed solutions to all in-chapter and odd-numbered end-of-chapter problems, as well as additional worked examples and a chapter self-test.

Acids and Bases

9.21 Which of the following species can be Brønsted–Lowry acids?
  a. HBr   c. $AlCl_3$ e. NO_2^-
  b. Br_2 d. HCOOH   f. HNO_2

9.22 Which of the following species can be Brønsted–Lowry acids?
  a. H_2O c. HOCl   e. CH_3CH_2COOH
  b. I^- d. $FeBr_3$ f. CO_2

9.23 Which of the following species can be Brønsted–Lowry bases?
  a. OH^- c. C_2H_6 e. OCl^-
  b. Ca^{2+} d. PO_4^{3-} f. $MgCO_3$

9.24 Which of the following species can be Brønsted–Lowry bases?
  a. Cl^- c. H_2O e. $Ca(OH)_2$
  b. BH_3 d. Na^+ f. $HCOO^-$

9.25 Draw the conjugate acid of each base.

  a. HS^- b. CO_3^{2-} c. NO_2^- d.

9.26 Draw the conjugate acid of each base.

  a. Br^- b. HPO_4^{2-} c. CH_3COO^- d.

9.27 Draw the conjugate base of each acid.
  a. HNO_2 b. NH_4^+ c. H_2O_2

9.28 Draw the conjugate base of each acid.
  a. H_3O^+ b. H_2Se c. HSO_4^-

9.29 Draw the structure of the conjugate base of each acid.

  a.   b.

9.30 Draw the structure of the conjugate base of each acid.

  a.   b.

9.31 Identify the acid, base, conjugate acid, and conjugate base in each diagram. Gray spheres correspond to H atoms.

  a.   +   ⟶   +

  b.   +   ⟶   +

9.32 Use the given representations for H_2Z, HZ^-, and Z^{2-}, as well as the space-filling structures of H_2O, H_3O^+, and OH^- that appear in Chapter 9, to depict each equation. Label the acid, base, conjugate acid, and conjugate base in each equation.

  ⬤ = H_2Z ⬤ = HZ^- ⬤ = Z^{2-}

  a. $H_2Z + H_2O \longrightarrow HZ^- + H_3O^+$
  b. $HZ^- + OH^- \longrightarrow Z^{2-} + H_2O$

9.33 Label the conjugate acid–base pairs in each equation.
  a. $HI(g) + NH_3(g) \rightleftharpoons NH_4^+(aq) + I^-(aq)$
  b. $HCOOH(l) + H_2O(l) \rightleftharpoons H_3O^+(aq) + HCOO^-(aq)$
  c. $HSO_4^-(aq) + H_2O(l) \rightleftharpoons H_2SO_4(aq) + OH^-(aq)$

9.34 Label the conjugate acid–base pairs in each equation.
  a. $Cl^-(aq) + HSO_4^-(aq) \rightleftharpoons HCl(aq) + SO_4^{2-}(aq)$
  b. $HPO_4^{2-}(aq) + OH^-(aq) \rightleftharpoons PO_4^{3-}(aq) + H_2O(l)$
  c. $NH_3(g) + HF(g) \rightleftharpoons NH_4^+(aq) + F^-(aq)$

9.35 Like H_2O, HCO_3^- is amphoteric. (a) Draw the conjugate acid of HCO_3^-. (b) Draw the conjugate base of HCO_3^-.

9.36 Like H_2O, $H_2PO_4^-$ is amphoteric. (a) Draw the conjugate acid of $H_2PO_4^-$. (b) Draw the conjugate base of $H_2PO_4^-$.

9.37 Fill in the missing product in each acid–base equation.
  a. $CH_3NH_2 + OH^- \rightleftharpoons (CH_3NH)^- +$ ☐
  b. $CH_3NH_2 + H_2SO_4 \rightleftharpoons$ ☐ $+ HSO_4^-$

9.38 Fill in the missing product in each acid–base equation.
  a. $CH_3OH + OH^- \rightleftharpoons (CH_3O)^- +$ ☐
  b. $CH_3OH + HCl \rightleftharpoons$ ☐ $+ Cl^-$

9.39 Write the equation for the acid–base reaction that takes place when nitric acid (HNO_3) dissolves in H_2O.

9.40 Write the equation for the acid–base reaction that takes place when formic acid (HCOOH) dissolves in H_2O.

Acid and Base Strength

9.41 Which diagram represents an aqueous solution of HF and which represents HCl? Explain your choice.

 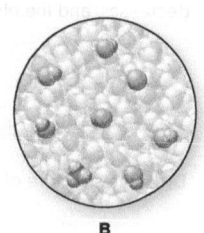

A   B

9.42 Which diagram represents what happens when HCN dissolves in water? Explain your choice.

A   B

9.43 (a) Which of the following represents a strong acid HZ dissolved in water? (b) Which represents a weak acid HZ dissolved in water?

 = HZ   = Z⁻

A   B

9.44 (a) Using molecular art, draw a diagram that represents an aqueous solution of a strong acid H_2Z. (b) Using molecular art, draw a diagram that represents an aqueous solution of a weak acid H_2Z.

 = H_2Z = HZ^-

9.45 Use the data in Tables 9.2 and 9.3 to label the stronger acid in each pair. Which acid in each pair has the stronger conjugate base?
  a. H_2O or CH_3COOH
  b. H_3PO_4 or HCO_3^-
  c. H_2SO_4 or HSO_4^-

9.46 Use the data in Tables 9.2 and 9.3 to label the stronger acid in each pair. Which acid in each pair has the stronger conjugate base?
  a. HPO_4^{2-} or HCN
  b. HSO_4^- or NH_4^+
  c. H_2O or HF

9.47 Which acid, **A** or **B**, is stronger in each part?
  a. **A** dissociates to a greater extent in water.
  b. **A** has a smaller K_a.
  c. The conjugate base of **A** is stronger than the conjugate base of **B**.

9.48 Which acid, **A** or **B**, is stronger in each part?
  a. **B** dissociates to a greater extent in water.
  b. **A** has a larger K_a.
  c. The conjugate base of **B** is stronger than the conjugate base of **A**.

9.49 Fill in the missing terms (strong or weak) and formulas in the following table.

	Acid	Formula	Conjugate Base	Formula
a.	strong	H_2SO_4		
b.		HOBr	strong	
c.			weak	NO_3^-
d.	weak			HCO_2^-

9.50 Fill in the missing terms (strong or weak) and formulas in the following table.

	Base	Formula	Conjugate Acid	Formula
a.	strong	OH^-		
b.			strong	H_3O^+
c.		CN^-	weak	
d.	weak			$HClO_4$

Equilibrium and Acid Dissociation Constants

9.51 For each pair of acids: [1] Label the stronger acid. [2] Draw the conjugate bases. [3] Label the stronger conjugate base.
  a. HSO_4^- or $H_2PO_4^-$
     bisulfate   dihydrogen phosphate
     $K_a = 1.2 \times 10^{-2}$ $K_a = 6.2 \times 10^{-8}$
  b. CH_3CH_2COOH or CH_3COOH
     propanoic acid   acetic acid
     $K_a = 1.3 \times 10^{-5}$ $K_a = 1.8 \times 10^{-5}$

9.52 For each pair of acids: [1] Label the stronger acid. [2] Draw the conjugate bases. [3] Label the stronger conjugate base.
  a. H_3PO_4 or HCOOH
     phosphoric acid   formic acid
     $K_a = 7.5 \times 10^{-3}$ $K_a = 1.8 \times 10^{-4}$
  b. HCOOH or C_6H_5COOH
     formic acid   benzoic acid
     $K_a = 1.8 \times 10^{-4}$ $K_a = 6.5 \times 10^{-5}$

9.53 (a) Which diagram illustrates the stronger acid? (b) Which diagram represents the acid with the larger K_a? (c) Which diagram contains the stronger conjugate base?

= HA   = A⁻   = H_3O^+

A   B

9.54 Consider the aqueous solutions of two weak acids depicted in diagrams **A** and **B**. (a) What is the formula of the acid and conjugate base in each solution? (b) Which of the following K_a values corresponds to each acid: 3.4×10^{-7} and 1.0×10^{-2}? (c) Which conjugate base is stronger?

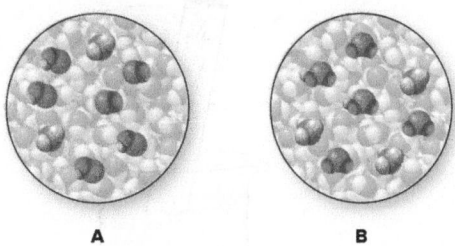

A   B

9.55 Calculate K_a for the weak acid HA dissolved in water depicted in the molecular art; $HA + H_2O \longrightarrow A^- + H_3O^+$

= HA   = A⁻   = H_3O^+

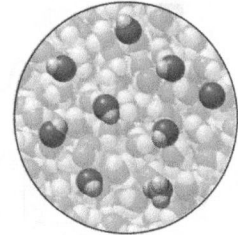

9.56 Calculate K_a for the weak acid HA dissolved in water depicted in the molecular art; $HA + H_2O \longrightarrow A^- + H_3O^+$

= HA   = A⁻   = H_3O^+

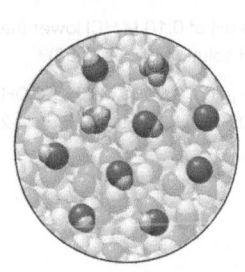

9.57 Label the acid in the reactants and the conjugate acid in the products in each reaction. Use the data in Tables 9.2 and 9.3 to determine whether the reactants or products are favored at equilibrium. Explain your reasoning.
a. $H_3PO_4(aq) + CN^-(aq) \rightleftharpoons H_2PO_4^-(aq) + HCN(aq)$
b. $Br^-(aq) + HSO_4^-(aq) \rightleftharpoons SO_4^{2-}(aq) + HBr(aq)$
c. $CH_3COO^-(aq) + H_2CO_3(aq) \rightleftharpoons CH_3COOH(aq) + HCO_3^-(aq)$

9.58 Label the acid in the reactants and the conjugate acid in the products in each reaction. Use the data in Tables 9.2 and 9.3 to determine whether the reactants or products are favored at equilibrium. Explain your reasoning.
a. $HF(g) + NH_3(g) \rightleftharpoons NH_4^+(aq) + F^-(aq)$
b. $Br^-(aq) + H_2O(l) \rightleftharpoons HBr(aq) + OH^-(aq)$
c. $HCN(aq) + HCO_3^-(aq) \rightleftharpoons H_2CO_3(aq) + CN^-(aq)$

Water and the pH Scale

9.59 Label each of the following statements as true or false. Correct any false statement to make it true.
a. A solution with a pH of 5 is 10 times more acidic than a solution with a pH of 6.
b. A solution with a pH of 2 is two times more acidic than a solution with a pH of 4.

9.60 Label each of the following statements as true or false. Correct any false statement to make it true.
a. A solution with a pH of 9 is three times more basic than a solution with a pH of 6.
b. A solution with a pH of 8 is 100 times more basic than a solution with a pH of 6.

9.61 Calculate the value of $[H_3O^+]$ from the given $[OH^-]$ in each liquid and label the solution as acidic or basic.

a.   b.

$[OH^-] = 1.1 \times 10^{-9}$ M $[OH^-] = 4.0 \times 10^{-12}$ M

(a): ©Davydenko Yulia/Shutterstock RF; (b): ©Ingram Publishing/SuperStock RF

352   **Chapter 9**   Acids and Bases

9.62   Calculate the value of $[OH^-]$ from the given $[H_3O^+]$ in each liquid and label the solution as acidic or basic.

a.

b.

$[H_3O^+] = 5.0 \times 10^{-7}$ $[H_3O^+] = 2.1 \times 10^{-4}$

(a): ©D. Hurst/Alamy RF; (b): ©Keith Homan/Shutterstock RF

9.63   Calculate the value of $[OH^-]$ from the given $[H_3O^+]$ and label the solution as acidic or basic.
a. 10^{-8} M   c. 3.0×10^{-4} M
b. 10^{-10} M   d. 2.5×10^{-11} M

9.64   Calculate the value of $[OH^-]$ from the given $[H_3O^+]$ and label the solution as acidic or basic.
a. 10^{-1} M   c. 2.6×10^{-7} M
b. 10^{-13} M   d. 1.2×10^{-12} M

9.65   Calculate the value of $[H_3O^+]$ from the given $[OH^-]$ and label the solution as acidic or basic.
a. 10^{-2} M   c. 6.2×10^{-7} M
b. 4.0×10^{-8} M   d. 8.5×10^{-13} M

9.66   Calculate the value of $[H_3O^+]$ from the given $[OH^-]$ and label the solution as acidic or basic.
a. 10^{-12} M   c. 6.0×10^{-4} M
b. 5.0×10^{-10} M   d. 8.9×10^{-11} M

9.67   Calculate the pH from each H_3O^+ concentration determined in Problem 9.65.

9.68   Calculate the pH from each H_3O^+ concentration determined in Problem 9.66.

9.69   Complete the following table with the needed $[H_3O^+]$, $[OH^-]$, and pH, and classify the solution as acidic, basic, or neutral.

$[H_3O^+]$	$[OH^-]$	pH	Classification
5.3×10^{-3}			
	2.0×10^{-8}		
		4.4	
	6.8×10^{-10}		

9.70   Complete the following table with the needed $[H_3O^+]$, $[OH^-]$, and pH, and classify the solution as acidic, basic, or neutral.

$[H_3O^+]$	$[OH^-]$	pH	Classification
6.3×10^{-4}			
	2.5×10^{-9}		
		9.4	
	6.8×10^{-4}		

9.71   Calculate the H_3O^+ concentration from each pH: (a) 12; (b) 1; (c) 1.80; (d) 8.90.

9.72   Calculate the H_3O^+ concentration from each pH: (a) 4; (b) 8; (c) 2.60; (d) 11.30.

9.73   If a urine sample has a pH of 5.90, calculate the concentrations of H_3O^+ and OH^- in the sample.

9.74   If pancreatic fluids have a pH of 8.2, calculate the concentrations of H_3O^+ and OH^- in the pancreas.

9.75   Calculate the concentrations of H_3O^+ and OH^- in the water sample with the given pH.

9.76   Calculate the concentrations of H_3O^+ and OH^- in the sample of milk of magnesia with the given pH.

9.77   Calculate the pH of each aqueous solution: (a) 0.0025 M HCl; (b) 0.015 M KOH.

9.78   Calculate the pH of each aqueous solution: (a) 0.015 M HNO_3; (b) 0.0025 M NaOH.

9.79   Why is the pH of 0.10 M HCl lower than the pH of 0.10 M CH_3COOH solution (1.0 vs. 2.88)?

9.80   Why is the pH of 0.0050 M CH_3COOH solution higher than the pH of 0.0050 M HCl solution (3.5 vs. 2.3)?

Acid–Base Reactions

9.81 Write a balanced equation for each reaction.
   a. $HBr(aq) + KOH(aq) \longrightarrow$
   b. $HNO_3(aq) + Ca(OH)_2(aq) \longrightarrow$
   c. $HCl(aq) + NaHCO_3(aq) \longrightarrow$
   d. $H_2SO_4(aq) + Mg(OH)_2(aq) \longrightarrow$

9.82 Write a balanced equation for each reaction.
   a. $HNO_3(aq) + LiOH(aq) \longrightarrow$
   b. $H_2SO_4(aq) + NaOH(aq) \longrightarrow$
   c. $K_2CO_3(aq) + HCl(aq) \longrightarrow$
   d. $HI(aq) + NaHCO_3(aq) \longrightarrow$

9.83 Marble statues, which are composed of calcium carbonate $(CaCO_3)$, are slowly eaten away by the nitric acid (HNO_3) in acid rain. Write a balanced equation for the reaction of $CaCO_3$ with HNO_3.

9.84 Some liquid antacids contain suspensions of aluminum hydroxide $[Al(OH)_3]$. Write a balanced equation for the reaction of $Al(OH)_3$ with the HCl in stomach acid.

Salt Solutions

9.85 Determine whether each salt forms an acidic, basic, or neutral solution when it dissolves in water.
   a. NaI   c. NH_4NO_3 e. $MgBr_2$
   b. LiF   d. $KHCO_3$ f. NaH_2PO_4

9.86 Determine whether each salt forms an acidic, basic, or neutral solution when it dissolves in water.
   a. NaBr   c. KCH_3COO e. $CaBr_2$
   b. NaCN   d. CsF   f. K_3PO_4

Titration

9.87 What is the molarity of an HCl solution if 35.5 mL of 0.10 M NaOH are needed to neutralize 25.0 mL of the sample?

9.88 What is the molarity of an HCl solution if 17.2 mL of 0.15 M NaOH are needed to neutralize 5.00 mL of the sample?

9.89 What is the molarity of an acetic acid (CH_3COOH) solution if 15.5 mL of 0.20 M NaOH are needed to neutralize 25.0 mL of the sample?

9.90 What is the molarity of an H_2SO_4 solution if 18.5 mL of 0.18 M NaOH are needed to neutralize 25.0 mL of the sample?

9.91 How many milliliters of 1.0 M NaOH solution are needed to neutralize 10.0 mL of 2.5 M CH_3COOH solution?

9.92 How many milliliters of 2.0 M NaOH solution are needed to neutralize 8.0 mL of 3.5 M H_2SO_4 solution?

Buffers

9.93 Consider a weak acid H_2A and its conjugate base HA^-. Which diagram represents a buffer? Explain your choice.

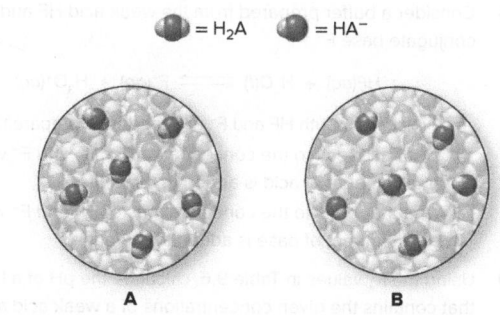

9.94 Consider a weak acid H_2A and its conjugate base HA^-. Which diagram represents a buffer? Explain your choice.

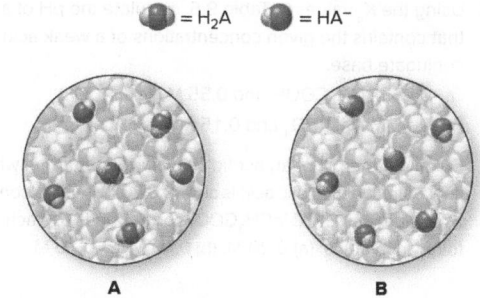

9.95 Consider a buffer that consists of equal concentrations of HZ and Z^-. Use the given representations for HZ and Z^-, as well as the space-filling structures for H_2O, H_3O^+, and OH^- that appear in Chapter 9, to answer the question. Which of the following equations depicts the reaction that occurs when the buffer is treated with a small amount of strong acid?

9.96 Which of the equations in Problem 9.95 depicts the reaction that occurs when the buffer is treated with a small amount of strong base?

9.97 Consider a buffer prepared from the weak acid HNO_2 and its conjugate base NO_2^-.

$$HNO_2(aq) + H_2O(l) \rightleftharpoons NO_2^-(aq) + H_3O^+(aq)$$

   a. Explain why both HNO_2 and NO_2^- are needed to prepare the buffer.
   b. What happens to the concentrations of HNO_2 and NO_2^- when a small amount of acid is added to the buffer?
   c. What happens to the concentrations of HNO_2 and NO_2^- when a small amount of base is added to the buffer?

9.98 Consider a buffer prepared from the weak acid HF and its conjugate base F^-.

$$HF(aq) + H_2O(l) \rightleftharpoons F^-(aq) + H_3O^+(aq)$$

  a. Explain why both HF and F^- are needed to prepare the buffer.
  b. What happens to the concentrations of HF and F^- when a small amount of acid is added to the buffer?
  c. What happens to the concentrations of HF and F^- when a small amount of base is added to the buffer?

9.99 Using the K_a values in Table 9.6, calculate the pH of a buffer that contains the given concentrations of a weak acid and its conjugate base.
  a. 0.10 M Na_2HPO_4 and 0.10 M Na_3PO_4
  b. 0.22 M $NaHCO_3$ and 0.22 M Na_2CO_3

9.100 Using the K_a values in Table 9.6, calculate the pH of a buffer that contains the given concentrations of a weak acid and its conjugate base.
  a. 0.55 M CH_3COOH and 0.55 M $NaCH_3COO$
  b. 0.15 M NaH_2PO_4 and 0.15 M Na_2HPO_4

9.101 Calculate the pH of an acetic acid/acetate buffer in which the concentration of acetic acid is always 0.20 M, but the concentration of sodium acetate ($NaCH_3COO$) corresponds to each of the following values: (a) 0.20 M; (b) 0.40 M; (c) 0.10 M.

9.102 Calculate the pH of a bicarbonate/carbonate buffer in which the concentration of sodium bicarbonate ($NaHCO_3$) is always 0.20 M, but the concentration of sodium carbonate (Na_2CO_3) corresponds to each of the following values: (a) 0.20 M; (b) 0.40 M; (c) 0.10 M.

Applications

9.103 Why is the pH of unpolluted rainwater lower than the pH of pure water?

9.104 The optimum pH of a swimming pool is 7.50. Calculate the value of $[H_3O^+]$ and $[OH^-]$ at this pH.

9.105 When an individual hyperventilates, he is told to blow into a paper bag held over his mouth. What effect should this process have on the CO_2 concentration and pH of the blood?

9.106 A sample of rainwater has a pH of 4.18. (a) Calculate the H_3O^+ concentration in the sample. (b) Suggest a reason why this pH differs from the pH of unpolluted rainwater (5.6).

9.107 How is CO_2 concentration related to the pH of the blood?

9.108 Explain why a lake on a bed of limestone is naturally buffered against the effects of acid rain.

CHALLENGE PROBLEMS

9.109 Calcium hypochlorite [$Ca(OCl)_2$] is used to chlorinate swimming pools. $Ca(OCl)_2$ acts as a source of the weak acid hypochlorous acid, HOCl, a disinfectant that kills bacteria. Write the acid–base reaction that occurs when OCl^- dissolves in water and explain why this reaction makes a swimming pool more basic.

9.110 Most buffer solutions are prepared using a weak acid and a salt of its conjugate base. Explain how the following combination can also form a buffer solution: 0.20 M H_3PO_4 and 0.10 M NaOH.

Radiation produced by cobalt-60 and other radioactive isotopes is used to treat many different forms of cancer.
©Martin Dohrn/Science Source

Nuclear Chemistry

CHAPTER OUTLINE

10.1 Introduction

10.2 Nuclear Reactions

10.3 Half-Life

10.4 Detecting and Measuring Radioactivity

10.5 FOCUS ON HEALTH & MEDICINE:
Medical Uses of Radioisotopes

10.6 Nuclear Fission and Nuclear Fusion

10.7 FOCUS ON HEALTH & MEDICINE:
Medical Imaging Without Radioactivity

CHAPTER GOALS

In this chapter you will learn how to:

1. Describe the different types of radiation emitted by a radioactive nucleus

2. Write equations for nuclear reactions

3. Define half-life

4. Recognize the units used for measuring radioactivity

5. Give examples of common radioisotopes used in medical diagnosis and treatment

6. Describe the general features of nuclear fission and nuclear fusion

7. Describe the features of medical imaging techniques that do not use radioactivity

*Why Study
Nuclear Chemistry?*

Thus far our study of reactions has concentrated on processes that involve the valence electrons of atoms. In these reactions, bonds that join atoms are broken and new bonds between atoms are formed, but the identity of the atoms does not change. In Chapter 10, we turn our attention to **nuclear reactions,** processes that involve changes in the nucleus of an atom. While certainly much less common than chemical reactions that occur with electrons, nuclear reactions form a useful group of processes with a wide range of applications. Nuclear medicine labs in hospitals use radioactive isotopes to diagnose disease, visualize organs, and treat tumors. Generating energy in nuclear power plants, dating archaeological objects using the isotope carbon-14, and designing a simple and reliable smoke detector all utilize the concepts of nuclear chemistry discussed here in Chapter 10.

10.1   Introduction

Although most reactions involve valence electrons, a small but significant group of reactions, **nuclear reactions,** involves the subatomic particles of the nucleus. To understand nuclear reactions we must first review facts presented in Chapter 2 regarding isotopes and the characteristics of the nucleus.

10.1A   Isotopes

The nucleus of an atom is composed of protons and neutrons.

- The atomic number (Z) = the number of protons in the nucleus.
- The mass number (A) = the number of protons and neutrons in the nucleus.

Atoms of the same type of element have the same atomic number, but the number of neutrons may vary.

- Isotopes are atoms of the same element having a different number of neutrons.

As a result, **isotopes have the same atomic number (Z) but different mass numbers (A).** Carbon, for example, has three naturally occurring isotopes. Each isotope has six protons in the nucleus (i.e., $Z = 6$), but the number of neutrons may be six, seven, or eight. Thus, the mass numbers (A) of these isotopes are 12, 13, and 14, respectively. As we learned in Chapter 2, we can refer to these isotopes as carbon-12, carbon-13, and carbon-14. Isotopes are also written with the mass number to the upper left of the element symbol and the atomic number to the lower left.

| 6 protons | 6 protons | 6 protons |
| 6 neutrons | 7 neutrons | 8 neutrons |

mass number ⟶ $^{12}_{6}C$ $^{13}_{6}C$ $^{14}_{6}C$
atomic number ⟶
carbon-12   carbon-13   carbon-14

Many isotopes are stable, but a larger number are not.

- A *radioactive isotope,* called a *radioisotope,* is unstable and spontaneously emits energy to form a more stable nucleus.

Radioactivity **is the nuclear radiation emitted spontaneously by an unstable radioactive isotope.** Of the known isotopes of all the elements, 264 are stable and 300 are naturally occurring but unstable. An even larger number of radioactive isotopes, called **artificial isotopes,** have been produced in the laboratory. Both carbon-12 and carbon-13 are stable isotopes and occur in higher natural abundance than carbon-14, a radioactive isotope.

SAMPLE PROBLEM 10.1 COMPARING THE CHARACTERISTICS OF TWO ISOTOPES

Iodine-123 and iodine-131 are radioactive isotopes used for the diagnosis or treatment of thyroid disease. Complete the following table for both isotopes.

	Atomic Number	Mass Number	Number of Protons	Number of Neutrons	Isotope Symbol
Iodine-123					
Iodine-131					

Analysis

- The atomic number = the number of protons.
- The mass number = the number of protons + the number of neutrons.
- Isotopes are written with the mass number to the upper left of the element symbol and the atomic number to the lower left.

Solution

	Atomic Number	Mass Number	Number of Protons	Number of Neutrons	Isotope Symbol
Iodine-123	53	123	53	$123 - 53 = 70$	$^{123}_{53}I$
Iodine-131	53	131	53	$131 - 53 = 78$	$^{131}_{53}I$

PRACTICE PROBLEM 10.1

Complete the following table for two isotopes of cobalt. Cobalt-60 is commonly used in cancer therapy.

	Atomic Number	Mass Number	Number of Protons	Number of Neutrons	Isotope Symbol
Cobalt-59					
Cobalt-60					

More Practice: Try Problems 10.19–10.22.

PROBLEM 10.1

Each of the following radioisotopes is used in medicine. For each isotope give its: [1] atomic number; [2] mass number; [3] number of protons; [4] number of neutrons.

a. $^{85}_{38}Sr$ b. $^{67}_{31}Ga$ c.   selenium-75
     used in bone scans   used in abdominal scans   used in pancreas scans

PROBLEM 10.2

Using the radioisotope whose nucleus is shown in the accompanying diagram, give its: (a) atomic number; (b) mass number; (c) number of protons; (d) number of neutrons; (e) isotope symbol.

10.1B   Types of Radiation

Different forms of radiation are emitted when a radioactive nucleus is converted to a more stable nucleus, including **alpha particles, beta particles, positrons,** and **gamma radiation.**

- An *alpha particle* is a high-energy particle that contains two protons and two neutrons.

$$\text{alpha particle:} \quad \alpha \quad \text{or} \quad {}^4_2\text{He}$$

An alpha particle, symbolized by the Greek letter **alpha (α)** or the element symbol for helium, has a +2 charge and a mass number of 4.

- A *beta particle* is a high-energy electron.

$$\text{beta particle:} \quad \beta \quad \text{or} \quad {}^0_{-1}\text{e}$$

An electron has a −1 charge and a negligible mass compared to a proton. A beta particle, symbolized by the Greek letter **beta (β),** is also drawn with the symbol for an electron, **e,** with a mass number of 0 in the upper left corner and a charge of −1 in the lower left corner. A β particle is formed when a neutron (n) is converted to a proton (p) and an electron.

$${}^1_0\text{n} \longrightarrow {}^1_1\text{p} + {}^0_{-1}\text{e}$$
$$\text{neutron} \qquad \text{proton} \quad \beta \text{ particle}$$

- A *positron* is called an *antiparticle* of a β particle, because their charges are different but their masses are the same.

Thus, a **positron** has a negligible mass like a β particle but is opposite in charge, +1. A positron, symbolized as β^+, is also drawn with the symbol for an electron, **e,** with a mass number of 0 in the upper left corner and a charge of +1 in the lower left corner. A positron, which can be thought of as a "positive electron," is formed when a proton is converted to a neutron.

$$\textbf{Symbol:} \quad {}^0_{+1}\text{e} \quad \text{or} \quad \beta^+ \qquad \textbf{Formation:} \quad {}^1_1\text{p} \longrightarrow {}^1_0\text{n} + {}^0_{+1}\text{e}$$
$$\text{positron} \qquad\qquad\qquad \text{proton} \quad \text{neutron} \quad \text{positron}$$

- *Gamma rays* are high-energy radiation released from a radioactive nucleus.

Gamma rays, symbolized by the Greek letter **gamma (γ),** are a form of energy and thus they have no mass or charge. Table 10.1 summarizes the properties of some of the different types of radiation.

$$\text{gamma ray:} \quad \gamma$$

Table 10.1   Types of Radiation

Type of Radiation	Symbol	Charge	Mass Number
Alpha particle	α or ${}^4_2\text{He}$	+2	4
Beta particle	β or ${}^0_{-1}\text{e}$	−1	0
Positron	β^+ or ${}^0_{+1}\text{e}$	+1	0
Gamma ray	γ	0	0

PROBLEM 10.3

What is the difference between an α particle and a helium atom?

PROBLEM 10.4

Identify Q in each of the following symbols.

a. ${}^0_{-1}\text{Q}$ b. ${}^4_2\text{Q}$ c. ${}^0_{+1}\text{Q}$

10.2　Nuclear Reactions

Radioactive decay **is the process by which an unstable radioactive nucleus emits radiation, forming a nucleus of new composition.** A nuclear equation can be written for this process, which contains the original nucleus, the new nucleus, and the radiation emitted. Unlike a chemical equation that balances atoms, in a nuclear equation the mass numbers and the atomic numbers of the nuclei must be balanced.

- The sum of the mass numbers (*A*) must be equal on both sides of a nuclear equation.
- The sum of the atomic numbers (*Z*) must be equal on both sides of a nuclear equation.

10.2A　Alpha Emission

Alpha emission **is the decay of a nucleus by emitting an α particle.** For example, uranium-238 decays to form thorium-234 by loss of an α particle.

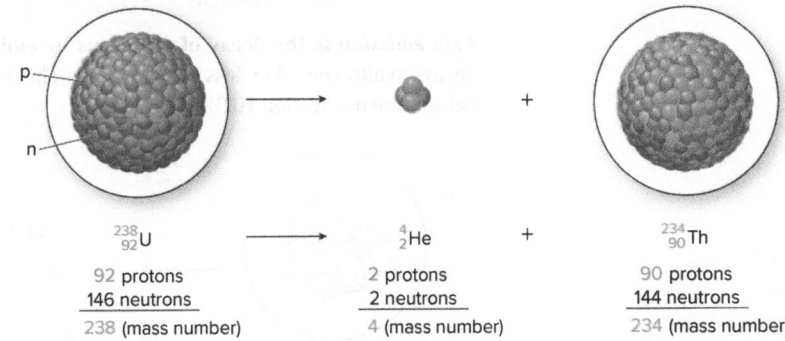

$^{238}_{92}\text{U}$	$\longrightarrow$	$^{4}_{2}\text{He}$	+	$^{234}_{90}\text{Th}$
92 protons		2 protons		90 protons
146 neutrons		2 neutrons		144 neutrons
238 (mass number)		4 (mass number)		234 (mass number)

Americium-241 is a radioactive element contained in smoke detectors. The decay of α particles creates an electric current that is interrupted when smoke enters the detector, sounding an alarm.
©S. Wanke/PhotoLink/Getty Images RF

Since an α particle has two protons, **the new nucleus has *two fewer protons* than the original nucleus.** Because it has a *different* number of protons, **the new nucleus represents a *different* element.** Uranium-238 has 92 protons, so loss of two protons forms the element thorium with 90 protons. The thorium nucleus has a mass number that is four fewer than the original—234—because it has been formed by loss of an α particle with a mass number of four.

As a result, the sum of the mass numbers is equal on both sides of the equation—238 = 4 + 234. The sum of the atomic numbers is also equal on both sides of the equation—92 = 2 + 90.

How To　**Balance an Equation for a Nuclear Reaction**

Example:　Write a balanced nuclear equation showing how americium-241, a radioactive element used in smoke detectors, decays to form an α particle.

Step [1]　**Write an incomplete equation with the original nucleus on the left and the particle emitted on the right.**
- Include the mass number and atomic number (from the periodic table) in the equation.

$$^{241}_{95}\text{Am} \longrightarrow {}^{4}_{2}\text{He} + ?$$

Step [2]　**Calculate the mass number and atomic number of the newly formed nucleus on the right.**
- Mass number: The sum of the mass numbers must be equal on both sides of the equation. **Subtract the mass of an α particle (4) to obtain the mass of the new nucleus;** 241 − 4 = 237.
- Atomic number: The sum of the atomic numbers must be equal on both sides of the equation. **Subtract the two protons of an α particle to obtain the atomic number of the new nucleus;** 95 − 2 = 93.

Step [3]　**Use the atomic number to identify the new nucleus and complete the equation.**
- From the periodic table, the element with an atomic number of 93 is neptunium, Np.
- Write the mass number and the atomic number with the element symbol to complete the equation.

$$241 = 4 + 237$$
$$^{241}_{95}\text{Am} \longrightarrow {}^{4}_{2}\text{He} + {}^{237}_{93}\text{Np}$$
$$95 = 2 + 93$$

PROBLEM 10.5

Radon, a radioactive gas formed in the soil, can cause lung cancers when inhaled in high concentrations for a long period of time. Write a balanced nuclear equation for the decay of radon-222, which emits an α particle.

PROBLEM 10.6

Radon (Problem 10.5) is formed in the soil as a product of radioactive decay that produces an α particle. Write a balanced nuclear equation for the formation of radon-222 and an α particle.

PROBLEM 10.7

Write a balanced equation showing how each nucleus decays to form a new element after releasing an α particle: (a) polonium-218; (b) thorium-230; (c) ^{252}Es.

10.2B   Beta Emission

***Beta emission* is the decay of a nucleus by emitting a β particle.** For example, carbon-14 decays to nitrogen-14 by loss of a β particle. The decay of carbon-14 is used to date archaeological specimens (Section 10.3).

In β emission, one neutron of the original nucleus decays to a β particle and a proton. As a result, the **new nucleus has *one more proton* and *one fewer neutron* than the original nucleus.** In this example, a carbon atom with six protons decays to a nitrogen atom with seven protons. Because the total number of particles in the nucleus does not change, the **mass number is constant.**

The subscripts that represent the atomic numbers are balanced because the β particle has a charge of −1. Seven protons on the right side plus a −1 charge for the β particle gives a total "charge" of +6, the atomic number of carbon on the left. The mass numbers are also balanced because a β particle has zero mass, and both the original nucleus and the new nucleus contain 14 subatomic particles (protons + neutrons).

Radioactive elements that emit β radiation are widely used in medicine. Because β radiation is composed of high-energy, rapidly moving electrons that penetrate tissue in a small, localized region, radioactive elements situated in close contact with tumor cells kill them. Although both healthy and diseased cells are destroyed by this internal radiation therapy, rapidly dividing tumor cells are more sensitive to its effects and therefore their growth and replication are affected the most.

Iodine-131, a radioactive element that emits β radiation, is used to treat hyperthyroidism, a condition resulting from an overactive thyroid gland (Figure 10.1). When iodine-131 is administered, it is incorporated into thyroxine, an iodine-containing hormone that is concentrated in the thyroid gland. The β radiation emitted by the iodine-131 kills some of the thyroid tissue, so that the gland is no longer overactive.

Figure 10.1   The Use of Iodine-131 to Treat Hyperthyroidism

thyroid gland

Radioactive iodine-131 is incorporated into the four I atoms (in purple) of thyroxine.

thyroxine
$C_{15}H_{11}I_4NO_4$

Iodine-131 is incorporated into the thyroid hormone thyroxine. Beta radiation emitted by the radioactive isotope destroys nearby thyroid cells, thus decreasing the activity of the thyroid gland and bringing the disease under control.

SAMPLE PROBLEM 10.2 BALANCING A NUCLEAR EQUATION INVOLVING β EMISSION

Write a balanced nuclear equation for the β emission of phosphorus-32, a radioisotope used to treat leukemia and other blood disorders.

Analysis

- Balance the atomic numbers and mass numbers on both sides of a nuclear equation.
- With β emission, treat the β particle as an electron with zero mass in balancing mass numbers and a −1 charge when balancing the atomic numbers.

Solution

[1] Write an incomplete equation with the original nucleus on the left and the particle emitted on the right.

- Use the identity of the element to determine the atomic number; phosphorus has an atomic number of 15.

$$^{32}_{15}P \longrightarrow {}^{0}_{-1}e + ?$$

[2] Calculate the mass number and the atomic number of the newly formed nucleus on the right.

- Mass number: Because a β particle has no mass, the masses of the new particle and the original particle are the same, 32.
- Atomic number: Because β emission converts a neutron into a proton, the new nucleus has one more proton than the original nucleus; 15 = −1 + ?. Thus the new nucleus has an atomic number of 16.

[3] Use the atomic number to identify the new nucleus and complete the equation.

- From the periodic table, the element with an atomic number of 16 is sulfur, S.
- Write the mass number and the atomic number with the element symbol to complete the equation.

$$^{32}_{15}P \longrightarrow {}^{0}_{-1}e + {}^{32}_{16}S$$

PRACTICE PROBLEM 10.2

Write a balanced nuclear equation for the β emission of iodine-131.

More Practice: Try Problems 10.29; 10.33a; 10.34c; 10.35a; 10.36a; 10.39b; 10.40a, d.

PROBLEM 10.8

Write a balanced nuclear equation for the β emission of each of the following isotopes.

a. $^{20}_{9}F$ b. $^{92}_{38}Sr$ c. chromium-55

10.2C   Positron Emission

***Positron emission* is the decay of a nucleus by emitting a positron (β⁺).** For example, carbon-11, an artificial radioactive isotope of carbon, decays to boron-11 by loss of a β⁺ particle. Positron emitters are used in a relatively new diagnostic technique, positron emission tomography (PET), described in Section 10.5.

$$^{11}_{6}\text{C} \longrightarrow ^{0}_{+1}\text{e} + ^{11}_{5}\text{B}$$

6 protons   +1 charge   5 protons
5 neutrons   0 mass   6 neutrons
11 (mass number)   11 (mass number)

The mass number is constant.

In positron emission, one proton of the original nucleus decays to a β⁺ particle and a neutron. As a result, the **new nucleus has *one fewer proton*** and ***one more neutron* than the original nucleus.** In this example, a carbon atom with six protons decays to a boron atom with five protons. Since the total number of particles in the nucleus does not change, the **mass number is constant.**

SAMPLE PROBLEM 10.3 BALANCING A NUCLEAR EQUATION INVOLVING POSITRON EMISSION

Write a balanced nuclear equation for the positron emission of fluorine-18, a radioisotope used for imaging in PET scans.

Analysis

- Balance the atomic numbers and mass numbers on both sides of a nuclear equation.
- With β⁺ emission, treat the positron as a particle with zero mass when balancing mass numbers and a +1 charge when balancing the atomic numbers.

Solution

[1] Write an incomplete equation with the original nucleus on the left and the particle emitted on the right.

- Use the identity of the element to determine the atomic number; fluorine has an atomic number of 9.

$$^{18}_{9}\text{F} \longrightarrow ^{0}_{+1}\text{e} + ?$$

[2] Calculate the mass number and the atomic number of the newly formed nucleus on the right.

- Mass number: Because a β⁺ particle has no mass, the masses of the new particle and the original particle are the same, 18.
- Atomic number: Because β⁺ emission converts a proton into a neutron, the new nucleus has one fewer proton than the original nucleus; 9 − 1 = 8. Thus, the new nucleus has an atomic number of 8.

[3] Use the atomic number to identify the new nucleus and complete the equation.

- From the periodic table, the element with an atomic number of 8 is oxygen, O.
- Write the mass number and the atomic number with the element symbol to complete the equation.

$$^{18}_{9}\text{F} \longrightarrow ^{0}_{+1}\text{e} + ^{18}_{8}\text{O}$$

PRACTICE PROBLEM 10.3

Write a balanced nuclear equation for the positron emission of each of the following nuclei:
(a) arsenic-74; (b) oxygen-15.

More Practice: Try Problems 10.31, 10.33c, 10.34a, 10.35b, 10.36b, 10.39c, 10.40c.

10.2D Gamma Emission

Gamma emission **is the decay of a nucleus by emitting γ radiation.** Since γ rays are simply a form of energy, their emission causes **no change in the atomic number or mass number** of a radioactive nucleus. Gamma emission sometimes occurs alone. For example, one form of technetium-99, written as technetium-99m, is an energetic form of the technetium nucleus that decays with emission of γ rays to technetium-99, a more stable but still radioactive element.

$$^{99m}_{43}\text{Tc} \longrightarrow {}^{99}_{43}\text{Tc} + \gamma$$

The mass number and atomic number are the same.

> The *m* in technetium-99m stands for *metastable*. This designation is meant to indicate that the isotope decays to a more stable form of the same isotope.

Technetium-99m is a widely used radioisotope in medical imaging. Because it emits high-energy γ rays but decays in a short period of time, it is used to image the brain, thyroid, lungs, liver, skeleton, and many other organs. It has also been used to detect ulcers in the gastrointestinal system, and combined with other compounds, it is used to map the circulatory system and gauge damage after a heart attack.

More commonly, γ emission accompanies α or β emission. For example, cobalt-60 decays with both β and γ emission. Because a β particle is formed, decay generates an element with the *same* mass but a *different* number of protons, and thus a new element, nickel-60.

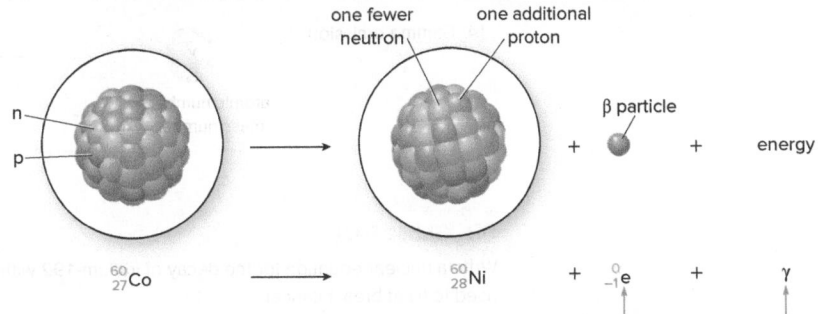

one fewer neutron   one additional proton

n

p

β particle

+   +   energy

$$^{60}_{27}\text{Co} \longrightarrow {}^{60}_{28}\text{Ni} + {}^{0}_{-1}e + \gamma$$

Both β particles and γ rays are emitted.

Cobalt-60 is used in external radiation treatment for cancer. Radiation generated by cobalt-60 decay is focused on a specific site in the body that contains cancerous cells (Figure 10.2). By directing the radiation on the tumor, damage to surrounding healthy tissues is minimized.

Figure 10.2 Focus on Health & Medicine: External Radiation Treatment for Tumors

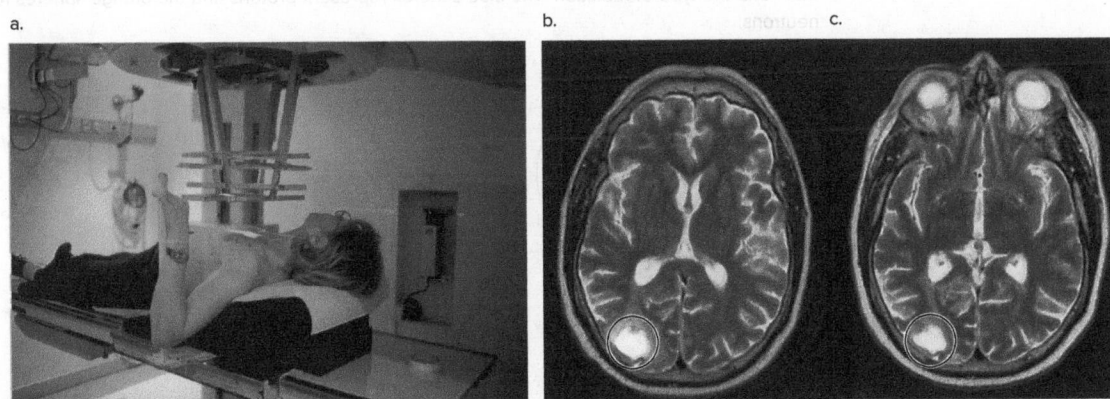

a.

b.

c.

a. Gamma radiation from the decay of cobalt-60 is used to treat a variety of tumors, especially those that cannot be surgically removed.

b. A tumor (bright area in circle) before radiation treatment

c. A tumor (bright area in circle) that has decreased in size after six months of radiation treatment

(a): ©Owen Franken/Corbis Documentary/Getty Images; (b & c): ©Custom Medical Stock Photo/CustomMedical

Table 10.2 summarizes the different types of nuclear reactions.

Table 10.2 Summary: Types of Nuclear Reactions

Type	Reaction		
[1] Alpha emission	X atomic number = Z mass number = A	$\longrightarrow$	^4_2He + Y atomic number = $Z-2$ mass number = $A-4$
[2] Beta emission	X atomic number = Z mass number = A	$\longrightarrow$	$^0_{-1}e$ + Y atomic number = $Z+1$ mass number = A
[3] Positron emission	X atomic number = Z mass number = A	$\longrightarrow$	$^0_{+1}e$ + Y atomic number = $Z-1$ mass number = A
[4] Gamma emission	X atomic number = Z mass number = A	$\longrightarrow$	γ + X atomic number = Z mass number = A

PROBLEM 10.9

Write a nuclear equation for the decay of iridium-192 with β and γ emission. Iridium implants have been used to treat breast cancer.

PROBLEM 10.10

Complete each nuclear equation.

a. $^{11}_5\text{B} \longrightarrow ? + \gamma$ b. $^{40}_{19}\text{K} \longrightarrow ? + {}^0_{-1}e + \gamma$

PROBLEM 10.11

Complete the nuclear equation by drawing the nucleus of the missing atom. Give the symbol for each atom and the type of radiation. The blue spheres represent protons and the orange spheres represent neutrons.

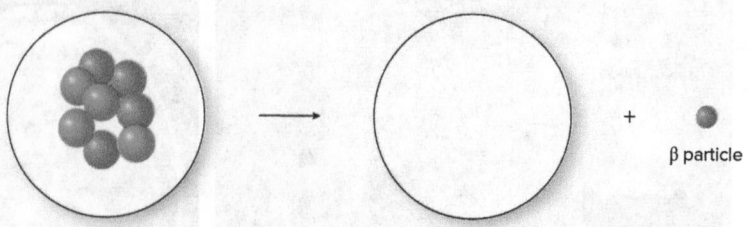
β particle

10.3 Half-Life

How fast do radioactive isotopes decay? It depends on the isotope.

- The *half-life* ($t_{1/2}$) of a radioactive isotope is the time it takes for one-half of the sample to decay.

10.3A   General Features

Suppose we have a sample that contains 16 g of phosphorus-32, a radioactive isotope that decays to sulfur-32 by β emission (Sample Problem 10.2). Phosphorus-32 has a half-life of approximately 14 days. Thus, after 14 days, the sample contains only half the amount of P-32—8.0 g. After another 14 days (a total of two half-lives), the 8.0 g of P-32 is again halved to 4.0 g. After another 14 days (a total of three half-lives), the 4.0 g of P-32 is halved to 2.0 g, and so on. Every 14 days, half of the P-32 decays.

Many naturally occurring isotopes have long half-lives. Examples include carbon-14 (5,730 years) and uranium-235 (7.0×10^8 years). Radioisotopes that are used for diagnosis and imaging in medicine have short half-lives so they do not linger in the body. Examples include technetium-99m (6.0 hours) and iodine-131 (8.0 days). The half-lives of several radioisotopes are given in Table 10.3.

The half-life of a radioactive isotope is a property of a given isotope and is independent of the amount of sample, temperature, and pressure. Thus, if the half-life and amount of a sample are known, it is possible to predict how much of the radioactive isotope will remain after a period of time.

Table 10.3 Half-Lives of Some Common Radioisotopes

Radioisotope	Symbol	Half-Life	Use
Carbon-14	$^{14}_{6}C$	5,730 years	Archaeological dating
Cobalt-60	$^{60}_{27}Co$	5.3 years	Cancer therapy
Iodine-131	$^{131}_{53}I$	8.0 days	Thyroid therapy
Potassium-40	$^{40}_{19}K$	1.3×10^9 years	Geological dating
Phosphorus-32	$^{32}_{15}P$	14.3 days	Leukemia treatment
Technetium-99m	$^{99m}_{43}Tc$	6.0 hours	Organ imaging
Uranium-235	$^{235}_{92}U$	7.0×10^8 years	Nuclear reactors

How To   **Use a Half-Life to Determine the Amount of Radioisotope Present**

Example: If the half-life of iodine-131 is 8.0 days, how much of a 100.-mg sample of iodine-131 remains after 32 days? Iodine-131 forms xenon-131 by β emission.

Step [1] **Determine how many half-lives occur in the given amount of time.**
   • Use the half-life of iodine-131 as a conversion factor to convert the number of days to the number of half-lives.

$$32 \text{ days} \times \frac{1 \text{ half-life}}{8.0 \text{ days}} = 4.0 \text{ half-lives}$$

—Continued

How To, continued . . .

Step [2] **For each half-life, multiply the initial mass by one-half to obtain the final mass.**

• Since 32 days corresponds to *four* half-lives, multiply the initial mass by ½ *four* times to obtain the final mass. After four half-lives, 6.25 mg of iodine-131 remains.

$$100. \text{ mg} \times \frac{1}{2} \times \frac{1}{2} \times \frac{1}{2} \times \frac{1}{2} = 6.25 \text{ mg of iodine-131 remains.}$$

initial mass

The mass is halved four times.

SAMPLE PROBLEM 10.4 USING A HALF-LIFE TO DETERMINE THE AMOUNT OF RADIOISOTOPE PRESENT

A radioactive element, shown with blue spheres, forms a decay product with a half-life of 2.0 min. Draw a diagram that illustrates the sample composition after 6.0 min.

initial sample

Analysis and Solution

[1] Determine how many half-lives occur in the given amount of time.

• Use the half-life as a conversion factor to convert the number of minutes to the number of half-lives.

$$6.0 \text{ min} \times \frac{1 \text{ half-life}}{2.0 \text{ min}} = 3.0 \text{ half-lives}$$

[2] For each half-life, halve the number of particles of the radioactive element.

• Because three half-lives elapse, halve the number of particles three times to show the number of radioactive particles remaining and the number of new particles (in green) formed.

initial sample   final sample
Answer

PRACTICE PROBLEM 10.4

A radioactive element (shown with blue spheres) forms a decay product (shown with green spheres) with a half-life of 22 min. (a) How many half-lives have elapsed to form the sample in diagram **A**? (b) How many minutes have elapsed in the conversion of the initial sample to **A**?

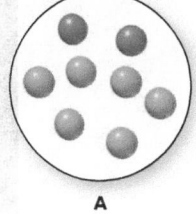

initial sample   **A**

More Practice: Try Problems 10.43–10.48.

PROBLEM 10.12

How much phosphorus-32 remains from a 1.00-g sample after each of the following number of half-lives: (a) 2; (b) 4; (c) 8?

PROBLEM 10.13

If a 160.-mg sample of technetium-99m is used for a diagnostic procedure, how much Tc-99m remains after each interval: (a) 6.0 h; (b) 18.0 h; (c) 24.0 h; (d) 2 days?

10.3B   Archaeological Dating

Archaeologists use the half-life of carbon-14 to determine the age of carbon-containing material derived from plants or animals. The technique, **radiocarbon dating,** is based on the fact that the ratio of radioactive carbon-14 to stable carbon-12 is a constant value in a living organism that is constantly taking in CO_2 and other carbon-containing nutrients from its surroundings. Once the organism dies, however, the radioactive isotope (C-14) decays (Section 10.2B) without being replenished, thus decreasing its concentration, while the stable isotope of carbon (C-12) remains at a constant value. By comparing the ratio of C-14 to C-12 in an artifact to the ratio of C-14 to C-12 in organisms today, the age of the artifact can be determined. Radiocarbon dating can be used to give the approximate age of wood, cloth, bone, charcoal, and many other substances that contain carbon.

The half-life of carbon-14 is 5,730 years, so half of the C-14 has decayed after about 6,000 years. Thus, a 6,000-year-old object has a ratio of C-14 to C-12 that has decreased by a factor of two, a 12,000-year-old object has a ratio of C-14 to C-12 that has decreased by a factor of four, and so forth.

Using this technique, archaeologists have determined the age of the paintings on cave walls in France to be about 30,000 years old (Figure 10.3). Because the amount of carbon-14 decreases with time, artifacts older than about 50,000 years have too little carbon-14 to accurately estimate their age.

PROBLEM 10.14

Estimate the age of an artifact that has 1/8 of the amount of C-14 (relative to C-12) compared to living organisms.

Figure 10.3   Radiocarbon Dating

Radiocarbon dating has been used to estimate the age of this cave painting in France at about 30,000 years. ©Javier Trueba/MSF/Science Source

A Geiger counter is a device used to detect radiation. ©Hank Morgan/Science Source

Individuals who work with radioactivity wear badges to monitor radiation levels. ©Landauer Corporation

10.4   Detecting and Measuring Radioactivity

We all receive a miniscule daily dose of radiation from cosmic rays and radioactive substances in the soil. Additional radiation exposure comes from television sets, dental X-rays, and other man-made sources. Moreover, we are still exposed to nuclear fallout, residual radiation resulting from the testing of nuclear weapons in the atmosphere decades ago.

Although this background radiation is unavoidable and minute, higher levels can be harmful and life-threatening because radiation is composed of high-energy particles and waves that damage cells and disrupt key biological processes, often causing cell death. How can radiation be detected and measured when it can't be directly observed by any of the senses?

A **Geiger counter** is a small portable device used for measuring radioactivity. It consists of a tube filled with argon gas that is ionized when it comes into contact with nuclear radiation. This in turn generates an electric current that produces a clicking sound or registers on a meter. Geiger counters are used to locate a radiation source or a site that has become contaminated by radioactivity.

Individuals who work with radioactivity wear radiation badges. These badges are regularly monitored to ensure that these individuals are not exposed to unhealthy levels of harmful radiation.

10.4A   Measuring the Radioactivity in a Sample

The amount of radioactivity in a sample is measured by the number of nuclei that decay per unit time—disintegrations per second. The most common unit is the **curie** (Ci), and smaller units are derived from it, the **millicurie** (mCi) and the **microcurie** (μCi). One curie equals 3.7×10^{10} disintegrations/second, which corresponds to the decay rate of 1 g of the element radium.

1 Ci = 3.7×10^{10} disintegrations/second

1 Ci = 1,000 mCi

1 Ci = 1,000,000 µCi

The **becquerel** (Bq), an SI unit, is also used to measure radioactivity; 1 Bq = 1 disintegration/second. Since each nuclear decay corresponds to one becquerel, 1 Ci = 3.7×10^{10} Bq. Radioactivity units are summarized in Table 10.4.

Often a dose of radiation is measured in the number of millicuries that must be administered. For example, a diagnostic test for thyroid activity uses sodium iodide that contains iodine-131—that is, $Na^{131}I$. The radioisotope is purchased with a known amount of radioactivity per milliliter, such as 3.5 mCi/mL. By knowing the amount of radioactivity a patient must be given, as well as the concentration of radioactivity in the sample, one can calculate the volume of radioactive isotope that must be administered (Sample Problem 10.5).

Table 10.4 Units Used to Measure Radioactivity

1 Ci = 3.7×10^{10} disintegrations/s

1 Ci = 3.7×10^{10} Bq

1 Ci = 1,000 mCi

1 Ci = 1,000,000 µCi

The curie is named for Polish chemist Marie Skłodowska Curie, who discovered the radioactive elements polonium and radium and received Nobel Prizes for both Chemistry and Physics in the early twentieth century.

SAMPLE PROBLEM 10.5 DETERMINING THE VOLUME OF A DOSE OF RADIOISOTOPE

A patient must be given a 4.5-mCi dose of iodine-131, which is available as a solution that contains 3.5 mCi/mL. What volume of solution must be administered?

Analysis

Use the amount of radioactivity (mCi/mL) as a conversion factor to convert the dose of radioactivity from millicuries to a volume in milliliters.

Solution

The dose of radioactivity is known in millicuries, and the amount of radioactivity per unit volume (3.5 mCi/mL) is also known. Use 3.5 mCi/mL as a millicurie–milliliter conversion factor.

mCi–mL conversion factor

$$4.5 \text{ m}\cancel{\text{Ci}} \text{ dose} \quad \times \quad \frac{1 \text{ mL}}{3.5 \text{ m}\cancel{\text{Ci}}} \quad = \quad 1.3 \text{ mL dose}$$

Millicuries cancel.

Answer

PRACTICE PROBLEM 10.5

To treat a thyroid tumor, a patient must be given a 110-mCi dose of iodine-131, supplied in a vial containing 25 mCi/mL. What volume of solution must be administered?

More Practice: Try Problems 10.55–10.58, 10.71c, 10.72c.

We can also use the half-life of a radioactive element to determine the amount of radioactivity remaining in a sample after a known interval of time (Sample Problem 10.6).

SAMPLE PROBLEM 10.6 USING HALF-LIFE TO DETERMINE THE AMOUNT OF RADIOISOTOPE REMAINING

A patient is injected with a sample of technetium-99m ($t_{1/2}$ = 6.0 h), which has an activity of 32 mCi. What activity is observed after 12 h?

Analysis

First determine how many half-lives have occurred in the time interval. Then, multiply the initial activity by the number of half-lives to determine the remaining activity.

Solution

[1] Use the half-life of technetium-99m as a conversion factor to convert the number of hours to the number of half-lives.

$$12 \ \cancel{h} \quad \times \quad \frac{1 \text{ half-life}}{6.0 \ \cancel{h}} \quad = \quad 2.0 \text{ half-lives}$$

[2] For each half-life, multiply the initial activity by 1/2 to obtain the final activity.

$$\underset{\text{initial activity}}{32 \text{ mCi}} \quad \times \quad \underbrace{\frac{1}{2} \quad \times \quad \frac{1}{2}}_{12 \text{ h} = \text{two half-lives}} \quad = \quad \underset{\textbf{Answer}}{8.0 \text{ mCi}}$$

PRACTICE PROBLEM 10.6

A sample of iodine-131 ($t_{1/2}$ = 8.0 days) has an activity of 240 mCi. What is the activity of the sample after 24 days?

More Practice: Try Problems 10.59, 10.60, 10.71b, 10.72b, 10.73c, 10.74c, 10.75c, 10.76b.

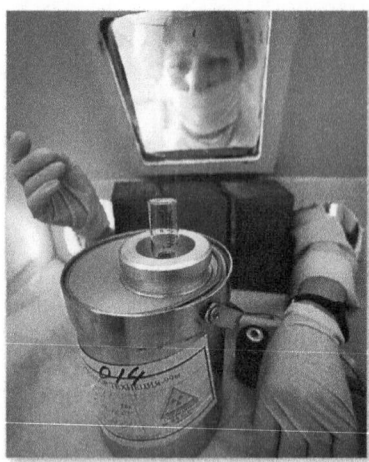

A lab worker must use protective equipment when working with radioactive substances. ©AFP/Getty Images

Strawberries that have been irradiated (on left) show no mold growth after two weeks, compared to strawberries that have not been irradiated (on right), which are moldy. ©Cordelia Molloy/Science Source

The Centers for Disease Control warns consumers that radioactive substances in cigarette smoke harm both smokers and those exposed to secondhand smoke. ©ClarkandCompany/Getty Images RF

10.4B   FOCUS ON HEALTH & MEDICINE
The Effects of Radioactivity

Radioactivity cannot be seen, smelled, tasted, heard, or felt, and yet it can have powerful effects. Because it is high in energy, nuclear radiation penetrates the surface of an object or living organism, where it can damage or kill cells. The cells that are most sensitive to radiation are those that undergo rapid cell division, such as those in bone marrow, reproductive organs, skin, and the intestinal tract. Because cancer cells rapidly divide, they are also particularly sensitive to radiation, a fact that makes radiation an effective method of cancer treatment (Section 10.5).

Alpha (α) particles, β particles, and γ rays differ in the extent to which they can penetrate a surface. Alpha particles are the heaviest of the radioactive particles, and as a result they move the slowest and penetrate the least. Individuals who work with radioisotopes that emit α particles wear lab coats and gloves that provide a layer of sufficient protection. Beta particles move much faster because they have negligible mass, and they can penetrate into body tissue. Lab workers and health professionals must wear heavy lab coats and gloves when working with substances that give off β particles. Gamma rays travel the fastest and readily penetrate body tissue. Working with substances that emit γ rays is extremely hazardous, and a thick lead shield is required to halt their penetration.

That γ rays kill cells is used to an advantage in the food industry. To decrease the incidence of harmful bacteria in foods, certain fruits and vegetables are irradiated with γ rays that kill any bacteria contained in them. **Foods do not come into contact with radioisotopes and the food is not radioactive after irradiation.** Gamma rays merely penetrate the food and destroy any live organism, and often as a result, the food product has a considerably longer shelf life.

Smokers are exposed to higher levels of radioactive elements like polonium-210. Although polonium-210 occurs naturally in soil and air and is found on tobacco leaves even after processing, when a cigarette is smoked, the smoke carries this radioactive element into the lungs. The sticky tar that builds up in the lungs of smokers traps the harmful radioactive material, and this can lead to lung cancer.

10.4C Measuring Human Exposure to Radioactivity

Several units are used to measure the amount of radiation *absorbed* by an organism.

- The rad—radiation absorbed dose—is the amount of radiation absorbed by one gram of a substance. The amount of energy absorbed varies with both the nature of the substance and the type of radiation.
- The rem—radiation equivalent for man—is the amount of radiation that also factors in its energy and potential to damage tissue. Using rem as a measure of radiation, 1 rem of any type of radiation produces the same amount of tissue damage.

Other units to measure absorbed radiation include the **gray** (1 Gy = 100 rad) and the **sievert** (1 Sv = 100 rem).

Although background radiation varies with location, the average radiation dose per year for an individual is estimated at 0.27 rem. Generally, no detectable biological effects are noticed when the dose of radiation is less than 25 rem. A single dose of 25–100 rem causes a temporary decrease in white blood cell count. The symptoms of radiation sickness—nausea, vomiting, fatigue, and prolonged decrease in white blood cell count—are visible at a dose of more than 100 rem.

Death results at still higher doses of radiation. The **LD$_{50}$—the lethal dose that kills 50% of a population**—is 500 rem in humans, and exposure to 600 rem of radiation is fatal for an entire population.

PROBLEM 10.15

The unit millirem (1 rem = 1,000 mrem) is often used to measure the amount of radiation absorbed. (a) The average yearly dose of radiation from radon gas is 200 mrem. How many rem does this correspond to? (b) If a thyroid scan exposes a patient to 0.014 rem of radiation, how many mrem does this correspond to? (c) Which represents the larger dose?

10.5 FOCUS ON HEALTH & MEDICINE
Medical Uses of Radioisotopes

Radioactive isotopes are used for both diagnostic and therapeutic procedures in medicine. In a diagnostic test to measure the function of an organ or to locate a tumor, low doses of radioactivity are generally given. When the purpose of using radiation is therapeutic, such as to kill diseased cells or cancerous tissue, a much higher dose of radiation is required.

10.5A Radioisotopes Used in Diagnosis

Radioisotopes are routinely used to determine if an organ is functioning properly or to detect the presence of a tumor. The isotope is ingested or injected and the radiation it emits can be used to produce a scan. Sometimes the isotope is an atom or ion that is not part of a larger molecule. Examples include iodine-131, which is administered as the salt sodium iodide (Na^{131}I), and xenon-133, which is a gas containing radioactive xenon atoms. At other times the radioactive atom is bonded to a larger molecule that targets a specific organ. An organ that has increased or decreased uptake of the radioactive element can indicate disease, the presence of a tumor, or other conditions.

A HIDA scan (hepatobiliary iminodiacetic acid scan) uses a technetium-99m-labeled molecule to evaluate the functioning of the gall bladder and bile ducts (Figure 10.4). After injection, the technetium-99m travels through the bloodstream and into the liver, gall bladder, and bile ducts, where, in a healthy individual, the organs are all clearly visible on a scan. When the gall bladder is inflamed or the bile ducts are obstructed by gallstones, uptake of the radioisotope does not occur and these organs are not visualized because they do not contain the radioisotope.

Figure 10.4   HIDA Scan Using Technetium-99m

a. Schematic showing the location of the liver, gall bladder, and bile ducts

b. A scan using technetium-99m showing bright areas for the liver, gall bladder, and bile ducts, indicating normal function

(b): ©Living Art Enterprises, LLC/Science Source

Figure 10.5   Bone Scan Using Technetium-99m

The bone scan of a patient whose lung cancer has spread to other organs. The anterior view [from the front in (a)] shows the spread of disease to the ribs, while the posterior view [from the back in (b)] shows spread of disease to the ribs and spine. The bright areas in the mid-torso and lower pelvis are due to a collection of radioisotope in the kidneys and bladder, before it is eliminated in the urine.
(a & b): ©Daniel C. Smith

Red blood cells tagged with technetium-99m are used to identify the site of internal bleeding in an individual. Bone scans performed with technetium-99m can show the location of metastatic cancer, so that specific sites can be targeted for radiation therapy (Figure 10.5).

Thallium-201 is used in stress tests to diagnose coronary artery disease. Thallium injected into a vein crosses cell membranes into normal heart muscle. Little radioactive thallium is found in

10.5 Focus on Health & Medicine: Medical Uses of Radioisotopes   **373**

areas of the heart that have a poor blood supply. This technique is used to identify individuals who may need bypass surgery or other interventions because of blocked coronary arteries.

PROBLEM 10.16

The half-life of thallium-201 is three days. What fraction of thallium-201 is still present in an individual after nine days?

Tiny seeds (shown next to a penny to illustrate their size) made of titanium with a small amount of iodine-125 are implanted near the prostate to treat prostate cancer. Because radiation is confined to a localized region, nearby organs such as the bladder and rectum receive only minimal radiation.
©David A. Tietz/Editorial Image, LLC RF

10.5B Radioisotopes Used in Treatment

The high-energy radiation emitted by radioisotopes can be used to kill rapidly dividing tumor cells. Two techniques are used. Sometimes the radiation source is external to the body. For example, a beam of radiation produced by decaying cobalt-60 can be focused at a tumor. Such a radiation source must have a much longer half-life—5.3 years in this case—than radioisotopes that are ingested for diagnostic purposes. With this method some destruction of healthy tissue often occurs, and a patient may experience some signs of radiation sickness, including vomiting, fatigue, and hair loss.

A more selective approach to cancer treatment involves brachytherapy, the implantation of a radioactive isotope internally at the site of the tumor within the body. Examples include using radioactive "seeds" or wire that can be implanted close to a tumor. Iodine-125 seeds are used to treat prostate cancer, and iridium-192 wire is used to treat some cancers of the breast.

Figure 10.6 illustrates radioisotopes that are used for diagnosis or treatment.

Figure 10.6   Common Radioisotopes Used in Medicine

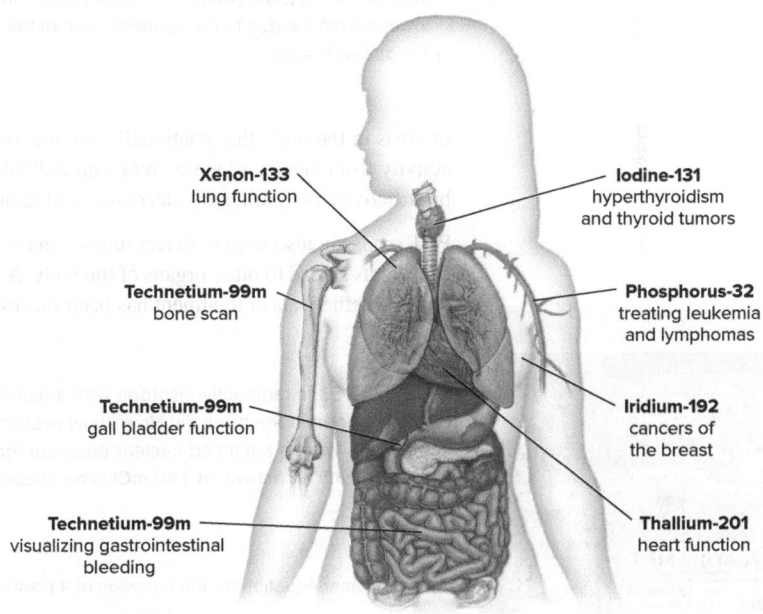

Xenon-133
lung function

Iodine-131
hyperthyroidism
and thyroid tumors

Technetium-99m
bone scan

Phosphorus-32
treating leukemia
and lymphomas

Technetium-99m
gall bladder function

Iridium-192
cancers of
the breast

Technetium-99m
visualizing gastrointestinal
bleeding

Thallium-201
heart function

10.5C Positron Emission Tomography—PET Scans

Positron emission tomography (PET) scans use radioisotopes that emit positrons when the nucleus decays. Once formed, a positron combines with an electron to form two γ rays, which create a scan of an organ.

Carbon-11, oxygen-15, nitrogen-13, and fluorine-18 are common radioactive isotopes used in PET scans. For example, a carbon-11 or fluorine-18 isotope can be incorporated in a glucose molecule. When this radioactive molecule is taken internally, its concentration becomes highest

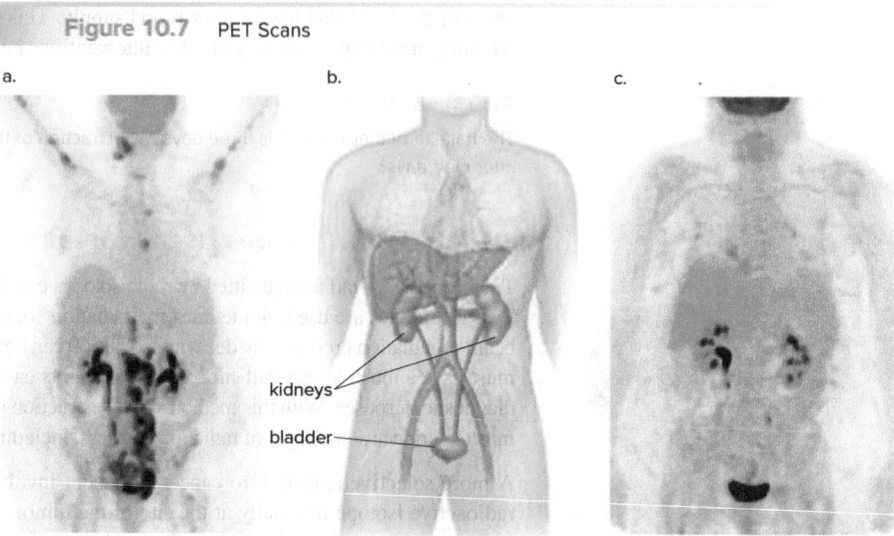

Figure 10.7   PET Scans

a.

b.

c.

kidneys

bladder

a. The PET scan shows cancer of the lymph nodes in the neck and abdomen, as well as scattered areas of tumor in the bone marrow of the arms and spine before treatment.

b. The schematic of selected organs in the torso and pelvis

c. The PET scan shows significant clearing of disease after chemotherapy by the decrease in intensity of the radioisotope. The dark regions in the kidneys (in the torso) and bladder (in the lower pelvis) are due to the concentration of the radioisotope before elimination in the urine.

(a & c): ©Daniel C. Smith

in areas in the body that continually use glucose. A healthy brain shows a high level of radio-activity from labeled glucose. When an individual suffers a stroke or has Alzheimer's disease, brain activity is significantly decreased and radioactivity levels are decreased.

PET scans are also used to detect tumors and coronary artery disease and to determine whether cancer has spread to other organs of the body. A PET scan is also a noninvasive method of moni-toring whether cancer treatment has been successful (Figure 10.7).

PROBLEM 10.17

Samarium-153, a radioactive isotope with a half-life of approximately 48 hours, is used to treat cancers lodged in the bone. (a) How many protons, neutrons, and electrons does samarium-153 contain? (b) Write a balanced nuclear equation for the emission of a β particle from samarium-153. (c) If a vial with an activity of 150 mCi is purchased, what is the activity of the solution after eight days?

PROBLEM 10.18

Write a nuclear equation for the emission of a positron from nitrogen-13.

10.6   Nuclear Fission and Nuclear Fusion

The nuclear reactions used in nuclear power plants occur by a process called *nuclear fission,* whereas the nuclear reactions that take place in the sun occur by a process called *nuclear fusion.*

- *Nuclear fission* is the splitting apart of a heavy nucleus into lighter nuclei and neutrons.
- *Nuclear fusion* is the joining together of two light nuclei to form a larger nucleus.

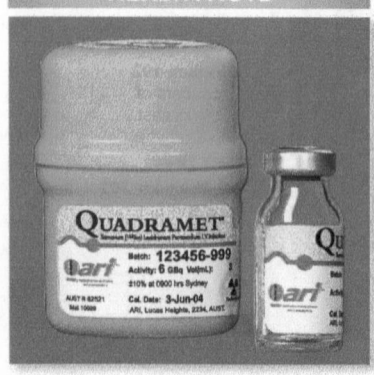

10.6A Nuclear Fission

When uranium-235 is bombarded by a neutron, it undergoes **nuclear fission** and splits apart into two lighter nuclei. Several different fission products have been identified. One common nuclear reaction is the fission of uranium-235 into krypton-91 and barium-142.

$$^{235}_{92}\text{U} \quad + \quad ^{1}_{0}\text{n} \quad \longrightarrow \quad ^{91}_{36}\text{Kr} \quad + \quad ^{142}_{56}\text{Ba} \quad + \quad 3\,^{1}_{0}\text{n}$$

Each neutron can react with more uranium-235.

More fission products and more neutrons are formed.

Three high-energy neutrons are also produced in the reaction as well as a great deal of energy. Whereas burning one gram of methane in natural gas releases 13 kcal of energy, fission of one gram of uranium-235 releases 3.4×10^8 kcal. Each neutron produced during fission can go on to bombard three other uranium-235 nuclei to produce more nuclei and more neutrons. Such a process is called a **chain reaction.**

In order to sustain a chain reaction there must be a sufficient amount of uranium-235. When that amount—the **critical mass**—is present, the chain reaction occurs over and over again and an atomic explosion occurs. When less than the critical mass of uranium-235 is present, there is a more controlled production of energy, as is the case in a nuclear power plant.

A nuclear power plant utilizes the tremendous amount of energy produced by fission of the uranium-235 nucleus to heat water to steam, which powers a generator to produce electricity (Figure 10.8). While nuclear energy accounts for a small but significant fraction of the electricity needs in the United States, most of the electricity generated in some European countries comes from nuclear power.

Figure 10.8 A Nuclear Power Plant

©Martin Bond/Science Source

a. Nuclear power plant with steam rising from a cooling tower

b. Fission occurs in a nuclear reactor core that is housed in a containment facility. Water surrounding the reactor is heated by the energy released during fission, and this energy drives a turbine, which produces electricity. Once the steam has been used to drive the turbine, it is cooled and re-circulated around the core of the reactor. To prevent the loss of any radioactive material to the environment, the water that surrounds the reactor core never leaves the containment building.

Two problems that surround nuclear power generation are the possibility of radiation leaks and the disposal of nuclear waste. Plants are designed and monitored to contain the radioactive materials within the nuclear reactor. The reactor core itself is located in a containment facility with thick walls, so that should a leak occur, the radiation should in principle be kept within the building. The nuclear reactor in Chernobyl, Russia, was built without a containment facility and in 1986 it exploded, releasing high levels of radioactivity to the immediate environment and sending a cloud of radioactivity over much of Europe.

The products of nuclear fission are radioactive nuclei with long half-lives, often hundreds or even thousands of years. As a result, nuclear fission generates radioactive waste that must be stored in a secure facility, so that it does not pose a hazard to the immediate surroundings. Burying waste far underground is currently considered the best option, but this issue is still unresolved.

SAMPLE PROBLEM 10.7 BALANCING A NUCLEAR EQUATION FOR A FISSION REACTION

Write a nuclear equation for the fission of uranium-235 by neutron bombardment to form strontium-90, an isotope of xenon, and three neutrons.

Analysis

Balance the atomic numbers and mass numbers on both sides of the nuclear equation. In fission reactions, include the neutron used for bombardment on the left and the high-energy neutrons produced on the right. Each neutron has a mass of one and zero charge.

Solution

[1] Write an incomplete equation with the original nucleus and neutron used for bombardment on the left, and the particles formed on the right.

- Use the identity of each element to determine its atomic number. Uranium has an atomic number of 92, strontium has an atomic number of 38, and xenon has an atomic number of 54.
- Include one neutron on the left side. In this reaction, three high-energy neutrons are formed, so include three neutrons on the right side.

$$^{235}_{92}U + ^{1}_{0}n \longrightarrow ^{90}_{38}Sr + ^{?}_{54}Xe + 3\,^{1}_{0}n$$

[2] Calculate the mass numbers and atomic numbers of all newly formed nuclei on the right.

- Atomic number: In this problem all atomic numbers are known from the identity of the elements.
- Mass number: **Balance mass numbers by taking into account the mass of the neutrons used or produced in the reaction.** On the left side, the total mass of the particles (the uranium nucleus and one neutron) is 236 (235 + 1). On the right side, the sum of the masses of Sr-90, xenon, and three neutrons (total mass of three) must also equal 236.

$$236 = 90 + ? + 3(1)$$ three neutrons / one mass unit from each neutron
$$236 = 93 + ?$$
$$143 = ?$$

The mass number of xenon is 143.

[3] Write the complete equation.

$$^{235}_{92}U + ^{1}_{0}n \longrightarrow ^{90}_{38}Sr + ^{143}_{54}Xe + 3\,^{1}_{0}n$$

PRACTICE PROBLEM 10.7

Write a nuclear equation for the fission of uranium-235 by neutron bombardment to form antimony-133, three neutrons, and one other isotope.

More Practice: Try Problems 10.65, 10.66.

10.6B Nuclear Fusion

Nuclear fusion occurs when two light nuclei join together to form a larger nucleus. For example, fusion of a deuterium nucleus with a tritium nucleus forms helium and a neutron. Recall from Section 2.3 that deuterium is an isotope of hydrogen that contains one proton and one neutron in its nucleus, whereas tritium is an isotope of hydrogen that contains one proton and two neutrons in its nucleus.

$$^2_1\text{H} + {}^3_1\text{H} \longrightarrow {}^4_2\text{He} + {}^1_0\text{n}$$

deuterium   tritium   helium

Like fission, fusion also releases a great deal of energy—namely, 5.3×10^8 kcal/mol of helium produced. The light and heat of the sun and other stars result from nuclear fusion.

One limitation of using fusion to provide energy for mankind is the extreme experimental conditions needed to produce it. Because it takes a considerable amount of energy to overcome the repulsive forces of the like charges of two nuclei, fusion can only be accomplished at high temperatures (greater than 100,000,000 °C) and pressures (greater than 100,000 atm). Since these conditions are not easily achieved, using controlled nuclear fusion as an energy source has yet to become a reality.

Controlled nuclear fusion has the potential of providing cheap and clean power. It is not plagued by the nuclear waste issues of fission reactors, and the needed reactants are readily available.

SAMPLE PROBLEM 10.8 DRAWING THE PRODUCTS OF NUCLEAR FUSION

Complete the nuclear fusion equation by drawing the nucleus of the missing species. Give the symbol for each reactant and product.

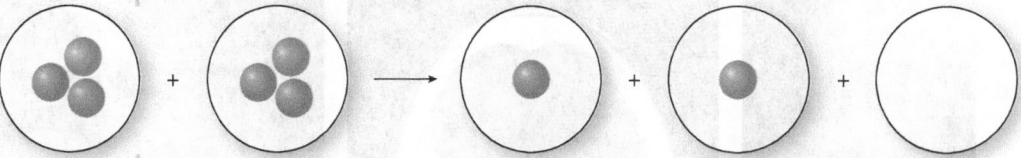

Analysis

Count the number of protons and neutrons on both sides of the equation and draw a new nucleus that has enough protons and neutrons to balance the atomic number and mass number.

Solution

The new nucleus needs two protons (in blue) and two neutrons (in orange) to make the mass number and atomic number equal on both sides of the equation. The number of protons determines the identity of the atom in the isotope symbol; He has two protons and H has one proton.

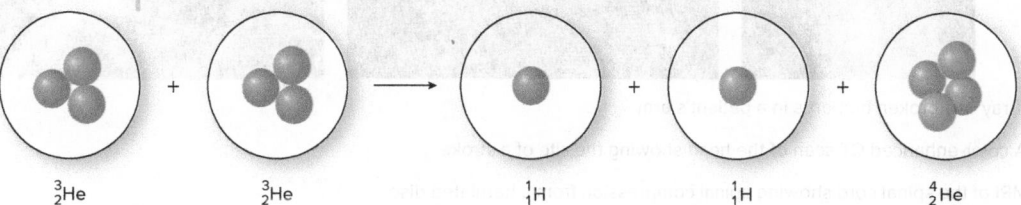

^3_2He ^3_2He ^1_1H ^1_1H ^4_2He

Answer

PRACTICE PROBLEM 10.8

Nuclear fusion in the stars occurs by a series of reactions. Identify **X, Y,** and **Z** in the following nuclear reactions that ultimately convert hydrogen into helium.

a. $^1_1H + X \longrightarrow {}^2_1H + {}^0_{+1}e$

b. $^1_1H + {}^2_1H \longrightarrow Y$

c. $^1_1H + {}^3_2He \longrightarrow {}^4_2He + Z$

More Practice: Try Problems 10.67–10.69, 10.77, 10.78.

10.7 FOCUS ON HEALTH & MEDICINE
Medical Imaging Without Radioactivity

X-rays, CT scans, and **MRIs** are also techniques that provide an image of an organ or extremity that is used for diagnosis of a medical condition. Unlike PET scans and other procedures discussed thus far, however, **these procedures are *not* based on nuclear reactions and they do *not* utilize radioactivity.** In each technique, an energy source is directed towards a specific region in the body, and a scan is produced that is analyzed by a trained medical professional.

X-rays are a high-energy type of radiation called electromagnetic radiation. Tissues of different density interact differently with an X-ray beam, so a map of bone and internal organs is created on an X-ray film. Dense bone is clearly visible in an X-ray, making it a good diagnostic technique for finding fractures (Figure 10.9a). Although X-rays are a form of high-energy radiation, they are lower in energy than the γ rays produced in nuclear reactions. Nonetheless, X-rays still cause adverse biological effects on the cells with which they come in contact, and the exposure of both the patient and X-ray technician must be limited.

Figure 10.9   Imaging the Human Body

a.

b.

c.

herniated disc

a. X-ray of a broken humerus in a patient's arm

b. A color-enhanced CT scan of the head showing the site of a stroke

c. MRI of the spinal cord showing spinal compression from a herniated disc

(a): ©Suttha Burawonk/Shutterstock RF; (b): ©Scott Camazine/Science Source; (c): ©Daniel C. Smith

CT (computed tomography) scans, which also use X-rays, provide high resolution images of "slices" of the body. Historically, CT images have shown a slice of tissue perpendicular to the long axis of the body. Modern CT scanners can now provide a three-dimensional view of the body's organs. CT scans of the head are used to diagnose bleeding and tumors in the brain (Figure 10.9b).

MRI (magnetic resonance imaging) uses low-energy radio waves to visualize internal organs. Unlike methods that use high-energy radiation, MRIs do not damage cells. An MRI is a good diagnostic method for visualizing soft tissue (Figure 10.9c), and thus it complements X-ray techniques.

CHAPTER HIGHLIGHTS

KEY TERMS

Alpha (α) particle (10.1)

Becquerel (10.4)

Beta (β) particle (10.1)

Chain reaction (10.6)

Critical mass (10.6)

Curie (10.4)

Gamma (γ) ray (10.1)

Geiger counter (10.4)

Gray (10.4)

Half-life (10.3)

LD_{50} (10.4)

Nuclear fission (10.6)

Nuclear fusion (10.6)

Nuclear reaction (10.2)

Positron (10.1)

Rad (10.4)

Radioactive decay (10.2)

Radioactive isotope (10.1)

Radioactivity (10.1)

Radiocarbon dating (10.3)

Rem (10.4)

Sievert (10.4)

X-ray (10.7)

KEY CONCEPTS

1 Describe the different types of radiation emitted by a radioactive nucleus. (10.1)

- A radioactive nucleus can emit α particles, β particles, positrons, or γ rays.
- An α particle is a high-energy nucleus that contains two protons and two neutrons.
- A β particle is a high-energy electron that has a −1 charge and negligible mass.
- A positron is an antiparticle of a β particle. A positron has a +1 charge and negligible mass.
- A γ ray is high-energy radiation with no mass or charge.

2 How are equations for nuclear reactions written? (10.2)

- In an equation for a nuclear reaction, the sum of the mass numbers (A) must be equal on both sides of the equation. The sum of the atomic numbers (Z) must be equal on both sides of the equation as well.

3 What is the half-life of a radioactive isotope? (10.3)

- The half-life ($t_{1/2}$) is the time it takes for one-half of a radioactive sample to decay. Knowing the half-life and the amount of a radioactive substance, one can calculate how much sample remains after a period of time.

4 What units are used to measure radioactivity? (10.4)

- Radiation in a sample is measured by the number of disintegrations per second, most often using the curie (Ci); $1 \text{ Ci} = 3.7 \times 10^{10}$ disintegrations/s. The becquerel (Bq) is also used; $1 \text{ Bq} = 1$ disintegration/s; $1 \text{ Ci} = 3.7 \times 10^{10}$ Bq.
- The exposure of a substance to radioactivity is measured with the rad (radiation absorbed dose) or the rem (radiation equivalent for man).

5 Give examples of common radioisotopes used in medicine. (10.5)

- Iodine-131 is used to diagnose and treat thyroid disease.
- Technetium-99m is used to evaluate the functioning of the gall bladder and bile ducts, and in bone scans to evaluate the spread of cancer.
- Red blood cells tagged with technetium-99m are used to find the site of a gastrointestinal bleed.
- Thallium-201 is used to diagnose coronary artery disease.
- Cobalt-60 is used as an external source of radiation for cancer treatment.
- Iodine-125 and iridium-192 are used in internal radiation treatment of prostate cancer and breast cancer, respectively.
- Carbon-11, oxygen-15, nitrogen-13, and fluorine-18 are used in positron emission tomography.

6 What are nuclear fission and nuclear fusion? (10.6)

- Nuclear fission is the splitting apart of a heavy nucleus into lighter nuclei and neutrons.
- Nuclear fusion is the joining together of two light nuclei to form a larger nucleus.
- Both nuclear fission and nuclear fusion release a great deal of energy. Nuclear fission is used in nuclear power plants to generate electricity. Nuclear fusion occurs in stars.

7 What medical imaging techniques do not use radioactivity? (10.7)

- X-rays and CT scans both use X-rays, a high-energy form of electromagnetic radiation.
- MRIs use low-energy radio waves to image soft tissue.

380   **Chapter 10** Nuclear Chemistry

PROBLEMS

Selected in-chapter and odd-numbered end-of-chapter problems have brief answers in Appendix B. The *Student Study Guide and Solutions Manual* contains detailed solutions to all in-chapter and odd-numbered end-of-chapter problems, as well as additional worked examples and a chapter self-test.

Isotopes and Radiation

10.19 For each isotope of fluorine, whose nuclei are shown in the accompanying diagrams, give its: (a) atomic number; (b) mass number; (c) number of protons; (d) number of neutrons; (e) isotope symbol. One isotope is a stable nucleus and one is a radioisotope used in PET scans.

A   B

10.20 For each isotope of nitrogen, whose nuclei are shown in the accompanying diagrams, give its: (a) atomic number; (b) mass number; (c) number of protons; (d) number of neutrons; (e) isotope symbol. One isotope is a stable nucleus and one is a radioisotope used in PET scans.

A   B

10.21 Complete the table of isotopes, each of which has found use in medicine.

	Atomic Number	Mass Number	Number of Protons	Number of Neutrons	Isotope Symbol
a. Chromium-51					
b.	46	103			
c.			19	23	
d.		133	54		

10.22 Complete the table of isotopes, each of which has found use in medicine.

	Atomic Number	Mass Number	Number of Protons	Number of Neutrons	Isotope Symbol
a. Sodium-24					
b.		89		51	
c.		59	26		
d. Samarium-153					

10.23 How much does the mass and charge of a nucleus change when each type of radiation is emitted: (a) α particle; (b) β particle; (c) γ ray; (d) positron?

10.24 Compare α particles, β particles, and γ rays with regard to each of the following: (a) speed the radiation travels; (b) penetrating power; (c) protective equipment that must be worn when handling.

10.25 What is the mass and charge of radiation that has each of the following symbols: (a) α; (b) n; (c) γ; (d) β?

10.26 What is the mass and charge of radiation that has each of the following symbols?

  a. $_{-1}^{0}e$ b. $_{+1}^{0}e$ c. $_{2}^{4}He$ d. $β^+$

Nuclear Reactions

10.27 What particle is emitted when each of the following nuclear reactions occurs? Write a balanced nuclear equation for the process.
  a. Cobalt-60 decays to nickel-60.
  b. Cobalt-55 decays to iron-55.
  c. Radon-220 decays to polonium-216.

10.28 What particle is emitted when each of the following nuclear reactions occurs? Write a balanced nuclear equation for the process.
  a. Platinum-175 decays to osmium-171.
  b. Magnesium-23 decays to sodium-23.
  c. Sodium-22 decays to neon-22.

10.29 Complete the nuclear equation by drawing the nucleus of the missing atom. Give the symbol for each atom and type of radiation. The blue spheres represent protons and the orange spheres represent neutrons.

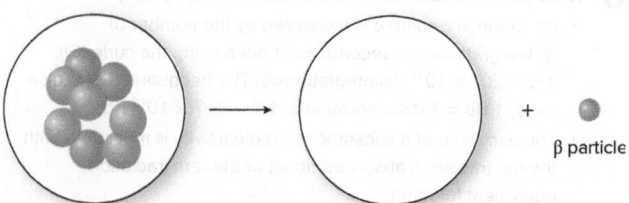

β particle

10.30 Complete the nuclear equation by drawing the nucleus of the missing atom. Give the symbol for each atom and the type of radiation. The blue spheres represent protons and the orange spheres represent neutrons.

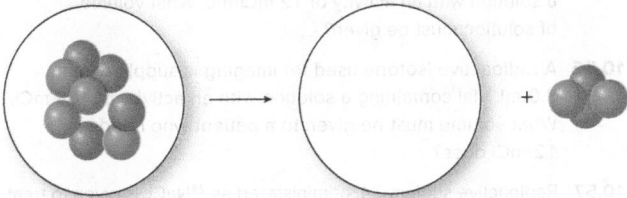

10.31 Complete the nuclear equation by drawing the nucleus of the missing atom. Give the symbol for each atom and type of radiation. (The blue spheres represent protons and the orange spheres represent neutrons.)

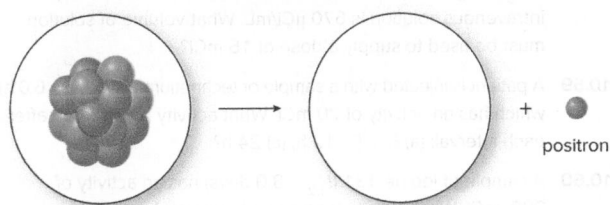

positron

10.32 Complete the nuclear equation by drawing the nucleus of the missing atom. Give the symbol for each atom and type of radiation. (The blue spheres represent protons and the orange spheres represent neutrons.)

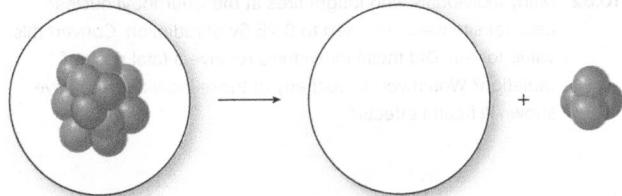

10.33 Complete each nuclear equation.
 a. $^{59}_{26}Fe \longrightarrow ? + ^{0}_{-1}e$ c. $^{178}_{80}Hg \longrightarrow ? + ^{0}_{+1}e$
 b. $^{190}_{78}Pt \longrightarrow ? + ^{4}_{2}He$

10.34 Complete each nuclear equation.
 a. $^{77}_{37}Rb \longrightarrow ? + ^{0}_{+1}e$ c. $^{66}_{29}Cu \longrightarrow ? + ^{0}_{-1}e$
 b. $^{251}_{102}No \longrightarrow ? + ^{4}_{2}He$

10.35 Complete each nuclear equation.
 a. $^{90}_{39}Y \longrightarrow ^{90}_{40}Zr + ?$ c. $^{210}_{83}Bi \longrightarrow ? + ^{4}_{2}He$
 b. $? \longrightarrow ^{135}_{59}Pr + ^{0}_{+1}e$

10.36 Complete each nuclear equation.
 a. $? \longrightarrow ^{90}_{39}Y + ^{0}_{-1}e$ c. $^{214}_{84}Po \longrightarrow ? + ^{4}_{2}He$
 b. $^{29}_{15}P \longrightarrow ^{29}_{14}Si + ?$

10.37 Bismuth-214 can decay to form either polonium-214 or thallium-210, depending on what type of radiation is emitted. Write a balanced nuclear equation for each process.

10.38 Lead-210 can be formed by the decay of either thallium-210 or polonium-214, depending on what type of radiation is

emitted. Write a balanced nuclear equation for each process.

10.39 Write a balanced nuclear equation for each reaction.
 a. decay of thorium-232 by α emission
 b. decay of sodium-25 by β emission
 c. decay of xenon-118 by positron emission
 d. decay of curium-243 by α emission

10.40 Write a balanced nuclear equation for each reaction.
 a. decay of sulfur-35 by β emission
 b. decay of thorium-225 by α emission
 c. decay of rhodium-93 by positron emission
 d. decay of silver-114 by β emission

10.41 If thorium-232 decays by emitting both an α particle and a β particle, what product is formed?

10.42 If polonium-216 decays by emitting an α particle and two β particles, what product is formed?

Half-Life

10.43 A radioactive element (shown with blue spheres) forms a decay product (shown with green spheres) with a half-life of three days. How many half-lives have elapsed in diagram **A?**

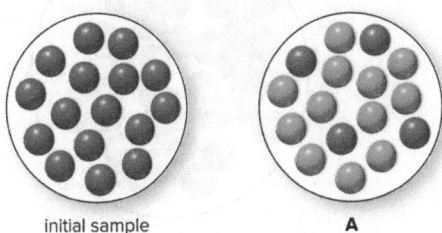

initial sample   A

10.44 A radioactive element (shown with blue spheres) forms a decay product (shown with green spheres) with a half-life of 10 min. How many minutes have elapsed to form the sample in diagram **B?**

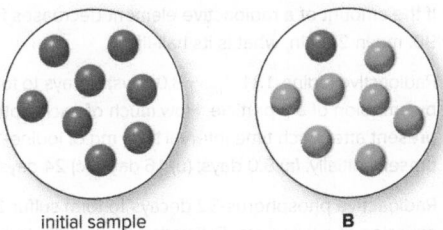

initial sample   B

10.45 Using the diagram in the *How To* in Section 10.3A as a guide, fill in the boxes in the following representation, which illustrates the decay of **A** to **B.** Indicate how many grams of **A** and **B** are present at each interval ($t_{1/2}$ = 2 days).

10.46 Using the diagram in the *How To* in Section 10.3A as a guide, fill in the boxes in the following representation, which illustrates the decay of **C** to **D**. Indicate how many grams of **C** and **D** are present at each interval.

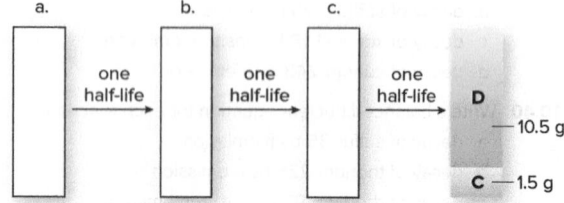

10.47 A radioactive sample consists of 32 particles of a radioisotope that has a half-life of decay of 2 minutes. (a) How many decays occur during the first two-minute interval? (b) How many decays occur during the second 2-minute interval?

10.48 A radioactive element, shown with blue spheres, forms a decay product with a half-life of 3 minutes. Draw a diagram that illustrates the sample composition after 12 minutes.

initial sample

10.49 If the amount of a radioactive element decreases from 2.4 g to 0.30 g in 12 days, what is its half-life?

10.50 If the amount of a radioactive element decreases from 0.36 g to 90. mg in 22 min, what is its half-life?

10.51 Radioactive iodine-131 ($t_{1/2}$ = 8.0 days) decays to form xenon-131 by emission of a β particle. How much of each isotope is present after each time interval if 64 mg of iodine-131 was present initially: (a) 8.0 days; (b) 16 days; (c) 24 days; (d) 32 days?

10.52 Radioactive phosphorus-32 decays to form sulfur-32 by emission of a β particle. Estimating the half-life to be 14 days, how much of each isotope is present after each time interval if 124 mg of phosphorus-32 was present initially: (a) 14 days; (b) 28 days; (c) 42 days; (d) 56 days?

Measuring Radioactivity

10.53 If a radioactive sample had an activity of 5.0 mCi, how many disintegrations per second does this correspond to?

10.54 Suggest a reason why the average amount of background radiation is generally higher at higher elevations.

10.55 A patient must be administered a 28-mCi dose of technetium-99m, which is supplied in a vial containing a solution with an activity of 12 mCi/mL. What volume of solution must be given?

10.56 A radioactive isotope used for imaging is supplied in an 8.0-mL vial containing a solution with an activity of 108 mCi. What volume must be given to a patient who needs a 12-mCi dose?

10.57 Radioactive sodium-24, administered as $^{24}NaCl$, is given to treat leukemia. If a patient must receive 190 μCi/kg and the isotope is supplied as a solution that contains 5.0 mCi/mL, what volume is needed for a 68-kg patient?

10.58 Radioactive phosphorus-32, administered as sodium phosphate ($Na_3{}^{32}PO_4$), is used to treat chronic leukemia. The activity of an intravenous solution is 670 μCi/mL. What volume of solution must be used to supply a dose of 15 mCi?

10.59 A patient is injected with a sample of technetium-99m ($t_{1/2}$ = 6.0 h), which has an activity of 20 mCi. What activity is observed after each interval: (a) 6 h; (b) 12 h; (c) 24 h?

10.60 A sample of iodine-131 ($t_{1/2}$ = 8.0 days) has an activity of 200. mCi. What activity is observed after each interval: (a) 8.0 days; (b) 24 days; (c) 48 days?

10.61 The initial responders to the Chernobyl nuclear disaster were exposed to 20 Sv of radiation. Convert this value to rem. Did these individuals receive a fatal dose of radiation?

10.62 Many individuals who fought fires at the Chernobyl nuclear disaster site were exposed to 0.25 Sv of radiation. Convert this value to rem. Did these individuals receive a fatal dose of radiation? Would you expect any of these individuals to have shown ill health effects?

Nuclear Fission and Nuclear Fusion

10.63 For which process does each statement apply—nuclear fission, nuclear fusion, both fission and fusion?
  a. The reaction occurs in the sun.
  b. A neutron is used to bombard a nucleus.
  c. A large amount of energy is released.
  d. Very high temperatures are required.

10.64 For which process does each statement apply—nuclear fission, nuclear fusion, both fission and fusion?
  a. The reaction splits a nucleus into lighter nuclei.
  b. The reaction joins two lighter nuclei into a heavier nucleus.
  c. The reaction is used to generate energy in a nuclear power plant.
  d. The reaction generates radioactive waste with a long half-life.

10.65 Complete each nuclear fission equation.

a. $^{235}_{92}U + ^{1}_{0}n \longrightarrow ? + ^{97}_{42}Mo + 2\,^{1}_{0}n$

b. $^{235}_{92}U + ^{1}_{0}n \longrightarrow ? + ^{140}_{56}Ba + 3\,^{1}_{0}n$

10.66 Complete each nuclear fission equation.

a. $^{235}_{92}U + ^{1}_{0}n \longrightarrow ? + ^{139}_{57}La + 2\,^{1}_{0}n$

b. $^{235}_{92}U + ^{1}_{0}n \longrightarrow ? + ^{140}_{58}Ce + 2\,^{1}_{0}n + 6\,^{0}_{-1}e$

10.67 Complete the nuclear fusion equation by drawing in the nucleus of the missing atom. Blue spheres represent protons and orange spheres represent neutrons.

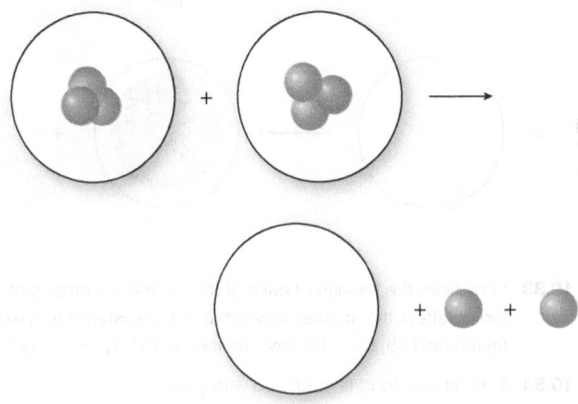

10.68 Complete the nuclear fusion equation by drawing in the nucleus of the missing atom. Blue spheres represent protons and orange spheres represent neutrons.

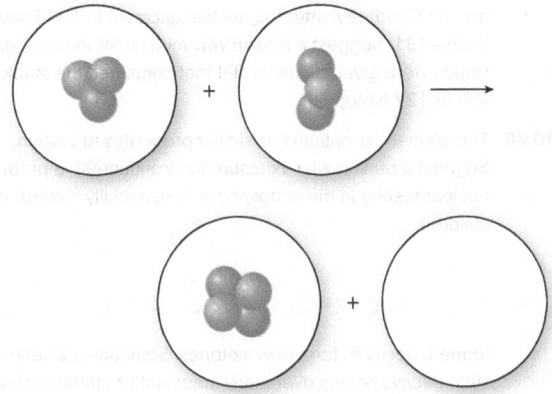

10.69 The fusion of two deuterium nuclei (hydrogen-2) forms a hydrogen nucleus (hydrogen-1) as one product. What other product is formed?

10.70 Discuss two problems that surround the generation of electricity from a nuclear power plant.

General Questions

10.71 Arsenic-74 is a radioisotope used for locating brain tumors.

a. Write a balanced nuclear equation for the positron emission of arsenic-74.

b. If $t_{1/2}$ for As-74 is 18 days, how much of a 120-mg sample remains after 90. days?

c. If the radioactivity of a 2.0-mL vial of arsenic-74 is 10.0 mCi, what volume must be administered to give a 7.5-mCi dose?

10.72 Sodium-24 is a radioisotope used for examining circulation.

a. Write a balanced nuclear equation for the β decay of sodium-24.

b. If $t_{1/2}$ for Na-24 is 15 h, how much of an 84-mg sample remains after 2.5 days?

c. If the radioactivity of a 5.0-mL vial of sodium-24 is 10.0 mCi, what volume must be administered to give a 6.5-mCi dose?

10.73 Strontium-89 is a radioactive isotope ($t_{1/2} = 50.$ days) used to reduce the pain of prostate and bone cancer. (a) How many protons, neutrons, and electrons does strontium-89 contain? (b) Write a balanced nuclear equation for the emission of a β particle from strontium-89. (c) If a vial contains 10.0 μg of strontium-89, how much of the radioisotope remains after 200. days?

10.74 Rhenium-186 is a radioactive isotope ($t_{1/2} = 4.0$ days) used for pain relief in bone cancer. (a) How many protons, neutrons, and electrons does rhenium-186 contain? (b) Write a balanced nuclear equation for the emission of a β particle from rhenium-186. (c) If a vial contains 200. μg of rhenium-186, how much of the radioisotope remains after 16 days?

10.75 Answer the following questions about radioactive iridium-192.

a. Write a balanced nuclear equation for the decay of iridium-192, which emits both a β particle and a γ ray.

b. If $t_{1/2}$ for Ir-192 is 74 days, estimate how much of a 120-mg sample remains after five 30-day months.

c. If a sample of Ir-192 had an initial activity of 36 Ci, estimate how much activity remains in the sample after ten 30-day months.

10.76 Answer the following questions about radioactive samarium-153 (Section 10.5C).

a. If $t_{1/2}$ for Sm-153 is 46 h, estimate how much of a 160-mg sample remains after four days.

b. If a sample of Sm-153 has an initial activity of 48 Ci, estimate how much activity remains in the sample after 6 days.

384   Chapter 10   Nuclear Chemistry

10.77 All nuclei with atomic numbers around 100 or larger do not exist naturally; rather, they have been synthesized by fusing two lighter-weight nuclei together. Using the principles for balancing nuclear reactions in Section 10.2, complete the nuclear equation by drawing the nucleus of the missing atom **X.** Give the element symbol, atomic number, and mass number of **X.**

10.78 Using the principles for balancing nuclear reactions in Section 10.2, complete the nuclear equation by drawing the nucleus of the missing atom **Y.** Give the element symbol, atomic number, and mass number of **Y.**

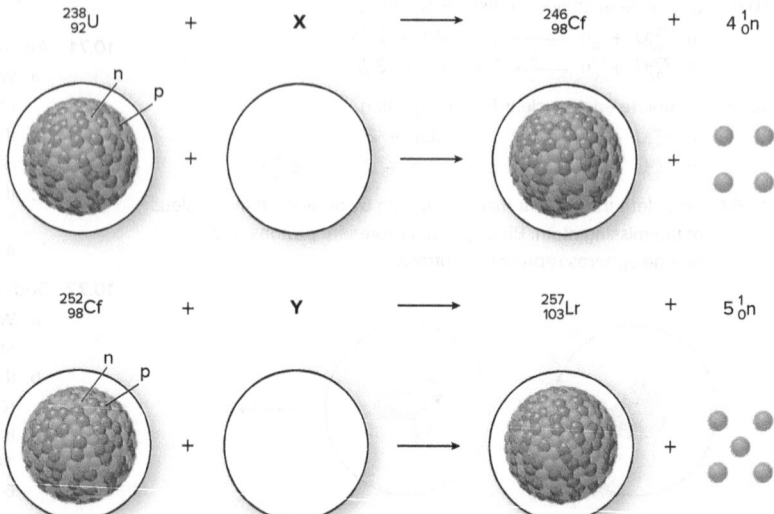

10.79 Complete the following nuclear equation by giving the name, atomic number, and mass number of the element made by this reaction.

$$^{209}_{83}Bi + ^{58}_{26}Fe \longrightarrow ? + ^{1}_{0}n$$

10.80 Complete the following nuclear equation, and give the name, atomic number, and mass number of the element made by this reaction.

$$^{235}_{92}U + ^{14}_{7}N \longrightarrow ? + 5\,^{1}_{0}n$$

Applications

10.81 Explain how each isotope is used in medicine.
  a. iodine-131
  b. iridium-192
  c. thallium-201

10.82 Explain how each isotope is used in medicine.
  a. iodine-125
  b. technetium-99m
  c. cobalt-60

10.83 How does the half-life of each of the following isotopes of iodine affect the manner in which it is administered to a patient: (a) iodine-125, $t_{1/2}$ = 60 days; (b) iodine-131, $t_{1/2}$ = 8 days?

10.84 Explain why food is irradiated with γ rays.

10.85 A mammogram is an X-ray of the breast. Why does an X-ray technician leave the room or go behind a shield when a mammogram is performed on a patient?

10.86 Why is a lead apron placed over a patient's body when dental X-rays are taken?

10.87 One of the radioactive isotopes that contaminated the area around Chernobyl after the nuclear accident in 1986 was iodine-131. Suggest a reason why individuals in the affected region were given doses of NaI that contained the stable iodine-127 isotope.

10.88 The element strontium has similar properties to calcium. Suggest a reason why exposure to strontium-90, a product of nuclear testing in the atmosphere, is especially hazardous for children.

CHALLENGE PROBLEMS

10.89 An article states that the fission of 1.0 g of uranium-235 releases 3.4×10^8 kcal, the same amount of energy as burning one ton (2,000. lb) of coal. If this report is accurate, how much energy is released when 1.0 g of coal is burned?

10.90 Radioactive isotopes with high atomic numbers often decay to form isotopes that are themselves radioactive and, once formed, decay to form new isotopes. Sometimes a series of such decays occurs over many steps until a stable nucleus is formed. The following series of decays occurs: Polonium-218 decays with emission of an α particle to form **X,** which emits a β particle to form **Y,** which emits an α particle to form **Z.** Identify **X, Y,** and **Z.**

11

Lidocaine, trade name Xylocaine, is an organic compound used as a local anesthetic by dentists and physicians.
©Kzenon/Alamy RF

Introduction to Organic Molecules and Functional Groups

CHAPTER OUTLINE

11.1 Introduction to Organic Chemistry

11.2 Characteristic Features of Organic Compounds

11.3 Shapes of Organic Molecules

11.4 Drawing Organic Molecules

11.5 Functional Groups

11.6 Properties of Organic Compounds

11.7 FOCUS ON HEALTH & MEDICINE: Vitamins

CHAPTER GOALS

In this chapter you will learn how to:

1. Recognize the characteristic features of organic compounds
2. Predict the shape around atoms in organic molecules
3. Use shorthand methods to draw organic molecules
4. Recognize the common functional groups and understand their importance
5. Distinguish organic compounds from ionic inorganic compounds
6. Determine whether an organic compound is polar or nonpolar
7. Determine solubility properties of organic compounds
8. Determine whether a vitamin is fat soluble or water soluble

Why Study Organic Molecules?

onsider for a moment the activities that occupied your past 24 hours. You likely showered with soap, drank a caffeinated beverage and ate a few meals, listened to a CD, and traveled in a vehicle that had rubber tires and was powered by fossil fuels. If you did any *one* of these, your life was touched by organic chemistry. In Chapter 11, we learn about the characteristic features of organic molecules.

11.1   Introduction to Organic Chemistry

What is organic chemistry?

Some compounds that contain the element carbon are *not* organic compounds. Examples include carbon dioxide (CO_2), sodium carbonate (Na_2CO_3), and sodium bicarbonate ($NaHCO_3$).

- **Organic chemistry is the study of compounds that contain the element carbon.**

While it may seem odd that an entire discipline is devoted to the study of a single element in the periodic table, millions of organic compounds are known, far more than the inorganic compounds discussed in Chapters 1–10. **These organic chemicals affect virtually every facet of our lives, and for this reason, it is important and useful to know something about them.**

Clothes, foods, medicines, gasoline, refrigerants, and soaps are composed almost solely of organic compounds. Some, like cotton, wool, or silk, are naturally occurring; that is, they can be isolated directly from natural sources. Others, such as nylon and polyester, are synthetic, meaning they are produced by chemists in the laboratory. By studying the principles and concepts of organic chemistry, you can learn more about compounds such as these and how they affect the world around you. Figure 11.1 illustrates some common products of organic chemistry used in medicine.

PROBLEM 11.1

Which chemical formulas represent organic compounds and which represent inorganic compounds?

a. C_6H_{12}	c. KI	e. CH_4O
b. H_2O	d. $MgSO_4$	f. NaOH

Figure 11.1   Some Common Products of Organic Chemistry Used in Medicine

a. Oral contraceptives   b. Plastic syringes   c. Antibiotics   d. Synthetic heart valves

Organic chemistry has given us contraceptives, plastics, antibiotics, synthetic heart valves, and a myriad of other materials. Our lives would be vastly different today without these products of organic chemistry. *(a): ©Comstock/Stockbyte/Getty Images RF; (b): ©Corbis Premium/Alamy RF; (c): ©Steven May/Alamy; (d): ©Layna Kennedy/Corbis Documentary/Getty Images*

11.2 Characteristic Features of Organic Compounds

Perhaps the best way to appreciate the variety of organic molecules is to look at a few. Simple organic compounds that contain just one or two carbon atoms, respectively, are methane and ethanol.

©Ingram Publishing/SuperStock RF

methane   ethanol

©Ingram Publishing RF

Methane, the main component of natural gas, burns in the presence of oxygen. The natural gas we use today was formed by the decomposition of organic material millions of years ago. **Ethanol,** the alcohol present in wine and other alcoholic beverages, is formed by the fermentation of sugar. Ethanol can also be made in the lab by a totally different process. **Ethanol produced in the lab is identical to the ethanol produced by fermentation.**

Two more complex organic molecules are capsaicin and caffeine. **Capsaicin,** the compound responsible for the characteristic spiciness of hot peppers, is the active ingredient in several topical creams for pain relief. **Caffeine** is the bitter-tasting stimulant found in coffee, tea, cola beverages, and chocolate.

©McGraw-Hill Education/Jill Braaten, photographer

capsaicin

©Comstock/Stockbyte/Getty Images RF

caffeine

What are the common features of these organic compounds?

[1] **All organic compounds contain carbon atoms and most contain hydrogen atoms. Carbon always forms four covalent bonds, and hydrogen forms one covalent bond.**

Carbon is located in group 4A of the periodic table, so a carbon atom has four valence electrons available for bonding (Section 4.1). Since hydrogen has a single valence electron, methane (CH_4) consists of four single bonds, each formed from one electron from a hydrogen atom and one electron from carbon.

Remember that each solid line represents one two-electron bond.

methane

[2] **Carbon forms single, double, and triple bonds to other carbon atoms.**

When a compound contains two or more carbon atoms, the type of bonding is determined by the number of atoms around carbon. Consider the three compounds drawn below:

| Each C forms four single bonds. | A double bond contains four electrons. | A triple bond contains six electrons. |

ethane   ethylene   acetylene

- A C atom surrounded by four atoms forms four single bonds. In ethane (C_2H_6), each carbon atom is bonded to three hydrogen atoms and one carbon atom. All bonds are single bonds.
- A C atom surrounded by three atoms forms one double bond. In ethylene (C_2H_4), each carbon atom is surrounded by three atoms (two hydrogens and one carbon); thus, each C forms a single bond to each hydrogen atom and a double bond to carbon.
- A C atom surrounded by two atoms generally forms one triple bond. In acetylene (C_2H_2), each carbon atom is surrounded by two atoms (one hydrogen and one carbon); thus, each C forms a single bond to hydrogen and a triple bond to carbon.

[3] **Some compounds have chains of atoms and some compounds have rings.**

For example, three carbon atoms can bond in a row to form propane, or form a ring called cyclopropane. Propane is the fuel burned in gas grills, and cyclopropane is an anesthetic.

propane
C_3H_8

cyclopropane
C_3H_6

Figure 11.2   Common Bonding Patterns for Atoms in Organic Compounds

	hydrogen	carbon	nitrogen	oxygen	halogen
Number of bonds	1	4	3	2	1
Number of nonbonded electron pairs	0	0	1	2	3

[4] **Organic compounds may also contain elements other than carbon and hydrogen. Any atom that is not carbon or hydrogen is called a _heteroatom_.**

The most common heteroatoms are nitrogen, oxygen, and the halogens (F, Cl, Br, and I).

- Each heteroatom forms a characteristic number of bonds, determined by its location in the periodic table.
- The common heteroatoms also have nonbonding, lone pairs of electrons, so that each atom is surrounded by eight electrons.

The number of bonds formed by common elements was first discussed in Section 4.1.

Thus, nitrogen forms three bonds and has one lone pair of electrons, whereas oxygen forms two bonds and has two additional lone pairs. The halogens form one bond and have three additional lone pairs. Common bonding patterns for atoms in organic compounds are summarized in Figure 11.2. Except for hydrogen, these common elements in organic compounds follow one rule in bonding:

$$\text{Number of bonds} \quad + \quad \text{Number of lone pairs} \quad = \quad 4$$

Oxygen and nitrogen form both single and multiple bonds to carbon. **The most common multiple bond between carbon and a heteroatom is a carbon–oxygen double bond (C=O).** The bonding patterns remain the same even when an atom is part of a multiple bond, as shown with methanol (CH_3OH) and formaldehyde ($H_2C=O$, a preservative).

These features explain why there are so many organic compounds: **Carbon forms four strong bonds with itself and other elements. Carbon atoms combine together to form rings and chains.**

SAMPLE PROBLEM 11.1 DRAWING H'S AND LONE PAIRS IN AN ORGANIC COMPOUND

Draw in all H's and lone pairs in each compound.

a. C—C—Cl   b. C—C=O   c. C—C≡N

Analysis

Each C and heteroatom must be surrounded by eight electrons. Use the common bonding patterns in Figure 11.2 to fill in the needed H's and lone pairs. C has four bonds; Cl has one bond and three lone pairs; O has two bonds and two lone pairs; N has three bonds and one lone pair.

Solution

a.

Cl has three lone pairs.

C needs 3 H's to have four bonds.

c.

N has one lone pair.

C already has four bonds.

b.

O has two lone pairs.

C needs 1 H to have four bonds.

PRACTICE PROBLEM 11.1

Fill in all H's and lone pairs in each compound.

a. $C-C=C-C$ b. $C-C-C$ c. $C-C-C$ d. $C-C-N-C$ e.

More Practice: Try Problems 11.23, 11.24.

Because **acetylene** (Section 11.3) produces a very hot flame on burning, it is often used in welding torches.
©Vol. 129 PhotoDisc/Getty Images RF

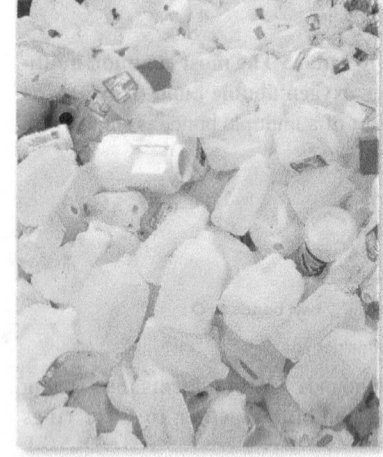

Ethylene is an important starting material in the preparation of the plastic polyethylene. Polyethylene is a synthetic plastic first produced in the 1930s, initially used as insulating material for radar during World War II. It is now a plastic in milk containers, sandwich bags, and plastic wrapping. Over 100 billion pounds of polyethylene are manufactured each year. ©Creatas/PunchStock RF

11.3 Shapes of Organic Molecules

The shape around atoms in organic molecules is determined by counting groups using the principles of VSEPR theory (Section 4.6). Recall that a group is either another atom or a lone pair of electrons. **The most stable arrangement keeps these groups as far away from each other as possible.**

- **An atom surrounded by two groups is linear and has a bond angle of 180°.**

Each carbon in acetylene (HC≡CH) is surrounded by two atoms and no lone pairs. Thus, each H—C—C bond angle is 180°, making all four atoms of acetylene linear.

180°

$H-C≡C-H$ =

180°

two atoms around each C

acetylene

ball-and-stick model

- **An atom surrounded by three groups is trigonal planar and has a bond angle of 120°.**

Each carbon in ethylene ($CH_2=CH_2$) is surrounded by three atoms and no lone pairs. Thus, each H—C—C bond angle is 120°, and all six atoms of ethylene lie in one plane.

120°

three atoms around each C

ethylene

- An atom surrounded by four groups places these four groups at the corners of a tetrahedron, giving bond angles of approximately 109.5°.

The carbon atom in methane (CH_4) is bonded to four hydrogen atoms, pointing to the corners of a tetrahedron.

109.5°

tetrahedral carbon

To draw the three-dimensional tetrahedron on a two-dimensional page, place two of the bonds in the plane, one bond in front, and one bond behind. Then, use the drawing conventions first presented in Section 4.6:

- A solid line is used for bonds in the plane.
- A wedge is used for a bond in front of the plane.
- A dashed wedge is used for a bond behind the plane.

bonds **in the plane**   bond **behind**

=

bond **in front**   methane

All carbons having four single bonds are tetrahedral. For example, each carbon of ethane is tetrahedral and can be drawn with two bonds in the plane, one in front on a wedge, and one behind on a dashed wedge.

ethane   tetrahedral C's   =

Ethane is a constituent of natural gas.
©Pakhnyushchy/Shutterstock RF

Don't forget about the lone pairs of electrons on nitrogen and oxygen when determining the shape around these atoms. The N atom in methylamine (CH_3NH_2) is surrounded by three atoms and one lone pair—four groups. To keep these four groups as far apart as possible, each of these groups occupies the corner of a tetrahedron. In this way, the N atom of methylamine resembles the N atom of ammonia (NH_3) discussed in Section 4.6. The H—N—C bond angle of 112° is close to the tetrahedral bond angle of 109.5°. This molecular shape is referred to as **trigonal pyramidal,** because one of the groups around the N is a lone pair, not another atom.

One corner of the tetrahedron has an **electron pair,** not a bond.

four groups around N
- three atoms
- one lone pair

methylamine   trigonal pyramidal   112°

Similarly, the O atom in methanol (CH_3OH) is surrounded by two atoms and two lone pairs—four groups. To keep these groups as far apart as possible, each of these groups occupies the corner of a tetrahedron. In this way the O atom of methanol resembles the O atom of water (H_2O) discussed in Section 4.6. The C—O—H bond angle of 109° is close to the tetrahedral bond angle of 109.5°. Methanol has a bent molecular shape around O because two of the groups around oxygen are lone pairs. Table 11.1 summarizes the possible shapes around atoms in organic compounds.

Two corners of the tetrahedron have **electron pairs,** not bonds.

four groups around O
• two atoms
• two lone pairs

methanol   bent shape   109°

Table 11.1 Molecular Shape Around Atoms in Organic Compounds

Total Number of Groups	Number of Atoms	Number of Lone Pairs	Shape Around an Atom (A)	Approximate Bond Angle (°)
2	2	0	linear	180
3	3	0	trigonal planar	120
4	4	0	tetrahedral	109.5
4	3	1	trigonal pyramidal	~109.5[a]
4	2	2	bent	~109.5[a]

[a]The symbol "~" means approximately.

SAMPLE PROBLEM 11.2 DETERMINING THE SHAPE AROUND AN ATOM

Determine the shape around each carbon and oxygen atom in dimethyl ether.

dimethyl ether

Analysis

• **Draw in all lone pairs on the heteroatom.** A heteroatom needs eight electrons around it, so add two lone pairs to O.
• **Count groups to determine the molecular shape.**

Solution

four groups
tetrahedral

H—C—O—C—H

two atoms + two lone pairs
bent shape

- Each C is surrounded by four atoms (3 H's and 1 O), making each C tetrahedral.
- The O atom is surrounded by 2 C's and two lone pairs (four groups), giving it a bent shape.
- This results in the following three-dimensional shape:

tetrahedral　　bent　　tetrahedral

PRACTICE PROBLEM 11.2

Determine the shape around the indicated atoms in each compound. Don't forget to add electron pairs to heteroatoms before determining the shape.

a. (1) (2) H—C=C—Br
b. (1) H—C≡C—C—O—H (2) (3)
c. (1) (2) H—C—O—H
d. (1) H—C=C, C=C—C—C≡N (2)

More Practice: Try Problems 11.25, 11.26.

PROBLEM 11.2

Predict the indicated bond angles in each compound.

a. (1) (2) F—C—C—Br (3)
halothane
(general anesthetic)

b. (1) H—C—C=C—H (2) (3)
propene
(petroleum product)

c. (2) (3) H—C—O—H (1)
phenol
(antiseptic)

PROBLEM 11.3

Draw the structure of each compound using solid lines, wedges, and dashed wedges to indicate the three-dimensional shape around each carbon.

a. H—C—Cl
b. H—C—C—Br

Don't let the size or complexity of an organic molecule intimidate you! Using the principles described in Section 11.3, you can predict the shape around any atom in any molecule no matter how complex it might be.

SAMPLE PROBLEM 11.3 DETERMINING THE SHAPE AROUND AN ATOM IN A COMPLEX MOLECULE

L-Dopa is a drug used to treat Parkinson's disease. Give the shape around each indicated atom.

L-dopa

Analysis

- **Add lone pairs of electrons to each heteroatom so that it is surrounded by eight electrons.** Each O gets two lone pairs and N gets one.
- Count groups to predict shape.

Solution

Adding electron pairs around O and N:

L-dopa

Pay special attention to the O and N atoms, and note the importance of adding the lone pairs before determining shape. O atoms are surrounded by *four* groups—two atoms *and* two electron pairs—giving them a bent shape. O atoms are *never* surrounded by two groups, making them linear.

PRACTICE PROBLEM 11.3

Enanthotoxin is a poisonous compound isolated from a common variety of hemlock grown in England. Predict the shape around the indicated atoms in enanthotoxin.

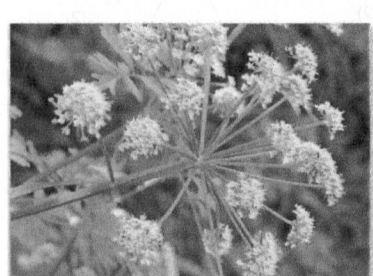

Hemlock is the source of the poison enanthotoxin. ©*John Somerville*

enanthotoxin

More Practice: Try Problems 11.29, 11.30.

PROBLEM 11.4

(a) How many lone pairs are present in lidocaine, the drug mentioned in the chapter opener, whose structure is shown in the ball-and-stick model? (b) Predict the shape around the indicated atoms in lidocaine.

Lidocaine deadens the nerve endings in the skin, so it is an effective topical local anesthetic. ©*Scott Camazine/Alamy*

lidocaine

11.4   Drawing Organic Molecules

Sections 11.1–11.3 illustrate that organic molecules can be represented in different ways. For example, all the atoms and bonds of pentane (C_5H_{12}) can be drawn (as in **A**), or a ball-and-stick model **B** can show the three-dimensional structure of pentane. Moreover, because organic molecules often contain many atoms, we use shorthand methods to simplify them. As a result, pentane can also be represented by the condensed structure **C** and the skeletal structure **D**.

| pentane complete structure | pentane ball-and-stick model | pentane condensed structure | pentane skeletal structure |
| **A** | **B** | **C** | **D** |

How to draw and interpret condensed and skeletal structures is explained in Sections 11.4A and 11.4B, respectively.

11.4A   Condensed Structures

Condensed structures are most often used for a compound having a chain of atoms bonded together, rather than a ring. The following conventions are used.

- All of the atoms are drawn in, but the two-electron bond lines are generally omitted.
- Lone pairs on heteroatoms are omitted.

To interpret a condensed formula, it is usually best to start at the *left side* of the molecule and remember that the *carbon atoms must have four bonds.*

- A carbon bonded to 3 H's becomes CH_3.
- A carbon bonded to 2 H's becomes CH_2.
- A carbon bonded to 1 H becomes CH.

Keep the vertical bond line to show where the CH_3 group is bonded.

Sometimes these structures are further simplified by using parentheses around like groups. Two CH_2 groups bonded together become $(CH_2)_2$. Two CH_3 groups bonded to the same carbon become $(CH_3)_2C$.

Additional examples of drawing condensed structures are shown in Figure 11.3.

Figure 11.3   Examples of Condensed Structures

- Entry [1]: Draw the H atom next to the C to which it is bonded, and use parentheses around CH_3 to show it is bonded to the carbon chain.
- Entry [2]: Keep the carbon–carbon double bond and draw the H atoms after each C to which they are bonded.
- Entry [3]: Omit the lone pairs on the O atom in the condensed structure.
- Entry [4]: Omit the lone pairs on Cl and O and draw the two CH_2 groups as $(CH_2)_2$.

SAMPLE PROBLEM 11.4 DRAWING A CONDENSED STRUCTURE

Convert each compound into a condensed structure.

Analysis

- Start at the left and proceed to the right, making sure that each carbon has four bonds.
- Omit lone pairs on the heteroatoms O and Cl.
- When like groups are bonded together or bonded to the same atom, use parentheses to further simplify the structure.

Solution

	Condensed structure	Further simplified

a. (structure) = $CH_3CHCH_2CHCH_3$ = $(CH_3)_2CHCH_2CH(CH_3)_2$

Use parentheses to show 2 CH_3 groups on one C.

b. (structure) = $CH_3CH_2CH_2OCH_2Cl$ = $CH_3(CH_2)_2OCH_2Cl$

PRACTICE PROBLEM 11.4

Convert each compound to a condensed formula.

a. (structure)   c. (structure)

b. (structure)   d. (structure)

More Practice: Try Problems 11.33, 11.34.

SAMPLE PROBLEM 11.5 CONVERTING A CONDENSED STRUCTURE TO A COMPLETE STRUCTURE

Convert each condensed structure to a complete structure with all lone pairs on heteroatoms.

a. $(CH_3)_3CCH_2NH_2$ b. $CH_3CH_2OCH(CH_3)_2$

Analysis

• Start at the left and proceed to the right and make sure each carbon gets four bonds.
• Give each heteroatom enough lone pairs to have an octet.

Solution

a. Place three CH_3 groups (labeled in blue) around the C atom in red. Add one lone pair to N to give an octet.

b. Place two CH_3 groups (labeled in blue) around the C atom in red. Add two lone pairs to O to give an octet.

$(CH_3)_3CCH_2NH_2$

$CH_3CH_2OCH(CH_3)_2$

PRACTICE PROBLEM 11.5

Convert each condensed formula to a complete structure with lone pairs on heteroatoms.

a. $CH_3(CH_2)_8CH_3$ c. CH_3CCl_3 e. $(CH_3)_2CHCH_2NH_2$

b. $CH_3(CH_2)_4OH$ d. $CH_3(CH_2)_4CH(CH_3)_2$

More Practice: Try Problems 11.37a–c, 11.38a–c.

11.4B   Skeletal Structures

Skeletal structures are used for organic compounds containing both rings and chains of atoms. Three important rules are used in drawing them.

- Assume there is a carbon atom at the junction of any two lines or at the end of any line.
- Assume there are enough hydrogens around each carbon to give it four bonds.
- Draw in all heteroatoms and the hydrogens directly bonded to them.

Rings are drawn as polygons with a carbon atom "understood" at each vertex, as shown for cyclohexane and cyclopentanol. All carbons and hydrogens in these molecules are understood, except for H's bonded to heteroatoms.

Figure 11.4 shows examples of converting cyclic skeletal structures into complete structures.

Figure 11.4   Examples of Skeletal Structures with Rings

- C's labeled in blue have 3 H's, so each C has four bonds.
- C's labeled in red have 1 H, so each C has four bonds.
- C labeled in green already has four bonds, so it has no H's bonded to it.
- All the other C's have 2 H's, so each C has four bonds.

SAMPLE PROBLEM 11.6 INTERPRETING THE SKELETAL STRUCTURE OF A CYCLIC COMPOUND

Convert each skeletal structure to a complete structure with all C's and H's drawn in.

a. □   b. ▷—Cl

Analysis

To draw each complete structure, place a C atom at the corner of each polygon and add H's to give carbon four bonds. Add lone pairs to a heteroatom to give an octet.

Solution

Each C needs 2 H's.

This C needs only 1 H.

Add three lone pairs to Cl.

PRACTICE PROBLEM 11.6

Convert each skeletal structure to a complete structure with all C's and H's drawn in. Add lone pairs on all heteroatoms.

lindane
(an insecticide)

More Practice: Try Problems 11.35, 11.36, 11.37d, 11.38d.

Carbon chains are also drawn with skeletal structures using the same principles. As shown for hexane, chains are drawn in a zigzag fashion, which resembles the zigzag arrangement shown in the ball-and-stick model.

hexane

hexane
skeletal structure

hexane
ball-and-stick model

How to interpret a skeletal structure for an organic molecule that contains both a chain of carbons and heteroatoms is shown in the stepwise procedure.

How To   Interpret a Skeletal Structure

Example: Draw in all C atoms, H atoms, and lone pairs in the following molecule:

Step [1] **Place a C atom at the intersection of any two lines and at the end of any line.**

- This molecule has six carbons, including the C labeled in red at the left end of the chain.
- There are two C's (labeled in green) between the C=C and the OH group.

—Continued

How To, continued . . .

Step [2]   **Add enough H's to make each C tetravalent.**

Add H's to give
C four bonds.

- The end C labeled in red needs three H's to be tetravalent.
- Each C on the C=C has three bonds already, so only one H must be drawn.
- There are two CH_2 groups between the C=C and the OH group.

Step [3]   **Add lone pairs to give each heteroatom an octet.**

two lone pairs

two lone pairs

Each O needs **two** lone pairs for an octet.

PROBLEM 11.5

Convert each skeletal structure to a complete structure with all C's and H's drawn in. Add lone pairs on all heteroatoms.

a.   b.   c.

SAMPLE PROBLEM 11.7 INTERPRETING THE SKELETAL STRUCTURE
OF A COMPLEX MOLECULE

Shorthand structures for more complex organic compounds are drawn with the same principles used for simpler structures. Answer the following questions about estradiol, a female sex hormone that controls the development of secondary sex characteristics.

estradiol
(female sex hormone)

a. How many C atoms are present in estradiol?

b. How many H atoms are bonded to C1? C2? C3? C4?

c. Draw a complete structure for estradiol, including all lone pairs on O atoms.

Analysis

Place a C atom at each corner of all polygons and at the end of any line that has no heteroatom bonded to it. Add enough H's to give each C four bonds. Each O needs two lone pairs to have eight electrons around it.

Solution

a. Estradiol has a total of 18 C's. Seventeen C atoms are located at the corners of the polygons. One C (labeled C4) is bonded to the rings.

b. C1, labeled in red, needs 2 H's to give it four bonds. C2, labeled in blue, needs 1 H to give it four bonds. C3, labeled in green, needs 1 H to give it four bonds. C4, labeled in gray, needs 3 H's to give it four bonds.

c.

estradiol
(female sex hormone)

PRACTICE PROBLEM 11.7

How many H's are bonded to each indicated carbon (C1–C8) in the following drugs?

ibuprofen
(anti-inflammatory agent)

fentanyl
(narcotic pain reliever)

More Practice: Try Problems 11.45, 11.46, 11.83d, 11.84c.

PROBLEM 11.6

Using the skeletal structure, determine the molecular formula of sitagliptin, a drug used to treat type 2 diabetes.

sitagliptin

11.5 Functional Groups

In addition to strong C—C and C—H bonds, organic molecules may have other structural features as well. Although over 50 million organic compounds are currently known, only a limited number of common structural features, called **functional groups,** are found in these molecules.

- A *functional group* is an atom or a group of atoms with characteristic chemical and physical properties.
- A functional group contains a heteroatom, a multiple bond, or sometimes both a heteroatom *and* a multiple bond.

A functional group determines a molecule's shape, properties, and the type of reactions it undergoes. A functional group behaves the same whether it is bonded to a carbon backbone having as few as two or as many as 20 carbons. For this reason, we often abbreviate the carbon and hydrogen portion of the molecule by a capital letter **R,** and draw the **R** bonded to a particular functional group.

> **R**─**Functional group**
>
> Carbon backbone...   bonded to...   a particular functional group.

Ethanol (CH_3CH_2OH), for example, has two carbons and five hydrogens in its carbon backbone, as well as an OH group, a functional group called a **hydroxyl** group. The hydroxyl group determines the physical properties of ethanol as well as the type of reactions it undergoes. Moreover, any organic molecule containing a hydroxyl group has properties similar to ethanol. Compounds that contain a hydroxyl group are called **alcohols.**

ethanol

The most common functional groups can be subdivided into three types.

- Hydrocarbons
- Compounds containing a single bond to a heteroatom
- Compounds containing a C═O group

11.5A   Hydrocarbons

Hydrocarbons are compounds that contain only the elements of carbon and hydrogen, as shown in Table 11.2.

- *Alkanes* have only C—C single bonds and no functional group. Ethane, CH_3CH_3, is a simple alkane.
- *Alkenes* have a C—C double bond as their functional group. Ethylene, $CH_2═CH_2$, is a simple alkene.
- *Alkynes* have a C—C triple bond as their functional group. Acetylene, $HC≡CH$, is a simple alkyne.
- *Aromatic compounds* contain a benzene ring, a six-membered ring with three double bonds.

Table 11.2 Hydrocarbons

Type of Compound	General Structure	Example	3-D Structure	Functional Group
Alkane	R—H	CH_3CH_3		—
Alkene				Carbon–carbon double bond
Alkyne	—C≡C—	H—C≡C—H		Carbon–carbon triple bond
Aromatic compound				Benzene ring

All hydrocarbons other than alkanes contain multiple bonds. Alkanes, which have no functional groups and therefore no reactive sites, are notoriously unreactive except under very drastic conditions. For example, **polyethylene** is a synthetic plastic and high molecular weight alkane, consisting of long chains of —CH_2— groups bonded together, hundreds or even thousands of atoms long. Because it has no reactive sites, it is a very stable compound that does not readily degrade and thus persists for years in landfills.

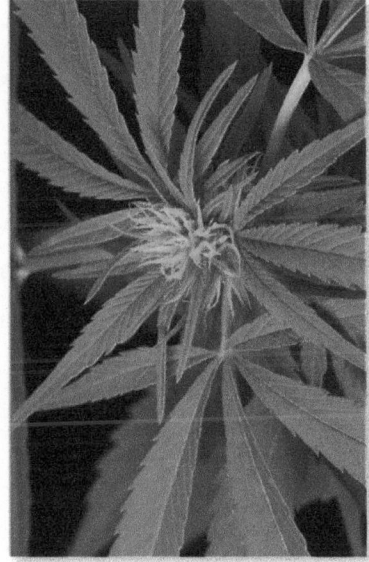

Tetrahydrocannabinol (THC) is the primary active constituent in marijuana. THC is approved for medical use in several states. ©Ted Kinsman/Science Source

polyethylene

The chain continues in both directions.

11.5B Compounds Containing a Single Bond to a Heteroatom

Several types of functional groups contain a carbon atom singly bonded to a heteroatom. Common examples include alkyl halides, alcohols, ethers, amines, and thiols, as shown in Table 11.3.

Several simple compounds in this category are widely used. Bromomethane (CH_3Br) is an alkyl halide that has been used to control the spread of the destructive Asian long-horned beetle to the United States. Chloroethane (CH_3CH_2Cl, commonly called ethyl chloride) is an alkyl halide used as a local anesthetic. When chloroethane is sprayed on a wound it quickly evaporates, causing a cooling sensation that numbs the site of injury.

Molecules containing these functional groups may be simple or very complex. It doesn't matter what else is present in other parts of the molecule. **Always dissect it into small pieces to identify the functional groups.** For example, diethyl ether, the first general anesthetic, is an ether because it has an O atom bonded to two C's. Tetrahydrocannabinol (THC), the active component

Table 11.3 Compounds Containing a Carbon–Heteroatom Single Bond

Type of Compound	General Structure	Example	3-D Structure	Functional Group
Alkyl halide	R—$\ddot{\underset{\cdot\cdot}{X}}$: (X = F, Cl, Br, I)	CH_3—$\ddot{\underset{\cdot\cdot}{Br}}$:		—X halo group
Alcohol	R—$\ddot{\underset{\cdot\cdot}{O}}H$	CH_3—$\ddot{\underset{\cdot\cdot}{O}}H$		—OH hydroxyl group
Ether	R—$\ddot{\underset{\cdot\cdot}{O}}$—R	CH_3—$\ddot{\underset{\cdot\cdot}{O}}$—$CH_3$		—OR alkoxy group
Amine	R—$\ddot{N}H_2$ or $R_2\ddot{N}H$ or $R_3\ddot{N}$	CH_3—$\ddot{N}H_2$		—NH_2 amino group
Thiol	R—$\ddot{\underset{\cdot\cdot}{S}}H$	CH_3—$\ddot{\underset{\cdot\cdot}{S}}H$		—SH sulfhydryl group

in marijuana, is also an ether because it contains an O atom bonded to two carbon atoms. In this case the O atom is also part of a ring.

diethyl ether

tetrahydrocannabinol
(THC)

PROBLEM 11.7

Identify the functional groups in each compound. Some compounds contain more than one functional group.

a. CH_3CHCH_3
OH

2-propanol
(disinfectant in
rubbing alcohol)

b. $-CH=CH_2$

styrene
(starting material used
to synthesize Styrofoam)

c. $H_2NCH_2CH_2CH_2CH_2NH_2$

putrescine
(putrid odor of rotting fish)

PROBLEM 11.8

Identify the functional groups in each skeletal structure.

a.

geraniol
(main component of rose oil)

b.

sevoflurane
(anesthetic)

c.

triethylamine
(organic base)

11.5C Compounds Containing a C=O Group

Many different kinds of compounds contain a carbon–oxygen double bond (**C=O, carbonyl group**), as shown in Table 11.4. Carbonyl compounds include aldehydes, ketones, carboxylic acids, esters, and amides. The type of atom bonded to the carbonyl carbon—hydrogen, carbon, or a heteroatom—determines the specific class of carbonyl compound.

carbonyl group

Take special note of the condensed structures used to draw aldehydes, carboxylic acids, and esters.

Table 11.4 Compounds Containing a C=O Group

Type of Compound	General Structure	Example	Condensed Structure	3-D Structure	Functional Group
Aldehyde	R–C(=O)–H	CH₃–C(=O)–H	CH_3CHO		C(=O)–H
Ketone	R–C(=O)–R	CH₃–C(=O)–CH₃	$(CH_3)_2CO$		C(=O)
Carboxylic acid	R–C(=O)–OH	CH₃–C(=O)–OH	CH_3CO_2H		C(=O)–OH carboxyl group
Ester	R–C(=O)–OR	CH₃–C(=O)–OCH₃	$CH_3CO_2CH_3$		C(=O)–OR
Amide	R–C(=O)–N(H or R)(H or R)	CH₃–C(=O)–NH₂	CH_3CONH_2		C(=O)–N

- **An aldehyde has a hydrogen atom bonded directly to the carbonyl carbon.**

CH₃–C(=O)–H = CH_3**CHO**   C is bonded to both H and O.

acetaldehyde   condensed structure

- **A carboxylic acid contains an OH group bonded directly to the carbonyl carbon.**

CH₃–C(=O)–OH = CH_3**COOH** or CH_3**CO₂H**   C is bonded to both O atoms.

acetic acid   condensed structures

- **An ester contains an OR group bonded directly to the carbonyl carbon.**

CH₃–C(=O)–OCH₂CH₃ = CH_3**COOCH₂CH₃** or CH_3**CO₂CH₂CH₃**

ethyl acetate   condensed structures   C is bonded to both O atoms.

Carbonyl compounds occur widely in nature, and many are responsible for the characteristic odor or flavor of the fruits shown in Figure 11.5.

Figure 11.5

What We Eat—Naturally Occurring
Carbonyl Compounds in Fruit

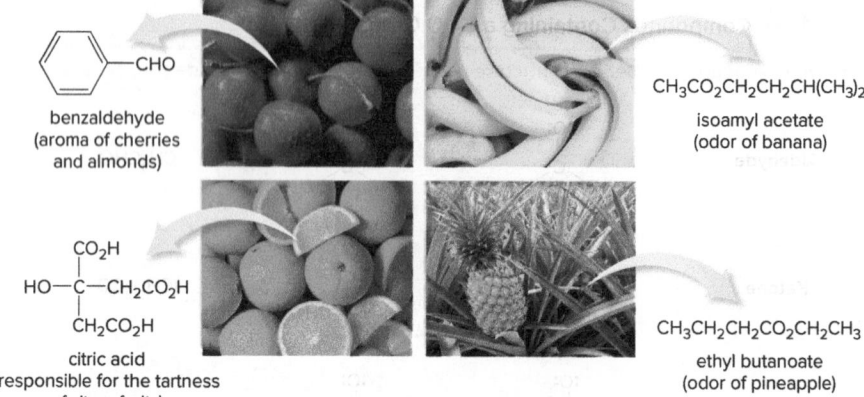

benzaldehyde
(aroma of cherries
and almonds)

isoamyl acetate
(odor of banana)

$CH_3CO_2CH_2CH_2CH(CH_3)_2$

citric acid
(responsible for the tartness
of citrus fruits)

ethyl butanoate
(odor of pineapple)

$CH_3CH_2CH_2CO_2CH_2CH_3$

- Benzaldehyde contains an aldehyde; citric acid contains one hydroxyl and three carboxyl groups; and both isoamyl acetate and ethyl butanoate contain esters.
- In addition to water, fruits (and other foods) contain a variety of organic compounds that give them taste, odor, texture, and nutritional value. Although one organic compound might be the major component in a food's flavor or odor, what we taste and smell is often a complex mixture of compounds. When even one of these components is missing, the odor and flavor can be somewhat different. This explains why artificial flavors and colors mimic, but don't really replace, the natural flavor. *(top left): ©Brand X Pictures/ Stockbyte/Getty Images RF; (top right): ©Ingram Publishing/SuperStock RF; (bottom left): ©Brand X Pictures/Stockbyte/ Getty Images RF; (bottom right): ©9comeback/Shutterstock RF*

SAMPLE PROBLEM 11.8 IDENTIFYING FUNCTIONAL GROUPS

Identify the functional group in each compound.

a.

$$\begin{array}{cc} H & CH_3 \\ \diagdown & \diagup \\ C=C \\ \diagup & \diagdown \\ H & CH_3 \end{array}$$

A

b.

⬡—OH

B

c.

⬠=O

C

Analysis

Concentrate on the multiple bonds and heteroatoms and refer to Tables 11.2, 11.3, and 11.4.

Solution

a.

$$\begin{array}{cc} H & CH_3 \\ \diagdown & \diagup \\ C=C \\ \diagup & \diagdown \\ H & CH_3 \end{array}$$

A

b.

⬡—OH

B

c.

⬠=O

C's on both sides
of the C=O

C

A is a hydrocarbon with a carbon–carbon double bond, making it an alkene.

B has a carbon atom bonded to a hydroxyl group (OH), making it an alcohol.

C contains a C=O. Since the carbonyl carbon is bonded to two other carbons in the ring, **C** is a ketone.

PRACTICE PROBLEM 11.8

For each compound: [1] Identify the functional group; [2] draw out the complete compound, including lone pairs on heteroatoms.

a. ⬡—CHO

c. ⬡=O

e.

$$\begin{array}{c} O \\ \parallel \\ \text{(cyclopentyl)}-C-NHCH_3 \end{array}$$

b. $CH_3CH_2CH_2CO_2H$

d. $CH_3CH_2CO_2CH_2CH_3$

More Practice: Try Problems 11.47, 11.48, 11.49.

PROBLEM 11.9

How do a carboxylic acid and an alcohol differ? Which ball-and-stick model represents a carboxylic acid and which represents an alcohol?

A   **B**

PROBLEM 11.10

Label each of the following condensed structures as an ether or a ketone.

a. $(CH_3)_2O$ b. $(CH_3)_2CO$ c. $(CH_3CH_2)_2CO$ d. $CH_3CH_2OCH(CH_3)_2$

PROBLEM 11.11

How do an amine and an amide differ? Which ball-and-stick model represents an amine and which represents an amide?

C   **D**

PROBLEM 11.12

How do an ether and an ester differ? Which ball-and-stick model represents an ether and which represents an ester?

E   **F**

Many useful organic compounds contain complex structures with two or more functional groups. Sample Problem 11.9 illustrates an example of identifying several functional groups in a single molecule.

SAMPLE PROBLEM 11.9 IDENTIFYING FUNCTIONAL GROUPS IN A COMPLEX MOLECULE

Identify all of the functional groups in the antiviral drug Tamiflu.

$(CH_3CH_2)_2CH$

$CO_2CH_2CH_3$

HN

NH_2

CH_3 O

Tamiflu

408   Chapter 11   Introduction to Organic Molecules and Functional Groups

Analysis

To identify functional groups, look for multiple bonds and heteroatoms. With functional groups that contain O atoms, look at what is bonded to the O's to decide if the group is an alcohol, ether, or other group. With carbonyl-containing groups, look at what is bonded to the carbonyl carbon.

Solution

Re-draw Tamiflu to further clarify the functional groups:

double bond—alkene

$(CH_3CH_2)_2$ CH

ether → O

O || C — OCH₂CH₃ ← ester

amide → HN C=O CH₃   NH₂ — amine

- Tamiflu contains a total of five functional groups: a carbon–carbon double bond (an alkene), ether, ester, amide, and amine.
- Note the difference between an amine and an amide. **An amine contains a N atom but no C=O. An amide contains a N atom bonded directly to a C=O.**

Atenolol and trandolapril (Practice Problem 11.9 and Problem 11.13) are two of the many drugs available to treat patients with high blood pressure.
©Russell Illig/Getty Images Rf

PRACTICE PROBLEM 11.9

Identify all of the functional groups in atenolol, an antihypertensive agent; that is, it is used to treat high blood pressure.

H_2N — C(=O) — CH₂ — ⟨benzene ring⟩ — O — CH₂CHCH₂NHCH(CH₃)₂ with OH

atenolol

More Practice: Try Problems 11.50, 11.58, 11.83a, 11.84a.

PROBLEM 11.13

Identify each carbonyl-containing functional group in trandolapril, a drug used to treat high blood pressure. Trandolapril is called an ACE inhibitor, which we will learn about in Chapter 21.

trandolapril

Methyl anthranilate (Sample Problem 11.10) is a component of neroli oil, a fragrant oil obtained from the flowers of the bitter orange tree and used in perfumery. Commercial products that contain methyl anthranilate are sprayed on fruit trees to keep birds away.
©Graham Titchmarsh/Alamy RF

SAMPLE PROBLEM 11.10 CONVERTING A BALL-AND-STICK MODEL TO A CONDENSED OR SKELETAL STRUCTURE

Convert each ball-and-stick model to a condensed or skeletal structure and identify the functional groups.

a.

cis-2-butene

b.

methyl anthranilate

Analysis

Use the common element colors shown on the inside back cover to convert the ball-and-stick model to a shorthand representation. Look for multiple bonds and heteroatoms to locate the functional groups, and refer to Tables 11.2, 11.3, and 11.4.

Solution

a.

cis-2-butene   carbon–carbon double bond
(an alkene)

b.

methyl anthranilate

PRACTICE PROBLEM 11.10

Convert each ball-and-stick model to a condensed or skeletal structure and identify the functional groups.

a.   b.

More Practice: Try Problems 11.51–11.54.

PROBLEM 11.14

Convert the ball-and-stick model of elemicin, a component of nutmeg, to a skeletal structure and identify the functional groups.

elemicin

The kernel of the fruit of the nutmeg tree contains elemicin (Problem 11.14) and several other organic compounds responsible for its characteristic flavor and fragrance. ©*National Geographic Image Collection/Alamy RF*

11.6   Properties of Organic Compounds

Because organic compounds are composed of covalent bonds, their properties differ a great deal from those of ionic inorganic compounds.

The intermolecular forces in covalent compounds were discussed in Section 7.7.

- Organic compounds exist as discrete molecules with much weaker intermolecular forces—the forces that exist *between* molecules—than those seen in ionic compounds, which are held together by very strong interactions of oppositely charged ions.

As a result, organic compounds resemble other covalent compounds in that they have much lower melting points and boiling points than ionic compounds. While ionic compounds are generally solids at room temperature, many organic compounds are liquids and some are even gases. Table 11.5 compares these and other properties of a typical organic compound (butane, $CH_3CH_2CH_2CH_3$) and a typical ionic inorganic compound (sodium chloride, NaCl).

Table 11.5   Comparing the Properties of an Organic Compound ($CH_3CH_2CH_2CH_3$) and an Ionic Inorganic Compound (NaCl)

or

$CH_3CH_2CH_2CH_3$
butane

discrete molecules
with covalent bonding

©Ingram Publishing/Fotosearch RF

Na⁺
Cl⁻

ionic bonding

©Fuse/Getty Images RF

Property	$CH_3CH_2CH_2CH_3$ (An Organic Compound)	NaCl (An Inorganic Compound)
Bonding	Covalent	Ionic
Physical state	Gas at room temperature	Solid at room temperature
Boiling point	Low (−0.5 °C)	High (1413 °C)
Melting point	Low (−138 °C)	High (801 °C)
Solubility in water	Insoluble	Soluble
Solubility in organic solvents	Soluble	Insoluble
Flammability	Flammable	Nonflammable

11.6A   Polarity

Are organic compounds polar or nonpolar? That depends. Like other covalent compounds, the polarity of an organic compound is determined by two factors: the polarity of the individual bonds and the overall shape of the molecule. **The polarity of an individual bond depends on the electronegativity of the atoms that form it.**

Review Sections 4.6 and 4.7 on electronegativity, bond polarity, and polar molecules. Recall that **electronegativity** measures how much a particular atom "wants" the electron density in a bond.

• A covalent bond is *nonpolar* when two atoms of identical or similar electronegativity are joined together. Thus, C—C and C—H bonds are nonpolar bonds.
• A covalent bond is *polar* when atoms of different electronegativity are joined together. Thus, bonds between carbon and common heteroatoms (N, O, and the halogens) are polar bonds.

Since the common heteroatoms are *more* electronegative than carbon, these atoms pull electron density away from carbon, making it partially positive and the heteroatom partially negative.

$$\delta+ \text{C}-\overset{\cdot\cdot}{\underset{\cdot\cdot}{\text{O}}}\delta- \qquad \delta+ \text{C}-\overset{\cdot\cdot}{\text{N}}\delta- \qquad \delta+ \text{C}-\overset{\cdot\cdot}{\underset{\cdot\cdot}{\text{X}}}\delta-$$

X = halogen

• The symbol δ+ is given to the less electronegative atom (usually C or H).
• The symbol δ− is given to the more electronegative atom (usually N, O, or a halogen).

PROBLEM 11.15

Indicate the polar bonds in each compound. Label the bonds with δ+ and δ−.

a.
$$\text{Cl}-\underset{\overset{|}{\text{Cl}}}{\overset{\overset{|}{\text{Cl}}}{\text{C}}}-\text{H}$$
chloroform
(once used as an anesthetic)

c.
$$\text{H}-\underset{\overset{|}{\text{F}}}{\overset{\overset{|}{\text{F}}}{\text{C}}}-\text{O}-\underset{\overset{|}{\text{F}}}{\overset{\overset{|}{\text{F}}}{\text{C}}}-\underset{\overset{|}{\text{Cl}}}{\overset{\overset{|}{\text{H}}}{\text{C}}}-\text{F}$$
enflurane
(anesthetic)

b.
$$\overset{\text{H}}{\underset{\text{H}}{}}\text{C}=\text{O}$$
formaldehyde
(preservative)

d.
methamphetamine
(illegal, addictive stimulant)

Hydrocarbons contain only nonpolar C—C and C—H bonds, so **hydrocarbons are nonpolar molecules.** In contrast, when an organic compound contains a *single* polar bond, as in the alkyl halide CH$_3$CH$_2$Cl, the molecule contains a net dipole and is therefore a polar molecule.

ethane
no polar bonds
nonpolar molecule

chloroethane
one polar bond
polar molecule

With organic compounds that have more than one polar bond, **the shape of the molecule determines the overall polarity.**

• If the individual bond dipoles cancel in a molecule, the molecule is nonpolar.
• If the individual bond dipoles do not cancel, the molecule is polar.

A bond dipole can be indicated by an arrow with the head of the arrow pointing toward the more electronegative element, and a perpendicular line drawn through the tail of the arrow (⊢→).

Thus, dichloroacetylene (ClC≡CCl) is a linear molecule with two polar C—Cl bonds, but the individual bond dipoles are equal in magnitude and opposite in direction. As a result, dichloroacetylene is a *nonpolar* molecule. In contrast, methanol, CH_3OH, has two polar bonds (C—O and O—H), and a bent shape around oxygen (Section 11.3). The individual bond dipoles do *not* cancel, so CH_3OH is a *polar* molecule.

Two bond dipoles cancel.   **Two bond dipoles do *not* cancel.**

:C̈l—C≡C—C̈l: net dipole

dichloroacetylene   methanol
nonpolar molecule   polar molecule

SAMPLE PROBLEM 11.11 DETERMINING POLARITY IN A MOLECULE

Explain why dichloromethane (CH_2Cl_2), a solvent used in paint remover, is a polar molecule.

Analysis

CH_2Cl_2 has two polar C—Cl bonds. We must determine the shape of the molecule around the carbon atom and check whether the two bond dipoles cancel or reinforce.

Solution

Since the C atom in CH_2Cl_2 is surrounded by four atoms, it is tetrahedral. The two bond dipoles do not cancel, and **CH_2Cl_2 is a polar molecule.**

Draw CH_2Cl_2 as a tetrahedron to see that the bond dipoles do not cancel.

Do *not* draw CH_2Cl_2 as:

net dipole

polar molecule

In this drawing it appears as if the bond dipoles cancel, but in reality they do *not.*

PRACTICE PROBLEM 11.11

Label each molecule as polar or nonpolar and explain your choice.

a. △   b. (CH₃)₂C=O   c. CCl_4 d. $CH_3CH_2CH_2NH_2$

More Practice: Try Problems 11.63, 11.64, 11.67, 11.68.

PROBLEM 11.16

Explain why dimethyl ether (CH_3OCH_3) is a polar molecule.

11.6B   Solubility

Review the general principles of solubility in Section 8.3.

Understanding the solubility properties of organic compounds allows us to learn about many interesting phenomena. One rule governs solubility: **"Like dissolves like."** Three facts can then be used to explain the solubility of organic compounds.

- Most organic compounds are soluble in organic solvents.
- Hydrocarbons and other nonpolar organic compounds are not soluble in water.
- Polar organic compounds are water soluble only if they are small (less than six carbons) and contain a nitrogen or oxygen atom that can hydrogen bond with water.

Three compounds—hexane, ethanol, and cholesterol—illustrate these principles. All of these compounds are organic and therefore soluble in an organic solvent like diethyl ether ($CH_3CH_2OCH_2CH_3$). Their water solubility depends on their polarity and size.

Since hexane ($CH_3CH_2CH_2CH_2CH_2CH_3$) is a nonpolar hydrocarbon, it is insoluble in water. Ethanol (CH_3CH_2OH), on the other hand, is water soluble because it is small and contains a polar OH group that can hydrogen bond to water. The ethanol in gin dissolves in the water of tonic water, resulting in the alcoholic beverage called a "gin and tonic."

Cholesterol has 27 carbon atoms and only one OH group. Its nonpolar hydrocarbon part is too large to dissolve in water, making it water insoluble. As a result, cholesterol can't dissolve in the aqueous medium of the blood. When it must be transported through the body in the bloodstream, cholesterol is bound to other substances that are water soluble.

CH_3CH_2—OH
ethanol

H$_2$O soluble

cholesterol

There are too many nonpolar C—C and C—H bonds for cholesterol to be soluble in water.

HO

H$_2$O insoluble

Table 11.6 summarizes the solubility characteristics of hexane, ethanol, and cholesterol.

Table 11.6   The Solubility Characteristics of Three Representative Organic Molecules

Compound	Solubility in an Organic Solvent	Solubility in Water
$CH_3CH_2CH_2CH_2CH_2CH_3$ Hexane	Soluble	Insoluble
CH_3CH_2OH Ethanol	Soluble	Soluble
Cholesterol	Soluble	Insoluble

SAMPLE PROBLEM 11.12 DETERMINING THE SOLUBILITY OF ORGANIC MOLECULES

Predict the solubility of acetic acid, CH_3CO_2H, and oleic acid, $CH_3(CH_2)_7CH$=$CH(CH_2)_7CO_2H$, whose structures are shown in Figure 11.6, in organic solvents and water.

Analysis

Use the general solubility rule, "Like dissolves like."

- Organic compounds are soluble in organic solvents.
- Organic compounds are water soluble only if they are small (less than six carbons) and contain a polar functional group that can hydrogen bond to water.

Solution

Acetic acid and oleic acid are both organic compounds that contain carbon atoms, so they are soluble in organic solvents. Acetic acid has only two carbons and a COOH group capable of hydrogen bonding to water, making it water soluble. Oleic acid has 18 carbons and only one COOH group, so its long nonpolar carbon chain makes it insoluble in water.

414   **Chapter 11**   Introduction to Organic Molecules and Functional Groups

---

PRACTICE PROBLEM 11.12

Predict the water solubility of each compound.

a. (octane structure)

octane
(gasoline component)

b. (acetone structure with CH₃ and CH₃ groups around C=O)

acetone
(solvent)

c. $CH_3(CH_2)_{16}CO_2H$

stearic acid
(a fatty acid)

More Practice: Try Problems 11.59–11.62, 11.69–11.72, 11.81d, 11.82d.

Figure 11.6   Carboxylic Acids in Vinegar and Olive Oil

acetic acid

oleic acid

- Balsamic vinegar contains the two-carbon carboxylic acid acetic acid, and olive oil contains esters formed from the 18-carbon carboxylic acid oleic acid.
©FoodCollection/StockFood RF

11.6C   FOCUS ON THE ENVIRONMENT
Environmental Pollutants

MTBE (*tert*-butyl methyl ether) and 4,4'–dichlorobiphenyl (a PCB, polychlorinated biphenyl) demonstrate that solubility properties can help to determine the fate of organic pollutants in the environment.

$CH_3-O-C(CH_3)_3$ Cl (4,4'-dichlorobiphenyl structure) Cl

MTBE
tert-butyl methyl ether

4,4'-dichlorobiphenyl
(a PCB)

MTBE is a small polar organic molecule that has been used as a high-octane additive in unleaded gasoline. The use of MTBE, however, has now also caused environmental concern. Although MTBE is not toxic or carcinogenic, it has a distinctive, nauseating odor, and **it is water soluble.** Small amounts of MTBE have contaminated the drinking water in several California communities, making it unfit for consumption. As a result, the use of MTBE as a gasoline additive has declined in the United States.

4,4'-Dichlorobiphenyl is one of a group of compounds called **PCBs,** which have been used in the manufacture of polystyrene coffee cups and other products. They have been released into the environment during production, use, storage, and disposal, making them one of the most widespread organic pollutants. **PCBs are insoluble in H_2O, but very soluble in organic media,** so they are soluble in fatty tissue, including that found in all types of fish and birds around the world. Although not acutely toxic, ingesting large quantities of fish contaminated with PCBs has been shown to retard growth and memory retention in children.

PROBLEM 11.17

DDT is a persistent environmental pollutant once widely used as an insecticide. Using solubility principles, explain why shorebirds that populate areas sprayed with DDT are found to have a high concentration of DDT in their tissues.

$$CCl_3$$

DDT

11.7 FOCUS ON HEALTH & MEDICINE
Vitamins

Vitamins **are organic compounds needed in small amounts for normal cell function.** Our bodies cannot synthesize these compounds, so they must be obtained in our diet. Most vitamins are identified by a letter, such as A, C, D, E, and K. There are several different B vitamins, though, so a subscript is added to distinguish them—for example, B_1, B_2, and B_{12}.

Vitamins are classified on the basis of their solubility properties.

- A *fat-soluble vitamin* dissolves in an organic solvent but is insoluble in water. Fat-soluble vitamins have many nonpolar C—C and C—H bonds and few polar functional groups.
- A *water-soluble vitamin* dissolves in water. Water-soluble vitamins have many polar bonds.

The name **vitamin** was first used in 1912 by the Polish chemist Casimir Funk, who called them *vitamines,* since he thought that they all contained an *amine* functional group. Later the word was shortened to vitamin, because some are amines but others, like vitamins A and C, are not.

Whether a vitamin is fat soluble or water soluble can be determined by applying the solubility principles discussed in Section 11.6. Vitamins A and C illustrate the differences between fat-soluble and water-soluble vitamins.

11.7A Vitamin A

Vitamin A, or **retinol,** is an essential component of the vision receptors in the eyes. It also helps to maintain the health of mucous membranes and the skin, so many anti-aging creams contain vitamin A. A deficiency of this vitamin leads to a loss of night vision.

OH

vitamin A

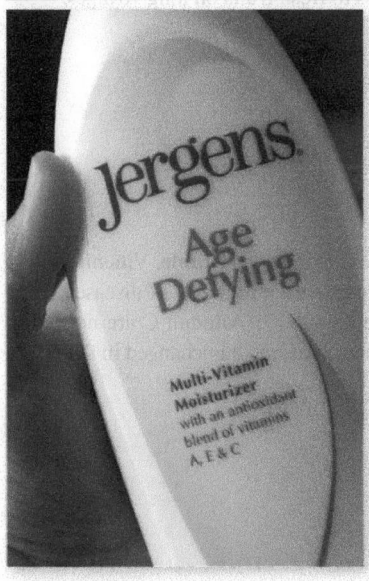

Some anti-aging creams contain vitamin A. ©McGraw-Hill Education/Jill Braaten, photographer

Vitamin A contains 20 carbons and a single OH group, making it **water insoluble.** Because it is organic, it is **soluble in any organic medium.** To understand the consequences of these solubility characteristics, we must learn about the chemical environment of the body.

About 70% of the body is composed of water. Fluids such as blood, gastric juices in the stomach, and urine are largely water with dissolved ions such as Na^+ and K^+. Vitamin A is insoluble in these fluids. There are also fat cells composed of organic compounds having C—C and C—H bonds. Vitamin A is soluble in this organic environment, and thus it is readily stored in these fat cells, particularly in the liver.

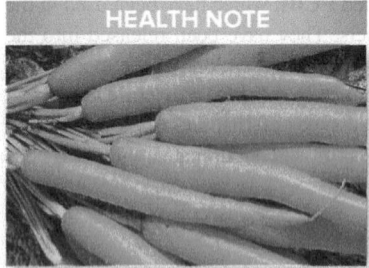

HEALTH NOTE

Vitamin A is synthesized in the body from β-carotene, the orange pigment found in carrots. ©*Ken Welsh/age fotostock RF*

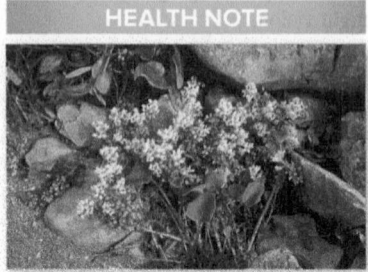

HEALTH NOTE

Vitamin C can be obtained from eating oranges and other citrus fruits. It can also be obtained by taking tablets that contain vitamin C synthesized in the laboratory. The vitamin C from both sources is exactly the same, so that "natural" vitamin C in oranges and "synthetic" vitamin C in tablets are identical. ©*McGraw-Hill Education/John Flournoy, photographer*

HEALTH NOTE

Scurvy grass is a low-growing plant found along the coasts of the Arctic region of the northern hemisphere. Scurvy grass was an excellent source of vitamin C for early Arctic explorers. ©*G.A. Matthews/Science Source*

In addition to obtaining vitamin A directly from the diet, β-carotene, the orange pigment found in many plants including carrots, is readily converted to vitamin A in our bodies.

β-carotene
(orange pigment in carrots)

Eating too many carrots does not result in storing an excess of vitamin A. If you consume more β-carotene in carrots than you need, the body stores this precursor until it needs more vitamin A. Some of the stored β-carotene reaches the surface tissues of the skin, giving it an orange color. This phenomenon is harmless and reversible. When stored β-carotene is converted to vitamin A and is no longer in excess, these tissues will return to their normal hue.

Ingesting a moderate excess of vitamin A doesn't cause any harm, but a large excess causes headaches, loss of appetite, and even death. Early Arctic explorers who ate polar bear livers that contain an unusually large amount of vitamin A are thought to have died from consuming too much vitamin A.

PROBLEM 11.18

(a) Convert the skeletal structure of vitamin A to a complete structure with all atoms and lone pairs drawn in. (b) Determine the molecular formula of β-carotene from its skeletal structure.

11.7B Vitamin C

Although most animal species can synthesize vitamin C, humans, the Indian fruit bat, and the bulbul bird must obtain this vitamin from dietary sources. Citrus fruits, strawberries, tomatoes, and sweet potatoes are all excellent sources of vitamin C.

Vitamin C, or ascorbic acid, is important in the formation of collagen, a protein that forms the connective tissues of skin, muscle, and blood vessels. A deficiency of vitamin C causes scurvy, a common disease of sailors in the 1600s who had no access to fresh fruits on long voyages.

vitamin C
(ascorbic acid)

Vitamin C has six carbon atoms and six oxygen atoms, making it **water soluble.** Vitamin C thus dissolves in urine. Although it has been acclaimed as a deterrent for all kinds of diseases, from the common cold to cancer, the benefits of taking large amounts of vitamin C are not really known, because an excess of the minimum daily requirement is excreted unchanged in the urine.

The solubility characteristics of vitamins A and C are shown in Figure 11.7.

PROBLEM 11.19

Predict the solubility of vitamin B_3 in water.

vitamin B_3
(niacin)

Figure 11.7   Solubility Characteristics of Vitamins A and C

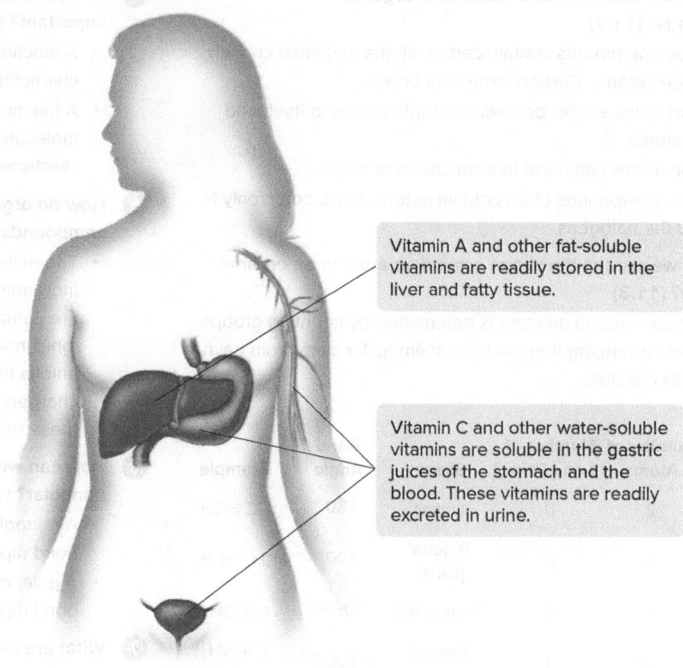

Vitamin A and other fat-soluble vitamins are readily stored in the liver and fatty tissue.

Vitamin C and other water-soluble vitamins are soluble in the gastric juices of the stomach and the blood. These vitamins are readily excreted in urine.

PROBLEM 11.20

Predict the solubility of vitamin K$_1$ in water and in organic solvents.

vitamin K$_1$
(phylloquinone)

CHAPTER HIGHLIGHTS

KEY TERMS

Alcohol (11.5)	Carbonyl group (11.5)	Hydroxyl group (11.5)
Aldehyde (11.5)	Carboxyl group (11.5)	Ketone (11.5)
Alkane (11.5)	Carboxylic acid (11.5)	"Like dissolves like" (11.6)
Alkene (11.5)	Condensed structure (11.4)	Nonpolar molecule (11.6)
Alkyl halide (11.5)	Ester (11.5)	Organic chemistry (11.1)
Alkyne (11.5)	Ether (11.5)	Polar molecule (11.6)
Amide (11.5)	Fat-soluble vitamin (11.7)	Skeletal structure (11.4)
Amine (11.5)	Functional group (11.5)	Thiol (11.5)
Amino group (11.5)	Heteroatom (11.2)	Vitamin (11.7)
Aromatic compound (11.5)	Hydrocarbon (11.5)	Water-soluble vitamin (11.7)

KEY CONCEPTS

❶ What are the characteristic features of organic compounds? (11.2)

- Organic compounds contain carbon atoms and most contain hydrogen atoms. Carbon forms four bonds.
- Carbon forms single, double, and triple bonds to itself and other atoms.
- Carbon atoms can bond to form chains or rings.
- Organic compounds often contain heteroatoms, commonly N, O, and the halogens.

❷ How can we predict the shape around an atom in an organic molecule? (11.3)

- The shape around an atom is determined by counting groups, and then arranging them to keep them as far away from each other as possible.

Number of Groups	Number of Atoms	Number of Lone Pairs	Shape	Bond Angle	Example
2	2	0	Linear	180°	$HC{\equiv}CH$
3	3	0	Trigonal planar	120°	$CH_2{=}CH_2$
4	4	0	Tetrahedral	109.5°	CH_3CH_3
4	3	1	Trigonal pyramidal	~109.5°	CH_3NH_2 (N atom)
4	2	2	Bent	~109.5°	CH_3OH (O atom)

❸ What shorthand methods are used to draw organic molecules? (11.4)

- In condensed structures, atoms are drawn in but the two-electron bonds are generally omitted. Lone pairs are omitted as well. Parentheses are used around like groups bonded together or to the same atom.
- Three assumptions are used in drawing skeletal structures: [1] There is a carbon at the intersection of two lines or at the end of any line. [2] Each carbon has enough hydrogens to give it four bonds. [3] Heteroatoms and the hydrogens bonded to them are drawn in.

❹ What is a functional group and why are functional groups important? (11.5)

- A functional group is an atom or a group of atoms with characteristic chemical and physical properties.
- A functional group determines all of the properties of a molecule—its shape, physical properties, and the type of reactions it undergoes.

❺ How do organic compounds differ from ionic inorganic compounds? (11.6)

- The main difference between organic compounds and ionic inorganic compounds is their bonding. Organic compounds are composed of discrete molecules with covalent bonds. Ionic inorganic compounds are composed of cations and anions held together by the strong attraction of oppositely charged ions. Other properties that are consequences of these bonding differences are summarized in Table 11.5.

❻ How can we determine if an organic molecule is polar or nonpolar? (11.6A)

- A nonpolar molecule has either no polar bonds or two or more bond dipoles that cancel.
- A polar molecule has either one polar bond, or two or more bond dipoles that do not cancel.

❼ What are the solubility properties of organic compounds? (11.6B)

- Most organic molecules are soluble in organic solvents.
- Hydrocarbons and other nonpolar organic molecules are not soluble in water.
- Polar organic molecules are water soluble only if they are small (less than six carbons) and contain a nitrogen or oxygen atom that can hydrogen bond with water.

❽ What are vitamins and when is a vitamin fat soluble or water soluble? (11.7)

- A vitamin is an organic compound that cannot be synthesized by the body but is needed in small amounts for cell function.
- A fat-soluble vitamin has many nonpolar C—C and C—H bonds and few polar bonds, making it insoluble in water.
- A water-soluble vitamin has many polar bonds, so it dissolves in water.

PROBLEMS

Selected in-chapter and odd-numbered end-of-chapter problems have brief answers in Appendix B. The *Student Study Guide and Solutions Manual* contains detailed solutions to all in-chapter and odd-numbered end-of-chapter problems, as well as additional worked examples and a chapter self-test.

General Characteristics of Organic Molecules

11.21 Which chemical formulas represent organic compounds and which represent inorganic compounds: (a) H_2SO_4; (b) Br_2; (c) C_5H_{12}?

11.22 Which chemical formulas represent organic compounds and which represent inorganic compounds: (a) LiBr; (b) HCl; (c) CH_5N?

11.23 Complete each structure by filling in all H's and lone pairs.

a. $C-C{=}C-C{\equiv}C$

b. $C{=}C-C-O$

c. $C{\equiv}C-\underset{\underset{\textstyle Cl}{|}}{C}-C$

d. $C{\equiv}C-C-\overset{\overset{\textstyle O}{\|}}{C}-N$

11.24 Complete the structure of mepivacaine by filling in all H's and lone pairs. Mepivacaine, sold under the trade name Carbocaine, is a fast-acting local anesthetic.

mepivacaine

Predicting Shape and Bond Angles

11.25 Determine the shape around the indicated atoms in each compound. Don't forget to add lone pairs to heteroatoms before determining the shape around them.

a.
$$\overset{(1)}{\underset{\underset{H}{\downarrow}}{\text{H}}}\text{—C}=\overset{(2)}{\text{C}}\text{—C}\equiv\text{N}$$
acrylonitrile
(used to prepare Orlon fibers)

b.
$$\text{CH}_3\text{—}\overset{(1)}{\text{O}}\text{—}\overset{(2)}{\text{C}}(\overset{(3)}{\text{CH}_3})_3$$
MTBE
(gasoline additive)

11.26 Ethambutol is a drug used to treat tuberculosis. Determine the shape around the indicated atoms in ethambutol. Don't forget to add lone pairs to heteroatoms before determining the shape around them.

$$\text{H—O—CH}_2\text{—}\underset{\underset{\text{H}}{|}}{\overset{\overset{\text{CH}_2\text{CH}_3}{|}}{\text{C}}}\text{—}\underset{\underset{\text{H}}{|}}{\text{N}}\text{—CH}_2\text{CH}_2\text{—}\underset{\underset{\text{H}}{|}}{\text{N}}\text{—}\underset{\underset{\text{H}}{|}}{\overset{\overset{\text{CH}_2\text{CH}_3}{|}}{\text{C}}}\text{—CH}_2\text{—O—H}$$

ethambutol

11.27 Predict the indicated bond angles in each compound.

a. $\text{CH}_3\overset{(1)}{\text{—}}\text{C}\equiv\text{C}\overset{(2)}{\text{—}}\text{Cl}$

b. $\text{CH}_2\text{=}\overset{(2)}{\underset{(1)}{\text{C}}}\text{—Cl}$ with H at (2)

c. $\text{CH}_3\text{—}\underset{\underset{\text{H}}{|}}{\overset{\overset{\text{H}}{|}}{\text{C}}}\text{—Cl}$ with (1) and (2)

11.28 Predict the indicated bond angles in each compound. Don't forget to add lone pairs to heteroatoms before determining the shape around them.

a. $\text{CH}_3(\text{CH}_2)_7\text{—}\underset{\underset{\text{H}}{|}}{\text{C}}\text{=}\underset{\underset{\text{H}}{|}}{\text{C}}\text{—}(\text{CH}_2)_7\text{—}\overset{\overset{\text{O}}{\|}}{\text{C}}\text{—O—H}$

oleic acid
(fatty acid in vegetable oil)

b. $\text{H—}\underset{\underset{\text{H}}{|}}{\text{N}}\text{—}\underset{\underset{\text{H}}{|}}{\overset{\overset{\text{H}}{|}}{\text{C}}}\text{—}(\text{CH}_2)_5\text{NH}_2$

1,6-diaminohexane
(used to synthesize nylon)

11.29 "Ecstasy" is a widely used illegal stimulant. Determine the shape around each indicated atom.

MDMA
"Ecstasy"

11.30 Fenfluramine is one component of the appetite suppressant Fen–Phen, which was withdrawn from the market in 1997 after it was shown to damage the heart valves in some patients. Determine the shape around each indicated atom.

fenfluramine

11.31 Explain why each C—C—C bond angle in benzene (Table 11.2) is 120°.

11.32 Hexachloroethane ($\text{Cl}_3\text{C—CCl}_3$), an alkyl chloride with a camphor-like odor, is a derivative of ethane (CH_3CH_3), formed by replacing each H by a Cl atom. Draw the structure of hexachloroethane using solid lines, wedges, and dashed wedges to indicate the three-dimensional shape around each atom.

Drawing Organic Molecules

11.33 Convert each compound to a condensed structure.

a., b., c. (structural formulas)

420   Chapter 11   Introduction to Organic Molecules and Functional Groups

11.34 Convert each compound to a condensed structure.

a. [structure: H-C-C-C-C-C-C-O-H with H's]

b. [structure with N]

c. [structure with O]

11.35 Convert each compound to a skeletal structure.

a. [structure with N]   b. [structure with Cl]

11.36 Convert each compound to a skeletal structure.

a. [structure with Br]   b. [structure with O]

11.37 Convert each shorthand structure to a complete structure with all atoms and lone pairs drawn in.

a. $(CH_3)_2CH(CH_2)_6CH_3$
b. $(CH_3)_3COH$
c. $CH_3CO_2(CH_2)_3CH_3$
d. [skeletal structure with Cl, Cl, O, HO]

11.38 Convert each shorthand structure to a complete structure with all atoms and lone pairs drawn in.

a. $(CH_3)_2CHO(CH_2)_4CH_3$
b. $(CH_3)_3C(CH_2)_3CBr_3$
c. $(CH_3)_2CHCONH_2$
d. [skeletal structure]

11.39 Convert each skeletal structure to a complete structure with all C's and H's drawn in. Add lone pairs to all heteroatoms.

a. [skeletal structure]   b. [skeletal structure with OH, O]

11.40 Convert each skeletal structure to a complete structure with all C's and H's drawn in. Add lone pairs to all heteroatoms.

a. [skeletal structure]   b. [skeletal structure with Br, OH, N]

11.41 **A** and **B** are ball-and-stick models of two compounds partly responsible for the scent of angel's trumpets, ornamental plants native to South America. (a) Convert **A** and **B** to complete structures with all atoms and lone pairs. (b) Convert each ball-and-stick model to a shorthand structure.

A   B

11.42 Theobromine is a stimulant in dark chocolate. (a) Convert the ball-and-stick model of theobromine to a complete structure with all atoms and lone pairs. (b) Convert the ball-and-stick model to a shorthand structure.

theobromine

11.43 What is wrong in each of the following shorthand structures?

a. $(CH_3)_3CHCH_2CH_3$
d. [cyclohexene structure with CH_3, CH_3]

b. $CH_3(CH_2)_4CH_3OH$
e. [cyclopentane structure with CH_3, CH_3, CH_3]

c. $(CH_3)_2C=CH_3$

11.44 What is wrong in each of the following shorthand structures?

a. $HC≡CCH_2C=CH_2$
d. [cyclopentadiene structure with Cl, Cl, Cl]

b. $CH_3C≡C(CH_3)_2$
e. [cyclohexanone structure with OH]

c. $HC≡CCH_2C(CH_3)_2$

11.45 Convert the shorthand structure of tyrosine to a complete structure with all atoms and lone pairs drawn in. Tyrosine is one of the 20 amino acids used for protein synthesis.

tyrosine

11.46 Albuterol (trade names Proventil and Ventolin) is a bronchodilator, a drug that widens airways, thus making it an effective treatment for individuals suffering from asthma. Draw a complete structure for albuterol with all atoms and lone pairs.

albuterol

Functional Groups

11.47 Identify the functional groups in each molecule.

a.

isoprene
(emitted by plants)

c. CH_3—C—$OCH_2CH_2CH_3$

propyl acetate
(from pears)

b. CH_3—C—$(CH_2)_4CH_3$

2-heptanone
(from blue cheese)

11.48 Identify the functional groups in each molecule.

a.

tartaric acid
(from grapes)

c. H—C—$N(CH_3)_2$

dimethylformamide
(solvent)

b.

butanedione
(component of butter flavor)

11.49 Identify the functional groups in each molecule.

a. H—C—$OCH_2CH(CH_3)_2$

isobutyl formate
(odor of raspberries)

b. CH_2=CHCHCH_2$—C≡C—C≡C—$CH_2CH$=CH(CH_2)_5CH_3$
       |
       OH

carotatoxin
(neurotoxin from carrots)

c. CH_3O— HO— —C—H

vanillin
(isolated from vanilla beans)

11.50 (a) Identify the functional groups in donepezil, trade name Aricept, used to treat dementia and Alzheimer's disease. (b) What is the molecular formula of donepezil?

donepezil

11.51 Dopamine, a molecule synthesized by nerve cells in the brain, affects movement, emotions, and pleasure. When dopamine-producing nerve cells die, Parkinson's disease results. Identify the functional groups in dopamine.

dopamine

11.52 GHB is an addictive, illegal recreational drug that depresses the central nervous system and results in intoxication. Identify the functional groups in GHB.

GHB

11.53 Convert the ball-and-stick model of neral, a compound isolated from lemons and limes, to a condensed or skeletal structure and identify the functional groups.

neral

11.54 Convert the ball-and-stick model of estragole, a compound isolated from tarragon, to a skeletal structure and identify the functional groups.

estragole

11.55 Draw an organic compound that fits each of the following criteria.

a. a hydrocarbon having molecular formula C_3H_4 that contains a triple bond

b. an alcohol containing three carbons

c. an aldehyde containing three carbons

d. a ketone having molecular formula C_4H_8O

11.56 Draw an organic compound that fits each of the following criteria.

a. an amine containing two CH_3 groups bonded to the N atom

b. an alkene that has the double bond in a ring

c. an ether having two different R groups bonded to the ether oxygen

d. an amide that has molecular formula C_3H_7NO

11.57 Draw the structure of an alkane, an alkene, and an alkyne, each having five carbon atoms. What is the molecular formula for each compound?

11.58 (a) Identify the functional groups in venlafaxine, trade name Effexor, an antidepressant. (b) What is the molecular formula of venlafaxine?

venlafaxine

Properties of Organic Compounds

11.59 You are given two unlabeled bottles of solids, one containing sodium chloride (NaCl) and one containing cholesterol ($C_{27}H_{46}O$, Section 11.6B). You are also given two labeled bottles of liquids, one containing water and one containing dichloromethane (CH_2Cl_2). How can you determine which solid is sodium chloride and which solid is cholesterol?

11.60 State how potassium iodide (KI) and pentane ($CH_3CH_2CH_2CH_2CH_3$) differ with regards to each of the following properties: (a) type of bonding; (b) solubility in water; (c) solubility in an organic solvent; (d) melting point; (e) boiling point.

11.61 The given beaker contains 100 mL of the organic solvent pentane (C_5H_{12}, density = 0.63 g/mL). Draw an illustration for what would be observed in each circumstance. (a) Water (50 mL) is added. (b) Ethanol (50 mL, CH_3CH_2OH, density = 0.79 g/mL) is added. (c) 1-Decanol (50 mL, $CH_3(CH_2)_9OH$, density = 0.83 g/mL) is added.

11.62 The given beaker contains 100 mL of water. Draw an illustration for what would be observed in each circumstance. (a) 1-Bromobutane (50 mL, $CH_3(CH_2)_3Br$, density = 1.27 g/mL) is added. (b) Ethanol (50 mL, CH_3CH_2OH, density = 0.79 g/mL) is added. (c) 1-Decanol (50 mL, $CH_3(CH_2)_9OH$, density = 0.83 g/mL) is added.

11.63 Why do we need to know the shape of a molecule with polar bonds before deciding if the molecule is polar or nonpolar?

11.64 1,1-Dichloroethylene (CH_2=CCl_2) is a starting material used to prepare the plastic packaging material Saran wrap. Your friend thinks that 1,1-dichloroethylene is a nonpolar molecule because the dipoles in the two C—Cl bonds cancel. Draw out the proper three-dimensional structure of 1,1-dichloroethylene, and then explain why your friend is correct or incorrect.

11.65 Indicate the polar bonds in each molecule. Label the bonds with δ+ and δ−.

a.
$$\begin{array}{c} Cl \\ | \\ F-C-Cl \\ | \\ Cl \end{array}$$

trichlorofluoromethane
(responsible for atmospheric
ozone destruction)

b. $HOCH_2CHCH_2OH$
$\qquad\quad |$
$\qquad\quad OH$

glycerol
(used in cosmetics)

11.66 Indicate the polar bonds in each molecule. Label the bonds with δ+ and δ−.

a.

vinyl chloride

b. —OCH₃

anisole

11.67 Classify each molecule as polar or nonpolar.

a.

c. CH_2Br_2

b. CH_3CH_2 —C(=O)— CH_2CH_3

11.68 Classify each molecule as polar or nonpolar.

a. $CH_3OCH_2CH_3$

c.

b. $(CH_3CH_2)_2NH$

11.69 Which molecule is more water soluble? Explain.

butane   ethylene glycol

11.70 Explain why pantothenic acid, vitamin B₅, is water soluble.

vitamin B₅

11.71 Sucrose (table sugar) and 1-dodecanol [(CH₃(CH₂)₁₁OH] both contain 12 carbon atoms and hydroxyl groups. Explain why sucrose is water soluble, but 1-dodecanol is not water soluble.

sucrose

11.72 Spermaceti wax [CH₃(CH₂)₁₄CO₂(CH₂)₁₅CH₃], a compound isolated from sperm whales, was once a common ingredient in cosmetics. Its use is now banned to help protect whales. (a) Identify the functional group in spermaceti wax. (b) Predict its solubility properties in water and organic solvents and explain your reasoning.

Vitamins

11.73 Explain why regularly taking a large excess of a fat-soluble vitamin can lead to severe health problems, whereas taking a large excess of a water-soluble vitamin often causes no major health problems.

11.74 You can obtain the minimum daily requirement of vitamin E by eating leafy greens or by taking vitamin E tablets. As a source of vitamin E, which of these methods is better for an individual?

11.75 Vitamin E is a natural antioxidant found in fish oil, almonds, hazelnuts, and leafy greens. Predict the solubility of vitamin E in water and in organic solvents.

vitamin E

11.76 Vitamin B₆ is obtained by eating a diet that includes meat, fish, wheat germ, and bananas. A deficiency of vitamin B₆ can cause convulsions and anemia. Predict the solubility of vitamin B₆ in water and in organic solvents.

vitamin B₆
pyridoxine

General Questions and Applications

11.77 Can a hydrocarbon have each of the following molecular formulas? Explain why or why not in each case. (a) C_3H_8; (b) C_3H_9; (c) C_3H_6.

11.78 Can an oxygen-containing organic compound have molecular formula C_2H_6O? Explain your reasoning.

11.79 (a) Draw a condensed structure for an amine having molecular formula $C_4H_{11}N$. (b) Label all polar bonds using the symbols δ+ and δ−. (c) Determine the geometry around the N atom. (d) Is the compound you drew polar or nonpolar?

11.80 (a) Draw a condensed structure for an alcohol having molecular formula $C_4H_{10}O$. (b) Label all polar bonds using the symbols δ+ and δ−. (c) Determine the geometry around the O atom. (d) Is the compound you drew polar or nonpolar?

11.81 Benzocaine is the active ingredient in topical pain relievers such as Orajel and Anbesol.

benzocaine

a. Give the molecular formula for benzocaine.

b. Draw in all lone pairs on heteroatoms using a skeletal structure.

c. How many trigonal planar carbons does benzocaine contain?

d. Predict the water solubility of benzocaine.

e. Label all polar bonds.

11.82 Methyl salicylate is responsible for the characteristic odor of the oil wintergreen.

methyl salicylate

a. Give the molecular formula for methyl salicylate.
b. Draw in all lone pairs on heteroatoms using a skeletal structure.
c. How many trigonal planar carbons does methyl salicylate contain?
d. Predict the water solubility of methyl salicylate.
e. Label all polar bonds.

11.83 Answer the following questions about aldosterone, a compound that helps to control the absorption of Na^+ and Cl^- ions in the kidneys and, as a result, affects water retention.

aldosterone

a. Identify the functional groups.
b. Draw in all lone pairs on O atoms.
c. How many C's does aldosterone contain?

CHALLENGE PROBLEMS

11.87 THC is the active component in marijuana (Section 11.5), and ethanol (CH_3CH_2OH) is the alcohol in alcoholic beverages. Using the solubility principles in Section 11.6, predict the water solubility of each of these compounds. Then, explain why drug screenings are able to detect the presence of THC but not ethanol weeks after these substances have been introduced into the body.

11.88 Cocaine is a widely abused, addicting drug. Cocaine is usually obtained as its hydrochloride salt (cocaine hydrochloride, an ionic salt). This salt can be converted to crack (a neutral molecule) by treatment with base.

d. How many H's are present at each C labeled with an asterisk (*)?
e. Give the shape around each atom labeled in gray.
f. Label all polar bonds.

11.84 Answer the following questions about levonorgestrel (trade name Plan B). Levonorgestrel interferes with ovulation, the release of an egg from an ovary, so it prevents pregnancy if taken within a few days of unprotected sex.

levonorgestrel

a. Identify the functional groups.
b. How many C's does levonorgestrel contain?
c. How many H's are present at each C labeled with an asterisk (*)?
d. Give the shape around each atom labeled in gray.
e. Label all polar bonds.
f. Is levonorgestrel soluble in an organic solvent?
g. Is levonorgestrel soluble in water?

11.85 Cabbage leaves are coated with a hydrocarbon of molecular formula $C_{29}H_{60}$. What purpose might this hydrocarbon coating serve?

11.86 Skin moisturizers come in two types. (a) One type of moisturizer is composed mainly of hydrocarbon material. Suggest a reason as to how a moisturizer of this sort helps to keep the skin from drying out. (b) A second type of moisturizer is composed mainly of propylene glycol [$CH_3CH(OH)CH_2OH$]. Suggest a reason as to how a moisturizer of this sort helps to keep the skin from drying out.

cocaine (crack)
(neutral organic molecule)

cocaine hydrochloride
(a salt)

a. Identify the functional groups in cocaine.
b. Given what you have learned about ionic and covalent bonding, which of the two compounds—crack or cocaine hydrochloride—has a higher boiling point?
c. Which compound is more soluble in water?
d. Can you use the relative solubility to explain why crack is usually smoked but cocaine hydrochloride is injected directly into the bloodstream?

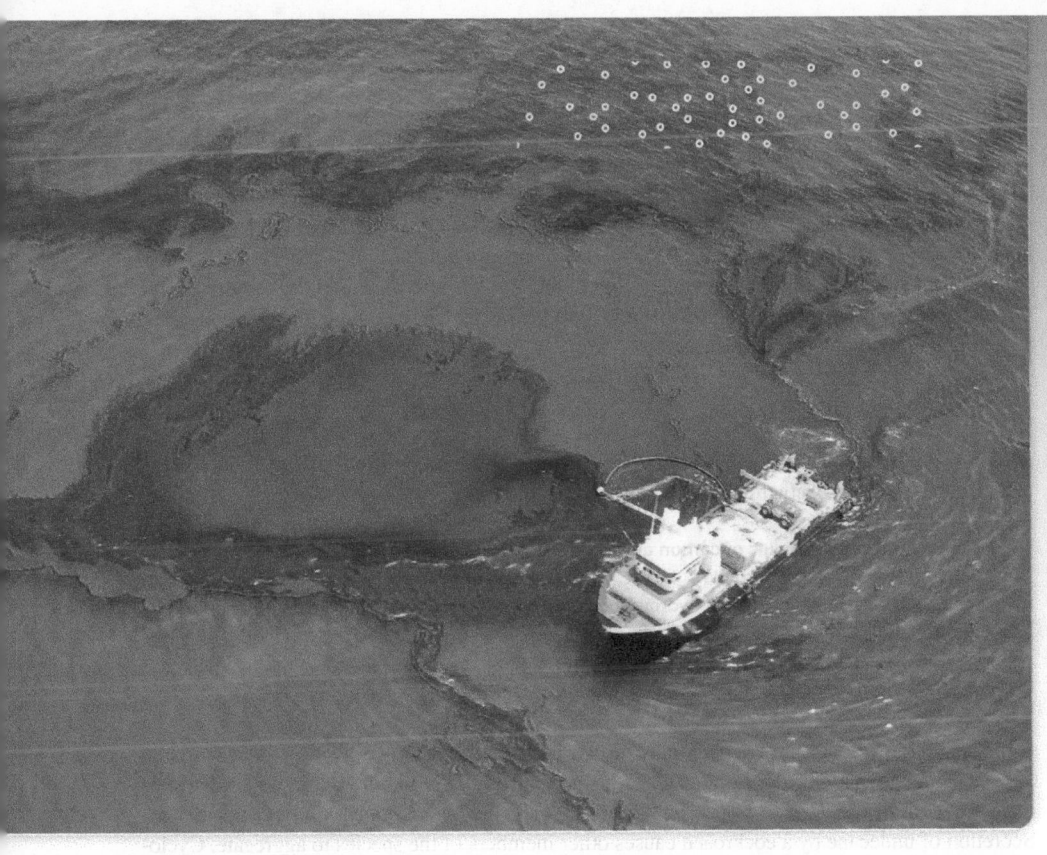

12

Crude petroleum spilled into
the sea creates an insoluble
oil slick. Petroleum is a
complex mixture that includes
the family of organic
compounds called **alkanes.**
Source: NOAA

Alkanes

CHAPTER OUTLINE

12.1 Introduction

12.2 Simple Alkanes

12.3 An Introduction to Nomenclature

12.4 Alkane Nomenclature

12.5 Cycloalkanes

12.6 FOCUS ON THE ENVIRONMENT: Fossil Fuels

12.7 Physical Properties

12.8 FOCUS ON THE ENVIRONMENT: Combustion

12.9 Halogenation of Alkanes

CHAPTER GOALS

In this chapter you will learn how to:

1. Identify and draw acyclic alkanes and cycloalkanes

2. Identify constitutional isomers

3. Name alkanes using the IUPAC system of nomenclature

4. Predict the physical properties of alkanes

5. Write equations for the complete and incomplete combustion of alkanes

6. Draw the products of the halogenation of alkanes

Why Study Alkanes?

In Chapter 12, we apply the principles of bonding, shape, and physical properties discussed in Chapter 11 to our first family of organic compounds, the **alkanes.** Since alkanes have no functional group, their chemical reactions are limited, and much of Chapter 12 is devoted to learning how to name and draw them. Alkanes do, however, undergo combustion, a process that powers automobiles and heats homes. The combustion of alkanes has also increased the carbon dioxide concentration in the atmosphere over the last 50 years, which may have long-term and far-reaching environmental consequences.

12.1   Introduction

Alkanes **are hydrocarbons having only C—C and C—H single bonds.** The carbons of an alkane can be joined together to form chains or rings of atoms.

The prefix *a-* means *not,* so an acyclic alkane is *not* cyclic.

- Alkanes that contain chains of carbon atoms but no rings are called *acyclic alkanes.* An acyclic alkane has the molecular formula C_nH_{2n+2}, where *n* is the number of carbons it contains. Acyclic alkanes are also called **saturated hydrocarbons** because they have the maximum number of hydrogen atoms per carbon.

- *Cycloalkanes* contain carbons joined in one or more rings. Since a cycloalkane has two fewer H's than an acyclic alkane with the same number of carbons, its general formula is C_nH_{2n}.

Undecane and cyclohexane are examples of two naturally occurring alkanes. Undecane is an acyclic alkane with molecular formula $C_{11}H_{24}$. Undecane is a *pheromone,* **a chemical substance used for communication** in a specific animal species, most commonly an insect population. Secretion of undecane by a cockroach causes other members of the species to aggregate. Cyclohexane, a cycloalkane with molecular formula C_6H_{12}, is one component of the mango, the most widely consumed fruit in the world.

$$CH_3CH_2CH_2CH_2CH_2CH_2CH_2CH_2CH_2CH_2CH_3$$

undecane   cyclohexane

(left): ©God of Insects; (right): ©Pixtal/age fotostock RF

PROBLEM 12.1

How many hydrogen atoms are present in each compound?

a. an acyclic alkane with three carbons

b. a cycloalkane with four carbons

c. a cycloalkane with nine carbons

d. an acyclic alkane with seven carbons

PROBLEM 12.2

Which formulas represent acyclic alkanes and which represent cycloalkanes?

a. C_5H_{12} b. C_4H_8 c. $C_{12}H_{24}$ d. $C_{10}H_{22}$

12.2   Simple Alkanes

We begin our study of alkanes with acyclic alkanes, and then move on to cycloalkanes in Section 12.5.

12.2A   Acyclic Alkanes Having Fewer Than Five Carbons

The structures for the two simplest acyclic alkanes were given in Chapter 11.

- **Methane, CH_4,** has a single carbon atom surrounded by four hydrogens to give it four bonds.
- **Ethane, CH_3CH_3,** has two carbon atoms joined together by a single bond. Each carbon is also bonded to three hydrogens to give it four bonds total.

Since each carbon in an alkane is surrounded by four atoms, each carbon is **tetrahedral,** and all bond angles are 109.5°.

> To draw the structure of an alkane, join the carbon atoms together with single bonds, and add enough H's to give each C four bonds.

3-D representation   ball-and-stick model

To draw a three-carbon alkane, draw three carbons joined together with single bonds and add enough hydrogens to give each carbon four bonds. This forms **propane, $CH_3CH_2CH_3$.**

3-D representation   ball-and-stick model   skeletal structure

Propane is the principal alkane in LPG (liquefied petroleum gas), a fuel used for vehicles and cooking. LPG has also been used as an aerosol propellant, replacing the ozone-depleting chlorofluorocarbons (Section 14.9). ©*Gary Gardiner/Bloomberg/ Getty Images*

The carbon skeleton in propane and other alkanes can be drawn in a variety of different ways and still represent the same molecule. For example, the three carbons of propane can be drawn in a horizontal row or with a bend. *These representations are equivalent.* **If you follow the carbon chain from one end to the other, you move across the *same* three carbon atoms in both representations.**

3 C's in a row   3 C's with a bend

Similarly, as long as a skeletal structure has three carbons in a row, it represents propane.

$CH_3CH_2CH_3$ $CH_3CH_2CH_3$ $CH_3CH_2CH_3$ $CH_3CH_2CH_3$

All of these skeletal structures represent propane, C_3H_8.

- **The bends in a carbon chain don't matter when it comes to identifying different compounds.**

There are two different ways to arrange four carbons, giving two compounds with molecular formula C_4H_{10}.

- **Butane, $CH_3CH_2CH_2CH_3$,** has four carbon atoms in a row. Butane is a **straight-chain alkane,** an alkane that has all of its carbons in one continuous chain.
- **Isobutane, $(CH_3)_3CH$,** has three carbon atoms in a row and one carbon bonded to the middle carbon. Isobutane is a **branched-chain alkane,** an alkane that contains one or more carbon branches bonded to a carbon chain.

butane | 4 C's in a row | skeletal structure | **straight-chain alkane**

isobutane | 3 C's with a one-carbon branch | skeletal structure | **branched-chain alkane**

Butane and isobutane are *isomers,* **two different compounds with the same molecular formula.** They belong to one of the two major classes of isomers called **constitutional isomers.**

Constitutional isomers are also called structural isomers.

- *Constitutional isomers* differ in the way the atoms are connected to each other.

Constitutional isomers like butane and isobutane belong to the same family of compounds: they are both **alkanes.** This is not always the case. For example, there are two different arrangements of atoms for a compound of molecular formula C_2H_6O.

$$H-\underset{\underset{H}{|}}{\overset{\overset{H}{|}}{C}}-\underset{\underset{H}{|}}{\overset{\overset{H}{|}}{C}}-O-H \qquad H-\underset{\underset{H}{|}}{\overset{\overset{H}{|}}{C}}-O-\underset{\underset{H}{|}}{\overset{\overset{H}{|}}{C}}-H$$

CH_3CH_2OH CH_3OCH_3
ethanol   dimethyl ether

Ethanol (CH_3CH_2OH) and dimethyl ether (CH_3OCH_3) are constitutional isomers with different functional groups: CH_3CH_2OH is an **alcohol** and CH_3OCH_3 is an **ether.**

SAMPLE PROBLEM 12.1 IDENTIFYING CONSTITUTIONAL ISOMERS

Are the compounds in each pair constitutional isomers or are they not isomers of each other?

a. $CH_3CH_2CH_3$ and $\underset{H}{\overset{H}{C}}=\underset{CH_3}{\overset{H}{C}}$

b. $CH_3CH_2CH_2NH_2$ and $CH_3-\underset{\underset{CH_3}{|}}{N}-CH_3$

Analysis

- **Compare molecular formulas;** two compounds are isomers only if they have the same molecular formula.
- **Check how the atoms are connected to each other.** Constitutional isomers have atoms bonded to *different* atoms.

Solution

a.   CH$_3$CH$_2$CH$_3$ and

$$\underset{H}{\overset{H}{\diagdown}}C=C\underset{CH_3}{\overset{H}{\diagup}}$$

   molecular formula
   C$_3$H$_8$

   molecular formula
   C$_3$H$_6$

The two compounds have the same number of C's but a different number of H's, so they have different molecular formulas. Thus, they are *not* isomers of each other.

b.   CH$_3$CH$_2$CH$_2$NH$_2$ and   CH$_3$—N—CH$_3$
                                                              |
                                                             CH$_3$

Both compounds have molecular formula C$_3$H$_9$N. Since one compound has C—C bonds and the other does not, the atoms are connected differently. These compounds are *constitutional isomers*.

PRACTICE PROBLEM 12.1

Are the compounds in each pair constitutional isomers or are they not constitutional isomers of each other?

a.   CH$_3$CH$_2$CH$_2$CH$_3$ and   CH$_3$CH$_2$CH$_3$

b.   CH$_3$CH$_2$CH$_2$OH   and   CH$_3$OCH$_2$CH$_3$

c.   [hexagon] and [pentagon]—CH$_3$

d.   [bowtie shape] and [square]

More Practice: Try Problems 12.29–12.34.

12.2B   Acyclic Alkanes Having Five or More Carbons

As the number of carbon atoms in an alkane increases, so does the number of isomers. There are three constitutional isomers for the five-carbon alkane, each having molecular formula C$_5$H$_{12}$: **pentane, isopentane** (or 2-methylbutane), and **neopentane** (or 2,2-dimethylpropane).

CH$_3$CH$_2$CH$_2$CH$_2$CH$_3$

$$CH_3-\underset{H}{\overset{CH_3}{\underset{|}{\overset{|}{C}}}}-CH_2CH_3$$

$$CH_3-\underset{CH_3}{\overset{CH_3}{\underset{|}{\overset{|}{C}}}}-CH_3$$

pentane

isopentane
(2-methylbutane)

neopentane
(2,2-dimethylpropane)

With alkanes having five or more carbons, the names of the straight-chain isomers are derived from Greek roots: *pent*ane for **five** carbons, *hex*ane for **six,** and so on. Table 12.1 lists the names and structures for the straight-chain alkanes having up to 10 carbons. The suffix *-ane* identifies a molecule as an alk*ane*. The remainder of the name—meth-, eth-, prop-, and so forth—indicates the number of carbons in the long chain.

The suffix *-ane* identifies a molecule as an alk*ane*.

SAMPLE PROBLEM 12.2 DRAWING ISOMERS

Draw two isomers with molecular formula C$_6$H$_{14}$ that have five carbon atoms in the longest chain and a one-carbon branch coming off the chain.

Analysis

Since isomers are different compounds with the same molecular formula, we must add a one-carbon branch to two different carbons to form two different products. Then add enough H's to give each C four bonds.

Solution

Compounds **A** and **B** are isomers because the CH_3 group is bonded to different atoms in the five-carbon chain. Note, too, that we cannot add the one-carbon branch to an *end* carbon because that creates a continuous six-carbon chain. Remember that **bends in the chain don't matter.**

Adding a C to an end C makes a six-carbon chain.

PRACTICE PROBLEM 12.2

Draw two isomers with molecular formula C_6H_{14} that have four carbon atoms in the longest chain and two one-carbon branches coming off the chain.

More Practice: Try Problems 12.35, 12.36, 12.39, 12.40c, 12.81b, 12.82b, 12.83b, 12.84b.

PROBLEM 12.3

Which of the following is *not* another representation for isopentane (2-methylbutane)?

Table 12.1 Straight-Chain Alkanes

Number of C's	Molecular Formula	Structure	Name
1	CH_4	CH_4	methane
2	C_2H_6	CH_3CH_3	ethane
3	C_3H_8	$CH_3CH_2CH_3$	propane
4	C_4H_{10}	$CH_3CH_2CH_2CH_3$	butane
5	C_5H_{12}	$CH_3CH_2CH_2CH_2CH_3$	pentane
6	C_6H_{14}	$CH_3CH_2CH_2CH_2CH_2CH_3$	hexane
7	C_7H_{16}	$CH_3CH_2CH_2CH_2CH_2CH_2CH_3$	heptane
8	C_8H_{18}	$CH_3CH_2CH_2CH_2CH_2CH_2CH_2CH_3$	octane
9	C_9H_{20}	$CH_3CH_2CH_2CH_2CH_2CH_2CH_2CH_2CH_3$	nonane
10	$C_{10}H_{22}$	$CH_3CH_2CH_2CH_2CH_2CH_2CH_2CH_2CH_2CH_3$	decane

12.2C   Classifying Carbon Atoms

Carbon atoms in alkanes and other organic compounds are classified by the number of other carbons directly bonded to them.

- A *primary carbon* (1° C) is bonded to *one* other C.
- A *secondary carbon* (2° C) is bonded to *two* other C's.
- A *tertiary carbon* (3° C) is bonded to *three* other C's.
- A *quaternary carbon* (4° C) is bonded to *four* other C's.

Classification of carbon atoms	Example

1° carbon   2° carbon   3° carbon   4° carbon

One example of each
type of C is labeled.

SAMPLE PROBLEM 12.3 CLASSIFYING CARBON ATOMS

Classify each carbon atom in the following molecule as 1°, 2°, 3°, or 4°.

$$CH_3-\overset{\overset{CH_3}{|}}{\underset{\underset{CH_3}{|}}{C}}-CH_2CH_2CH_3$$

Analysis

To classify a carbon atom, count the number of C's bonded to it. Draw a complete structure with all bonds and atoms to clarify the structure if necessary.

Solution

All C's labeled in red are 1° C's.

PRACTICE PROBLEM 12.3

Classify the carbon atoms in each compound as 1°, 2°, 3°, or 4°.

a. $CH_3CH_2CH_2CH_3$ b. $(CH_3)_3CH$ c. $CH_3-\overset{\overset{CH_3}{|}}{\underset{\underset{H}{|}}{C}}-CH_2CH_3$ d. $CH_3-\overset{\overset{CH_3}{|}}{\underset{\underset{CH_3}{|}}{C}}-CH_3$

More Practice: Try Problems 12.27, 12.28.

PROBLEM 12.4

Draw a condensed structure for an alkane that fits each description.

a. an alkane that contains only 1° and 2° carbons
b. an alkane of molecular formula C_5H_{12} that has one 3° carbon
c. an alkane with two 4° carbons

PROBLEM 12.5

Classify the carbon atoms in the following skeletal structures.

a.   b.

12.2D   Bond Rotation and Skeletal Structures for Acyclic Alkanes

A ball-and-stick model of ethane with two labeled hydrogens reveals an important feature. **Rotation can occur around carbon–carbon single bonds.** This allows the hydrogens on one CH_3

group to adopt different orientations relative to the hydrogens on the other CH_3 group. This is a characteristic of *all* carbon–carbon single bonds.

In a similar fashion, each carbon–carbon bond in butane ($CH_3CH_2CH_2CH_3$) undergoes rotation, a process that is rapid at room temperature. As a result, the carbon backbone of butane can be arranged in a variety of ways. The most stable arrangement avoids crowding between nearby carbons, so that the carbon skeleton is extended in a zigzag fashion.

preferred butane arrangement

Take care in interpreting skeletal structures. Although pentane is typically drawn using a zigzag structure, the carbon skeleton can be drawn in a variety of ways, and still represent the same compound. Each of the following representations has five carbon atoms in a row, so each represents pentane, not an isomer of pentane.

pentane C_5H_{12} 5 C's in a row   5 C's in a row   5 C's in a row

---

PROBLEM 12.6

Draw a skeletal structure for each compound: (a) $CH_3CH_2CH_2CH_2CH_2CH_3$ (hexane); (b) $CH_3(CH_2)_5CH_3$ (heptane).

PROBLEM 12.7

Convert each skeletal structure to a complete structure with all atoms and bond lines.

a.   b.   c.

PROBLEM 12.8

How are the ball-and-stick models **A** and **B** related to each other? Do they represent constitutional isomers or identical molecules?

A   **B**

PROBLEM 12.9

(a) Which two representations are identical molecules? (b) Which structure is an isomer of the other two representations?

A   **B**   **C**

12.3   An Introduction to Nomenclature

12.3A   The IUPAC System of Nomenclature

Garlic has been used in Chinese herbal medicine for over 4,000 years. Today it is sold as a dietary supplement because of its reported health benefits. **Allicin,** the molecule responsible for garlic's odor, is not stored in the garlic bulb, but rather is produced by the action of enzymes when the bulb is crushed or bruised.
©Stockbyte/Getty Images RF

How are organic compounds named? Long ago, the name of a compound was often based on the plant or animal source from which it was obtained. For example, the name allicin, the principal component of the odor of garlic, is derived from the botanical name for garlic, *Allium sativum.* Other compounds were named by their discoverer for more personal reasons. Adolf von Baeyer supposedly named barbituric acid after a woman named Barbara, although no one knows Barbara's identity—a lover, a Munich waitress, or even St. Barbara.

$$CH_2{=}CHCH_2SSCH_2CH{=}CH_2$$

allicin
(odor of garlic)

barbituric acid
(named for Barbara whom?)

With the isolation and preparation of thousands of new organic compounds, it became obvious that each organic compound must have an unambiguous name. A systematic method of naming compounds (a system of **nomenclature**) was developed by the *I*nternational *U*nion of *P*ure and *A*pplied *C*hemistry. It is referred to as the **IUPAC** system of nomenclature, and how it can be used to name alkanes is explained in Section 12.4.

12.3B   FOCUS ON HEALTH & MEDICINE
Naming New Drugs

Naming organic compounds has become big business for drug companies. The IUPAC name of an organic compound can be long and complex. As a result, most drugs have three names:

- **Systematic:** The systematic name follows the accepted rules of nomenclature; this is the IUPAC name.
- **Generic:** The generic name is the official, internationally approved name for the drug.
- **Trade:** The trade name for a drug is assigned by the company that manufactures it. Trade names are often "catchy" and easy to remember. Companies hope that the public will continue to purchase a drug with an easily recalled trade name long after a cheaper generic version becomes available.

Consider the world of over-the-counter anti-inflammatory agents. The compound a chemist calls 2-[4-(2-methylpropyl)phenyl]propanoic acid has the generic name ibuprofen. It is marketed under a variety of trade names, including Motrin and Advil.

©Jill Braaten RF

Systematic name:	2-[4-(2-methylpropyl)phenyl]propanoic acid
Generic name:	ibuprofen
Trade name:	Motrin or Advil

12.4   Alkane Nomenclature

Although the names of the straight-chain alkanes having 10 carbons or fewer were already given in Table 12.1, we must also learn how to name alkanes that have carbon branches, called **substituents,** bonded to a long chain. The names of these organic molecules have three parts.

> • The parent name indicates the number of carbons in the longest continuous carbon chain in the molecule.
> • The suffix indicates what functional group (if any) is present.
> • The prefix tells us the identity, location, and number of substituents attached to the carbon chain.

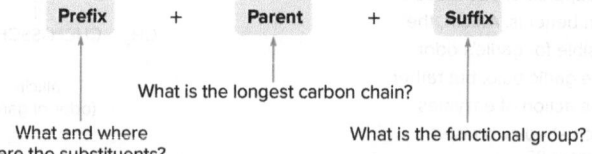

The names of the straight-chain alkanes in Table 12.1 consist of two parts. The suffix *-ane* indicates that the compounds are alkanes. The remainder of the name is the parent name, which indicates the number of carbon atoms in the longest carbon chain. The parent name for **one carbon is *meth-*,** for **two carbons is *eth-*,** and so on. Thus, we are already familiar with two parts of the name of an organic compound.

To determine the third part of a name, the prefix, we must learn how to name the substituents that are bonded to the longest carbon chain.

12.4A   Naming Substituents

Carbon substituents bonded to a long carbon chain are called *alkyl groups.*

> • An *alkyl group* is formed by removing one hydrogen from an alkane.

An alkyl group is a part of a molecule that is now able to bond to another atom or a functional group. **To name an alkyl group, change the *-ane* ending of the parent alkane to *-yl.*** Thus, methane (CH_4) becomes **methyl** (CH_3—) and ethane (CH_3CH_3) becomes **ethyl** (CH_3CH_2—).

Removing one hydrogen from an *end* carbon in any straight-chain alkane forms other alkyl groups named in a similar fashion. Thus, propane ($CH_3CH_2CH_3$) becomes propyl ($CH_3CH_2CH_2$—) and butane ($CH_3CH_2CH_2CH_3$) becomes butyl ($CH_3CH_2CH_2CH_2$—). The names of alkyl groups having six carbons or fewer are summarized in Table 12.2. Figure 12.1 shows some alkyl groups drawn in skeletal structures.

Table 12.2 Some Common Alkyl Groups

Number of C's	Structure	Name
1	CH_3-	methyl
2	CH_3CH_2-	ethyl
3	$CH_3CH_2CH_2-$	propyl
4	$CH_3CH_2CH_2CH_2-$	butyl
5	$CH_3CH_2CH_2CH_2CH_2-$	pentyl
6	$CH_3CH_2CH_2CH_2CH_2CH_2-$	hexyl

Figure 12.1 Alkyl Groups Drawn in Skeletal Structures

methyl group
(CH_3 group)

ethyl group
(CH_2CH_3 group)

butyl group
($CH_2CH_2CH_2CH_3$ group)

12.4B Naming an Acyclic Alkane

Four steps are needed to name an alkane.

How To Name an Alkane Using the IUPAC System

Step [1] Find the parent carbon chain and add the suffix.

- **Find the longest continuous carbon chain,** and name the molecule using the parent name for that number of carbons, given in Table 12.1. To the name of the parent, add the suffix *-ane* for an alkane. Each functional group has its own suffix.

$$CH_3-\overset{\overset{\displaystyle CH_3}{|}}{CH}-CH_2-CH_2-CH_2-CH_3$$

6 C's in the longest chain

6 C's ---→ hexane

- The longest chain may not be written horizontally across the page. Remember that **it does not matter if the chain is *straight* or has *bends.*** All of the following representations are equivalent.

6 C's in the longest chain of each structure

Step [2] Number the atoms in the carbon chain to give the first substituent the lower number.

CORRECT Start numbering here.

first substituent at C2

INCORRECT

first substituent at C5

—*Continued*

436   Chapter 12   Alkanes

Step [3] **Name and number the substituents.**

• Name the substituents as alkyl groups, and use the numbers from step [2] to designate their location.

methyl at C2

CH₃

CH₃—CH—CH₂—CH₂—CH₂—CH₃ ← longest chain (6 C's)
hexane

1   2

• Every carbon belongs to *either* the longest chain or a substituent, but *not both.*
• Each substituent needs its *own* number.
• If two or more identical substituents are bonded to the longest chain, use **prefixes** to indicate how many: **di-** for two groups, **tri-** for three groups, **tetra-** for four groups, and so forth. The following compound has two methyl groups so its name contains the prefix *di-* before methyl → *di*methyl.

methyl at C2

CH₃

CH₃—CH—CH—CH₂—CH₂—CH₃   Use the prefix *di-*.
CH₃

1   2 3   methyl at C3

Step [4] **Combine substituent names and numbers + parent + suffix.**

• Precede the name of the parent by the names of the substituents. **Alphabetize** the names of the substituents, ignoring any prefixes like *di-.* For example, triethyl precedes dimethyl because the e of **e**thyl comes before the m of **m**ethyl in the alphabet.
• Precede the name of each substituent by the number that indicates its location. There must be **one number for each substituent.**
• Separate numbers by commas and separate numbers from letters by dashes.

methyl at C2   methyl at C2

CH₃   CH₃

CH₃—CH—CH₂—CH₂—CH₂—CH₃   CH₃—CH—CH—CH₂—CH₂—CH₃ ← **hexane**

1   2   longest chain (6 C's)   CH₃
hexane   1   2 3   methyl at C3

To help identify which carbons belong to the longest chain and which are substituents, always box in the atoms of the long chain. Every other carbon atom then becomes a substituent that needs its own name as an alkyl group.

• Two numbers are needed, one for each methyl group.

Answer: 2-methylhexane   **Answer: 2,3-dimethylhexane**

Sample Problem 12.4 illustrates the naming of an alkane with all C's and H's drawn in. Sample Problem 12.5 gives an example of naming an alkane drawn in a skeletal structure.

SAMPLE PROBLEM 12.4 NAMING AN ALKANE

Give the IUPAC name for the following compound.

Analysis and Solution

[1] Name the parent and use the suffix -*ane* because the molecule is an alkane.

CH₃   CH₃CH₂ H
CH₃—C—CH₂CH₂—C—C—CH₂CH₃
H   H   CH₃

8 C's in the longest chain ---→ **octane**

• Box in the atoms of the longest chain to clearly show which carbons are part of the longest chain and which carbons are substituents.

[2] Number the chain to give the first substituent the lower number.

- Numbering from left to right puts the first substituent at C2.

[3] Name and number the substituents.

- This compound has three substituents: two methyl groups at C2 and C6 and an ethyl group at C5.

[4] Combine the parts.

- Write the name as one word and use the prefix *di-* before methyl because there are two methyl groups.
- Alphabetize the *e* of **e**thyl before the *m* of **m**ethyl. The prefix *di-* is ignored when alphabetizing.

Answer: 5-ethyl-2,6-dimethyloctane

PRACTICE PROBLEM 12.4

Give the IUPAC name for each compound.

a. CH$_3$CH$_2$CHCH$_2$CH$_3$
           |
          CH$_3$

b. CH$_3$CH$_2$CH$_2$—C—C—CH$_2$CH$_2$CH$_2$CH$_3$ with CH$_3$ CH$_2$CH$_2$CH$_3$ above and H H below

c. H—C—CH$_2$—CHCH$_3$ with CH$_2$CH$_3$ above, CH$_3$ and CH$_3$ below

More Practice: Try Problems 12.41; 12.43a; 12.44a; 12.45 a–c, e; 12.46 a–d; 12.81a; 12.82a.

PROBLEM 12.10

How many carbons are in the longest chain of each molecule?

a. CH$_3$CH$_2$CHCH$_2$CH$_2$CHCH$_3$ with CH$_3$ above and CH$_3$ below

b. (CH$_3$)$_2$CH(CH$_2$)$_3$CH$_3$

c.

d.

PROBLEM 12.11

Give the IUPAC name for each compound.

a. (CH$_3$)$_2$CHCH(CH$_3$)$_2$

b. CH$_3$CH$_2$CH$_2$CHCH$_2$C—H   with CH$_2$CH$_2$CH$_2$CH$_3$ above, CH$_3$CH$_2$ and H below

c. CH$_3$CH$_2$CH$_2$CH$_2$—C—C—CH$_2$CH$_3$ with CH$_3$ H above, CH$_2$ CH$_3$ below and CH$_3$ at bottom

SAMPLE PROBLEM 12.5 DETERMINING THE IUPAC NAME FOR A SKELETAL STRUCTURE

Give the IUPAC name for the following compound.

Analysis and Solution

[1] Name the parent and use the suffix -ane because the molecule is an alkane.

- Highlight the atoms in the longest continuous carbon chain, remembering that the longest chain need not be drawn horizontally across the page.

7 C's in the longest chain - - - → **heptane**

[2] Number the chain to give the first substituent the lower number.

- Numbering from right to left puts the first substituent at C2.

[3] Name and number the substituents.

methyl at C5

methyl at C2

ethyl at C4

methyl at C3

- This compound has four substituents: three methyl groups at C2, C3, and C5, and an ethyl group at C4.

[4] Combine the parts.

- Write the name as one word and use the prefix *tri-* before methyl because there are three methyl groups.
- Alphabetize the *e* of **e**thyl before the *m* of **m**ethyl.

methyl at C5

methyl at C2

ethyl at C4

heptane

methyl at C3

three methyl groups - - - → **trimethyl**

Answer: 4-ethyl-2,3,5-trimethylheptane

PRACTICE PROBLEM 12.5

Give the IUPAC name for each compound.

a.

b.

More Practice: Try Problems 12.45d, f; 12.46e, f.

You must also know how to derive a structure from a given name. Sample Problem 12.6 demonstrates a stepwise method.

SAMPLE PROBLEM 12.6 DERIVING A STRUCTURE FROM A NAME

Give the structure with the following IUPAC name: 2,3,3-trimethylpentane.

Analysis

To derive a structure from a name, first look at the end of the name to find the parent name and suffix. From the parent we know the number of C's in the longest chain, and the suffix tells us the functional group; the suffix -*ane* = an alkane. Then, number the carbon chain from either end and add the substituents. Finally, add enough H's to give each C four bonds.

Solution

2,3,3-Trimethyl**pentane** has **pentane** (5 C's) as the longest chain and three methyl groups at carbons 2, 3, and 3.

2,3,3-trimethylpentane

skeletal structure

PRACTICE PROBLEM 12.6

Give the structure corresponding to each IUPAC name.

  a. 3-methylhexane   b. 3,3-dimethylpentane   c. 3,5,5-trimethyloctane   d. 3-ethyl-4-methylhexane

More Practice: Try Problems 12.49, 12.50.

PROBLEM 12.12

Give the structure corresponding to each IUPAC name.

  a. 2,2-dimethylbutane   c. 4,4,5,5-tetramethylnonane

  b. 6-butyl-3-methyldecane   d. 3-ethyl-5-propylnonane

12.5 Cycloalkanes

Cycloalkanes contain carbon atoms arranged in a ring. Think of a cycloalkane as being formed by removing two H's from the end carbons of a chain, and then bonding the two carbons together.

12.5A Simple Cycloalkanes

Simple cycloalkanes are named by adding the prefix *cyclo-* to the name of the acyclic alkane having the same number of carbons. Cycloalkanes having three to six carbon atoms are shown in the accompanying figure. They are drawn using polygons in skeletal representations (Section 11.4). Each corner of the polygon has a carbon atom with two hydrogen atoms to give it four bonds.

cyclopropane C_3H_6　　cyclobutane C_4H_8　　cyclopentane C_5H_{10}　　cyclohexane C_6H_{12}

Cyclic compounds occur widely in nature and many have interesting and important biological properties. For example, **pyrethrin I,** a naturally occurring insecticide obtained from chrysanthemums, contains both a three- and five-membered ring. **Vitamin D₃,** a fat-soluble vitamin that regulates calcium and phosphorus metabolism, contains six- and five-membered rings. Many foods, particularly milk, are fortified with vitamin D₃ so that we get enough of this vital nutrient in our diet.

pyrethrin I

vitamin D₃

(left): ©Brand X Pictures/PunchStock RF; (right): ©McGraw-Hill Education/Suzie Ross, photographer

Although we draw cycloalkanes as flat polygons, in reality cycloalkanes with more than three carbons are not planar molecules. Cyclohexane, for example, adopts a puckered arrangement called the **chair** form, in which all bond angles are 109.5°.

cyclohexane

skeletal structure

nonplanar cyclohexane
chair form

ball-and-stick model

PROBLEM 12.13

Review: Label the functional groups in pyrethrin I.

PROBLEM 12.14

(a) Give the molecular formula for vitamin D₃. (b) From what you learned in Chapter 11, explain why vitamin D₃ is a fat-soluble vitamin.

12.5B   Naming Cycloalkanes

Cycloalkanes are named using the rules in Section 12.4, but the prefix *cyclo-* immediately precedes the name of the parent.

A ring is present.

Prefix   +   **cyclo-**   +   **Parent**   +   **Suffix**

What and where
are the substituents?

How many C's are in the ring?

What is the functional group?

How To Name a Cycloalkane Using the IUPAC System

Step [1] Find the parent cycloalkane.

- Count the number of carbon atoms in the ring and use the parent name for that number of carbons. Add the prefix *cyclo-* and the suffix *-ane* to the parent name.

6 C's in the ring ⟶

cyclohexane

Step [2] Name and number the substituents.

- No number is needed to indicate the location of a **single** substituent.

methyl

methylcyclohexane

butyl

butylcyclopentane

- For rings with more than one substituent, begin numbering at one substituent, and then give the **second substituent** the lower number. With two **different** substituents, number the ring to assign the lower number to the substituents **alphabetically.**

- Place CH$_3$ groups at C1 and C3.

1,3-dimethylcyclohexane
(*not* 1,5-dimethylcyclohexane)

Earlier letter ----→ lower number

- ethyl group at **C1**
- methyl group at **C3**

1-ethyl-3-methylcyclohexane
(*not* 3-ethyl-1-methylcyclohexane)

SAMPLE PROBLEM 12.7 NAMING A CYCLOALKANE

Give the IUPAC name for the following compound.

Analysis and Solution

[1] Name the ring. The ring has 5 C's, so the molecule is named as a cyclopentane.

[2] Name and number the substituents.

- There are two substituents: CH$_3$CH$_2$– is an ethyl group and CH$_3$CH$_2$CH$_2$– is a propyl group.
- Number to put the two groups at C1 and C2 (not C1 and C5).
- Place the ethyl group at C1 because the *e* of **e**thyl comes before the *p* of **p**ropyl in the alphabet.

Start numbering here.

ethyl at C1

5 C's ---→ cyclopentane

propyl at C2 (not C5)

Answer: 1-ethyl-2-propylcyclopentane

PRACTICE PROBLEM 12.7

Give the IUPAC name for each compound.

a.   b.   c.   d.

More Practice: Try Problems 12.42, 12.43b, 12.44b, 12.47, 12.48, 12.83a, 12.84a.

PROBLEM 12.15

Give the structure corresponding to each IUPAC name.

a. propylcyclopentane
b. 1,2-dimethylcyclobutane

c. 1,1,2-trimethylcyclopropane
d. 4-ethyl-1,2-dimethylcyclohexane

12.6   FOCUS ON THE ENVIRONMENT
Fossil Fuels

Many alkanes occur in nature, primarily in natural gas and petroleum. Both of these fossil fuels serve as energy sources, formed long ago by the degradation of organic material.

Natural gas is composed largely of **methane** (60–80% depending on its source), with lesser amounts of ethane, propane, and butane. These organic compounds burn in the presence of oxygen, releasing energy for cooking and heating (Section 12.8).

Petroleum is a complex mixture of compounds, most of which are hydrocarbons containing 1–40 carbon atoms. Distilling crude petroleum, a process called **refining**, separates it into usable fractions that differ in boiling point (Figure 12.2). Most products of petroleum refining provide fuel for home heating, automobiles, diesel engines, and airplanes. Each fuel type has a different composition of hydrocarbons: gasoline (C_5H_{12}–$C_{12}H_{26}$), kerosene ($C_{12}H_{26}$–$C_{16}H_{34}$), and diesel fuel ($C_{15}H_{32}$–$C_{18}H_{38}$).

CONSUMER NOTE

Natural gas is odorless. The smell observed in a gas leak is due to minute amounts of a sulfur additive such as methanethiol, CH_3SH, which provides an odor for easy detection and safety.

Figure 12.2   Refining Crude Petroleum into Usable Fuel and Other Petroleum Products

a.

b.

An oil refinery. At an oil refinery, crude petroleum is separated into fractions of similar boiling point.
©Ingram PublishingRF

A refinery tower. As crude petroleum is heated, the lower-boiling components come off at the top of the tower, followed by fractions of higher boiling point.

Petroleum provides more than fuel. About 3% of crude oil is used to make plastics and other synthetic compounds, including drugs, fabrics, dyes, and pesticides. These products are responsible for many of the comforts we now take for granted in industrialized countries. Imagine what life would be like without air-conditioning, refrigeration, anesthetics, and pain relievers, all products of the petroleum industry.

Barrel of crude oil

petroleum starting materials for chemical synthesis (1.3 gal)

asphalt and road oil (1.3 gal)

boiler oil (2.9 gal)

lubricants, waxes, solvents (4.2 gal)

jet fuel (4.2 gal)

diesel and home heating oil (8.4 gal)

gasoline (19.7 gal)

1 barrel = 42 gal

products made from petroleum

©McGraw-Hill Education/Jill Braaten, photographer

Energy from petroleum is *nonrenewable,* and the remaining known oil reserves are limited. Given our dependence on petroleum, not only for fuel, but also for the many necessities of modern society, it becomes obvious that we must both conserve what we have and find alternate energy sources.

The high cost of energy and limited petroleum reserves have prompted many ingenious approaches to energy production. Several large cattle farms in the United States use manure digesters to convert animal waste into methane, called "biogas," which in turn is used to generate electricity (Figure 12.3). The manure is pumped into large oxygen-free tanks, where anaerobic bacteria break down the organic material in the manure to form methane. The methane is collected and then combusted to generate electricity. The residue is compressed and used for fertilizer. In this way, a large volume of animal waste is transformed into two useful products—electricity and fertilizer.

Figure 12.3   Methane from Manure

digester cover

biogas

to flame for electricity generation

biogas outlet

manure inlet

Bubbles of CH$_4$ gas form and escape from the mixture.

effluent outlet

fertilizer

444   Chapter 12 Alkanes

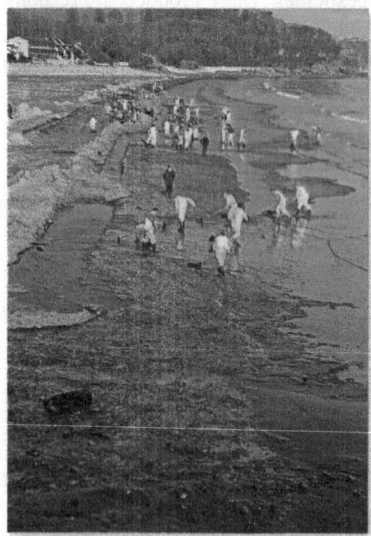

Crude oil that leaks into the sea forms an insoluble layer on the surface.
©Vince Bevan/Alamy

The insolubility of nonpolar oil and very polar water leads to the expression "Oil and water don't mix."

Vaseline petroleum jelly (Problem 12.17), a skin lubricant often used for chapped lips and diaper rash, is a mixture of high molecular weight alkanes.
©Jill Braaten RF

12.7   Physical Properties

Alkanes contain only nonpolar C—C and C—H bonds, so they exhibit only **weak intermolecular forces.** As a result, alkanes have low melting points and boiling points. Low molecular weight alkanes are gases at room temperature, and alkanes used in gasoline are all liquids.

The melting points and boiling points of alkanes increase as the number of carbons increases. Increased surface area increases the force of attraction between molecules, thus raising the boiling point and melting point. This is seen in comparing the boiling points of three straight-chain alkanes.

$CH_3CH_2CH_2CH_3$	$CH_3CH_2CH_2CH_2CH_3$	$CH_3CH_2CH_2CH_2CH_2CH_3$
butane	pentane	hexane
bp = −0.5 °C	bp = 36 °C	bp = 69 °C

Increasing surface area
Increasing boiling point

Because nonpolar alkanes are water insoluble and less dense than water, crude petroleum spilled into the sea from a ruptured oil tanker creates an insoluble oil slick on the surface. The insoluble hydrocarbon oil poses a special threat to birds whose feathers are coated with natural nonpolar oils for insulation. Because these oils dissolve in the crude petroleum, birds lose their layer of natural protection and many die.

PROBLEM 12.16

Answer the following questions about pentane (C_5H_{12}), heptane (C_7H_{16}), and decane ($C_{10}H_{22}$).

a. Which compound has the highest boiling point?
b. Which compound has the lowest boiling point?
c. Which compound has the highest melting point?
d. Which compound has the lowest melting point?

PROBLEM 12.17

Explain why Vaseline, a complex mixture of hydrocarbons used as a skin lubricant and ointment, is insoluble in water and soluble in dichloromethane (CH_2Cl_2).

PROBLEM 12.18

Polyisobutylene, a synthetic high molecular weight alkane with many properties similar to those of polyethylene (Section 11.5A), is the principal component of Elastol, a product used to clean up oil spills. Elastol dissolves oil to form a thick mat that can be skimmed or suctioned from the surface. Explain why oil dissolves in Elastol.

polyisobutylene

12.8   FOCUS ON THE ENVIRONMENT
Combustion

Alkanes are the only family of organic molecules that has no functional group, so **alkanes undergo few reactions.** In this section, we consider one reaction of alkanes—**combustion.** Combustion is an example of an **oxidation–reduction** reaction, a class of reactions first discussed in Section 5.4. In Section 12.9, we examine the reaction of alkanes with halogen.

To determine if an organic compound undergoes oxidation or reduction, we concentrate on the carbon atoms of the starting material and product, and **compare the relative number of C—H and C—O bonds.**

- *Oxidation* results in an *increase* in the number of C—O bonds or a *decrease* in the number of C—H bonds.
- *Reduction* results in a *decrease* in the number of C—O bonds or an *increase* in the number of C—H bonds.

Alkanes undergo **combustion**—that is, **they burn in the presence of oxygen to form carbon dioxide (CO_2) and water.** This is a practical example of oxidation. Every C—H and C—C bond in the starting material is converted to a C—O bond in the product. Equations are written with two different alkanes.

Review Section 5.2 on how to balance a chemical equation.

$$CH_4 \;+\; 2\,O_2 \xrightarrow{\text{flame}} CO_2 \;+\; 2\,H_2O \;+\; \text{energy}$$
methane
(natural gas)

$$2\,(CH_3)_3CCH_2CH(CH_3)_2 \;+\; 25\,O_2 \xrightarrow{\text{flame}} 16\,CO_2 \;+\; 18\,H_2O \;+\; \text{energy}$$
isooctane
(high-octane component of gasoline)

Note that the products, **$CO_2 + H_2O$,** are the same regardless of the identity of the starting material. Combustion of alkanes in the form of natural gas, gasoline, or heating oil releases energy for heating homes, powering vehicles, and cooking food.

A spark or a flame is needed to initiate combustion. Gasoline, which is composed largely of alkanes, can be safely handled and stored in the air, but the presence of a spark or open flame causes immediate and violent combustion.

The combustion of alkanes and other hydrocarbons obtained from fossil fuels adds a tremendous amount of CO_2 to the atmosphere each year. Quantitatively, data show over a 25% increase in the atmospheric concentration of CO_2 in the last 58 years (from 315 parts per million in 1958 to 402 parts per million in 2016; Figure 12.4). Although the composition of the atmosphere has changed over the lifetime of the earth, this is likely the first time that the actions of mankind have altered that composition significantly and so quickly.

ENVIRONMENTAL NOTE

Driving an automobile 10,000 miles at 25 miles per gallon releases 10,000 lb of CO_2 into the atmosphere. ©*Tim McCaig/ Getty Images RF*

An increased CO_2 concentration in the atmosphere may have long-range and far-reaching effects. CO_2 is a **greenhouse gas** because it absorbs thermal energy that normally radiates from the earth's surface, and redirects it back to the surface. Higher levels of CO_2 may therefore contribute to an increase in the average temperature of the earth's atmosphere. The global climate change resulting from these effects may lead to the melting of polar ice caps, the rise in sea level, and many more unforeseen consequences.

The 2007 Nobel Peace Prize was awarded to former Vice President Al Gore and the Intergovernmental Panel on Climate Change for their roles in focusing attention on the potentially disastrous effects of rapid climate change caused by human activity.

PROBLEM 12.19

Write a balanced equation for each combustion reaction.

a. $CH_3CH_2CH_3 \;+\; O_2 \xrightarrow{\text{flame}}$
   propane

b. $CH_3CH_2CH_2CH_3 \;+\; O_2 \xrightarrow{\text{flame}}$
   butane

When there is not enough oxygen available to completely burn a hydrocarbon, **incomplete combustion** may occur and **carbon monoxide (CO)** is formed instead of carbon dioxide (CO_2).

Incomplete combustion
$$2\,CH_4 \;+\; 3\,O_2 \xrightarrow{\text{flame}} 2\,CO \;+\; 4\,H_2O \;+\; \text{energy}$$
methane
carbon monoxide

HEALTH NOTE

Meters that measure CO levels can be purchased, as described in Section 5.7. When wood is burned in a poorly ventilated fireplace situated in a well-insulated room, the CO concentration can reach an unhealthy level.

Carbon monoxide is a poisonous gas that binds to hemoglobin in the blood, thus reducing the amount of oxygen that can be transported through the bloodstream to cells. CO can be formed whenever hydrocarbons burn. When an automobile engine burns gasoline, unwanted carbon monoxide can be produced. Yearly car inspections measure CO and other pollutant levels and are

Figure 12.4   The Changing Concentration of CO_2 in the Atmosphere

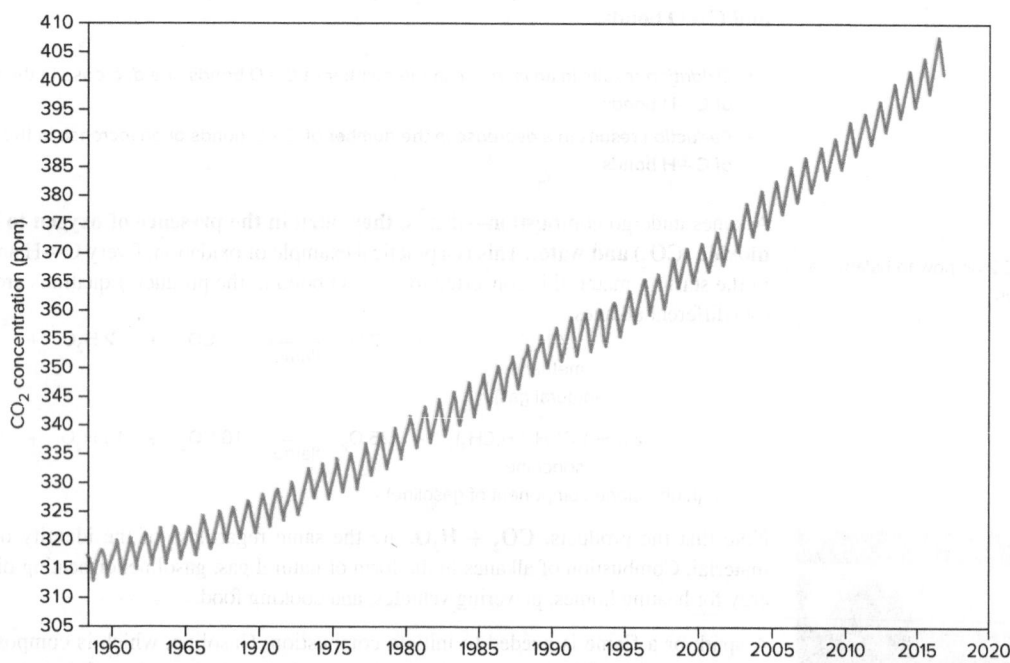

The graph clearly shows the increasing level of CO_2 in the atmosphere (1958–2016). Two data points are recorded each year. The sawtooth nature of the graph is due to seasonal variation of CO_2 level with the seasonal variation in photosynthesis. (Data recorded at Mauna Loa, Hawaii.)

designed to prevent cars from emitting potentially hazardous substances into ambient air. Carbon monoxide is also formed when cigarettes burn, so heavy smokers have an unhealthy concentration of CO in their bloodstreams.

12.9 Halogenation of Alkanes

The reaction of an alkane with a halogen, usually chlorine (Cl_2) or bromine (Br_2), is called **halogenation.** Halogenation of an alkane forms an **alkyl halide** (RCl or RBr) and a hydrogen halide (HCl or HBr). This reaction occurs only when the reactants are heated together or when they are exposed to light, and this is typically indicated over or under the reaction arrow.

Halogenation $-\overset{|}{\underset{|}{C}}-H$ + X—X $\xrightarrow{\text{light or heat}}$ $-\overset{|}{\underset{|}{C}}-X$ + H—X

alkane   alkyl halide

For example, the treatment of methane with Cl_2 in the presence of light forms CH_3Cl (chloromethane) and HCl. Heating ethane with bromine forms CH_3CH_2Br (bromoethane) and HBr.

$$H-\overset{\overset{\displaystyle H}{|}}{\underset{\underset{\displaystyle H}{|}}{C}}-H \ + \ Cl-Cl \ \xrightarrow{\text{light}} \ H-\overset{\overset{\displaystyle H}{|}}{\underset{\underset{\displaystyle H}{|}}{C}}-Cl \ + \ H-Cl$$

methane   chloromethane

$$H-\overset{\overset{\displaystyle H}{|}}{\underset{\underset{\displaystyle H}{|}}{C}}-\overset{\overset{\displaystyle H}{|}}{\underset{\underset{\displaystyle H}{|}}{C}}-H \ + \ Br-Br \ \xrightarrow{\text{heat}} \ H-\overset{\overset{\displaystyle H}{|}}{\underset{\underset{\displaystyle H}{|}}{C}}-\overset{\overset{\displaystyle H}{|}}{\underset{\underset{\displaystyle H}{|}}{C}}-Br \ + \ H-Br$$

ethane   bromoethane

Halogenation is an example of a *substitution* reaction.

- **Substitution is a reaction in which an atom is replaced by another atom or a group of atoms.**

In halogenation, a hydrogen atom of an alkane is replaced by a halogen atom. Both acyclic alkanes and cycloalkanes undergo substitution.

substitution of H by Br

We will learn more about the alkyl halides formed in this reaction in Chapter 14.

PROBLEM 12.20

Draw the products formed in each of the following halogenation reactions.

a. $CH_3-\overset{\overset{\displaystyle CH_3}{|}}{\underset{\underset{\displaystyle CH_3}{|}}{C}}-CH_3$ + Br_2 $\xrightarrow{\text{light}}$ b. ▷ + Cl_2 $\xrightarrow{\text{heat}}$

PROBLEM 12.21

Reaction of butane ($CH_3CH_2CH_2CH_3$) with Cl_2 in the presence of light forms two different alkyl chlorides that have molecular formula C_4H_9Cl. Draw the structures of both alkyl chlorides.

PROBLEM 12.22

What alkane is needed as a starting material to prepare each of the following alkyl halides by a halogenation reaction?

a. $CH_3-\overset{\overset{\displaystyle CH_3}{|}}{\underset{\underset{\displaystyle Br}{|}}{C}}-CH_3$ b. ⬠—Cl   c. ⬜—Br with CH₃

CHAPTER HIGHLIGHTS

KEY TERMS

Acyclic alkane (12.1)
Alkane (12.1)
Alkyl group (12.4)
Branched-chain alkane (12.2)
Combustion (12.8)
Constitutional isomer (12.2)
Cycloalkane (12.1)
Greenhouse gas (12.8)
Halogenation (12.9)

Incomplete combustion (12.8)
Isomer (12.2)
IUPAC nomenclature (12.3)
Oxidation (12.8)
Parent name (12.4)
Petroleum (12.6)
Pheromone (12.1)
Primary carbon, 1° C (12.2)
Quaternary carbon, 4° C (12.2)

Reduction (12.8)
Refining (12.6)
Saturated hydrocarbon (12.1)
Secondary carbon, 2° C (12.2)
Straight-chain alkane (12.2)
Substitution (12.9)
Tertiary carbon, 3° C (12.2)

KEY CONCEPTS

❶ What are the characteristics of an alkane? (12.1, 12.2)
- Alkanes are hydrocarbons having only nonpolar C—C and C—H single bonds.
- There are two types of alkanes: Acyclic alkanes (C_nH_{2n+2}) have no rings. Cycloalkanes (C_nH_{2n}) have one or more rings.

- A carbon is classified as 1°, 2°, 3°, or 4° by the number of carbons bonded to it. A 1° C is bonded to one carbon; a 2° C is bonded to two carbons, and so forth.

❷ What are constitutional isomers? (12.2)
- Isomers are different compounds with the same molecular formula.
- Constitutional isomers differ in the way the atoms are connected to each other. $CH_3CH_2CH_2CH_3$ and $HC(CH_3)_3$ are constitutional isomers because they have molecular formula C_4H_{10}, but one compound has a chain of four carbons in a row and the other does not.

❸ How are alkanes named? (12.4, 12.5)
- Alkanes are named using the IUPAC system of nomenclature. A name has three parts: the parent indicates the number of carbons in the longest chain or the ring; the suffix indicates the functional group (-*ane* = alkane); the prefix tells the number and location of substituents coming off the chain or ring.
- Alkyl groups are formed by removing one hydrogen from an alkane. Alkyl groups are named by changing the -*ane* ending of the parent alkane to the suffix -*yl*.

❹ Characterize the physical properties of alkanes. (12.7)
- Alkanes are nonpolar, so they have weak intermolecular forces, low melting points, and low boiling points.

- The melting points and boiling points of alkanes increase as the number of carbons increases due to increased surface area.
- Alkanes are insoluble in water.

❺ What are the products of the combustion and incomplete combustion of an alkane? (12.8)
- Alkanes burn in the presence of air. Combustion forms CO_2 and H_2O as products. Incomplete combustion forms CO and H_2O.
- Alkane combustion has increased the level of CO_2, a greenhouse gas, in the atmosphere.
- Incomplete combustion forms carbon monoxide, a toxin and air pollutant.

❻ What products are formed during the halogenation of an alkane? (12.9)
- Reaction of an alkane with a halogen (X_2) forms an alkyl halide (RX) and a hydrogen halide (HX). Halogenation is a substitution reaction in which a halogen atom X replaces a hydrogen atom.

PROBLEMS

Selected in-chapter and odd-numbered end-of-chapter problems have brief answers in Appendix B. The *Student Study Guide and Solutions Manual* contains detailed solutions to all in-chapter and odd-numbered end-of-chapter problems, as well as additional worked examples and a chapter self-test.

Alkanes and Isomers

12.23 The waxy coating that covers tobacco leaves contains a straight-chain alkane having 31 carbons. How many hydrogens does this alkane contain?

©Zbigniew Guzowski/Shutterstock RF

12.24 The sex attractant of the female tiger moth is an alkane of molecular formula $C_{18}H_{38}$. Is this molecule an acyclic alkane or a cycloalkane?

12.25 The waxy coating on the surface of apple skins contains an alkane with 27 carbon atoms. What is the molecular formula of this alkane?

©lynx/iconotec.com/Glow Images RF

12.26 An alkane has 20 hydrogen atoms. How many carbon atoms would it contain if it were (a) a straight-chain alkane; (b) a branched-chain alkane; (c) a cycloalkane?

12.27 Classify each carbon as 1°, 2°, 3°, or 4°.
a. $CH_3(CH_2)_3CH_3$ c. $(CH_3)_3CC(CH_3)_3$

b.   d.

12.28 Give the structure of an alkane that fits each description.
a. an alkane that contains only 1° and 4° carbons
b. a cycloalkane that contains only 2° carbons
c. an alkane of molecular formula C_6H_{14} that contains a 4° carbon
d. a cycloalkane that contains 2° and 3° carbons

12.29 Label each pair of compounds as constitutional isomers or identical molecules.

a. CH₃CHCHCH₃ (with CH₂CH₃ above and CH₂CH₃ below) and CH₃CH₂CHCH₂CH(CH₃)₂ (with CH₃ above)

b. [skeletal structure] and [skeletal structure]

c. [skeletal structure] and [skeletal structure]

d. [skeletal structure] and [skeletal structure]

12.30 Label each pair of compounds as constitutional isomers, identical molecules, or not isomers of each other.

a. CH₃CH₂CH₂CH₃ and CH₃CH₂CH₂CH₂CH₃

b. [skeletal structure] and [skeletal structure]

c. [skeletal structure] and [skeletal structure]

d. CH₃—C(=O)—OCH₃ and CH₃CH₂—C(=O)—OH

12.31 Consider compounds **A**, **B**, and **C**. Label each pair of compounds as constitutional isomers or identical molecules: (a) **A** and **B**; (b) **A** and **C**; (c) **B** and **C**.

A   **B**   **C**

12.32 Consider compounds **D**, **E**, and **F**. Label each pair of compounds as constitutional isomers or identical molecules: (a) **D** and **E**; (b) **D** and **F**; (c) **E** and **F**.

D   **E**   **F**

12.33 How is each of the following compounds related to (CH₃)₂CHCH₂CH₂CH₃? Choose from constitutional isomers or identical molecules.

a. CH₃CHCHCH₃ (with CH₃ above and CH₃ below)

b. CH₃CHCH₂CH₂ (with CH₃ above and CH₃ below)

c. CH₃CHCH₃ (with CH₂CH₂CH₃ below)

d. CH₃CHCH₂CH₃ (with CH₂CH₃ below)

e. [skeletal structure]

12.34 Consider compounds **A–E** and label each pair of compounds as identical molecules, constitutional isomers, or not isomers of each other: (a) **A** and **B**; (b) **A** and **C**; (c) **B** and **D**; (d) **D** and **E**; (e) **B** and **E**.

[skeletal structure]   CH₃(CH₂)₃CHCH₃ (with CH₃ below)   H—C(CH₃)(H)—CH₂CH₂CH₂—C(H)(CH₃)—H

A   **B**   **C**

CH₃CH₂CH₂CHCH₂CH₃ (with CH₃ above) [skeletal structure]

D   **E**

12.35 Draw structures that fit the following descriptions:
a. two cycloalkanes that are constitutional isomers with molecular formula C₇H₁₄
b. an ether and an alcohol that are constitutional isomers with molecular formula C₅H₁₂O
c. two constitutional isomers of molecular formula C₃H₇Cl

12.36 Draw the five constitutional isomers having molecular formula C₆H₁₄.

12.37 How many carbons are present in the longest chain of each molecule?

a.   b.

12.38 Locate the longest continuous carbon chain in each molecule.

a.   b.

12.39 Draw the five constitutional isomers that have molecular formula C₅H₁₀ and contain one ring.

12.40 Pristane is a high molecular weight alkane found in shark liver oil obtained from sharks that inhabit the cold waters of the northern Atlantic and southern Pacific Oceans. (a) Give the molecular formula for pristane from the ball-and-stick model. (b) Draw a skeletal structure for pristane. (c) Draw a constitutional isomer that contains the same number of carbon atoms in the longest chain.

pristane

©Paul Nicklen/National Geographic/Getty Images RF

Alkane Nomenclature

12.41 Give the IUPAC name for each of the five constitutional isomers of molecular formula C_6H_{14} in Problem 12.36.

12.42 Give the IUPAC name for each of the five cyclic isomers of molecular formula C_5H_{10} in Problem 12.39.

12.43 Give the IUPAC name for each compound.

a.

b.

12.44 Give the IUPAC name for each compound.

a.   b.

12.45 Give the IUPAC name for each compound.

a. $CH_3CH_2CHCH_2CH_2CH_2CH_3$
    |
    CH_3

b. $CH_3CH_2CHCH_2CHCH_2CH_2CH_3$
    | |
    CH_3 CH_3

c. $CH_3CH_2CH_2C(CH_2CH_3)_3$

d.

e. $(CH_3CH_2)_2CHCH_2CH_2CH_2CH(CH_3)_2$

f.

12.46 Give the IUPAC name for each compound.

a.   d. $(CH_3CH_2)_2CHCH(CH_2CH_3)_2$

```
      H    CH3
      |    |
CH3—C—CHCH3
      |
      CH2CH3
```

b.   e.

```
          CH3
          |
CH3CH2—C—CH2CH2CH3
          |
          CH3
```

```
              CH2CH2CH2CH3
              |
c.  CH3CH2CHCH2CH2CH3        f.
```

12.47 Give the IUPAC name for each cycloalkane.

a.   c.

b. ▷—CH3   d.

12.48 Give the IUPAC name for each cycloalkane.

a.   c.

b.   d.

12.49 Give the structure corresponding to each IUPAC name.
   a. 3-ethylhexane
   b. 3-ethyl-3-methyloctane
   c. 2,3,4,5-tetramethyldecane
   d. cyclononane
   e. 1,1,3-trimethylcyclohexane
   f. 1-ethyl-2,3-dimethylcyclopentane

12.50 Give the structure corresponding to each IUPAC name.
   a. 3-ethyl-3-methylhexane
   b. 2,2,3,4-tetramethylhexane
   c. 4-ethyl-2,2-dimethyloctane
   d. 1,3,5-triethylcycloheptane
   e. 3-ethyl-3,4-dimethylnonane
   f. 2-ethyl-1-methyl-3-propylcyclopentane

12.51 Each of the following IUPAC names is incorrect. Explain why it is incorrect and give the correct IUPAC name.
 a. 3-methylbutane d. 5-ethyl-2-methylhexane
 b. 1-methylcyclopentane e. 1,5-dimethylcyclohexane
 c. 1,3-dimethylbutane f. 1-propyl-2-ethylcyclopentane

12.52 Each of the following IUPAC names is incorrect. Explain why it is incorrect and give the correct IUPAC name.
 a. 4-methylpentane d. 3-methyl-5-ethylhexane
 b. 2,3,3-trimethylbutane e. 2-ethyl-2-methylcycloheptane
 c. 1,3-dimethylpentane f. 1,6-diethylcyclohexane

12.53 Draw three constitutional isomers having molecular formula C_7H_{14} that contain a five-membered ring and two CH_3 groups bonded to the ring. Give the IUPAC name for each isomer.

12.54 Draw four constitutional isomers having molecular formula C_6H_{12} that contain a four-membered ring. Give the IUPAC name for each isomer.

Drawing Acyclic Alkanes and Cycloalkanes

12.55 Draw a skeletal structure for each compound.
 a. octane
 b. 1,2-dimethylcyclopentane
 c. $CH_3CHCH_2CH_2CH_2CH_2CH_3$
    $|$
    CH_3

12.56 Convert each compound to a skeletal structure.
 a. $CH_3(CH_2)_7CH_3$ c. $(CH_3CH_2)_2CHCH_2CH_2CH_3$
 b. 1,1-diethylcyclohexane

12.57 Convert each skeletal structure to a complete structure with all atoms drawn in.

12.58 Convert each skeletal structure to a complete structure with all atoms drawn in.

Physical Properties

12.59 Which compound in each pair has the higher melting point?

12.60 Which compound in each pair has the higher boiling point?

12.61 Branching in an alkane chain decreases surface area. As a result, a branched-chain alkane tends to have a lower boiling point than a straight-chain alkane with the same number of carbons. Keeping this in mind, rank the alkane isomers in each group in order of increasing boiling point.
 a. $CH_3CH_2CH_2CH_2CH_3$, $(CH_3)_2CHCH_2CH_3$, $(CH_3)_4C$
 b. $(CH_3)_2CHCH(CH_3)_2$, $CH_3(CH_2)_4CH_3$, $CH_3CH_2CH_2CH(CH_3)_2$

12.62 Explain why the boiling points of heptane [$CH_3(CH_2)_5CH_3$] and H_2O are similar even though heptane has a much higher molecular weight and greater surface area.

12.63 Explain why hexane is more soluble in dichloromethane (CH_2Cl_2) than in water.

12.64 Mineral oil and Vaseline are both mixtures of alkanes, but mineral oil is a liquid at room temperature and Vaseline is a solid. Which product is composed of alkanes that contain a larger number of carbon atoms? Explain your choice.

Reactions

12.65 Write a balanced equation for the combustion of each alkane: (a) CH_3CH_3; (b) $(CH_3)_2CHCH_2CH_3$.

12.66 Write a balanced equation for the combustion of each cycloalkane.

 a. [hexagon] b. [pentagon]

12.67 Write a balanced equation for the incomplete combustion of each alkane: (a) $CH_3CH_2CH_3$; (b) $CH_3CH_2CH_2CH_3$.

12.68 Benzene (C_6H_6) is a fuel additive sometimes used to make gasoline burn more efficiently. Write a balanced equation for the incomplete combustion of benzene.

12.69 In the body, glucose, a simple carbohydrate with molecular formula $C_6H_{12}O_6$, is oxidized to CO_2 and H_2O with the release of a great deal of energy. Thus, the metabolism of glucose provides energy for our bodies, in much the same way as the oxidation of an alkane provides energy to power an automobile. Write a balanced equation for the oxidation of glucose to form CO_2 and H_2O.

12.70 Gasohol is a mixture of 90% gasoline and 10% ethanol, CH_3CH_2OH. Ethanol is considered an environmentally friendly fuel additive because it can be made from a renewable source— sugarcane. Ethanol burns in air to form CO_2 and H_2O, and, like the combustion of alkanes, this reaction also releases a great deal of energy. Write a balanced equation for the combustion of ethanol.

452   **Chapter 12**   Alkanes

12.71 What alkyl halide is formed when each of the following compounds is heated with bromine?

a. CH_4 b. ⬡   c. ▢

12.72 Draw all the alkyl halides with molecular formula $C_5H_{11}Cl$ formed when pentane ($CH_3CH_2CH_2CH_2CH_3$) is heated with Cl_2.

12.73 Draw the products formed when $(CH_3)_3CC(CH_3)_3$ is treated with each reagent.

a. O_2 (flame)   c. Br_2 and heat
b. Cl_2 and light

12.74 What alkane is needed as a starting material to prepare each of the following alkyl halides by a halogenation reaction?

a. CH_3—$\overset{\overset{\displaystyle CH_3}{|}}{\underset{\underset{\displaystyle Cl}{|}}{C}}$—$CH_2CH_2CH_3$ b. $CH_3CH_2CH_2CH_2CH_2CH_2Cl$

Applications

12.75 The gasoline industry seasonally changes the composition of gasoline in locations where it gets very hot in the summer and very cold in the winter. Gasoline is refined to contain a larger fraction of higher molecular weight alkanes in warmer weather. In colder weather, it is refined to contain a larger fraction of lower molecular weight alkanes. What is the purpose of producing different types of gasoline for different temperatures?

12.76 Polyethylene (Section 11.5) is a high molecular weight alkane that contains hundreds or even thousands of carbon atoms, bonded together in long carbon chains. When a new home is built, the concrete foundation is often wrapped with polyethylene (sold under the trade name of Tyvek). What purpose does the polyethylene serve?

12.77 Mineral oil, a mixture of high molecular weight alkanes, is sometimes used as a laxative. Individuals who use mineral oil for this purpose are advised to avoid taking it at the same time they consume foods rich in fat-soluble vitamins such as vitamin A. Why is this advice given?

12.78 Explain why having a fire in a fireplace in a poorly ventilated room poses a health hazard.

12.79 You went running on a newly paved asphalt road, which soiled your sneakers. What solvent might be best for removing asphalt, a mixture of high molecular weight hydrocarbons, from your sneakers: (a) water; (b) nail polish remover, which is mainly acetone [$(CH_3)_2C{=}O$]; (c) paint thinner, which is largely liquid alkanes? Explain your choice.

CHALLENGE PROBLEMS

12.85 What is the molecular formula for a compound with 10 carbons and two rings?

12.86 Draw the structure of the 12 constitutional isomers that have the molecular formula C_6H_{12} and contain one ring.

12.80 A major component of animal fat is tristearin. (a) Identify the three functional groups in tristearin. (b) Label all the polar bonds. (c) Explain why tristearin will dissolve in an organic solvent like hexane but is insoluble in water.

$$H_2C-O-\overset{\overset{\displaystyle O}{\|}}{C}-(CH_2)_{16}CH_3$$
$$H-C-O-\overset{\overset{\displaystyle O}{\|}}{C}-(CH_2)_{16}CH_3$$
$$H_2C-O-\overset{\overset{\displaystyle O}{\|}}{C}-(CH_2)_{16}CH_3$$

tristearin

General Questions

12.81 Answer the following questions about the alkane drawn below.

$$CH_3CH_2CH_2-\overset{\overset{\displaystyle CH_3}{|}}{\underset{\underset{\displaystyle CH_3}{|}}{C}}-\overset{\overset{\displaystyle CH_2CH_3}{|}}{\underset{\underset{\displaystyle H}{|}}{C}}-CH_2CH_3$$

a. Give the IUPAC name.
b. Draw one constitutional isomer.
c. Predict the solubility in water.
d. Predict the solubility in an organic solvent.
e. Write a balanced equation for complete combustion.
f. Draw a skeletal structure.

12.82 Answer the questions in Problem 12.81 for the alkane drawn below.

$$CH_3CH_2CH_2-\overset{\overset{\displaystyle H}{|}}{\underset{\underset{\displaystyle CH_3CH_2}{|}}{C}}-\overset{\overset{\displaystyle CH_2CH_3}{|}}{\underset{\underset{\displaystyle CH_3}{|}}{C}}-CH_2CH_3$$

12.83 Answer the questions in Problem 12.81 for the cycloalkane depicted in the given ball-and-stick model.

12.84 Answer the questions in Problem 12.81 for the cycloalkane depicted in the given ball-and-stick model.

12.87 Cyclopentane has a higher boiling point than pentane even though both compounds have the same number of carbons (49 °C vs. 36 °C). Can you suggest a reason for this phenomenon?

12.88 Draw the structure of the six constitutional isomers formed when ethylcyclohexane is treated with Cl_2 in the presence of light.

Candlenuts, known as kukui nuts in Hawaii, are rich in oils derived from unsaturated fatty acids, such as linoleic acid and linolenic acid.
©Inga Spence/Science Source

Unsaturated Hydrocarbons

CHAPTER OUTLINE

13.1 Alkenes and Alkynes

13.2 Nomenclature of Alkenes and Alkynes

13.3 Cis–Trans Isomers

13.4 Interesting Alkenes in Food and Medicine

13.5 FOCUS ON HEALTH & MEDICINE: Oral Contraceptives

13.6 Reactions of Alkenes

13.7 FOCUS ON HEALTH & MEDICINE: Margarine or Butter?

13.8 Polymers—The Fabric of Modern Society

13.9 Aromatic Compounds

13.10 Nomenclature of Benzene Derivatives

13.11 FOCUS ON HEALTH & MEDICINE: Aromatic Drugs, Sunscreens, and Carcinogens

13.12 FOCUS ON HEALTH & MEDICINE: Phenols as Antioxidants

13.13 Reactions of Aromatic Compounds

CHAPTER GOALS

In this chapter you will learn how to:

1. Identify the three major types of unsaturated hydrocarbons—alkenes, alkynes, and aromatic compounds

2. Name alkenes, alkynes, and substituted benzenes

3. Recognize the difference between constitutional isomers and stereoisomers, as well as identify cis and trans isomers

4. Identify saturated and unsaturated fatty acids and predict their relative melting points

5. Draw the products of addition reactions of alkenes

6. Draw the products of reactions that follow Markovnikov's rule

7. Explain what products are formed when a vegetable oil is partially hydrogenated

8. Draw the structure of polymers formed from alkene monomers

9. Draw the products of substitution reactions of benzene

Why Study
Alkenes, Alkynes, and
Aromatic Hydrocarbons?

In Chapter 13 we continue our study of hydrocarbons by examining three families of compounds that contain carbon–carbon multiple bonds. **Alkenes** contain a double bond and **alkynes** contain a triple bond. **Aromatic hydrocarbons** contain a benzene ring, a six-membered ring with three double bonds. These compounds differ from the alkanes of Chapter 12 because they each have a functional group, making them much more reactive. Thousands of biologically active molecules contain these functional groups, and many useful synthetic products result from their reactions.

13.1   Alkenes and Alkynes

Alkenes and alkynes are two families of organic molecules that contain multiple bonds.

CONSUMER NOTE

A ripe banana speeds up the ripening of green tomatoes because the banana gives off ethylene, a plant growth hormone. ©McGraw-Hill Education/Jill Braaten, photographer

• Alkenes are compounds that contain a carbon–carbon double bond.

Alkene

double bond $CH_2=CH_2$ Each C is trigonal planar.
                     ethylene   120°

The general molecular formula of an alkene is C_nH_{2n}, so an alkene has **two** fewer hydrogens than an acyclic alkane, which has a general molecular formula of C_nH_{2n+2}. Ethylene (C_2H_4) is the simplest alkene. Since each carbon of ethylene is surrounded by three atoms, each carbon is **trigonal planar.** All six atoms of ethylene lie in the same plane, and all bond angles are **120°.**

Ethylene is a hormone that regulates plant growth and fruit ripening. This allows individuals to enjoy bananas, strawberries, and tomatoes that were grown in faraway countries. Fruit can be picked green and then sprayed with ethylene when ripening is desired upon arrival at its destination.

• Alkynes are compounds that contain a carbon–carbon triple bond.

Alkyne

triple bond   acetylene   Each C is linear.
                                         180°
                                         180°

The general molecular formula for an alkyne is C_nH_{2n-2}, so an alkyne has **four** fewer hydrogens than an acyclic alkane. Acetylene (C_2H_2) is the simplest alkyne. Each carbon of acetylene is surrounded by two atoms, making each carbon **linear** with bond angles of **180°.**

Because alkenes and alkynes are composed of nonpolar carbon–carbon and carbon–hydrogen bonds, their physical properties are similar to those of other hydrocarbons. Like alkanes:

• Alkenes and alkynes have low melting points and boiling points and are insoluble in water.

Recall from Chapter 12 that acyclic alkanes are called saturated hydrocarbons, because they contain the maximum number of hydrogen atoms per carbon. In contrast, **alkenes and alkynes are called *unsaturated* hydrocarbons.**

• Unsaturated hydrocarbons are compounds that contain fewer than the maximum number of hydrogen atoms per carbon.

The multiple bond of an alkene or alkyne is always drawn in a condensed structure. To translate a condensed structure to a complete structure with all bond lines drawn in, make sure that **each carbon of a double bond has three atoms around it, and each carbon of a triple bond has two atoms around it,** as shown in Sample Problem 13.1. Keep in mind that in every structure, each carbon always has four bonds.

SAMPLE PROBLEM 13.1 INTERPRETING A CONDENSED STRUCTURE OF AN ALKENE AND AN ALKYNE

Draw a complete structure for each alkene or alkyne.

a. $CH_2=CHCH_2CH_3$ b. $CH_3C≡CCH_2CH_3$

Analysis

First, draw the multiple bond in each structure. Draw an alkene so that each C of the double bond has three atoms around it. Draw an alkyne so that each C of the triple bond has two atoms around it. All other C's have four single bonds.

Solution

a. The C labeled in red has single bonds to 2 H's. The C labeled in blue has single bonds to 1 H and a CH_2CH_3 group.

b. The C labeled in red has a single bond to a CH_3 group. The C labeled in blue has a single bond to a CH_2CH_3 group.

PRACTICE PROBLEM 13.1

Convert each condensed structure to a complete structure with all atoms, bond lines, and lone pairs drawn in.

a. $CH_2=CHCH_2OH$ b. $(CH_3)_2C=CH(CH_2)_2CH_3$ c. $(CH_3)_2CHC≡CCH_2C(CH_3)_3$

More Practice: Try Problems 13.22–13.24.

PROBLEM 13.1

Give the molecular formula for each of the following compounds.

a. an alkene that has four carbons
b. a saturated hydrocarbon that has six carbons
c. an alkyne that has seven carbons
d. an alkene that has five carbons

Zingiberene is obtained from ginger root. Ginger is used as a spice in Indian and Chinese cooking. Ginger candy is sometimes used to treat nausea resulting from seasickness. ©*Alvis Upitis/ Photgrapher's Choice/Getty Images RF*

PROBLEM 13.2

Complete the structure of zingiberene, a component of ginger root, by drawing in all H's on the carbon skeleton. Then draw a skeletal structure for zingiberene.

zingiberene

13.2   Nomenclature of Alkenes and Alkynes

Whenever we encounter a new functional group, we must learn how to use the IUPAC system to name it. There are two new facts to learn: how to name the suffix that identifies the functional group, and how to number the carbon skeleton. In the IUPAC system:

- An alkene is identified by the suffix *-ene*.
- An alkyne is identified by the suffix *-yne*.

How To   **Name an Alkene or an Alkyne**

Example: Give the IUPAC name of each alkene and alkyne.

a. $CH_2{=}CHCHCH_3$ (with CH_3 substituent)   b. $CH_3CH_2CHC{\equiv}CCH_3$ (with CH_2CH_3 substituent)

Step [1]   **Find the longest chain that contains *both* carbon atoms of the double or triple bond.**

a. $CH_2{=}CHCHCH_3$ (with CH_3)

  4 C's in the longest chain

  but*ane* – – – → but*ene*

  • The compound is an alkene, so change the *-ane* ending of the parent alkane to *-ene*.

b. $CH_3CH_2CHC{\equiv}CCH_3$ (with CH_2CH_3)

  6 C's in the longest chain

  hex*ane* – – – → hex*yne*

  • The compound is an alkyne, so change the *-ane* ending of the parent alkane to *-yne*.

Step [2]   **Number the carbon chain from the end that gives the multiple bond the lower number.**

For each compound, number the chain and name the compound using the *first* number assigned to the multiple bond.

a.   Start numbering here.

  $CH_2{=}CHCHCH_3$ (with CH_3)
  1   2 3 4

  1-butene

  • Numbering the chain from left to right puts the double bond at C1 (not C3). The alkene is named using the *first* number assigned to the double bond, making it 1-butene.

b.   Start numbering here.

  $CH_3CH_2CHC{\equiv}CCH_3$ (with CH_2CH_3)
  6   5 4 3   2 1

  2-hexyne

  • Numbering the chain from right to left puts the triple bond at C2 (not C4). The alkyne is named using the *first* number assigned to the triple bond, making it 2-hexyne.

—Continued

How To, continued . . .

Step [3] **Number and name the substituents, and write the name.**

a.   CH₂=CHCHCH₃   methyl group at C3
      1   3
         Answer: **3-methyl-1-butene**

b.   CH₃CH₂CHC≡CCH₃   ethyl group at C4
            4   2
         Answer: **4-ethyl-2-hexyne**

Compounds with two double bonds are called **dienes.** They are named by changing the *-ane* ending of the parent alkane to the suffix *-adiene*. Each double bond gets its own number.

CH₂=CHCH=CH₂   CH₃C=CHCH₂CH=CH₂
                                        |
                                        CH₃

Numbering: 1   2 3   4   Numbering: 6 5 4 3 2   1

Name: **1,3-butadiene**   Name: **5-methyl-1,4-hexadiene**

In naming cycloalkenes, the double bond is located between C1 and C2, and the "1" is usually omitted in the name. The ring is numbered to give the first substituent the lower number.

1-methylcyclopentene   **3-methylcycloheptene**   **1,6-dimethylcyclohexene**

[Number clockwise beginning at the C=C and place the CH₃ at C3.]   [Number counterclockwise beginning at the C=C and place the first CH₃ at C1.]

A few simple alkenes and alkynes have names that do not follow the IUPAC system. The simplest alkene, CH₂=CH₂, is called *ethene* in the IUPAC system, but it is commonly called **ethylene.** The simplest alkyne, HC≡CH, is called *ethyne* in the IUPAC system, but it is commonly named **acetylene.** We will use these common names since they are more widely used than their systematic IUPAC names.

SAMPLE PROBLEM 13.2 NAMING AN ALKENE

Give the IUPAC name for the following compound.

CH₃CH₂   CH₃
        \   /
         C=C
        /   \
    CH₃   CH₃

Analysis and Solution

[1] Find the longest chain containing both carbon atoms of the multiple bond.

CH₃CH₂   CH₃
        \   /
         C=C
        /   \
    CH₃   CH₃

5 C's in the longest chain - - - → **pentene**

458   Chapter 13   Unsaturated Hydrocarbons

[2] Number the chain to give the double bond the lower number.

CH₃CH₂   CH₃
  5   4   C=C
      CH₃ 3   2 CH₃
          1

• Numbering from right to left is preferred because the double bond begins at C2 (not C3). The molecule is named as a **2-pentene.**

[3] Name and number the substituents and write the complete name.

• The alkene has two methyl groups located at C2 and C3. Use the prefix *di-* before methyl → 2,3-**di**methyl.

CH₃CH₂   CH₃ methyl at C2
       C=C
   CH₃ 3   2 CH₃
methyl at C3

Answer: 2,3-dimethyl-2-pentene

PRACTICE PROBLEM 13.2

Give the IUPAC name for each alkene.

a. CH₂=CHCHCH₂CH₃
              |
             CH₃

c. CH₃CH₂CH=CHCH=CHCH₃

b. (CH₃CH₂)₂C=CHCH₂CH₂CH₃

d.

More Practice: Try Problems 13.27–13.30.

PROBLEM 13.3

Give the IUPAC name for each alkyne.

a. CH₃CH₂CH₂CH₂CH₂C≡CCH(CH₃)₂

b. CH₃CH₂—C≡C—CH₂—C—CH₃
                         |
                        CH₃
with CH₂CH₃ above the C and CH₃ below.

SAMPLE PROBLEM 13.3 NAMING AN ALKENE FROM A SKELETAL STRUCTURE

Give the IUPAC name of the following alkene.

Analysis and Solution

[1] Find the longest continuous carbon chain that contains both atoms of the double bond.

7 C's in the longest chain - - - → **heptene**

[2] Number the chain to give the double bond the lower number.

• Numbering from left to right places the double bond at C3 (not C4), so the molecule is named as a 3-heptene.

3-heptene

[3] Name and number the substituents and write the complete name.

• The alkene has one ethyl group at C3.

ethyl at C3

Answer: 3-ethyl-3-heptene

PRACTICE PROBLEM 13.3

Give the IUPAC name of the following alkenes.

a.

b.

More Practice: Try Problems 13.31–13.34.

SAMPLE PROBLEM 13.4 DRAWING THE STRUCTURE FROM THE NAME OF AN ALKENE OR ALKYNE

Draw the structure corresponding to each IUPAC name: (a) 5,5-dimethyl-3-heptyne; (b) 1,3-dimethylcyclohexene.

Analysis

First identify the parent name to find the longest carbon chain or ring, and then use the suffix to determine the functional group; the suffix *-ene* = **an alkene** and *-yne* = **an alkyne.** Then number the carbon chain or ring and place the functional group at the indicated carbon. Add the substituents and enough hydrogens to give each carbon four bonds.

Solution

a. 5,5-Dimethyl-3-heptyne has 7 C's as its longest chain (hept-) and a triple bond that begins at C3 (3-heptyne). Two methyl groups are bonded to C5.

Draw 7 C's and number the chain:

C—C—C—C—C—C—C — — — → C—C—C≡C—C—C—C — — — →
1 2 3 4 5 6 7   Add C≡C.   3   Add CH₃'s and H's.

Answer:

CH_3CH_2—C≡C—C—CH_2CH_3
                3   5 CH_3
           CH_3

5,5-dimethyl-3-heptyne

b. 1,3-Dimethylcyclohexene contains a six-membered ring with a double bond (cyclohexene). Number the ring to put the double bond between C1 and C2, and then add two methyl groups at C1 and C3.

• Draw a 6 C ring.
• Begin numbering at any C.

[6-membered ring numbered 1-6] — — — → [ring with C=C, 1 and 2] — — — → [ring with methyls at 1 and 3]

Place C=C between C1 and C2.   Add CH₃'s.

Answer:

1,3-dimethylcyclohexene

> **PRACTICE PROBLEM 13.4**
>
> Give the structure corresponding to each name.
>
> a. 4-methyl-1-hexene
> b. 5-ethyl-2-methyl-2-heptene
> c. 2,5-dimethyl-3-hexyne
> d. 1-propylcyclobutene
> e. 1,3-cyclohexadiene
> f. 4-ethyl-1-decyne
>
> More Practice: Try Problems 13.35, 13.36.

13.3   Cis–Trans Isomers

As we learned in Section 12.2 on alkanes, constitutional isomers are possible for alkenes of a given molecular formula. For example, there are three constitutional isomers for an alkene of molecular formula C_4H_8—1-butene, 2-butene, and 2-methylpropene.

$$CH_2{=}CHCH_2CH_3 \qquad CH_3CH{=}CHCH_3 \qquad \overset{\overset{\textstyle CH_3}{|}}{CH_2{=}CCH_3}$$

| 1-butene | 2-butene | 2-methylpropene |

These compounds are constitutional isomers because the atoms are bonded to each other in different ways. 1-Butene and 2-butene both have a four-carbon chain, but the location of the double bond is different, and 2-methylpropene has a longest chain containing only three carbon atoms.

13.3A   Stereoisomers—A New Class of Isomer

2-Butene illustrates another important aspect about alkenes. In contrast to the free rotation observed around carbon–carbon single bonds (Section 12.2D), there is **restricted rotation** around the carbon atoms of a double bond. As a result, the groups on one side of the double bond *cannot* rotate to the other side.

With 2-butene, there are two ways to arrange the atoms on the double bond. The two CH_3 groups can be on the *same side* of the double bond or they can be on *opposite sides* of the double bond. These molecules are *different* compounds with the same molecular formula; that is, they are **isomers.**

$$CH_3CH{=}CHCH_3$$

2-butene

skeletal structure

The two CH_3 groups are on the **same side** of the line that joins the doubly bonded C's.

The two CH_3 groups are on **opposite sides** of the line that joins the doubly bonded C's.

skeletal structure

- When the two CH_3 groups are on the *same side* of the double bond, the compound is called the *cis* isomer.

- When the two CH_3 groups are on *opposite sides* of the double bond, the compound is called the *trans* isomer.

General, Organic, & Biological Chemistry, Fourth Edition

13.3 Cis–Trans Isomers **461**

To give these compounds unique IUPAC names, we use the prefixes *cis* and *trans* before the remainder of the name to indicate the relative location of the two alkyl groups on the double bond. Thus, one isomer is called ***cis*-2-butene,** and the other isomer is called ***trans*-2-butene.**

two CH₃ groups on the **same** side

two CH₃ groups on **opposite** sides

cis-2-butene   *trans*-2-butene

different compounds

The cis and trans isomers of 2-butene are a specific example of a general class of isomer that occurs at carbon–carbon double bonds. **Whenever the two groups on *each* end of a C=C are *different from each other*, two isomers are possible.**

These two groups must be **different from each other...**

...*and* these two groups must also be **different from each other.**

When the two groups on one end of the double bond are identical, there is still restricted rotation, but no cis and trans isomers are possible. With 1-butene, $CH_2=CHCH_2CH_3$, one end of the double bond has two hydrogens, so the ethyl group (CH_2CH_3) is always cis to a hydrogen, no matter how the molecule is drawn.

two identical groups

No cis and trans isomers are possible.

1-butene   **identical**

SAMPLE PROBLEM 13.5 DRAWING CIS AND TRANS ISOMERS

Draw *cis*- and *trans*-3-hexene.

Analysis

First, use the parent name to draw the carbon skeleton, and place the double bond at the correct carbon; 3-hexene indicates a 6 C chain with the double bond beginning at C3. Then use the definitions of cis and trans to draw the isomers.

Solution

Each C of the double bond is bonded to a CH_3CH_2 group and a hydrogen. A cis isomer has the CH_3CH_2 groups bonded to the same side of the double bond. A trans isomer has the two CH_3CH_2 groups bonded to the opposite sides of the double bond.

$CH_3CH_2CH=CHCH_2CH_3$ - - - →

1 2 3   4 5 6

3-hexene

cis-3-hexene

trans-3-hexene

PRACTICE PROBLEM 13.5

Draw a condensed structure for each compound: (a) *cis*-2-octene; (b) *trans*-3-heptene;
(c) *trans*-4-methyl-2-pentene.

More Practice: Try Problems 13.39–13.46.

The female silkworm moth, *Bombyx mori*, secretes the sex pheromone bombykol. Pheromones like bombykol have been used to control insect populations. In one method, the pheromone is placed in a trap containing a poison or sticky substance, and the male is lured to the trap by the pheromone. Alternatively, the pheromone can be released into infested areas, confusing males who are then unable to find females.
©*Pascal Goetgheluck/Science Source*

PROBLEM 13.4

Bombykol is secreted by the female silkworm moth (*Bombyx mori*) to attract mates. Bombykol contains two double bonds, and each double bond must have a particular three-dimensional arrangement of groups around it to be biologically active. Label the double bonds of bombykol as cis or trans.

bombykol

Cis and trans compounds are isomers, but they are *not* constitutional isomers. Each carbon atom of *cis-* and *trans*-2-butene is bonded to the same atoms. The only difference is the three-dimensional arrangement of the groups around the double bond. Isomers of this sort are called **stereoisomers.**

- *Stereoisomers* are isomers that differ *only* in the 3-D arrangement of atoms.

Thus, *cis*-2-butene and *trans*-2-butene are stereoisomers, but each of these compounds is a constitutional isomer of 1-butene, as shown in Figure 13.1.

We have now learned the two major classes of isomers.

- Constitutional isomers differ in the way the atoms are bonded to each other.
- Stereoisomers differ only in the three-dimensional arrangement of atoms.

Figure 13.1   Comparing Three Isomers: 1-Butene, *cis*-2-Butene, and *trans*-2-Butene

<table>
<tr><td colspan="3" align="center">constitutional isomers</td><td colspan="2" align="center">stereoisomers</td></tr>
</table>

H₂C=CH—CH₂CH₃
1-butene

CH₃—CH=CH—CH₃
cis-2-butene

CH₃—CH=CH—CH₃
trans-2-butene

constitutional isomers

SAMPLE PROBLEM 13.6 IDENTIFYING STEREOISOMERS AND CONSTITUTIONAL ISOMERS

Label each pair of compounds as stereoisomers or constitutional isomers: (a) **A** and **B**; (b) **A** and **C**.

A   **B**   **C**

Analysis

- Constitutional isomers differ in the way the atoms are bonded to each other. **Atoms are bonded to *different* atoms.**
- Stereoisomers differ only in the three-dimensional arrangement of atoms. **Atoms are bonded to the *same* atoms.**

Solution

a. Compounds **A** and **B** are constitutional isomers because the double bond is located between different atoms in the chain. **A** has an ethyl group (CH_3CH_2) bonded to the C=C, whereas **B** has a methyl group (CH_3) on the C=C.

different groups

CH₃CH₂ ... H
    C=C
  H   CH₂OH
    A

CH₃ ... H
    C=C
  H   CH₂CH₂OH
    B

b. Compounds **A** and **C** are stereoisomers because all the atoms are bonded to the same atoms, but the arrangement of groups on the carbon–carbon double bond is different. In **A**, the CH_3CH_2 and CH_2OH groups are on opposite sides of the double bond, making them trans, whereas in **C**, the CH_3CH_2 and CH_2OH groups are on the same side of the double bond, making them cis.

CH₃CH₂ ... H
    C=C
  H   CH₂OH
    A
two groups on opposite sides
trans isomer

CH₃CH₂ ... CH₂OH
    C=C
  H   H
    C
two groups on the same side
cis isomer

PRACTICE PROBLEM 13.6

Label each pair of alkenes as constitutional isomers or stereoisomers.

a. $CH_3CH=CHCH_2CH_3$ and $CH_2=CHCH_2CH_2CH_3$

b.
CH₃CH₂ ... CH₃
    C=C
  H   H
   and
CH₃CH₂ ... H
    C=C
  H   CH₃

c.
CH₃CH₂ ... H
    C=C
  CH₃   H
   and
CH₃CH₂ ... CH₃
    C=C
  H   H

More Practice: Try Problems 13.49–13.52.

> We will learn more about stereoisomers in Chapter 15.

> Cis–trans isomers are also called **geometric isomers.**

PROBLEM 13.5

Double bonds in rings can also be characterized as cis or trans. Label each double bond in the following compounds as cis or trans.

a. [hexagon ring structure]   b. [ring structure with double bond]

13.3B   FOCUS ON HEALTH & MEDICINE
Saturated and Unsaturated Fatty Acids

Naturally occurring animal fats and vegetable oils are formed from fatty acids. **Fatty acids are carboxylic acids (RCOOH) with long carbon chains of 12–20 carbon atoms.** Because a fatty acid has many nonpolar C—C and C—H bonds and few polar bonds, fatty acids are insoluble in water. There are two types of fatty acids.

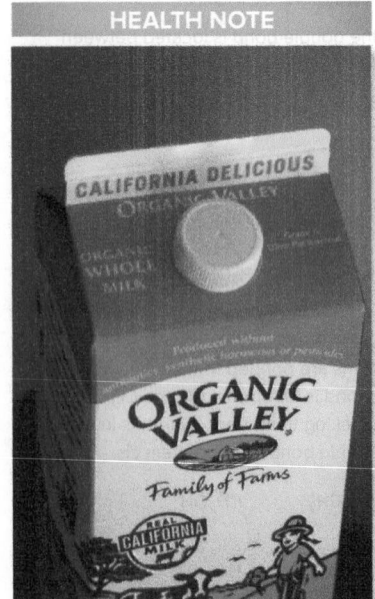

Linoleic and linolenic acids are **essential fatty acids,** meaning they cannot be synthesized in the human body and must therefore be obtained in the diet. A common source of these essential fatty acids is whole milk. Babies fed a diet of nonfat milk in their early months do not thrive because they do not obtain enough of these essential fatty acids.
©Jill Braaten RF

Table 13.1 Common Saturated and Unsaturated Fatty Acids

Name	Structure	Mp (°C)
Stearic acid (0 C=C)		71
Oleic acid (1 C=C)		16
Linoleic acid (2 C=C)		−5
Linolenic acid (3 C=C)		−11

- *Saturated* fatty acids have no double bonds in their long hydrocarbon chains.
- *Unsaturated* fatty acids have one or more double bonds in their long hydrocarbon chains.

Table 13.1 lists the structure and melting point of four fatty acids containing 18 carbon atoms. Stearic acid is one of the two most common saturated fatty acids, while oleic and linoleic acids are the most common unsaturated ones.

One structural feature of unsaturated fatty acids is especially noteworthy.

- Generally, double bonds in naturally occurring fatty acids are cis.

The presence of cis double bonds affects the melting point of these fatty acids greatly.

- As the number of double bonds in the fatty acid *increases*, the melting point *decreases*.

The cis double bonds introduce kinks in the long hydrocarbon chain, as shown in Figure 13.2. This makes it difficult for the molecules to pack closely together in a solid. **The larger the number of cis double bonds, the more kinks in the hydrocarbon chain, and the lower the melting point.**

Fats and oils are organic molecules synthesized in plant and animal cells from fatty acids. Fats and oils have different physical properties.

- Fats are solids at room temperature. Fats are generally formed from fatty acids having few double bonds.
- Oils are liquids at room temperature. Oils are generally formed from fatty acids having a larger number of double bonds.

Saturated fats are typically obtained from animal sources, whereas unsaturated oils are common in vegetable sources. Thus, butter and lard are formed from saturated fatty acids, while olive oil and safflower oil are formed from unsaturated fatty acids. An exception to this generalization is coconut oil, which is composed largely of saturated fatty acids.

Considerable evidence suggests that an elevated cholesterol level is linked to increased risk of heart disease. Saturated fats stimulate cholesterol synthesis in the liver, resulting in an increase in cholesterol concentration in the blood. We will learn more about fats and oils in Section 13.7 and Chapter 19.

Figure 13.2   The Three-Dimensional Structure of Four Fatty Acids

stearic acid

oleic acid

linoleic acid

linolenic acid

PROBLEM 13.6

Draw out a skeletal structure of arachidonic acid, indicating the arrangement of groups around the four double bonds.

$$CH_3(CH_2)_4CH{=}CHCH_2CH{=}CHCH_2CH{=}CHCH_2CH{=}CHCH_2(CH_2)_2CO_2H$$

arachidonic acid

PROBLEM 13.7

You have two fatty acids, one with a melting point of 63 °C, and one with a melting point of 1 °C. Which structure corresponds to each melting point?

palmitic acid

palmitoleic acid

PROBLEM 13.8

Conjugated linoleic acids (CLAs) are a group of unsaturated fatty acids that contain 18 carbons and two carbon–carbon double bonds separated by one single bond. Conjugated linoleic acids are found in meat and dairy products obtained from grass-fed sheep and cows. Some dietary supplements purported to reduce body fat contain CLAs. (a) Label the double bonds in conjugated linoleic acid **A** as cis or trans. (b) Draw the structure of a stereoisomer of **A**. (c) Would this stereoisomer have a higher or lower melting point than **A**? (d) Is **A** a stereoisomer or constitutional isomer of linoleic acid?

A

13.4   Interesting Alkenes in Food and Medicine

In addition to the plant hormone ethylene, $CH_2{=}CH_2$ (Section 13.1), many useful compounds contain one or more carbon–carbon double bonds.

More examples of antioxidants are given in Section 13.12.

Lycopene, the red pigment in tomatoes and watermelon, contains 13 double bonds. Lycopene is an **antioxidant,** a compound that prevents an unwanted oxidation reaction from occurring. Diets that contain a high intake of antioxidants like lycopene have been shown to decrease the risk of heart disease and certain forms of cancer. Unlike other antioxidants that can be destroyed when fresh fruits or vegetables are processed, even foods such as tomato paste, tomato juice, and ketchup are high in lycopene.

lycopene

Processed tomato products contain the antioxidant lycopene. ©McGraw-Hill Education/Jill Braaten, photographer

Lycopene's red color is due to the 11 double bonds that are each separated by one single bond (labeled in red). These double bonds absorb some (but not all) wavelengths of visible light. When a compound absorbs visible light, it takes on the color of those wavelengths of light it does *not* absorb. Since lycopene absorbs blue-green light, it appears red because it does not absorb the red light of the visible spectrum.

Lycopene absorbs this part of the visible region.

visible region

This part of the spectrum is *not* absorbed.

Lycopene appears red.

Tamoxifen is a potent anticancer drug that contains a carbon–carbon double bond in addition to other functional groups. Tamoxifen is used widely in the treatment of certain breast cancers that require the female sex hormone estrogen for growth. Tamoxifen binds to estrogen receptors, and in this way it inhibits the growth of breast cancers that are estrogen dependent. Tamoxifen is sold under the trade name of Nolvadex.

tamoxifen

©Sergio Piumatti

Most oral contraceptives are made up of two synthetic female sex hormones, each containing a carbon–carbon triple bond. ©Comstock/Punchstock RF

13.5 FOCUS ON HEALTH & MEDICINE
Oral Contraceptives

The development of synthetic oral contraceptives in the 1960s revolutionized the ability to control fertility. Prior to that time, women ingested all sorts of substances—iron rust, gunpowder, tree bark, sheep's urine, elephant dung, and others—in the hope of preventing pregnancy.

Synthetic birth control pills are similar in structure to the female sex hormones **estradiol** and **progesterone,** but they also contain a carbon–carbon triple bond. Most oral contraceptives contain two synthetic hormones that are more potent than these natural hormones, so they can be administered in lower doses.

estradiol   progesterone

Two common components of birth control pills are **ethynylestradiol** and **norethindrone.** Ethynylestradiol is a synthetic estrogen that resembles the structure and biological activity of estradiol. Norethindrone is a synthetic progesterone that is similar to the natural hormone progesterone. These compounds act by artificially elevating hormone levels in a woman, and this prevents pregnancy, as illustrated in Figure 13.3.

Figure 13.3 How Oral Contraceptives Work

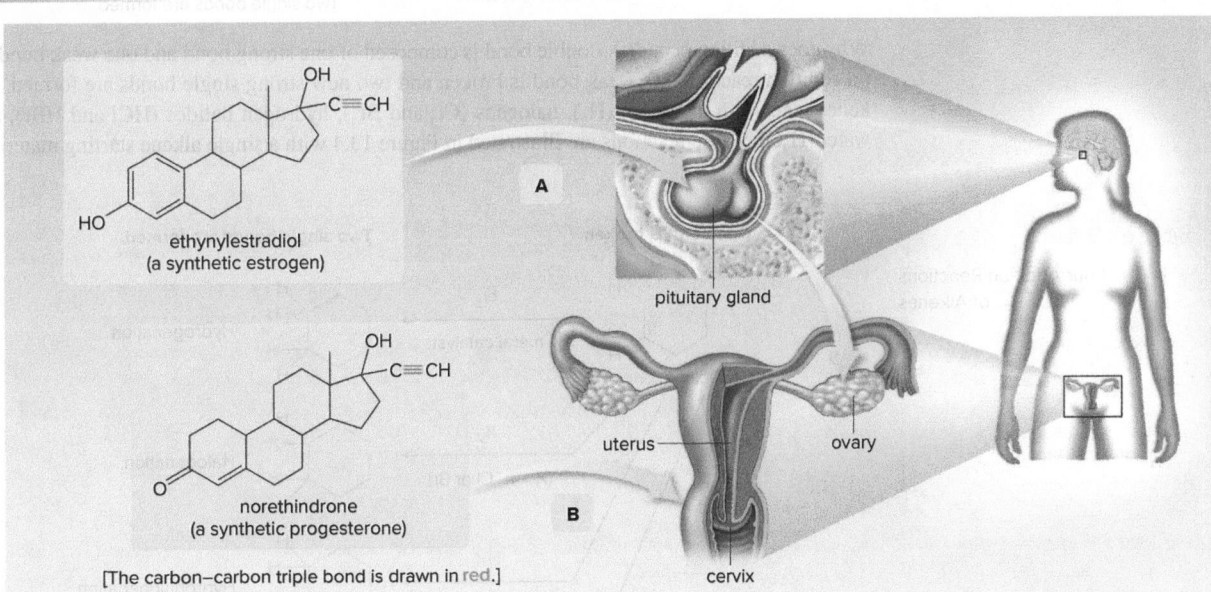

ethynylestradiol
(a synthetic estrogen)

norethindrone
(a synthetic progesterone)

[The carbon–carbon triple bond is drawn in red.]

pituitary gland

uterus   ovary

cervix

Monthly cycles of hormones from the pituitary gland cause ovulation, the release of an egg from an ovary. To prevent pregnancy, the two synthetic hormones in many oral contraceptives have different effects on the female reproductive system. **A:** The elevated level of **ethynylestradiol,** a synthetic estrogen, "fools" the pituitary gland into thinking a woman is pregnant, so ovulation does not occur. **B:** The elevated level of **norethindrone,** a synthetic progesterone, stimulates the formation of a thick layer of mucus in the cervix, making it difficult for sperm to reach the uterus.

Two other synthetic hormones with triple bonds are **RU 486** and **levonorgestrel.** RU 486 blocks the effects of progesterone and, by this means, prevents implantation of a fertilized egg. RU 486 is used to induce abortions within the first few weeks of pregnancy. Levonorgestrel interferes with ovulation, and thereby prevents pregnancy if taken within a few days of unprotected sex.

RU 486
(Trade name Mifepristone)

levonorgestrel
(Trade name Plan B)

[The carbon–carbon triple bond is drawn in red.]

13.6   Reactions of Alkenes

Most families of organic compounds undergo a characteristic type of reaction. **Alkenes undergo addition reactions.** In an addition reaction, new groups X and Y are added to a starting material. One bond of the double bond is broken and two new single bonds are formed.

- Addition is a reaction in which elements are added to a compound.

Addition

One bond is broken.   Two single bonds are formed.

Why does addition occur? A double bond is composed of one strong bond and one weak bond. In an addition reaction, the weak bond is broken and two new strong single bonds are formed. Alkenes react with hydrogen (H_2), halogens (Cl_2 and Br_2), hydrogen halides (HCl and HBr), and water (H_2O). These reactions are illustrated in Figure 13.4 with a single alkene starting material.

Figure 13.4

Four Addition Reactions of Alkenes

One bond is broken.

Two single bonds are formed.

cyclohexene

H_2 / metal catalyst → Hydrogenation

X_2 (X = Cl or Br) → Halogenation

HX (X = Cl or Br) → Hydrohalogenation

H_2O / H_2SO_4 → Hydration

13.6A   Addition of Hydrogen—Hydrogenation

Reaction of an alkene with hydrogen (H_2) is called **hydrogenation.** Hydrogenation is an addition reaction in which two bonds are broken—one bond of the carbon–carbon double bond and the H—H bond—and two new C—H bonds are formed.

The addition of H_2 occurs only in the presence of a **metal catalyst** such as palladium (Pd). The metal provides a surface that binds both the alkene and H_2, and this speeds up the rate of reaction. Hydrogenation of an alkene forms an **alkane** because the product has only C—C single bonds.

SAMPLE PROBLEM 13.7 DRAWING THE PRODUCT OF HYDROGENATION

Draw the product of the following reaction.

$$CH_3CH_2CH_2CH{=}CH_2 \ + \ H_2 \ \xrightarrow{\ \ Pd\ \ }$$

Analysis

To draw the product of a hydrogenation reaction:

- Locate the C=C and mentally break one bond in the double bond.
- Mentally break the H—H bond of the reagent.
- Add one H atom to each C of the C=C, thereby forming two new C—H single bonds.

Solution

PRACTICE PROBLEM 13.7

What product is formed when each alkene is treated with H_2 and a Pd catalyst?

a. $CH_3CH_2CH{=}CHCH_2CH_3$

b.

c.

More Practice: Try Problems 13.53, 13.57a, 13.58b, 13.95b, 13.96b.

470   **Chapter 13**   Unsaturated Hydrocarbons

13.6B   Addition of Halogen—Halogenation

Halogenation results in the addition of halogen (X$_2$) to an alkene. Two bonds are broken—one
bond of the carbon–carbon double bond and the X—X bond—and two new C—X bonds are formed.

Halogenation readily occurs with Cl$_2$ and Br$_2$. The product of halogenation is a **dihalide.**

When an alkene such as hex-1-ene
(1-hexene) is treated with red liquid
bromine, the Br$_2$ adds to the carbon–
carbon double bond to give a colorless
product, as seen in the right test tube.
With the alkane hexane (test tube on the
left), no reaction occurs unless heat or
light is added, and the red color of Br$_2$
remains. ©Andrew Lambert Photography/
Science Source

Halogenation with bromine is a simple chemical test used to determine if a double bond is present in an unknown compound. Bromine is a fuming red liquid. When bromine is added to an alkene, the bromine adds to the double bond and the red color disappears. The disappearance of the
red color shows that a double bond is present.

PROBLEM 13.9

Draw the product of each reaction.

a. CH$_3$CH$_2$CH═CH$_2$ +   Cl$_2$ ⟶

b. [structure] + Br$_2$ ⟶

13.6C   Addition of Hydrogen Halides—Hydrohalogenation

Hydrohalogenation results in the addition of HX (X = Cl or Br) to an alkene. Two bonds are
broken—one bond of the carbon–carbon double bond and the H—X bond—and new C—H and
C—X bonds are formed.

Hydrohalogenation readily occurs with HCl and HBr. The product of hydrohalogenation is an
alkyl halide.

chloroethane

bromocyclohexane

There is one important difference in this addition reaction compared to the addition of H_2 and X_2. In this case, addition puts different atoms—H and X—on the two carbons of the double bond. As a result, HX can add to the double bond to give two constitutional isomers when an unsymmetrical alkene is used as starting material.

propene   2-chloropropane   1-chloropropane

only product

For example, the addition of HCl to propene could in theory form two products. If H adds to the end carbon (labeled C1) and Cl adds to the middle carbon (C2), 2-chloropropane is formed. If Cl adds to the end carbon (C1) and H adds to the middle carbon (C2), 1-chloropropane is formed. In fact, **addition forms *only* 2-chloropropane.** This is a specific example of a general trend called **Markovnikov's rule,** named for the Russian chemist who first determined the selectivity of the addition of HX to an alkene.

- In the addition of HX to an unsymmetrical alkene, the H atom bonds to the less substituted carbon atom—that is, the carbon that has more H's to begin with.

The end carbon (C1) of propene has two hydrogens while the middle carbon (C2) has just one hydrogen. Addition puts the H of HCl on C1 because it had more hydrogens (two versus one) to begin with.

This C has only 1 H, so the Cl bonds here.

This C has 2 H's, so the H bonds here.

SAMPLE PROBLEM 13.8 DRAWING THE PRODUCT OF HYDROHALOGENATION

What product is formed when 2-methylpropene [$(CH_3)_2C=CH_2$] is treated with HBr?

Analysis

Alkenes undergo addition reactions, so the elements of H and Br must be added to the double bond. Since the alkene is unsymmetrical, the H atom of HBr bonds to the carbon that has more H's to begin with.

Solution

This C has no H's, so the Br bonds here.

This C has 2 H's, so the H bonds here.

PRACTICE PROBLEM 13.8

What product is formed in each of the following reactions?

a. $CH_3CH=CHCH_3$ + HBr $\longrightarrow$ c. $(CH_3)_2C=CHCH_3$ + HCl $\longrightarrow$

b. + HBr $\longrightarrow$ d. + HCl $\longrightarrow$

More Practice: Try Problems 13.55; 13.57d, e; 13.58e; 13.97c; 13.98b.

Gasohol contains 10% ethanol.
Source: Ethanol Promotion and Information Council (EPIC)

13.6D   Addition of Water—Hydration

Hydration results in the addition of water to an alkene. Two bonds are broken—one bond of the carbon–carbon double bond and the H—OH bond—and new C—H and C—OH bonds are formed.

Hydration occurs only if a strong acid such as H_2SO_4 is added to the reaction mixture. The product of hydration is an **alcohol.** For example, hydration of ethylene forms ethanol.

Ethanol is used as a solvent in many reactions in the laboratory. **Ethanol is also used as a gasoline additive** because, like alkanes, it burns in the presence of oxygen to form CO_2 and H_2O with the release of a great deal of energy. Although ethanol can also be formed by the fermentation of carbohydrates in grains and potatoes, much of the ethanol currently used in gasoline and solvent comes from the hydration of ethylene.

The hydration of unsymmetrical alkenes follows Markovnikov's rule.

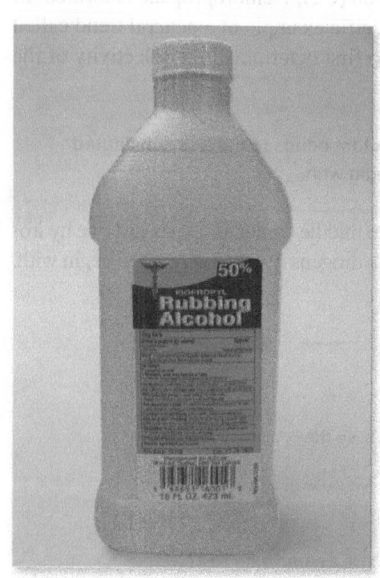

Addition of H_2O to propene forms 2-propanol [$(CH_3)_2CHOH$], the main component of rubbing alcohol.
©McGraw-Hill Education/Mark Dierker, photographer

- In the addition of H_2O to an unsymmetrical alkene, the H atom bonds to the less substituted carbon atom—that is, the carbon that has more H's to begin with.

This C has only 1 H, so the OH bonds here.

This C has 2 H's, so the H bonds here.

SAMPLE PROBLEM 13.9 DRAWING THE PRODUCT OF HYDRATION

What product is formed when 1-methylcyclohexene is treated with H_2O?

+ H_2O $\xrightarrow{H_2SO_4}$

1-methylcyclohexene

Analysis

- Add the elements of H and OH to the double bond.
- Because the alkene is unsymmetrical, the H atom bonds to the carbon that has more H's to begin with.

Solution

This C has no H's, so the **OH** bonds here.

This C has 1 H, so the **H** bonds here.

PRACTICE PROBLEM 13.9

What alcohol is formed when each alkene is treated with H_2O in the presence of H_2SO_4?

a. $CH_3CH=CHCH_3$

b. $CH_3CH_2CH=CH_2$

c.

More Practice: Try Problems 13.56, 13.57f, 13.58f, 13.95c, 13.96c, 13.98c.

PROBLEM 13.10

What product is formed when 1-pentene ($CH_3CH_2CH_2CH=CH_2$) is treated with each reagent?

a. H_2, Pd

b. Cl_2

c. Br_2

d. HBr

e. HCl

f. H_2O, H_2SO_4

13.7 FOCUS ON HEALTH & MEDICINE
Margarine or Butter?

One addition reaction of alkenes, hydrogenation, is especially important in the food industry. It lies at the heart of the debate over which product, butter or margarine, is better for the consumer.

As we learned in Section 13.3, butter is derived from saturated fatty acids like stearic acid [$CH_3(CH_2)_{16}COOH$], compounds with long carbon chains that contain only carbon–carbon single bonds. As a result, butter is a solid at room temperature.

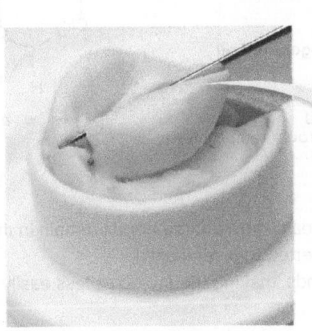

A portion of a fat molecule in butter

$CH_2CH_2CH_2CH_2CH_2CH_2CH_2CH_2CH_2CH_2CH_2CH_2CH_2CH_2CH_2CH_2CH_3$

all C—C single bonds in the carbon chain

©Fuse/Getty Images RF

Peanut butter is a common consumer product that contains partially hydrogenated vegetable oil.
©McGraw-Hill Education/Elite Images

Margarine, on the other hand, is a synthetic product that mimics the taste and texture of butter. It is prepared from vegetable oils derived from unsaturated fatty acids like linoleic acid [CH$_3$(CH$_2$)$_4$CH=CHCH$_2$CH=CH(CH$_2$)$_7$COOH]. Margarine is composed mainly of *partially hydrogenated* vegetable oils formed by adding hydrogen to the double bonds in the carbon chain derived from unsaturated fatty acids.

When an unsaturated liquid vegetable oil is treated with hydrogen, some (or all) of the double bonds add H$_2$, as shown in Figure 13.5. This increases the melting point of the oil, thus giving it a semi-solid consistency that more closely resembles butter. This process is called *hardening.*

As we will learn in Section 19.4, unsaturated oils with carbon–carbon double bonds are healthier than saturated fats with no double bonds. Why, then, does the food industry partially hydrogenate oils, thus reducing the number of double bonds? The reasons relate to texture and shelf life. Consumers prefer the semi-solid consistency of margarine to a liquid oil. Imagine pouring vegetable oil on a piece of toast or pancakes!

Furthermore, unsaturated oils are more susceptible than saturated fats to oxidation at the carbons adjacent to the double bond carbons. Oxidation makes the oil rancid and inedible. Hydrogenating the double bonds reduces the number of carbons bonded to double bonds (also illustrated in Figure 13.5), thus reducing the likelihood of oxidation and increasing the shelf life of the food product. This process reflects a delicate balance between providing consumers with healthier food products, while maximizing shelf life to prevent spoilage.

Figure 13.5   Partial Hydrogenation of the Double Bonds in a Vegetable Oil

- When an oil is *partially* hydrogenated, some double bonds react with H$_2$, whereas some double bonds remain in the product. Since the product has fewer double bonds, it has a higher melting point. Thus, a liquid oil is converted to a semi-solid.
- Partial hydrogenation decreases the number of carbons bonded to double bonds, making the molecule less easily oxidized, thereby increasing its shelf life.

©McGraw-Hill Education/Jill Braaten, photographer

One other fact is worthy of note. During hydrogenation, some of the cis double bonds in vegetable oils are converted to trans double bonds, forming so-called "trans fats." The shape of the resulting fatty acid chain is very different, closely resembling the shape of a *saturated* fatty acid chain. As a result, trans fats are thought to have the same negative effects on blood cholesterol levels as saturated fats; that is, trans fats stimulate cholesterol synthesis in the liver, thus increasing blood cholesterol levels, a factor linked to increased risk of heart disease.

A "trans" fat and a saturated fat have a similar 3-D shape.

trans double bond

a trans fatty acid chain

similar shape

a saturated fatty acid chain

Which should you choose—butter or margarine—and if it's margarine, which of the many varieties is best for you? Margarine can be hard or soft. It can be made from olive oil, corn oil, safflower oil, or even yogurt. One fact remains clear to nutritionists. It is best to limit your intake of both butter (high in saturated fat) and margarine (high in trans fat).

PROBLEM 13.11

As mentioned in the chapter opener, oil from the kukui nut contains linolenic acid (Table 13.1). (a) When linolenic acid is partially hydrogenated with one equivalent of H_2 in the presence of a Pd catalyst, three constitutional isomers are formed. One of them is linoleic acid. Draw the structures of the other two possible products. (b) What product is formed when linolenic acid is completely hydrogenated with three equivalents of H_2?

13.8 Polymers—The Fabric of Modern Society

Polymers **are large molecules made up of repeating units of smaller molecules—called** *monomers*—**covalently bonded together.** Polymers include the naturally occurring proteins that compose hair, tendons, and fingernails. They also include such industrially important plastics as polyethylene, poly(vinyl chloride) (PVC), and polystyrene. Since 1976, the U.S. production of synthetic polymers has exceeded its steel production.

13.8A Synthetic Polymers

Many synthetic polymers—that is, those synthesized in the lab—are among the most widely used organic compounds in modern society. Soft drink bottles, plastic bags, food wrap, compact discs, Teflon, and Styrofoam are all made of synthetic polymers. Figure 13.6 illustrates several consumer products and the polymers from which they are made.

To form a polymer from an alkene monomer, the weak bond that joins the two carbons of the double bond is broken and new strong carbon–carbon single bonds join the monomers together.

General, Organic, and Biochemisty

Figure 13.6 Polymers in Some Common Products

poly(vinyl chloride)
PVC

polyacrylonitrile

polyisobutylene

polystyrene
(Styrofoam)

(topleft): ©McGraw-Hill Education/John Thoeming, photographer; (topright): ©Dynamic Graphics Group/Getty Images RF; (bottomleft): ©Fernando Bengoechea/Corbis/Getty Images; (bottomright): ©McGraw-Hill Education/John Thoeming, photographer

CONSUMER NOTE

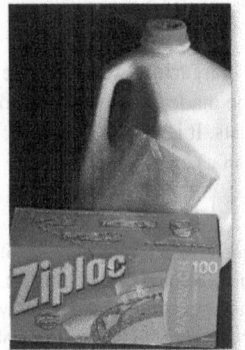

HDPE (high-density polyethylene) and **LDPE** (low-density polyethylene) are common types of polyethylene prepared under different reaction conditions and having different physical properties. HDPE is opaque and rigid, and used in milk containers and water jugs. LDPE is less opaque and more flexible, and used in plastic bags and electrical insulation. ©Jill Braaten RF

For example, joining **ethylene monomers** together forms the polymer **polyethylene,** a plastic used in milk containers and sandwich bags.

ethylene **monomers** $CH_2\!=\!CH_2$ + $CH_2\!=\!CH_2$ + $CH_2\!=\!CH_2$

$\downarrow$ polymerization

polyethylene **polymer**

three monomer units joined together

[New bonds are shown in red.]

- *Polymerization* is the joining together of monomers to make polymers.

Many ethylene derivatives having the general structure $CH_2\!=\!CHZ$ are also used as monomers for polymerization. The identity of Z affects the physical properties of the resulting polymer, making some polymers more suitable for one consumer product (e.g., plastic bags or food wrap) than another (e.g., soft drink bottles or compact discs). Polymerization of $CH_2\!=\!CHZ$ usually yields polymers with the Z groups on every other carbon atom in the chain.

$CH_2\!=\!CHZ$ + $CH_2\!=\!CHZ$ + $CH_2\!=\!CHZ$ $\longrightarrow$

Repeating unit: Many monomers are joined together.

shorthand structure

Polymer structures are often abbreviated by placing the atoms in the repeating unit in brackets, as shown. Table 13.2 lists some common monomers and polymers used in medicine and dentistry.

Table 13.2 **Common Monomers and Polymers Used in Medicine and Dentistry**

PVC blood bags and tubing

polypropylene syringes

dental floss

(top): ©Image Source/Getty Images RF; (middle): ©Steve Allen/Shutterstock RF; (bottom): ©Jill Braaten RF

SAMPLE PROBLEM 13.10 DRAWING THE PRODUCT OF POLYMERIZATION

What polymer is formed when CH_2=$CHCO_2CH_3$ (methyl acrylate) is polymerized?

Analysis

Draw three or more alkene molecules and arrange the carbons of the double bonds next to each other. Break one bond of each double bond, and join the alkenes together with single bonds. With unsymmetrical alkenes, substituents are bonded to every other carbon.

Solution

Join these 2 C's.   Join these 2 C's.

Answer:

Break one bond that joins each C=C.

[New bonds are drawn in red.]

PRACTICE PROBLEM 13.10

What polymer is formed when each compound is polymerized?

a. CH_2=C with CH_3 and CH_2CH_3

b. CH_2=C with CH_3 and CN

c. CH_2=C with H and (benzene ring with Cl)

More Practice: Try Problems 13.61–13.64, 13.95d, 13.96d.

CONSUMER NOTE

Disposable diapers contain
poly(acrylic acid), a polymer that can
absorb 30 times its weight in water.
©Image Source RF

CONSUMER NOTE

Many new varieties of lawn furniture
are built from recycled polyethylene.
Source: Photo courtesy of Poly-Wood, Inc.

PROBLEM 13.12

Draw the structure of poly(acrylic acid), the polymer formed by polymerizing acrylic acid (CH_2=CHCOOH).

PROBLEM 13.13

What monomer is used to form poly(vinyl acetate), a polymer used in paints and adhesives?

poly(vinyl acetate)

13.8B   FOCUS ON THE ENVIRONMENT
Polymer Recycling

The same desirable characteristics that make polymers popular materials for consumer products—durability, strength, and lack of reactivity—also contribute to environmental problems. Polymers do not degrade readily, and as a result, billions of pounds of polymers end up in landfills every year. Estimates suggest that synthetic polymers comprise 11% of solid municipal waste, 30% of which comes from packaging materials. Recycling existing polymer types to make new materials is one solution to the waste problem created by polymers.

Although thousands of different synthetic polymers have now been prepared, six compounds comprise the bulk of the synthetic polymers produced in the United States each year. Each polymer is assigned a recycling code (1–6) that indicates its ease of recycling; **the lower the number, the easier it is to recycle.** Table 13.3 lists these six most common polymers, as well as the type of products made from each recycled polymer.

Table 13.3 Recyclable Polymers

Recycling Code	Polymer Name	Shorthand Structure	Recycled Product
1	PET polyethylene terephthalate	$\left[CH_2CH_2-O-\overset{\displaystyle O}{\underset{\displaystyle O}{C}}-\text{(benzene ring)}-\overset{\displaystyle O}{C}-O\right]_n$	fleece clothing carpeting plastic bottles
2	HDPE high-density polyethylene	$[CH_2CH_2]_n$	Tyvek insulation outdoor furniture sports clothing
3	PVC poly(vinyl chloride)	$\left[CH_2CH\underset{\displaystyle Cl}{}\right]_n$	floor mats
4	LDPE low-density polyethylene	$[CH_2CH_2]_n$	trash bags
5	PP polypropylene	$\left[CH_2CH\underset{\displaystyle CH_3}{}\right]_n$	furniture
6	PS polystyrene	$\left[CH_2CH\text{(benzene ring)}\right]_n$	molded trays trash cans

Recycling begins with sorting plastics by type, shredding into small chips, and washing to remove adhesives and labels. After drying and removing any metal caps or rings, the polymer is melted and molded for reuse.

Of the six most common polymers, only the polyethylene terephthalate (PET) in soft drink bottles and the high-density polyethylene (HDPE) in milk jugs and juice bottles are recycled to any great extent. Since recycled polymers are often still contaminated with small amounts of adhesives and other materials, these recycled polymers are generally not used for storing food or drink products. Recycled HDPE is converted to Tyvek, an insulating wrap used in new housing construction, and outdoor furniture. Recycled PET is used to make fibers for fleece clothing and carpeting.

13.9 Aromatic Compounds

Aromatic compounds represent another example of unsaturated hydrocarbons. Aromatic compounds were originally named because many simple compounds in this family have characteristic odors. Today, the word *aromatic* **refers to compounds that contain a benzene ring,** or rings that react in a similar fashion to benzene.

Benzene, the simplest and most widely known aromatic compound, contains a six-membered ring and three double bonds. Each carbon of the ring is also bonded to a hydrogen atom, so the molecular formula for benzene is C_6H_6. Each carbon is surrounded by three groups, making it trigonal planar. Thus, **benzene is a planar molecule,** and all bond angles are **120°.**

benzene
C_6H_6

planar molecule

Although benzene is drawn with a six-membered ring and three double bonds, there are two different ways to arrange the double bonds so that they alternate with single bonds around the ring.

This bond is a single bond in one structure and a double bond in the second structure.

Each of these representations has the same arrangement of atoms. Only the location of the electrons is different. These structures are called **resonance structures.**

- **Resonance structures are Lewis structures with the same arrangement of atoms but a different arrangement of electrons.**

Drawing resonance structures was first presented in Section 4.4.

A **double-headed arrow** indicates that the two structures are resonance structures. In actuality, neither structure represents the true structure of benzene. The true structure of benzene is really a combination of both resonance structures, called a **hybrid.** Because the electron pair in a given double bond in a benzene ring is not really located between two particular carbon atoms, we say that the three electron pairs in the double bonds are *delocalized* in the six-membered ring. This gives benzene added stability compared to other unsaturated hydrocarbons.

Sometimes, a benzene ring is drawn with a circle inside a hexagon in place of the three double bonds.

three equivalent representations of benzene

The circle is meant to show that the six electrons from the three double bonds move freely around the ring. Realize, however, that we can draw benzene using either resonance structure or a benzene ring with a circle inside. Each of these representations is equivalent.

The physical properties of aromatic hydrocarbons are similar to other hydrocarbons—they have low melting points and boiling points and are water insoluble. Their chemical properties, however, are very different. **Aromatic hydrocarbons do not undergo the addition reactions that characterize alkenes.** For example, bromine adds to ethylene to form an addition product with two new C—Br bonds, but benzene does not react under similar conditions.

ethylene   addition product

benzene

- Aromatic compounds resemble benzene—they are unsaturated compounds that do not undergo the addition reactions characteristic of alkenes.

13.10   Nomenclature of Benzene Derivatives

Many organic molecules contain a benzene ring with one or more substituents, so we must learn how to name them. Many common names are recognized by the IUPAC system, however, so this complicates the nomenclature of benzene derivatives somewhat.

13.10A   Monosubstituted Benzenes

To name a benzene ring with one substituent, **name the substituent and add the word** *benzene.* Carbon substituents are named as alkyl groups. When a halogen is a substituent, name the halogen by changing the *-ine* ending of the name of the halogen to the suffix *-o*; for example, chlor*ine* → chlor*o*.

ethyl group   butyl group   chloro group
ethylbenzene   butylbenzene   chlorobenzene

Many monosubstituted benzenes, such as those with methyl (CH_3—), hydroxyl (—OH), and amino (—NH_2) groups, have common names that you must learn, too.

toluene   phenol   aniline
(methylbenzene)   (hydroxybenzene)   (aminobenzene)

13.10B Disubstituted Benzenes

There are three different ways that two groups can be attached to a benzene ring, so a prefix—**ortho, meta,** or **para**—is used to designate the relative position of the two substituents. Ortho, meta, and para are generally abbreviated as *o, m,* and *p,* respectively.

1,2-Disubstituted benzene ortho isomer	**1,3-Disubstituted benzene** meta isomer	**1,4-Disubstituted benzene** para isomer

o-diethylbenzene
or
1,2-diethylbenzene

m-diethylbenzene
or
1,3-diethylbenzene

p-diethylbenzene
or
1,4-diethylbenzene

If the two groups on the benzene ring are different, **alphabetize the name of the substituents** preceding the word *benzene.* If one of the substituents is part of a **common root,** name the **molecule as a derivative of that monosubstituted benzene.**

Alphabetize two different substituent names:

o-bromochloro-benzene   *m*-ethylfluoro-benzene

Use a common root name:

toluene   phenol

p-bromo**toluene**   *o*-chloro**phenol**

13.10C Polysubstituted Benzenes

For three or more substituents on a benzene ring:

1. **Number to give the lowest possible numbers around the ring.**
2. **Alphabetize the substituent names.**
3. **When substituents are part of common roots, name the molecule as a derivative of that monosubstituted benzene. The substituent that comprises the common root is located at C1, but the "1" is omitted from the name.**

- Assign the lowest set of numbers.
- Alphabetize the names of all the substituents.

4-chloro-1-ethyl-2-propylbenzene

- Name the molecule as a derivative of the common root **aniline.**
- Designate the position of the NH_2 group as "1," and then assign the lowest possible set of numbers to the other substituents.

2,5-dichloroaniline

13.10D   Aromatic Compounds with More Than One Ring

Some aromatic compounds contain two or more benzene rings joined together. Naphthalene has two benzene rings joined together. There are two different aromatic hydrocarbons with three benzene rings, named anthracene and phenanthrene.

naphthalene   anthracene   phenanthrene

SAMPLE PROBLEM 13.11 NAMING AROMATIC COMPOUNDS

Name each of the following aromatic compounds.

a. CH_3CH_2 —   — $CH_2CH_2CH_3$

b. CH_3 —   —Cl, —Br

Analysis

- Name the substituents on the benzene ring.
- With two groups, alphabetize the substituent names and use the prefix ortho, meta, or para to indicate their location.
- With three substituents, alphabetize the substituent names, and number to give the lowest set of numbers.

Solution

a. CH_3CH_2 —   — $CH_2CH_2CH_3$

ethyl   propyl
group   group

- The two substituents are located 1,3- or **meta** to each other.
- Alphabetize the *e* of **e**thyl before the *p* of **p**ropyl.

Answer: *m*-ethylpropylbenzene

b. CH_3 — 1, 3 —Cl, 4 —Br

toluene

- Since a CH_3 group is bonded to the ring, name the molecule as a derivative of toluene.
- Place the CH_3 group at the "1" position, and number to give the lowest set of numbers.

Answer: 4-bromo-3-chlorotoluene

PRACTICE PROBLEM 13.11

Give the IUPAC name of each compound.

a. — $CH_2CH_2CH_3$

b. I— —CH_2CH_3

c. OH— —$CH_2CH_2CH_2CH_3$

d. CH_3 —Br, Cl—

More Practice: Try Problems 13.69–13.72.

PROBLEM 13.14

Draw the structure corresponding to each name.

a. pentylbenzene

b. *o*-dichlorobenzene

c. *m*-bromoaniline

d. 4-chloro-1,2-diethylbenzene

13.11 FOCUS ON HEALTH & MEDICINE
Aromatic Drugs, Sunscreens, and Carcinogens

Many widely used drugs contain an aromatic ring. Notable examples include the analgesic acetaminophen, the antidepressant sertraline, and the antihistamine loratadine (Figure 13.7). These drugs are better known by their trade names Tylenol, Zoloft, and Claritin, respectively.

All commercially available sunscreens contain a benzene ring. A sunscreen absorbs ultraviolet radiation and thus shields the skin for a time from its harmful effects. Two sunscreens that have been used for this purpose are *p*-aminobenzoic acid (PABA) and Padimate O.

p-aminobenzoic acid
(PABA)

Padimate O

Compounds containing two or more benzene rings that share carbon–carbon bonds are called **polycyclic aromatic hydrocarbons (PAHs).** **Benzo[*a*]pyrene,** a PAH containing five rings

---

Figure 13.7   Three Drugs That Contain a Benzene Ring

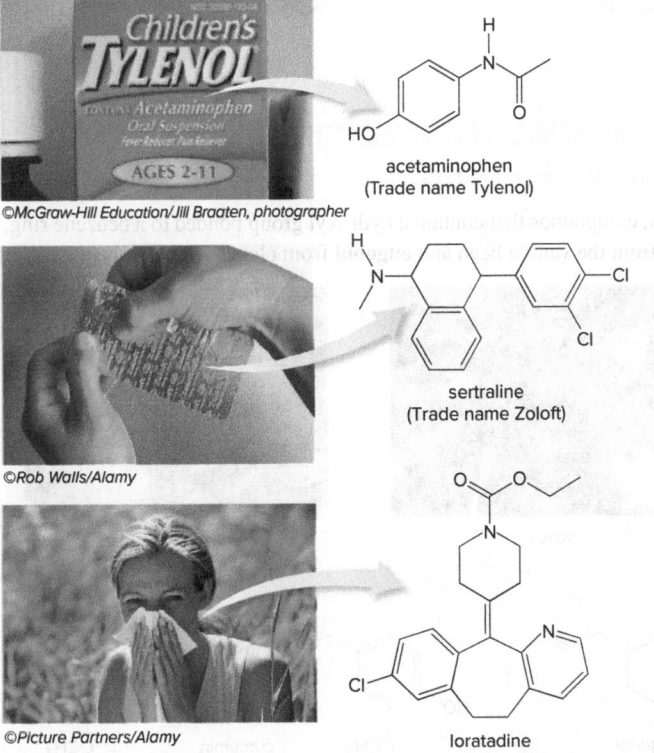

©McGraw-Hill Education/Jill Braaten, photographer

acetaminophen
(Trade name Tylenol)

©Rob Walls/Alamy

sertraline
(Trade name Zoloft)

©Picture Partners/Alamy

loratadine
(Trade name Claritin)

• Acetaminophen reduces fever and pain, but it is not anti-inflammatory. Thus, it is ineffective in treating conditions like arthritis, which have a significant inflammatory component.

• Sertraline is a widely used antidepressant discussed in more detail in Section 18.8.

• Loratadine is an over-the-counter antihistamine used for the treatment of seasonal allergies. Loratadine is an antihistamine that does not cause drowsiness.

484   **Chapter 13**   Unsaturated Hydrocarbons

joined together, is a widespread environmental pollutant, produced during the combustion of all types of organic material—gasoline, fuel oil, wood, garbage, and cigarettes.

tobacco plant

Source: Photo by Bob Nichols, USDA Natural Resources Conservation Service

©C. Zachariasen/PhotoAlto RF

benzo[a]pyrene
(a polycyclic aromatic hydrocarbon)

When benzo[a]pyrene, a nonpolar and water-insoluble hydrocarbon, is inhaled or ingested, it is oxidized in the liver. Oxidation is a common fate of foreign substances that are not useful nutrients for the body. The oxidation products are more polar, making them much more water soluble and more readily excreted in urine. The oxidation product from benzo[a]pyrene is also a potent **carcinogen;** that is, it causes cancer. The carcinogen binds to a needed protein or DNA in the cell and disrupts normal cell function, causing cancer or cell death.

PROBLEM 13.15

Which of the following compounds might be an ingredient in a commercial sunscreen? Explain why or why not.

a.

b.

13.12   FOCUS ON HEALTH & MEDICINE
Phenols as Antioxidants

A wide variety of **phenols,** compounds that contain a hydroxyl group bonded to a benzene ring, occur in nature. **Vanillin** from the vanilla bean and **eugenol** from cloves are both phenols.

vanilla bean

cloves

turmeric

vanillin

eugenol

curcumin

(left): ©MonikaMaria/Shutterstock RF; (middle): ©Peter Arnold, Inc./Alamy; (right): ©FLPA/Alamy

Curcumin is a yellow pigment isolated from turmeric, a tropical perennial in the ginger family and a principal ingredient in curry powder. Curcumin has long been used as an anti-inflammatory agent in traditional eastern medicine.

Some phenols are antiseptics and others are irritants. The disinfectant Lysol contains 2-benzyl-4-chlorophenol. The phenol urushiol in poison ivy causes an irritating rash on contact.

2-benzyl-4-chlorophenol
(active ingredient in Lysol)

urushiol
(found in poison ivy)

Like lycopene (Section 13.4), many **phenols are antioxidants.** Two examples are naturally occurring vitamin E and synthetic BHT. **The OH group on the benzene ring is the key functional group that prevents unwanted oxidation reactions from occurring.**

vitamin E

BHT
(**b**utylated **h**ydroxy **t**oluene)

Vitamin E is a natural antioxidant found in fish oil, peanut oil, wheat germ, and leafy greens. Although the molecular details of its function remain obscure, it is thought that vitamin E prevents the unwanted oxidation of unsaturated fatty acid residues in cell membranes. In this way, vitamin E helps retard the aging process.

Synthetic antioxidants such as **BHT**—**b**utylated **h**ydroxy **t**oluene—are added to packaged and prepared foods to prevent oxidation and spoilage. BHT is a common additive in breakfast cereals.

PROBLEM 13.16

Which of the following compounds might be antioxidants?

a. CH_3 — ⟨⟩ — $CH(CH_3)_2$
OH
menthol

b. curcumin

c. CH_3 — ⟨⟩ — CH_3
p-xylene
(gasoline additive)

13.13 Reactions of Aromatic Compounds

Like the alkenes, aromatic compounds undergo a characteristic type of reaction. In contrast to the alkenes, however, aromatic compounds undergo **substitution** *not* addition. In substitution, a hydrogen atom on a benzene ring is replaced by another atom or a group of atoms.

Substitution

⟨benzene⟩—H + X—Y ⟶ ⟨benzene⟩—X + H—Y

substitution of **H** by **X**

HEALTH NOTE

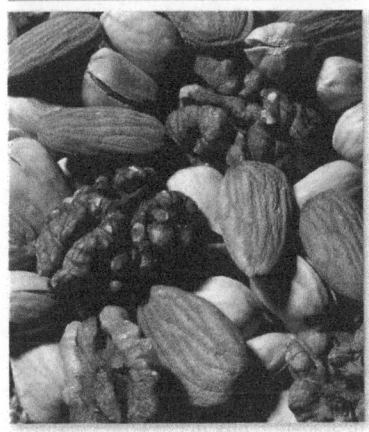

The purported health benefits of antioxidants have made them a popular component in anti-aging formulations.
©McGraw-Hill Education/Elite Images

HEALTH NOTE

Nuts are an excellent source of vitamin E.
©Stockbyte/Getty Images RF

Why does substitution occur? **Substitution of H by X keeps the stable aromatic ring intact.** Benzene does *not* undergo addition reactions like other unsaturated hydrocarbons because the product would not contain a benzene ring.

Addition does *not* occur.

$$+ \quad X{-}Y \quad \xmapsto{\ \ \times\ \ } $$

The product is *not* aromatic.

Three specific reactions of benzene are considered: **chlorination, nitration,** and **sulfonation.** In each reaction, one hydrogen atom on the benzene ring is replaced by another atom or group: —Cl, NO_2, or —SO_3H, respectively.

13.13A Chlorination and the Synthesis of the Pesticide DDT

Benzene reacts with Cl_2 in the presence of an iron catalyst ($FeCl_3$) to yield chlorobenzene. Chlorobenzene is an **aryl halide,** an organic halide with the halogen bonded directly to the aromatic ring. Reaction with chlorine is called **chlorination.** In chlorination, a Cl atom substitutes for a hydrogen atom on the benzene ring.

Chlorination

$$+ \quad Cl{-}Cl \quad \xrightarrow{FeCl_3} \quad \text{chlorobenzene} \quad + \quad H{-}Cl$$

chlorobenzene

Time Magazine, June 30, 1947.

Winston Churchill called DDT a "miraculous" chemical in 1945 for the many lives it saved during World War II. Less than 20 years later, as prolonged use of large quantities of this nonspecific pesticide led to harmful environmental effects, Rachel Carson called DDT the "elixir of death" in her book *Silent Spring.* DDT use was banned in the United States in 1973, but given its low cost, it is still widely used to control insect populations in developing countries.

The chlorination of benzene is the first step in the two-step synthesis of the pesticide **DDT** (*d*ichloro*d*iphenyl*t*richloroethane).

DDT
(nonbiodegradable pesticide)

DDT is an organic molecule with valuable short-term effects that has caused long-term problems. DDT kills insects that spread diseases such as malaria and typhus, and in controlling insect populations, DDT has saved millions of lives worldwide. DDT is a weakly polar and very stable organic compound, and so it (and compounds like it) persists in the environment for years. Since DDT is soluble in organic media, it accumulates in the fatty tissues of most animals. Most adults in the United States have low concentrations of DDT (or a degradation product of DDT) in them. The long-term effect on humans is not known, but DDT has had a direct harmful effect on the eggshell formation of certain predator birds such as eagles and hawks.

13.13B FOCUS ON HEALTH & MEDICINE
Nitration and Sulfa Drugs

Benzene reacts with nitric acid (HNO_3) in the presence of sulfuric acid (H_2SO_4) to yield nitrobenzene. Substitution of a **nitro group** (NO_2) for a hydrogen is called **nitration.**

Nitration

$$+ \quad HO{-}NO_2 \quad \xrightarrow{H_2SO_4} \quad \text{nitrobenzene} \quad + \quad H{-}OH$$

nitrobenzene

Nitration is a very valuable reaction because nitro groups are readily converted to amino groups, (NH$_2$) with H$_2$ and a palladium catalyst.

Many of the antibacterial sulfa drugs have NH$_2$ groups bonded to the benzene ring. Examples include sulfanilamide, one of the first antibiotics synthesized in the 1930s, and newer sulfa drugs such as sulfamethoxazole (trade name Bactrim) and sulfisoxazole (trade name Gantrisin), which are used to treat ear and urinary tract infections.

sulfanilamide

sulfamethoxazole
(Trade name Bactrim)

sulfisoxazole
(Trade name Gantrisin)

In cells, sulfamethoxazole and sulfisoxazole are both metabolized to sulfanilamide, the active agent. To understand how sulfanilamide functions as an antibacterial agent we must examine **folic acid,** which microorganisms synthesize from *p*-aminobenzoic acid.

p-aminobenzoic acid
PABA

folic acid

Sulfanilamide and *p*-aminobenzoic acid are similar in size and shape and have related functional groups. Thus, when sulfanilamide is administered, bacteria attempt to use it in place of *p*-aminobenzoic acid to synthesize folic acid. Derailing folic acid synthesis means that the bacteria cannot grow and reproduce. Sulfanilamide affects only bacterial cells, though, because humans do not synthesize folic acid and must obtain it from their diets.

sulfanilamide

p-aminobenzoic acid

13.13C   Sulfonation and Detergent Synthesis

Benzene reacts with sulfur trioxide (SO$_3$) in the presence of sulfuric acid (H$_2$SO$_4$) to yield benzenesulfonic acid. Substitution of SO$_3$H for a hydrogen is called **sulfonation.**

Sulfonation

benzenesulfonic acid

Figure 13.8   Synthesis of a Detergent Using Sulfonation

a benzenesulfonic acid

sodium salt of
a benzenesulfonic acid

synthetic detergent

Although less widely used than chlorination and nitration, sulfonation is an important step in the synthesis of detergents. Many detergents are sodium salts of sulfonic acids, and are prepared by the two-step sequence shown in Figure 13.8.

PROBLEM 13.17

What product is formed when *p*-dichlorobenzene is treated with each reagent: (a) Cl_2, $FeCl_3$; (b) HNO_3, H_2SO_4; (c) SO_3, H_2SO_4?

PROBLEM 13.18

When toluene (methylbenzene) is treated with Cl_2 and $FeCl_3$, a total of three products are possible. Draw the structure of the three products and give their IUPAC names.

CHAPTER HIGHLIGHTS

KEY TERMS

Addition reaction (13.6)	Hardening (13.7)	Para isomer (13.10)
Alkene (13.1)	Hybrid (13.9)	Partial hydrogenation (13.7)
Alkyne (13.1)	Hydration (13.6)	Phenol (13.12)
Antioxidant (13.4)	Hydrogenation (13.6)	Polycyclic aromatic hydrocarbon (PAH, 13.11)
Aromatic compound (13.9)	Hydrohalogenation (13.6)	Polymer (13.8)
Aryl halide (13.13)	Markovnikov's rule (13.6)	Polymerization (13.8)
Chlorination (13.13)	Meta isomer (13.10)	Resonance structure (13.9)
Cis isomer (13.3)	Monomer (13.8)	Stereoisomer (13.3)
Double-headed arrow (13.9)	Nitration (13.13)	Sulfonation (13.13)
Fat (13.3)	Nitro group (13.13)	Trans isomer (13.3)
Fatty acid (13.3)	Oil (13.3)	Unsaturated hydrocarbon (13.1)
Halogenation (13.6)	Ortho isomer (13.10)	

KEY REACTIONS

[1]   Addition reactions of alkenes (13.6)

a. Hydrogenation (13.6A)

c. Hydrohalogenation (13.6C)

b. Halogenation (13.6B)

d. Hydration (13.6D)

[2] Substitution reactions of benzene (13.13)

a. Chlorination (13.13A)

$$C_6H_6 + Cl_2 \xrightarrow{FeCl_3} C_6H_5Cl + HCl$$

b. Nitration (13.13B)

$$C_6H_6 + HNO_3 \xrightarrow{H_2SO_4} C_6H_5NO_2 + H_2O$$

c. Sulfonation (13.13C)

$$C_6H_6 + SO_3 \xrightarrow{H_2SO_4} C_6H_5SO_3H$$

KEY CONCEPTS

1 What are the characteristics of alkenes, alkynes, and aromatic compounds?

- Alkenes are unsaturated hydrocarbons that contain a carbon–carbon double bond and have molecular formula C_nH_{2n}. Each carbon of the double bond is trigonal planar. (13.1)
- Alkynes are unsaturated hydrocarbons that contain a carbon–carbon triple bond and have molecular formula C_nH_{2n-2}. Each carbon of the triple bond is linear. (13.1)
- Benzene, molecular formula C_6H_6, is the most common aromatic hydrocarbon. Benzene is a stable hybrid of two resonance structures, each containing a six-membered ring and three double bonds. Each carbon of benzene is trigonal planar. (13.9)

2 How are alkenes, alkynes, and substituted benzenes named?

- An alkene is identified by the suffix -ene, and the carbon chain is numbered to give the C=C the lower number. (13.2)
- An alkyne is identified by the suffix -yne, and the carbon chain is numbered to give the C≡C the lower number. (13.2)
- Substituted benzenes are named by naming the substituent and adding the word benzene. When two substituents are bonded to the ring, the prefixes ortho, meta, and para are used to show the relative positions of the two groups: 1,2-, 1,3-, or 1,4-, respectively. With three substituents on a benzene ring, number to give the lowest possible numbers. (13.10)

3 What is the difference between constitutional isomers and stereoisomers? How are cis and trans isomers different? (13.3)

- Constitutional isomers differ in the way the atoms are bonded to each other.
- Stereoisomers differ only in the three-dimensional arrangement of atoms.
- Cis and trans isomers are one type of stereoisomer. A cis alkene has two alkyl groups on the same side of the double bond. A trans alkene has two alkyl groups on opposite sides of the double bond.

4 How do saturated and unsaturated fatty acids differ? (13.3B)

- Fatty acids are carboxylic acids (RCOOH) with long carbon chains. Saturated fatty acids have no double bonds in the carbon chain, and unsaturated fatty acids have one or more double bonds in their long carbon chains.

- Double bonds in naturally occurring fatty acids are generally cis.
- As the number of double bonds in the fatty acid increases, the melting point decreases.

5 What types of reactions do alkenes undergo? (13.6)

- Alkenes undergo addition reactions with reagents X—Y. One bond of the double bond and the X—Y bond break and two new single bonds (C—X and C—Y) are formed.
- Alkenes react with four different reagents—H_2 (Pd catalyst), X_2 (X = Cl or Br), HX (X = Cl or Br), and H_2O (with H_2SO_4).

6 What is Markovnikov's rule? (13.6)

- Markovnikov's rule explains the selectivity observed when an unsymmetrical reagent HX adds to an unsymmetrical alkene like propene ($CH_3CH{=}CH_2$). The H of HX is added to the end of the C=C that has more H's to begin with, forming $CH_3CH(X)CH_3$.

7 What products are formed when a vegetable oil is partially hydrogenated? (13.7)

- When an unsaturated oil is partially hydrogenated, some but not all of the cis C=C's add H_2, reducing the number of double bonds and increasing the melting point.
- Some of the cis double bonds are converted to trans double bonds, forming trans fats, whose shape and properties closely resemble those of saturated fats.

8 What are polymers, and how are they formed from alkene monomers? (13.8)

- Polymers are large molecules made up of repeating smaller molecules called monomers covalently bonded together. When alkenes are polymerized, one bond of the double bond breaks, and two new single bonds join the alkene monomers together in long carbon chains.

9 What types of reactions does benzene undergo? (13.13)

- To keep the stable aromatic ring intact, benzene undergoes substitution, not addition, reactions. One H atom on the ring is replaced by another atom or group of atoms. Reactions include chlorination (substitution by Cl), nitration (substitution by NO_2), and sulfonation (substitution by SO_3H).

PROBLEMS

Selected in-chapter and odd-numbered end-of-chapter problems have brief answers in Appendix B. The *Student Study Guide and Solutions Manual* contains detailed solutions to all in-chapter and odd-numbered end-of-chapter problems, as well as additional worked examples and a chapter self-test.

Alkene, Alkyne, and Benzene Structure

13.19 Anethole, the major constituent of anise oil, is used in licorice-flavored sweets and flavored brandy. Answer the following questions using the ball-and-stick model of anethole.

anethole

a. What is the molecular formula of anethole?

b. Identify the functional groups.

c. Label the carbon–carbon double bond as cis or trans.

d. Draw the structure of anethole and label each carbon as trigonal planar or tetrahedral.

13.20 Methyl cinnamate, isolated from red clover flowers, is used in perfumery and as a flavoring agent because of its strawberry-like taste and odor. Answer the following questions using the ball-and-stick model of methyl cinnamate.

methyl cinnamate

a. What is the molecular formula of methyl cinnamate?

b. Identify the functional groups.

c. Label the carbon–carbon double bond as cis or trans.

d. Draw the structure of methyl cinnamate and label each carbon as trigonal planar or tetrahedral.

13.21 What is the molecular formula for a hydrocarbon with 10 carbons that is (a) completely saturated; (b) an alkene; (c) an alkyne?

13.22 Draw the structure of a hydrocarbon with molecular formula C_6H_{10} that also contains: (a) a carbon–carbon triple bond; (b) two carbon–carbon double bonds; (c) one ring and one C=C.

13.23 Draw structures for the three alkynes having molecular formula C_5H_8.

13.24 Draw the structures of the five constitutional isomers of molecular formula C_5H_{10} that contain a double bond.

13.25 Label each carbon in the following molecules as tetrahedral, trigonal planar, or linear.

a.

b. ──C≡CH

c.

13.26 Falcarinol is a natural pesticide found in carrots that protects them from fungal diseases. Predict the indicated bond angles in falcarinol.

falcarinol

Nomenclature of Alkenes and Alkynes

13.27 Give the IUPAC name for each molecule depicted in the ball-and-stick models.

a.   b.

13.28 Give the IUPAC name for each molecule depicted in the ball-and-stick models.

a.   b.

13.29 Give the IUPAC name for each compound.

a. CH_2=$CHCH_2CH_2C(CH_3)_3$

b. $(CH_3CH_2)_2C$=$CHCHCH_2CHCH_3$
   with CH_3 and CH_3 substituents

c. CH_2=CCH_2CH_3
   with $CH_2CH_2CH_2CH_2CH_3$

d. CH_3C≡$CCH_2C(CH_3)_3$

e. CH_3C≡C—CH_2—CH—C—CH_2CH_3
   with CH_3, CH_3, and CH_2CH_3 substituents

f. CH_2=$CHCH_2$—C—CH=CH_2
   with CH_3 and CH_3 substituents

13.30 Give the IUPAC name for each compound.

a. CH$_2$=CHCH$_2$CHCH$_2$CH$_3$
                      |
                      CH$_3$

b. (CH$_3$)$_2$C=CHCH$_2$CHCH$_2$CH$_3$
                           |
                          CH$_2$CH$_2$CH$_3$

c. CH$_3$C≡CCHCH$_3$
                 |
                 CH$_2$CH$_2$CH$_3$

d. (CH$_3$)$_3$CC≡CC(CH$_3$)$_3$

e. (CH$_3$CH$_2$CH$_2$CH$_2$)$_2$C=CHCH$_3$

f. (CH$_3$)$_2$C=CHCH$_2$CH$_2$CH$_2$CH=C(CH$_3$)$_2$

13.31 Give the IUPAC name for each alkene.

a.   b.

13.32 Give the IUPAC name for each alkene.

a. b.

13.33 Give the IUPAC name for each cyclic compound.

a. b.

13.34 Give the IUPAC name for each cyclic compound.

a. b.

13.35 Give the structure corresponding to each IUPAC name.

a. 3-methyl-1-octene
b. 1-ethylcyclobutene
c. 2-methyl-3-hexyne
d. 3,5-diethyl-2-methyl-3-heptene
e. 1,3-heptadiene
f. *cis*-7-methyl-2-octene

13.36 Give the structure corresponding to each IUPAC name.

a. 1,2-dimethylcyclopentene
b. 6-ethyl-2-octyne
c. 3,3-dimethyl-1,4-pentadiene
d. *trans*-5-methyl-2-hexene
e. 5,6-dimethyl-2-heptyne
f. 3,4,5,6-tetramethyl-1-decyne

13.37 Each of the following IUPAC names is incorrect. Explain why it is incorrect and give the correct IUPAC name.

a. 5-methyl-4-hexene
b. 1-methylbutene
c. 2,3-dimethylcyclohexene
d. 3-butyl-1-butyne

13.38 Each of the following IUPAC names is incorrect. Explain why it is incorrect and give the correct IUPAC name.

a. *cis*-2-methyl-2-hexene
b. 2-methyl-2,4-pentadiene
c. 2,4-dimethylcyclohexene
d. 1,1-dimethyl-2-cyclohexene

Isomers

13.39 **A** is one component of the queen substance, a mixture secreted by a queen bee that prevents the development of ovaries in worker bees. Label the alkene in **A** as cis or trans.

A

©Jocelyn Winwood, NZ. Specialist in nature shots/Getty Images

13.40 Ichthyothereol is a toxic compound isolated from several Central and South American plants of the genus *Ichthyothere*. Identify the functional groups in ichthyothereol and label any alkene as cis or trans.

ichthyothereol

©Mauricio Mercadante

13.41 Leukotriene C$_4$ is a key compound that causes the constriction of small airways and, in this way contributes to the asthmatic response. Label each double bond in leukotriene C$_4$ as cis or trans.

leukotriene C$_4$

13.42 Draw a skeletal structure of each naturally occurring compound using the proper cis or trans arrangement around the carbon–carbon double bond. Muscalure is the sex attractant of the housefly. Cinnamaldehyde is responsible for the odor of cinnamon.

a. CH$_3$(CH$_2$)$_8$CH=CH(CH$_2$)$_{12}$CH$_3$
              muscalure
         (cis double bond)

b. ⬡—CH=CHCHO
     cinnamaldehyde
    (trans double bond)

13.43 Label the carbon–carbon double bond as cis or trans, and give the IUPAC name for the alkene depicted in the ball-and-stick model.

13.44 Label the carbon–carbon double bond as cis or trans, and give the IUPAC name for the alkene depicted in the ball-and-stick model.

13.45 Draw a skeletal structure for the cis and trans isomers for each compound: (a) 2-nonene; (b) 2-methyl-3-heptene.

13.46 Draw a skeletal structure for the cis and trans isomers for each compound: (a) 3-heptene; (b) 4,4-dimethyl-2-hexene.

13.47 Double bonds in cycloalkenes can also be characterized as cis or trans. Label each double bond in the following compound as cis or trans.

13.48 Draw all of the possible stereoisomers for 2,4-hexadiene ($CH_3CH=CH-CH=CHCH_3$).

13.49 How are the compounds in each pair related? Choose from constitutional isomers, stereoisomers, or identical.

a.   and

b.   and

13.50 How are the compounds in each pair related? Choose from constitutional isomers, stereoisomers, or identical.

a.   and

b.   and

13.51 Consider compounds **A, B,** and **C.** Label each pair of compounds as constitutional isomers, stereoisomers, or not isomers of each other: (a) **A** and **B;** (b) **A** and **C;** (c) **B** and **C.**

A   B   C

13.52 (a) Convert the ball-and-stick model of **A** to a skeletal or complete structure that clearly shows the stereochemistry at the carbon–carbon double bond. (b) Draw a stereoisomer of **A.** (c) Draw a constitutional isomer of **A.**

A

Reactions of Alkenes

13.53 What alkane is formed when each alkene is treated with H_2 in the presence of a Pd catalyst?

a. $CH_2=CHCH_2CH_2CH_2CH_3$ c.

b. $(CH_3)_2C=CHCH_2CH_2CH_3$ d.

13.54 What dihalide is formed when each of the alkenes in Problem 13.53 is treated with Br_2?

13.55 What alkyl halide is formed when each alkene is treated with HCl?

a.   c. $CH_2=CHCH_2CH(CH_3)_2$

b. $(CH_3)_2C=C(CH_3)_2$ d.

13.56 What alcohol is formed when each alkene in Problem 13.55 is treated with H_2O and H_2SO_4?

13.57 Draw the product formed when 1-ethylcyclohexene is treated with each reagent.

CH$_2$CH$_3$ a. H_2, Pd   d. HCl
b. Cl_2 e. HBr
c. Br_2 f. H_2O, H_2SO_4

1-ethylcyclohexene

13.58 Draw the products formed in each reaction.

a. $CH_3CH=CHCH_3$ + HCl ⟶

b.   + H_2 →(Pd)

c.   CH$_3$
        + Cl_2 ⟶
    CH$_3$

d. $CH_3CH=CHCH_2CH_2CH_3$ + Br_2 ⟶

e. $(CH_3)_2C=CHCH_2CH_3$ + HBr ⟶

f.   CH$_3$
         CH$_3$ + H_2O →(H_2SO_4)
    CH$_3$

13.59 What alkene is needed as a starting material to prepare each of the following alkyl halides or dihalides? In each case, also indicate what reagent is needed to react with the alkene.

a. CH₃CH₂Br

c.

b.

d. BrCH₂CHCH₂CH(CH₃)₂
$\qquad$ |
$\qquad$ Br

13.60 What three alkenes yield pentane (CH₃CH₂CH₂CH₂CH₃) when treated with hydrogen and a palladium catalyst? Don't forget about stereoisomers.

Polymers

13.61 What is the structure of polychlorotrifluoroethylene, the polymer formed by polymerizing chlorotrifluoroethylene (F₂C=CFCl)? Polychlorotrifluoroethylene is used in packaging materials for some medications.

13.62 What polymer is formed when methyl α-methylacrylate [CH₂=C(CH₃)CO₂CH₃] is polymerized? This polymer is used in Lucite and Plexiglas, transparent materials that are lighter but more impact resistant than glass.

13.63 What polymer is formed when each compound is polymerized?

a. [ball-and-stick model]   b. [ball-and-stick model]

13.64 What polymer is formed when each compound is polymerized?

a. [ball-and-stick model]   b. [ball-and-stick model]

13.65 What monomer is used to form the following polymer?

$$\begin{matrix} & Br & & Br & & Br \\ & | & & | & & | \\ -CH_2-C-CH_2-C-CH_2-C- \\ & | & & | & & | \\ & Cl & & Cl & & Cl \end{matrix}$$

13.66 What monomer is used to form the following polymer?

$$\begin{matrix} & CH_3 & & CH_3 & & CH_3 \\ & | & & | & & | \\ -CH_2-C-CH_2-C-CH_2-C- \\ & | & & | & & | \\ & C=O & & C=O & & C=O \\ & | & & | & & | \\ & OCH_2CH_3 & OCH_2CH_3 & OCH_2CH_3 \end{matrix}$$

Structure and Nomenclature of Benzene

13.67 Draw two resonance structures for chlorobenzene.

13.68 Explain why structures **A** and **B** are the same compound, even though **A** has the two Cl atoms on the same double

bond and **B** has the two Cl atoms on different double bonds.

[structure A with Cl atoms]   [structure B with Cl atoms]

A   **B**

13.69 Name each aromatic compound.

a. [ball-and-stick model]   b. [ball-and-stick model]

13.70 Name each aromatic compound.

a. [ball-and-stick model]   b. [ball-and-stick model]

13.71 Give the IUPAC name for each substituted benzene.

a.

c. [structure with ethyl and butyl substituents]

b. H₂N—[benzene]—NO₂

d. [structure with Cl, OH, Cl substituents]

13.72 Give the IUPAC name for each substituted benzene.

a.

b. [structure with ethyl and Br substituents]

c. [structure with H₂N and ethyl substituents]

d. [structure with Br, CH₃, I substituents]

13.73 Draw the structure of the three constitutional isomers that have a Cl atom and an NH₂ group bonded to a benzene ring. Name each compound using the IUPAC system.

13.74 Are o-bromochlorobenzene and m-bromochlorobenzene constitutional isomers or stereoisomers?

13.75 Give the structure corresponding to each IUPAC name.
a. p-nitropropylbenzene
d. 2-bromo-4-chlorotoluene
b. m-dibutylbenzene
e. 2-chloro-6-iodoaniline
c. o-iodophenol

494   Chapter 13   Unsaturated Hydrocarbons

13.76 Give the structure corresponding to each IUPAC name.
   a. *m*-ethylnitrobenzene   d. 1,3,5-trinitrobenzene
   b. *o*-difluorobenzene   e. 2,4-dibromophenol
   c. *p*-bromotoluene

Reactions of Aromatic Compounds

13.77 What product is formed when *p*-dimethylbenzene (also called *p*-xylene) is treated with each reagent?

CH_3—⬡—CH_3

p-dimethylbenzene

   a. Cl_2, $FeCl_3$
   b. HNO_3, H_2SO_4
   c. SO_3, H_2SO_4

13.78 What reagents (**A–D**) are needed to carry out each reaction in the following sequence?

⬡ →**A**→ ⬡—Cl →**B**→ O_2N—⬡—Cl →**C**→

O_2N—⬡(Cl)(SO_3H) →**D**→ H_2N—⬡(Cl)(SO_3H)

13.79 When bromobenzene is treated with HNO_3 and H_2SO_4, three different products are formed. Draw the structures of the three products formed.

13.80 You have three bottles (labeled **A, B,** and **C**) and each contains one of the *o*-, *m*-, or *p*-dibromobenzene isomers, but you don't know which isomer is in which bottle. When the dibromobenzene isomer in bottle **A** is treated with Cl_2 and $FeCl_3$, one product of molecular formula $C_6H_3Br_2Cl$ is obtained. When the dibromobenzene isomer in bottle **B** is treated with Cl_2 and $FeCl_3$, three products of molecular formula $C_6H_3Br_2Cl$ are obtained. When the dibromobenzene isomer in bottle **C** is treated with Cl_2 and $FeCl_3$, two products of molecular formula $C_6H_3Br_2Cl$ are obtained. Which isomer (ortho, meta, or para) is contained in which bottle (**A, B,** or **C**)?

Applications

13.81 Rosemary contains the antioxidant rosmarinic acid. Identify each functional group that contains an OH group as an alcohol, carboxylic acid, or phenol.

rosmarinic acid

13.82 Why is BHA an ingredient in some breakfast cereals and other packaged foods?

CH_3O—⬡(OH)—C(CH_3)_3

BHA
(**b**utylated **h**ydroxy **a**nisole)

13.83 Although nonpolar compounds tend to dissolve and remain in fatty tissues, polar substances are more water soluble, and more readily excreted into an environment where they may be degraded by other organisms. Explain why methoxychlor is more biodegradable than DDT.

CH_3O—⬡—CH(—⬡—OCH_3)(CCl_3)

methoxychlor

13.84 Explain why the pesticide DDT is insoluble in water, but the herbicide 2,4-D is water soluble. 2,4-D is one component of the defoliant Agent Orange used extensively during the Vietnam War.

Cl—⬡—CH(—⬡—Cl)(CCl_3)   Cl—⬡(Cl)—OCH_2COOH

DDT   2,4-D

13.85 Kukui nuts contain oil that is high in linoleic acid content (Table 13.1). (a) What two constitutional isomers are formed when linoleic acid is partially hydrogenated with one equivalent of H_2? (b) What product is formed when linoleic acid is completely hydrogenated with H_2? (c) What product would be formed if, during hydrogenation, one equivalent of H_2 is added *and* one of the cis double bonds is converted to a trans double bond?

13.86 Eleostearic acid is an unsaturated fatty acid found in tung oil, obtained from the seeds of the tung oil tree (*Aleurites fordii*) a deciduous tree native to China. Eleostearic acid is unusual in that the double bond at C9 is cis, but the other two double bonds are trans. (a) Draw the structure of eleostearic acid, showing the arrangement of groups around each double bond. (b) Draw a stereoisomer of eleostearic acid in which all of the double bonds are trans. (c) Which compound, eleostearic acid or its all-trans isomer, has the higher melting point? Explain your reasoning.

$$CH_3(CH_2)_3CH=CHCH=CHCH=CH(CH_2)_7CO_2H$$
                                              ⌐C9

eleostearic acid

13.87 Which of the following compounds might be an antioxidant?

   a. ⬡—$CH_2CH_2CH_2OH$ c. HO—⬡—OCH_3

   b. ⬡—OCH_3

13.88 Which of the following compounds might be an ingredient in a commercial sunscreen?

a.

b.

13.89 When benzene enters the body, it is oxidized to phenol (C_6H_5OH). What is the purpose of this oxidation reaction?

13.90 Explain what a PAH is, and give an example of a PAH mentioned in this chapter, other than benzo[*a*]pyrene.

13.91 Macadamia nuts have a high concentration of unsaturated oils formed from palmitoleic acid [$CH_3(CH_2)_5CH{=}CH(CH_2)_7COOH$]. (a) Draw the structure of the naturally occurring fatty acid with a cis double bond. (b) Draw a stereoisomer of palmitoleic acid. (c) Draw a constitutional isomer of palmitoleic acid.

13.92 What products are formed when polyethylene is completely combusted?

General Questions

13.93 Why is the six-membered ring in benzene flat but the six-membered ring in cyclohexane is puckered (not flat)?

13.94 Explain why *p*-dichlorobenzene is a nonpolar molecule but *o*-dichlorobenzene is a polar molecule.

13.95 Answer the following questions about compound **A,** represented in the given ball-and-stick model.

A

a. Convert **A** to a condensed structure and give its IUPAC name.
b. What product is formed when **A** is treated with H_2 in the presence of a metal catalyst?
c. What product is formed when **A** is treated with H_2O in the presence of H_2SO_4?
d. What polymer is formed when **A** is polymerized?

13.96 Answer the following questions about compound **B,** represented in the given ball-and-stick model.

B

a. Convert **B** to a condensed structure and give its IUPAC name.
b. What product is formed when **B** is treated with H_2 in the presence of a metal catalyst?
c. What product is formed when **B** is treated with H_2O in the presence of H_2SO_4?
d. What polymer is formed when **B** is polymerized?

13.97 Answer the following questions about alkene **C,** depicted in the ball-and-stick model.

C

a. Convert alkene **C** to a skeletal structure and give its IUPAC name.
b. What product is formed when **C** is treated with Cl_2?
c. What product is formed when **C** is treated with HCl?

13.98 Answer the following questions about alkene **D,** depicted in the ball-and-stick model.

D

a. Convert **D** to a skeletal structure.
b. What product is formed when **D** reacts with HBr?
c. What product is formed when **D** reacts with H_2O in the presence of H_2SO_4?

13.99 Several complex organic compounds are often identified by abbreviations. For each of the following abbreviations: [1] give the name that corresponds to the abbreviation; [2] identify the functional group(s) present; [3] write one fact about the compound.
  a. HDPE
  b. PS
  c. PAH

13.100 Answer the questions in Problem 13.99 for each of the following abbreviations.
  a. LDPE
  b. PET
  c. PP

CHALLENGE PROBLEMS

13.101 Are *cis*-2-hexene and *trans*-3-hexene constitutional isomers or stereoisomers? Explain.

13.102 Ignoring stereoisomers, draw the structures of the 13 constitutional isomers of molecular formula C_6H_{12} that contain one carbon–carbon double bond.

14

Linalool, a component of lavender oil, is used in scented soaps and lotions, and as an insecticide for controlling fleas and roaches.
©Daniel C. Smith

Organic Compounds That Contain Oxygen, Halogen, or Sulfur

CHAPTER OUTLINE

14.1 Introduction

14.2 Structure and Properties of Alcohols

14.3 Nomenclature of Alcohols

14.4 Interesting Alcohols

14.5 Reactions of Alcohols

14.6 FOCUS ON HEALTH & MEDICINE: Ethanol, the Most Widely Abused Drug

14.7 Structure and Properties of Ethers

14.8 FOCUS ON HEALTH & MEDICINE: Ethers as Anesthetics

14.9 Alkyl Halides

14.10 Organic Compounds That Contain Sulfur

CHAPTER GOALS

In this chapter you will learn how to:

1. Identify alcohols, ethers, alkyl halides, and thiols
2. Classify alcohols and alkyl halides as 1°, 2°, or 3°
3. Determine the properties of alcohols, ethers, alkyl halides, and thiols
4. Name alcohols, ethers, alkyl halides, and thiols
5. Draw the products of the dehydration of alcohols
6. Determine the products of alcohol oxidation
7. Convert thiols to disulfides

Why Study Alcohols, Ethers, Alkyl Halides, and Thiols?

Chapter 14 concentrates on four families of organic compounds that contain a carbon singly bonded to a heteroatom—**alcohols** (ROH), **ethers** (ROR), **alkyl halides** (RX, X = F, Cl, Br, or I), and **thiols** (RSH). The polar carbon–heteroatom bond gives these compounds different properties than the hydrocarbons of Chapters 12 and 13. Of the four families, alcohols are the most widely occurring, represented by simple compounds such as ethanol (CH_3CH_2OH) and by complex compounds such as starch and cellulose. Ethers are the most common anesthetics in use today, and alkyl halides, widely used as industrial solvents and refrigerants, are responsible for the destruction of the ozone layer. The –SH group of thiols plays an important role in protein chemistry. In Chapter 14, we learn about the properties of these four groups of organic compounds.

14.1 Introduction

Alcohols, ethers, alkyl halides, and **thiols** are four families of compounds that contain a carbon atom singly bonded to a heteroatom—oxygen, halogen, or sulfur.

Alcohols and **ethers** are organic derivatives of H_2O, formed by replacing one or two hydrogens on the oxygen by alkyl groups, respectively. *Alcohols* **contain a hydroxyl group (OH group)** bonded to a tetrahedral carbon atom, while *ethers* **have two alkyl groups bonded to an oxygen atom.** The oxygen atom in both compounds has two lone pairs of electrons, so it is surrounded by eight electrons.

General structures	Examples
R—Ö—H R—Ö—R	CH_3CH_2—Ö—H CH_3CH_2—Ö—CH_2CH_3
alcohol ether	ethanol diethyl ether

Alkyl halides contain a halogen atom (X = F, Cl, Br, or I) bonded to a tetrahedral carbon. Each halogen atom forms one bond to carbon and has three lone pairs of electrons. **Thiols contain a sulfhydryl group (SH group)** bonded to a tetrahedral carbon atom. A thiol is a sulfur analogue of an alcohol, formed by replacing the oxygen by sulfur. Like oxygen, the sulfur atom has two lone pairs of electrons around it.

General structures	Examples
R—Ẍ: R—S̈—H	CH_3CH_2—C̈l: CH_3CH_2—S̈—H
alkyl halide thiol	chloroethane ethanethiol
X = F, Cl, Br, I	

Mercaptomethylfuran (characteristic aroma of coffee), sevoflurane (a common anesthetic), and Taxol (an anticancer drug) are compounds that contain these functional groups.

2-mercaptomethylfuran
(coffee aroma)

sevoflurane
(general anesthetic)

paclitaxel
(Trade name Taxol)

[The OH, SH, halogen, and ether O atoms are labeled in red.]

(left): ©FoodCollection/StockFood RF; (middle): ©Mira/Alamy; (right): ©George Ostertag/Alamy

Taxol, a complex anticancer agent active against ovarian, breast, and some lung tumors, is especially interesting. Initial biological studies with Taxol were carried out with natural material isolated from the bark of the Pacific yew tree, but stripping the bark killed these magnificent trees. Taxol can now be prepared by a plant cell fermentation process, thus providing ample quantities for patients.

PROBLEM 14.1

a. Label the hydroxyl groups, sulfhydryl groups, halogens, and ether oxygens in each compound.

b. Which –OH group in salmeterol (**C**) is *not* part of an alcohol? Explain.

A
chondrochole A
(isolated from red seaweed,
Chondrococcus hornemanni)

B
3-methyl-3-sulfanyl-1-hexanol
(onion-like odor in human sweat)

C
salmeterol
Trade name Serevent
(dilates airways; used to treat asthma)

14.2 Structure and Properties of Alcohols

Alcohols contain a **hydroxyl group (OH group)** bonded to a tetrahedral carbon atom. Alcohols are classified as **primary (1°), secondary (2°),** or **tertiary (3°)** based on the number of carbon atoms bonded to the carbon with the OH group.

Alcohol	Classification of alcohols				Example

hydroxyl group

1°   2°   3°

2° alcohol   1° alcohol

3° alcohol

- A primary (1°) alcohol has an OH group on a carbon bonded to one carbon.
- A secondary (2°) alcohol has an OH group on a carbon bonded to two carbons.
- A tertiary (3°) alcohol has an OH group on a carbon bonded to three carbons.

SAMPLE PROBLEM 14.1 CLASSIFYING AN ALCOHOL AS 1°, 2°, OR 3°

Classify each alcohol as 1°, 2°, or 3°.

a. [structure]—CH₂CH₂OH

b. [structure]—OH

Analysis

To determine whether an alcohol is 1°, 2°, or 3°, locate the C with the OH group and count the number of C's bonded to it. A 1° alcohol has the OH group on a C bonded to one C, and so forth.

Solution

Draw out the structure or add H's to the skeletal structure to clearly see how many C's are bonded to the C bearing the OH group.

a. [structure] This C is bonded to 1 C.
1° alcohol

b. [structure] This C is bonded to 2 C's in the ring.
2° alcohol

PRACTICE PROBLEM 14.1

Classify each alcohol as 1°, 2°, or 3°.

a. $(CH_3)_2C$=CHCH₂CH₂—C—CH=CH₂ with CH₃ above and OH below

linalool
(isolated from lavender)

b. $(CH_3)_2C$=CHCH₂—C—C(CH₃)=CH₂ with CH₂OH above and H below

lavandulol
(isolated from lavender)

c. [structure]
menthol

Linalool (the chapter-opening molecule) and lavandulol (Practice Problem 14.1) are two of the over 300 compounds that determine the characteristic fragrance of lavender. ©Ingram Publishing RF

More Practice: Try Problems 14.23, 14.24, 14.35b, 14.36b, 14.66a, 14.93b, 14.94b.

500   **Chapter 14**   Organic Compounds That Contain Oxygen, Halogen, or Sulfur

Sorbitol occurs naturally in some berries and fruits. It is used as a substitute sweetener in sugar-free—that is, sucrose-free—candy and gum.
©McGraw-Hill Education/Jill Braaten, photographer

PROBLEM 14.2

Classify each hydroxyl group in sorbitol as 1°, 2°, or 3°.

sorbitol

An alcohol contains an oxygen atom surrounded by two atoms and two lone pairs of electrons, giving the oxygen atom a **bent** shape like H_2O. The C—O—H bond angle is similar to the tetrahedral bond angle of 109.5°.

CH₃—Ö—H = [bent shape 109.5°]
methanol   bent shape

Because oxygen is much more electronegative than carbon or hydrogen, the C—O and O—H bonds are polar. Since an alcohol contains two polar bonds and a bent shape, it has a net dipole. **Alcohols are also capable of intermolecular hydrogen bonding,** because they possess a hydrogen atom bonded to an oxygen. This gives alcohols much stronger intermolecular forces than the hydrocarbons of Chapters 12 and 13.

An alcohol has a net dipole.   Alcohols exhibit intermolecular hydrogen bonding.

CH₃—Ö—H net dipole / two polar bonds   CH₃—Ö—H = ... hydrogen bond ... = H—Ö—CH₃

As a result:

- Alcohols have higher boiling points and melting points than hydrocarbons of comparable molecular weight and shape.

CH₃CH₂CH₂CH₃   CH₃CH₂CH₂OH   ← stronger intermolecular forces higher boiling point and melting point

butane   1-propanol

melting point: −138 °C   melting point: −127 °C
boiling point: −0.5 °C   boiling point: 97 °C

The general rule governing solubility—**"like dissolves like"**—explains the solubility properties of alcohols, as we learned in Section 11.6B.

- Alcohols are soluble in organic solvents.
- Low molecular weight alcohols (those having fewer than six carbons) are soluble in water.
- Higher molecular weight alcohols (those having six carbons or more) are not soluble in water.

Thus, both ethanol (CH_3CH_2OH) and 1-octanol [$CH_3(CH_2)_7OH$] are soluble in organic solvents, but ethanol is water soluble and 1-octanol is not.

only 2 C's in the chain	many nonpolar C—C and C—H bonds
water soluble	**water insoluble**

PROBLEM 14.3

Which compound in each pair has the higher boiling point?

a.   or

b. $(CH_3)_3C$—OH or $(CH_3)_4C$

PROBLEM 14.4

Label each compound as water soluble or water insoluble.

a.   b.   c.

14.3   Nomenclature of Alcohols

In the IUPAC system, alcohols are identified by the suffix *-ol.*

How To Name an Alcohol Using the IUPAC System

Example: Give the IUPAC name of the following alcohol.

Step [1] Find the longest carbon chain containing the carbon bonded to the OH group.

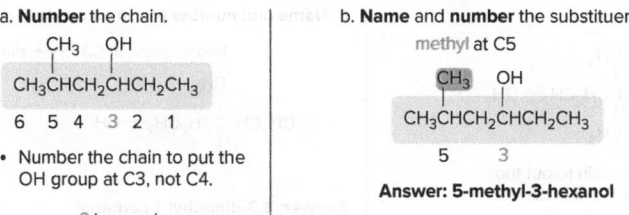

6 C's in the longest chain

hexane - - - → hexan*ol*

- Change the **-e** ending of the parent alkane to the suffix *-ol.*

Step [2] Number the carbon chain to give the OH group the lower number, and apply all other rules of nomenclature.

a. **Number** the chain.

$$CH_3CHCH_2CHCH_2CH_3$$

6 5 4 3 2 1

- Number the chain to put the OH group at C3, not C4.

3-hexanol

b. **Name** and **number** the substituents.

methyl at C5

$$CH_3CHCH_2CHCH_2CH_3$$

5   3

Answer: 5-methyl-3-hexanol

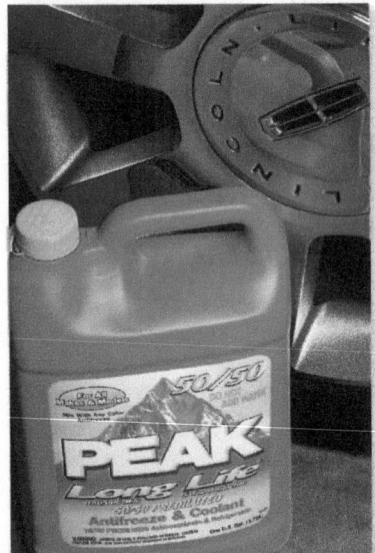

Ethylene glycol (HOCH$_2$CH$_2$OH) is used in antifreeze. It is sweet tasting but extremely toxic. Ethylene glycol is a starting material in the synthesis of synthetic fibers such as Dacron (Section 17.10). ©Jill Braaten RF

When an OH group is bonded to a ring, the **ring is numbered beginning with the OH group,** and the "1" is usually omitted from the name. The ring is then numbered in a clockwise or counterclockwise fashion to give the next substituent the lower number.

3-methylcyclohexanol

[The OH group is at C1; the second substituent (CH$_3$) gets the lower number.]

2-ethylcyclopentanol

[The OH group is at C1; the second substituent (CH$_3$CH$_2$) gets the lower number.]

Common names are often used for simple alcohols. To assign a common name:

- **Name all the carbon atoms of the molecule as a single alkyl group.**
- **Add the word *alcohol*, separating the words with a space.**

alcohol

OH = CH$_3$CH$_2$CH$_2$—OH ----> **propyl alcohol**

propyl group   a common name

Compounds with two hydroxyl groups are called **diols** (using the IUPAC system) or **glycols.** Compounds with three hydroxyl groups are called **triols,** and so forth. To name a diol, for example, the suffix **-diol** is added to the name of the parent alkane and numbers are used in the prefix to indicate the location of the two OH groups.

HOCH$_2$CH$_2$OH

IUPAC name: 1,2-ethanediol
Common name: **ethylene glycol**

1,2-cyclopentanediol

SAMPLE PROBLEM 14.2 NAMING AN ALCOHOL

Give the IUPAC name of the following alcohol.

$$CH_3CH_2\overset{\overset{\displaystyle CH_3}{|}}{\underset{\underset{\displaystyle CH_3}{|}}{C}}CH_2CH_2OH$$

Analysis and Solution

[1] Find the longest carbon chain that contains the carbon bonded to the OH group.

CH$_3$CH$_2$CCH$_2$CH$_2$ —OH
    |
    CH$_3$

5 C's in the longest chain ----> **pentanol**

- Change the **-e** ending of the parent alkane to the suffix **-ol.**

[2] Number the carbon chain to give the OH group the lower number, and apply all other rules of nomenclature.

a. **Number** the chain.

CH$_3$CH$_2$CCH$_2$CH$_2$—OH
    |
5   3   CH$_3$ 1

- Number the chain to put the OH group at C1, not C5.

1-pentanol

b. **Name** and **number** the substituents.

two methyls at C3 ⟶ dimethyl

CH$_3$CH$_2$CCH$_2$CH$_2$—OH
    |
    CH$_3$ 1
    3

Answer: 3,3-dimethyl-1-pentanol

PRACTICE PROBLEM 14.2

Give the IUPAC name for each compound.

a. $CH_3CH(CH_2)_4CH_3$ with OH

b. $(CH_3CH_2)_2CHCHCH_2CH_3$ with OH

c. (cyclohexane with CH₃ and OH)

d. (branched structure with OH)

More Practice: Try Problems 14.33a, 14.35c, 14.36c, 14.37, 14.38, 14.93a, 14.94a.

PROBLEM 14.5

Give the structure corresponding to each name.

a. 7,7-dimethyl-4-octanol

b. 5-methyl-4-propyl-3-heptanol

c. 2-ethyl-3-methylcyclohexanol

d. 1,3-cyclohexanediol

14.4   Interesting Alcohols

The most well known alcohol is ethanol, CH_3CH_2OH. **Ethanol** (Figure 14.1), formed by the fermentation of carbohydrates in grains and grapes, is the alcohol present in alcoholic beverages. Fermentation requires yeast, which provides the needed enzymes for the conversion. Ethanol is likely the first organic compound synthesized by humans, since alcohol has been produced for at least 4,000 years.

Ethanol is also a common laboratory solvent, which is sometimes made unfit to ingest by adding small amounts of benzene or methanol (CH_3OH), both of which are toxic. Ethanol is used as a

Figure 14.1   Ethanol—The Alcohol in Alcoholic Beverages

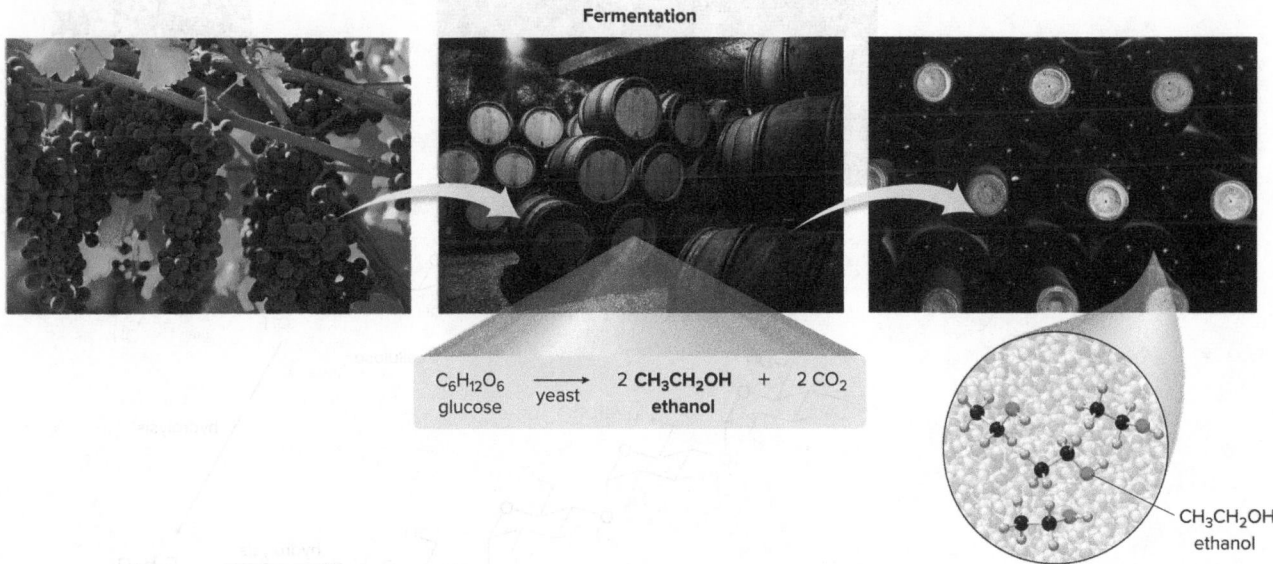

Fermentation

$$C_6H_{12}O_6 \xrightarrow{\text{yeast}} 2\ CH_3CH_2OH + 2\ CO_2$$
glucose / ethanol

CH_3CH_2OH
ethanol

Ethanol is the alcohol in red wine, obtained by the fermentation of grapes. All alcoholic beverages are mixtures of ethanol and water in various proportions. Beer has 3–8% ethanol, wines have 10–14% ethanol, and other liquors have 35–90% ethanol. *(left): ©Dynamic Graphics Group/Getty Images RF; (middle): ©Goodshoot/Getty Images RF; (right): ©Image Source RF*

Figure 14.2 Some Simple Alcohols

CH₃OH

- **Methanol (CH₃OH)** is a useful solvent and starting material for the synthesis of plastics. Methanol is extremely toxic because of the oxidation products formed when metabolized in the liver (Section 14.6A). Ingestion of as little as 15 mL (about half an ounce) causes blindness and 100 mL causes death.

(CH₃)₂CHOH

- **2-Propanol [(CH₃)₂CHOH, isopropyl alcohol]** is the major component of rubbing alcohol. When rubbed on the skin it evaporates readily, producing a pleasant cooling sensation. 2-Propanol is used to clean skin before medical procedures and to sterilize medical instruments.

HOCH₂CHCH₂OH
        |
        OH

- **Glycerol [(HOCH₂)₂CHOH]** is a triol used in lotions, liquid soap, and shaving cream. Since it is sweet tasting and nontoxic, it is also an additive in candy and some prepared foods. Its three OH groups readily hydrogen bond to water, so it helps to retain moisture in these products.

gasoline additive because it readily combusts to form CO_2 and H_2O with the release of energy. Other simple alcohols are listed in Figure 14.2.

Starch and **cellulose** are two polymers that contain many OH groups and belong to the family of molecules called **carbohydrates.**

The six-membered rings in starch and cellulose are drawn in the puckered "chair" form mentioned in Section 12.5A.

cellulose

amylose
(one form of starch)

hydrolysis

hydrolysis

$C_6H_{12}O_6$

glucose

(left): ©Vol. 1 PhotoDisc/Getty Images RF; (right): ©Fuse/Getty Images RF

Starch is the main carbohydrate in the seeds and roots of plants. When humans ingest wheat, rice, and potatoes, for example, they consume starch, which is then hydrolyzed to the simple sugar **glucose. Cellulose,** nature's most abundant organic material, gives rigidity to tree trunks and plant stems. Wood, cotton, and flax are composed largely of cellulose. Complete hydrolysis of cellulose also forms glucose, but unlike starch, humans cannot metabolize cellulose to glucose; that is, humans can digest starch but not cellulose.

14.5 Reactions of Alcohols

Alcohols undergo two useful reactions—**dehydration** and **oxidation.**

14.5A Dehydration

When an alcohol is treated with a strong acid such as H_2SO_4, the elements of water are lost and an alkene is formed as product. **Loss of H_2O from a starting material is called** *dehydration.* Dehydration takes place by breaking bonds on two adjacent atoms—the C—OH bond and an adjacent C—H bond.

H_2O is "lost."

Dehydration is an example of a general type of organic reaction called an **elimination reaction.**

- *Elimination* is a reaction in which elements of the starting material are "lost" and a new multiple bond is formed.

For example, dehydration of ethanol (CH_3CH_2OH) with H_2SO_4 forms ethylene ($CH_2\!=\!CH_2$), as shown. To draw the product of any dehydration, **remove the elements of H and OH from two adjacent atoms and draw a carbon–carbon double bond in the product.**

ethylene

cyclohexene

Sometimes more than one alkene can be formed as the product of a dehydration reaction, as is the case when 2-butanol [$CH_3CH(OH)CH_2CH_3$] is the starting material. If H and OH are removed from C1 and C2, 1-butene is formed. If H and OH are removed from C3 and C2, 2-butene is formed.

2-butanol   1-butene

two possible organic products of elimination

2-butanol   2-butene

Although both products are formed, **the major product is the alkene with more alkyl groups bonded to the carbons of the double bond.** In this case, therefore, 2-butene is the major product, because its C=C has two alkyl groups (two CH_3 groups) bonded to it, whereas the C=C of 1-butene has only one alkyl group (one CH_2CH_3 group) bonded to it.

This is a specific example of a general trend called the **Zaitsev rule.**

- **The Zaitsev rule: The major product in elimination is the alkene that has more alkyl groups bonded to it.**

SAMPLE PROBLEM 14.3 DRAWING THE PRODUCTS OF DEHYDRATION

Draw all possible products of dehydration of the following alcohol, and predict which one is the major product.

$$CH_3CHCH_2CH(CH_3)_2$$
$$|$$
$$OH$$

Analysis

To draw the products of dehydration:

- Find the carbon bonded to the OH group, and identify all carbons with H's bonded to this carbon.
- **Remove the elements of H and OH from two adjacent C's,** and draw a double bond between these C's in the product.
- When two different alkenes are formed, **the major product has more C's bonded to the C=C.**

Solution

In this example, there are two different C's bonded to the C with the OH. Elimination of H and OH from C1 and C2 forms 4-methyl-1-pentene. Elimination of H and OH from C3 and C2 forms 4-methyl-2-pentene. The major product is 4-methyl-2-pentene because it has two C's bonded to the C=C, whereas 4-methyl-1-pentene has only one C bonded to the C=C.

PRACTICE PROBLEM 14.3

Draw the products formed when each alcohol is dehydrated with H_2SO_4.

More Practice: Try Problems 14.57–14.60, 14.69a, 14.70a.

PROBLEM 14.6

What alkenes are formed when each alcohol is treated with H_2SO_4? Use the Zaitsev rule to predict the major product.

a. $CH_3CHCH_2CH_2CH_3$
        |
        OH

b. CH_3
        |
    CH_3—$\overset{CH_3}{\underset{OH}{C}}$—$CH_2CH_3$

c. (structure: cyclohexane ring with a methyl group and OH group on the same carbon)

PROBLEM 14.7

Explain why alcohol **A** readily undergoes dehydration in the presence of acid, while alcohol **B** does not.

(structure A: benzene ring attached to a carbon bearing CH_3, OH, and H)   (structure B: benzene ring attached to CH_2OH)

A   **B**

14.5B   Oxidation

Recall from Section 12.8 that to determine if an organic compound has been oxidized, we compare the relative number of C—H and C—O bonds in the starting material and product.

- Oxidation results in an increase in the number of C—O bonds or a decrease in the number of C—H bonds.

Thus, an organic compound like CH_4 can be oxidized by replacing C—H bonds with C—O bonds, as shown in Figure 14.3. When an alkane like CH_4 undergoes complete oxidation, as it does during combustion, all C—H bonds are converted to C—O bonds, forming CO_2. Organic chemists use the symbol [O] to indicate oxidation.

Alcohols can be oxidized to a variety of compounds, depending on the type of alcohol and the reagent. **Oxidation occurs by replacing the C—H bonds** *on the carbon bearing the OH group* **by C—O bonds.** All oxidation products from alcohol starting materials contain a **C=O, a carbonyl group.**

Alcohol   **Carbonyl compound**

(reaction scheme)   [O]   — A new C—O bond is formed.

Two bonds are broken.

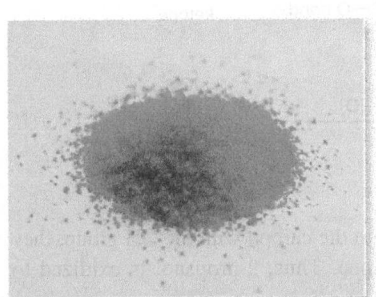

$K_2Cr_2O_7$, potassium dichromate, is a red-orange solid used to oxidize alcohols and other types of organic compounds.
Source: Ben Mills

A common reagent for alcohol oxidation is potassium dichromate, $K_2Cr_2O_7$. During oxidation the reagent is converted to a green Cr^{3+} product. Thus, these oxidations are accompanied by a characteristic color change. Since a variety of reagents can be used, we will write oxidation with the general symbol for oxidation, [O].

Figure 14.3

A General Scheme for Oxidizing an Organic Compound

(reaction scheme)

H—$\overset{H}{\underset{H}{C}}$—$H$ [O] H—$\overset{H}{\underset{H}{C}}$—$OH$ [O] $\overset{H}{\underset{H}{C}}$=$O$ [O] $\overset{H}{\underset{HO}{C}}$=$O$ [O] O=C=O

4 C—H bonds   3 C—H bonds   2 C—H bonds   1 C—H bond   0 C—H bonds
0 C—O bonds   1 C—O bond   2 C—O bonds   3 C—O bonds   4 C—O bonds

Increasing number of C—O bonds

- Primary (1°) alcohols are first oxidized to aldehydes (RCHO), which are further oxidized to carboxylic acids (RCOOH) by replacing one and then two C—H bonds by C—O bonds.

Replace 1 C—H bond by 1 C—O bond.

OH
|
R—C—H   [O]   [O]
| $\longrightarrow$ $\longrightarrow$
H

1° alcohol   aldehyde   carboxylic acid

Replace 2 C—H bonds by 2 C—O bonds.

Thus, oxidation of one C—H bond of ethanol forms acetaldehyde. Since acetaldehyde still contains a hydrogen atom on the carbonyl carbon, converting this C—H bond to a C—O bond forms acetic acid, a carboxylic acid with three C—O bonds.

OH
|
CH_3—C—H   [O]   [O]
| $\longrightarrow$ CH_3 $\longrightarrow$ CH_3
H

ethanol   acetaldehyde   acetic acid

- Secondary (2°) alcohols are oxidized to ketones (R_2CO), by replacing one C—H bond by one C—O bond.

General reaction

OH
|
R—C—H   [O]
| $\longrightarrow$
R

2° alcohol

Replace 1 C—H bond by 1 C—O bond.

ketone

Example

OH
|
CH_3—C—H   [O]
| $\longrightarrow$
CH_3

2-propanol

CH_3 CH_3

acetone

Since 2° alcohols have only one hydrogen atom bonded to the carbon with the OH group, they can be oxidized to only one type of compound, a ketone. Thus, 2-propanol is oxidized to acetone.

- Tertiary 3° alcohols have no H atoms on the carbon with the OH group, so they are not oxidized.

R
|
R—C—OH   [O]
| $\longrightarrow$ No reaction
R

no C—H bond

3° alcohol

SAMPLE PROBLEM 14.4 DRAWING THE PRODUCT OF ALCOHOL OXIDATION

Draw the carbonyl products formed when each alcohol is oxidized with $K_2Cr_2O_7$.

a.

⬡—OH

cyclohexanol

b. $CH_3CH_2CH_2CH_2OH$

1-butanol

Analysis

Classify the alcohol as 1°, 2°, or 3° by drawing in all of the H atoms on the C with the OH. Then **concentrate on the C with the OH group** and replace H atoms by bonds to O. Keep in mind:

- RCH_2OH (1° alcohols) are oxidized to RCHO, which are then oxidized to RCOOH.
- R_2CHOH (2° alcohols) are oxidized to R_2CO.
- R_3COH (3° alcohols) are not oxidized because they have no H atom on the C with the OH.

Solution

a. Cyclohexanol is a 2° alcohol with only one H atom on the C bonded to the OH group, so it is oxidized to a ketone, cyclohexanone.

only 1 H atom

cyclohexanol   cyclohexanone
2° alcohol   ketone

b. 1-Butanol is a 1° alcohol with two H atoms on the C bonded to the OH group. Thus, it is first oxidized to an aldehyde and then to a carboxylic acid.

$CH_3CH_2CH_2-\overset{OH}{\underset{H}{\overset{|}{C}}}-H$ →[O]→ $CH_3CH_2CH_2-\overset{O}{\overset{||}{C}}-H$ →[O]→ $CH_3CH_2CH_2-\overset{O}{\overset{||}{C}}-OH$

2 H atoms

1-butanol   butanal   butanoic acid
1° alcohol   aldehyde   carboxylic acid

PRACTICE PROBLEM 14.4

What products are formed when each alcohol is oxidized with $K_2Cr_2O_7$? In some cases, no reaction occurs.

a. $CH_3CHCH_2CH_2CH_3$ b. $(CH_3)_3CCH_2CH_2OH$ c. ⬠—OH   d. ⬡—OH
   $\overset{|}{\underset{OH}{}}$

More Practice: Try Problems 14.63–14.65; 14.66b, c; 14.69b; 14.70b.

14.5C FOCUS ON THE HUMAN BODY
Oxidation and Blood Alcohol Screening

Oxidations with chromium reagents are characterized by a color change, as the **red-orange chromium reagent** is reduced to a **green Cr^{3+} product.** The first devices used to measure blood alcohol content in individuals suspected of "driving under the influence" made use of this color change. Oxidation of CH_3CH_2OH, the 1° alcohol in alcoholic beverages, with red-orange $K_2Cr_2O_7$ forms CH_3COOH and green Cr^{3+}.

CH_3CH_2-OH +   **$K_2Cr_2O_7$** red-orange   → $CH_3-\overset{O}{\overset{||}{C}}-OH$ +   **Cr^{3+}** green

ethanol "alcohol"   acetic acid

Blood alcohol level can be determined by having an individual blow into a tube containing $K_2Cr_2O_7$ and an inert solid. The alcohol in the exhaled breath is oxidized by the chromium

Figure 14.4   Blood Alcohol Screening

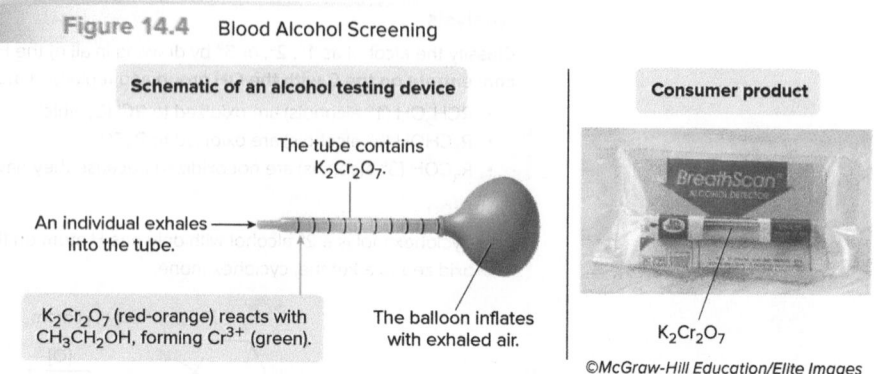

Schematic of an alcohol testing device

The tube contains
$K_2Cr_2O_7$.

An individual exhales →
into the tube.

$K_2Cr_2O_7$ (red-orange) reacts with
CH_3CH_2OH, forming Cr^{3+} (green).

The balloon inflates
with exhaled air.

Consumer product

$K_2Cr_2O_7$

©McGraw-Hill Education/Elite Images

- The oxidation of CH_3CH_2OH with $K_2Cr_2O_7$ to form CH_3COOH and Cr^{3+} was the first available method for the routine testing of alcohol concentration in exhaled air. Some consumer products for alcohol screening are still based on this technology.
- A driver is considered "under the influence" in most states with a blood alcohol concentration of 0.08%.

reagent, which turns green in the tube (Figure 14.4). The higher the concentration of CH_3CH_2OH in the breath, the more chromium reagent is reduced, and the farther the green color extends down the length of the sample tube. This value is then correlated with blood alcohol content to determine if an individual has surpassed the legal blood alcohol limit.

14.6   FOCUS ON HEALTH & MEDICINE
Ethanol, the Most Widely Abused Drug

Throughout history, humans have ingested alcoholic beverages for their pleasant taste and the feeling of euphoria they impart. Although we think of alcohol as a stimulant, largely because small amounts decrease social inhibitions, the ethanol (CH_3CH_2OH) in an alcoholic beverage actually depresses the central nervous system. The chronic and excessive consumption of alcoholic beverages has become a major health and social crisis, making ethanol the most widely abused drug in the United States. One estimate suggests that there are 40 times more alcoholics than heroin addicts.

14.6A   The Metabolism of Ethanol

When ethanol is consumed, it is quickly absorbed in the stomach and small intestines and then rapidly transported in the bloodstream to other organs. Ethanol is metabolized in the liver by a two-step oxidation sequence. The body does not use chromium reagents as oxidants. Instead, high molecular weight enzymes, alcohol dehydrogenase and aldehyde dehydrogenase, and a small molecule called a **coenzyme** carry out these oxidations.

The products of the biological oxidation of ethanol are the same as the products formed in the laboratory. When ethanol (CH_3CH_2OH, a 1° alcohol) is ingested, it is oxidized in the liver first to CH_3CHO (acetaldehyde) and then to CH_3COOH (acetic acid).

$$CH_3CH_2-OH \xrightarrow[\text{dehydrogenase}]{\text{alcohol} \atop [O]} \underset{\text{acetaldehyde}}{CH_3CHO} \xrightarrow[\text{dehydrogenase}]{\text{aldehyde} \atop [O]} \underset{\text{acetic acid}}{CH_3COOH}$$

ethanol

If more ethanol is ingested than can be metabolized in a given time period, the concentration of acetaldehyde accumulates. This toxic compound is responsible for the feelings associated with a hangover.

The oxygen atom of an ether is surrounded by two carbon atoms and two lone pairs of electrons, giving it a **bent** shape like the oxygen in H_2O. The C—O—C bond angle is similar to the tetrahedral bond angle of 109.5°.

CH_3—O—CH_3

dimethyl ether

109.5°

bent shape

The ether oxygen can be contained in a ring. **A ring that contains a heteroatom is called a heterocycle.** When the ether is part of a three-membered ring, the ether is called an *epoxide.*

epoxide

a three-membered ring with an ether O atom

Many compounds that contain ether heterocycles are naturally occurring. **Disparlure,** the sex pheromone of the female gypsy moth, is an epoxide used to control the spread of the gypsy moth caterpillar. This pest has periodically devastated the forests of the northeastern United States by eating the leaves of many shade and fruit-bearing trees. **Hemibrevetoxin B,** a complex neurotoxin with four ether oxygens, is produced by algal blooms referred to as "red tides," because of the color of the ocean waters when these algae proliferate.

disparlure

hemibrevetoxin B

[Cyclic ethers are labeled in red.]

(top): ©Ed Reschke; (bottom): ©Peter J.S. Franks, Scripps Institution of Oceanography

PROBLEM 14.9

Draw the structure of the three constitutional isomers of molecular formula $C_4H_{10}O$ that contain an ether.

14.7A   Physical Properties

Because oxygen is more electronegative than carbon, the C—O bonds of an ether are both polar. Since an ether contains two polar bonds and a bent shape, it has a **net dipole.** In this way, ethers resemble alcohols.

net dipole

two polar bonds

Ethers do not contain a hydrogen atom bonded to oxygen, so unlike alcohols, two ether molecules *cannot* intermolecularly hydrogen bond to each other. **This gives ethers stronger intermolecular forces than alkanes but weaker intermolecular forces than alcohols.** As a result:

- Ethers have *higher* melting points and boiling points than hydrocarbons of comparable molecular weight and shape.
- Ethers have *lower* melting points and boiling points than alcohols of comparable molecular weight and shape.

$CH_3CH_2CH_2CH_3$	$CH_3OCH_2CH_3$	$CH_3CH_2CH_2OH$
butane	ethyl methyl ether	1-propanol
boiling point −0.5 °C	boiling point 11 °C	boiling point 97 °C

Increasing boiling point

All ethers are soluble in organic solvents. Like alcohols, **low molecular weight ethers are water soluble,** because the oxygen atom of the ether can hydrogen bond to one of the hydrogens of water. When the alkyl groups of the ether have more than a total of five carbons, the nonpolar portion of the molecule is too large, so the ether is water insoluble.

$CH_3—\ddot{O}:$

CH_3

dimethyl ether

hydrogen bond

$H—\ddot{O}—H$

SAMPLE PROBLEM 14.5 DETERMINING THE RELATIVE BOILING POINTS OF AN ALCOHOL, ETHER, AND ALKANE

Rank the following compounds in order of increasing boiling point:

—OCH₃

A

B

OH

C

Analysis

Look at the functional groups to determine the strength of the intermolecular forces—**the stronger the forces, the higher the boiling point.**

Solution

B is an alkane with nonpolar C—C and C—H bonds, so it has the weakest intermolecular forces and therefore the lowest boiling point. **C** is an alcohol capable of intermolecular hydrogen bonding, so it has the strongest intermolecular forces and the highest boiling point. **A** is an ether, so it contains a net dipole but is incapable of intermolecular hydrogen bonding. **A**, therefore, has intermolecular forces of intermediate strength and has a boiling point between the boiling points of **B** and **C**.

B   **A**   **C**

Increasing intermolecular forces
Increasing boiling point

PRACTICE PROBLEM 14.5

Which compound in each pair has the higher boiling point?

a. $CH_3(CH_2)_6CH_3$ or $CH_3(CH_2)_5OCH_3$

c. $CH_3(CH_2)_6OH$ or $CH_3(CH_2)_5OCH_3$

b. [hexane ring] or [oxane ring]

d. $CH_3(CH_2)_5OCH_3$ or CH_3OCH_3

More Practice: **Try Problems 14.49–14.56.**

PROBLEM 14.10

Label each ether as water soluble or water insoluble.

a. $CH_3CH_2{-}O{-}CH_3$ b. [cyclohexyl-O-cyclohexyl]   c. [decalin with OCH₃]

14.7B Naming Ethers

Simple ethers are usually assigned common names. To do so, **name both alkyl groups** bonded to the oxygen, arrange these names alphabetically, and add the word *ether*. For ethers with identical alkyl groups, name the alkyl group and add the prefix *di-*.

$CH_3CH_2CH_2{-}O{-}CH_2CH_3$ $CH_3CH_2{-}O{-}CH_2CH_3$

propyl   ethyl   ethyl   ethyl
ethyl propyl ether   **diethyl ether**

More complex ethers are named using the IUPAC system. One alkyl group is named as a hydrocarbon chain, and the other is named as part of a substituent bonded to that chain.

- **Name the simpler alkyl group + O atom as an alkoxy substituent by changing the *-yl* ending of the alkyl group to *-oxy*.**

$CH_3O{-}$ $CH_3CH_2O{-}$
methoxy   ethoxy

- **Name the remaining alkyl group as an alkane, with the alkoxy group as a substituent bonded to this chain.**

SAMPLE PROBLEM 14.6 NAMING AN ETHER

Give the IUPAC name for the following ether.

$$CH_3CH_2CH_2CH_2CHCH_2CH_2CH_3$$
$$OCH_2CH_3$$

Analysis and Solution

[1] Name the longer chain as an alkane and the shorter chain as an alkoxy group.	[2] Apply other nomenclature rules to complete the name.

CH₃CH₂CH₂CH₂CHCH₂CH₂CH₃

$$CH_3CH_2CH_2CH_2CHCH_2CH_2CH_3$$

OCH₂CH₃
ethoxy group

8 C's ----→ octane

4   1
$$CH_3CH_2CH_2CH_2CHCH_2CH_2CH_3$$

OCH₂CH₃

Answer: 4-ethoxyoctane

PRACTICE PROBLEM 14.6

Name each ether.

a. CH₃—O—CH₂CH₂CH₂CH₃

b. OCH₃

c.

More Practice: Try Problems 14.34a, 14.41, 14.42.

PROBLEM 14.11

Draw the structure corresponding to each name.

a. dibutyl ether

b. ethyl propyl ether

c. 1-methoxypentane

d. 3-ethoxyhexane

14.8   FOCUS ON HEALTH & MEDICINE
Ethers as Anesthetics

diethyl ether

A general anesthetic is a drug that interferes with nerve transmission in the brain, resulting in a loss of consciousness and the sensation of pain. The discovery that **diethyl ether** (CH₃CH₂OCH₂CH₃) is a general anesthetic revolutionized surgery in the nineteenth century. Early experiments performed by a dentist, Dr. William Morton, resulted in a public demonstration of diethyl ether as an anesthetic in Boston in 1846. Diethyl ether quickly supplanted the crude methods then used for a patient to tolerate the excruciating pain of surgery—making an individual unconscious by excess alcohol intake or by striking a blow to the head.

Diethyl ether is an imperfect anesthetic, but considering the alternatives in the nineteenth century, it was considered revolutionary. It is safe and easy to administer with low patient mortality, but it is highly flammable, and it causes nausea in many patients.

For these reasons, alternatives to diethyl ether are now widely used. Many of these newer general anesthetics, which cause little patient discomfort, are also ethers. These include isoflurane, enflurane, and methoxyflurane. Replacing some of the hydrogen atoms in the ether by halogens results in compounds with similar anesthetic properties but decreased flammability.

isoflurane
(Trade name Forane)

enflurane
(Trade name Ethrane)

methoxyflurane
(Trade name Penthrane)

desflurane

PROBLEM 14.12

(a) Translate the ball-and-stick model of desflurane, a potent general anesthetic, into a complete structure with all atoms, bond lines, and lone pairs. (b) The solubility properties of desflurane resemble other general anesthetics, in that it readily crosses the nonpolar medium of the blood–brain barrier. Explain why desflurane is soluble in organic solvents and other organic media.

PROBLEM 14.13

Halothane ($CF_3CHClBr$) is a general anesthetic that is not an ether. Draw a three-dimensional structure for halothane using solid lines, wedges, and dashed wedges (see Section 11.3).

Alkyl halides have the general molecular formula $C_nH_{2n+1}X$, and are formally derived from an alkane by replacing a hydrogen atom with a halogen. Alkyl halides are prepared from alkanes by halogenation (Section 12.9).

14.9 Alkyl Halides

Alkyl halides **are organic molecules containing a halogen atom X (X = F, Cl, Br, I) bonded to a tetrahedral carbon atom.** Alkyl halides are classified as **primary (1°), secondary (2°),** or **tertiary (3°)** depending on the number of carbons bonded to the carbon with the halogen.

Alkyl halide	Classification of alkyl halides			Example

$X = F, Cl, Br, I$ $1°$ $2°$ $3°$ 2° chloride   1° fluoride   3° iodide

- A primary (1°) alkyl halide has a halogen on a carbon bonded to one carbon.
- A secondary (2°) alkyl halide has a halogen on a carbon bonded to two carbons.
- A tertiary (3°) alkyl halide has a halogen on a carbon bonded to three carbons.

PROBLEM 14.14

Classify each alkyl halide as 1°, 2°, or 3°.

a. $CH_3CH_2CH_2CH_2CH_2Br$

b. (structure with CH₃ and F)

c. CH_3—C(CH₃)₂—CHCH₃ with Cl

PROBLEM 14.15

Dexamethasone is a halogen-containing steroid used to treat inflammation in rheumatoid arthritis and other conditions. (a) Classify the alkyl halide in dexamethasone as 1°, 2°, or 3°. (b) Classify the hydroxyl groups as 1°, 2°, or 3°.

dexamethasone

14.9A Physical Properties

Alkyl halides contain a polar C—X bond, but because they have all of their hydrogens bonded to carbon, they are incapable of intermolecular hydrogen bonding. Alkyl halides with one halogen are polar molecules, therefore, because they contain a net dipole. As a result, they have higher melting points and boiling points than alkanes with the same number of carbons.

The size of the alkyl groups and the halogen also affects the physical properties of an alkyl halide.

- The boiling point and melting point of an alkyl halide increase with the size of the alkyl group because of increased surface area.
- The boiling point and melting point of an alkyl halide increase with the size of the halogen.

Thus, $CH_3CH_2CH_2Cl$ has a higher boiling point than CH_3CH_2Cl because it has one more carbon, giving it a larger surface area. $CH_3CH_2CH_2Br$ has a higher boiling point than $CH_3CH_2CH_2Cl$ because Br is farther down the column of the periodic table, making it larger than Cl.

CH_3CH_2Cl	$CH_3CH_2CH_2Cl$	$CH_3CH_2CH_2Br$
chloroethane	1-chloropropane	1-bromopropane
bp = 12 °C	bp = 47 °C	bp = 71 °C

Increasing boiling point
Increasing size of the alkyl group
Increasing size of the halogen

Alkyl halides are incapable of hydrogen bonding, so they are insoluble in water regardless of size.

PROBLEM 14.16

Rank the compounds in each group in order of increasing boiling point.

a. $CH_3CH_2CH_2I$, $CH_3CH_2CH_2Cl$, $CH_3CH_2CH_2F$
b. $CH_3(CH_2)_4CH_3$, $CH_3(CH_2)_5Br$, $CH_3(CH_2)_5Cl$

14.9B Nomenclature

In the IUPAC system, an alkyl halide is named as an alkane with a halogen substituent—that is, as a **halo alkane.** To name a halogen substituent, change the **-ine** ending of the name of the halogen to the suffix **-o** (e.g., chlor*ine* → chlor*o*).

How To Name an Alkyl Halide Using the IUPAC System

Example: Give the IUPAC name of the following alkyl halide.

$$CH_3CH_2CHCH_2CH_2CHCH_3$$

Step [1] Find the parent carbon chain containing the carbon bonded to the halogen.

$$CH_3CH_2CHCH_2CH_2CHCH_3$$

7 C's in the longest chain

7 C's - - - → heptane

- Name the parent chain as an **alkane,** with the halogen as a substituent bonded to the longest chain.

—Continued

How To, continued . . .

Step [2]   **Apply all other rules of nomenclature.**

a. **Number** the chain.

$$CH_3 \qquad\qquad Cl$$
$$CH_3CH_2CHCH_2CH_2CHCH_3$$
$$7 \quad 6 \quad 5 \quad 4 \quad\; 3 \quad 2 \quad 1$$

- Begin at the end nearest the first substituent, either alkyl or halogen.

b. **Name** and **number** the substituents.

methyl at C5   chloro at C2

$$CH_3 \qquad\qquad Cl$$
$$CH_3CH_2CHCH_2CH_2CHCH_3$$
$$5 \qquad\qquad\qquad 2$$

c. Alphabetize: **c** for **c**hloro, then **m** for **m**ethyl.

Answer: 2-chloro-5-methylheptane

Common names for alkyl halides are used only for simple alkyl halides. To assign a common name, name the carbon atoms as an alkyl group. Then name the halogen by changing the *-ine* ending of the halogen name to the suffix *-ide;* for example, **brom*ine* → brom*ide.***

$$CH_3CH_2—Cl \quad = \quad \diagup\!\!\!\diagdown\!\!Cl \qquad \text{chlor}ine \;\rightarrow\; \text{chlor}ide$$

ethyl
group

Common name:
ethyl chloride

PROBLEM 14.17

Give the IUPAC name for each compound.

a. $CH_3CHCH_2CH_2CH_2CH_3$
        |
        Br

b. (structure with Cl)

c. (cyclohexane with CH₃ and Br)

PROBLEM 14.18

Give the structure corresponding to each name.

a. 3-chloro-2-methylhexane

b. 4-ethyl-5-iodo-2,2-dimethyloctane

c. 1,1,3-tribromocyclohexane

d. propyl chloride

14.9C   Interesting Alkyl Halides

Many simple alkyl halides make excellent solvents because they are not flammable and they dissolve a wide variety of organic compounds. Two compounds in this category include $CHCl_3$ (chloroform or trichloromethane) and CCl_4 (carbon tetrachloride or tetrachloromethane). Large quantities of these solvents are produced industrially each year, but like many chlorinated organic compounds, both chloroform and carbon tetrachloride are toxic if inhaled or ingested. Two other simple alkyl halides are given in Figure 14.5.

Figure 14.5   Two Simple Alkyl Halides

- **Chloromethane (CH_3Cl)** is produced by giant kelp and algae and is also found in emissions from volcanoes such as Hawaii's Kilauea. Almost all of the atmospheric chloromethane results from these natural sources.

CH_3Cl

- **Dichloromethane (or methylene chloride, CH_2Cl_2)** is an important solvent, once used to decaffeinate coffee. Coffee is now decaffeinated using liquid CO_2 due to concerns over the possible ill effects of trace amounts of residual CH_2Cl_2 in the coffee. Subsequent studies on rats have shown, however, that no cancers occurred when animals ingested the equivalent of over 100,000 cups of decaffeinated coffee per day.

CH_2Cl_2

Giant kelp forests in the ocean release chloromethane (CH_3Cl) into the atmosphere. *Source: Claire Fackler, CINMS, NOAA*

Fluticasone is used as an aerosol inhalation to treat seasonal and recurrent allergies and to combat chronic lung inflammation in asthma. ©McGraw-Hill Education/Mark Dierker, photographer

The 1995 Nobel Prize in Chemistry was awarded to Professors Mario Molina, Paul Crutzen, and F. Sherwood Rowland for their work in elucidating the interaction of ozone with CFCs. What began as a very fundamental research project turned out to have important implications in the practical world.

Propane and butane are now used as propellants in spray cans in place of CFCs. ©McGraw-Hill Education/Jill Braaten, photographer

PROBLEM 14.19

Classify each of the labeled functional groups in the drug fluticasone as 1°, 2°, or 3°.

fluticasone

14.9D   FOCUS ON THE ENVIRONMENT
Alkyl Halides and the Ozone Layer

While the beneficial effects of many organic halides are undisputed, certain synthetic chlorinated organics, such as the **chlorofluorocarbons,** have caused lasting harm to the environment. **Chlorofluorocarbons (CFCs)** are simple halogen-containing compounds having the general molecular structure CF_xCl_{4-x}. CFCs are manufactured under the trade name Freons. Two examples are $CFCl_3$ (Freon 11) and CF_2Cl_2 (Freon 12).

CFCs are inert and nontoxic, and they have been used as refrigerants, solvents, and aerosol propellants. Because CFCs have low boiling points and are water insoluble, they readily escape into the upper atmosphere. There, CFCs are decomposed by sunlight. This process forms highly reactive intermediates that have been shown to destroy the ozone layer (Figure 14.6).

Figure 14.6   CFCs and Ozone Destruction

ENVIRONMENTAL NOTE

O_3 destruction is most severe in the region of the South Pole, where a large ozone hole (shown in purple) is visible with satellite imaging. *Source: NASA*

The ozone (O_3) in the upper atmosphere is vital to life: it acts as a shield, protecting the earth's surface from destructive ultraviolet radiation. A decrease in ozone concentration in this protective layer will have some immediate consequences, including an increase in the incidence of skin cancer and eye cataracts. Other long-term effects include a reduced immune response, interference with photosynthesis in plants, and harmful effects on the growth of plankton, the mainstay of the ocean food chain.

These findings led to a ban on the use of CFCs in aerosol propellants in the United States in 1978 and to the phasing out of their use in refrigeration systems. While it is now easy to second-guess the extensive use of CFCs, it is also easy to see why they were used so widely. **CFCs made refrigeration available to the general public.** Would you call your refrigerator a comfort or a necessity?

There are two newer alternatives to CFCs. **Hydrochlorofluorocarbons (HCFCs)** such as CF_3CHCl_2 contain the elements of H, Cl, and F bonded to carbon, and **hydrofluorocarbons (HFCs)** such as FCH_2CF_3 contain the elements of H and F bonded to carbon. These compounds have many properties in common with CFCs, but they are decomposed more readily before they reach the upper atmosphere, so they are less destructive to the O_3 layer.

PROBLEM 14.20

Classify each compound as a CFC, HCFC, or HFC: (a) CF_3Cl; (b) $CHFCl_2$; (c) CH_2F_2.

14.10   Organic Compounds That Contain Sulfur

Thiols **are organic compounds that contain a sulfhydryl group (SH group) bonded to a tetrahedral carbon.** Since sulfur is directly below oxygen in the periodic table, thiols can be considered sulfur analogues of alcohols. Because the sulfur atom is surrounded by two atoms and two lone pairs, thiols have a bent shape around sulfur.

Thiol

$$-\overset{|}{\underset{|}{C}}-\ddot{\underset{..}{S}}H \qquad CH_3CH_2-\ddot{\underset{..}{S}}-H \quad = \qquad = \qquad \diagdown\diagup^{SH}$$

sulfhydryl group   ethanethiol   bent shape around S

Thiols differ from alcohols in one important way. They contain no O—H bonds, so they are incapable of intermolecular hydrogen bonding. **This gives thiols lower boiling points and melting points compared to alcohols having the same size and shape.**

Hydrogen bonding can occur. stronger intermolecular forces **higher boiling point** ⟶ CH_3CH_2-OH CH_3CH_2-SH ⟵ Hydrogen bonding is impossible. weaker intermolecular forces **lower boiling point**

ethanol bp 78 °C   ethanethiol bp 35 °C

To name a thiol in the IUPAC system:

- Name the parent hydrocarbon as an alkane and add the suffix *-thiol*.
- Number the carbon chain to give the SH group the lower number.

$$CH_3-SH \qquad CH_3CH_2CH_2CH_2-SH \qquad \overset{\overset{\displaystyle CH_3}{|}}{CH_3\underset{4}{C}HCH_2CH_2CH_2\underset{1}{-}SH}$$

methanethiol   1-butanethiol   4-methyl-1-pentanethiol

SAMPLE PROBLEM 14.7 NAMING A THIOL

Give the IUPAC name for the following thiol.

$$CH_3CH_2CHCH_2CH_2CH_2CHCH_3$$

with substituents CH_2CH_3 and SH

Analysis and Solution

[1] Find the longest carbon chain that contains the carbon bonded to the SH group.

$$CH_3CH_2CHCH_2CH_2CH_2CHCH_3$$

8 C's in the longest chain ----→ **octane**

- Name the alkane and add the suffix *-thiol:* **octanethiol.**

[2] Number the carbon chain to give the SH group the lower number and apply all other rules of nomenclature.

a. Number the chain.

$$CH_3CH_2CHCH_2CH_2CH_2CHCH_3$$
  8   6   2 1

- Number to put the SH at C2, not C7.
  2-octanethiol

b. Name and **number** the substituents.

ethyl at C6

$$CH_3CH_2CHCH_2CH_2CH_2CHCH_3$$
        6   2

Answer: 6-ethyl-2-octanethiol

PRACTICE PROBLEM 14.7

Give the IUPAC name for each thiol.

a. $CH_3CH_2CHCH_2CH_3$
           |
          SH

b. (cyclohexane with SH)

c. (branched chain with SH)

More Practice: Try Problems 14.34b, 14.45c, 14.46c.

The potent odor of grapefruit mercaptan contributes to the characteristic aroma of grapefruit. ©Purestock/SuperStock

The most obvious physical property of thiols is their distinctive foul odor. For example, 3-methyl-3-sulfanyl-1-hexanol is responsible for the onion-like odor of human sweat.

(structure) SH ... OH
3-methyl-3-sulfanyl-1-hexanol

Thiols undergo one important reaction: **thiols are oxidized to disulfides,** compounds that contain a sulfur–sulfur bond. This is an oxidation reaction because two hydrogen atoms are removed in forming the disulfide.

Oxidation $2\ CH_3CH_2-S-H$ $\xrightarrow{[O]}$ $CH_3CH_2-S-S-CH_2CH_3$
                        thiol   disulfide
                                                    new S—S bond

Disulfides can also be converted back to thiols with a reducing agent. The symbol for a general reducing agent is **[H],** since hydrogen atoms are often added to a molecule during reduction.

Reduction $CH_3CH_2-S-S-CH_2CH_3$ $\xrightarrow{[H]}$ $2\ CH_3CH_2-S-H$
                        disulfide   thiol
                                                    new S—H bond

Figure 14.7   Focus on the Human Body: Making Straight Hair Curly

Reduce the disulfide bonds.

Re-form the disulfide bonds
to form curled strands of hair.

Straight hair

Curly hair

To make straight hair curly, the disulfide bonds holding the protein chains together are reduced. This forms free SH groups. The hair is turned around curlers and then an oxidizing agent is applied. This re-forms the disulfide bonds in the hair, now giving it a curly appearance.
(left&right): ©McGraw-Hill Education/Suzi Ross, photographer

Diallyl disulfide (Problem 14.22), which is formed by the decomposition of allicin (Section 12.3) when garlic cloves are cut or crushed, is principally responsible for the pungent odor of garlic oil. ©McGraw-Hill Education/Mark Dierker, photographer

diallyl disulfide

The chemistry of thiols and disulfides plays an important role in determining the properties and shape of some proteins, as we will learn in Chapter 21. For example, α-keratin, the protein in hair, contains many disulfide bonds. Straight hair can be made curly by cleaving the disulfide bonds in α-keratin, then rearranging and re-forming them, as shown schematically in Figure 14.7.

First, the disulfide bonds in the straight hair are reduced to thiol groups, so the bundles of α-keratin chains are no longer held in their specific "straight" orientation. Then, the hair is wrapped around curlers and treated with an oxidizing agent that converts the thiol groups back to disulfide bonds, now with twists and turns in the keratin backbone. This makes the hair look curly and is the chemical basis for a "permanent."

PROBLEM 14.21

(a) Draw the disulfide formed when $CH_3CH_2CH_2SH$ is oxidized. (b) Draw the product formed when the following disulfide is reduced: $CH_3CH_2CH_2CH_2SSCH_2CH_3$.

PROBLEM 14.22

What product is formed when diallyl disulfide, a major component of garlic oil, is reduced?

CHAPTER HIGHLIGHTS
KEY TERMS

Alcohol (14.1)

Alkoxy group (14.7)

Alkyl halide (14.1)

Carbonyl group (14.5)

Chlorofluorocarbon (14.9)

Coenzyme (14.6)

Dehydration (14.5)

Diol (14.3)

Disulfide (14.10)

Elimination (14.5)

Epoxide (14.7)

Ether (14.1)

Glycol (14.3)

Heterocycle (14.7)

Hydrochlorofluorocarbon (14.9)

Hydrofluorocarbon (14.9)

Hydroxyl group (14.1)

Oxidation (14.5)

Primary (1°) alcohol (14.2)

Primary (1°) alkyl halide (14.9)

Secondary (2°) alcohol (14.2)

Secondary (2°) alkyl halide (14.9)

Sulfhydryl group (14.1)

Tertiary (3°) alcohol (14.2)

Tertiary (3°) alkyl halide (14.9)

Thiol (14.1)

Triol (14.3)

Zaitsev rule (14.5)

KEY REACTIONS

[1]　Dehydration of alcohols (14.5A)

$$\underset{\substack{| \;\;\;| \\ H \;\; OH}}{-\overset{|}{C}-\overset{|}{C}-} \quad \xrightarrow{H_2SO_4} \quad \overset{\diagdown}{\underset{\diagup}{C}}=\overset{\diagup}{\underset{\diagdown}{C}} \;+\; H_2O$$

[2]　Oxidation of alcohols (14.5B)

　　a.　Primary (1°) alcohols　　$RCH_2OH \xrightarrow{[O]} \underset{\text{aldehyde}}{RCHO} \xrightarrow{[O]} \underset{\text{carboxylic acid}}{RCOOH}$

　　b.　Secondary (2°) alcohols　　$R_2CHOH \xrightarrow{[O]} \underset{\text{ketone}}{R_2CO}$

　　c.　Tertiary (3°) alcohols　　$R_3COH \xrightarrow{[O]} \text{No reaction}$

[3]　Oxidation of thiols and reduction of disulfides (14.10)

$$2 \; \underset{\text{thiol}}{R-S-H} \;\; \underset{[H]}{\overset{[O]}{\rightleftharpoons}} \;\; \underset{\text{disulfide}}{R-S-S-R}$$

KEY CONCEPTS

❶ What are the characteristics of alcohols, ethers, alkyl halides, and thiols?

- Alcohols contain a hydroxyl group (OH group) bonded to a tetrahedral carbon. Since the O atom is surrounded by two atoms and two lone pairs, alcohols have a bent shape around O. (14.2)
- Ethers have two alkyl groups bonded to an oxygen atom. Since the O atom is surrounded by two atoms and two lone pairs, ethers have a bent shape around O. (14.7)
- Alkyl halides contain a halogen atom (X = F, Cl, Br, I) singly bonded to a tetrahedral carbon. (14.9)
- Thiols contain a sulfhydryl group (SH group) bonded to a tetrahedral carbon. Since the S atom is surrounded by two atoms and two lone pairs, thiols have a bent shape around S. (14.10)

❷ How are alcohols and alkyl halides classified?

- Alcohols and alkyl halides are classified by the number of C's bonded to the C with the functional group.
- $RCH_2OH = 1°$ alcohol; $R_2CHOH = 2°$ alcohol; $R_3COH = 3°$ alcohol. (14.2)
- $RCH_2X = 1°$ alkyl halide; $R_2CHX = 2°$ alkyl halide; $R_3CX = 3°$ alkyl halide. (14.9)

❸ What are the properties of alcohols, ethers, alkyl halides, and thiols?

- Alcohols have a bent shape and polar C—O and O—H bonds, so they have a net dipole. Their OH bond allows for intermolecular hydrogen bonding between two alcohol molecules or between an alcohol molecule and water. As a result, alcohols have the

strongest intermolecular forces of the four families of molecules in this chapter. (14.2)
- Ethers have a bent shape and two polar C—O bonds, so they have a net dipole. (14.7)
- Alkyl halides with one halogen have one polar bond and a net dipole. (14.9)
- Thiols have a bent shape and lower boiling points than alcohols with the same number of carbons. (14.10)

❹ How are alcohols, ethers, alkyl halides, and thiols named?

- Alcohols are identified by the suffix -ol. (14.3)
- Ethers are named in two ways. Simple ethers are named by naming the alkyl groups bonded to the ether oxygen and adding the word *ether.* More complex ethers are named as *alkoxy alkanes;* that is, the simpler alkyl group is named as an alkoxy group (RO) bonded to an alkane. (14.7B)
- Alkyl halides are named as *halo alkanes;* that is, the halogen is named as a substituent (halo group) bonded to an alkane. (14.9B)
- Thiols are identified by the suffix -thiol. (14.10)

❺ What products are formed when an alcohol undergoes dehydration? (14.5A)

- Alcohols form alkenes on treatment with strong acid. The elements of H and OH are lost from two adjacent atoms and a new double bond is formed.
- Dehydration follows the Zaitsev rule: When more than one alkene can be formed, the major product of elimination is the alkene that has more alkyl groups bonded to it.

524   **Chapter 14**   Organic Compounds That Contain Oxygen, Halogen, or Sulfur

6 **What products are formed when an alcohol is oxidized? (14.5B)**
- Primary alcohols (RCH_2OH) are oxidized to aldehydes (RCHO), which are further oxidized to carboxylic acids (RCO_2H).
- Secondary alcohols (R_2CHOH) are oxidized to ketones.
- Tertiary alcohols have no C—H bond on the carbon with the OH group, so they are not oxidized.

7 **What product is formed when a thiol is oxidized? (14.10)**
- Thiols (RSH) are oxidized to disulfides (RSSR).
- Disulfides are reduced to thiols.

PROBLEMS

Selected in-chapter and odd-numbered end-of-chapter problems have brief answers in Appendix B. The *Student Study Guide and Solutions Manual* contains detailed solutions to all in-chapter and odd-numbered end-of-chapter problems, as well as additional worked examples and a chapter self-test.

Alcohols, Ethers, Alkyl Halides, and Thiols

14.23 Classify each alcohol as 1°, 2°, or 3°.

a. $CH_3CH_2CH_2OH$

b. $(CH_3CH_2)_3COH$

c.

d.

14.24 Classify each labeled alcohol in the anticancer drug doxorubicin (trade name Adriamycin) as 1°, 2°, or 3°.

doxorubicin

14.25 Classify each alkyl halide as 1°, 2°, or 3°.

a. $CH_3(CH_2)_5CHCH_3$
     |
     Cl

b. $CH_3CH_2CCH_2CH_3$
     |
     Cl
     (with CH₃ above)

c.

d.

14.26 Classify each halide in **A** as 1°, 2°, or 3°. **A** is a component of the red seaweed *C. hornemanni* found in Sri Lanka.

$CH_3C=CHCH_2CH_2CCH=CH_2$
(with CH₃ and CH₂Br and Cl substituents)

A

14.27 Draw the structure of a molecule that fits each description:
a. a 2° alcohol of molecular formula $C_6H_{14}O$
b. an ether with molecular formula $C_6H_{14}O$ that has a methyl group bonded to oxygen
c. a 3° alkyl halide with molecular formula $C_5H_{11}Br$

14.28 Draw the structure of a molecule that fits each description:
a. a 2° alcohol of molecular formula $C_6H_{12}O$
b. a cyclic ether with molecular formula $C_5H_{10}O$
c. a 1° alkyl halide with molecular formula $C_5H_{11}Cl$

14.29 Draw the structure of the six constitutional isomers of molecular formula $C_5H_{12}O$ that contain an ether as functional group.

14.30 Draw the structure of the four constitutional isomers of molecular formula $C_3H_6Br_2$.

Nomenclature

14.31 Draw the structure of 1-propanethiol, a compound partly responsible for the characteristic odor of onions.

©I. Rozenbaum & F. Cirou/PhotoAlto RF

14.32 Draw the structure of 3-methyl-1-butanethiol, which is partly responsible for the disagreeable odor of skunks.

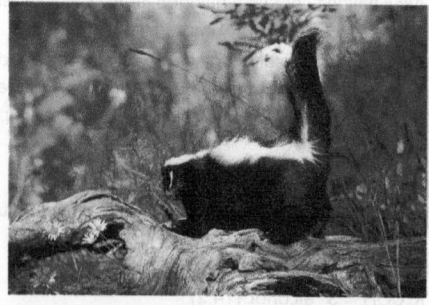

©Comstock/PunchStock RF

14.33 Name each molecule depicted in the ball-and-stick models.

a.   b.

14.34 Name each molecule depicted in the ball-and-stick models.

a.

b.

14.35 Answer each question about alcohol **A.**

A

a. Draw a condensed or skeletal structure for **A.**
b. Classify the hydroxyl group as 1°, 2°, or 3°.
c. Give the IUPAC name for **A.**

14.36 Answer each question about alcohol **B.**

B

a. Draw a skeletal structure for **B.**
b. Classify the hydroxyl group as 1°, 2°, or 3°.
c. Give the IUPAC name for **B.**

14.37 Give the IUPAC name for each alcohol.

a. CH₃CHCH₂CH₂CH₃ (with OH on carbon 2)

b. CH₃CHCCH₂CH₂CH₃ (with HO and CH₃, and CH₃)

c. (branched structure with OH)

d. (cyclohexane with HO and butyl group)

e. (cyclobutane with OH and dimethyl)

f. (cyclopentane with OH and two ethyl groups)

14.38 Give the IUPAC name for each alcohol.

a. CH₃CH₂CHCH₂CH₂CH(CH₃)₂ (with OH)

b. CH₃CH₂CH₂CHCH₂CH₃ (with CH₂OH)

c. CH₃(CH₂)₃CHCH₃ (with CH₂CH₂OH)

d. HO—(structure)—OH

e. (cyclopentane with OH and ethyl, methyl)

f. HO—(cyclohexane with two methyl groups)

14.39 Give the structure corresponding to each IUPAC name.
a. 3-hexanol
b. propyl alcohol
c. 2-methylcyclopropanol
d. 1,2-butanediol
e. 4,4,5-trimethyl-3-heptanol
f. 3,5-dimethyl-1-heptanol

14.40 Give the structure corresponding to each IUPAC name.
a. 3-methyl-3-pentanol
b. 4-methyl-2-pentanol
c. 2,4-dimethyl-2-hexanol
d. 1,3-propanediol
e. 3,5-dimethylcyclohexanol
f. 6,6-diethyl-4-nonanol

14.41 Give an acceptable name (IUPAC or common) for each ether.

a. CH₃CH₂OCH₂CH₂CH₂CH₃   c. (cyclopentane—O—CH₂CH₃)

b. CH₃CH₂CH₂CHCH₃ (with OCH₂CH₃)

14.42 Give an acceptable name (IUPAC or common) for each ether.

a. CH₃OCH₂CH₂CH₃   c. (cyclopropane—OCH₃)

b. (CH with OCH₃)

14.43 Draw the structures and give the IUPAC names for all constitutional isomers of molecular formula C₇H₁₆O that contain an OH group and have seven carbons in the longest chain.

14.44 Draw structures for the four constitutional isomers of molecular formula C₄H₁₀O that contain an OH group. Give the IUPAC name for each alcohol.

14.45 Give the IUPAC name for each alkyl halide and thiol.
a. (CH₃CH₂CH₂)₂CHBr   c. CH₃CH₂CH₂CH₂CH₂SH

b. (cyclobutane with Cl and methyl)

14.46 Give the IUPAC name for each alkyl halide and thiol.

a. CH₃CH₂CHCH₂CH(CH₂)₄CH₃ (with F and CH₂CH₃)   c. (CH₃)₂CHSH

b. (cyclopentane with Cl and ethyl)

14.47 Give the structure corresponding to each IUPAC name.
a. 2-methoxypropane
b. cyclobutyl ethyl ether
c. 1-ethoxy-2-ethylcyclohexane
d. butyl chloride
e. 2-methylcyclohexanethiol
f. 1-ethyl-2-fluorocyclobutane

526   **Chapter 14** Organic Compounds That Contain Oxygen, Halogen, or Sulfur

14.48 Give the structure corresponding to each IUPAC name.

a. dicyclohexyl ether

b. 2-ethoxy-2-methylpropane

c. propyl iodide

d. 3-methyl-1-pentanethiol

e. 1-chloro-2-methylpropane

f. 2-bromo-3-methylheptane

Physical Properties

14.49 Which compound in each pair has the higher boiling point?

a. $CH_3CH_2CH_2Cl$ or $CH_3CH_2CH_2I$

b. $CH_3CH_2CH_2OH$ or $HOCH_2CH_2OH$

c. $CH_3CH_2CH_2OH$ or $CH_3CH_2CH_2F$

14.50 Rank the compounds in order of increasing melting point: $CH_3CH_2CH_2CH_2OH$, $CH_3CH_2CH_2OH$, CH_3CH_2OH.

14.51 Rank the following compounds in order of increasing boiling point.

A   B   C

14.52 Rank the following compounds in order of increasing boiling point.

D   E   F

14.53 Explain the following observation. Dimethyl ether [$(CH_3)_2O$] and ethanol (CH_3CH_2OH) are both water-soluble compounds. The boiling point of ethanol (78 °C), however, is much higher than the boiling point of dimethyl ether (−24 °C).

14.54 Explain why 1,6-hexanediol [$HO(CH_2)_6OH$] is much more water soluble than 1-hexanol [$CH_3(CH_2)_5OH$].

14.55 Match compounds **A** and **B** to the observed boiling points: 118 °C and 98 °C. Explain your choice.

A   B

14.56 Name each compound and explain why one compound is water soluble and one is not water soluble.

X   Y

Reactions of Alcohols

14.57 Draw the products formed when each alcohol is dehydrated with H_2SO_4. Use the Zaitsev rule to predict the major product when a mixture forms.

a. [structure: cyclobutanol with OH]

b. [structure: 1-phenyl-1-propanol]

c. $CH_3CHCH_2CH_2CH_2CH_3$ with OH

d. $CH_3CH_2CCH_2CH_3$ with OH and CH_3

14.58 Draw the products formed when each alcohol is dehydrated with H_2SO_4. Use the Zaitsev rule to predict the major product when a mixture forms.

a. $(CH_3)_2CHCH_2CH_2CH_2OH$

b. $(CH_3CH_2)_3COH$

c. [structure: heptane chain with OH]

d. [structure: cyclopentane with CH_3 and OH]

14.59 Dehydration of 3-hexanol [$CH_3CH_2CH(OH)CH_2CH_2CH_3$] yields a mixture of two alkenes. (a) Draw the structures of both constitutional isomers formed. (b) Use the Zaitsev rule to explain why both products are formed in roughly equal amounts.

14.60 Dehydration of 3-methylcyclohexanol yields a mixture of two alkenes. (a) Draw the structures of both constitutional isomers formed. (b) Use the Zaitsev rule to explain why both products are formed in roughly equal amounts.

14.61 What alcohol is needed to form each alkene as a product of a dehydration reaction?

a. [structure: diphenyl–CH=CH– diphenyl]

b. [structure: cyclooctene]

14.62 What alcohol is needed to form each alkene as the major product of a dehydration reaction?

a. [structure: cyclohexene with two CH_3]

b. [structure: $(CH_3)_2C=C(CH_3)_2$]

14.63 Draw the products formed when each alcohol is oxidized with $K_2Cr_2O_7$. In some cases, no reaction occurs.

a. $CH_3(CH_2)_6CH_2OH$

b. $(CH_3CH_2)_2CHOH$

c. [structure with OH]

d. [structure with OH]

14.64 Draw the products formed when each alcohol is oxidized with $K_2Cr_2O_7$. In some cases, no reaction occurs.

a. [structure: cyclopentane with OH and methyl]

b. $CH_3(CH_2)_8CH_2OH$

c. [structure: cyclopentane with OH]

d. $(CH_3CH_2)_3COH$

14.65 Cortisol is an anti-inflammatory agent that also regulates carbohydrate metabolism. What oxidation product is formed when cortisol is treated with $K_2Cr_2O_7$?

cortisol

14.66 Xylitol is a nontoxic compound as sweet as table sugar but with only one-third the calories, so it is often used as a sweetening agent in gum and hard candy.

xylitol

a. Classify the OH groups as 1°, 2°, or 3°.
b. What product is formed when only the 1° OH groups are oxidized?
c. What product is formed when all of the OH groups are oxidized?

14.67 What alcohol starting material is needed to prepare each carbonyl compound as a product of an oxidation reaction?

a.   b.

14.68 What alcohol starting material is needed to prepare each carbonyl compound as a product of an oxidation reaction?

a.   b.

14.69 What products are formed when **X** is treated with each reagent: (a) H_2SO_4; (b) $K_2Cr_2O_7$?

X

14.70 What products are formed when **Y** is treated with each reagent: (a) H_2SO_4; (b) $K_2Cr_2O_7$?

Y

14.71 Draw the structure of an alcohol that forms only $CH_3CH_2CH_2CH_2CH_2CH=CH_2$ in a dehydration reaction, and yields $CH_3(CH_2)_5CO_2H$ on oxidation with $K_2Cr_2O_7$.

14.72 Draw the structure of an alcohol that forms only $(CH_3)_3CCH=CH_2$ in a dehydration reaction, and yields ketone **X** on oxidation with $K_2Cr_2O_7$.

X

14.73 An unknown alcohol of molecular formula $C_4H_{10}O$ forms only one alkene when treated with H_2SO_4. No reaction is observed when the alcohol is treated with an oxidizing agent. Draw the structure of the alcohol.

14.74 You have two test tubes, one containing $(CH_3CH_2)_3COH$ and one containing $CH_3(CH_2)_6OH$, but you do not know which alcohol is in which tube. Explain how treating the alcohols with an oxidizing agent like $K_2Cr_2O_7$ can help you to determine which test tube contains which alcohol.

Reactions of Thiols

14.75 What disulfide is formed when each thiol is oxidized?

a.   —SH   b. $CH_3(CH_2)_4SH$

14.76 As we will learn in Chapter 21, cysteine is a naturally occurring amino acid that contains a thiol group. What disulfide is formed when cysteine is oxidized?

cysteine

14.77 The smell of fried onions is in part determined by the two disulfides drawn below. What thiols are formed when each disulfide is reduced?

a. CH_3S—$SCH_2CH_2CH_3$ b. $CH_2=CHCH_2S$—$SCH_2CH_2CH_3$

14.78 Sometimes disulfide bonds occur in a ring. As we will learn in Chapter 21, these disulfide bonds play an important role in determining the shape and properties of proteins. What *di*thiol is formed when the following disulfide is reduced?

Applications

14.79 Diethyl ether [$(CH_3CH_2)_2O$] is an imperfect anesthetic in part because it readily combusts in air to form CO_2 and H_2O. Write a balanced equation for the complete combustion of diethyl ether.

14.80 Methanol (CH_3OH) is used as a fuel for some types of race cars, because it readily combusts in air to form CO_2 and H_2O. Write a balanced equation for the complete combustion of methanol.

14.81 With reference to the halogenated organic compounds called CFCs, HCFCs, and HFCs: (a) How do these compounds differ in structure? (b) How do these compounds differ in their interaction with ozone?

14.82 Give an example of a CFC and explain why the widespread use of CFCs has been detrimental to the environment.

14.83 As we learned in Chapter 13, polymers have very different properties depending (in part) on their functional groups. For example, poly(ethylene glycol) is commonly used in shampoos, where it forms viscous solutions in water. Poly(vinyl chloride), on the other hand, repels water and is used to make pipes and garden hoses. Discuss the water solubility of these polymers, and explain why there is a difference, even though both polymers have several polar bonds.

poly(ethylene glycol)
PEG

poly(vinyl chloride)
PVC

14.84 (a) Translate the ball-and-stick model of sevoflurane, an inhaled, sweet-smelling general anesthetic, into a complete structure with all atoms, bond lines, and lone pairs. (b) Give two reasons why halogenated ethers such as sevoflurane are now used in place of diethyl ether as anesthetics.

sevoflurane

14.85 Write out the chemical reaction that occurs when a breathalyzer test is carried out. How does this test give an indication of blood alcohol content?

14.86 2,3-Butanedione is commonly used to give microwave popcorn a buttery flavor. What diol is needed to prepare 2,3-butanedione by an oxidation reaction?

2,3-butanedione
(butter flavor)

14.87 In contrast to ethylene glycol ($HOCH_2CH_2OH$), which is extremely toxic, propylene glycol [$CH_3CH(OH)CH_2OH$] is nontoxic because it is oxidized in the body to a product formed during the metabolism of carbohydrates. What product is formed when propylene glycol is oxidized?

14.88 Lactic acid [$CH_3CH(OH)CO_2H$] gives sour milk its distinctive taste. What product is formed when lactic acid is oxidized by $K_2Cr_2O_7$?

14.89 Write out the chemical reactions that occur during the metabolism of ethanol. Explain how Antabuse is used in the treatment of alcoholism.

14.90 What chemical reactions occur when straight hair is made curly with a "permanent"?

General Questions

14.91 Explain why two ether molecules can't hydrogen bond to each other, but an ether molecule can hydrogen bond to a water molecule.

14.92 When an alcohol hydrogen bonds with water, two different hydrogen bonding interactions are possible. The oxygen atom of the alcohol (ROH) can hydrogen bond with a hydrogen atom of water, or a hydrogen atom of the alcohol can hydrogen bond to the oxygen atom of water. Illustrate both of these possibilities with CH_3CH_2OH.

14.93 Answer the following questions about alcohol **A.**

A

a. Give the IUPAC name.
b. Classify the alcohol as 1°, 2°, or 3°.
c. Draw the products formed when **A** is dehydrated with H_2SO_4.
d. What product is formed when **A** is oxidized with $K_2Cr_2O_7$?
e. Draw a constitutional isomer of **A** that contains an OH group.
f. Draw a constitutional isomer of **A** that contains an ether.

14.94 Answer the following questions about alcohol **B**.

B

a. Give the IUPAC name.

b. Classify the alcohol as 1°, 2°, or 3°.

c. Draw the products formed when **B** is dehydrated with H_2SO_4.

d. What product is formed when **B** is oxidized with $K_2Cr_2O_7$?

e. Draw a constitutional isomer of **B** that contains an OH group.

f. Draw a constitutional isomer of **B** that contains an ether.

CHALLENGE PROBLEMS

14.95 2-Methyl-1-butene can be formed by dehydrating two different alcohols (**A** and **B**) of molecular formula ($C_5H_{12}O$). When **A** undergoes dehydration, 2-methyl-1-butene is formed as the *only* product of dehydration. When alcohol **B** undergoes dehydration, two different alkenes are formed and 2-methyl-1-butene is formed as the *minor* product. (a) Identify the structures of **A** and **B**. (b) What is the major alkene formed when **B** undergoes dehydration?

14.96 Dehydration of alcohol **C** forms two products of molecular formula $C_{14}H_{12}$ that are isomers, but they are not constitutional isomers. Draw the structures of these two products.

C

Like helical seashells, many organic molecules possess handedness that determines their properties.
©PeskyMonkey/Getty Images RF

The Three-Dimensional Shape of Molecules

CHAPTER OUTLINE

15.1 Isomers—A Review

15.2 Looking Glass Chemistry—Molecules and Their Mirror Images

15.3 Chirality Centers

15.4 Chirality Centers in Cyclic Compounds

15.5 FOCUS ON HEALTH & MEDICINE: Chiral Drugs

15.6 Fischer Projections

15.7 Optical Activity

15.8 Compounds with Two or More Chirality Centers

15.9 FOCUS ON THE HUMAN BODY: The Sense of Smell

CHAPTER GOALS

In this chapter you will learn how to:

1. Recognize whether a molecule is chiral or achiral

2. Identify chirality centers

3. Draw two enantiomers in three dimensions around the chirality center

4. Explain why some chiral drugs have very different properties from their mirror images

5. Draw Fischer projection formulas

6. Compare the physical properties of enantiomers

7. Recognize the difference between enantiomers and diastereomers

8. Explain the relationship between the shape and odor of a molecule

Why Study
The Three-Dimensional
Shape of Molecules?

Are you left-handed or right-handed? If you're right-handed, you've probably spent little time thinking about your hand preference. If you're left-handed, though, you probably learned at an early age that many objects—like scissors and baseball gloves—"fit" for righties, but are "backwards" for lefties. **Hands, like many objects in the world around us, are mirror images that are *not* identical.** In Chapter 15 we examine the "handedness" of molecules, and ask, "How important is the three-dimensional shape of a molecule?"

15.1 Isomers—A Review

Chapter 15 concentrates on *stereochemistry*—that is, **the three-dimensional structure of molecules.** Since an understanding of isomers is needed in the discussion of stereochemistry, let's begin with an overview of isomers. Recall from Section 12.2:

• **Isomers are different compounds with the same molecular formula.**

There are two major classes of isomers: **constitutional isomers** (Section 12.2) and **stereoisomers** (Section 13.3).

• *Constitutional isomers* differ in the way the atoms are connected to one another.

Constitutional isomers have atoms bonded to *different* atoms. As a result, constitutional isomers have different IUPAC names. Constitutional isomers may have the same functional group or they may have different functional groups.

For example, 2-methylpentane and 3-methylpentane are constitutional isomers with molecular formula C_6H_{14}. 2-Methylpentane has a CH_3 group bonded to the second atom (C2) of a five-carbon chain, whereas 3-methylpentane has a CH_3 group bonded to the middle atom (C3) of a five-carbon chain. Both molecules are alkanes, so they both belong to the same family of organic compounds.

Constitutional isomers with the same functional group

CH_3 group at C2 CH_3 group at C3

$CH_3CHCH_2CH_2CH_3$ and $CH_3CH_2CHCH_2CH_3$
         | |
        CH_3 CH_3

2-methylpentane   **3**-methylpentane
C_6H_{14} C_6H_{14}

Ethanol and dimethyl ether are constitutional isomers with molecular formula C_2H_6O. Ethanol contains an O—H bond and dimethyl ether does not. Thus, the atoms are bonded to different atoms and these constitutional isomers have *different* functional groups. Dimethyl ether is an ether and ethanol is an alcohol.

Constitutional isomers with different functional groups

CH_3CH_2—O—H CH_3—O—CH_3

ethanol   dimethyl ether
C_2H_6O C_2H_6O

• *Stereoisomers* differ only in the three-dimensional arrangement of atoms.

Stereoisomers always have the *same* functional group, because they differ *only* in the way the atoms are oriented in space. Two stereoisomers need a prefix like cis or trans added to their IUPAC names to distinguish them. The cis and trans isomers of 2-butene are an example of stereoisomers. Each stereoisomer of 2-butene contains the same sequence of atoms. The only difference is the three-dimensional arrangement of the two methyl groups on the double bond.

One example of stereoisomers—Isomers at a double bond

$$CH_3 \quad CH_3 \qquad\qquad CH_3 \quad H$$
$$C=C \qquad\qquad\qquad C=C$$
$$H \quad\quad H \qquad\qquad H \quad\quad CH_3$$

cis-2-butene   *trans*-2-butene

- The *cis* isomer of 2-butene has the two CH_3 groups on the same side of the double bond.
- The *trans* isomer of 2-butene has the two CH_3 groups on opposite sides of the double bond.

Cis and trans isomers on a carbon–carbon double bond are one example of stereoisomers. In Section 15.2, we learn about another type of stereoisomer that occurs at a tetrahedral carbon.

PROBLEM 15.1

Classify each pair of compounds as identical molecules, constitutional isomers, or stereoisomers.

a. $CH_3CH_2CHCHCH_3$ and $CH_3CHCH_2CHCH_3$
   with CH_3 on the first and CH_3, CH_3

b.
$$CH_3CH_2 \quad CH_3 \qquad CH_3CH_2 \quad H$$
$$C=C \qquad\qquad C=C$$
$$H \quad\quad H \qquad\qquad H \quad\quad CH_3$$

c. $CH_2=CHCH_2CH_2CH_3$ and $CH_3CH_2CH_2CH=CH_2$

d. [cyclobutane with O] and [cyclopropane]—OH

SAMPLE PROBLEM 15.1 IDENTIFYING ISOMERS FROM SKELETAL REPRESENTATIONS

Label each pair of compounds as stereoisomers, constitutional isomers, or identical molecules:
(a) **A** and **B**; (b) **A** and **C**.

A   B   C

Analysis

- Constitutional isomers have **atoms bonded to *different* atoms.**
- Stereoisomers differ *only* in the three-dimensional arrangement of atoms, so **atoms are bonded to the *same* atoms.**

Solution

a. Compounds **A** and **B** are constitutional isomers because **A** and **B** have the same molecular formula (C_6H_{12}), but the atoms are bonded to different atoms. **A** is an alkene and **B** is a cycloalkane.

b. Compounds **A** and **C** are stereoisomers because all the atoms are bonded to the same atoms, but the arrangement of groups on the carbon–carbon double bond is different. In **A**, the CH_3CH_2 groups are on opposite sides of the line joining the carbons of the double bond, making them trans. In **C**, the CH_3CH_2 groups are on the same side of the line joining the atoms of the double bond, making them cis.

A   C
trans isomer   cis isomer

PRACTICE PROBLEM 15.1

Label each pair of compounds as stereoisomers, constitutional isomers, or identical molecules:
(a) **A** and **B**; (b) **A** and **C**; (c) **A** and **D**.

A   **B**   **C**   **D**

PROBLEM 15.2

For *trans*-2-hexene: (a) draw a stereoisomer; (b) draw a constitutional isomer that contains a carbon–carbon double bond; (c) draw a constitutional isomer that does not contain a carbon–carbon double bond.

15.2   Looking Glass Chemistry—Molecules and Their Mirror Images

To learn more about stereoisomers that occur at tetrahedral carbon atoms, we must turn our attention to molecules and their mirror images. **Everything, including molecules, has a mirror image.** What's important in chemistry is **whether a molecule is *identical* to or *different* from its mirror image.**

15.2A   What It Means to Be Chiral or Achiral

Some molecules are like hands. **Left and right hands are mirror images of each other, but they are *not* identical.** If you try to mentally place one hand inside the other hand you can never superimpose either all the fingers, or the tops and palms. To *superimpose* an object on its mirror image means to align *all* parts of the object with its mirror image. With molecules, this means aligning all atoms and all bonds.

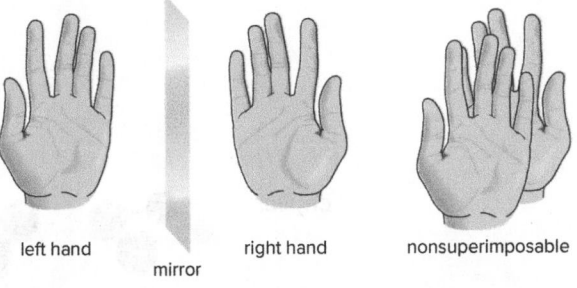

left hand   right hand   nonsuperimposable

mirror

- A molecule (or object) that is *not* superimposable on its mirror image is said to be *chiral*.

Other molecules are like socks. **Two socks from a pair are mirror images that *are* superimposable.** One sock can fit inside another, aligning toes and heels, and tops and bottoms. A sock and its mirror image are *identical*.

mirror   superimposable

- A molecule (or object) that *is* superimposable on its mirror image is said to be *achiral*.

The dominance of right-handedness over left-handedness occurs in all races and cultures. Despite this fact, even identical twins can exhibit differences in hand preference. Pictured as infants are Zachary (left-handed) and Matthew (right-handed), identical twin sons of the author. ©*Daniel C. Smith*

The adjective *chiral* (pronounced ky-rel) comes from the Greek *cheir*, meaning *hand*. Left and right hands are **chiral:** they are mirror images that do not superimpose on each other.

PROBLEM 15.3

Classify each object as chiral or achiral.

a.   b.   c.   d.

15.2B The Chirality of Molecules

Let's determine whether three molecules—H_2O, CH_2BrCl, and $CHBrClF$—are superimposable on their mirror images; that is, **are H_2O, CH_2BrCl, and $CHBrClF$ chiral or achiral?**

To test **chirality**—that is, to test whether a molecule and its mirror image are identical or different:

1. Draw the molecule in three dimensions.
2. Draw its mirror image.
3. Try to align all bonds and atoms. To superimpose a molecule and its mirror image, you can perform any rotation but you cannot break bonds.

Following this procedure, H_2O and CH_2BrCl are both **achiral** molecules: each molecule is superimposable on its mirror image.

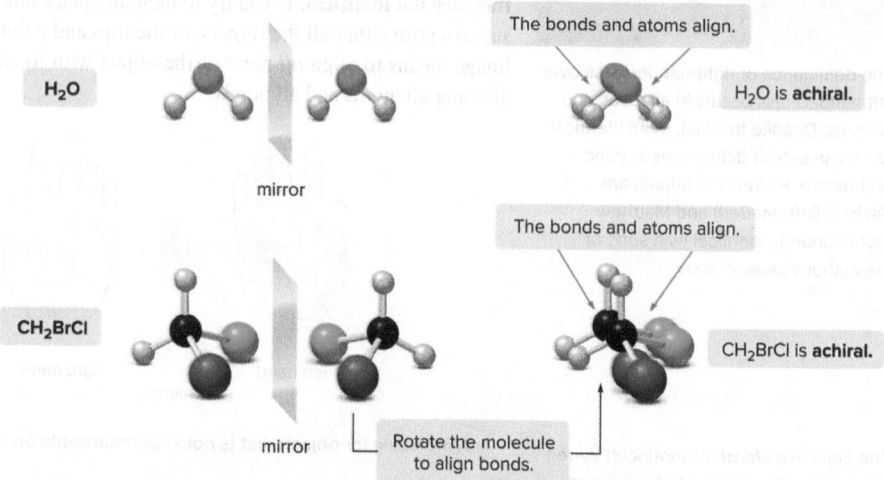

With $CHBrClF$, the result is different. The molecule (labeled **A**) and its mirror image (labeled **B**) are not superimposable. No matter how you rotate **A** and **B**, all of the atoms never align. **$CHBrClF$ is thus a chiral molecule,** and **A** and **B** are different compounds.

A and **B** are **stereoisomers** because they are isomers differing only in the three-dimensional arrangement of substituents. They represent a new type of stereoisomer that occurs at tetrahedral carbon atoms. These stereoisomers are called *enantiomers.*

- **Enantiomers are mirror images that are not superimposable.**

CHBrClF contains a carbon atom bonded to four different groups. **A carbon atom bonded to four different groups is called a *chirality center*.**

We have now learned two related but different concepts, and it is necessary to distinguish between them.

- **A molecule that is not superimposable on its mirror image is a *chiral molecule*.**
- **A carbon atom surrounded by four different groups is a *chirality center*.**

CHBrClF is a chiral molecule because it is not superimposable on its mirror image. CHBrClF contains one chirality center, one carbon atom bonded to four different groups. Molecules can contain zero, one, or more chirality centers.

15.2C   Chirality in Nature

Why must we study a topic like stereochemistry that may seem so esoteric? In truth, chirality pervades our existence. On a molecular level, many biological molecules discussed in Chapters 19–22 are chiral. On a macroscopic level, many naturally occurring objects possess handedness. Examples include helical seashells shaped like right-handed screws, and plants such as honeysuckle that wind in a left-handed helix (Figure 15.1). The human body is chiral, and hands, feet, and ears are not superimposable.

PROBLEM 15.4

Explain the difference between the terms *chiral* and *chirality center.*

> Naming a carbon atom with four different groups is a topic that currently has no firm agreement among organic chemists. IUPAC recommends the term *chirality center,* and so this is the term used in this text. Other terms in common use are chiral center, chiral carbon, asymmetric carbon, and stereogenic center.

Figure 15.1   Chirality in Nature

a.

b.

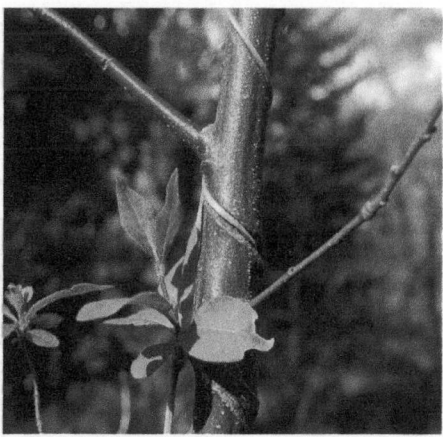

a. Many types of snails possess a chiral, right-handed helical shell. When a right-handed shell is held in the right hand with the thumb pointing toward the wider end, the opening is on the right side.

b. Plants like honeysuckle wind in a chiral left-handed helix.

(a): ©McGraw-Hill Education/Jill Braaten, photographer; (b): ©biosphoto/Claude Thouvenin

15.3   Chirality Centers

A necessary skill in studying the three-dimensional structure of molecules is the ability to locate and draw chirality centers—carbon atoms bonded to four different groups.

15.3A   Locating Chirality Centers

To locate a chirality center, examine each **tetrahedral** carbon atom in a molecule, and look at the four *groups*—not the four *atoms*—bonded to it. CBrClFI has one chirality center because its carbon atom is bonded to four different elements—Br, Cl, F, and I. 3-Bromohexane also has one chirality center because one carbon is bonded to H, Br, CH_2CH_3, and $CH_2CH_2CH_3$. We consider all atoms in a group as a *whole unit,* not just the atom directly bonded to the carbon in question.

chirality center

chirality center
3-bromohexane

This C is bonded to: H
Br
CH_2CH_3
$CH_2CH_2CH_3$
two *different* alkyl groups

Keep in mind the following:

- A carbon atom bonded to two or more like groups is *never* a chirality center. CH_2 and CH_3 groups have more than one H atom bonded to the same carbon, so each of these carbons is *never* a chirality center.
- A carbon that is part of a multiple bond does not have four groups around it, so it can *never* be a chirality center.

SAMPLE PROBLEM 15.2 LOCATING CHIRALITY CENTERS

Locate the chirality center in each drug. Penicillamine is used to treat Wilson's disease, a genetic disorder that leads to a buildup of copper in the liver, kidneys, and the brain. Albuterol is a bronchodilator—that is, it widens air passages—so it is used to treat asthma.

a. penicillamine

b. albuterol

Analysis

In compounds with many C's, look at each C individually and eliminate those C's that can't be chirality centers. Thus, omit all CH_2 and CH_3 groups and all multiply bonded C's. Check all remaining C's to see if they are bonded to four different groups.

Solution

a. The CH_3 groups and COOH group in penicillamine are not chirality centers. One C is bonded to two CH_3 groups, so it can be eliminated from consideration as well. This leaves one C with four different groups bonded to it.

b. In albuterol, omit all CH_2 and CH_3 groups and all C's that are part of a double bond. Also omit from consideration the one C bonded to three CH_3 groups. This leaves one C with four different groups bonded to it.

penicillamine

chirality center

albuterol

chirality center

PRACTICE PROBLEM 15.2

Label the chirality center in the given molecules. The compounds contain zero or one chirality center.

a. $CH_3CHCH_2CH_3$
        |
        Cl

b. $(CH_3)_3CH$

c. $CH_2{=}CHCHCH_3$
                    |
                    OH

d.

More Practice: Try Problems 15.29a, b; 15.30a, b; 15.63a; 15.64a; 15.65a; 15.66a.

PROBLEM 15.5

Locate the chirality center in the carbohydrate erythrulose, an ingredient in sunless tanning agents.

erythrulose

Larger organic molecules can have two, three, or even hundreds of chirality centers. Tartaric acid, isolated from grapes, and ephedrine, isolated from the herb ma huang (used to treat respiratory ailments in traditional Chinese medicine), each have two chirality centers. Once a popular drug to promote weight loss and enhance athletic performance, ephedrine use has now been linked to episodes of sudden death, heart attack, and stroke.

tartaric acid

ephedrine
(bronchodilator, decongestant)

[Chirality centers are labeled in blue.]

©FoodCollection/StockFood RF

©WILDLIFE GmbH/Alamy

PROBLEM 15.6

Label the chirality centers in each molecule. Compounds may have one or two chirality centers.

a.
                        H
                        |
$CH_3CH_2CH_2{-}C{-}CH_3$
                        |
                        OH

b.
          COOH
          |
$H_2N{-}C{-}H$
          |
          $CH_3{-}C{-}H$
                  |
                  CH_2CH_3

c.
                Br   Cl
                | |
$CH_3CH_2{-}C{-}CH_2CH_2{-}C{-}CH_3$
                | |
                H   H

In locating chirality centers in skeletal structures, always remember that **each carbon has enough hydrogens to make it tetravalent.** 2-Chloropentane has one chirality center, because C2 is bonded to four different groups—H, CH_3, $CH_2CH_2CH_3$, and Cl.

Cl   chirality center

2-chloropentane

H Cl

C2 is bonded to four
different groups.

SAMPLE PROBLEM 15.3 LOCATING CHIRALITY CENTERS IN SKELETAL STRUCTURES

Label the chirality center in the antidepressant fluoxetine (trade name Prozac).

fluoxetine

Analysis

- In skeletal structures, remember that H's are understood and that each C has enough H's to make it tetravalent.
- Omit all CH_2 and CH_3 groups, as well as all C's that are part of a multiple bond.
- Check the remaining C's to see if they are bonded to four different groups.

Solution

In fluoxetine, omit all C's that are part of a multiple bond or bonded to identical groups. That leaves only one C that is bonded to four different groups.

This C is bonded to 1 H.   chirality center

PRACTICE PROBLEM 15.3

Locate the chirality center in the antihistamine brompheniramine.

brompheniramine

More Practice: Try Problems 15.28, 15.30d, 15.62a.

PROBLEM 15.7

Translate the ball-and-stick model to a shorthand structure, and label the two chirality centers in vitamin K. Vitamin K is essential to blood clot formation. A deficiency of this vitamin may lead to excessive and often fatal bleeding.

vitamin K

15.3B Drawing a Pair of Enantiomers

How are chirality centers related to chiral molecules?

> • **Any molecule with one chirality center is a chiral compound.**

Recall from Section 15.2 that a **chiral compound is not superimposable on its mirror image,** and that these mirror image isomers are called **enantiomers.** Let's learn how to draw two enantiomers using 2-butanol [$CH_3CH(OH)CH_2CH_3$], a compound with one chirality center, as an example.

How To Draw Two Enantiomers of a Chiral Compound

Example: Draw two enantiomers of 2-butanol in three dimensions around the chirality center.

H ——— chirality center
|
CH_3—C—CH_2CH_3
|
OH
2-butanol

Step [1] **Draw one enantiomer by arbitrarily placing the four different groups on any bond to the chirality center.**

• Use the convention learned in Section 11.3 for drawing a tetrahedron: **place two bonds in the plane, one in front of the plane on a wedge, and one behind the plane on a dashed wedge.**

• Arbitrarily place the four groups—H, OH, CH_3, and CH_2CH_3—on any bond to the chirality center, forming enantiomer **A.**

Draw the bonds: Add the groups:

CH_3
|
CH_3CH_2—C''''H
OH

= [ball-and-stick model] —— chirality center

A

Step [2] **Draw a mirror plane and arrange the substituents in the mirror image so that they are a reflection of the groups in the first molecule.**

• Place the four groups—H, OH, CH_3, and CH_2CH_3—on the chirality center in the mirror image to form enantiomer **B.**

• **A** and **B** are mirror images, but no matter how **A** and **B** are rotated their bonds do not align, so **A** and **B** are chiral compounds.

Draw the molecule...then the mirror image.

A   **B**

mirror
not superimposable

enantiomers

The foul odor of human sweat is due in part to the presence of unequal amounts of both enantiomers of 3-methyl-3-sulfanyl-1-hexanol (Problem 15.9).
©Andersen Ross/Blend Images LLC RF

PROBLEM 15.8

Locate the chirality center in each compound and draw both enantiomers.

a. $CH_3CHCH_2CH_3$
          |
          Cl

b. $CH_3CH_2CHCH_2OH$
              |
              OH

PROBLEM 15.9

Although fresh human sweat has no odor, enzymes in skin bacteria form a variety of compounds with distinctive, pungent odors. The two enantiomers of 3-methyl-3-sulfanyl-1-hexanol (**A**), which smell somewhat differently, contribute to the characteristic foul odor of sweat. Locate the chirality center in **A** and draw both enantiomers.

$$ HOCH_2CH_2 \overset{\overset{\displaystyle CH_3}{|}}{\underset{\underset{\displaystyle SH}{|}}{C}} CH_2CH_2CH_3 $$

A

15.4   Chirality Centers in Cyclic Compounds

Chirality centers may also occur at carbon atoms that are part of a ring. To find chirality centers on ring carbons, always draw the rings as flat polygons, and look for tetrahedral carbons that are bonded to four different groups, as usual.

15.4A   Locating Chirality Centers on Ring Carbons

Does methylcyclopentane have a chirality center?

Is C1 a chirality center?

methylcyclopentane   two identical groups on C1   **NO,** C1 is **not** a chirality center.

All of the carbon atoms are bonded to two or three hydrogen atoms except for C1, the ring carbon bonded to the methyl group. Next, compare the ring atoms and bonds on both sides the same distance from C1, and continue until a point of difference is reached, or until both sides meet. In this case, there is no point of difference on either side, so C1 is considered to be bonded to identical alkyl groups that happen to be part of a ring. **C1 is therefore *not* a chirality center.**

With 3-methylcyclohexene, the result is different.

Is C3 a chirality center?

These 2 C's are different.

3-methylcyclohexene   **YES,** C3 is a chirality center.

All carbon atoms are bonded to two or three hydrogen atoms or are part of a double bond except for C3, the ring carbon bonded to the methyl group. In this case, the atoms equidistant from C3 are different, so C3 is considered to be bonded to *different* alkyl groups in the ring. **C3 is therefore bonded to four different groups, making it a chirality center.**

Since 3-methylcyclohexene has one tetrahedral chirality center, it is a chiral compound, and exists as a pair of enantiomers. Substituents above and below the ring are drawn with wedges and dashed wedges.

Sample Problem 15.4 illustrates how to draw an enantiomer and constitutional isomer for a compound that contains a chirality center on a ring.

SAMPLE PROBLEM 15.4 DRAWING AN ENANTIOMER AND A CONSTITUTIONAL ISOMER

Consider proline, one of the 20 naturally occurring amino acids. (a) Draw the enantiomer of proline. (b) Draw a constitutional isomer of proline.

proline

Analysis and Solution

a. To draw an enantiomer, draw a mirror plane, and arrange the substituents in the mirror image so that they are a reflection of the groups in the first molecule. In drawing the mirror image of proline, keep the CO_2H group on a wedge and the H atom bonded to the chirality center on a dashed wedge.

proline   enantiomer

b. To draw a constitutional isomer, draw a molecule with the same molecular formula, but have atoms bonded to different atoms. One possible constitutional isomer has the CO_2H group bonded to a different carbon of the ring.

Move CO_2H

proline
$C_5H_9NO_2$

constitutional isomer
$C_5H_9NO_2$

PRACTICE PROBLEM 15.4

(a) Draw the enantiomer of (R)-limonene, a compound isolated from oranges. (b) Draw a constitutional isomer of (R)-limonene.

(R)-limonene

More Practice: Try Problems 15.35; 15.36; 15.61b; 15.63b; 15.64b; 15.65b, d; 15.66b.

542 **Chapter 15** The Three-Dimensional Shape of Molecules

PROBLEM 15.10

Label the chirality centers in each compound. A molecule may have zero, one, or two chirality centers.

a. [cyclohexene ring with —OH]   b. [benzene ring with CH₂CH₃]   c. [cyclobutane ring with Cl and Cl]

PROBLEM 15.11

Label the two chirality centers in sertraline, the generic name for the antidepressant Zoloft.

CH₃NH— [sertraline structure with Cl, Cl]

sertraline

15.4B FOCUS ON HEALTH & MEDICINE
The Unforgettable Legacy of Thalidomide

Many biologically active compounds contain one or more chirality centers on ring carbons. For example, **thalidomide,** which contains one such chirality center, was once used as a sedative and anti-nausea drug for pregnant women in Europe and Great Britain from 1959 to 1962.

Two enantiomers of thalidomide

chirality center [thalidomide enantiomer structures] chirality center

anti-nausea drug   teratogen

Unfortunately, thalidomide was sold as a mixture of its two enantiomers, and each of these stereoisomers has a different biological activity, a property not uncommon to chiral drugs, as we will see in Section 15.5. While one enantiomer has the desired therapeutic effect, the other enantiomer was responsible for thousands of catastrophic birth defects in children born to women who took the drug during pregnancy. Thalidomide was never approved for use in the United States due to the diligence of Frances Oldham Kelsey, a medical reviewing officer for the Food and Drug Administration, who insisted that the safety data on thalidomide were inadequate.

PROBLEM 15.12

Label the two chirality centers in captopril, a drug used to treat high blood pressure.

HS— [captopril structure with OH, O, N]

captopril

15.5 FOCUS ON HEALTH & MEDICINE
Chiral Drugs

A living organism is a sea of chiral molecules. Many drugs are chiral, and often they must interact with a chiral receptor to be effective. One enantiomer of a drug may be effective in treating a disease whereas its mirror image may be ineffective.

Why should such a difference in biological activity be observed? For an everyday analogy, consider what happens when you are given a right-handed glove. A glove is a chiral object, and your right and left hands are also chiral—they are mirror images that are not identical. Only your right hand can fit inside a right glove, not your left. Thus, the glove's utility depends on the hand—either it fits or it doesn't fit.

The same phenomenon is observed with drugs that must interact with a chiral receptor in a cell. One enantiomer "fits" the receptor and evokes a specific response. Its mirror image doesn't fit the same receptor, making it ineffective; or if it "fits" another receptor, it can evoke a totally different response. Figure 15.2 schematically illustrates this difference in binding between two enantiomers and a chiral receptor.

Figure 15.2   The Interaction of Two Enantiomers with a Chiral Receptor

One enantiomer of the amino acid phenylalanine, labeled **A,** has three groups that can interact with the appropriate binding sites of the chiral receptor. The groups around the chirality center in the mirror image **B,** however, can never be arranged so that all three groups can bind to these same three binding sites. Thus, enantiomer **B** does not "fit" the same receptor, so it does not evoke the same response.

15.5A   Chiral Pain Relievers

Ibuprofen and naproxen are nonsteroidal anti-inflammatory drugs (NSAIDs) that illustrate how two enantiomers can have different biological activities. Both drugs are common over-the-counter remedies that relieve pain and fever, and reduce inflammation.

Ibuprofen is the generic name for the pain relievers known as Motrin and Advil. Ibuprofen has one chirality center and thus exists as a pair of enantiomers. Only one enantiomer, labeled **A,** is an active anti-inflammatory agent. Its enantiomer **B** is inactive. **B,** however, is slowly converted

544   **Chapter 15**   The Three-Dimensional Shape of Molecules

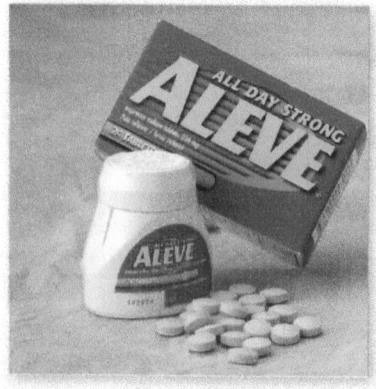
to **A** in the body. Ibuprofen is sold as a mixture of both enantiomers. **An equal mixture of two enantiomers is called a** *racemic mixture* (pronounced ra-see′-mik).

ibuprofen
active anti-inflammatory agent
A

inactive enantiomer
B

One enantiomer of **naproxen,** the pain reliever in Naprosyn and Aleve, is an active anti-inflammatory agent, but its enantiomer is a harmful liver toxin. Changing the orientation of two substituents to form a mirror image can thus alter biological activity to produce an undesirable side effect in the other enantiomer.

naproxen
active anti-inflammatory agent
A

enantiomer
liver toxin
B

These examples illustrate the benefit of marketing a chiral drug as a single active enantiomer. In these instances it should be possible to use smaller doses with fewer side effects, yet many chiral drugs continue to be sold as racemic mixtures, because it is more difficult and therefore more costly to obtain a single enantiomer.

The Food and Drug Administration has encouraged the development of so-called *racemic switches,* the patenting and marketing of a single enantiomer that was originally sold as a racemic mixture. To obtain a new patent on a single enantiomer, however, a company must show evidence that it provides significant benefit over the racemic mixture.

PROBLEM 15.13

Propranolol (trade name Inderal) is used in the treatment of high blood pressure and heart disease. (a) Locate the chirality center in propranolol. (b) Draw both enantiomers of propranolol. Only one of these enantiomers is biologically active.

propranolol

15.5B Parkinson's Disease and L-Dopa

L-Dopa was first isolated from the seeds of the broad bean *Vicia faba,* and since 1967 it has been the drug of choice for the treatment of Parkinson's disease. L-Dopa is a chiral molecule with one chirality center. Unlike ibuprofen, which is still marketed as a racemic mixture, L-dopa, also called levodopa, is sold as a single enantiomer. Like many chiral drugs, only one enantiomer is active against Parkinson's disease. The inactive enantiomer is also responsible for neutropenia, a decrease in certain white blood cells that help to fight infection.

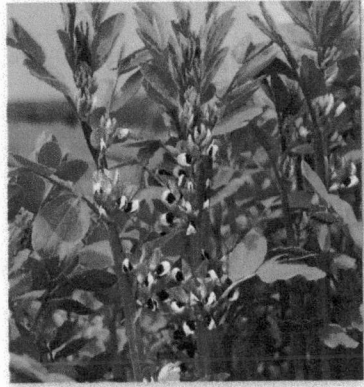

The broad bean *Vicia faba* produces the drug L-dopa. To meet the large demand for L-dopa today, the commercially available drug is synthesized in the laboratory.
©Nigel Cattlin/Alamy

L-dopa
active against
Parkinson's disease

D-dopa
enantiomer responsible for
undesired side effects

Parkinson's disease, which afflicts 1.5 million individuals in the United States, results from the degeneration of neurons that produce the neurotransmitter dopamine in the brain. Dopamine affects brain processes that control movement and emotions, so proper dopamine levels are needed to maintain an individual's mental and physical health. When the level of dopamine drops, the loss of motor control symptomatic of Parkinson's disease results.

L-Dopa is an oral medication that is transported to the brain by the bloodstream. In the brain it is converted to dopamine (Figure 15.3). Dopamine itself cannot be given as a medication because it cannot pass from the bloodstream into the brain; that is, it does not cross the blood–brain barrier.

Figure 15.3   L-Dopa, Dopamine, and Parkinson's Disease

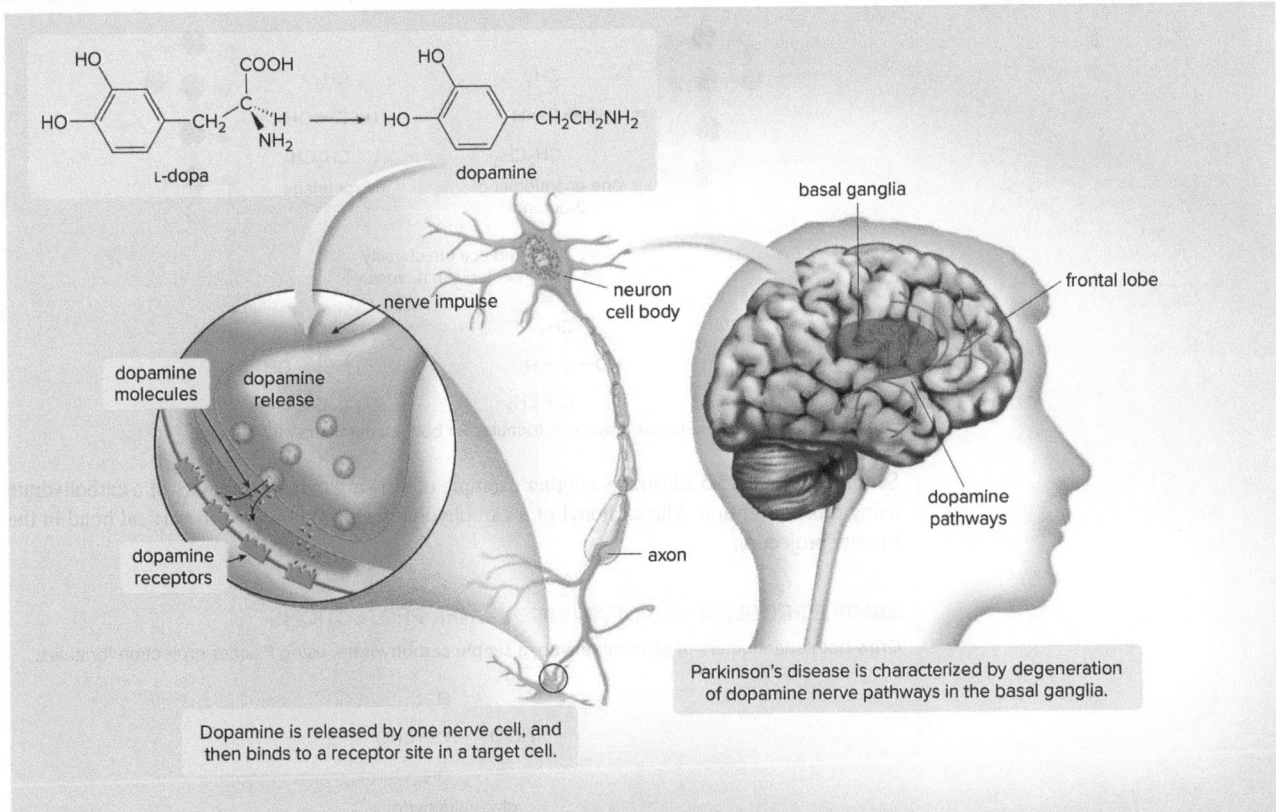

L-dopa ⟶ dopamine

nerve impulse

neuron
cell body

basal ganglia

frontal lobe

dopamine
molecules

dopamine
release

dopamine pathways

dopamine
receptors

axon

Parkinson's disease is characterized by degeneration of dopamine nerve pathways in the basal ganglia.

Dopamine is released by one nerve cell, and then binds to a receptor site in a target cell.

15.6 Fischer Projections

The chirality centers in some organic compounds, most notably carbohydrates (Chapter 20), are often drawn using a different convention than is used for other chirality centers.

Instead of drawing a tetrahedron with two bonds in the plane, one in front of the plane, and one behind it, the **tetrahedron is tipped so that both horizontal bonds come forward (drawn on wedges) and both vertical bonds go behind (on dashed wedges).** This structure is then abbreviated by a **cross formula,** also called a **Fischer projection formula.** In a Fischer projection formula, therefore,

Draw a tetrahedron as: Abbreviate it as a cross formula:

Horizontal bonds come forward, on wedges.   Z—C—X   =   Z—|—X

Vertical bonds go back, on dashed wedges.   Fischer projection formula   chirality center

- A carbon atom is located at the intersection of the two lines of the cross.
- The horizontal bonds come forward, on wedges.
- The vertical bonds go back, on dashed wedges.

For example, to draw the chirality center of 2-butanol [$CH_3CH(OH)CH_2CH_3$, Section 15.3B] using this convention, **draw the tetrahedron with horizontal bonds on wedges and vertical bonds on dashed wedges.** Then, **replace the chirality center with a cross** to draw the Fischer projection. The carbon skeleton is often drawn vertically.

Fischer projection formulas for both enantiomers of 2-butanol

Sample Problem 15.5 illustrates another example of drawing two enantiomers of a carbohydrate using this convention. The carbonyl of a carbohydrate is placed on the top vertical bond in the Fischer projection.

SAMPLE PROBLEM 15.5 DRAWING FISCHER PROJECTIONS

Draw both enantiomers of glyceraldehyde, a simple carbohydrate, using Fischer projection formulas.

$$HOCH_2—\underset{\underset{\displaystyle OH}{|}}{\overset{\overset{\displaystyle H}{|}}{C}}—CHO$$

glyceraldehyde

Analysis

- **Draw the tetrahedron of one enantiomer with the horizontal bonds on wedges, and the vertical bonds on dashed wedges.** Arrange the four groups on the chirality center—H, OH, CHO, and CH$_2$OH—arbitrarily in the first enantiomer.
- Draw the second enantiomer by arranging the substituents in the mirror image so that they are a reflection of the groups in the first molecule.
- Replace the chirality center with a cross to draw the Fischer projections.

Solution

Draw the compound.

Then, draw the mirror image.

- Horizontal bonds come forward.
- Vertical bonds go back.

Fischer projection of one enantiomer

Fischer projection of the second enantiomer

PRACTICE PROBLEM 15.5

Convert each molecule into a Fischer projection formula.

a. H►C◄Br with CH$_3$ up and Cl down

b. H►C◄OH with COOH up and CH$_2$Cl down

More Practice: Try Problems 15.43–15.46.

PROBLEM 15.14

Convert each Fischer projection formula into a representation that uses wedges and dashed wedges.

a. CH$_3$CH$_2$—C—Br with CH$_3$ up and Cl down

b. CH$_3$CH$_2$—C—CH$_3$ with H up and NH$_2$ down

PROBLEM 15.15

Draw Fischer projections of both enantiomers for each compound.

a. CH$_3$CHCH$_2$CH$_2$CH$_3$ with OH

b. CH$_3$CH$_2$CHCH$_2$Cl with Cl

15.7 Optical Activity

15.7A   The Physical Properties of Enantiomers

How do the physical properties of enantiomers compare?

- Two enantiomers have identical physical properties—melting point, boiling point, and solubility—except for how they interact with plane-polarized light.

What is **plane-polarized light?** Ordinary light consists of waves that oscillate in all planes at right angles to the direction in which the light travels. Passing light through a device called a polarizer allows light in only one plane to come through. This is plane-polarized light and it consists of light waves in a single plane.

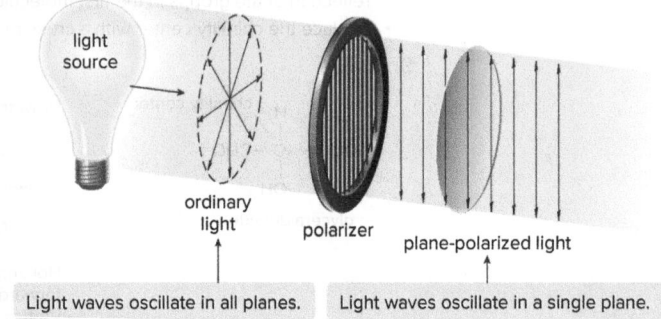

A **polarimeter** is an instrument that allows plane-polarized light to travel through a sample tube containing an organic compound. After the light exits the sample tube, an analyzer slit is rotated to determine the direction of the plane of the polarized light exiting the sample tube.

- An achiral compound does not change the direction of the plane-polarized light and is said to be *optically inactive.*
- A chiral compound rotates the plane of polarized light through an angle α, measured in degrees (°). A compound that rotates plane-polarized light is said to be *optically active.*

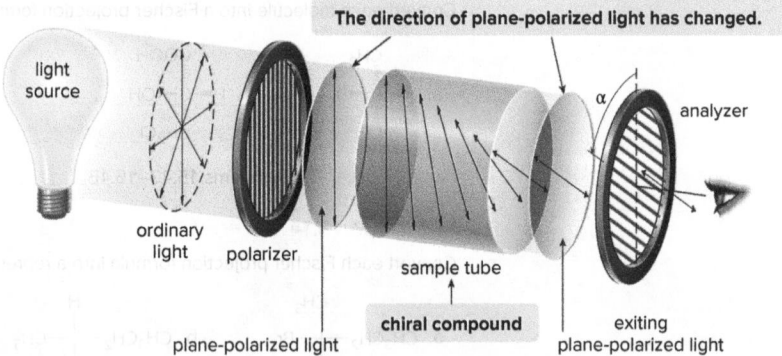

For example, the achiral compound CH_2BrCl is optically *inactive,* whereas a single enantiomer of CHBrClF, a chiral compound, is optically *active.*

The rotation of polarized light can be in the **clockwise** or **counterclockwise** direction.

- If the rotation is *clockwise,* the compound is called *dextrorotatory* and is labeled as the (+)-enantiomer.
- If the rotation is *counterclockwise,* the compound is called *levorotatory* and is labeled as the (−)-enantiomer.

How does the rotation of two enantiomers compare?

- Two enantiomers rotate plane-polarized light *to an equal extent* but in the *opposite* direction.

Thus, if enantiomer **A** rotates polarized light +5°, then the same concentration of enantiomer **B** rotates it −5°. Enantiomer **A** is dextrorotatory, whereas enantiomer **B** is levorotatory.

PROBLEM 15.16

Label each compound as optically active or optically inactive.

a. $CH_3(CH_2)_6CH_3$

b.
COOH
CH₃—C⋯H
OH

c.
CH₃
CH₃—C⋯H
OH

d.

PROBLEM 15.17

Suppose a sample tube contained an equal amount of two enantiomers. Would you expect this solution to be optically active or optically inactive?

15.7B   Specific Rotation

The observed rotation of an optically active sample depends on the number of chiral molecules that interact with polarized light. This depends on the concentration of the sample and the length of the sample tube. To standardize data, the quantity **specific rotation** ($[\alpha]$) is defined using a specific sample tube length (usually 10 cm), concentration (reported in g/mL), temperature (25 °C), and wavelength. A specific rotation is reported as a positive (+) or negative (−) value without units.

For example, naturally occurring (S)-glyceraldehyde has a specific rotation of −8.7, while its enantiomer, (R)-glyceraldehyde, has a specific rotation of +8.7.

CHO
HOCH₂—C⋯H
OH

(S)-glyceraldehyde
$[\alpha]$ = −8.7
levorotatory

CHO
H⋯C—CH₂OH
HO

(R)-glyceraldehyde
$[\alpha]$ = +8.7
dextrorotatory

SAMPLE PROBLEM 15.6 COMPARING THE PHYSICAL PROPERTIES OF ENANTIOMERS

The specific rotation of camphor, an aromatic compound isolated from the wood of the camphor laurel, a large Asian evergreen, is +44. (a) Is camphor a dextrorotatory or levorotatory compound? (b) What is the specific rotation of the enantiomer of camphor? (c) If camphor melts at 174 °C, what is the melting point of its enantiomer?

Analysis

Two enantiomers have identical melting points, boiling points, and solubility properties. The specific rotation of two enantiomers is the same numerical value, but opposite in sign.

Camphor, a fragrant compound obtained from the wood of camphor laurel, has been utilized for centuries in cooking, ointments, and medicine. Much of the camphor used today is synthesized from petroleum products. ©GYRO PHOTOGRAPHY/amanaimages/Getty Images RF

Solution

a. Camphor is dextrorotatory because its specific rotation is a positive value.

b. The enantiomer has a specific rotation of −44, the same value but opposite in sign to the specific rotation of camphor.

c. Camphor's enantiomer melts at 174 °C, because two enantiomers have identical melting points.

PRACTICE PROBLEM 15.6

Pure cholesterol has a specific rotation of −32. (a) Is cholesterol a dextrorotatory or levorotatory compound? (b) What is the specific rotation of the enantiomer of cholesterol?

More Practice: Try Problems 15.55, 15.56.

PROBLEM 15.18

(S)-Alanine is an amino acid that is used to synthesize the complex proteins that make up the muscles of the body. (S)-Alanine has a melting point of 297 °C and a specific rotation of +8.5.

a. Draw the enantiomer of (S)-alanine, called (R)-alanine.

b. What is the melting point of (R)-alanine?

c. What is the specific rotation of (R)-alanine?

(S)-alanine

15.8   Compounds with Two or More Chirality Centers

Although most chiral compounds we have seen thus far have one chirality center, molecules may have two, three, or hundreds of chirality centers. Two examples—tartaric acid and ephedrine— were shown in Section 15.3.

- A compound with one chirality center has two stereoisomers—a pair of enantiomers.
- A compound with two chirality centers has a maximum of four possible stereoisomers.

Let's examine the four stereoisomers of the amino acid threonine. The two chirality centers in threonine are labeled in the given structure. Threonine is one of the 20 naturally occurring amino acids needed for protein synthesis. Since humans cannot synthesize threonine, it is an essential amino acid, meaning that it must be obtained in the diet.

[The chirality centers are labeled in blue.]

carbon skeleton of the
amino acid threonine

There are four different ways that the groups around two chirality centers can be arranged, shown in structures **A–D.**

A and B are mirror images, but they are not superimposable, so they are enantiomers. C and D are also mirror images, but they are not superimposable, so they are enantiomers as well. In other words, with *two* chirality centers, there can be *two* pairs of enantiomers.

Because these structures are drawn with the horizontal bonds of the chirality centers on wedges and the vertical bonds on dashed wedges, Fischer projection formulas can be drawn for each stereoisomer by replacing each chirality center by a cross.

Figure 15.4

Summary—Types of Isomers

Isomers
different compounds with
the same molecular formula

Constitutional isomers
isomers having
atoms bonded to different atoms

Stereoisomers
isomers with
a difference in 3-D arrangement only

Enantiomers
mirror images

Diastereomers
not mirror images

Thus, there are four stereoisomers for threonine: enantiomers **A** and **B,** and enantiomers **C** and **D.** What is the relationship between two stereoisomers like **A** and **C? A** and **C** are stereoisomers, but if you arrange a mirror plane between **A** and **C** you can see that they are *not* mirror images of each other. **A** and **C** represent a second broad class of stereoisomers, called **diastereomers.**

- *Diastereomers* are stereoisomers, but they are *not* mirror images of each other.

A and **B** are diastereomers of **C** and **D,** and vice versa. Naturally occurring threonine is a single stereoisomer corresponding to structure **A.** The other stereoisomers do not occur in nature and cannot be used to synthesize biologically active proteins.

You have now been introduced to all of the possible types of isomers for organic molecules. A flowchart in Figure 15.4 illustrates the relationships among the major classes of isomers.

SAMPLE PROBLEM 15.7 CLASSIFYING STEREOISOMERS AS ENANTIOMERS OR DIASTEREOMERS

Considering the four stereoisomers of 2,3-pentanediol (**E–H**): (a) Which compound is an enantiomer of **E?** (b) Which compound is an enantiomer of **F?** (c) What two compounds are diastereomers of **G?**

Four stereoisomers
of 2,3-pentanediol:

Analysis

Keep in mind the definitions:

- **Enantiomers are stereoisomers that are nonsuperimposable mirror images of each other.**
  Look for two compounds that when placed side-by-side have the groups on both chirality centers drawn as a *reflection* of each other. A given compound has only one possible enantiomer.
- **Diastereomers are stereoisomers that are *not* mirror images of each other.**

552   **Chapter 15**   The Three-Dimensional Shape of Molecules

Solution

a. **E** and **G** are enantiomers because they are mirror images that do not superimpose on each other.

b. **F** and **H** are enantiomers for the same reason.

c. Any compound that is a stereoisomer of **G** but is not its mirror image is a diastereomer. Thus, **F** and **H** are diastereomers of **G**.

PRACTICE PROBLEM 15.7

Answer the following questions about the four stereoisomers of 3-bromo-2-chloropentane (**W–Z**).
(a) Which compound is the enantiomer of **W?** (b) Which compound is the enantiomer of **X?** (c) What two compounds are diastereomers of **Y?** (d) What two compounds are diastereomers of **Z?**

More Practice: Try Problems 15.57a, 15.58a.

PROBLEM 15.19

Consider the ball-and-stick representations labeled **A–C.** How are the compounds in each pair related:
(a) **A** and **B;** (b) **A** and **C;** (c) **B** and **C?** Choose from enantiomers, diastereomers, or identical molecules.

15.9   FOCUS ON THE HUMAN BODY
The Sense of Smell

Research suggests that the odor of a particular molecule is determined more by its shape than by the presence of a particular functional group (Figure 15.5). For example, hexachloroethane (Cl_3CCCl_3) and cyclooctane have no obvious structural similarities. However, both molecules have a camphor-like odor, a fact attributed to their similar spherical shape, which is readily shown using space-filling models.

cyclooctane   space-filling model   space-filling model   hexachloroethane

Figure 15.5   The Shape of Molecules and the Sense of Smell

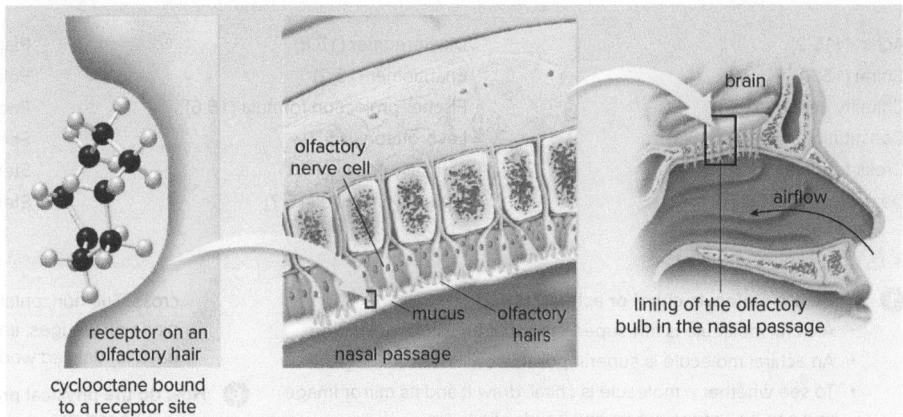

olfactory nerve cell

brain

airflow

olfactory hairs

mucus

lining of the olfactory bulb in the nasal passage

receptor on an olfactory hair

nasal passage

cyclooctane bound to a receptor site

Cyclooctane and other molecules similar in shape bind to a particular olfactory receptor on the nerve cells that lie at the top of the nasal passage. Binding results in a nerve impulse that travels to the brain, which interprets impulses from particular receptors as specific odors.

Since enantiomers interact with chiral smell receptors, some enantiomers have different odors. There are a few well-characterized examples of this phenomenon in nature. For example, one enantiomer of carvone is responsible for the odor of caraway, whereas the other carvone enantiomer is responsible for the odor of spearmint.

caraway seeds

carvone enantiomer **A**

carvone enantiomer **B**

spearmint leaves

A has the odor of caraway.

B has the odor of spearmint.

(left): ©McGraw-Hill Education/Elite Images; (right): ©DAJ/Getty Images RF

Thus, the three-dimensional structure of a molecule is important in determining its odor.

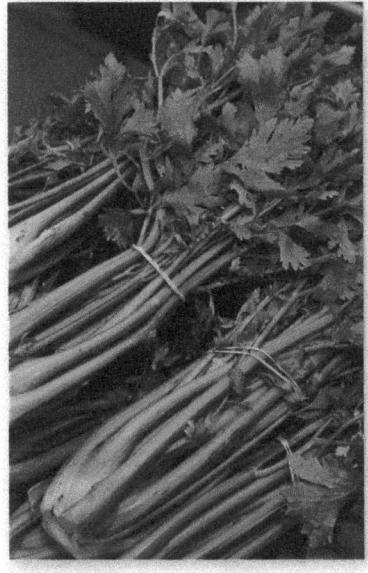

One enantiomer of celery ketone (Problem 15.20) has an odor reminiscent of celery leaves. ©Aaron Roeth Photography RF

PROBLEM 15.20

Celery ketone is similar to carvone in that each enantiomer has a different odor; one enantiomer has the characteristic odor of celery leaves, whereas the other has an odor reminiscent of licorice, fennel, or anise. Identify the chirality center in celery ketone and draw both enantiomers.

CH_3 — — $CH_2CH_2CH_3$

O

celery ketone

CHAPTER HIGHLIGHTS

KEY TERMS

Achiral (15.2)

Chiral (15.2)

Chirality center (15.2)

Constitutional isomer (15.1)

Cross formula (15.6)

Dextrorotatory (15.7)

Diastereomer (15.8)

Enantiomer (15.2)

Fischer projection formula (15.6)

Levorotatory (15.7)

Optically active (15.7)

Optically inactive (15.7)

Plane-polarized light (15.7)

Polarimeter (15.7)

Racemic mixture (15.5)

Specific rotation (15.7)

Stereochemistry (15.1)

Stereoisomer (15.1)

KEY CONCEPTS

① When is a molecule chiral or achiral? (15.2)
- A chiral molecule is not superimposable on its mirror image.
- An achiral molecule is superimposable on its mirror image.
- To see whether a molecule is chiral, draw it and its mirror image and see if all of the atoms and bonds align.

② What is a chirality center? (15.2, 15.3)
- A chirality center is a carbon with four different groups around it.
- A molecule with one chirality center is chiral.

③ What are enantiomers? (15.2, 15.3)
- Enantiomers are mirror images that are not superimposable on each other. To draw two enantiomers, draw one molecule in three dimensions around the chirality center. Then draw the mirror image so that the substituents are a reflection of the groups in the first molecule.

④ Why do some chiral drugs have different properties from their mirror-image isomers? (15.5)
- When a chiral drug must interact with a chiral receptor, only one enantiomer fits the receptor properly and evokes a specific response. Ibuprofen, naproxen, and L-dopa are examples of chiral drugs in which the two enantiomers have very different properties.

⑤ What is a Fischer projection? (15.6)
- A Fischer projection is a specific way of depicting a chirality center. The chirality center is located at the intersection of a

cross. The horizontal lines represent bonds that come out of the plane on wedges, and the vertical lines represent bonds that go back on dashed wedges.

⑥ How do the physical properties of two enantiomers compare? (15.7)
- Two enantiomers have identical physical properties except for their interaction with plane-polarized light.
- The specific rotation of two enantiomers is the same numerical value, but opposite in sign.

⑦ What is the difference between an enantiomer and a diastereomer? (15.8)
- Enantiomers are stereoisomers that are nonsuperimposable mirror images of each other.
- Diastereomers are stereoisomers that are *not* mirror images of each other.

⑧ How is the shape of a molecule related to its odor? (15.9)
- It is thought that the odor of a molecule is determined more by its shape than the presence of a particular functional group, so compounds of similar shape have similar odors. For an odor to be perceived, a molecule must bind to an olfactory receptor, resulting in a nerve impulse that travels to the brain. Enantiomers may have different odors because they bind with chiral receptors and each enantiomer fits the chiral receptors in a different way.

PROBLEMS

Selected in-chapter and odd-numbered end-of-chapter problems have brief answers in Appendix B. The *Student Study Guide and Solutions Manual* contains detailed solutions to all in-chapter and odd-numbered end-of-chapter problems, as well as additional worked examples and a chapter self-test.

Chiral Compounds, Chirality Centers, and Enantiomers

15.21 Classify each object as chiral or achiral.

a.   b.   c.

(a): ©Glow Images RF; (b): ©McGraw-Hill Education/Mark Dierker, photographer; (c): ©Sylvain Sonnet/Getty Images RF

15.22 Classify each object as chiral or achiral.

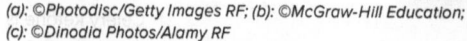

(a): ©Photodisc/Getty Images RF; (b): ©McGraw-Hill Education; (c): ©Dinodia Photos/Alamy RF

15.23 Draw a mirror image for each compound. Label each compound as chiral or achiral.

a.

halothane
(general anesthetic)

b.

dichloromethane
(common solvent)

15.24 Draw a mirror image for each compound. Label each compound as chiral or achiral.

a. CH_3CH_2—O—CH_2CH_3

diethyl ether
(general anesthetic)

b. glycerol
(triol used in lotions)

15.25 Consider the ball-and-stick model of **A**, and label **B** and **C** as either identical to **A** or an enantiomer of **A**.

A   B   C

15.26 Consider the ball-and-stick model of **D**, and label **E** and **F** as either identical to **D** or an enantiomer of **D**.

D   E   F

15.27 Locate the chirality center in nicotine, the addictive stimulant in tobacco.

nicotine

©Jetsadaphoto/Shutterstock RF

15.28 Locate the chirality centers in aspartame, the synthetic sweetener sold under the trade name Equal.

aspartame

©McGraw-Hill Education/Jill Braaten, photographer

15.29 Label the chirality center (if one exists) in each compound. Compounds contain zero or one chirality center.

a. CH_3CH_2CHCl
         |
         Cl

c.

b. $CH_3CCH_2CHCH_3$ (with CH_3 and Cl above, H below)

d.

15.30 Label the chirality center (if one exists) in each compound. Compounds contain zero or one chirality center.

a. CH_3—C(=O)—CH_2CH_3

c.

b. CH_3—C(=O)—$CHCH_2CH_3$
                        |
                      CH_3

d.   OH

15.31 Label the chirality center (if one exists) in each compound. A compound may contain zero or one chirality center.

a.   b.

15.32 Label the chirality center (if one exists) in each compound. A compound may contain zero or one chirality center.

a.   b.

15.33 Draw the structure of a compound that fits each description:
a. an alkane of molecular formula C_7H_{16} that contains one chirality center
b. an alcohol of molecular formula $C_6H_{14}O$ that contains one chirality center

15.34 Draw the structure of a compound that fits each description:
a. an alkyl bromide of molecular formula C_4H_9Br that contains one chirality center
b. a diol of molecular formula $C_5H_{12}O_2$ that contains two chirality centers

15.35 Methamphetamine is an addictive stimulant sold illegally as "speed," "meth," or "crystal meth." Identify the chirality center in methamphetamine, and then draw both enantiomers in three dimensions around the chirality center.

methamphetamine

15.36 Dobutamine is a heart stimulant used in stress tests to measure cardiac fitness. Identify the chirality center in dobutamine, and then draw both enantiomers in three dimensions around the chirality center.

dobutamine

Isomers

15.37 How are the compounds in each pair related? Are they identical molecules or enantiomers?

a.   and

b.   and

15.38 How are the compounds in each pair related? Are they identical molecules or enantiomers?

a.   and

b.   and

15.39 How are the molecules in each pair related? Choose from: identical molecules, constitutional isomers, enantiomers, diastereomers, or not isomers of each other.

a. $CH_3CH_2CH_2OCH_3$ and $CH_3CH_2OCH_2CH_3$

b. ⬡—OH   and   HO—⬡

c. $CH_3CH_2CH_2$—C—CH_3 and CH_3—C—$CH_2CH_2CH_3$
   (Br above/below)   (Br above/below)

d.
```
      CH3                    CH3
  Cl—┼—H                 Cl—┼—H
   H—┼—Cl                 Cl—┼—H
      CH2CH3                 CH2CH3
```
        and

15.40 How are the molecules in each pair related? Choose from: identical molecules, constitutional isomers, enantiomers, diastereomers, or not isomers of each other.

a.
```
        OH                        OH
         |                         |
         C                         C
 CH3CH2 / ''CO2H    and    HO2C'' /  CH2CH3
         H                         H
```

b. $CH_3CH_2CH_2CHOH$ and $CH_3CH_2OCH(CH_3)_2$
            |
            CH_3

c. $CH_3CH_2OCH_2CH_3$ and
```
              O
              ‖
       CH3    C    CH2CH3
```

d.
```
          ⬡                       ⬡
   H—┼—OH                  HO—┼—H
   H—┼—OH                  HO—┼—H
      CH2CH3                  CH2CH3
```
        and

15.41 Draw the structure of the four constitutional isomers of molecular formula $C_5H_{10}O$ that contain an aldehyde (—CHO) as a functional group. Label any chirality center present in each compound. Some compounds have no chirality centers.

15.42 Although there are four constitutional isomers of molecular formula C_4H_9Cl, only one contains a chirality center and can therefore exist as a pair of enantiomers. Draw both enantiomers of this alkyl chloride in three dimensions around the chirality center.

Fischer Projections

15.43 Convert the given ball-and-stick model to a Fischer projection.

15.44 Convert the given ball-and-stick model to a Fischer projection.

15.45 Convert each three-dimensional representation into a Fischer projection.

a.
```
   CHO
    |
H━C◀OH
    |
   CH₃
```

b.
```
     OCH₃
      |
CH₃━C◀H
      |
CH₃━C◀OH
      |
    CH₂CH₃
```

15.46 Convert each three-dimensional representation into a Fischer projection.

a.
```
     OCH₂CH₃
      |
CH₃━C◀H
      |
   N(CH₃)₂
```

b.
```
     COCH₂CH₃
      |
H━C◀Br
      |
H━C◀OH
      |
     CH₃
```

15.47 Convert each Fischer projection into a three-dimensional representation with wedges and dashed wedges.

a.
```
     CH₃
      |
H ───┼─── F
      |
   CH(CH₃)₂
```

b.
```
     COOH
      |
H ───┼─── NH₂
      |
CH₃ ──┼── H
      |
    CH₂CH₃
```

15.48 Convert each Fischer projection into a three-dimensional representation with wedges and dashed wedges.

a.
```
     CH₂CH₃
      |
HO ──┼── CH₃
      |
   (phenyl)
```

b.
```
      CH₃
       |
H ───┼─── Cl
       |
H ───┼─── Cl
       |
     CH₂Cl
```

15.49 How are the Fischer projection formulas in each pair related to each other? Are they identical or are they enantiomers?

a.
```
    CH₃                CH₃
     |                  |
Cl──┼──H    and    H──┼──Cl
     |                  |
    CH₃                CH₃
```

b.
```
     COOH                COOH
      |                   |
CH₃──┼──OH   and   HO──┼──CH₃
      |                   |
      H                   H
```

c.
```
    CO₂H                CO₂H
     |                   |
H──┼──NH₂    and   H₂N──┼──H
     |                   |
   CH₂OH               CH₂OH
```

15.50 How are the Fischer projection formulas in each pair related to each other? Are they identical or are they enantiomers?

a.
```
    COOH              COOH
     |                 |
H───┼───H    and   H───┼───H
     |                 |
    NH₂               NH₂
```

b.
```
         Cl                    Cl
          |                     |
CH₃CH₂──┼──CH₃   and   CH₃──┼──CH₂CH₃
          |                     |
         Cl                    Cl
```

c.
```
      CH₂OH              CH₂OH
       |                  |
CH₃──┼──OH   and   HO──┼──CH₃
       |                  |
       H                  H
```

Physical Properties of Enantiomers

15.51 (a) Define the terms "optically active" and "optically inactive." (b) Give an example of a compound with molecular formula $C_4H_{10}O$ that is optically inactive. (c) Give an example of a compound with molecular formula $C_4H_{10}O$ that is optically active.

15.52 (a) Draw the structure of a compound with molecular formula $C_5H_{10}O$ that contains an aldehyde and is optically inactive. (b) Draw the structure of a compound with molecular formula $C_5H_{10}O$ that contains an aldehyde and is optically active.

15.53 Label each compound as optically active or optically inactive.

a.   b.

15.54 Label each compound as optically active or optically inactive.

a.   b.

15.55 Lactose, the major carbohydrate in milk, has a specific rotation of +52 and is water soluble (22 g per 100 mL of H_2O). (a) Is lactose a dextrorotatory or levorotatory compound? (b) What is the specific rotation of the enantiomer of lactose? (c) How much of the enantiomer of lactose dissolves in 100 mL of water?

15.56 The anticancer drug Taxol has a specific rotation of −49. (a) What is the specific rotation of the enantiomer of Taxol? (b) How does the boiling point of Taxol compare to the boiling point of its enantiomer? (c) How do the solubility properties of Taxol compare to those of its enantiomer?

Enantiomers and Diastereomers

15.57 Consider the stereoisomers (**A–D**) drawn below. These compounds are four-carbon sugars, as we will learn in Chapter 20.

A   B   C   D

a. How are the compounds in each pair related? Are the compounds enantiomers or diastereomers: [1] **A** and **B**; [2] **A** and **C**; [3] **A** and **D**; [4] **B** and **C**; [5] **B** and **D**; [6] **C** and **D**?

b. Draw a constitutional isomer of **A** that contains a ketone, not an aldehyde.

15.58 Consider the stereoisomers (**E–H**) drawn below. These compounds are five-carbon sugars, as we will learn in Chapter 20.

E   F   G   H

a. How are the compounds in each pair related? Are the compounds enantiomers or diastereomers: [1] **E** and **F**; [2] **E** and **G**; [3] **E** and **H**; [4] **F** and **G**; [5] **F** and **H**; [6] **G** and **H**?

b. Draw a constitutional isomer of **E** that contains an aldehyde, not a ketone.

15.59 In Chapter 13 we learned that cis and trans alkenes are stereoisomers. Are *cis*-2-butene and *trans*-2-butene enantiomers or diastereomers? Explain your choice.

15.60 Are *cis*-2-butene and *trans*-2-butene chiral or achiral compounds? Explain your choice.

Applications

15.61 Lactic acid is a product of glucose metabolism. During periods of strenuous exercise, lactic acid forms faster than it can be oxidized, resulting in the aching feeling of tired muscles.

CH_3CHCO_2H
        |
        OH
lactic acid

a. Locate the chirality center in lactic acid.

b. Draw both enantiomers of lactic acid in three dimensions around the chirality center.

c. Draw Fischer projection formulas for both enantiomers of lactic acid.

15.62 Locate the chirality centers in each vitamin.

a.
vitamin E

b.
vitamin C

15.63 Hydroxydihydrocitronellal is another example of a compound that has two enantiomers that smell different. One enantiomer smells minty, and the other smells like lily of the valley.

hydroxydihydrocitronellal

a. Locate the chirality center in this compound.

b. Draw both enantiomers in three dimensions around the chirality center.

c. Draw Fischer projection formulas for both enantiomers.

15.64 Two enantiomers can sometimes taste very different. L-Leucine, a naturally occurring amino acid used in protein synthesis, tastes bitter, but its enantiomer, D-leucine, tastes sweet.

leucine

a. Locate the chirality center in leucine.

b. Draw both enantiomers in three dimensions around the chirality center.

c. Draw Fischer projection formulas for both enantiomers.

15.65 Answer the following questions about the analgesic propoxyphene (trade name Darvon).

Darvon

a. Label the chirality centers.
b. Draw the enantiomer. Like many of the drugs discussed in Section 15.5, the enantiomer, levopropoxyphene (trade name Novrad) has different biological properties. Levopropoxyphene is an antitussive agent, meaning it relieves coughs. (Do you notice anything about the trade names Darvon and Novrad?)
c. Draw the structure of one diastereomer.
d. Draw the structure of one constitutional isomer.
e. Convert Darvon to a Fischer projection formula.

15.66 Plavix, the trade name for the generic drug clopidogrel, is used in the treatment of coronary artery disease. Like many newer drugs, Plavix is sold as a single enantiomer.

clopidogrel
(Trade name Plavix)

a. Locate the chirality center.
b. Draw both enantiomers in three dimensions around the chirality center.
c. Convert both enantiomers to Fischer projection formulas.

CHALLENGE PROBLEMS

15.67 Identify the nine chirality centers in sucrose, the sweet-tasting carbohydrate we use as table sugar.

sucrose

15.68 Identify the six chirality centers in the anabolic steroid nandrolone. Nandrolone is used to increase muscle mass in body builders and athletes, although it is not permitted in competitive sports.

nandrolone

Solanine, a toxin that contains three acetals, is formed in the leaves, stems, and green spots on the skin of potatoes as a defense against insects and predators.
©WILDLIFE GmbH/Alamy

Aldehydes and Ketones

CHAPTER OUTLINE

16.1 Structure and Bonding

16.2 Nomenclature

16.3 Physical Properties

16.4 FOCUS ON HEALTH & MEDICINE: Interesting Aldehydes and Ketones

16.5 Reactions of Aldehydes and Ketones

16.6 Reduction of Aldehydes and Ketones

16.7 FOCUS ON THE HUMAN BODY: The Chemistry of Vision

16.8 Acetal Formation

CHAPTER GOALS

In this chapter you will learn how to:

1 Identify the characteristics of aldehydes and ketones

2 Name aldehydes and ketones

3 Give examples of useful aldehydes and ketones

4 Draw the products of oxidation reactions of aldehydes

5 Draw the products of reduction reactions of aldehydes and ketones

6 Understand the basic reactions involved in vision

7 Identify and prepare hemiacetals and acetals

**Why Study
Aldehydes and Ketones?**

Chapter 16 is the first of two chapters that concentrate on compounds that contain a **carbonyl group (C=O)**, perhaps the most important functional group in organic chemistry. In this chapter we examine **aldehydes** and **ketones,** compounds that contain a carbonyl carbon bonded to hydrogen or carbon atoms. Aldehydes and ketones occur widely in nature, and also serve as useful starting materials and solvents in industrial processes. All simple carbohydrates contain a carbonyl group, and more complex carbohydrates are derived from reactions discussed in this chapter.

16.1   Structure and Bonding

Two broad classes of compounds contain a *carbonyl group.*

carbonyl group

1. Compounds that have only carbon and hydrogen atoms bonded to the carbonyl group

aldehyde   ketone

- An *aldehyde* has at least one H atom bonded to the carbonyl group.
- A *ketone* has two alkyl groups bonded to the carbonyl group.

2. Compounds that contain an electronegative atom bonded to the carbonyl group

carboxylic acid   ester   amide

These compounds include **carboxylic acids, esters,** and **amides,** which contain an electronegative oxygen or nitrogen atom bonded directly to the carbonyl carbon. Esters and amides are called **carboxylic acid derivatives,** because they can be prepared from carboxylic acids. Carboxylic acids and their derivatives are discussed in Chapter 17, whereas aldehydes and ketones are the subject of this chapter.

Two structural features dominate the properties and chemistry of the carbonyl group.

trigonal planar

- The carbonyl carbon atom is trigonal planar, and all bond angles are 120°. In this way the carbonyl carbon resembles the carbons of a carbon–carbon double bond.
- Because oxygen is more electronegative than carbon, a carbonyl group is polar. The carbonyl carbon is electron poor (δ+) and the oxygen is electron rich (δ−). In this way the carbonyl carbon is very different from the carbons of a nonpolar carbon–carbon double bond.

As mentioned in Chapter 11, the double bond of a carbonyl group is usually omitted in drawing shorthand structures. An aldehyde is often written as **RCHO.** Remember that the **H atom is**

bonded to the carbon atom, not the oxygen. Likewise, a ketone is written as **RCOR,** or if both alkyl groups are the same, **R₂CO.**

$= \quad CH_3CHO$

acetaldehyde

- C is singly bonded to H.
- C is doubly bonded to O.

$= \quad CH_3COCH_3 \quad$ or $\quad (CH_3)_2CO$

acetone

- C is singly bonded to 2 C's.
- C is doubly bonded to O.

Many simple aldehydes and ketones are naturally occurring. For example, octanal, decanal, and piperitone are among the 70 organic compounds that contribute to the flavor and odor of an orange.

©evdayan/Getty Images RF

piperitone

$CH_3(CH_2)_6$ ... H

octanal

$CH_3(CH_2)_8$ ... H

decanal

PROBLEM 16.1

Draw out each compound to clearly show what groups are bonded to the carbonyl carbon. Label each compound as a ketone or aldehyde.

a. CH_3CH_2CHO b. $CH_3CH_2COCH_3$ c. $(CH_3)_3CCOCH_3$ d. $(CH_3CH_2)_2CHCHO$

PROBLEM 16.2

Draw the structure of the three constitutional isomers of molecular formula C_4H_8O that contain a carbonyl group. Label each compound as a ketone or aldehyde.

16.2 Nomenclature

Both IUPAC and common names are used for aldehydes and ketones.

16.2A Naming Aldehydes

- In IUPAC nomenclature, aldehydes are identified by the suffix -*al.*

To name an aldehyde using the IUPAC system:

1. **Find the longest chain containing the CHO group, and change the -e ending of the parent alkane to the suffix -*al.***

2. **Number the chain or ring to put the CHO group at C1, but omit this number from the name. Apply all of the other usual rules of nomenclature.**

Simple aldehydes have common names that are widely used. In fact, the common names **formaldehyde, acetaldehyde,** and **benzaldehyde** are virtually always used instead of their IUPAC names. Common names all contain the suffix *-aldehyde.*

formaldehyde	acetaldehyde	benzaldehyde
(methanal)	(ethanal)	(benzenecarbaldehyde)

(IUPAC names are in parentheses.)

SAMPLE PROBLEM 16.1 NAMING AN ALDEHYDE

Give the IUPAC name for each aldehyde.

a. $CH_3CHCH-\overset{O}{\overset{\|}{C}}-H$ with CH_3 above and CH_3 below

b. $CH_3CH_2CH_2-\overset{H}{\overset{|}{\underset{CHO}{C}}}-CH_2CH_3$

Analysis and Solution

a. [1] Find and name the longest chain containing the CHO.

butane ---→ butan*al*
(4 C's)

[2] Number and name substituents, making sure the CHO group is at C1.

Answer: 2,3-dimethylbutanal

b. [1] Find and name the longest chain containing the CHO.

pentane ----→ pentan*al*
(5 C's)

[2] Number and name substituents, making sure the CHO group is at C1.

Answer: 2-ethylpentanal

PRACTICE PROBLEM 16.1

Give the IUPAC name for each aldehyde.

a. $(CH_3)_2CHCH_2CH_2CH_2CHO$ b. $(CH_3)_3CC(CH_3)_2CH_2CHO$ c.

More Practice: Try Problems 16.19a, 16.20a, 16.21, 16.22.

PROBLEM 16.3

Give the structure corresponding to each IUPAC name.

a. 2-chloropropanal

b. 3,4,5-triethylheptanal

c. 3,6-diethylnonanal

d. *o*-ethylbenzaldehyde

Yuzu is a small citrus fruit used widely in Japanese cooking. Its unusual aroma is partly due to the aldehydes depicted in Problem 16.4. ©Aflo Foto Agency/Alamy RF

PROBLEM 16.4

Give the IUPAC name for each aldehyde depicted in the ball-and-stick models. Both aldehydes are isolated from yuzu, a citrus fruit extensively cultivated in Japan.

a.   b.

16.2B   Naming Ketones

- In the IUPAC system, ketones are identified by the suffix *-one.*

To name an acyclic ketone using IUPAC rules:

1. **Find the longest chain containing the carbonyl group, and change the *-e* ending of the parent alkane to the suffix *-one.***
2. **Number the carbon chain to give the carbonyl carbon the lower number. Apply all of the other usual rules of nomenclature.**

With cyclic ketones, numbering always begins at the carbonyl carbon, but the "1" is usually omitted from the name. The ring is then numbered clockwise or counterclockwise to give the first substituent the lower number.

Most common names for ketones are formed by **naming both alkyl groups** on the carbonyl carbon, **arranging them alphabetically,** and adding the word *ketone.* Using this method, the common name for 2-butanone becomes ethyl methyl ketone.

methyl group   ethyl group

$$CH_3 \overset{\overset{\displaystyle O}{\|}}{C} CH_2CH_3 \qquad CH_3 \overset{\overset{\displaystyle O}{\|}}{C} CH_2CH_3$$

IUPAC name: **2-butanone**   Common name: **ethyl methyl ketone**

Three widely used common names for some simple ketones do not follow this convention:

acetone   acetophenone   benzophenone

SAMPLE PROBLEM 16.2 NAMING A KETONE

Give the IUPAC name for each ketone.

a. $CH_3 \overset{\overset{\displaystyle O}{\|}}{C} CHCH_2CH_3$
            |
           CH_3

b. (cyclohexanone ring with CH_2CH_3 and CH_3 substituents)

Analysis and Solution

a. **[1] Find and name the longest chain containing the carbonyl group.**

$$CH_3-\overset{\overset{\displaystyle O}{\|}}{C}-\underset{\underset{\displaystyle CH_3}{|}}{CH}CH_2CH_3$$

pentane – – – → pentan*one*
(5 C's)

[2] Number and name substituents, making sure the carbonyl carbon has the lower number.

$$CH_3-\overset{\overset{\displaystyle O}{\|}}{C}-\underset{2\ \ \underset{\displaystyle CH_3}{|}}{\overset{3}{CH}}CH_2CH_3$$

Answer: 3-methyl-2-pentanone

b. **[1] Name the ring.**

cyclohexane – – – → cyclohexan*one*
(6 C's)

[2] Number and name substituents, making sure the carbonyl carbon is at C1.

Answer: 3-ethyl-4-methylcyclohexanone

PRACTICE PROBLEM 16.2

Give the IUPAC name for each ketone.

a. $CH_3CH_2\overset{\overset{\displaystyle O}{\|}}{C}\underset{\underset{\displaystyle CH_3}{|}}{CH}CH_2CH_2CH_3$

b.

c.

More Practice: Try Problems 16.19b, 16.20b, 16.25, 16.26.

PROBLEM 16.5

Give the structure corresponding to each name.

a. butyl ethyl ketone

b. 2-methyl-3-pentanone

c. *p*-ethylacetophenone

d. 2-propylcyclobutanone

16.3 Physical Properties

Because aldehydes and ketones have a polar carbonyl group, they are **polar molecules** with stronger intermolecular forces than the hydrocarbons of Chapters 12 and 13. Since they have no OH bond, two molecules of RCHO or RCOR are incapable of intermolecular hydrogen bonding, giving them weaker intermolecular forces than alcohols.

polar bond

$$\underset{CH_3}{\overset{CH_3}{C}}=\ddot{\ddot{O}}$$

acetone

$\delta+$ $\delta-$ $\delta+$ $\delta-$

Oppositely charged ends of the dipoles interact.

566 **Chapter 16** Aldehydes and Ketones

As a result:

- Aldehydes and ketones have *higher* boiling points than hydrocarbons of comparable molecular weight.
- Aldehydes and ketones have *lower* boiling points than alcohols of comparable molecular weight.

CH₃CH₂CH₂CH₂CH₃	CH₃CH₂CH₂CHO	CH₃CH₂CH₂CH₂OH
pentane	butanal	1-butanol
bp 36 °C	bp 76 °C	bp 118 °C

Increasing strength of intermolecular forces
Increasing boiling point

Based on the general rule governing solubility (i.e., **"like dissolves like,"** Section 8.3), aldehydes and ketones are soluble in organic solvents. Moreover, because aldehydes and ketones contain an oxygen atom with an available lone pair, they can intermolecularly hydrogen bond to water.

As a result:

- Low molecular weight aldehydes and ketones (those having fewer than six carbons) are soluble in both organic solvents and water.
- Higher molecular weight aldehydes and ketones (those having six or more carbons) are soluble in organic solvents, but insoluble in water.

PROBLEM 16.6

Which compound in each pair has the higher boiling point?

a.　　　　　　　or

A　　　　　　　B

b.　　　　　　　or

C　　　　　　　D

PROBLEM 16.7

Acetone and progesterone are two ketones that occur naturally in the human body. Discuss the solubility properties of both compounds in water and organic solvents.

acetone

progesterone

16.4 FOCUS ON HEALTH & MEDICINE
Interesting Aldehydes and Ketones

formaldehyde
CH_2=O

acetone
$(CH_3)_2C$=O

Formaldehyde (CH_2=O, the simplest aldehyde) is a starting material for the synthesis of many resins and plastics, and billions of pounds are produced annually in the United States. Formaldehyde is also sold as a 37% aqueous solution called **formalin,** a disinfectant and preservative for biological specimens. As a product of the incomplete combustion of coal and other fossil fuels, formaldehyde is partly responsible for the irritation caused by smoggy air.

Acetone [$(CH_3)_2C$=O, the simplest ketone] is an industrial solvent and a starting material in the synthesis of some organic polymers. Acetone is produced naturally in cells during the breakdown of fatty acids. In diabetes, a disease where normal metabolic processes are altered because of the inadequate secretion of insulin, individuals often have unusually high levels of acetone in the bloodstream. The characteristic odor of acetone can be detected on the breath of diabetic patients when their disease is poorly controlled.

Many aldehydes with characteristic odors occur in nature, as shown in Figure 16.1. It is thought that the shape of these molecules is an important factor in determining their odors, as discussed in Section 15.9.

Ketones play an important role in the tanning industry. Dihydroxyacetone is the active ingredient in commercial tanning agents that produce sunless tans. Dihydroxyacetone reacts with proteins in the skin, producing a complex colored pigment that gives the skin a brown hue. In addition, many commercial sunscreens are ketones that have the carbonyl carbon bonded to one or two benzene rings (see also Section 13.11). Examples include avobenzone, oxybenzone, and dioxybenzone.

sunless tanning agent

dihydroxyacetone

avobenzone

oxybenzone

dioxybenzone

sunscreen

[Ketone carbonyls are shown in red.]

(left & right): ©McGraw-Hill Education/Jill Braaten, photographer

Figure 16.1   Some Naturally Occurring Aldehydes with Characteristic Odors

cinnamaldehyde
(odor of cinnamon)

geranial
(lemony odor,
isolated from lemongrass)

vanillin
(flavoring agent isolated
from vanilla beans)

[Aldehyde carbonyls are shown in red.]

citronellal
(lemony odor, isolated from lemongrass
and citronella grass)

- **Cinnamaldehyde,** the major component of cinnamon bark, is a common flavoring agent.

- **Vanillin** is the primary component of the extract of the vanilla bean. Because natural sources cannot meet the high demand, most vanilla flavoring agents are made synthetically from starting materials derived from petroleum.

- **Geranial** has the lemony odor characteristic of lemongrass. Geranial is used in perfumery and as a starting material for synthesizing vitamin A.

- **Citronellal** gives the distinctive lemon odor to citronella candles, commonly used to repel mosquitoes.

Some naturally occurring compounds do not contain a carbonyl group, but they are converted to aldehydes and ketones by enzymes in cells. One such compound is **amygdalin.**

amygdalin   enzymes   glucose
(two molecules)   +   benzaldehyde   +   HCN
hydrogen
cyanide
toxic gas

Amygdalin is present in the seeds and pits of apricots, peaches, and wild cherries. In the body, amygdalin is converted to two aldehydes, glucose and benzaldehyde. Also formed as a by-product is hydrogen cyanide, **HCN,** a toxic gas. Amygdalin, like a closely related compound called laetrile, was once touted as an anticancer drug, and is still available in some countries for this purpose, although its effectiveness is unproven. It appears as if the toxic HCN produced from amygdalin indiscriminately kills cells without targeting cancer cells. Patients in some clinical trials involving amygdalin show signs of cyanide poisoning but not cancer remission.

PROBLEM 16.8

Which sunscreen—avobenzone, oxybenzone, or dioxybenzone—is probably most soluble in water, and therefore most readily washed off when an individual goes swimming? Explain your choice.

16.5 Reactions of Aldehydes and Ketones

16.5A General Considerations

Aldehydes and ketones undergo two general types of reactions.

1. Aldehydes can be oxidized to carboxylic acids.

Since aldehydes contain a hydrogen atom bonded to the carbonyl carbon, they can be oxidized to carboxylic acids, as discussed in Section 16.5B.

2. Aldehydes and ketones undergo addition reactions.

Like alkenes, aldehydes and ketones contain a multiple bond (the carbonyl group) that is readily broken. As a result, aldehydes and ketones undergo addition reactions with a variety of reagents. In the addition reaction, new groups X and Y are added to the carbonyl group of the starting material. One bond of the double bond is broken and two new single bonds are formed. We examine the addition of H_2 in Section 16.6 and the addition of alcohols (ROH) in Section 16.8.

16.5B Oxidation of Aldehydes

Because aldehydes contain a hydrogen atom bonded directly to the carbonyl carbon, they can be oxidized to carboxylic acids; that is, the aldehyde C—H bond can be converted to a C—OH bond. Since ketones have no hydrogen atom bonded to the carbonyl group, they are *not* oxidized under similar reaction conditions.

A common reagent for this oxidation is potassium dichromate, $K_2Cr_2O_7$, a red-orange solid that is converted to a green Cr^{3+} product during oxidation.

Aldehydes are easily oxidized by oxygen in the air. When $CH_3CH_2CH_2CHO$ (butanal) stands at room temperature, it slowly develops the characteristic smell of its oxidation product, $CH_3CH_2CH_2COOH$ (butanoic acid), a compound that contributes to the distinctive odor of human sweat.

570   **Chapter 16**   Aldehydes and Ketones

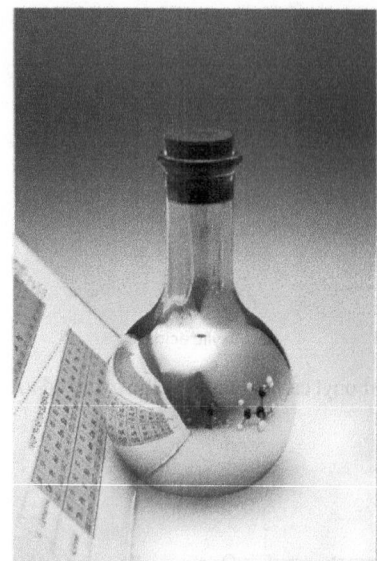

Aldehydes are said to give a *positive* Tollens test; that is, they react with Ag⁺ to form RCOOH and Ag. When the reaction is carried out in a glass flask, a silver mirror is formed on its walls. Other functional groups give a *negative* Tollens test; that is, no silver mirror forms.
©McGraw-Hill Education/Charles D. Winters/ Timeframe Photography, Inc.

As we learned in Section 14.5, $K_2Cr_2O_7$ oxidizes other functional groups (most notably 1° and 2° alcohols), as well. Aldehydes can be oxidized *selectively* in the presence of other functional groups using **silver(I) oxide (Ag_2O) in aqueous ammonium hydroxide (NH_4OH).** This is called **Tollens reagent.** Only aldehydes react with Tollens reagent; all other functional groups are inert. Oxidation with Tollens reagent provides a distinct color change because the Ag^+ reagent is converted to silver metal (Ag), which precipitates out of the reaction mixture as a silver mirror.

Only the aldehyde is oxidized.

SAMPLE PROBLEM 16.3 DRAWING THE PRODUCT OF CARBONYL OXIDATION WITH $K_2Cr_2O_7$

What product is formed when each carbonyl compound is treated with $K_2Cr_2O_7$?

a.   b.

Analysis

Compounds that contain a C—H and C—O bond on the *same* carbon are oxidized with $K_2Cr_2O_7$. Thus,
- Aldehydes (RCHO) are oxidized to RCO_2H.
- Ketones (R_2CO) are *not* oxidized with $K_2Cr_2O_7$.

Solution

The aldehyde in part (a) is oxidized with $K_2Cr_2O_7$ to a carboxylic acid, but the ketone in part (b) is inert to oxidation.

a. $K_2Cr_2O_7$

Replace 1 C—H bond by 1 C—O bond.

b. $K_2Cr_2O_7$ No reaction

This C is bonded only to other C's.

PRACTICE PROBLEM 16.3

What product is formed when each carbonyl compound is treated with $K_2Cr_2O_7$? In some cases, no reaction occurs.

a. CH_3CH_2CHO b. $(CH_3CH_2)_2C{=}O$ c. $CH_3\overset{\underset{|}{CH_3}}{C}{=}CHCH_2CH_2\overset{\underset{|}{CH_3}}{C}HCH_2CHO$

More Practice: Try Problems 16.41, 16.42, 16.45d, 16.75b, 16.76b, 16.77b, 16.78b, 16.81b.

SAMPLE PROBLEM 16.4 DRAWING THE PRODUCT OF OXIDATION WITH TOLLENS REAGENT

What product is formed when each compound is treated with Tollens reagent (Ag_2O, NH_4OH)?

a. CH_3—C—H (with =O)   b. $HOCH_2$— —C—H (with =O)

Analysis

Only aldehydes (RCHO) react with Tollens reagent. Ketones and alcohols are inert to oxidation.

Solution

The aldehyde in both compounds is oxidized to RCO_2H, but the 1° alcohol in part (b) does not react with Tollens reagent.

a.

Replace 1 C—H bond by 1 C—O bond.

b.   HOCH₂—

Only the aldehyde is oxidized.

PRACTICE PROBLEM 16.4

What product is formed when each compound is treated with Tollens reagent (Ag_2O, NH_4OH)? In some cases, no reaction occurs.

a. $CH_3(CH_2)_6CHO$ b.   c.   d.

More Practice: Try Problems 16.43, 16.44, 16.45c, 16.46d, 16.75c, 16.76c, 16.77c, 16.78c.

PROBLEM 16.9

(a) Draw the structure of a constitutional isomer of 3-heptanone that is not oxidized with Tollens reagent. (b) Draw the structure of a constitutional isomer of 3-heptanone that reacts with Tollens reagent, and give the structure of the product formed.

16.6   Reduction of Aldehydes and Ketones

Recall from Section 12.8 that to determine if an organic compound has been reduced, we compare the number of C—H and C—O bonds. **Reduction is the *opposite* of oxidation.**

| Reduction | | |

carbonyl group

2 C—O bonds

alcohol

1 C—O bond
1 C—H bond

- Reduction results in a *decrease* in the number of C—O bonds or an *increase* in the number of C—H bonds.

The conversion of a carbonyl group (C=O) to an alcohol (C—OH) is a reduction, because the starting material has more C—O bonds than the product (two versus one). Reduction of a carbonyl is also an **addition reaction,** because the elements of H_2 are added across the double bond, forming new C—H and O—H bonds. The symbol **[H]** is often used to represent a general reduction reaction.

16.6A   Specific Features of Carbonyl Reductions

The identity of the carbonyl starting material determines the type of alcohol formed as product in a reduction reaction.

- Aldehydes (RCHO) are reduced to 1° alcohols (RCH$_2$OH).

R—C(=O)(H)   → [H] →   R—C(H)(H)—O—H

aldehyde   1° alcohol

- Ketones (RCOR) are reduced to 2° alcohols (R$_2$CHOH).

R—C(=O)(R)   → [H] →   R—C(R)(H)—O—H

ketone   2° alcohol

Many different reagents can be used to reduce an aldehyde or ketone to an alcohol. For example, the addition of H$_2$ to a carbonyl group (C=O) takes place with the same reagents used for the addition of H$_2$ to a C=C—namely, **H$_2$ gas in the presence of palladium (Pd) metal** (Section 13.6). The metal is a catalyst that provides a surface to bind both the carbonyl compound and H$_2$, and this speeds up the rate of reduction. The addition of hydrogen to a multiple bond is called **hydrogenation.**

CH$_3$—C(=O)(H)   → H$_2$/Pd →   CH$_3$—C(H)(H)—O—H = CH$_3$CH$_2$OH

aldehyde   1° alcohol

CH$_3$CH$_2$—C(=O)(CH$_2$CH$_3$)   → H$_2$/Pd →   CH$_3$CH$_2$—C(CH$_2$CH$_3$)(H)—O—H = (CH$_3$CH$_2$)$_2$CHOH

ketone   2° alcohol

SAMPLE PROBLEM 16.5 DRAWING THE PRODUCT OF HYDROGENATION

What alcohol is formed when each aldehyde or ketone is treated with H$_2$ in the presence of a Pd catalyst?

a. (cyclohexane ring)—C(=O)(H)   b. (cyclohexanone ring)=O

Analysis

To draw the products of reduction:

- Locate the C=O and mentally break one bond in the double bond.
- Mentally break the H—H bond of the reagent.
- Add one H atom to each atom of the C=O, forming new C—H and O—H single bonds.

Solution

The aldehyde (RCHO) in part (a) forms a 1° alcohol (RCH$_2$OH) and the ketone in part (b) forms a 2° alcohol (R$_2$CHOH).

a. Break one bond. / Break the single bond. / 1° alcohol

b. Break one bond. / Break the single bond. / 2° alcohol

PRACTICE PROBLEM 16.5

What alcohol is formed when each compound is treated with H$_2$ and a Pd catalyst?

a. CH$_3$CH$_2$CH$_2$CHO   b.   c. CH$_3$COCH$_2$CH$_3$ d.

More Practice: Try Problems 16.49, 16.50c, 16.51, 16.52, 16.74d, 16.75a, 16.76a, 16.77a, 16.78a.

16.6B   Examples of Carbonyl Reduction in Organic Synthesis

The reduction of aldehydes and ketones is a common reaction used in the laboratory synthesis of many useful compounds.

Chemists synthesize compounds for many different reasons. Sometimes a naturally occurring compound has useful properties but is produced by an organism in only minute amounts. Chemists then develop a method to prepare this molecule from simpler starting materials to make it more readily available and less expensive. For example, **muscone,** a strongly scented ketone isolated from musk, is an ingredient in many perfumes. Originally isolated from the male musk deer, muscone is now prepared synthetically in the lab. One step in the synthesis involves reducing a ketone to a 2° alcohol.

ketone   2° alcohol

[H]   →   four steps   →   muscone odor of musk (perfume component)

male musk deer
©M.K. Ranjitsinh/Science Source

Sometimes chemists prepare molecules that do not occur in nature because they have useful medicinal properties. For example, **fluoxetine** (trade name Prozac) is a prescription antidepressant that does not occur in nature. One step in a laboratory synthesis of fluoxetine involves reduction of a ketone to a 2° alcohol. Fluoxetine is widely used because it has excellent medicinal properties *and* because it is readily available by laboratory synthesis.

©McGraw-Hill Education/
Jill Braaten, photographer

PROBLEM 16.10

What carbonyl starting material is needed to prepare alcohol **A** by a reduction reaction? **A** can be converted to the anti-inflammatory agent ibuprofen in three steps.

A   ibuprofen

PROBLEM 16.11

What product is formed when muscone is reduced with H_2 and a Pd catalyst?

muscone

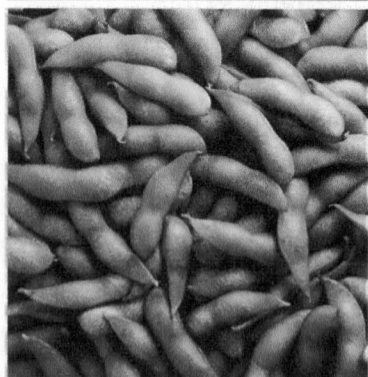

Niacin can be obtained from foods such as soybeans, which contain it naturally, and from breakfast cereals, which are fortified with it.
©C Squared Studios/Getty Images RF

niacin
vitamin B$_3$

16.6C FOCUS ON THE HUMAN BODY
Biological Reductions

The reduction of carbonyl groups is common in biological systems. Biological systems do not use H_2 and Pd as a reducing agent. Instead, they use the coenzyme **NADH** (nicotinamide adenine dinucleotide, reduced form) in the presence of an enzyme. The enzyme binds both the carbonyl compound and NADH, holding them closely together, and this facilitates the addition of H_2 to the carbonyl group, forming an alcohol. The NADH itself is oxidized in the process, forming NAD^+. **NAD^+,** a biological oxidizing agent, is a coenzyme synthesized from the vitamin niacin, which can be obtained from soybeans, among other dietary sources.

Biological reduction

$+$ NADH → $+$ NAD^+
coenzyme   enzyme

For example, the reduction of pyruvic acid with NADH, catalyzed by the enzyme lactate dehydrogenase, yields lactic acid. Pyruvic acid is formed during the metabolism of the simple sugar glucose.

$$CH_3-\underset{\underset{O}{\parallel}}{C}-COOH \xrightarrow[\text{dehydrogenase}]{\text{NADH}}{\text{lactate}} CH_3-\underset{\underset{H}{|}}{\overset{\overset{OH}{|}}{C}}-COOH + NAD^+$$

pyruvic acid   lactic acid

16.7   FOCUS ON THE HUMAN BODY
The Chemistry of Vision

The human eye consists of two types of light-sensitive cells—the rod cells, which are responsible for sight in dim light; and the cone cells, which are responsible for color vision and sight in bright light. Animals like pigeons, whose eyes have only cone cells, have color vision but see poorly in dim light, whereas owls, which have only rod cells, are color blind but see well in dim light.

The chemistry of vision in the rod cells centers around the aldehyde, **11-*cis*-retinal.**

11-*cis*-Retinal is the light-sensitive aldehyde that plays a key role in the chemistry of vision for all vertebrates, arthropods, and mollusks. ©*Daniel C. Smith*

Although 11-*cis*-retinal is a stable molecule, the cis geometry around one of the double bonds causes crowding; a hydrogen atom on one double bond is close to the methyl group on an adjacent double bond. In the human retina (Figure 16.2), 11-*cis*-retinal is bonded to the protein opsin, forming rhodopsin or visual purple. When light hits the retina, the 11-cis double bond is isomerized to its more stable trans isomer, and all-*trans*-retinal is formed. This process sends a nerve impulse to the brain, which is then converted into a visual image.

In order for the process to continue, the all-*trans*-retinal must be converted back to 11-*cis*-retinal. This occurs by a series of reactions that involve biological oxidation (Section 14.5) and reduction (Section 16.6). As shown in Figure 16.3, NADH is the coenzyme that reduces the aldehyde in all-*trans*-retinal to all-*trans*-retinol, **vitamin A** (Reaction [1]). NAD+ is the coenzyme that oxidizes 11-*cis*-retinol back to 11-*cis*-retinal (Reaction [3]), so the chemical cycle of vision can continue.

This scheme explains the role of vitamin A (Section 11.7) in vision. Vitamin A can be obtained either directly in the diet or from the orange pigment β-carotene in carrots. Vitamin A, also called all-*trans*-retinol, is converted in two steps to 11-*cis*-retinal, the aldehyde essential for vision in the rod cells. Since the rod cells are responsible for vision in dim light, a deficiency of vitamin A causes night blindness.

576   Chapter 16   Aldehydes and Ketones

Figure 16.2   Vision

In the rod cells of the eye, the 11-*cis*-retinal bonded to opsin absorbs light, and the crowded 11-cis double bond is isomerized to the trans isomer. This process generates a nerve impulse that is converted to a visual image by the brain.

Figure 16.3   Vitamin A and the Chemistry of Vision

- Reaction [1] (reduction): The aldehyde in all-*trans*-retinal (labeled in blue) is reduced to a 1° alcohol using the coenzyme NADH. The product is all-*trans*-retinol.
- Reaction [2] (isomerization): The trans double bond (labeled in red) is isomerized to a cis double bond, forming 11-*cis*-retinol.
- Reaction [3] (oxidation): The 1° alcohol in 11-*cis*-retinol (labeled in blue) is oxidized with the coenzyme NAD+ to an aldehyde. This re-forms 11-*cis*-retinal and the chemical cycle of vision continues.

How are the compounds in each pair related? Choose from stereoisomers, constitutional isomers, or not isomers of each other.

    a. all-*trans*-retinal and 11-*cis*-retinal

    b. all-*trans*-retinal and vitamin A

    c. vitamin A and 11-*cis*-retinol

16.8 Acetal Formation

Aldehydes and ketones undergo addition reactions with alcohols (ROH) to form hemiacetals and acetals. Acetal formation is done in the presence of sulfuric acid (H_2SO_4).

16.8A Acetals and Hemiacetals

Addition of one molecule of alcohol (ROH) to an aldehyde or ketone forms a **hemiacetal.** Like other addition reactions, one bond of the C=O is broken and two new single bonds are formed. Acyclic hemiacetals are unstable. They react with a second molecule of alcohol to form **acetals.**

- A *hemiacetal* contains an OH (hydroxyl) group and an OR (alkoxy) group bonded to the *same* carbon.
- *Acetals* are compounds that contain two OR groups (alkoxy groups) bonded to the *same* carbon.

Two examples of acetal formation using ethanol (CH_3CH_2OH) as the alcohol component are given.

How To **Draw a Hemiacetal and Acetal from a Carbonyl Compound**

Example: Draw the hemiacetal and acetal formed when acetaldehyde (CH_3CHO) is treated with two equivalents of methanol (CH_3OH) in the presence of H_2SO_4.

Step [1] **Convert the carbonyl group to a hemiacetal by adding one equivalent of alcohol (ROH).**
- Locate the C=O in the aldehyde or ketone.
- Break one C—O bond and add one equivalent of CH_3OH across the double bond, placing the OCH_3 group on the carbonyl carbon to form the hemiacetal.

Step [2] **Convert the hemiacetal to an acetal with the second equivalent of ROH.**
- Replace the OH group of the hemiacetal by OCH_3 to form the acetal.

SAMPLE PROBLEM 16.6 DRAWING A HEMIACETAL AND ACETAL

Draw the hemiacetal and acetal formed when cyclohexanone is treated with methanol (CH_3OH) in the presence of H_2SO_4.

cyclohexanone   methanol
     (2 equivalents)

Analysis

To form a hemiacetal and acetal from a carbonyl compound:
- Locate the C=O in the starting material.
- Break one C—O bond and add one equivalent of CH_3OH across the double bond, placing the OCH_3 group on the carbonyl carbon. This forms the hemiacetal.
- Replace the OH group of the hemiacetal by OCH_3 to form the acetal.

Solution

hemiacetal   acetal

PRACTICE PROBLEM 16.6

Draw the hemiacetal and acetal formed when each carbonyl compound is treated with two equivalents of the given alcohol in the presence of H_2SO_4.

a. CH_3CH_2—C(=O)—CH_2CH_3 + CH_3OH

b.   (benzaldehyde structure)   + CH_3CH_2OH

More Practice: Try Problems 16.63–16.66; 16.73d; 16.74c; 16.75d, e; 16.76d, e; 16.77d, e; 16.78d, e.

Acetals are *not* ethers, even though both compounds contain a C—OR bond.

—C(OR)(OR)—	—C—O—C—
acetal	ether
2 OR groups on one carbon	2 C's on a single O atom

- An acetal contains one carbon atom bonded to *two* OR groups.
- An ether contains only *one* oxygen atom bonded to two carbons.

SAMPLE PROBLEM 16.7 IDENTIFYING AN ETHER, A HEMIACETAL, AND AN ACETAL

Identify each compound as an ether, hemiacetal, or acetal.

a. CH_3CH_2—O—CH_2CH_3

b. (five-membered ring with two O's and C bonded to two CH_3)

Analysis

Recall the definitions to identify the functional groups:

- An ether has the general structure ROR.
- A hemiacetal has one C bonded to OH and OR.
- An acetal has one C bonded to two OR groups.

Solution

a. CH_3CH_2—O—CH_2CH_3
    2 C's on one O atom
    ether

b. (ring structure)
    This C is bonded to 2 O's.
    acetal

Note that the acetal in part (b) is part of a ring. It contains one ring carbon bonded to two oxygens, making it an acetal.

PRACTICE PROBLEM 16.7

Identify each compound as an ether, hemiacetal, or acetal.

a. (cyclohexane ring with OCH_3)

b. (cyclohexane ring with two OCH_3)

c. $CH_3CH_2CH_2CH_2$—C(OH)(H)—OCH_3

d. (bicyclic ring with two O's and C bonded to two CH_3)

More Practice: Try Problems 16.59, 16.60.

PROBLEM 16.13

Label the functional group(s) in each compound as ethers or acetals.

a.   b.

16.8B   Cyclic Hemiacetals

Although acyclic hemiacetals are generally unstable, **cyclic hemiacetals containing five- and six-membered rings are stable compounds** that are readily isolated.

Hemiacetal General structure	Cyclic hemiacetals

One C is bonded to:
• one OH group
• one OR group

Each indicated C is bonded to:
• an OH group
• an OR group that is part of a ring

These cyclic hemiacetals are formed by an *intramolecular* reaction of a compound that contains *both* a hydroxyl group and an aldehyde or ketone.

HOCH₂CH₂CH₂CH₂ — 5-hydroxypentanal

Cyclic hemiacetals are especially important in carbohydrate chemistry. **The most common simple carbohydrate, glucose, exists predominantly as a cyclic hemiacetal.** Glucose has five OH groups, but only one OH group is bonded to a carbon that is also bonded to another oxygen atom, making it a hemiacetal. All of the other OH groups in glucose are "regular" alcohols. We will learn much more about these stable cyclic hemiacetals in Chapter 20.

glucose
(cyclic hemiacetal form)

Cyclic hemiacetals are converted to acetals by reaction with another alcohol (ROH). To draw the structure of the resulting acetal, replace the OH group of the hemiacetal by the OR group of the alcohol.

Many biologically active molecules contain acetals and cyclic hemiacetals. For example, lactose, the principal carbohydrate in milk, contains one acetal and one hemiacetal. Many individuals, mainly of Asian and African descent, lack adequate amounts of lactase, the enzyme needed to digest and absorb lactose. This condition, lactose intolerance, is associated with abdominal cramping and recurrent diarrhea.

©Mitch Hrdlicka/Stockbyte/Getty Images RF

SAMPLE PROBLEM 16.8 LOCATING AN ACETAL, HEMIACETAL, AND ETHER IN A CYCLIC COMPOUND

Label the acetal, hemiacetal, and ether in the following compound.

Analysis

Label functional groups in cyclic acetals, hemiacetals, and ethers in the same manner as for acyclic compounds.

- An ether has two C's bonded to one O atom.
- An acetal has two OR groups bonded to one C atom.
- A hemiacetal has one OH group and one OR group bonded to one C.

Solution

- The hemiacetal has the C atom bonded to an OH group and an O atom that is part of a ring.
- The ether has an O atom bonded to two C atoms that are part of rings.
- The acetal has the C atom bonded to an OCH_3 group and an O atom that is part of a ring.

PRACTICE PROBLEM 16.8

Locate the ether and acetal in oleandrin, a complex toxin isolated from the sap of the oleander plant.

oleandrin

More Practice: Try Problems 16.61a, 16.62a, 16.85, 16.86.

Oleandrin, obtained from the sap of the oleander plant (*Nerium oleander*), is used in some countries for the treatment of congestive heart failure.
©alessandro0770/Getty Images RF

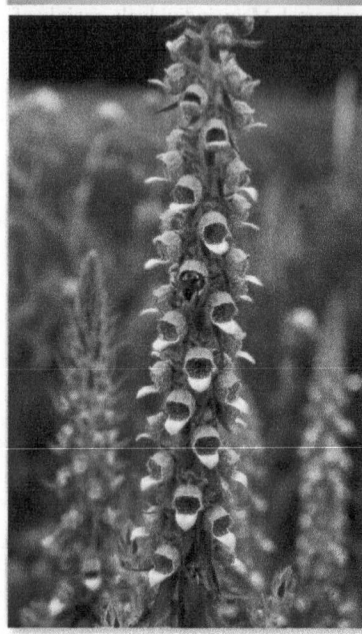

The leaves of the woolly foxglove plant are the source of the potent cardiac drug digoxin. ©*Richo Cech, Horizon Herbs, LLC.*

SAMPLE PROBLEM 16.9 IDENTIFYING ACETALS IN A COMPLEX MOLECULE

Identify the three acetals in digoxin, a naturally occurring drug prescribed for patients with congestive heart failure and other heart ailments.

digoxin

Analysis

Although the structure of digoxin is complicated, look at each O atom individually and recall that an **acetal has one C bonded to two OR groups.**

Solution

The acetal carbons in digoxin are indicated with arrows and the oxygen atoms of the acetals are drawn in red.

acetal   acetal

acetal

digoxin

PRACTICE PROBLEM 16.9

Label the three acetals in solanine, the toxic compound mentioned in the chapter opener.

solanine

$R = C_{27}H_{42}N$

More Practice: Try Problem 16.58.

PROBLEM 16.14

What acetal is formed in each reaction?

a. [structure] $-OH$ + CH_3CH_2OH $\xrightarrow{H_2SO_4}$

b. [structure] $-OH$ + [structure] $-OH$ $\xrightarrow{H_2SO_4}$

16.8C   Acetal Hydrolysis

Acetals are stable molecules, but they can be converted back to aldehydes and ketones by treatment with acid and water. This reaction is a *hydrolysis*, **since bonds are cleaved by reaction with water.**

SAMPLE PROBLEM 16.10 DRAWING THE PRODUCTS OF ACETAL HYDROLYSIS

What hydrolysis products are formed when the acetal $(CH_3CH_2)_2C(OCH_3)_2$ is treated with H_2SO_4 in H_2O?

Analysis

To draw the products of hydrolysis:

- Locate the two C—OR bonds on the same carbon.
- Replace the two C—O single bonds with a carbonyl group (C=O).
- Each OR group then becomes a molecule of alcohol (ROH) product.

Solution

PRACTICE PROBLEM 16.10

What products are formed by hydrolysis of each acetal?

More Practice: Try Problems 16.71, 16.72.

CHAPTER HIGHLIGHTS

KEY TERMS

Acetal (16.8)

Aldehyde (16.1)

Carbonyl group (16.1)

Cyclic hemiacetal (16.8)

Hemiacetal (16.8)

Hydrogenation (16.6)

Hydrolysis (16.8)

Ketone (16.1)

NAD$^+$ (16.6)

NADH (16.6)

Oxidation (16.5)

Reduction (16.6)

Tollens reagent (16.5)

KEY REACTIONS

[1] Oxidation of aldehydes (16.5)

$$RCHO \xrightarrow[\text{or Tollens reagent}]{K_2Cr_2O_7} RCOOH$$
carboxylic acid

[2] Reduction (16.6)

a. Aldehydes $RCHO \xrightarrow[\text{Pd}]{H_2} RCH_2OH$
1° alcohol

b. Ketones $R_2CO \xrightarrow[\text{Pd}]{H_2} R_2CHOH$
2° alcohol

c. Biological reduction

$$+ \quad NAD^+$$

[3] Acetals and hemiacetals (16.8)

a. General reaction

hemiacetal   acetal

b. Cyclic hemiacetal

$$HOCH_2CH_2CH_2CH_2 \overset{O}{\underset{H}{C}} \xrightarrow{\text{re-draw}} \cdots \rightarrow$$
5-hydroxypentanal

cyclic hemiacetal

c. Cyclic acetals

cyclic hemiacetal   cyclic acetal

d. Acetal hydrolysis

$$R\overset{OR'}{\underset{H \,(or\, R)}{\overset{|}{C}}}OR' \; + \; H_2O \; \underset{}{\overset{H_2SO_4}{\rightleftharpoons}} \; R\overset{O}{\underset{H \,(or\, R)}{C}} \; + \; 2\, R'O-H$$

KEY CONCEPTS

❶ **What are the characteristics of aldehydes and ketones?**
  • An aldehyde has the general structure RCHO and contains a carbonyl group (C=O) bonded to at least one hydrogen atom. (16.1)
  • A ketone has the general structure RCOR' and contains a carbonyl group (C=O) bonded to two carbon atoms. (16.1)
  • The carbonyl carbon is trigonal planar, with bond angles of approximately 120°. (16.1)

  • The carbonyl group is polar, giving an aldehyde or ketone stronger intermolecular forces than hydrocarbons. (16.3)
  • Aldehydes and ketones have lower boiling points than alcohols but higher boiling points than hydrocarbons of comparable size. (16.3)
  • Aldehydes and ketones are soluble in organic solvents, but those having less than six C's are water soluble, too. (16.3)

2 **How are aldehydes and ketones named? (16.2)**

- Aldehydes are identified by the suffix -*al*, and the carbon chain is numbered to put the carbonyl group at C1.
- Ketones are identified by the suffix -*one*, and the carbon chain is numbered to give the carbonyl group the lower number.

3 **Give examples of useful aldehydes and ketones. (16.4)**

- Formaldehyde (CH_2=O) is an irritant in smoggy air, a preservative, and a disinfectant, and it is a starting material for synthesizing polymers.
- Acetone [$(CH_3)_2$C=O] is an industrial solvent and polymer starting material.
- Several aldehydes—cinnamaldehyde, vanillin, geranial, and citronellal—have characteristic odors and occur naturally in fruits and plants.
- Dihydroxyacetone [$(HOCH_2)_2$C=O] is the active ingredient in artificial tanning agents, and many other ketones are useful sunscreens.
- Amygdalin, a naturally occurring carbonyl derivative, forms toxic HCN on hydrolysis.

4 **What products are formed when aldehydes are oxidized? (16.5)**

- Aldehydes are oxidized to carboxylic acids (RCOOH) with $K_2Cr_2O_7$ or Tollens reagent.
- Ketones are not oxidized because they contain no H atom on the carbonyl carbon.

5 **What products are formed when aldehydes and ketones are reduced? (16.6)**

- Aldehydes are reduced to 1° alcohols with H_2 and a Pd catalyst.
- Ketones are reduced to 2° alcohols with H_2 and a Pd catalyst.
- Biological reduction occurs with the coenzyme NADH.

6 **What reactions occur during vision? (16.7)**

- When light hits the retina, the crowded C=C in 11-*cis*-retinal is isomerized to a more stable trans double bond, and a nerve impulse is generated. All-*trans*-retinal is converted back to the cis isomer by a three-step sequence—reduction, isomerization, and oxidation.

7 **What are hemiacetals and acetals, and how are they prepared? (16.8)**

- Hemiacetals contain an OH group and an OR group bonded to the same carbon.
- Acetals contain two OR groups bonded to the same carbon.
- Treatment of an aldehyde or ketone with an alcohol (ROH) first forms an unstable hemiacetal, which reacts with more alcohol to form an acetal.
- Cyclic hemiacetals are stable compounds present in carbohydrates and some drugs.
- Acetals are converted back to aldehydes and ketones by hydrolysis with water and acid.

PROBLEMS

Selected in-chapter and odd-numbered end-of-chapter problems have brief answers in Appendix B. The *Student Study Guide and Solutions Manual* contains detailed solutions to all in-chapter and odd-numbered end-of-chapter problems, as well as additional worked examples and a chapter self-test.

Structure and Bonding

16.15 Draw the structure of a compound that fits each description:
   a. an aldehyde of molecular formula $C_8H_{16}O$ that has six carbons in its longest chain
   b. a ketone of molecular formula $C_6H_{12}O$ that contains five carbons in its longest chain
   c. a ketone of molecular formula C_5H_8O that contains a ring
   d. an aldehyde of molecular formula $C_6H_{10}O$ that has the CHO group bonded to a ring

16.16 Draw the structure of a constitutional isomer of 2-heptanone ($CH_3COCH_2CH_2CH_2CH_2CH_3$) that:
   a. contains an aldehyde
   b. contains a ketone
   c. contains a hydroxyl group (OH)

16.17 How do a C=O and a C=C compare with regard to the following: (a) geometry; (b) polarity; (c) type of reaction?

16.18 Can an aldehyde have molecular formula $C_5H_{12}O$? Explain why or why not.

Nomenclature

16.19 Give an acceptable name for each carbonyl compound depicted in the ball-and-stick models.

a.   b.

16.20 Give an acceptable name for each carbonyl compound depicted in the ball-and-stick models.

a.   b.

586   **Chapter 16**   Aldehydes and Ketones

16.21   Give an acceptable name for each aldehyde.

a. CH₃CH₂CH₂CHCH₂CHO
          |
          CH₃

b. CH₃CH₂CHCH₂CHCH₂CHO
          | |
          CH₃   CH₃

c.
       CH₂CHO
       |
CH₃CH₂CH₂CHCH₂CH₂CH₃

d.

e.

16.22   Give an acceptable name for each aldehyde.

a. (CH₃)₃CCH₂CHO

b. (CH₃CH₂)₂CHCH₂CH₂CHO

c.

d. (CH₃CH₂CH₂CH₂)₂CHCH₂CHO

e.

16.23   Draw the structure corresponding to each name.

a. 3,3-dichloropentanal

b. 3,4-dimethylhexanal

c. o-bromobenzaldehyde

d. 4-hydroxyheptanal

16.24   Draw the structure corresponding to each name.

a. 2-bromooctanal

b. 2-propylheptanal

c. 3,4-dimethoxybenzaldehyde

d. 3,4-dihydroxynonanal

16.25   Give an acceptable name for each ketone.

a. (CH₃)₂CHCH₂C(=O)CH₃   d. (CH₃)₂CHC(=O)CHCH₂CH₃
                                           |
                                           CH₃

b.

e.

c.

16.26   Give an acceptable name for each ketone.

a. CH₃CH₂CH₂CH₂CHCH₂CH₃
                      |
                  O=C-CH₃

b.

c.
CH₃CH₂C(=O)(CH₂)₅CH(CH₃)₂

d.

e.

16.27   Draw the structure corresponding to each name.

a. 3,3-dimethyl-2-hexanone

b. methyl propyl ketone

c. m-ethylacetophenone

d. 2,4,5-triethylcyclohexanone

16.28   Draw the structure corresponding to each name.

a. dibutyl ketone

b. 1-chloro-3-pentanone

c. p-bromoacetophenone

d. 3-hydroxycyclopentanone

16.29   Draw the structure of the four constitutional isomers of molecular formula C₆H₁₂O that contain an aldehyde and four carbons in the longest chain. Give the IUPAC name for each aldehyde.

16.30   Draw the structure of the three isomeric ketones of molecular formula C₅H₁₀O. Give the IUPAC name for each ketone.

16.31   Each of the following names is incorrect. Draw the structure of the compound and name it correctly.

a. 1-pentanone

b. 4-hexanone

c. 3-propyl-2-butanone

d. 2-methyl-1-octanal

16.32   Each of the following names is incorrect. Draw the structure of the compound and name it correctly.

a. 6-octanone

b. 1-heptanone

c. 3-propyl-1-cyclopentanone

d. 5-methylcyclohexanone

Physical Properties and Intermolecular Forces

16.33   Draw out the structure of benzaldehyde, including any lone pairs on oxygen. Then, show the hydrogen bonding interactions between benzaldehyde and water.

16.34 Can hydrogen bonding occur between the compounds in each pair? If hydrogen bonding is possible, draw out the compounds and indicate how that interaction would take place.
  a. two molecules of acetaldehyde (CH₃CHO)
  b. CH₃CHO and H₂O
  c. CH₃CHO and CH₃OH

16.35 Which compound in each pair has the higher boiling point?
  a. (CH₃)₃CCH₂CH₂CH₃ or (CH₃)₃CCH₂CHO

  b.

16.36 Which compound in each pair has the higher boiling point?
  a. CH₃(CH₂)₆CHO or CH₃(CH₂)₇OH
  b. CH₃(CH₂)₆CHO or CH₃(CH₂)₂CHO

16.37 Rank the following compounds in order of increasing melting point.

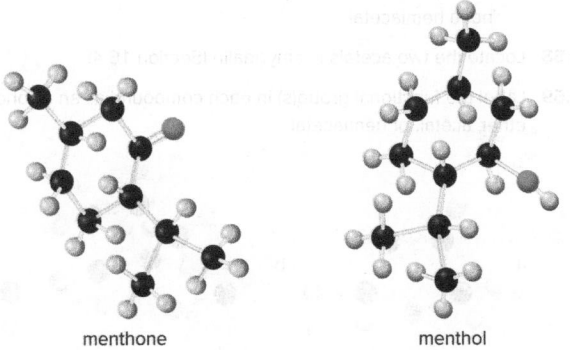

16.38 Menthone and menthol are both isolated from mint. Explain why menthol is a solid at room temperature but menthone is a liquid.

menthone   menthol

16.39 Label each compound as water soluble or water insoluble.
  a.
  b. CH₃—C(=O)—CH₂CH₃
  c. CH₃CH₂CH₂CH₃

16.40 Label each compound as water soluble or water insoluble.
  a. [cyclohexanone with methyl]
  b. CH₃CH₂CH₂CHO
  c. CH₃CH₂CH₂OH

Oxidation and Reduction

16.41 What product is formed when each compound is treated with K₂Cr₂O₇? With some compounds, no reaction occurs.
  a. CH₃(CH₂)₄CHO
  b. [cyclopentane-CH₂CHO]
  c. [cyclopentanone with ethyl]
  d. [chain with OH]

16.42 What product is formed when each compound is treated with K₂Cr₂O₇? With some compounds, no reaction occurs.
  a. [benzene with Cl and CHO]
  b. CH₃(CH₂)₈CHO
  c. [OH on chain]
  d. [cyclohexane with C(=O)CH₃]

16.43 What product is formed when each compound in Problem 16.41 is treated with Tollens reagent (Ag₂O, NH₄OH)? With some compounds, no reaction occurs.

16.44 Which of the following compounds react with Tollens reagent?
  a. [cyclopentanone]
  b. [cyclopentane-CHO]
  c. [chain with OH]
  d. [cyclopentane-C(=O)CH₃]

16.45 Answer the following questions about the carbohydrate erythrulose, an ingredient in sunless tanning agents.

erythrulose
  a. Does erythrulose contain an aldehyde or ketone?
  b. Classify each hydroxyl group as 1°, 2°, or 3°.
  c. What product is formed when erythrulose is treated with Tollens reagent?
  d. What product is formed when erythrulose is treated with K₂Cr₂O₇?

16.46 Consider the following ball-and-stick model.

  a. Locate the chirality center.
  b. Is the carbonyl group part of an aldehyde or a ketone?
  c. Classify each hydroxyl group as 1°, 2°, or 3°.
  d. What product is formed when this compound is treated with Tollens reagent?

588   **Chapter 16**   Aldehydes and Ketones

16.47 What aldehyde is needed to prepare each carboxylic acid by an oxidation reaction?

a. $CH_3CH_2CHCH_2CO_2H$ (with CH_3 branch)   b. CH_3—⬡—CO_2H

16.48 What aldehyde is needed to prepare each carboxylic acid by an oxidation reaction?

a. ⬠—$CH_2CH_2CO_2H$ b. (benzene ring with Br and CO_2H)

16.49 What alcohol is formed when each carbonyl compound is treated with H_2 and a Pd catalyst?

a. CH_3CH_2—⬡—CHO c. $CH_3CH_2\overset{\displaystyle O}{\overset{\|}{C}}CH_2CH(CH_3)_2$

b. (4-methylcyclohexanone)   d. $CH_3(CH_2)_6CHO$

16.50 (a) Draw the structure of 6-methyloctanal, a component of yuzu (Section 16.2). (b) Label the chirality center. (c) What product is formed when 6-methyloctanal is treated with H_2 and a palladium catalyst?

16.51 Using the information in Sections 16.6 and 13.6A, draw the product that results when citronellal (Figure 16.1) is treated with excess H_2 in the presence of a Pd catalyst.

(structure of citronellal)

citronellal

16.52 What product is formed when 2,3-butanedione, an additive that imparts a butter flavor to products, is treated with two equivalents of H_2 in the presence of a palladium catalyst?

(structure of 2,3-butanedione)

2,3-butanedione

16.53 What carbonyl compound is needed to make each alcohol by a reduction reaction?

a. $CH_3CH_2CH_2CH_2CH_2OH$ b. (3-methylcyclohexanol)

16.54 What carbonyl compound is needed to make each alcohol by a reduction reaction?

a. $CH_3CH_2\overset{\displaystyle OH}{\overset{|}{C}H}CH_2CH_2CH_3$ b. $(CH_3)_2CHCH_2CH_2OH$

16.55 Why can't 1-methylcyclohexanol be prepared by the reduction of a carbonyl compound?

1-methylcyclohexanol

16.56 Why can't 2-methyl-2-propanol be prepared by the reduction of a carbonyl compound?

2-methyl-2-propanol

Hemiacetals and Acetals

16.57 Draw the structure of a compound of molecular formula $C_5H_{12}O_2$ that fits each description.
   a. a compound that contains an acetal
   b. a compound that contains a hemiacetal
   c. a compound that contains two ethers
   d. a compound that contains an alcohol and an ether, but is not a hemiacetal

16.58 Locate the two acetals in amygdalin (Section 16.4).

16.59 Label the functional group(s) in each compound as an alcohol, ether, acetal, or hemiacetal.

a.   b.

16.60 Label the functional group(s) in each compound as an alcohol, ether, acetal, or hemiacetal.

a.   b.

16.61 (a) Label the hemiacetal in glucosamine, available in over-the-counter remedies for the treatment of osteoarthritis. (b) Label all the other functional groups in glucosamine.

glucosamine

16.62 (a) Label the acetal in salicin, a naturally occurring pain reliever isolated from the bark of the willow tree. (b) How many 1° OH groups does salicin contain?

salicin

16.63 What acetal is formed when each aldehyde or ketone is treated with two equivalents of methanol (CH₃OH) in the presence of H₂SO₄?

16.64 What acetal is formed when each aldehyde or ketone is treated with two equivalents of ethanol (CH₃CH₂OH) in the presence of H₂SO₄?

a. CH₃CH₂CH₂COCH₂CH₃   c. (CH₃)₂CHCH₂CH₂CHO

b. [cyclohexanone methyl]   d. CH₃CH₂CHO

16.65 (a) What hemiacetal is formed when acetone [(CH₃)₂CO] is treated with one equivalent of cyclopentanol? (b) What acetal is formed when acetone is treated with two equivalents of cyclopentanol in the presence of H₂SO₄?

16.66 (a) What hemiacetal is formed when benzaldehyde (C₆H₅CHO) is treated with one equivalent of cyclohexanol? (b) What acetal is formed when benzaldehyde is treated with two equivalents of cyclohexanol in the presence of H₂SO₄?

16.67 a. Identify the hemiacetal carbon in compound **A**.
b. What hydroxy aldehyde would form this hemiacetal in a cyclization reaction?
c. What product is formed when **A** is treated with CH₃OH and H₂SO₄?

16.68 a. Identify the hemiacetal carbon in compound **B**.
b. What hydroxy aldehyde would form this hemiacetal in a cyclization reaction?
c. What product is formed when **B** is treated with CH₃CH₂OH and H₂SO₄?

16.69 What hemiacetal is formed when hydroxy aldehyde **C** is cyclized?

HOCH₂CH₂CH₂CH(CH₃)CHO **C**

16.70 What hemiacetal is formed when hydroxy aldehyde **D** is cyclized?

HOCHCH₃CH₂CH₂CHO **D**

16.71 What products are formed when each acetal is hydrolyzed with water and sulfuric acid?

16.72 What products are formed when each acetal is hydrolyzed with water and sulfuric acid?

General Reactions

16.73 Answer each question about carbonyl compound **A**, depicted in the ball-and-stick model, and one of the many components of the mango.

©Africa Studio/Shutterstock RF

a. Draw a skeletal structure for **A**.
b. Give an acceptable name for **A**.
c. How many trigonal planar carbons are present in **A**?
d. What product is formed when **A** is treated with two equivalents of CH₃OH in the presence of acid?

590   Chapter 16 Aldehydes and Ketones

16.74 Answer each question about phenylacetaldehyde, depicted in the ball-and-stick model, and one of the components responsible for the fragrance of the plumeria flower.

©Don Mammoser/Shutterstock RF

phenylacetaldehyde

a. Draw a skeletal structure for phenylacetaldehyde.
b. How many trigonal planar carbons are present in phenylacetaldehyde?
c. What product is formed when phenylacetaldehyde is treated with two equivalents of CH_3OH in the presence of acid?
d. What product is formed when phenylacetaldehyde is treated with one equivalent of hydrogen gas in the presence of a metal catalyst?

16.75 Benzaldehyde is the compound principally responsible for the odor of almonds. What products are formed when benzaldehyde is treated with each reagent?

benzaldehyde

a. H_2, Pd
b. $K_2Cr_2O_7$
c. Ag_2O, NH_4OH
d. CH_3OH (2 equivalents), H_2SO_4
e. CH_3CH_2OH (2 equivalents), H_2SO_4
f. Product in (e), then H_2O, H_2SO_4

16.76 Anisaldehyde is a component of anise, a spice with a licorice odor used in cooking and aromatherapy. What products are formed when anisaldehyde is treated with each reagent?

anisaldehyde

a. H_2, Pd
b. $K_2Cr_2O_7$
c. Ag_2O, NH_4OH
d. CH_3OH (2 equivalents), H_2SO_4
e. CH_3CH_2OH (2 equivalents), H_2SO_4
f. Product in (e), then H_2O, H_2SO_4

16.77 2-Heptanone is an alarm pheromone of the bee. What products are formed when 2-heptanone is treated with each reagent? With some reagents, no reaction occurs.

©ElementalImaging/Getty Images RF

$$CH_3\overset{O}{\underset{||}{C}}(CH_2)_4CH_3$$

2-heptanone

a. H_2, Pd
b. $K_2Cr_2O_7$
c. Ag_2O, NH_4OH
d. CH_3OH (2 equivalents), H_2SO_4
e. CH_3CH_2OH (2 equivalents), H_2SO_4
f. Product in (e), then H_2O, H_2SO_4

16.78 2,6-Dimethyl-3-heptanone is a communication pheromone of the bee. What products are formed when 2,6-dimethyl-3-heptanone is treated with each reagent? With some reagents, no reaction occurs.

$$(CH_3)_2CH\overset{O}{\underset{||}{C}}(CH_2)_2CH(CH_3)_2$$

2,6-dimethyl-3-heptanone

a. H_2, Pd
b. $K_2Cr_2O_7$
c. Ag_2O, NH_4OH
d. CH_3OH (2 equivalents), H_2SO_4
e. CH_3CH_2OH (2 equivalents), H_2SO_4
f. Product in (e), then H_2O, H_2SO_4

16.79 Three constitutional isomers of molecular formula C_5H_8O can be converted to 1-pentanol ($CH_3CH_2CH_2CH_2CH_2OH$) on treatment with two equivalents of H_2 in the presence of a Pd catalyst. Draw the structures of the three possible compounds, all of which contain a carbonyl group.

16.80 Identify **A–C** in the following reaction sequence.

$$\underset{C_5H_8O}{\textbf{A}} \xrightarrow[\text{Pd}]{H_2} \underset{C_5H_{10}O}{\textbf{B}} \xrightarrow{H_2SO_4}$$

$$\underset{C_5H_8}{\textbf{C}} \xrightarrow[\text{Pd}]{H_2} \bigcirc$$

Applications

16.81 Androsterone is a male sex hormone that controls the development of secondary sex characteristics in males. Draw the organic products formed when androsterone is treated with each reagent.

HO

androsterone

a. H_2, Pd
b. $K_2Cr_2O_7$
c. CH_3OH (2 equivalents), H_2SO_4
d. CH_3CH_2OH (2 equivalents), H_2SO_4

16.82 Salmeterol (trade name Serevent) is a drug that dilates airways and is used to treat asthma. It can be formed by the reduction of a dicarbonyl compound **X** with excess H$_2$ and a Pd catalyst.

X

a. Draw the structure of salmeterol.
b. Label the one chirality center in salmeterol.
c. Draw both enantiomers of salmeterol in three dimensions using wedges and dashed wedges (see Section 15.3).

16.83 When cinnamon is ingested, the cinnamaldehyde it contains is oxidized by the coenzyme NAD$^+$ and an enzyme in a similar fashion to the biological oxidation described in Section 14.6. What oxidation product is formed from cinnamaldehyde?

cinnamaldehyde

16.84 Safrole is a naturally occurring compound isolated from sassafras plants. Once used as a common food additive in root beer and other beverages, it is now banned because it is carcinogenic.

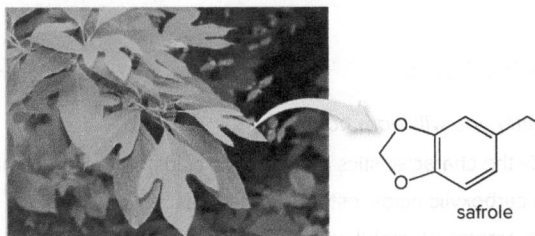

©kj2011/Getty Images RF

safrole

a. Label the functional groups in safrole.
b. What products are formed when safrole undergoes hydrolysis with water and sulfuric acid?

16.85 2-Deoxyribose is a building block of DNA, very large organic molecules that store all genetic information. Label each OH group in 2-deoxyribose as being part of a regular alcohol or a hemiacetal.

2-deoxyribose

16.86 Paraldehyde, a hypnotic and sedative once commonly used to treat seizures and induce sleep in some hospitalized patients, is formed from three molecules of acetaldehyde (CH$_3$CHO). Label the acetal carbons in paraldehyde.

paraldehyde

16.87 Describe the main reaction that occurs in the rod cells in the retina, which generates a nerve impulse that allows us to see. What role does the geometry of 11-*cis*-retinal play in this process?

16.88 What reactions convert all-*trans*-retinal back to 11-*cis*-retinal so that the process of vision can continue?

CHALLENGE PROBLEMS

16.89 Monensin, a complex antibiotic produced by the bacterium *Streptomyces cinamonsis,* is added to cattle feed to protect the cattle from infection. Identify each oxygen-containing functional group.

monensin

16.90 Chloral hydrate is a sedative formed by the addition of water to chloral (Cl$_3$CCHO). Chloral hydrate is sometimes used to calm a patient prior to a surgical procedure. It has also been used for less reputable purposes. Adding it to an alcoholic beverage forms a so-called "knock-out drink," causing an individual to pass out. Although we have not studied the formation of hydrates from aldehydes, this reaction resembles the addition of alcohols to aldehydes to form hemiacetals. What is the structure of chloral hydrate?

17

Soaps are salts derived from
carboxylic acids, which clean
clothes by dissolving the
hydrocarbons of dirt in their long
nonpolar carbon chains.
©Jill Braaten RF

Carboxylic Acids, Esters, and Amides

CHAPTER OUTLINE

17.1   Structure and Bonding

17.2   Nomenclature

17.3   Physical Properties

17.4   Interesting Carboxylic Acids in Consumer
         Products and Medicines

17.5   Interesting Esters and Amides

17.6   The Acidity of Carboxylic Acids

17.7   FOCUS ON HEALTH & MEDICINE: Aspirin

17.8   The Conversion of Carboxylic Acids to Esters
         and Amides

17.9   Hydrolysis of Esters and Amides

17.10 Synthetic Polymers in Modern Society—
         Polyamides and Polyesters

17.11 FOCUS ON HEALTH & MEDICINE: Penicillin

CHAPTER GOALS

In this chapter you will learn how to:

1. Identify the characteristics of carboxylic acids, esters, and amides
2. Name carboxylic acids, esters, and amides
3. Give examples of useful carboxylic acids
4. Give examples of useful esters and amides
5. Draw the products of acid–base reactions of carboxylic acids
6. Explain how soap cleans away dirt
7. Discuss the acid–base chemistry of aspirin
8. Convert carboxylic acids to esters and amides
9. Draw the products of the hydrolysis of esters and amides
10. Draw the structures of polyesters and polyamides
11. Explain how penicillin works

Chapter 17 is the second of two chapters that concentrates on compounds that contain a carbonyl group (C=O). Whereas Chapter 16 focused on aldehydes (RCHO) and ketones (R_2CO), Chapter 17 discusses the chemistry and properties of **carboxylic acids (RCOOH), esters (RCOOR'), and amides (RCONR'$_2$).** All three families of organic compounds occur widely in nature, and many useful synthetic compounds have been prepared as well. Simple carboxylic acids like acetic acid (CH_3COOH) have a sour taste and a biting odor, and long-chain carboxylic acids form vegetable oils and animal fat. Simple esters have easily recognized fragrances, and the most abundant lipids contain three ester groups. Several useful drugs are amides, and all proteins, such as those that form hair, muscle, and connective tissue, contain many amide units.

17.1   Structure and Bonding

Carboxylic acids, esters, and **amides** are three families of organic molecules that contain a **carbonyl group (C=O)** bonded to an element more electronegative than carbon.

The word *carboxyl* (for a COOH group) is derived from *carb*onyl (C=O) + hydr*oxyl* (OH).

- *Carboxylic acids* are organic compounds containing a carboxyl group (COOH).

General structure

carboxylic acid   **carboxyl group**   acetic acid CH_3CO_2H

Although the structure of a carboxylic acid is often abbreviated as **RCOOH** or **RCO$_2$H,** keep in mind that the central carbon atom of the functional group has a double bond to one oxygen atom and a single bond to another.

- *Esters* are carbonyl compounds that contain an alkoxy group (OR') bonded to the carbonyl carbon.

General structure

ester   methyl acetate $CH_3CO_2CH_3$

The structure of an ester is often abbreviated as RCOOR' or RCO$_2$R'.

- *Amides* are carbonyl compounds that contain a nitrogen atom bonded to the carbonyl carbon.

General structure

amide   **1° amide**   **2° amide**   **3° amide**
R' = H or alkyl   1 C—N bond   2 C—N bonds   3 C—N bonds

The N atom of an amide may be bonded to other hydrogen atoms or alkyl groups. Amides are classified as **1°, 2°,** or **3°** depending on the number of carbon atoms bonded directly to the *nitrogen* atom.

- A primary (1°) amide contains one C—N bond. A 1° amide has the structure RCONH$_2$.
- A secondary (2°) amide contains two C—N bonds. A 2° amide has the structure RCONHR'.
- A tertiary (3°) amide contains three C—N bonds. A 3° amide has the structure RCONR'$_2$.

Cyclic esters and amides are known. **A cyclic ester is called a *lactone*. A cyclic amide is called a *lactam*.**

The carbonyl carbon is bonded to an OR group that is part of a ring.

The carbonyl carbon is bonded to a nitrogen atom that is part of a ring.

cyclic ester
lactone

cyclic amide
lactam

Carboxylic acids, esters, and amides are called **acyl compounds,** because they contain an **acyl group (RCO)** bonded to an electronegative atom.

N or O atom bonded here

acyl group

The two most important features of acyl compounds, like other carbonyl compounds, are the following:

120°   120°

trigonal planar

polar bond

δ−

δ+

- **The carbonyl carbon is trigonal planar, so all bond angles are 120°.**
- **The electronegative oxygen atom makes the carbonyl group polar, so the carbonyl carbon is electron poor (δ+) and the carbonyl oxygen is electron rich (δ−).**

Oxalic acid (a carboxylic acid) in spinach, propyl acetate (an ester) in pears, and capsaicin (an amide) in hot peppers are examples of acyl compounds.

CH_3 —— $OCH_2CH_2CH_3$

propyl acetate

HO —— OH

oxalic acid

CH_3O

HO

capsaicin

PROBLEM 17.1

Draw out each compound to clearly show what groups are bonded to the carbonyl carbon. Label each compound as a carboxylic acid, ester, or amide.

a. $CH_3CH_2CO_2CH_2CH_3$ b. $CH_3CONHCH_3$ c. $(CH_3)_3CCO_2H$ d. $(CH_3)_2CHCON(CH_3)_2$

PROBLEM 17.2

Classify the four amides in thyrotropin-releasing hormone (TRH), a hormone produced in the hypothalamus region of the brain, as 1°, 2°, or 3°.

PROBLEM 17.3

(a) Label each functional group in lisinopril, a drug used to treat high blood pressure. (b) How many trigonal planar carbons does lisinopril contain?

lisinopril

17.2 Nomenclature

To name carboxylic acids, esters, and amides, we must learn the suffix that identifies each functional group in the IUPAC system. Since the names of esters and amides are derived from carboxylic acids, we must first learn how to name carboxylic acids. With esters, 2° amides, and 3° amides, the name of the acyl compound has two distinct portions: an acyl group that contains the carbonyl, and one or two alkyl groups bonded to the oxygen or nitrogen atom.

17.2A Naming a Carboxylic Acid—RCOOH

- In the IUPAC system, carboxylic acids are identified by the suffix -oic acid.

To name a carboxylic acid using the IUPAC system:

1. Find the longest chain containing the COOH group, and change the -e ending of the parent alkane to the suffix -oic acid.
2. Number the carbon chain to put the COOH group at C1, but omit this number from the name. Apply all of the other usual rules of nomenclature.

Many simple carboxylic acids are often referred to by their common names. A common name uses the suffix -ic acid. Three common names are virtually always used.

formic acid (methanoic acid)   acetic acid (ethanoic acid)   benzoic acid (benzenecarboxylic acid)

[IUPAC names are given in parentheses, and are rarely used.]

Greek letters are sometimes used to designate the carbons near carbonyl groups. These terms can be used for any carbonyl group.

$$\beta \text{ carbon} \quad \text{C}-\text{C}-\overset{\displaystyle O}{\text{C}} \quad \alpha \text{ carbon}$$

- The carbon adjacent to the COOH is called the α (alpha) carbon.
- The carbon bonded to the α carbon is the β (beta) carbon.

SAMPLE PROBLEM 17.1 NAMING A CARBOXYLIC ACID

Give the IUPAC name of the following carboxylic acid.

$$\underset{\overset{|}{CH_3}}{CH_3CHCHCH_2CH_2}-\overset{\displaystyle O}{\underset{OH}{C}}$$

Analysis and Solution

[1] Find and name the longest chain containing COOH.

$$\underset{\overset{|}{CH_3}}{CH_3CHCHCH_2CH_2}-\overset{\displaystyle O}{\underset{OH}{C}}$$

hexane ----> hexanoic acid
(6 C's)

The COOH contributes one C to the longest chain.

[2] Number and name the substituents, making sure the COOH group is at C1.

$$\underset{5\;\;\overset{|}{CH_3}}{CH_3CHCHCH_2CH_2}-\overset{\displaystyle O}{\underset{1\;\;OH}{C}}$$

two methyl substituents on C4 and C5

Answer: 4,5-dimethylhexanoic acid

PRACTICE PROBLEM 17.1

Give the IUPAC name for each compound.

a. $CH_3CH_2CH_2\underset{\overset{|}{CH_3}}{\overset{\overset{\displaystyle CH_3}{|}}{C}}CH_2COOH$

b. $CH_3\underset{\overset{|}{Cl}}{CH}CH_2CH_2COOH$

c. $(CH_3CH_2)_2CHCH_2\underset{\overset{|}{CH_2CH_3}}{\overset{\overset{\displaystyle CH_2CH_3}{|}}{CH}}COOH$

More Practice: Try Problems 17.31c, 17.32b, 17.33, 17.34, 17.39c, 17.40d, 17.77a, 17.78a.

PROBLEM 17.4

Give the structure corresponding to each IUPAC name.

a. 2-bromobutanoic acid
b. 2,3-dimethylpentanoic acid
c. 2-ethyl-5,5-dimethyloctanoic acid
d. 3,4,5,6-tetraethyldecanoic acid

PROBLEM 17.5

Give the IUPAC names for valeric acid and isovaleric acid, carboxylic acids with odors reminiscent of unwashed feet.

Extracts of valerian, a flowering perennial that contains valeric acid and isovaleric acid (Problem 17.5), were used as a sedative in ancient Greece and Rome. Valerian is a dietary supplement used to treat sleep disorders and anxiety, although its efficacy is unproven.
©shapencolour/Alamy RF

valeric acid   isovaleric acid

17.2B   Naming an Ester—RCOOR'

The names of esters are derived from the names of the parent carboxylic acids. Keep in mind that the common names **formic acid, acetic acid,** and **benzoic acid** are used for the parent acid, so these common parent names are used for their derivatives as well.

An ester has two parts to its structure, each of which must be named separately: an **acyl group** that contains the carbonyl group (**RCO—**) and an **alkyl group** (designated as **R'**) bonded to the oxygen atom.

- In the IUPAC system, esters are identified by the suffix *-ate*.

How To   Name an Ester (RCO₂R') Using the IUPAC System

Example: Give a systematic name for the ester $CH_3CO_2CH_2CH_3$.

   Step [1]   **Name the R' group bonded to the oxygen atom as an alkyl group.**

- The name of the alkyl group, ending in the suffix *-yl*, becomes the *first* part of the ester name. In this case, a two-carbon *ethyl* group is bonded to the ester oxygen atom.

$$CH_3-\overset{\overset{\displaystyle O}{\|}}{C}-OCH_2CH_3 \quad \text{ethyl group}$$

   Step [2]   **Name the acyl group (RCO—) by changing the *-ic acid* ending of the parent carboxylic acid to the suffix *-ate*.**

- The name of the acyl group becomes the *second* part of the name.
- In this case, the name of the parent two-carbon carboxylic acid, acet*ic acid,* becomes acet*ate*.

Esters are often written as RCOOR', where the alkyl group (R') is written *last*. When an ester is named, however, the R' group appears *first* in the name.

$$CH_3-\overset{\overset{\displaystyle O}{\|}}{C}-OCH_2CH_3 \qquad \textbf{Answer: ethyl acetate}$$

derived from
acet*ic acid* - - - → acet*ate*

SAMPLE PROBLEM 17.2 NAMING AN ESTER

Give the IUPAC name of the following ester, which occurs naturally in apples.

$$CH_3CH_2CH_2-\overset{\overset{\displaystyle O}{\|}}{C}-OCH_3$$

Analysis and Solution

[1] Name the alkyl group on the O atom.

$$CH_3CH_2CH_2-\overset{\overset{\displaystyle O}{\|}}{C}-OCH_3 \quad \text{methyl group}$$

The word *methyl* becomes the first part of the name.

[2] To name the acyl group, find and name the longest chain containing the carbonyl group, placing the C=O at C1.

$$CH_3CH_2CH_2-\overset{\overset{\displaystyle O}{\|}}{C}-OCH_3$$

butano*ic acid* - - - → butano*ate*
(4 C's)

Answer: methyl butanoate

598   **Chapter 17**   Carboxylic Acids, Esters, and Amides

Ethyl formate is one of the many compounds that contribute to the characteristic flavor of raspberries.
©FoodCollection/StockFood RF

PRACTICE PROBLEM 17.2

Give an acceptable name for each ester.

a. $CH_3(CH_2)_4CO_2CH_3$ b.   c.

More Practice: Try Problems 17.31b, 17.32a, 17.35, 17.36, 17.39d, 17.40a, 17.41.

PROBLEM 17.6

Give the structure corresponding to each name.

a. propyl propanoate   b. butyl acetate   c. ethyl hexanoate   d. methyl benzoate

PROBLEM 17.7

Draw the structure of ethyl formate, a compound with a rum-like odor that is partly responsible for the flavor of raspberries.

17.2C   Naming an Amide

• In the IUPAC system, amides are identified by the suffix *-amide*.

All 1° amides are named by replacing the *-oic acid* ending (or *-ic acid* ending of a common name) with the suffix *-amide.*

Naming 1° amides

derived from
acet*ic acid* ----▸ **acet*amide***

derived from
benz*oic acid* ----▸ **benz*amide***

A 2° or 3° amide has two parts to its structure: an **acyl group** that contains the carbonyl group (**RCO—**) and one or two **alkyl groups** bonded to the nitrogen atom.

How To   **Name a 2° or 3° Amide**

Example: Give a systematic name for each amide.

a.   b.

Step [1]   **Name the alkyl group (or groups) bonded to the N atom of the amide. Use the prefix "*N-*" preceding the name of each alkyl group.**

• The name of the alkyl groups forms the first part of each amide name.
• For 3° amides, use the prefix *di-* if the two alkyl groups on N are the same. If the two alkyl groups are different, **alphabetize** their names. One "*N-*" is needed for each alkyl group, even if both R groups are identical.

a.

ethyl group

• The compound is a 2° amide with one ethyl group ⟶ *N*-ethyl.

b.

two methyl groups

• The compound is a 3° amide with two methyl groups.
• Use the prefix *di-* and two "*N-*" to begin the name ⟶ *N,N*-dimethyl.

—Continued

How To, continued . . .

Step [2] **Name the acyl group (RCO—) with the suffix -amide.**

a.

derived from
form*ic acid* - - - -→ **form*amide***

- Change the *-ic acid* or *-oic acid* suffix of the parent carboxylic acid to the suffix *-amide*.
- Put the two parts of the name together.
Answer: *N*-ethylformamide

b.

derived from
benz*oic acid* - - - -→ **benz*amide***

- Change benz*oic acid* to benz*amide*.
- Put the two parts of the name together.
Answer: *N,N*-dimethylbenzamide

PROBLEM 17.8

Give an acceptable name for each amide.

a.

b.

c.

PROBLEM 17.9

Draw the structure of each amide.

a. propanamide

b. *N*-ethylhexanamide

c. *N,N*-dimethylacetamide

d. *N*-butyl-*N*-methylbutanamide

17.3 Physical Properties

Carboxylic acids, esters, and amides are polar compounds because they possess a polar carbonyl group. All C—O, O—H, C—N, and N—H bonds in these compounds are polar bonds as well, and thus contribute to the net dipole of each compound.

Carboxylic acids also exhibit intermolecular **hydrogen bonding** because they possess a hydrogen atom bonded to an electronegative oxygen atom. Carboxylic acids often exist as **dimers,** held together by *two* intermolecular hydrogen bonds, as shown in Figure 17.1. The carbonyl oxygen atom of one molecule hydrogen bonds to the hydrogen atom of another molecule.

Figure 17.1   Two Molecules of Acetic Acid (CH_3COOH) Held Together by Two Hydrogen Bonds

hydrogen bond

hydrogen bond

As a result:

• **Carboxylic acids have stronger intermolecular forces than esters, giving them higher boiling points and melting points, when comparing compounds of similar molecular weight.**

$$CH_3-C\overset{O}{\underset{OCH_3}{\big|}}$$

bp 58 °C

no hydrogen bonding possible

$$CH_3CH_2-C\overset{O}{\underset{OH}{\big|}}$$

bp 141 °C   hydrogen bonding possible

stronger intermolecular forces
higher boiling point

Carboxylic acids also have stronger intermolecular forces than alcohols, even though both functional groups exhibit hydrogen bonding; two molecules of a carboxylic acid are held together by *two* intermolecular hydrogen bonds, whereas only *one* hydrogen bond is possible between two molecules of an alcohol (Section 14.2). As a result:

• **Carboxylic acids have higher boiling points and melting points than alcohols of comparable molecular weight.**

$$CH_3CH_2CH_2OH$$

1-propanol
bp 97 °C

$$CH_3-C\overset{O}{\underset{OH}{\big|}}$$

acetic acid
bp 118 °C

more hydrogen-bonding interactions possible
higher boiling point

Primary (1°) and 2° amides contain N—H bonds, so hydrogen bonding is possible between two molecules of the amide, as shown in Figure 17.2. This gives 1° and 2° amides stronger intermolecular forces than 3° amides and esters, which can't intermolecularly hydrogen bond. As a result:

• **Primary (1°) and 2° amides have higher boiling points and melting points than esters and 3° amides of comparable molecular weight.**

$$CH_3-C\overset{O}{\underset{OCH_3}{\big|}}$$

ester
bp 58 °C

$$H-C\overset{O}{\underset{N(CH_3)_2}{\big|}}$$

3° amide
bp 153 °C

$$CH_3CH_2-C\overset{O}{\underset{NH_2}{\big|}}$$

1° amide   hydrogen bonding possible
bp 213 °C

strongest intermolecular forces
highest boiling point

Like other oxygen-containing compounds, carboxylic acids, esters, and amides having fewer than six carbons are soluble in water. Higher molecular weight acyl compounds are insoluble in water because the nonpolar portion of the molecule, the C—C and C—H bonds, gets larger than the polar carbonyl group.

Figure 17.2   Intermolecular Hydrogen Bonding Between Two CH_3CONH_2 Molecules

hydrogen bond

PROBLEM 17.10

Which compound in each pair has the higher boiling point?

17.4 Interesting Carboxylic Acids in Consumer Products and Medicines

Simple carboxylic acids have biting or foul odors.

$$HCO_2H \qquad CH_3CO_2H \qquad CH_3CH_2CH_2CH_2CH_2CO_2H$$

* Formic acid (HCO_2H) is responsible for the sting of some types of ants.
* Acetic acid (CH_3CO_2H) is the sour-tasting component of vinegar. Air oxidation of ethanol (CH_3CH_2OH) to acetic acid makes "bad" wine taste sour.
* Hexanoic acid [$CH_3(CH_2)_4COOH$] has the foul odor associated with dirty socks and locker rooms. It also contributes to the unpleasant odor of ginkgo seeds. The common name for hexanoic acid is caproic acid, derived from the Latin word *caper*, meaning "goat."

17.4A FOCUS ON HEALTH & MEDICINE
Skin Care Products

Several skin care products that purportedly smooth fine lines and improve skin texture contain α-hydroxy acids. **α-Hydroxy acids contain a hydroxyl group on the α (alpha) carbon to the carboxyl group.** Two common α-hydroxy acids are glycolic acid and lactic acid. Glycolic acid occurs naturally in sugarcane, and lactic acid gives sour milk its distinctive taste.

General structure

Do products that contain α-hydroxy acids make the skin look younger? α-Hydroxy acids react with the outer layer of skin cells, causing them to loosen and flake off. Underneath is a layer of healthier looking skin that has not been exposed to the sun. In this way, these skin products do not actually reverse the aging process; rather, they remove a layer of old skin that may be less pliant or contain small age spots. They can, however, give the appearance of younger skin for a time.

Ginkgo trees have existed for over 280 million years. Extracts of the ginkgo tree have long been used in China, Japan, and India in medicine and cooking.
Source: Photo by Forest and Kim Starr

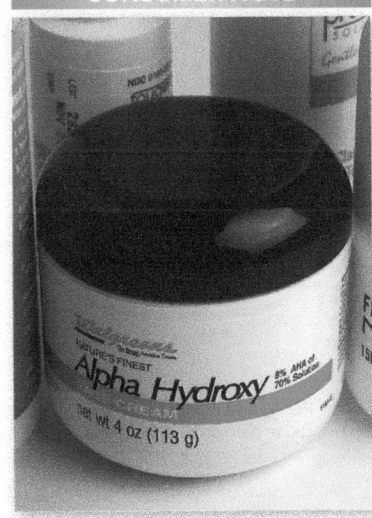

α-Hydroxy acids are used in skin care products that are promoted to remove wrinkles and age spots. ©McGraw-Hill Education/Jill Braaten, photographer

602   **Chapter 17**   Carboxylic Acids, Esters, and Amides

PROBLEM 17.11

Which compounds are α-hydroxy acids?

a.

tartaric acid
(isolated from grapes)

b. CH_3CHCH_2-C

3-hydroxybutanoic acid
(starting material for
polymer synthesis)

c.

salicylic acid
(isolated from meadowsweet)

17.4B   FOCUS ON HEALTH & MEDICINE
Aspirin and Anti-Inflammatory Agents

Three common pain relievers that are also anti-inflammatory agents contain a carboxyl group—aspirin, ibuprofen, and naproxen.

aspirin

ibuprofen

naproxen

How does aspirin relieve pain and reduce inflammation? Although aspirin is the most widely used pain reliever and anti-inflammatory agent and has been sold since the late 1800s, its mechanism of action remained unknown until the 1970s. At that time it was shown that aspirin blocks the synthesis of **prostaglandins,** carboxylic acids containing 20 carbons that are responsible for mediating pain, inflammation, and a wide variety of other biological functions.

Prostaglandins are not stored in cells. Rather, they are synthesized on an as-needed basis from arachidonic acid, an unsaturated fatty acid with four cis double bonds. **Aspirin relieves pain and decreases inflammation because it prevents the synthesis of prostaglandins, the compounds responsible for both of these physiological responses, from arachidonic acid.**

arachidonic acid

Aspirin blocks this process.

$PGF_{2\alpha}$ and compounds like it
cause pain and inflammation.

$PGF_{2\alpha}$
a prostaglandin

The 1982 Nobel Prize in Physiology or Medicine was awarded to John Vane, Bengt Samuelsson, and Sune Bergstrom for unraveling the details of prostaglandin synthesis, thus showing how aspirin acts.

17.5 Interesting Esters and Amides

Many low molecular weight esters have pleasant and very characteristic odors. These include ethyl butanoate (from mangoes), pentyl butanoate (from apricots), and methyl salicylate (oil of wintergreen).

$CH_3CH_2CH_2COOCH_2CH_3$

ethyl butanoate
(isolated from mangoes)

$CH_3CH_2CH_2COO(CH_2)_4CH_3$

pentyl butanoate
(isolated from apricots)

methyl salicylate
(oil of wintergreen)

(left): ©Jiang Hongyan/Shutterstock RF; (middle): ©I. Rozenbaum & F. Cirou/PhotoAlto RF; (right): ©Westend61 GmbH/Alamy RF

Esters are a common functional group in many lipids, as we will learn in Section 17.9 and Chapter 19.

Melatonin, an amide synthesized by the brain's pineal gland, is thought to induce sleep. Melatonin levels in the body rise as less light falls upon the eye and drop quickly at dawn. For this reason, melatonin has become a popular supplement for travelers suffering from jet lag and individuals with mild sleep disorders.

melatonin

©McGraw-Hill Education/Jill Braaten, photographer

We will learn about proteins, naturally occurring polyamides, in Chapter 21.

Many useful drugs are esters or amides. **Benzocaine,** an ester, is the active ingredient in many over-the-counter oral topical anesthetics such as Orajel. **Acetaminophen,** an amide, is the active ingredient in Tylenol. Acetaminophen relieves pain and fever. In large doses acetaminophen causes liver damage, so dosage recommendations must be carefully followed.

benzocaine
(local anesthetic)

acetaminophen
(pain reliever in Tylenol)

(left–right): ©McGraw-Hill Education/Jill Braaten, photographer

---

PROBLEM 17.12

In addition to ethyl butanoate (Section 17.5), mangoes contain several other esters. Draw the structure of each of the following esters that has been isolated from the mango: (a) butyl formate; (b) ethyl octanoate; (c) ethyl propanoate.

17.6   The Acidity of Carboxylic Acids

As their name implies, **carboxylic acids are acids;** that is, **they are *proton donors*.** When a carboxylic acid is dissolved in water, an acid–base equilibrium occurs: the carboxylic acid donates a proton to H_2O, forming its conjugate base, a **carboxylate anion,** and water gains a proton, forming its conjugate acid, H_3O^+.

K_a values for a variety of acids are given in Section 9.4.

While carboxylic acids are more acidic than other families of organic compounds, they are weak acids compared to inorganic acids like HCl or H_2SO_4. Typical acid dissociation constants (K_a) for carboxylic acids fall in the range 10^{-4} to 10^{-5}. Thus, only a small percentage of a carboxylic acid is ionized in aqueous solution. For example, dissolving acetic acid in H_2O forms a low concentration of acetate and H_3O^+.

17.6A   Reaction with Bases

Carboxylic acids react with bases such as NaOH to form water-soluble salts. In this reaction, the acid–base equilibrium is shifted to the right, and essentially all of the carboxylic acid is converted to its carboxylate anion.

- A proton is removed from acetic acid (CH_3COOH) to form its conjugate base, the acetate anion (CH_3COO^-), which is present in solution as its sodium salt, sodium acetate.
- Hydroxide (OH^-) gains a proton to form neutral H_2O.

Similar acid–base reactions occur with other hydroxide bases (KOH), sodium bicarbonate ($NaHCO_3$), and sodium carbonate (Na_2CO_3). **In each reaction, a proton is transferred from the acid (RCOOH) to the base.**

SAMPLE PROBLEM 17.3 DRAWING THE PRODUCTS FORMED WHEN A CARBOXYLIC ACID REACTS WITH A BASE

What products are formed when propanoic acid (CH_3CH_2COOH) reacts with potassium hydroxide (KOH)?

Analysis

In any acid–base reaction with a carboxylic acid:

- **Remove a proton from the carboxyl group** (COOH) and form the carboxylate anion ($RCOO^-$).
- **Add a proton to the base.** If the base has a −1 charge to begin with, it becomes a neutral product when a proton (H^+) is added to it.
- Balance the charge of the carboxylate anion by drawing it as a salt with a metal cation.

Solution

propanoic acid   base   The carboxylate anion is formed as a potassium salt.

This proton is transferred from the acid to the base.

Thus, CH_3CH_2COOH loses a proton to form $CH_3CH_2COO^-$, which is present in solution as its potassium salt, $CH_3CH_2COO^-\ K^+$. Hydroxide (OH^-) gains a proton to form H_2O.

PRACTICE PROBLEM 17.3

Draw the products of each acid–base reaction.

a.   + NaOH ⟶   b.   + Na_2CO_3 ⟶

More Practice: Try Problems 17.53, 17.54, 17.77d, 17.78d, 17.81a.

PROBLEM 17.13

What products are formed when benzoic acid (C_6H_5COOH) is treated with each base: (a) NaOH; (b) Na_2CO_3; (c) $NaHCO_3$?

17.6B Carboxylate Anions—Salts of Carboxylic Acids

The salts of carboxylic acids that are formed by acid–base reactions are water-soluble ionic solids. Thus, a water-*insoluble* carboxylic acid like octanoic acid can be converted to its water-*soluble* sodium salt by reaction with NaOH. This reaction is important in determining the solubility of drugs that contain a carboxyl group, as we will learn in Section 17.7.

octanoic acid   base   sodium octanoate

The acid has more than 5 C's, so it is **insoluble** in water.

The ionic salt is **soluble** in water.

SAMPLE PROBLEM 17.4 DETERMINING THE WATER SOLUBILITY OF CARBOXYLIC ACIDS AND CARBOXYLATES

Label each compound as water soluble or water insoluble.

A   B   C

Analysis

- Carboxylic acids containing fewer than six carbons are soluble in water.
- Carboxylic acids containing six or more carbons are insoluble in water, because the nonpolar portion of the molecule is larger than the polar carboxyl group.
- Carboxylate salts are ionic, so they are soluble in water.

Solution

- **A** is a carboxylic acid with 9 C's, so it is insoluble in water.
- **B** is a carboxylate salt, so it is soluble in water.
- **C** is a low molecular weight carboxylic acid (4 C's), so it is soluble in water.

PRACTICE PROBLEM 17.4

Which compound in each pair is more water soluble?

a. $CH_3(CH_2)_3CO_2H$ or $CH_3(CH_2)_6CO_2H$
b. $CH_3(CH_2)_6CO_2H$ or $CH_3(CH_2)_6CO_2^-Li^+$
c. $CH_3(CH_2)_3CO_2H$ or CH_3CO_2H

More Practice: Try Problem 17.52.

To name the metal salts of carboxylate anions, three parts must be put together: the name of the metal cation, the parent name indicating the number of carbons in the parent carboxylic acid, and the suffix indicating that the species is a salt. The suffix is added by changing the *-ic acid* ending of the parent carboxylic acid to the suffix *-ate.*

> name of the metal cation   +   parent   +   *-ate* (suffix)

SAMPLE PROBLEM 17.5 NAMING A SALT OF A CARBOXYLATE ANION

Give an acceptable name for each salt.

Analysis

Name the carboxylate salt by putting three parts together:

- the name of the metal cation
- the parent name that indicates the number of carbons in the parent chain
- the suffix, *-ate*

Solution

- The first part of the name is the metal cation, sodium.
- The parent name is derived from the common name, acetic acid. Change the *-ic acid* ending to *-ate;* acetic acid → acetate.

Answer: sodium acetate

b.

potassium cation

parent + suffix
propano-   -ate

- The first part of the name is the metal cation, potassium.
- The parent name is derived from the IUPAC name, propanoic acid. Change the *-ic acid* ending to *-ate;* propanoic acid → propanoate.
  Answer: potassium propanoate

PRACTICE PROBLEM 17.5

Name each salt of a carboxylic acid.

a. $CH_3CH_2CH_2CO_2^-\ Na^+$

b. ⬡—$COO^-\ Li^+$

More Practice: Try Problems 17.39b, 17.40c.

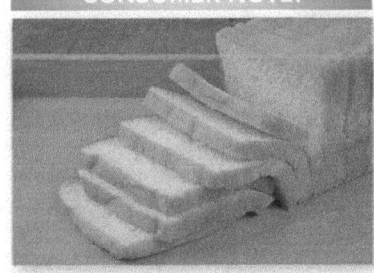

Sodium or calcium propanoate is used as a preservative to keep packaged breads from getting moldy.
©KSSphotographer/Shutterstock RF

Salts of carboxylic acids are commonly used as preservatives. **Sodium benzoate,** which inhibits the growth of fungus, is a preservative used in soft drinks, and potassium sorbate is an additive that prolongs the shelf-life of baked goods and other foods. These salts do not kill bacteria or fungus. They increase the pH of the product, thus preventing further growth of microorganisms.

sodium benzoate   potassium sorbate

PROBLEM 17.14

Draw the structure of sodium propanoate, a common preservative used in baked goods.

17.6C   How Does Soap Clean Away Dirt?

Soap has been used by humankind for some 2,000 years. Historical records describe its manufacture in the first century and document the presence of a soap factory in Pompeii. Prior to this time, clothes were cleaned by rubbing them on rocks in water, or by forming soapy lathers from the roots, bark, and leaves of certain plants. These plants produced natural materials called *saponins,* which act in much the same way as modern-day soaps.

Soaps are salts of carboxylic acids that have many carbon atoms in a long hydrocarbon chain. A soap has two parts.

- The ionic end is called the *polar head.*
- The carbon chain of nonpolar C—C and C—H bonds is called the *nonpolar tail.*

ionic end
polar head

long, hydrocarbon chain
nonpolar tail

Figure 17.3   Dissolving Soap in Water

When soap is dissolved in H_2O, spherical droplets are formed with the nonpolar tails in the interior and the polar heads on the surface.

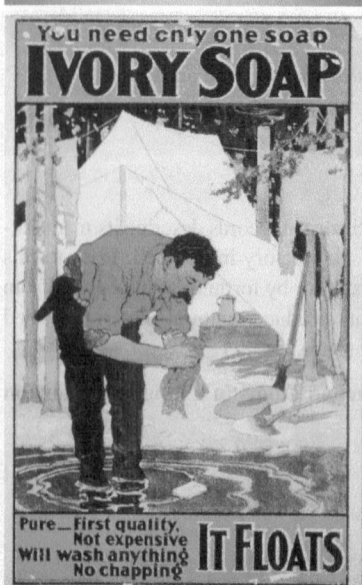

CONSUMER NOTE

All soaps are metal salts of carboxylate anions. The main difference between brands is the addition of other ingredients that do not alter their cleaning properties: dyes for color, scents for fragrance, and oils for lubrication. *Source: Library of Congress, Prints and Photographs Division [LC-USZC4-106]*

Dissolving soap in water forms **spherical droplets having the ionic heads on the surface and the nonpolar tails packed together in the interior.** These spherical droplets are called *micelles* and are illustrated in Figure 17.3. In this arrangement, the ionic heads can interact with the polar solvent water, and this brings the nonpolar, "greasy" hydrocarbon portion of the soap into solution.

How does soap dissolve grease and oil? The polar solvent water alone cannot dissolve dirt, which is composed largely of nonpolar hydrocarbons. When soap is mixed with water, however, the nonpolar hydrocarbon tails dissolve the dirt in the interior of the micelle. The polar head of the soap remains on the surface to interact with water. The nonpolar tails of the soap molecules are so well sealed off from the water by the polar head groups that the micelles are water soluble, so they can separate from the fibers of our clothes and be washed down the drain with water. In this way, soaps do a seemingly impossible task: they remove nonpolar hydrocarbon material from skin and clothes by dissolving it in the polar solvent water.

Cross-section of a soap micelle with a grease particle dissolved in the interior

PROBLEM 17.15

Draw the structure of a soap composed of a potassium cation and a carboxylate anion containing 16 carbons.

17.7   FOCUS ON HEALTH & MEDICINE
Aspirin

Aspirin is one of the most widely used over-the-counter drugs. Whether you purchase Anacin, Bufferin, Bayer, or a generic, the active ingredient is the same—**acetylsalicylic acid.** Aspirin is a synthetic compound; that is, it does not occur in nature, but it is similar in structure to salicin found in willow bark and salicylic acid found in meadowsweet blossoms.

> The modern history of aspirin dates back to 1763 when Reverend Edmund Stone reported on the analgesic effects of chewing on the bark of the willow tree. Willow bark is now known to contain salicin, which is structurally similar to aspirin.

> The word *aspirin* is derived from the prefix *a-* for *acetyl* + *spir* from the Latin name *spirea* for the meadowsweet plant.

(left): ©Skip Brown/National Geographic/Getty Images; (right): ©Biopix. http://www.biopix.dk

Both salicylic acid and sodium salicylate, its sodium salt, were used to relieve pain in the nineteenth century, but both had undesirable side effects. Salicylic acid irritated the mucous membranes of the mouth and stomach, and sodium salicylate was too sweet for most patients. This prompted a search for a related compound that did not have these same drawbacks. In 1899, Felix Hoffmann, a German chemist at Bayer Company, developed an economical commercial synthesis of acetylsalicylic acid, and aspirin was marketed to the general public. Hoffmann's work was motivated by personal reasons; his father suffered from rheumatoid arthritis and he was unable to tolerate the sweet taste of sodium salicylate.

Aspirin was first used in medicine for its analgesic (pain-relieving), antipyretic (fever-reducing), and anti-inflammatory properties. Today it is also commonly used as an antiplatelet agent; that is, it is used to prevent blood clots from forming in arteries. In this way, it is used to treat and prevent heart attacks and strokes.

Like other carboxylic acids, **aspirin is a proton donor.** When aspirin is dissolved in water, an acid–base equilibrium occurs, and the carboxyl group (COOH) donates a proton to form its

Figure 17.4

The Acid–Base Chemistry of Aspirin

Passage through the cell membrane occurs in the neutral form.

esophagus

In the stomach, aspirin exists as a neutral organic compound.

aspirin
neutral form

stomach

small intestine

In the intestines, aspirin exists as an ionic compound.

carboxylate anion
ionic form

conjugate base, a carboxylate anion. Because it is a weak acid, only a small percentage of the carboxylic acid is ionized in water.

This proton is removed.

aspirin

$+ \ H_2O$ carboxylate anion $+ \ H_3O^+$

After ingestion, aspirin travels first into the stomach and then the intestines. In the acidic environment of the stomach, aspirin remains in its neutral form. When aspirin travels into the basic environment of the small intestines, however, aspirin is converted to its carboxylate anion, as shown in Figure 17.4. In the intestines, therefore, aspirin is predominantly in its ionic form.

Why is this acid–base reaction important? Whether aspirin is a neutral acid or an ionic conjugate base affects its transport throughout the body and its ability to pass through a cell membrane. In its ionic form, aspirin is readily soluble in the aqueous environment of the blood, so it is transported in the bloodstream to tissues. Once aspirin has reached its target location, however, its conjugate base must be re-protonated to form the neutral acid that can pass through a cell membrane and act as a pain reliever and anti-inflammatory agent.

PROBLEM 17.16

Ibuprofen is another pain reliever that is a carboxylic acid. (a) Draw the acid–base reaction that occurs when ibuprofen is treated with NaOH. (b) What form of ibuprofen (neutral or ionic) exists in the stomach? (c) What form of ibuprofen exists in the intestines?

ibuprofen

17.8 The Conversion of Carboxylic Acids to Esters and Amides

All acyl compounds undergo a common type of reaction—*substitution*. When an acyl compound (RCOZ) undergoes substitution, the group Z containing an electronegative atom bonded to the carbonyl carbon is *replaced* by another atom or group of atoms (Y).

Substitution

$$R\text{--}C(=O)\text{--}Z + H\text{--}Y \longrightarrow R\text{--}C(=O)\text{--}Y + H\text{--}Z$$

Y replaces Z.

Z = OH, OR', NR'$_2$ Y = OH, OR', NR'$_2$

For example, carboxylic acids react with alcohols to form esters and with ammonia to form amides.

Ester formation

$$R\text{--}C(=O)\text{--}OH + H\text{--}OR' \underset{}{\overset{H_2SO_4}{\rightleftharpoons}} R\text{--}C(=O)\text{--}OR' + H\text{--}OH$$

carboxylic acid   alcohol   ester   OR' replaces OH.

The Greek letter Δ (delta) is used over the arrow to indicate that a reaction requires heat (Section 5.1).

Amide formation

$$R\text{--}C(=O)\text{--}OH + H\text{--}NH_2 \overset{\Delta}{\longrightarrow} R\text{--}C(=O)\text{--}NH_2 + H\text{--}OH$$

carboxylic acid   ammonia   amide   NH$_2$ replaces OH.

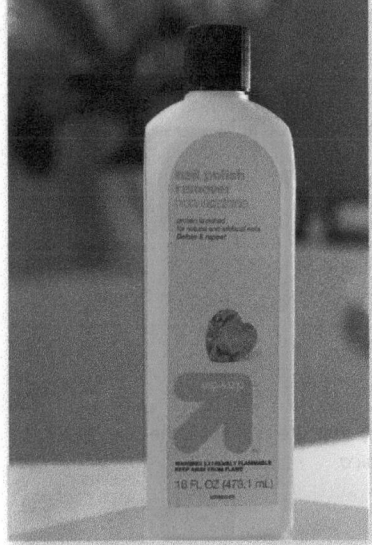

CONSUMER NOTE

The ester ethyl acetate, a common organic solvent with a very characteristic odor, is used in non-acetone nail polish remover. ©Jill Braaten RF

17.8A Ester Formation

Treatment of a carboxylic acid (RCOOH) with an alcohol (R'OH) in the presence of an acid catalyst forms an ester (RCOOR'). This reaction is called a **Fischer esterification.** Esterification is a substitution because the OR' group of an alcohol replaces the OH group of the starting carboxylic acid.

Fischer esterification

$$CH_3\text{--}C(=O)\text{--}OH + H\text{--}OCH_2CH_3 \underset{}{\overset{H_2SO_4}{\rightleftharpoons}} CH_3\text{--}C(=O)\text{--}OCH_2CH_3 + H\text{--}OH$$

acetic acid   ethanol   ethyl acetate

$$C_6H_5\text{--}C(=O)\text{--}OH + H\text{--}OCH_3 \underset{}{\overset{H_2SO_4}{\rightleftharpoons}} C_6H_5\text{--}C(=O)\text{--}OCH_3 + H\text{--}OH$$

benzoic acid   methanol   methyl benzoate

This reaction is an equilibrium process. According to Le Châtelier's principle (Section 6.6), it is driven to the right by using excess alcohol or by removing the water as it is formed. Note where the elements of H$_2$O originate: the OH group comes from the carboxylic acid, and one H atom comes from the hydrogen of the alcohol (R'OH).

SAMPLE PROBLEM 17.6 DRAWING THE PRODUCT OF FISCHER ESTERIFICATION

What ester is formed when propanoic acid (CH_3CH_2COOH) is treated with methanol (CH_3OH) in the presence of H_2SO_4?

Analysis

To draw the products of any acyl substitution, arrange the carboxyl group of the carboxylic acid next to the functional group with which it reacts—the OH group of the alcohol in this case. Then, replace the OH group of the carboxylic acid by the OR' group of the alcohol, forming a new C—O bond at the carbonyl carbon.

Remove OH and H to form H_2O.
new C—O bond

carboxylic acid + H—OR' ⟶ ester + H—OH

Solution

Replace the OH group of propanoic acid by the OCH_3 group of methanol to form the ester.

new C—O bond

CH_3CH_2—COOH + H—OCH_3 ⇌ (H_2SO_4) CH_3CH_2—COOCH_3 + H—OH

OCH_3 replaces OH.

PRACTICE PROBLEM 17.6

What ester is formed when each carboxylic acid is treated with ethanol (CH_3CH_2OH) in the presence of H_2SO_4?

a. $(CH_3)_2CH$—C(=O)OH

b. HCO_2H

c. $CH_3(CH_2)_6$—C(=O)OH

d. (cyclohexyl)—CO_2H

More Practice: Try Problems 17.55, 17.56, 17.58, 17.75a, 17.77f, 17.78f.

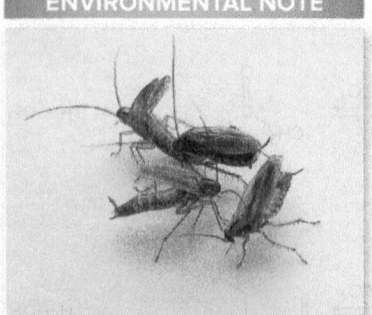

A short laboratory synthesis of the ester blattellaquinone, the sex pheromone of the female German cockroach (Problem 17.17), opens new possibilities for cockroach population control using pheromone-baited traps. ©Coby Schal/NC State University

Fischer esterification can be used to synthesize aspirin from salicylic acid.

salicylic acid + acetic acid ⇌ (H_2SO_4) aspirin + H—OH

new C—O bond

PROBLEM 17.17

Identify **A** in the following reaction. **A** was converted in one step to blattellaquinone, the sex pheromone of the female German cockroach, *Blattella germanica*.

(structure) + HO—C(=O)CH(CH_3)_2 ⟶ (H_2SO_4) **A** ⟶ blattellaquinone

PROBLEM 17.18

What carboxylic acid and alcohol are needed to synthesize the local anesthetic benzocaine (Section 17.5)?

benzocaine

17.8B   Amide Formation

**Heating a carboxylic acid (RCOOH) with ammonia (NH₃) or an amine (R'NH₂ or R'₂NH)
forms an amide.** Formation of an amide from a carboxylic acid is a substitution because the OH
group of the acid is replaced by a nitrogen-containing group.

Amide formation

$$\underset{\text{carboxylic acid}}{\text{R}-\overset{\overset{\displaystyle O}{\|}}{\text{C}}-\text{OH}} \;+\; \underset{\text{R'} = \text{H or alkyl}}{\text{H}-\overset{\overset{\displaystyle |}{\text{N}}}{\underset{\text{R'}}{|}}-\text{R'}} \;\overset{\Delta}{\longrightarrow}\; \underset{\text{amide}}{\text{R}-\overset{\overset{\displaystyle O}{\|}}{\text{C}}-\text{NR'}_2} \;+\; \text{H}-\text{OH}$$

The identity of the nitrogen compound determines the type of amide formed.

- Reaction of RCOOH with NH₃ forms a 1° amide (RCONH₂).
- Reaction of RCOOH with R'NH₂ forms a 2° amide (RCONHR').
- Reaction of RCOOH with R'₂NH forms a 3° amide (RCONR'₂).

$$\underset{\text{acetic acid}}{\text{CH}_3-\overset{\overset{\displaystyle O}{\|}}{\text{C}}-\text{OH}} \;+\; \underset{\text{ammonia}}{\text{H}-\text{NH}_2} \;\overset{\Delta}{\longrightarrow}\; \underset{\text{1° amide}}{\text{CH}_3-\overset{\overset{\displaystyle O}{\|}}{\text{C}}-\text{NH}_2} \;+\; \text{H}-\text{OH}$$

$$\underset{\text{acetic acid}}{\text{CH}_3-\overset{\overset{\displaystyle O}{\|}}{\text{C}}-\text{OH}} \;+\; \underset{\text{methylamine}}{\text{H}-\overset{\text{H}}{\underset{}{\text{N}}}-\text{CH}_3} \;\overset{\Delta}{\longrightarrow}\; \underset{\text{2° amide}}{\text{CH}_3-\overset{\overset{\displaystyle O}{\|}}{\text{C}}-\text{NHCH}_3} \;+\; \text{H}-\text{OH}$$

$$\underset{\text{acetic acid}}{\text{CH}_3-\overset{\overset{\displaystyle O}{\|}}{\text{C}}-\text{OH}} \;+\; \underset{\text{dimethylamine}}{\text{H}-\overset{\text{CH}_3}{\underset{}{\text{N}}}-\text{CH}_3} \;\overset{\Delta}{\longrightarrow}\; \underset{\text{3° amide}}{\text{CH}_3-\overset{\overset{\displaystyle O}{\|}}{\text{C}}-\text{N(CH}_3)_2} \;+\; \text{H}-\text{OH}$$

Useful amides can be made by this reaction. Heating carboxylic acid **X** with diethylamine forms
the 3° amide *N,N*-diethyl-*m*-toluamide, popularly known as **DEET**. DEET, the active ingredient
in the most widely used insect repellents, is effective against mosquitoes, fleas, and ticks.

Insect repellents containing DEET have
become particularly popular because of
the spread of many insect-borne
diseases, such as West Nile virus and
Lyme disease. DEET does not kill
insects—it repels them. It is thought that
DEET somehow confuses insects, so that
they can no longer sense the warm moist
air that surrounds a human body. *Source:
Photo by Scott Bauer/USDA*

**SAMPLE PROBLEM 17.7 DRAWING THE PRODUCT OF THE REACTION
OF A CARBOXYLIC ACID WITH AN AMINE**

What amide is formed when propanoic acid (CH_3CH_2COOH) is heated with ethylamine ($CH_3CH_2NH_2$)?

Analysis

To draw the products of amide formation, arrange the carboxyl group of the carboxylic acid next to the H—N bond of the amine. Then, replace the OH group of the carboxylic acid by the $NHCH_2CH_3$ group of the amine, forming a new C—N bond at the carbonyl carbon.

Solution

Reaction of RCOOH with an amine that has one alkyl group on the N atom ($R'NH_2$) forms a 2° amide (RCONHR').

PRACTICE PROBLEM 17.7

What amide is formed when $CH_3CH_2CH_2CH_2COOH$ is treated with each compound?

a. NH_3 b. $(CH_3)_2NH$ c. ⬡—NH_2 d. CH_3NH_2

More Practice: Try Problems 17.59, 17.60, 17.77g, 17.78g.

PROBLEM 17.19

What carboxylic acid and amine are needed to synthesize the pain reliever phenacetin? Phenacetin was once a component of the over-the-counter pain reliever APC (aspirin, phenacetin, caffeine), but it is no longer used because of its kidney toxicity.

phenacetin

17.9 Hydrolysis of Esters and Amides

Esters and amides undergo substitution at the carbonyl carbon as well. For example, **esters and amides react with water to form carboxylic acids.** This reaction is another example of **hydrolysis,** because bonds are cleaved on reaction with water.

17.9A   Ester Hydrolysis

Esters are hydrolyzed with water in the presence of acid or base. **Treatment of an ester (RCOOR') with water in the presence of an acid catalyst forms a carboxylic acid (RCOOH) and a molecule of alcohol (R'OH).** The hydrolysis of esters in aqueous acid is an equilibrium reaction that is driven to the right by using a large excess of water.

Esters are hydrolyzed in aqueous base to form carboxylate anions and a molecule of alcohol. Basic hydrolysis of an ester is called **saponification.**

SAMPLE PROBLEM 17.8 DRAWING THE PRODUCTS OF ESTER HYDROLYSIS IN ACID

What products are formed when ethyl propanoate ($CH_3CH_2CO_2CH_2CH_3$) is hydrolyzed with water in the presence of H_2SO_4?

Analysis

To draw the products of hydrolysis in acid, replace the OR' group of the ester by an OH group from water, forming a new C—O bond at the carbonyl carbon. A molecule of alcohol (R'OH) is also formed from the alkoxy group (OR') of the ester.

Solution

Replace the OCH_2CH_3 group of ethyl propanoate by the OH group of water to form propanoic acid ($CH_3CH_2CO_2H$) and ethanol (CH_3CH_2OH).

PRACTICE PROBLEM 17.8

What products are formed when each ester is treated with H_2O and H_2SO_4?

More Practice: Try Problems 17.65, 17.67, 17.75b.

PROBLEM 17.20

What products are formed when each ester in Practice Problem 17.8 is treated with H_2O and NaOH?

PROBLEM 17.21

Aspirin cannot be sold as a liquid solution for children because it slowly undergoes hydrolysis in water. What products are formed when aspirin is hydrolyzed?

aspirin

PROBLEM 17.22

What products are formed when both esters in the addictive drug cocaine are hydrolyzed in aqueous acid? Cocaine is obtained from the leaves of the coca plant, *Erythroxylon coca*.

cocaine

coca plant
©blickwinkel/Alamy

17.9B   Amide Hydrolysis

Amides are much less reactive than esters in substitution reactions. Nonetheless, under forcing conditions amides can be hydrolyzed with water in the presence of acid or base. **Treatment of an amide (RCONHR') with water in the presence of an acid catalyst (HCl) forms a carboxylic acid (RCOOH) and an amine salt (R'NH$_3$$^+$ Cl$^-$).**

Amides are also hydrolyzed in aqueous base to form carboxylate anions and a molecule of ammonia (NH_3) or amine.

amide   carboxylate anion   ammonia

The relative lack of reactivity of the amide bond is important in the proteins in the body. Proteins are polymers connected by amide linkages, as we will learn in Chapter 21. Proteins are stable in water in the absence of acid or base, so they can perform their various functions in the cell without breaking down. The hydrolysis of the amide bonds in proteins requires a variety of specific enzymes.

SAMPLE PROBLEM 17.9 DRAWING THE PRODUCTS OF AMIDE HYDROLYSIS IN BASE

What products are formed when *N*-methylacetamide ($CH_3CONHCH_3$) is hydrolyzed with water in the presence of NaOH?

Analysis

To draw the products of amide hydrolysis in base, replace the NHR' group of the amide by an oxygen anion (O^-), forming a new C—O bond at the carbonyl carbon. A molecule of amine ($R'NH_2$) is also formed from the nitrogen group (NHR') of the amide.

new C—O bond

amide

O^- replaces NHR'.

Solution

Replace the $NHCH_3$ group of *N*-methylacetamide by a negatively charged oxygen atom (O^-) to form sodium acetate ($CH_3CO_2^-$ Na^+) and methylamine (CH_3NH_2).

N-methylacetamide

O^- replaces $NHCH_3$.

PRACTICE PROBLEM 17.9

What products are formed when each amide is treated with H_2O and H_2SO_4?

a. $CH_3(CH_2)_8$—C(=O)—NH_2

b. CH_3CHCH_2—C(=O)—$NHCH_3$ (CH_3)

c. (cyclohexyl)—C(=O)—N(propyl)(propyl)

More Practice: Try Problems 17.69; 17.70; 17.76b, c.

PROBLEM 17.23

What products are formed when each amide in Practice Problem 17.9 is treated with H_2O and NaOH?

17.9C FOCUS ON HEALTH & MEDICINE
Olestra, a Synthetic Fat

The most prevalent naturally occurring esters are the **triacylglycerols.** *Triacylglycerols* contain **three ester groups, each having a long carbon chain (abbreviated as R, R', and R'') bonded to the carbonyl group.** Triacylglycerols are **lipids;** that is, they are water-insoluble organic compounds found in biological systems. Animal fats and vegetable oils are composed of triacylglycerols.

CH_2—O—C(=O)—R

CH—O—C(=O)—R'   R groups have 11–19 C's.

CH_2—O—C(=O)—R''   [Three ester groups are labeled in red.]

triacylglycerol

CONSUMER NOTE

This product contains the "fake fat" olestra, giving it fewer calories for the calorie-conscious consumer. ©McGraw-Hill Education/Jill Braaten, photographer

Animals store energy in the form of triacylglycerols kept in a layer of fat cells below the surface of the skin. This fat serves to insulate the organism, as well as provide energy for its metabolic needs for long periods of time. The first step in the metabolism of a triacylglycerol is hydrolysis of the ester bonds to form glycerol and three fatty acids—long-chain carboxylic acids. **This reaction is simply ester hydrolysis.** In cells, this reaction is carried out with enzymes called **lipases.**

The three bonds drawn in red are broken in hydrolysis.

triacylglycerol

glycerol

Three carboxylic acids containing 12–20 C's are formed as products.

We will learn more about triacylglycerols in Chapter 19.

The fatty acids produced on hydrolysis are then oxidized, yielding CO_2 and H_2O, as well as a great deal of energy. Diets high in fat content can lead to a large amount of stored fat, ultimately causing an individual to be overweight. One recent attempt to reduce calories in common snack foods has been to substitute "fake fats" such as **olestra** (trade name **Olean**) for triacylglycerols.

olestra
a "fake fat"

R groups have long chains of C's joined together.

The ester groups are so crowded that hydrolysis does not readily take place.

Olestra has many ester groups (shown in red) formed from long-chain carboxylic acids and sucrose, the sweet-tasting carbohydrate in table sugar. Olestra has many properties similar to those of the triacylglycerols in fats and oils. In one way, however, olestra is different. Olestra has so many ester units clustered together that they are too crowded to be hydrolyzed. As a result, olestra is *not* metabolized nor is it absorbed. Instead, it passes through the body unchanged, *providing no calories to the consumer.*

PROBLEM 17.24

What products are formed when the following triacylglycerol is hydrolyzed with water and H_2SO_4?

17.10 Synthetic Polymers in Modern Society—Polyamides and Polyesters

All natural and synthetic fibers are polymers. Natural fibers are obtained from either plant or animal sources, and this determines the fundamental nature of their chemical structure. Fibers like **wool and silk obtained from animals are proteins,** and so they are joined together by many amide linkages.

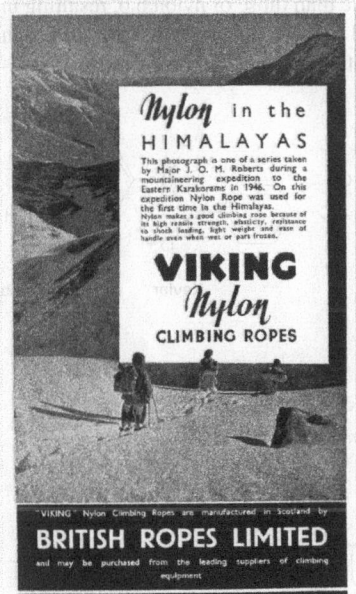

DuPont built the first commercial nylon plant in 1938. Although it was initially used by the military to make parachutes, nylon quickly replaced silk in many common products after World War II.
©*Jeff Morgan 14/Alamy*

wool and silk—polymers with many amide bonds
(labeled in red)

An important practical application of organic chemistry has been the synthesis of synthetic fibers, many of which have properties that are different from and sometimes superior to their naturally occurring counterparts. Two common classes of synthetic polymers are polyamides and polyesters.

17.10A Nylon—A Polyamide

The search for a synthetic fiber with properties similar to silk led to the discovery of **nylon,** a **polyamide.** There are several different kinds of nylon, but the best known is nylon 6,6.

nylon 6,6
[The amide bonds are labeled in red.]

To synthesize nylon 6,6, two monomers are needed. Each monomer has six carbons (hence its name) and two functional groups. One monomer is a dicarboxylic acid, adipic acid $[HO_2C(CH_2)_4CO_2H]$, and the second monomer is a diamine, hexamethylenediamine $[H_2N(CH_2)_6NH_2]$. Heating the two monomers together at high temperature forms the amide bonds of the long polymer chain. When each amide is formed, a molecule of H_2O is lost from the starting materials. Nylon is an example of a **condensation polymer.**

Nylon is used in a wide variety of consumer products, including rope, fabric, backpacks, hot air balloons, and parachutes. Nylon sutures are used in medicine.
©*Patrick Foto/Shutterstock RF*

Polymers were first discussed in detail in Section 13.8.

Each NH₂ and COOH react.

$H_2N-(CH_2)_6-NH_2$ + $HO-C(=O)-(CH_2)_4-C(=O)-OH$ + $H_2N-(CH_2)_6-NH_2$ + $HO-C(=O)-(CH_2)_4-C(=O)-OH$

loss of H₂O   loss of H₂O   loss of H₂O

Δ

nylon 6,6

new amide bonds

- A *condensation polymer* is a polymer formed when monomers containing two functional groups come together with loss of a small molecule such as water.

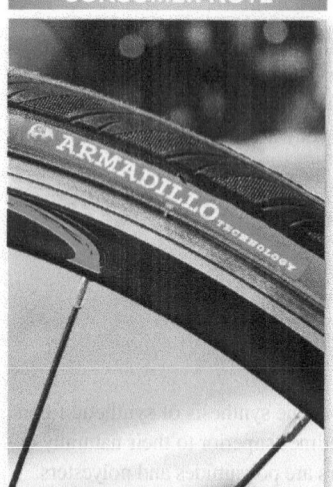

Armadillo bicycle tires reinforced with Kevlar are hard to pierce with sharp objects, so a cyclist rarely gets a flat tire. ©McGraw-Hill Education/ John Thoeming, photographer

Kevlar is a polyamide formed from terephthalic acid and 1,4-diaminobenzene. The aromatic rings of the polymer backbone make the chains less flexible than those of nylon 6,6, resulting in a very strong material. Kevlar is light in weight compared to other materials that are similar in strength, so it is used in many products, such as bulletproof vests, army helmets, and the protective clothing used by firefighters.

terephthalic acid   +   1,4-diaminobenzene $\xrightarrow[\text{(−H}_2\text{O)}]{\Delta}$ Kevlar   new amide bond

SAMPLE PROBLEM 17.10 DETERMINING THE DIAMINE AND THE DICARBOXYLIC ACID NEEDED TO PREPARE A POLYAMIDE

What diamine and dicarboxylic acid are needed to prepare polyamide **A**?

A

Analysis

To find the starting materials:

- Locate the amide bonds that join the atoms of the polymer chain.
- Replace the N—C bond of the amide by an N—H bond (to form an amine) and an HO—C bond to form a carboxylic acid.

Add **H** to **N**.   Add **OH** to **C**═**O**.

amine   +   carboxylic acid

Solution

Locate the amides.

amide   amide   amide

A

A is prepared from a diamine and a diacid.

diamine   dicarboxylic acid   diamine   dicarboxylic acid

PRACTICE PROBLEM 17.10

What two monomers are needed to prepare nylon 6,10?

nylon 6,10

More Practice: Try Problems 17.71, 17.72.

17.10B Polyesters

Polyesters constitute a second major class of condensation polymers. The most common polyester is polyethylene terephthalate (**PET**), which is sold under a variety of trade names depending on its use (Dacron, Terylene, and Mylar). Plastic soft drink bottles are made of PET.

polyethylene terephthalate
PET
[Ester bonds are drawn in red.]

©McGraw-Hill Education/Jill Braaten, photographer

One method of synthesizing PET is by the acid-catalyzed reaction of a dicarboxylic acid (terephthalic acid) with ethylene glycol ($HOCH_2CH_2OH$) in a Fischer esterification reaction.

Each OH and COOH react.

loss of H_2O

HO terephthalic acid OH + $HOCH_2CH_2OH$ + HO OH + $HOCH_2CH_2OH$

loss of H_2O

acid catalyst

loss of H_2O

CH_2CH_2

$O-CH_2CH_2-O$

CH_2CH_2

polyethylene terephthalate
PET

Figure 17.5   Medical Uses of PET

a. PET is used to make the knitted material present in artificial heart valves. ©*Antonia Reeve/Science Source*

b. Some replacement blood vessels are made with PET. ©*Antonia Reeve/Science Source*

Because these polymers are easily and cheaply prepared and they form strong and chemically stable materials, they have been used in clothing, films, tires, and plastic drink bottles. Polyester fiber is also used in artificial heart valves and replacement blood vessels (Figure 17.5).

PROBLEM 17.25

Draw the structure of Kodel, a polyester formed from 1,4-dihydroxymethylcyclohexane and terephthalic acid. Suggest a reason why fabrics made from Kodel are stiff and crease resistant.

HOCH₂—⬡—CH₂OH   +   terephthalic acid

1,4-dihydroxymethylcyclohexane   terephthalic acid

17.10C   FOCUS ON HEALTH & MEDICINE
Dissolving Sutures

Although PET is a stable material, the ester bonds in some other polyesters are quite readily hydrolyzed to carboxylic acids and alcohols in aqueous medium. Polyesters of this sort are suited for applications in which slow degradation is a useful feature. One example of a degradable polymer is formed from two α-hydroxy acids—glycolic acid ($HOCH_2COOH$) and lactic acid [$CH_3CH(OH)COOH$].

dissolving suture material

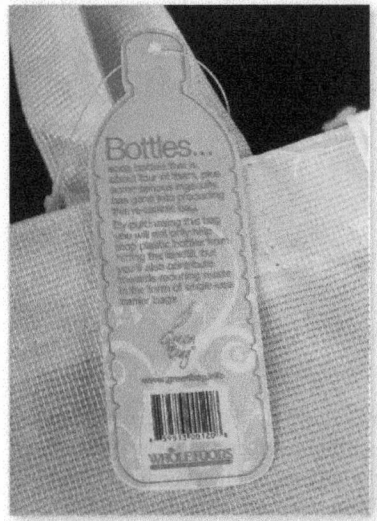

Recycled PET is used to make shopping bags. ©*Jill Braaten RF*

When glycolic acid and lactic acid are combined, the hydroxyl group of one α-hydroxy acid reacts with the carboxyl group of the second α-hydroxy acid. The resulting polymer is used by surgeons in dissolving sutures. Within weeks, the polymer is hydrolyzed to the monomers from which it was prepared, which are metabolized readily by the body. These sutures are used internally to hold tissues together while healing and scar formation occur.

17.10D FOCUS ON THE ENVIRONMENT
Polymer Recycling

The same desirable characteristics that make polymers popular materials for consumer products—durability, strength, and lack of reactivity—also contribute to environmental problems. Many polymers do not degrade readily, and as a result, billions of pounds of polymers end up in landfills every year. Recycling polymers is one way to help combat the waste problem they create.

The most common polymers are each assigned a recycling code (1–6); **the lower the number, the easier the polymer is to recycle.** PET materials are assigned recycling code "1" because they are the easiest to recycle. Since recycled polymers are often still contaminated with small amounts of adhesives and other materials, these recycled polymers are generally not used for storing food or drink products. Recycled PET is used to make fibers for fleece clothing and carpeting.

PET can also be converted back to the monomers from which it was made. For example, heating PET with water and acid breaks the ester bonds of the polymer chain to give ethylene glycol ($HOCH_2CH_2OH$) and terephthalic acid. These monomers then serve as starting materials for more PET.

polyethylene terephthalate
PET

terephthalic acid

+ $HOCH_2CH_2OH$
ethylene glycol

chemical recycling

Penicillin was used to treat injured soldiers in World War II before its structure had been conclusively determined. *Source: Library of Congress, Prints & Photographs Division [LC-USZC4-1986]*

17.11 FOCUS ON HEALTH & MEDICINE
Penicillin

In the twenty-first century it is hard to imagine that an infected cut or scrape could be life-threatening. Before antibiotics were discovered in the early twentieth century, however, that was indeed the case.

The antibiotic properties of **penicillin** were first discovered in 1928 by Sir Alexander Fleming, who noticed that a mold of the genus *Penicillium* inhibited the growth of certain bacteria. After years of experimentation, penicillin was first used to treat a female patient who had developed a streptococcal infection in 1942. By 1944, penicillin production was given high priority by the United States government, because it was needed to treat the many injured soldiers in World War II.

The penicillins are a group of related antibiotics. All penicillins contain two amide units. One amide is part of a four-membered ring called a **β-lactam.** The second amide is bonded to the α carbon of the β-lactam carbonyl group. Particular penicillins differ in the identity of the R group in the amide side chain. The first penicillin to be discovered was penicillin G. Amoxicillin is another example in common use today.

**General structure
Penicillin**

α carbon

β-lactam

penicillin G

amoxicillin

Penicillin has no effect on mammalian cells because they are surrounded by a flexible membrane composed of a lipid bilayer (Chapter 19) and not a cell wall.

Unlike mammalian cells, bacterial cells are surrounded by a fairly rigid cell wall, which allows the bacterium to live in many different environments. **Penicillin interferes with the synthesis of the bacterial cell wall.** Penicillin kills bacteria by a substitution reaction that occurs at the amide that is part of the β-lactam. The β-lactam is more reactive than a regular amide because the bond angles in the small ring must be 90°. This feature makes the ring unstable. The β-lactam ring of the penicillin molecule reacts with an enzyme needed to synthesize the cell wall, and this deactivates the enzyme. Cell wall construction is halted, killing the bacterium. This process is discussed further in Section 21.10.

PROBLEM 17.26

The conversion of **A** to **B** illustrates how penicillin inactivates a bacterial enzyme needed for the synthesis of the bacterial cell wall. (a) What functional groups are present in **A** that are missing in **B**? (b) What new functional groups are present in **B**?

active enzyme

penicillin

inactive enzyme

penicillin bound to an enzyme

A   **B**

CHAPTER HIGHLIGHTS

KEY TERMS

Acyl group (17.1)	Fischer esterification (17.8)	Polyamide (17.10)
Alpha (α) carbon (17.2)	Hydrolysis (17.9)	Polyester (17.10)
Amide (17.1)	α-Hydroxy acid (17.4)	Primary (1°) amide (17.1)
Beta (β) carbon (17.2)	Lactam (17.1)	Prostaglandin (17.4)
Carboxyl group (17.1)	Lactone (17.1)	Saponification (17.9)
Carboxylate anion (17.6)	Lipid (17.9)	Secondary (2°) amide (17.1)
Carboxylic acid (17.1)	Micelle (17.6)	Soap (17.6)
Condensation polymer (17.10)	Nylon (17.10)	Tertiary (3°) amide (17.1)
Ester (17.1)	Penicillin (17.11)	Triacylglycerol (17.9)

KEY REACTIONS

[1] Acid–base reaction of carboxylic acids (17.6)

$$\underset{R}{\overset{O}{\underset{}{\overset{\parallel}{C}}}}\!\!-\!O\!-\!H \;+\; Na^{+}\,OH^{-} \longrightarrow \underset{R}{\overset{O}{\underset{}{\overset{\parallel}{C}}}}\!\!-\!O^{-}\,Na^{+} \;+\; H_2O$$

[2] Substitution reactions of carboxylic acids (17.8)

a. Formation of esters
$$\underset{R}{\overset{O}{\overset{\parallel}{C}}}\!\!-\!OH \;+\; R'OH \;\underset{}{\overset{H_2SO_4}{\rightleftharpoons}}\; \underset{R}{\overset{O}{\overset{\parallel}{C}}}\!\!-\!OR' \;+\; H_2O$$

b. Formation of amides
$$\underset{R}{\overset{O}{\overset{\parallel}{C}}}\!\!-\!OH \;+\; R'_2NH \;\overset{\Delta}{\longrightarrow}\; \underset{R}{\overset{O}{\overset{\parallel}{C}}}\!\!-\!NR'_2 \;+\; H_2O$$
$$R' = H \text{ or alkyl}$$

[3] Hydrolysis of acyl compounds (17.9)

a. Ester hydrolysis
$$\underset{R}{\overset{O}{\overset{\parallel}{C}}}\!\!-\!OR' \;+\; H_2O \begin{cases} \overset{H^{+}}{\longrightarrow} & \underset{R}{\overset{O}{\overset{\parallel}{C}}}\!\!-\!OH \;+\; R'OH \\[2ex] \overset{OH^{-}}{\longrightarrow} & \underset{R}{\overset{O}{\overset{\parallel}{C}}}\!\!-\!O^{-} \;+\; R'OH \end{cases}$$

b. Amide hydrolysis
$$\underset{R}{\overset{O}{\overset{\parallel}{C}}}\!\!-\!NR'_2 \;+\; H_2O \begin{cases} \overset{H^{+}}{\longrightarrow} & \underset{R}{\overset{O}{\overset{\parallel}{C}}}\!\!-\!OH \;+\; (R'_2NH_2)^{+} \\[2ex] \overset{OH^{-}}{\longrightarrow} & \underset{R}{\overset{O}{\overset{\parallel}{C}}}\!\!-\!O^{-} \;+\; R'_2NH \end{cases}$$
$$R' = H \text{ or alkyl}$$

KEY CONCEPTS

1 What are the characteristics of carboxylic acids, esters, and amides?

- Carboxylic acids have the general structure RCOOH; esters have the general structure RCOOR'; amides have the general structure RCONR'$_2$, where R' = H or alkyl. (17.1)
- The carbonyl carbon is trigonal planar with bond angles of 120°. (17.1)
- All acyl compounds have a polar C=O. RCO$_2$H, RCONH$_2$, and RCONHR' are capable of intermolecular hydrogen bonding. (17.3)

2 How are carboxylic acids, esters, and amides named? (17.2)

- Carboxylic acids are identified by the suffix -oic acid.
- Esters are identified by the suffix -ate.
- Amides are identified by the suffix -amide.

3 Give examples of useful carboxylic acids. (17.4)

- α-Hydroxy carboxylic acids are used in skin care products.
- Aspirin, ibuprofen, and naproxen are pain relievers and anti-inflammatory agents.
- Aspirin is an anti-inflammatory agent because it blocks the synthesis of prostaglandins from arachidonic acid.

4 Give examples of useful esters and amides. (17.5)

- Some esters—ethyl butanoate, pentyl butanoate, and methyl salicylate—have characteristic odors and flavors.
- Benzocaine is the active ingredient in over-the-counter oral topical anesthetics.
- Acetaminophen is the active ingredient in Tylenol.

5 What products are formed when carboxylic acids are treated with base? (17.6)

- Carboxylic acids react with bases to form carboxylate anions (RCOO⁻).
- Carboxylate anions are water soluble and commonly used as preservatives.

6 How does soap clean away dirt? (17.6C)

- Soaps are salts of carboxylic acids that have many carbon atoms in a long hydrocarbon chain.
- Soap forms micelles in water with its polar heads on the surface and the hydrocarbon tails in the interior. Grease and dirt dissolve in the nonpolar tails, so they can be washed away with water.

626   Chapter 17 Carboxylic Acids, Esters, and Amides

7 **Discuss the acid–base chemistry of aspirin. (17.7)**
- Aspirin remains in its neutral form in the stomach, and in this form it can cross a cell membrane and serve as an anti-inflammatory agent.
- A proton is removed from aspirin in the basic environment of the intestines to form an ionic carboxylate anion. This form is not absorbed.

8 **How are carboxylic acids converted to esters and amides? (17.8)**
- Carboxylic acids are converted to esters by reaction with alcohols (R'OH) and acid (H$_2$SO$_4$).
- Carboxylic acids are converted to amides by heating with ammonia (NH$_3$) or amines (R'NH$_2$ or R'$_2$NH).

9 **What hydrolysis products are formed from esters and amides? (17.9)**
- Esters are hydrolyzed to carboxylic acids (RCOOH) in the presence of an acid catalyst (H$_2$SO$_4$). Esters are converted to carboxylate anions (RCOO$^-$) with aqueous base (NaOH in H$_2$O).

- Amides are hydrolyzed to carboxylic acids (RCOOH) in the presence of an acid catalyst (HCl). Amides are converted to carboxylate anions (RCOO$^-$) with aqueous base (NaOH in H$_2$O).

10 **What are polyamides and polyesters, and how are they formed? (17.10)**
- Polyamides like nylon are polymers that contain many amide bonds. They are formed when a dicarboxylic acid is heated with a diamine.
- Polyesters like PET are polymers that contain many ester bonds. They are formed when a dicarboxylic acid is treated with a diol in the presence of acid (H$_2$SO$_4$).

11 **How does penicillin act as an antibiotic? (17.11)**
- The β-lactam of penicillin is more reactive than a regular amide, and it reacts with an enzyme needed to synthesize the cell wall of a bacterium. Without a cell wall, the bacterium dies.

PROBLEMS

Selected in-chapter and odd-numbered end-of-chapter problems have brief answers in Appendix B. The *Student Study Guide and Solutions Manual* contains detailed solutions to all in-chapter and odd-numbered end-of-chapter problems, as well as additional worked examples and a chapter self-test.

Structure and Bonding

17.27 Draw the structure of a compound that fits each description:
- a. a carboxylic acid of molecular formula C$_8$H$_{16}$O$_2$ that has six carbons in its longest chain
- b. an ester of molecular formula C$_6$H$_{12}$O$_2$ that contains a methoxy group (OCH$_3$) bonded to the carbonyl group
- c. an ester of molecular formula C$_6$H$_{10}$O$_2$ that contains a ring

17.28 Draw the structure of a constitutional isomer of octanoic acid [CH$_3$(CH$_2$)$_6$CO$_2$H] that:
- a. contains a carboxyl group and no chirality center
- b. contains a carboxyl group and a chirality center
- c. contains an ester

17.29 Draw the structure of a compound of molecular formula C$_5$H$_{11}$NO that contains a: (a) 1° amide; (b) 2° amide; (c) 3° amide.

17.30 Draw the structure of four constitutional isomers of molecular formula C$_4$H$_8$O$_2$ that contain an ester.

Nomenclature

17.31 Give an acceptable name for each compound depicted in the ball-and-stick models.

17.32 Give an acceptable name for each compound depicted in the ball-and-stick models.

17.33 Give an acceptable name for each carboxylic acid.
- a. (CH$_3$)$_2$CHCH$_2$CH$_2$COOH
- b. CH$_3$CH$_2$CH$_2$CHCHCH$_2$CH$_2$COOH, with CH$_2$CH$_3$ and CH$_2$CH$_3$ substituents
- c. (structure shown)

17.34 Give an acceptable name for each carboxylic acid.
- a. (CH$_3$)$_2$CHCH$_2$CH$_2$CH$_2$CH$_2$CH$_2$COOH
- b. CH$_3$CHCHCHCH$_2$COOH, with CH$_3$, CH$_3$, and CH$_3$ substituents
- c. (structure shown)

17.35 Give an acceptable name for each ester.

a. CH₃CH₂CH₂CO₂CH₂CH₂CH₃   b. ⬡—CO₂(CH₂)₃CH₃

17.36 Give an acceptable name for each ester.

a. CH₃CO₂(CH₂)₄CH₃   b. HCO₂(CH₂)₅CH₃

17.37 Give an acceptable name for each amide.

a. [skeletal structure with O and NH₂]   b. [benzene ring with O and N(CH₂CH₃)(CH₃)]

17.38 Give an acceptable name for each amide.

a. [skeletal structure with O and NH₂]

b. [benzene ring with O and N(CH₂CH₃)₂]

17.39 Give an acceptable name for each compound.

a. HCONH₂   c. CH₃CH₂CHCOOH with OH

b. [CH₃—C(=O)—O⁻ Li⁺]   d. [ester skeletal structure with O]

17.40 Give an acceptable name for each compound.

a. CH₃(CH₂)₈CO₂CH₃   c. [H—C(=O)—O⁻ K⁺]

b. (CH₃)₂CHCH₂CONH₂   d. [skeletal structure with O and OH]

17.41 Give an acceptable name for CH₃CO₂(CH₂)₇CH₃, a compound found in oranges and grapefruits.

©Len44ik/Shutterstock RF

17.42 Draw a skeletal structure of ethyl heptanoate, a compound with a fruity odor reminiscent of grapes.

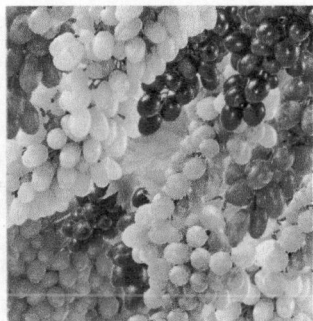

©cooperr/Shutterstock RF

17.43 Draw the structure corresponding to each name.

a. 2-hydroxyheptanoic acid
b. 4-chlorononanoic acid
c. 3,4-dibromobenzoic acid
d. lithium propanoate
e. 2,2-dibromobutanoic acid
f. ethyl 2-methylpropanoate

17.44 Draw the structure corresponding to each name.

a. 3-methylhexanoic acid
b. 3-hydroxy-4-methylheptanoic acid
c. *p*-nitrobenzoic acid
d. sodium hexanoate
e. *m*-ethylbenzoic acid
f. propyl decanoate

17.45 Draw the structure corresponding to each name.

a. propyl formate
b. butyl butanoate
c. heptyl benzoate
d. *N*-ethylhexanamide
e. *N*-ethyl-*N*-methylheptanamide

17.46 Draw the structure corresponding to each name.

a. octyl acetate
b. hexyl pentanoate
c. propyl hexanoate
d. *N*-butylbenzamide
e. *N,N*-dimethyloctanamide

Physical Properties and Intermolecular Forces

17.47 Which compound(s) can hydrogen bond to another molecule like itself? Which compounds can hydrogen bond to water? (a) HCO₂CH₃; (b) CH₃CH₂CO₂H.

17.48 Which compound(s) can hydrogen bond to another molecule like itself? Which compounds can hydrogen bond to water? (a) CH₃CONHCH₃; (b) HCON(CH₃)₂.

17.49 Rank the following compounds in order of increasing boiling point.

A   B   C

17.50 Rank the following compounds in order of increasing boiling point.

D   E   F

17.51 Explain why the boiling point of $CH_3CH_2CONH_2$ is higher than the boiling point of $CH_3CO_2CH_3$.

17.52 Which compound in each pair is more water soluble? Which compound in each pair is more soluble in an organic solvent? (a) $CH_3CH_2CH_2CH_3$ or $CH_3CH_2CH_2CH_2CO_2H$; (b) $CH_3(CH_2)_4COOH$ or $CH_3(CH_2)_4COO^- Na^+$.

Acidity

17.53 Draw the products of each acid–base reaction.

a.
$$CH_3(CH_2)_3 \overset{\overset{O}{\|}}{C} OH \quad + \quad KOH \longrightarrow$$

b. $(CH_3)_2CHCH_2CH_2COOH \quad + \quad Na_2CO_3 \longrightarrow$

17.54 Draw the products of each acid–base reaction.

a.
$$CH_3 \!-\!\! \overset{\overset{O}{\|}}{\underset{OH}{C}} \quad + \quad NaOH \longrightarrow$$

b. $Cl_3CCOOH \quad + \quad NaHCO_3 \longrightarrow$

Formation of Esters and Amides

17.55 What ester is formed when butanoic acid ($CH_3CH_2CH_2CO_2H$) is treated with each alcohol in the presence of H_2SO_4?

a. CH_3OH

c. ⬡—OH

b. $CH_3CH_2CH_2OH$

d. ⬡—CH_2CH_2OH

17.56 What ester is formed when each carboxylic acid is treated with 2-propanol [$(CH_3)_2CHOH$] in the presence of H_2SO_4?

a. CH_3CH_2COOH

c. HCO_2H

b.
$$CH_3(CH_2)_{10} \overset{\overset{O}{\|}}{C} OH$$

d. CH_3O—⬡—COOH

17.57 Methylparaben is a common preservative used in cosmetics. What carboxylic acid and alcohol are needed to synthesize methylparaben by Fischer esterification?

methylparaben

17.58 Draw the structure of 2-octyl cyanoacrylate, an ester formed from α-cyanoacrylic acid and 2-octanol [$CH_3CH(OH)CH_2CH_2CH_2CH_2CH_2CH_3$]. 2-Octyl cyanoacrylate, a clear liquid that rapidly polymerizes in moist air, is sold under the trade name Dermabond, a tissue adhesive used to close wounds.

α-cyanoacrylic acid

17.59 What amide is formed when butanoic acid ($CH_3CH_2CH_2CO_2H$) is heated with each nitrogen-containing compound?

a. NH_3

c. $(CH_3CH_2)_2NH$

b. $CH_3CH_2NH_2$

d. $CH_3NHCH_2CH_3$

17.60 What amide is formed when propylamine ($CH_3CH_2CH_2NH_2$) is heated with each carboxylic acid?

a. CH_3CH_2COOH

c. HCO_2H

b.
$$CH_3(CH_2)_{10} \overset{\overset{O}{\|}}{C} OH$$

d. CH_3O—⬡—COOH

17.61 What carboxylic acid and alcohol are needed to synthesize each ester by Fischer esterification?

a. ⬡—CO_2CH_3

b. ⬡—O—$\overset{\overset{O}{\|}}{C}$—$CH_3$

17.62 What carboxylic acid and alcohol are needed to synthesize each ester by Fischer esterification?

a.

b. (structure)

17.63 What carboxylic acid and amine are needed to synthesize acetaminophen, the active ingredient in Tylenol?

(molecular model)

acetaminophen

17.64 What carboxylic acid and amine are needed to synthesize each amide?

a. (structure)

b. (structure)

Hydrolysis

17.65 Ethyl phenylacetate ($C_6H_5CH_2CO_2CH_2CH_3$) is a naturally occurring ester in honey. What hydrolysis products are formed when this ester is treated with water and H_2SO_4?

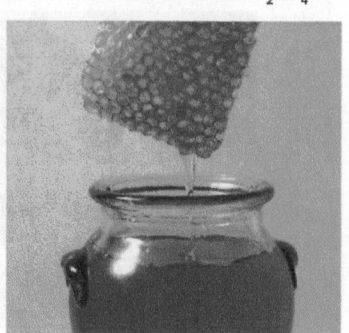

17.66 Benzyl acetate ($CH_3CO_2CH_2C_6H_5$) is a naturally occurring ester in peaches. What hydrolysis products are formed when this ester is treated with water and NaOH?

©Pixtal/SuperStock RF

17.67 What products are formed when each ester is hydrolyzed with water and H_2SO_4?

a. $CH_3CH_2CH_2$—C(=O)—$OCH(CH_3)_2$

b. (decalin ring with —O—C(=O)—CH₃ substituent)

c. cyclohexyl—CH_2CH_2—O—C(=O)—H

17.68 What products are formed when each ester in Problem 17.67 is hydrolyzed with water and NaOH?

17.69 What products are formed when each amide is hydrolyzed with water and HCl?

a. (benzene ring with $CONH_2$ and OCH_3)

b. $(CH_3)_3CCON(CH_3)_2$

c. cyclohexyl—N(H)—C(=O)—CH₃

17.70 What products are formed when each amide in Problem 17.69 is hydrolyzed with water and NaOH?

Polyesters and Polyamides

17.71 What dicarboxylic acid and diamine are needed to prepare the following polyamide?

(polyamide structure: —C(=O)—C₆H₄—C(=O)—N(H)—(CH₂)₄—N(H)—C(=O)—C₆H₄—C(=O)—N(H)—(CH₂)₄—N(H)—)

17.72 What dicarboxylic acid and diol are needed to form the following polyester?

(polyester structure: —C(=O)—(CH₂)₂—C(=O)—O—cyclohexyl—O—C(=O)—(CH₂)₂—C(=O)—O—cyclohexyl—O—C(=O)—(CH₂)₂—C(=O)—O—cyclohexyl—O—)

17.73 PTT (polytrimethylene terephthalate) is a polyester formed from 1,3-propanediol ($HOCH_2CH_2CH_2OH$) by the given reaction. PTT is sold under the trade name Sorona by DuPont. 1,3-Propanediol can now be made from a plant source like corn, rather than from petroleum starting materials. This makes PTT a more environmentally friendly polyester than PET. What is the structure of PTT?

HOOC—C₆H₄—COOH + $HOCH_2CH_2CH_2OH$ $\xrightarrow{H_2SO_4}$ PTT

terephthalic acid   1,3-propanediol

17.74 Compounds that contain both a hydroxyl group and a COOH can be used to form polyesters by reaction of the OH group in one molecule with the COOH group in another molecule. What polyester is formed from 4-hydroxycyclohexanecarboxylic acid?

HO—cyclohexyl—COOH

4-hydroxycyclohexanecarboxylic acid

General Questions

17.75 Draw the products formed in each reaction.

a. CH_3—C(=O)—OH + CH_3OH $\underset{}{\overset{H_2SO_4}{\rightleftharpoons}}$

b. $(CH_3)_2CHO$—C(=O)—CH_3 + H_2O $\underset{}{\overset{H_2SO_4}{\rightleftharpoons}}$

c. isobutyl—O—C(=O)—isopropyl + H_2O $\xrightarrow{NaOH}$

d. $CH_3(CH_2)_4$—C(=O)—OH + NaOH $\longrightarrow$

17.76 Draw the products formed in each reaction.

a. $(CH_3)_2CH$—C(=O)—OH + CH_3NH_2 $\xrightarrow{\Delta}$

b. $(CH_3)_2CHCH_2NH$—C(=O)—CH_3 + H_2O $\xrightarrow{HCl}$

c. isopropyl—N(H)—C(=O)—CH₂CH₃ + H_2O $\xrightarrow{NaOH}$

d. HO—C(=O)—$CH_2CH(CH_3)_2$ + NaOH $\longrightarrow$

630 **Chapter 17** Carboxylic Acids, Esters, and Amides

17.77 Answer the following questions about **A,** depicted in the ball-and-stick model.

A

a. What is the IUPAC name for **A?**
b. Draw an isomer of **A** that has the same functional group.
c. Draw an isomer of **A** that has a different functional group.
d. What products are formed when **A** is treated with NaOH?
e. Predict the solubility properties of **A** in H_2O; in an organic solvent.
f. What product is formed when **A** is treated with CH_3CH_2OH and H_2SO_4?
g. What product is formed when **A** is heated with $CH_3CH_2NH_2$?

17.78 Answer the following questions about **B,** depicted in the ball-and-stick model.

B

a. What is the IUPAC name for **B?**
b. Draw an isomer of **B** that has the same functional group.
c. Draw an isomer of **B** that has a different functional group.
d. What products are formed when **B** is treated with NaOH?
e. Predict the solubility properties of **B** in H_2O; in an organic solvent.
f. What product is formed when **B** is treated with CH_3CH_2OH and H_2SO_4?
g. What product is formed when **B** is heated with $CH_3CH_2NH_2$?

Applications

17.79 Which of the following structures represent soaps? Explain your answers.
a. $CH_3CO_2^-Na^+$ c. $CH_3(CH_2)_{12}COOH$
b. $CH_3(CH_2)_{14}CO_2^-Na^+$

17.80 Which of the following structures represent soaps? Explain your answers.
a. $CH_3CH_2CO_2^-K^+$ c. $CH_3(CH_2)_9CO_2^-Na^+$
b. $CH_3(CH_2)_{16}COOH$

17.81 Like aspirin, naproxen contains a carboxyl group, so it undergoes similar acid–base reactions.

naproxen

a. Draw the reaction that occurs when naproxen is treated with NaOH.
b. What form of naproxen exists in the stomach?
c. What form of naproxen exists in the intestines?

17.82 Sunscreens that contain an ester can undergo hydrolysis. What products are formed when **A,** a commercial sunscreen, is hydrolyzed with water?

A

17.83 How does aspirin act as an anti-inflammatory agent?

17.84 What structural feature is important in making penicillin a biologically active antibiotic? How does the biological activity of penicillin come about?

17.85 Explain how soap is able to dissolve nonpolar hydrocarbons in a polar solvent like H_2O.

17.86 Today, synthetic detergents like the compound drawn below are used to clean clothes, not soaps. Synthetic detergents are similar to soaps in that they contain an ionic head bonded to a large hydrocarbon group (the nonpolar tail). Explain how this detergent cleans away dirt.

$$CH_3(CH_2)_9 \underset{\text{a detergent}}{\longrightarrow} SO_3^-\ Na^+$$

17.87 Draw the products formed by acidic hydrolysis of **aspartame,** the artificial sweetener used in Equal and many diet beverages. One of the hydrolysis products of this reaction is the naturally occurring amino acid phenylalanine. Infants afflicted with phenylketonuria cannot metabolize this amino acid so it accumulates, causing mental retardation. When the condition is identified early, a diet limiting the consumption of phenylalanine (and compounds like aspartame that are converted to it) can allow for a normal life.

aspartame

17.88 Polyhydroxybutyrate (PHB) is a biodegradable polyester; that is, the polymer is degraded by microorganisms that naturally occur in the environment. Such biodegradable polymers are attractive alternatives to the commonly used polymers that persist in landfills for years. What is the single product formed when PHB is hydrolyzed with acid and water?

PHB

CHALLENGE PROBLEMS

17.89 Compounds that contain both a hydroxyl group (OH) and a carboxyl group (COOH) can undergo an intramolecular esterification reaction. What product is formed when each hydroxy acid undergoes an intramolecular reaction?
a. $HOCH_2CH_2CH_2CH_2CO_2H$
b. $HOCH_2CH_2CH_2CO_2H$

17.90 Lactams can be hydrolyzed with base, just like other amides. When a lactam is hydrolyzed, the ring is opened to form a product with two functional groups and no ring. What product is formed when caprolactam, the starting material for the synthesis of one type of nylon, is hydrolyzed with water and base?

caprolactam

18

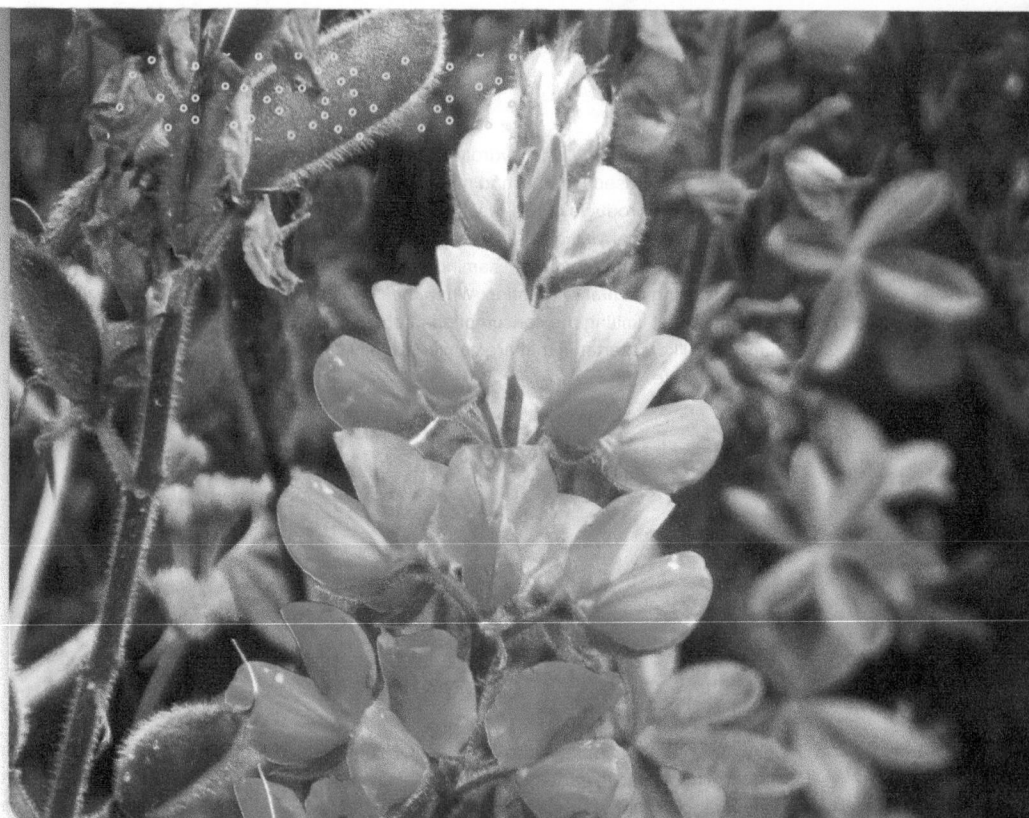

Lupin, a genus of flowering
plant found in the Andes of Peru
and along the roadsides of
Alaska, contains alkaloids,
naturally occurring amines
obtained from plants.
©Daniel C. Smith

Amines and Neurotransmitters

CHAPTER OUTLINE

18.1   Structure and Bonding

18.2   Nomenclature

18.3   Physical Properties

18.4   FOCUS ON HEALTH & MEDICINE:
Caffeine and Nicotine

18.5   Alkaloids—Amines from Plant Sources

18.6   Amines as Bases

18.7   FOCUS ON HEALTH & MEDICINE: Ammonium
Salts as Useful Drugs

18.8   Neurotransmitters

18.9   FOCUS ON THE HUMAN BODY: Epinephrine and
Related Compounds

18.10   FOCUS ON HEALTH & MEDICINE: Histamine and
Antihistamines

CHAPTER GOALS

In this chapter you will learn how to:

1. Identify the characteristics of amines

2. Name amines

3. Give examples of common alkaloids

4. Draw the products of acid–base reactions of amines

5. Identify and name ammonium salts

6. Discuss the function of neurotransmitters and explain how
neurotransmitters and hormones differ

7. Discuss the role of dopamine and serotonin in the body

8. Give examples of important derivatives of 2-phenylethylamine

9. Discuss the chemistry of histamine, antihistamines, and anti-ulcer
drugs

In Chapter 18 we turn our attention to **amines,** organic compounds that contain nitrogen atoms. The amine nitrogen atom can be bonded to one, two, or three alkyl groups, and many amines have a nitrogen atom in a ring. All proteins contain amines, as do many vitamins and hormones. Many common amines, such as the caffeine in coffee and the nicotine in tobacco, are naturally occurring. Synthetic drugs used as sedatives, antihistamines, and bronchodilators also contain the amine functional group. Chapter 18 concludes with a discussion of **neurotransmitters,** important chemical messengers in the body, and many other related physiologically active amines.

18.1   Structure and Bonding

Amines **are organic nitrogen compounds,** formed by replacing one or more hydrogen atoms of ammonia (NH_3) with alkyl groups. Amines are classified as 1°, 2°, or 3° by the number of alkyl groups bonded to the *nitrogen* atom.

- A primary (1°) amine has one C—N bond and the general structure RNH_2.
- A secondary (2°) amine has two C—N bonds and the general structure R_2NH.
- A tertiary (3°) amine has three C—N bonds and the general structure R_3N.

Like ammonia, **the amine nitrogen atom has a lone pair of electrons,** which is generally omitted in condensed structures. In Section 18.7, we will also learn about **quaternary ammonium ions** that contain a fourth alkyl group bonded to nitrogen. In this case, the nitrogen atom has no lone pair and bears a positive charge.

General structure		Example
$R{-}\overset{\overset{\displaystyle R}{|}}{\underset{\underset{\displaystyle R}{|}}{N^{+}}}{-}R$		$CH_3{-}\overset{\overset{\displaystyle CH_2CH_3}{|}}{\underset{\underset{\displaystyle CH_3}{|}}{N^{+}}}{-}CH_2CH_2CH_3$
quaternary ammonium ion		N has no lone pair.

The amine nitrogen atom can also be part of a ring to form a **heterocycle.** For example, piperidine, one compound isolated from black pepper, and coniine, the poisonous principle of hemlock, both contain a nitrogen atom in a six-membered ring.

pepper plant   hemlock

piperidine   coniine

(left): ©Maximilian Weinzierl/Alamy; (right): ©Steven P. Lynch RF

An amine nitrogen atom is surrounded by three atoms and one nonbonded electron pair, making it trigonal pyramidal in shape, with bond angles of approximately 109.5°.

CH_3NH_2
methylamine

$CH_3 \overset{\ddot{N}}{\underset{109.5°}{\diagup}} \overset{H}{\underset{H}{}}$

trigonal pyramidal

$(CH_3)_3N$
trimethylamine

$CH_3 \overset{\ddot{N}}{\underset{109.5°}{\diagup}} \overset{CH_3}{\underset{CH_3}{}}$

trigonal pyramidal

SAMPLE PROBLEM 18.1 CLASSIFYING AMINES

Classify each amine in the following compounds as 1°, 2°, or 3°. Putrescine is partly responsible for the foul odor of decaying fish. MDMA is the illegal stimulant commonly called "Ecstasy."

a. $H_2N(CH_2)_4NH_2$

putrescine

b.

MDMA
"Ecstasy"

Analysis

To determine whether an amine is 1°, 2°, or 3°, count the number of carbons bonded to the nitrogen atom. A 1° amine has one C—N bond, and so forth.

Solution

Draw out the structure or add H's to the skeletal structure to clearly see how many C—N bonds the amine contains.

a. $H-\overset{H}{\underset{H}{N}}-CH_2CH_2CH_2CH_2-\overset{H}{\underset{H}{N}}-H$

putrescine

Each N is bonded to only 1 C.
Both amines are **1°**.

b.

MDMA
"Ecstasy"

This N is bonded to 2 C's,
making it a **2° amine.**

PRACTICE PROBLEM 18.1

Classify each amine in the following compounds as 1°, 2°, or 3°.

a. $H_2N(CH_2)_3NH(CH_2)_4NH(CH_2)_3NH_2$

spermine
(isolated from semen)

b.

meperidine
(Trade name Demerol)

More Practice: Try Problems 18.23–18.28, 18.32, 18.73a, 18.74a, 18.75b, 18.76b.

PROBLEM 18.1

Label the amine and hydroxyl group in lupinine, a compound obtained from lupin, as 1°, 2°, or 3°.

lupinine

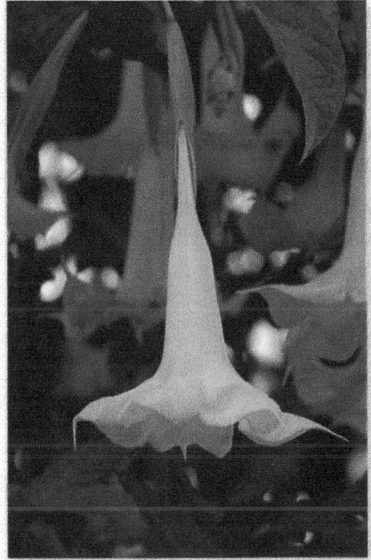

Angel's trumpets are ornamental plants that contain the toxic amine scopolamine (Problem 18.2). Transdermal patches that release a minute dose of scopolamine are used to treat the nausea and vomiting associated with motion sickness. ©James Forte/Getty Images RF

PROBLEM 18.2

Label the amine and hydroxyl group in scopolamine, a drug used to treat motion sickness, as 1°, 2°, or 3°.

scopolamine

Methamphetamine (Figure 18.1) is one of the many biologically active amines discussed in this chapter. Because it imparts to the user a pleasurable "high," methamphetamine is a widely abused illegal drug that has profound effects on the body and mind. Methamphetamine, known as speed, meth, or crystal meth, is highly addictive, easy to synthesize, and has adverse effects on the heart, lungs, blood vessels, and other organs. Prolonged use can lead to sleeplessness, seizures, hallucinations, paranoia, and serious heart disease.

PROBLEM 18.3

(a) What type of amine does methamphetamine contain? (b) Give the molecular shape around each indicated atom in methamphetamine.

methamphetamine

Figure 18.1

Effects of Methamphetamine Use

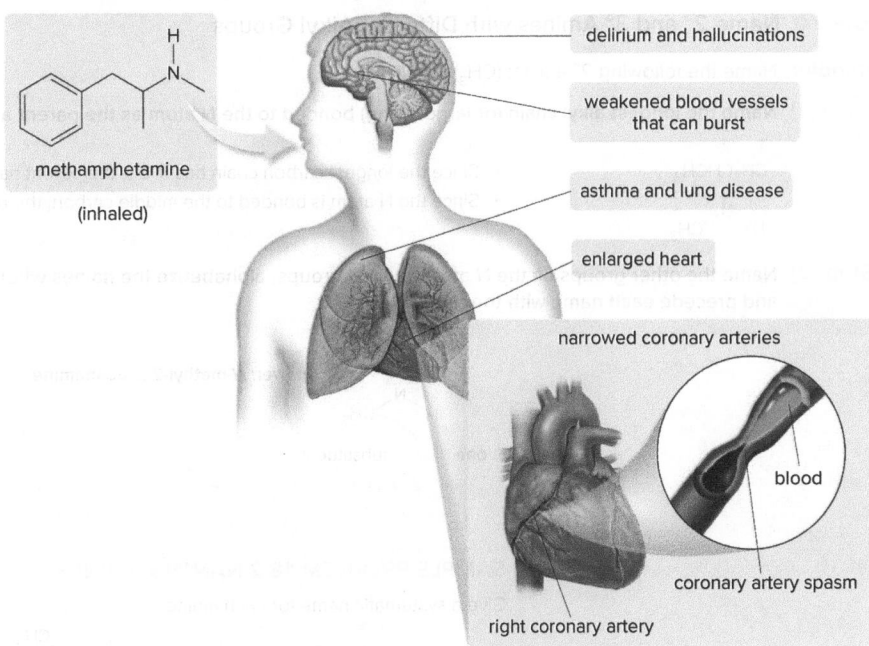

Blood flow is constricted during an artery spasm, resulting in a heart attack.

18.2 Nomenclature

18.2A Primary Amines

Primary (1°) amines are named using either systematic or common names. Systematic names can be used for any amine. To assign the **systematic name,** find the longest carbon chain bonded to the amine nitrogen, and change the *-e* ending of the parent alkane to the suffix *-amine.* Then use the usual rules of nomenclature to number the chain and name the substituents.

Common names are used only for simple amines. To assign a **common name,** name the alkyl group bonded to the nitrogen atom and add the suffix *-amine,* forming a single word.

$$CH_3NH_2$$

Common name: methylamine
Systematic name: methanamine

$$CH_3CH_2CH_2CH_2NH_2 \ = \ \text{(structure)} NH_2$$

4   3   2   1

Common name: butylamine
Systematic name: 1-butanamine

18.2B Secondary and Tertiary Amines

Secondary (2°) and 3° amines having identical alkyl groups are named by using the prefix *di-* or *tri-* with the name of the primary amine.

$$\text{(structure)} = CH_3CH_2-N-CH_2CH_3$$
with CH_2CH_3

triethylamine

$$CH_3CH_2CH_2-N-CH_2CH_2CH_3 = \text{(structure)}$$
with H

dipropylamine

Secondary and tertiary amines having more than one kind of alkyl group are named as **N-substituted primary amines** using the following *How To* procedure.

How To **Name 2° and 3° Amines with Different Alkyl Groups**

Example: Name the following 2° amine: $(CH_3)_2CHNHCH_3$.

Step [1] Name the longest alkyl chain (or largest ring) bonded to the N atom as the parent amine.

1   2
$$CH_3CHCH_3$$
H CH_3

- Since the longest carbon chain has 3 C's, the parent name is *propanamine.*
- Since the N atom is bonded to the middle carbon, the name becomes *2-propanamine.*

Step [2] Name the other groups on the N atom as alkyl groups, alphabetize the names when there is more than one substituent, and precede each name with the prefix N-.

$$CH_3CHCH_3$$
H CH_3

Answer: *N*-methyl-2-propanamine

one methyl substituent

SAMPLE PROBLEM 18.2 NAMING AMINES

Give a systematic name for each amine.

a. $CH_3CH_2CH_2CH_2CH_2NH_2$

b. (structure: cyclopentyl group bonded to N with CH_3 and CH_2CH_3 substituents)

Analysis and Solution

a. [1] For a 1° amine, find and name the longest chain containing the amine group.

$$CH_3CH_2CH_2CH_2CH_2NH_2$$

pentane - - - → pentan*amine*
(5 C's)

[2] Number the carbon skeleton.

$$CH_3CH_2CH_2CH_2CH_2NH_2$$
   5   2   1

You must use a number to show the location of the NH_2 group.
Answer: 1-pentanamine

b. For a 3° amine, one alkyl group on N is the principal R group and the others are substituents.

[1] Name the ring bonded to the N.

CH₃ / N / CH₂CH₃

5 C's in the ring

↓

cyclopentanamine

[2] Name the substituents.

CH₃ / N / CH₂CH₃

methyl and ethyl groups on N

• 2 N's are needed, one for each alkyl group.
• Alphabetize the *e* of **e**thyl before the *m* of **m**ethyl.

Answer: *N*-ethyl-*N*-methylcyclopentanamine

PRACTICE PROBLEM 18.2

Give an acceptable name for each amine.

a. $CH_3CH_2CHCH_3$
              |
             NH_2

b. $CH_3CH_2CH_2NHCH_3$

c. cyclohexane—N(CH₃)₂

d. (structure)

More Practice: Try Problems 18.33a, 18.34a, 18.35, 18.36.

18.2C   Aromatic Amines

Aromatic amines, amines having a nitrogen atom bonded directly to a benzene ring, are named as derivatives of aniline.

benzene—NH₂   benzene—NHCH₂CH₃   benzene—NH₂ / Br

aniline   *N*-ethylaniline   *o*-bromoaniline

PROBLEM 18.4

Draw a structure corresponding to each name: (a) *N*-methylaniline; (b) *m*-ethylaniline; (c) 3,5-diethylaniline; (d) *N,N*-diethylaniline.

18.2D   Miscellaneous Nomenclature Facts

An **NH_2** group named as a substituent is called an **amino group.**

There are many different **nitrogen heterocycles,** and each ring type is named differently, depending on the number of N atoms in the ring and the ring size. The structures and names of four common nitrogen heterocycles are shown.

piperidine   pyrrolidine   pyridine   pyrrole

PROBLEM 18.5

Draw a structure corresponding to each name.

a. 3-hexanamine

b. *N*-methylpentylamine

c. *p*-nitroaniline

d. *N*-methylpiperidine

e. *N,N*-dimethylethylamine

f. 2-aminocyclohexanone

g. 1-propylcyclohexanamine

h. *N*-propylaniline

18.3   Physical Properties

Many low molecular weight amines have *very* foul odors. **Trimethylamine** [$(CH_3)_3N$], formed when enzymes break down certain fish proteins, has the characteristic odor of rotting fish. **Cadaverine** ($NH_2CH_2CH_2CH_2CH_2CH_2NH_2$) is a poisonous diamine with a putrid odor also present in rotting fish, and partly responsible for the odor of semen, urine, and bad breath.

Because nitrogen is much more electronegative than carbon or hydrogen, amines contain polar C—N and N—H bonds. **Primary (1°) and 2° amines are also capable of intermolecular hydrogen bonding,** because they contain N—H bonds.

intermolecular
hydrogen bonding

Since nitrogen is less electronegative than oxygen, however, intermolecular hydrogen bonds between N and H are *weaker* than those between O and H. As a result:

- In comparing compounds of similar molecular weight, 1° and 2° amines have higher boiling points than compounds incapable of hydrogen bonding, but lower boiling points than alcohols that have stronger intermolecular hydrogen bonds.

$CH_3CH_2OCH_2CH_3$	$CH_3CH_2CH_2CH_2NH_2$	$CH_3CH_2CH_2CH_2OH$
diethyl ether	1-butanamine	1-butanol
bp = 38 °C	bp = 78 °C	bp = 118 °C

Increasing intermolecular forces
Increasing boiling point

- Tertiary (3°) amines have lower boiling points than 1° and 2° amines of comparable molecular weight, because they have no N—H bonds.

3 C's bonded to N	$CH_3CH_2N(CH_3)_2$	CH_3CH_2—N—CH_2CH_3 (one N—H bond)	2 C's bonded to N
3° amine	no N—H bond bp = 38 °C	bp = 56 °C	2° amine

higher boiling point

Amines are soluble in organic solvents regardless of size. Amines with fewer than six carbons are water soluble because they can hydrogen bond with water. Larger amines are water insoluble because the nonpolar alkyl portion is too large to dissolve in the polar water solvent.

SAMPLE PROBLEM 18.3 DETERMINING RELATIVE BOILING POINTS

Which compound in each pair has the higher boiling point: (a) $CH_3CH_2NHCH_3$ or $CH_3CH_2OCH_3$; (b) $(CH_3)_3N$ or $CH_3CH_2CH_2NH_2$?

Analysis

Keep in mind the general rule: For compounds of comparable molecular weight, **the stronger the intermolecular forces, the higher the boiling point.**

- Compounds that can hydrogen bond have higher boiling points than compounds that are polar but cannot hydrogen bond.
- Polar compounds have higher boiling points than nonpolar compounds.

Solution

a. The 2° amine ($CH_3CH_2NHCH_3$) has an N—H bond, so intermolecular hydrogen bonding is possible. The ether ($CH_3CH_2OCH_3$) has only C—H bonds, so there is no possibility of intermolecular hydrogen bonding. $CH_3CH_2NHCH_3$ has a higher boiling point because it has stronger intermolecular forces.

$$CH_3CH_2\!-\!\underset{\underset{H}{|}}{N}\!-\!CH_3 \qquad\qquad CH_3CH_2\!-\!O\!-\!CH_3$$

a 2° amine with an N—H bond
intermolecular hydrogen bonding
higher boiling point

an ether with only C—H bonds

b. The 1° amine ($CH_3CH_2CH_2NH_2$) has N—H bonds, so intermolecular hydrogen bonding is possible. The 3° amine [$(CH_3)_3N$] has only C—H bonds, so there is no possibility of intermolecular hydrogen bonding. $CH_3CH_2CH_2NH_2$ has a higher boiling point because it has stronger intermolecular forces.

$$CH_3CH_2CH_2NH_2 \qquad\qquad CH_3\!-\!\underset{\underset{CH_3}{|}}{N}\!-\!CH_3$$

a 1° amine with N—H bonds
intermolecular hydrogen bonding
higher boiling point

a 3° amine with only C—H bonds

PRACTICE PROBLEM 18.3

Which compound in each pair has the higher boiling point?

More Practice: Try Problems 18.43, 18.45, 18.46, 18.49.

18.4   FOCUS ON HEALTH & MEDICINE
Caffeine and Nicotine

Caffeine and **nicotine** are widely used stimulants of the central nervous system that contain amine heterocycles. Caffeine and nicotine, like other amines discussed in Section 18.5, are *alkaloids*, **naturally occurring amines derived from plant sources.**

caffeine   nicotine

18.4A   Caffeine

Caffeine (Figure 18.2) is a bitter-tasting amine found in coffee and tea. Caffeine is also present in soft drinks and chocolate bars. The pain reliever Anacin contains aspirin and caffeine, and over-the-counter remedies like NoDoz used to ward off sleep contain caffeine. Table 18.1 lists the average caffeine content of several products.

Caffeine is a mild stimulant, usually imparting a feeling of alertness after consumption. It also increases heart rate, dilates airways, and stimulates the secretion of stomach acid. These effects are observed because caffeine increases glucose production, making an individual feel energetic. Caffeine's effects are temporary, so an individual must consume it throughout the day to maintain the same "high."

Figure 18.2

Caffeine—An Alkaloid from the Coffee Plant

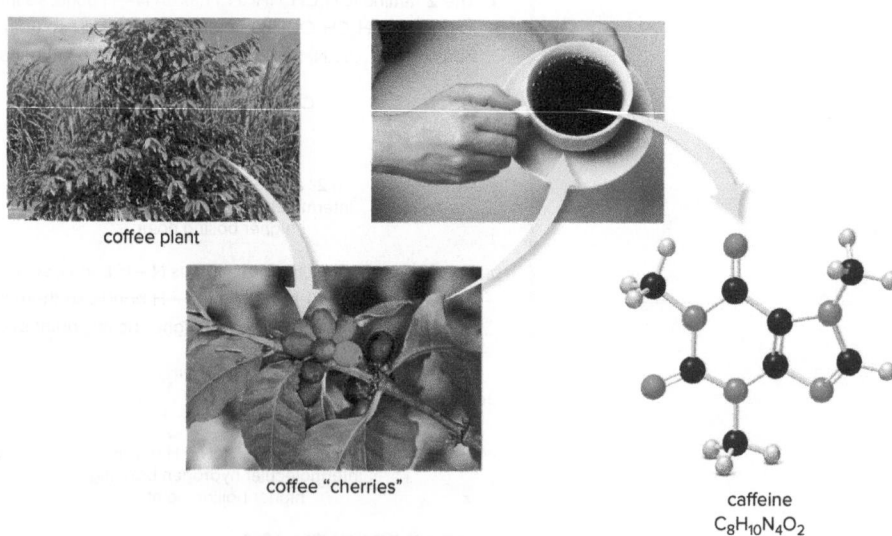

coffee plant

coffee "cherries"

caffeine
$C_8H_{10}N_4O_2$

Coffee is grown in 50 tropical countries worldwide, and ranks second only to oil in the amount traded internationally. The coffee "cherries" are picked by hand and dried to give two seeds per fruit. Raw beans are shipped to roasting facilities around the world. *(left): ©mediacolor's/Alamy; (right): ©GFC Collection/Alamy RF; (bottom): ©Nick Koudis/Gettty Images RF*

Some chocolate bars contain as much caffeine as a 12-oz can of cola. *©Andrew Brett Wallis/Getty Images RF*

Table 18.1 Average Caffeine Content in Common Foods and Drugs

Product	Serving Size	Caffeine (mg)
Coffee, brewed	8 oz	133
Coffee, instant	16 oz	47
Coffee, decaffeinated	8 oz	5
Tea, brewed	8 oz	53
Coca-Cola Classic	12 oz	35
Diet Coke	12 oz	47
Hershey's Chocolate Bar	1.55 oz	9
Hershey's Special Dark Chocolate	1.45 oz	31
Anacin	2 tablets	64
NoDoz	1 tablet	200

[Data taken from the web, Center for Science in the Public Interest.]

In moderation, caffeine consumption poses no health risks, but large quantities can cause insomnia, anxiety, and dehydration. Since caffeine is somewhat addicting, withdrawal symptoms—headache, irritability, and mild depression—can be observed when it is eliminated from the diet. Several studies suggest that pregnant women should limit their intake of caffeine, and that excessive caffeine consumption increases the risk of miscarriage. Nursing mothers are likewise advised to limit caffeine intake, because it passes into breast milk and can adversely affect newborn babies.

PROBLEM 18.6

Decaffeinated coffee is produced by extracting the caffeine from coffee with a solvent. Initially dichloromethane (CH_2Cl_2) was used, but concerns arose over the ill health effects of trace amounts of CH_2Cl_2 remaining in the coffee. Why is caffeine soluble in CH_2Cl_2?

18.4B Nicotine

Nicotine (Figure 18.3) is a highly toxic amine isolated from tobacco. In small doses it acts as a stimulant, but in larger doses causes depression, nausea, and even death. Nicotine is synthesized in tobacco plants as a defense against insect predators, and is used commercially as an insecticide.

Although inhaled tobacco smoke contains over 4,000 compounds, many of which are toxic or cancer causing, nicotine is the compound that makes smoking addictive. Nicotine imparts a sense of pleasure to the smoker, and once a smoker is "hooked," he or she needs to continue smoking to avoid the extreme discomforts of withdrawal—restlessness, anxiety, and craving.

Figure 18.3 Nicotine—An Alkaloid from the Tobacco Plant

tobacco plant

dried tobacco leaves

nicotine
$C_{10}H_{14}N_2$

Tobacco is grown in temperate climates. The leaves are harvested and dried, and then converted to cigarettes and other tobacco products.

(left): ©kai4107/Shutterstock RF; (right): ©Glow Images RF; (bottom): ©Wyne Hutchinson/Alamy

Nicotine patches and nicotine-containing chewing gum have been effectively used by many individuals to quit smoking.
©Stockbyte/Getty Images RF

The word *alkaloid* is derived from the word *alkali*, because aqueous solutions of alkaloids are slightly basic.

Cigarette smoking causes lung disease, heart disease, and cancer, and it is recognized today as the leading cause of avoidable death in the United States. Despite this well-known fact, the nicotine addiction makes it difficult for current smokers to quit. In fact, the sale of nicotine-free cigarettes many years ago was an unsuccessful enterprise because the nicotine in cigarettes is what smokers really crave when they light up.

One method employed by some to quit smoking involves the use of a nicotine patch. The patch is applied to the skin and nicotine diffuses through the skin and into the bloodstream. In this way, a smoker still derives pleasure from the nicotine in the system, but is no longer exposed to the ill effects of the other components of cigarette smoke. Slowly the concentration of nicotine in the patch is reduced, with the hope that eventually the smoker will no longer need nicotine. A similar strategy is used with chewing gum that contains nicotine.

PROBLEM 18.7

What two types of nitrogen heterocycles are present in nicotine?

18.5 Alkaloids—Amines from Plant Sources

Morphine, quinine, and **atropine** are three alkaloids with useful medicinal properties. All three compounds contain nitrogen heterocycles and have a complex structure with several functional groups.

18.5A Morphine and Related Alkaloids

The psychological and analgesic effects of the opium poppy *Papaver somniferum* have been known for probably 6,000 years, and it has been widely used as a recreational drug and pain-killing remedy for centuries. The analgesic and narcotic effects of opium are largely due to **morphine. Codeine,** an alkaloid of similar structure with a single methyl ether, is also present, but in much smaller amounts.

morphine   codeine

Morphine is especially useful in relieving severe chronic pain, so it is often prescribed for patients with terminal cancer. Morphine is also very addictive, and with time, higher doses are needed to produce the same effects. Approximately 95% of the morphine obtained from legally grown poppies is converted to codeine, a useful drug for the relief of less severe pain.

Heroin, a widely used, very addictive illicit drug, is readily prepared by converting the two hydroxyl groups of morphine to acetate esters. Heroin is less polar than morphine, making it more soluble in fat cells in the body. As a result, it is two to three times more potent than morphine in producing euphoria and pain relief.

Poppy seed tea, which contains morphine, was used as a folk remedy in parts of England until World War II. Since poppy seeds contain morphine, eating poppy seed cake or bagels can introduce enough morphine into the system to produce a positive test in a drug screen. ©John Foxx/Getty Images RF

Both OH groups are converted to esters.

morphine   heroin

PROBLEM 18.8

(a) Classify the amine in heroine as 1°, 2°, or 3°. (b) Identify all the functional groups in heroin.

PROBLEM 18.9

Naloxone is a drug used to treat overdoses of heroin and prescription opioids. (a) Label the amine in naloxone as 1°, 2°, or 3°. (b) Identify the functional groups in heroin and naloxone that differ. (c) Considering their functional groups, which drug is more polar?

naloxone

18.5B Quinine

Quinine is an alkaloid isolated from the bark of the cinchona tree native to the Andes Mountains. Quinine is a powerful antipyretic—that is, it reduces fever—and for centuries it was the only effective treatment for malaria. Its bitter taste gives tonic water its characteristic flavor.

quinine

cinchona tree

Source: Photo by Forest and Kim Starr

18.5C Atropine

Atropine is an alkaloid isolated from *Atropa belladonna*, the deadly nightshade plant.

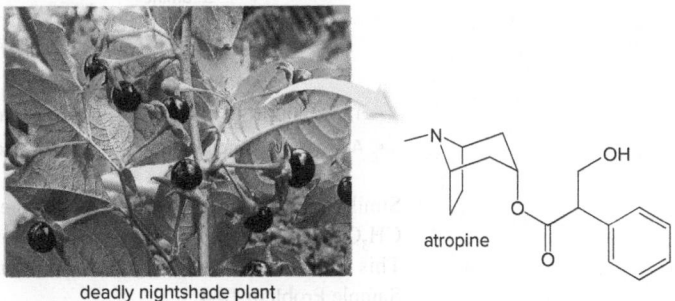

atropine

deadly nightshade plant

©Werner Arnold

During the Renaissance (fourteenth to seventeenth centuries), women used the juice of the berries of the nightshade to enlarge the pupils of their eyes for cosmetic reasons. Sometimes ophthalmologists today use atropine to dilate pupils. Atropine also increases heart rate, so physicians administer atropine for this purpose. Atropine relaxes smooth muscles and interferes with nerve impulses. In higher doses atropine is toxic, leading to convulsions, coma, and death.

18.6 Amines as Bases

Like ammonia (NH_3), **amines are bases;** that is, **they are *proton acceptors*.** When an amine is dissolved in water, an acid–base equilibrium occurs: the amine accepts a proton from H_2O, forming its conjugate acid, an **ammonium ion,** and water loses a proton, forming hydroxide, OH^-.

This acid–base reaction occurs with 1°, 2°, and 3° amines. While amines are more basic than other families of organic compounds, they are weak bases compared to inorganic bases like NaOH.

18.6A Reaction of Amines with Acids

Amines also react with acids such as HCl to form water-soluble salts. The lone pair of electrons from the amine nitrogen atom is always used to form a new bond to a proton from the acid.

- The amine [$(CH_3)_3N$] gains a proton to form its conjugate acid, an ammonium cation [$(CH_3)_3NH^+$].
- A proton is removed from the acid (HCl) to form its conjugate base, the chloride anion (Cl^-).

Similar acid–base reactions occur with other inorganic acids (H_2SO_4), and with organic acids like CH_3COOH, as well. **In each reaction, the amine gains a proton and the acid loses a proton.** This fundamental reaction of amines occurs no matter how complex the amine, as shown in Sample Problem 18.4.

- In an acid–base reaction of an amine, the amine nitrogen always forms a new bond to a proton forming an ammonium ion.

SAMPLE PROBLEM 18.4 DRAWING THE PRODUCTS WHEN AN AMINE REACTS WITH ACID

What products are formed when methamphetamine (Section 18.1) reacts with HCl?

methamphetamine

Analysis

In any acid–base reaction with an amine:

- Locate the N atom of the amine and add a proton to it. Since the amine nitrogen is neutral to begin with, adding a proton gives it a +1 charge.
- Remove a proton from the acid (HCl) and form its conjugate base (Cl^-).

Solution

Transfer a proton from the acid to the base. Use the lone pair on the N atom to form the new bond to the proton of the acid.

methamphetamine

This proton is transferred from the acid to the amine base.

Thus, HCl loses a proton to form Cl^-, and the N atom of methamphetamine gains a proton to form an ammonium cation.

PRACTICE PROBLEM 18.4

What products are formed when each of the following amines is treated with HCl: (a) $CH_3CH_2NH_2$; (b) $(CH_3CH_2)_2NH$; (c) $(CH_3CH_2)_3N$?

More Practice: Try Problems 18.51, 18.53, 18.54, 18.73g, 18.74f.

PROBLEM 18.10

Draw the products of each acid–base reaction.

a. $CH_3CH_2CH_2CH_2-NH_2$ + HCl $\longrightarrow$

b. $(CH_3)_2NH$ + C_6H_5COOH $\longrightarrow$

c. + H_2O $\longrightarrow$

PROBLEM 18.11

What products are formed when epinephrine is treated with H_2SO_4?

epinephrine
(adrenaline)

18.6B Ammonium Salts

When an amine reacts with an acid, the product is an *ammonium salt:* **the amine forms its conjugate acid, a positively charged ammonium ion, and the acid forms its conjugate base, an anion.**

To name an ammonium salt, change the suffix *-amine* of the parent amine from which the salt is formed to the suffix *-ammonium.* Then add the name of the anion as a separate word. Two examples are shown in Sample Problem 18.5.

SAMPLE PROBLEM 18.5 NAMING AN AMMONIUM SALT

Name each ammonium salt.

a. $(CH_3CH_2NH_3)^+$ Cl^- b. $[(CH_3)_3NH]^+$ CH_3COO^-

Analysis

To name an ammonium salt, identify the four groups bonded to the N atom. Remove one hydrogen from the N atom to draw the structure of the parent amine. Then put the two parts of the name together.

- Name the ammonium ion by changing the suffix *-amine* of the parent amine to the suffix *-ammonium.*
- Add the name of the anion.

Solution

a. Cl^- chloride
- Change the name ethyl*amine* to ethyl*ammonium.*
- Add the name of the anion, chloride.
  Answer: ethylammonium chloride

derived from $CH_3CH_2{-}N{-}H$
ethylamine

b. CH_3COO^- acetate
- Change the name trimethyl*amine* to trimethyl*ammonium.*
- Add the name of the anion, acetate.
  Answer: trimethylammonium acetate

derived from $CH_3{-}N{-}CH_3$
trimethylamine

PRACTICE PROBLEM 18.5

Name each ammonium salt.

a. $(CH_3NH_3)^+$ Cl^- b. $[(CH_3CH_2CH_2)_2NH_2]^+$ Br^- c. $[(CH_3)_2NHCH_2CH_3]^+$ CH_3COO^-

More Practice: Try Problems 18.39, 18.40.

Ammonium salts are ionic compounds, and as a result:

- **Ammonium salts are water-soluble solids.**

In this way, the solubility properties of an amine can be changed by treatment with acid. For example, octylamine has eight carbons, making it water insoluble. Reaction with HCl forms octylammonium chloride. This ionic solid is now soluble in water.

$$CH_3CH_2CH_2CH_2CH_2CH_2CH_2CH_2-\underset{\underset{H}{|}}{\overset{}{N}}-H \quad + \quad H-Cl \quad \longrightarrow \quad \left[CH_3CH_2CH_2CH_2CH_2CH_2CH_2CH_2-\underset{\underset{H}{|}}{\overset{\overset{H}{|}}{N}}-H \right]^+ \; Cl^-$$

octylamine   octylammonium chloride

water-insoluble amine - → **water-soluble salt**

The solubility properties change.

- **A water-insoluble amine can be converted to a water-soluble ammonium salt by treatment with acid.**

SAMPLE PROBLEM 18.6   DETERMINING THE WATER SOLUBILITY OF AMINES AND AMMONIUM SALTS

Label each compound as water soluble or water insoluble.

A   **B**   **C**

Analysis

- Amines containing fewer than six carbons are soluble in water.
- Amines containing six or more carbons are insoluble in water, because the nonpolar portion of the molecule is larger than the polar NH_2 group.
- Ammonium salts are ionic, so they are soluble in water.

Solution

- **A** is an amine with 8 C's, so it is insoluble in water.
- **B** is an ammonium salt, so it is soluble in water.
- **C** is a low molecular weight amine (4 C's), so it is soluble in water.

PRACTICE PROBLEM 18.6

Label each compound as water soluble or water insoluble.

a. $(CH_3CH_2)_3N$ c. $CH_3CH_2NH_2$

b. $\left[(CH_3CH_2)_3NH \right]^+ \; Br^-$ d.

More Practice: Try Problems 18.44, 18.50.

Ammonium salts can be re-converted to amines by treatment with base. Base removes a proton from the nitrogen atom of the amine, regenerating the neutral amine.

This proton is removed by the base.

$$\left[CH_3CH_2CH_2CH_2CH_2CH_2CH_2CH_2-\overset{\overset{H}{|}}{\underset{|}{N}}-H \right]^+ Cl^- \;+\; Na^+OH^- \;\longrightarrow\; CH_3CH_2CH_2CH_2CH_2CH_2CH_2CH_2-\overset{}{\underset{H}{N}}-H \;+\; H-OH \;+\; NaCl$$

octylammonium chloride
water-soluble salt

octylamine
water-insoluble amine

PROBLEM 18.12

What product is formed when each ammonium salt is treated with NaOH?

a. $\left[(CH_3CH_2)_3NH \right]^+$ Br^- b. $(CH_3CH_2NH_3)^+$ HSO_4^- c.

18.7 FOCUS ON HEALTH & MEDICINE
Ammonium Salts as Useful Drugs

CONSUMER NOTE

Many antihistamines and decongestants are sold as their hydrochloride salts.
©McGraw-Hill Education/Jill Braaten, photographer

Many amines with useful medicinal properties are sold as their ammonium salts. Since the ammonium salts are more water soluble than the parent amine, they are easily transported through the body in the aqueous medium of the blood.

For example, diphenhydramine is a 3° amine that is sold as its ammonium salt under the name of Benadryl. Benadryl, formed by treating diphenhydramine with HCl, is an over-the-counter antihistamine that is used to relieve the itch and irritation of skin rashes and hives.

diphenhydramine   +   HCl   ⟶   ammonium salt
                                                Benadryl

The names of medicines sold as ammonium salts are often derived from the names of the amine and the acid used to form them. Since Benadryl is formed from diphenhydramine and HCl, it is called **diphenhydramine hydrochloride.**

Two other examples of amines sold as their ammonium salts are phenylephrine hydrochloride, the decongestant in Sudafed PE, Theraflu, and DayQuil, and methadone hydrochloride, a long-acting narcotic taken orally to treat chronic painful conditions. Methadone hydrochloride is also used as a substitute narcotic for heroin addicts.

phenylephrine hydrochloride
(decongestant in Sudafed PE,
Theraflu, and DayQuil)

methadone hydrochloride
(narcotic analgesic)

Some **quaternary ammonium salts** ($R_4N^+ X^-$, Section 18.1)—that is, ammonium salts with nitrogen atoms bonded to *four* alkyl groups—are also useful agents. Bitrex is a foul-tasting nontoxic salt used on children's fingers to keep them from biting their nails or sucking their thumbs. Benzalkonium chloride is a disinfectant and antiseptic in mouthwash.

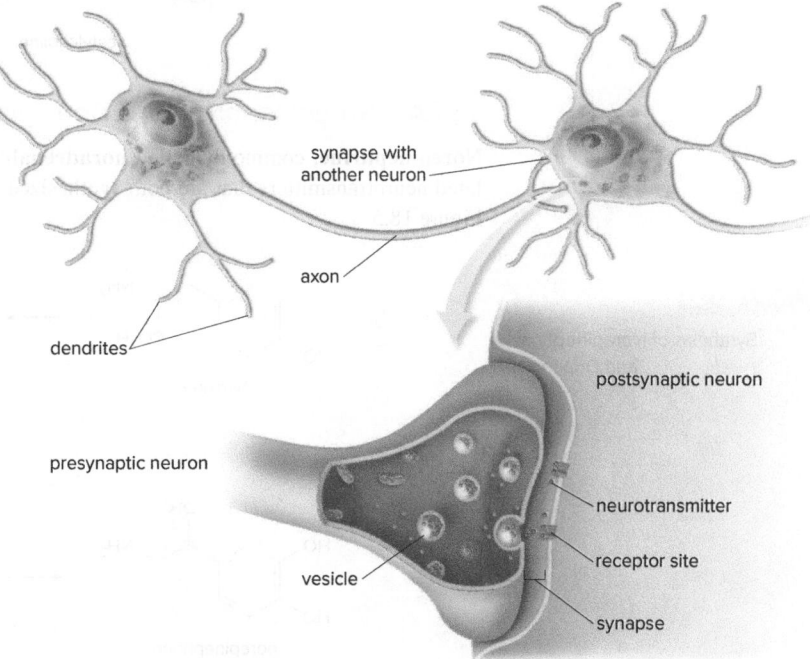

Bitrex

N is bonded to 4 C's.

benzalkonium chloride

N is bonded to 4 C's.

PROBLEM 18.13

When Benadryl is treated with a base like NaOH, the free amine, diphenhydramine, is re-formed, as we learned in Section 18.6. Explain why a similar reaction does not occur with a quaternary ammonium salt like Bitrex.

PROBLEM 18.14

Draw the structures of the amines from which phenylephrine hydrochloride and methadone hydrochloride are derived.

18.8 Neurotransmitters

A *neurotransmitter* is a chemical messenger that transmits nerve impulses from one nerve cell—neuron—to another cell. As shown in Figure 18.4, a neuron consists of many short filaments called **dendrites** connected to a cell body. A long stem called an **axon** also protrudes from

Figure 18.4

Neurotransmitters—Transmitting Information Between Neurons

synapse with another neuron

axon

dendrites

postsynaptic neuron

presynaptic neuron

neurotransmitter

receptor site

vesicle

synapse

Neurotransmitters are released from vesicles in the presynaptic neuron and diffuse through the synapse to bind to the receptor sites on the postsynaptic neuron.

the cell body. The axon ends in numerous small filaments at its opposite end. These filaments are separated from the dendrites of a nearby neuron by a small gap called the **synapse.**

Neurotransmitters are stored in small packets called **vesicles** in the filaments of the axon near the synapse. When an electrical signal flows from the cell body of the neuron along the axon to the filaments, the neurotransmitter is released, diffuses across the synapse, and binds to a receptor on the dendrites of an adjacent neuron.

- The presynaptic neuron releases the neurotransmitter.
- The postsynaptic neuron contains the receptors that bind the neurotransmitter.

Once the neurotransmitter is bound to the receptor, the chemical message is delivered. The neurotransmitter is then degraded or it is returned to the presynaptic neuron to begin the process again.

Drugs may be used to affect neurotransmitters in many different ways. Some drugs prevent the release of a neurotransmitter or prevent its binding to a receptor. Other drugs increase the amount of neurotransmitter released. Some drugs affect the degradation of a neurotransmitter or prevent its reuptake by the presynaptic neuron.

All neurotransmitters contain nitrogen atoms. Three important neurotransmitters are amines— **norepinephrine, dopamine,** and **serotonin**—and one is an ammonium ion—**acetylcholine.**

norepinephrine
(noradrenaline)

dopamine

serotonin

acetylcholine

18.8A Norepinephrine and Dopamine

Norepinephrine, commonly called **noradrenaline,** and **dopamine** are two structurally related neurotransmitters that are both synthesized from the amino acid tyrosine, as shown in Figure 18.5.

Figure 18.5

Synthesis of Norepinephrine and Dopamine

tyrosine

L-dopa

norepinephrine

dopamine

Norepinephrine and dopamine are both synthesized from the amino acid tyrosine by a multistep route. The newly introduced group at each stage is shown in red.

norepinephrine

Proper levels of both amines are needed for good mental health. For example, when **norepinephrine** levels are above normal, an individual feels unusually elated, and very high levels are associated with manic behavior. Norepinephrine is also converted to adrenaline when an individual experiences fear or stress, as we will learn in Section 18.9.

Dopamine affects brain processes that control movement, emotions, and pleasure. When dopamine-producing neurons die and there is too little dopamine in the brain, an individual loses control of fine motor skills and Parkinson's disease results. As we learned in Section 15.5, the level of dopamine in the brain cannot be increased simply by giving an individual dopamine, because dopamine does not cross the blood–brain barrier. L-Dopa, a precursor of dopamine shown in Figure 18.5, can travel from the bloodstream to the brain, so it is an effective treatment for Parkinson's disease. Elevated dopamine levels are also unhealthy and are associated with schizophrenia.

Dopamine plays an important role in addiction. Normal dopamine levels give an individual a pleasurable, satisfied feeling. Increased levels result in an intense "high." Drugs such as heroin, cocaine, and alcohol increase dopamine levels. When dopamine receptors are stimulated more than normal, the number and sensitivity of the receptors decreases, and an individual requires more of a drug to feel the same sense of pleasure.

dopamine

PROBLEM 18.15

(a) Classify the amine in rasagiline, a drug sold under the trade name Azilect for treatment of Parkinson's disease, as 1°, 2°, or 3°. (b) What other functional groups are present in the drug? (c) Locate the chirality center in rasagiline.

rasagiline

©2017 Teva Neuroscience, Inc. AZILECT is a registered trademark of Teva Pharmaceutical Industries Ltd.

PROBLEM 18.16

Indicate the chirality center in each of the compounds in Figure 18.5. Which compounds are achiral and contain no chirality centers?

18.8B Serotonin

The neurotransmitter **serotonin** is synthesized from the amino acid tryptophan. Serotonin plays an important role in mood, sleep, perception, and temperature regulation. We get sleepy after eating a turkey dinner on Thanksgiving because the unusually high level of tryptophan in turkey is converted to serotonin.

serotonin

tryptophan   serotonin

652   **Chapter 18**   Amines and Neurotransmitters

A deficiency of serotonin causes depression. Understanding the central role of serotonin in determining one's mood has led to the development of a wide variety of drugs for the treatment of depression. The most widely used antidepressants today are **selective serotonin reuptake inhibitors (SSRIs).** These drugs act by inhibiting the reuptake of serotonin by the presynaptic neuron, thus effectively increasing its concentration. Fluoxetine (trade name Prozac) and sertraline (trade name Zoloft) are two common antidepressants that act in this way.

fluoxetine
(Trade name Prozac)

sertraline
(Trade name Zoloft)

The discovery that migraine headaches result from improper levels of serotonin in the brain has led to the synthesis of several drugs that combat the pain, nausea, and light sensitivity that are associated with this condition. These drugs include sumatriptan (trade name Imitrex) and rizatriptan (trade name Maxalt).

sumatriptan
(Trade name Imitrex)

rizatriptan
(Trade name Maxalt)

Drugs that interfere with the metabolism of serotonin have a profound effect on mental state. For example, bufotenin, isolated from *Bufo* toads from the Amazon jungle, and psilocin isolated from *Psilocybe* mushrooms, are very similar in structure to serotonin and both cause intense hallucinations.

Bufo toad

Psilocybe mushrooms

bufotenin

psilocin

(left): ©Daniel C. Smith; (right): ©IT Stock/age fotostock RF

PROBLEM 18.17

The conversion of tryptophan to serotonin is a two-step process. What functional groups must be added or removed during this process?

PROBLEM 18.18

How are serotonin, bufotenin, and psilocin similar in structure? Classify the amines in these three compounds as 1°, 2°, or 3°.

18.8C Acetylcholine and Nicotine Addiction

Acetylcholine is a quaternary ammonium ion that serves as a neurotransmitter between neurons and muscle cells. In the brain, acetylcholine is involved in memory, mood, and other functions.

acetylcholine

nicotine

The pleasurable high that a smoker feels is due to nicotine interacting with acetylcholine receptors. At low concentrations, nicotine is a stimulant because it binds to these receptors, resulting in a feeling of well-being and alertness. Other nerve cells are also activated and this releases dopamine. The sense of pleasure resulting from the release of dopamine is what causes nicotine to be addictive. Over time receptors are inactivated and some degenerate, so tolerance to nicotine develops and larger quantities are needed to maintain the same sense of pleasure.

18.9 FOCUS ON THE HUMAN BODY
Epinephrine and Related Compounds

While neurotransmitters are the chemical messengers of the nervous system, **hormones** are the chemical messengers of the endocrine system. A *hormone* is a compound produced by an endocrine gland, which then travels through the bloodstream to a target tissue or organ.

Epinephrine, or **adrenaline** as it is commonly called, is a hormone synthesized in the adrenal glands from norepinephrine (noradrenaline).

norepinephrine
(noradrenaline)

epinephrine
(adrenaline)

When an individual senses danger or is confronted by stress, the hypothalamus region of the brain signals the adrenal glands to synthesize and release epinephrine, which enters the bloodstream and

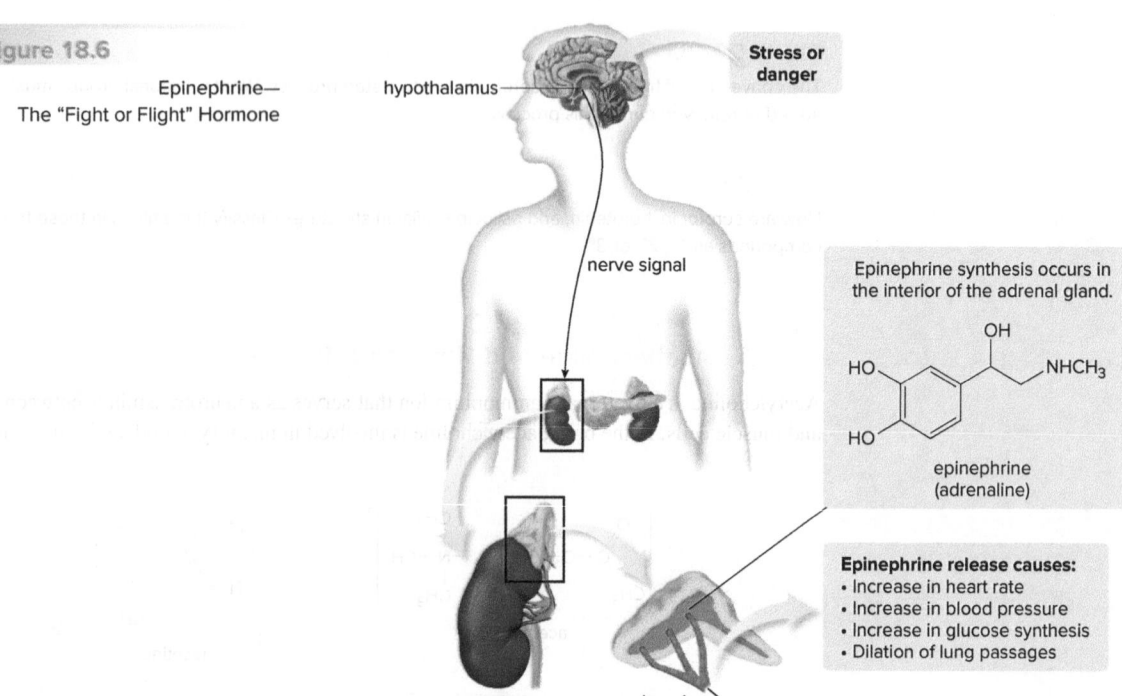

Figure 18.6

Epinephrine—
The "Fight or Flight" Hormone

then stimulates a response in many organs (Figure 18.6). Stored carbohydrates are metabolized in the liver to form glucose, which is further metabolized to provide an energy boost. Heart rate and blood pressure increase, and lung passages are dilated. These physiological changes are commonly referred to as a "rush of adrenaline," and they prepare an individual for "fight or flight."

18.9A Derivatives of 2-Phenylethylamine

Like epinephrine and norepinephrine, a large number of physiologically active compounds are derived from **2-phenylethylamine, $C_6H_5CH_2CH_2NH_2$.** Each of these compounds has a common structural unit: a benzene ring bonded to a two-carbon chain that is bonded to a nitrogen atom.

2-phenylethylamine   common structural feature shown in red

For example, **amphetamine** and **methamphetamine** are derivatives of 2-phenylethylamine that are powerful stimulants of the central nervous system. Both amines increase heart rate and respiratory rate. Since they increase glucose concentration in the bloodstream, they decrease hunger and fatigue. While amphetamine and methamphetamine may be prescribed for attention deficit hyperactivity disorder (ADHD) and weight reduction under the trade names Adderall and Desoxyn, respectively, they are highly addictive and widely abused drugs that must be used with extreme care. Both amphetamine and methamphetamine increase the level of dopamine in the brain, causing a pleasurable "high."

amphetamine   methamphetamine

The atoms of 2-phenylethylamine are shown in red.

Sudafed contains the decongestant pseudoephedrine, while Sudafed PE contains the decongestant phenylephrine.
©McGraw-Hill Education/Jill Braaten, photographer

Pseudoephedrine, the decongestant in Sudafed, is another derivative of 2-phenylethylamine. Since pseudoephedrine can be readily converted to methamphetamine, it has been replaced in many products by a related amine, **phenylephrine.** For example, Pfizer markets its pseudoephedrine-free decongestant as Sudafed PE. Products that contain pseudoephedrine are still over-the-counter remedies, but they are now stocked behind the pharmacy counter so their sale can be more closely monitored.

pseudoephedrine
(decongestant in Sudafed) → methamphetamine ✗ phenylephrine
(decongestant in Sudafed PE)

PROBLEM 18.19

Pseudoephedrine can be readily converted to methamphetamine by replacing one OH group by a hydrogen atom. Examine the structure of phenylephrine, and suggest a reason why it cannot be readily converted to methamphetamine.

PROBLEM 18.20

Label the atoms of 2-phenylethylamine in each compound. Mescaline is the active hallucinogen in peyote, a cactus native to the southwestern United States and Mexico. LSD, a hallucinogen commonly called "acid," was first synthesized in 1938 by Swiss chemist Albert Hofmann.

a. mescaline

b. LSD

18.9B   Drugs to Treat Asthma

The search for drugs that were structurally related to epinephrine but exhibited only some components of its wide range of biological activities led to the discovery of some useful medications. Both **albuterol** and **salmeterol** are derivatives of 2-phenylethylamine that dilate lung passages; that is, they are *bronchodilators.* They do not, however, stimulate the heart. This makes both compounds useful for the treatment of asthma. Albuterol is a short-acting drug used to relieve the wheezing associated with asthma. Salmeterol is much longer acting, and thus it is often used before bedtime to keep an individual symptom free overnight.

albuterol
(Trade names Ventolin, Proventil)

salmeterol
(Trade name Serevent)

PROBLEM 18.21

Classify the amines and the alcohols (not the phenols) in albuterol and salmeterol as 1°, 2°, or 3°.

18.10   FOCUS ON HEALTH & MEDICINE
Histamine and Antihistamines

Histamine is a biologically active amine formed in many tissues from the amino acid histidine.

Scombroid fish poisoning, associated with facial flushing, hives, and general itching, is caused by the ingestion of inadequately refrigerated fish, typically mahimahi and tuna. Bacteria convert the amino acid histidine to histamine, and when consumed in large amounts, this clinical syndrome results. ©Daniel C. Smith

Histamine is a neurotransmitter that binds to two different receptors, the H1 and H2 receptors, and produces a wide range of physiological effects on the body. Histamine is a vasodilator (it dilates capillaries), so it is released at the site of an injury or infection to increase blood flow. It is also responsible for the symptoms of allergies, including a runny nose and watery eyes. In the stomach, histamine stimulates the secretion of acid.

Antihistamines bind to the H1 histamine receptor, but they evoke a different response. An antihistamine like chlorpheniramine or diphenhydramine, for example, inhibits vasodilation, so it is used to treat the symptoms of the common cold and environmental allergies. These antihistamines also cause drowsiness by crossing the blood–brain barrier and binding to H1 receptors in the central nervous system. Newer antihistamines like fexofenadine (trade name Allegra) also bind to H1 receptors, but they do not cause drowsiness because they cannot cross the blood–brain barrier and bind to the H1 receptors in the central nervous system.

chlorpheniramine
(antihistamine)

diphenhydramine
(antihistamine)

fexofenadine
(nonsedating antihistamine)

Drugs that bind to the H2 receptor produce a different effect. For example, cimetidine (trade name Tagamet) binds to the H2 histamine receptor and, as a result, reduces acid secretion in the stomach. Thus, cimetidine is an effective **anti-ulcer** medication.

cimetidine
(Trade name Tagamet)
anti-ulcer drug

Cetirizine is an over-the-counter, nonsedating antihistamine. ©*Elizabeth Leyden/Alamy*

PROBLEM 18.22

Cetirizine (trade name Zyrtec) is an antihistamine that does not cross the blood–brain barrier, so it does not cause drowsiness. (a) Classify the amines in cetirizine as 1°, 2°, or 3°. (b) Locate the chirality center in cetirizine. (c) What is the molecular formula of cetirizine?

cetirizine

CHAPTER HIGHLIGHTS

KEY TERMS

Alkaloid (18.4)

Amine (18.1)

Ammonium salt (18.6)

Antihistamine (18.10)

Anti-ulcer drug (18.10)

Axon (18.8)

Dendrite (18.8)

Heterocycle (18.1)

Hormone (18.9)

Neuron (18.8)

Neurotransmitter (18.8)

Postsynaptic neuron (18.8)

Presynaptic neuron (18.8)

Primary (1°) amine (18.1)

Quaternary ammonium ion (18.1)

Secondary (2°) amine (18.1)

SSRI (18.8)

Synapse (18.8)

Tertiary (3°) amine (18.1)

Vesicle (18.8)

KEY REACTIONS

Amines react as bases with inorganic and organic acids (18.6).

$$R-\overset{\cdot\cdot}{\underset{H}{N}}-H \;+\; H-Cl \;\rightleftharpoons\; \left[R-\overset{H}{\underset{H}{N}}-H\right]^{+} \;+\; Cl^{-}$$

KEY CONCEPTS

1 **What are the characteristics of amines? (18.1, 18.3)**

- Amines are organic nitrogen compounds, formed by replacing one or more hydrogen atoms of NH_3 by alkyl groups.
- Primary (1°) amines have one C—N bond; 2° amines have two C—N bonds; 3° amines have three C—N bonds.
- An amine has a lone pair of electrons on the N atom, and is trigonal pyramidal in shape.
- Amines contain polar C—N and N—H bonds. Primary (1°) and 2° amines can hydrogen bond. Intermolecular hydrogen bonds between N and H are weaker than those between O and H.
- Tertiary (3°) amines have lower boiling points than 1° and 2° amines because they cannot hydrogen bond.

2 **How are amines named? (18.2)**

- Primary (1°) amines are identified by the suffix -*amine*.
- Secondary (2°) and 3° amines with identical alkyl groups are named by adding the prefix *di*- or *tri*- to the name of the 1° amine.
- Secondary (2°) and 3° amines with different alkyl groups are named as *N*-substituted 1° amines.

3 **What are alkaloids? Give examples of common alkaloids. (18.4, 18.5)**

- Alkaloids are naturally occurring amines isolated from plant sources.
- Examples of alkaloids include caffeine (from coffee and tea), nicotine (from tobacco), morphine and codeine (from the opium poppy), quinine (from the cinchona tree), and atropine (from the deadly nightshade plant).

4 **What products are formed when an amine is treated with acid? (18.6)**

- Amines act as proton acceptors in water and acid. For example, the reaction of RNH_2 with HCl forms the water-soluble ammonium salt $RNH_3^+ Cl^-$.

5 **What are the characteristics of ammonium salts and how are they named? (18.6, 18.7)**

- An ammonium salt consists of a positively charged ammonium ion and an anion.

- An ammonium salt is named by changing the suffix -*amine* of the parent amine to the suffix -*ammonium* followed by the name of the anion.
- Ammonium salts are water-soluble solids.
- Water-insoluble amine drugs are sold as their ammonium salts to increase their solubility in the aqueous environment of the blood.

6 **What are neurotransmitters and how do they differ from hormones? (18.8, 18.9)**
- A neurotransmitter is a chemical messenger that transmits a nerve impulse from a neuron to another cell.
- A hormone is a compound produced by an endocrine gland that travels through the bloodstream to a target tissue or organ.

7 **What roles do dopamine and serotonin play in the body? (18.8)**
- Dopamine affects movement, emotions, and pleasure. Too little dopamine causes Parkinson's disease. Too much dopamine causes schizophrenia. Dopamine plays a role in addiction.
- Serotonin is important in mood, sleep, perception, and temperature regulation. A deficiency of serotonin causes depression. SSRIs are antidepressants that effectively increase the concentration of serotonin.

8 **Give examples of important derivatives of 2-phenylethylamine. (18.9)**
- Derivatives of 2-phenylethylamine contain a benzene ring bonded to a two-carbon chain that is bonded to a nitrogen atom.
- Examples of 2-phenylethylamine derivatives include epinephrine, norepinephrine, amphetamine, and methamphetamine. Albuterol and salmeterol are also derivatives of 2-phenylethylamine that are used to treat asthma.

9 **What is histamine, and how do antihistamines and anti-ulcer drugs work? (18.10)**
- Histamine is an amine with a wide range of physiological effects. Histamine dilates capillaries, is responsible for the runny nose and watery eyes of allergies, and stimulates the secretion of stomach acid.
- Antihistamines bind to the H1 histamine receptor and inhibit vasodilation, so they are used to treat the symptoms of colds and allergies.
- Anti-ulcer drugs bind to the H2 histamine receptor and reduce the production of stomach acid.

PROBLEMS

Selected in-chapter and odd-numbered end-of-chapter problems have brief answers in Appendix B. The *Student Study Guide and Solutions Manual* contains detailed solutions to all in-chapter and odd-numbered end-of-chapter problems, as well as additional worked examples and a chapter self-test.

Structure and Bonding

18.23 Label each nitrogen-containing functional group in lidocaine, a local anesthetic, as an amine or amide, and classify it as 1°, 2°, or 3°.

lidocaine

18.24 Label each nitrogen-containing functional group in fentanyl, a narcotic pain reliever, as an amine or amide, and classify it as 1°, 2°, or 3°.

fentanyl

18.25 Aripiprazole, sold under the trade name Abilify, is a drug used to treat depression and bipolar disorder. Label each nitrogen-containing functional group as an amine or amide, and classify each as 1°, 2°, or 3°.

aripiprazole

18.26 Benazepril, sold under the trade name Lotensin, is a drug used to treat high blood pressure and congestive heart failure. Label each nitrogen-containing functional group as an amine or amide, and classify each as 1°, 2°, or 3°.

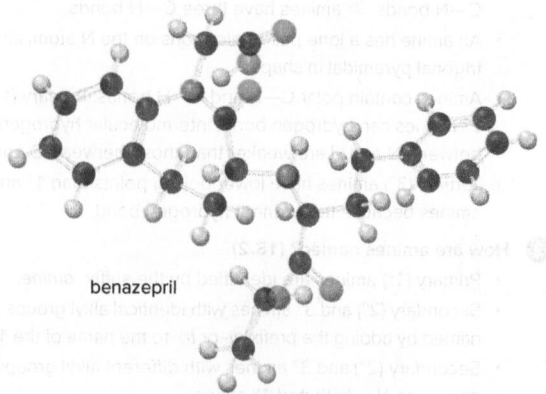

benazepril

18.27 Classify each amine as 1°, 2°, or 3°.

a. CH₃CHCH₂CH₂NHCH₃
         |
         CH₃

b.

18.28 Hygrine is an amine isolated from coca leaves. (a) Classify the amine as 1°, 2°, or 3°. (b) What type of nitrogen heterocycle is present in hygrine?

©Jordi Cami/Getty Images

hygrine

18.29 Match the description to one of the compounds **A–D.**
   a. a compound that contains a 1° amine and a 1° alcohol
   b. a compound that contains a 2° amine and a 2° alcohol
   c. a compound that contains a 1° amine and a 3° alcohol
   d. a compound that contains a 3° amine and a 1° alcohol

A   **B**

C   **D**

18.30 Draw the structure of three constitutional isomers of molecular formula C₅H₁₃N that contain a 1° amine and one chirality center.

18.31 Match the description to one of the compounds **E–H.**
   a. a compound that contains a 1° amine and a 1° amide
   b. a compound that contains a 1° amine and a 2° amide
   c. a compound that contains a 2° amine and a 3° amide
   d. a compound that contains a 3° amine and a 3° amide

E   **F**

G   **H**

18.32 Identify each nitrogen-containing functional group in U-47700, an illicit street drug called "pink" or "pinky," as an amine or amide, and classify it as 1°, 2°, or 3°.

U-47700

Nomenclature

18.33 Give an acceptable name for each amine.

a.   b.

18.34 Give an acceptable name for each amine.

a.

b.

18.35 Give an acceptable name for each amine.

a.
       H
       |
   CH₃CH₂—N—CH₂CH₃

b.
            NH₂
            |
   CH₃CH₂CHCH₂CH₂CH₂CH₃

c.
             NHCH₃
             |
   CH₃CH₂CH₂CHCH₂CH₃

d.

18.36 Give an acceptable name for each amine.

a. CH₃(CH₂)₆NH₂

b. [cyclopentyl]—NHCH₂CH₃

c.

d.

18.37 Draw the structure corresponding to each name.
   a. 1-decanamine
   b. tricyclohexylamine
   c. p-bromoaniline
   d. 3-aminobutanoic acid
   e. N,N-dipropyl-2-octanamine
   f. N-ethylhexylamine

660   **Chapter 18**   Amines and Neurotransmitters

18.38 Draw the structure corresponding to each name.
  a. cyclobutylamine
  b. 4-nonanamine
  c. *N*-pentylaniline
  d. 3-amino-2-butanone
  e. 3-methyl-1-butanamine
  f. *N*-ethyl-*N*-propylcyclopentylamine

18.39 Draw the structure of each ammonium salt.
  a. dipropylammonium chloride
  b. butylammonium bromide
  c. ethyldimethylammonium hydroxide

18.40 Draw the structure of each ammonium salt.
  a. cyclohexylammonium fluoride
  b. triethylammonium iodide
  c. ethylmethylammonium chloride

18.41 Draw the structures for the four amines of molecular formula C_3H_9N. Give the systematic name for each amine.

18.42 (a) Draw the structures for the eight constitutional isomers of molecular formula $C_4H_{11}N$. (b) Give the systematic name for each amine. (c) Identify the chirality center present in one of the amines.

Physical Properties and Intermolecular Forces

18.43 Explain why pyridine is more water soluble than benzene. How would you expect the boiling points of pyridine and benzene to compare?

18.44 Explain why $CH_3CH_2CH_2NH_2$ is water soluble but $CH_3CH_2CH_2CH_3$ is not water soluble.

18.45 Which compound in each pair has the higher boiling point?

18.46 Which compound in each pair has the higher boiling point?

18.47 Draw the hydrogen-bonding interactions that occur between two molecules of diethylamine [$(CH_3CH_2)_2NH$].

18.48 Draw the hydrogen-bonding interactions that occur between diethylamine [$(CH_3CH_2)_2NH$] and water.

18.49 Explain why a 1° amine and a 3° amine having the same number of carbons are soluble in water to a similar extent, but the 1° amine has a higher boiling point.

18.50 Which compound has the higher water solubility: $CH_3(CH_2)_5NH_2$ or $CH_3(CH_2)_5NH_3^+$ Cl⁻? Explain your choice.

Acid–Base Reactions of Amines

18.51 Draw the acid–base reaction that occurs when each amine dissolves in water: (a) $CH_3CH_2NH_2$; (b) $(CH_3CH_2)_2NH$; (c) $(CH_3CH_2)_3N$.

18.52 What ammonium salt is formed when each amine is treated with HCl?

  a. [benzene ring]—NH₂

  b. [benzene ring]—CH₂NHCH₃

  c. [benzene ring]—N(CH₂CH₃)₂

18.53 Draw the products of each acid–base reaction.
  a. $CH_3CH_2CH_2N(CH_3)_2$ + HCl ⟶

  b. [structure with NH₂] + H_2SO_4 ⟶

  c. [pyridine] + HBr ⟶

  d. $\left[CH_3CH_2-\overset{\overset{H}{|}}{\underset{\underset{CH_2CH_3}{|}}{N}}-CH_2CH_3 \right]^+$ + NaOH ⟶

18.54 Draw the products of each acid–base reaction.
  a. [quinoline] + HCl ⟶

  b. $CH_3CH_2CHCH_2CH_3$ + H_2SO_4 ⟶
        |
        NHCH₃

  c. CH_3NH_2 + CH_3COOH ⟶

  d. $\left[CH_3(CH_2)_5NH_3 \right]^+$ + NaOH ⟶

18.55 What ammonium salt is formed when each alkaloid is treated with HCl?

  a. [piperidine structure]
        N   CH₂CH₂CH₃
        H
     coniine

  b. [morphine structure]
     morphine

18.56 Oxycodone (trade name OxyContin) is an addictive, narcotic pain reliever prescribed for chronic or severe pain. (a) Identify the functional groups in oxycodone and label any alcohol or amine as 1°, 2°, or 3°. (b) What hydrochloride salt is formed when oxycodone reacts with HCl?

©PureRadiancePhoto/Shutterstock RF

oxycodone

Neurotransmitters, Alkaloids, and Other Biologically Active Amines

18.57 What type of nitrogen heterocycle occurs in both coniine and morphine (Problem 18.55)?

18.58 Only one of the N atoms in nicotine has a trigonal pyramidal shape. Identify which N is trigonal pyramidal and explain why the other N atom has a different molecular shape.

18.59 What physiological effects does caffeine produce on the body?

18.60 Why should caffeine intake be limited in pregnant and nursing mothers?

18.61 Why are aqueous solutions of an alkaloid slightly basic?

18.62 For each alkaloid, list its natural source and give one of its uses in medicine: (a) morphine; (b) quinine; (c) atropine.

18.63 What are the physiological effects of dopamine? What conditions result when dopamine levels are too high or too low?

18.64 Explain why patients with Parkinson's disease cannot be treated by giving them dopamine, even though the disease results from low dopamine levels.

18.65 What are the physiological effects of serotonin? What condition results when there is too little serotonin?

18.66 Give two examples of SSRIs and explain how they combat depression.

18.67 Which of the following amines are derivatives of 2-phenylethylamine? Label the atoms of 2-phenylethylamine in those amines that contain this unit.

a. [structure] C(CH₃)₂—CH₂N(CH₃)₂

b. [structure] CH₂CH₂CH₂NH₂

c. [structure] CH₂—[piperidine with HN]

18.68 Which of the following amines are derivatives of 2-phenylethylamine? Label the atoms of 2-phenylethylamine in those amines that contain this unit.

a. [structure with CH₃ CH₃ / C—C—CH₃ / CH₃ NHCH₃]

b. [structure] CH₂NH—[cyclohexane]

c. [structure] CH₂CH₂—N—[piperidine]

18.69 Locate the atoms of 2-phenylethylamine in the banned diet drug phentermine. (See also Problem 18.74.)

phentermine

18.70 Locate the atoms of 2-phenylethylamine in the broncodilator albuterol.

albuterol

18.71 Give an example of an antihistamine. Explain how an antihistamine relieves the runny nose and watery eyes of a cold or allergies.

18.72 Give an example of an anti-ulcer drug, and explain how it is used to treat a stomach ulcer.

General Questions

18.73 Benzphetamine (trade name Didrex) is a habit-forming diet pill with many of the same properties as amphetamine.

[structure of benzphetamine]

benzphetamine

a. Label the amine as 1°, 2°, or 3°.

b. Label the chirality center in benzphetamine.

c. Draw the two enantiomers of benzphetamine.

d. Draw a constitutional isomer that contains a 1° amine.

e. Draw a constitutional isomer that contains a 3° amine.

f. Draw the structure of benzphetamine hydrochloride.

g. What products are formed when benzphetamine is treated with acetic acid, CH₃COOH?

662   Chapter 18   Amines and Neurotransmitters

18.74 Phentermine is one component of the banned diet drug fen–phen.

phentermine

a. Label the amine as 1°, 2°, or 3°.
b. Indicate the molecular shape around each atom.
c. Draw a constitutional isomer that contains a 1° amine.
d. Draw a constitutional isomer that contains a 2° amine.
e. Draw the structure of phentermine hydrobromide.
f. What products are formed when phentermine is treated with benzoic acid, C_6H_5COOH?

18.75 Ritalin is the trade name for methylphenidate, a drug used to treat attention deficit hyperactivity disorder (ADHD).

methylphenidate
(Trade name Ritalin)

a. Identify the functional groups.
b. Label the amine as 1°, 2°, or 3°.
c. Locate the chirality centers.
d. Locate the atoms of 2-phenylethylamine.
e. Draw the structure of methylphenidate hydrochloride.

18.76 Seldane is the trade name for terfenadine, an antihistamine once used in the United States but withdrawn from the market because of cardiac side effects observed in some patients.

terfenadine
(Trade name Seldane)

a. Identify the functional groups.
b. Label the amine as 1°, 2°, or 3°.
c. Label any alcohol as 1°, 2°, or 3°.

d. Label any 4° carbon.
e. Locate any chirality centers.
f. Draw the structure of terfenadine hydrochloride.

Applications

18.77 The antihistamine in the over-the-counter product Chlortrimeton is chlorpheniramine maleate. Draw the structure of the amine and carboxylic acid that are used to form this ammonium salt.

chlorpheniramine maleate

18.78 Dextromethorphan hydrobromide is a cough suppressant used in many over-the-counter cough and cold medications. Given the structure of the parent amine dextromethorphan, what is the structure of its hydrobromide salt?

dextromethorphan

18.79 What is the difference between a vasodilator and a bronchodilator? Give an example of a drug that fits each category.

18.80 Why do some antihistamines cause drowsiness while others do not?

18.81 In Section 17.7 we learned that aspirin exists in different forms (neutral or ionic) in the stomach and the intestines. Similar behavior occurs with amines that are ingested, since they undergo acid–base reactions. In what form does the drug albuterol (Section 18.9B) exist in the stomach? In the intestines?

18.82 Explain why eating a poppy seed bagel can produce a positive test in a drug screening.

CHALLENGE PROBLEMS

18.83 Compare the structures of morphine and heroin. Suggest a method to convert morphine to heroin.

18.84 Heroin and the morphine from which it is made are both odorless solids. Drug-sniffing dogs can sometimes locate heroin because of a biting odor that is present in a small enough

concentration that humans cannot detect, but the keen nose of a canine can. Suggest what compound might cause the odor that allows for heroin detection. (Hint: What products would be formed by the hydrolysis of heroin in moist air?)

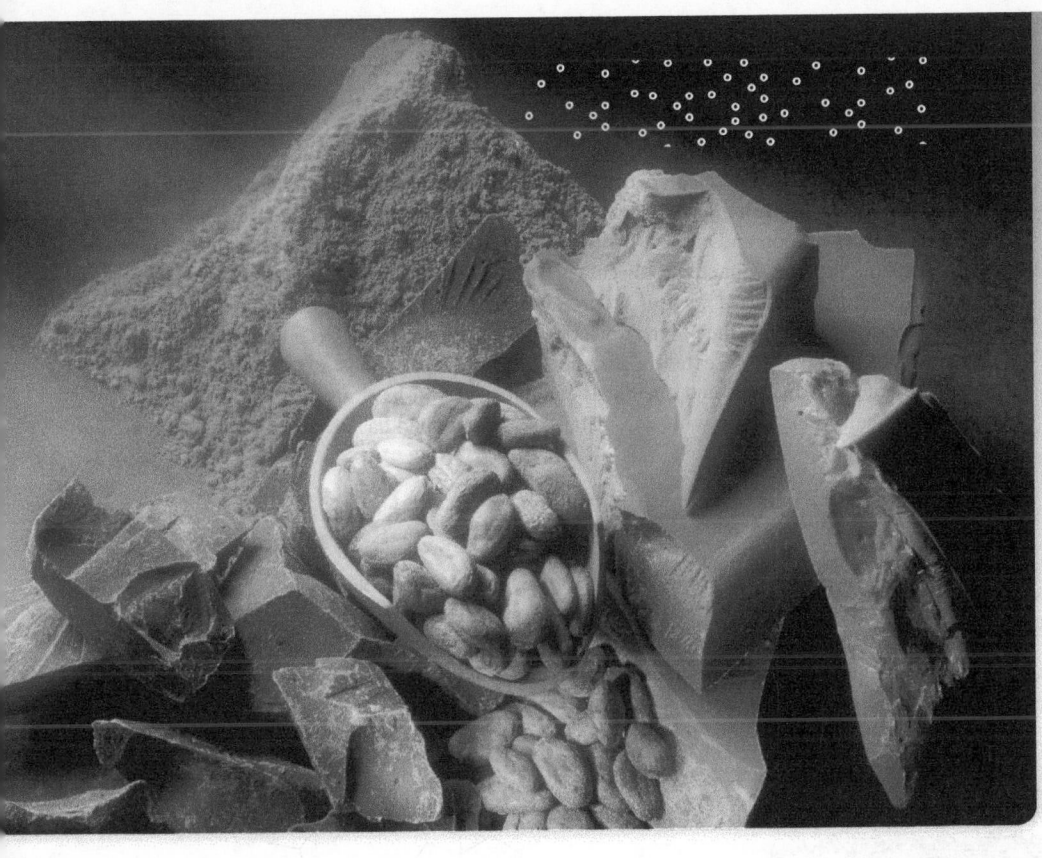

The cocoa butter in chocolate is rich in triacylglycerols, the most abundant lipids. ©Deborah Van Kirk/The Image Bank/Getty Images

Lipids

CHAPTER OUTLINE

19.1 Introduction to Lipids

19.2 Fatty Acids

19.3 Waxes

19.4 Triacylglycerols—Fats and Oils

19.5 Hydrolysis of Triacylglycerols

19.6 Phospholipids

19.7 Cell Membranes

19.8 FOCUS ON HEALTH & MEDICINE: Cholesterol, the Most Prominent Steroid

19.9 Steroid Hormones

19.10 FOCUS ON HEALTH & MEDICINE: Fat-Soluble Vitamins

19.11 FOCUS ON HEALTH & MEDICINE: Prostaglandins and Leukotrienes

CHAPTER GOALS

In this chapter you will learn how to:

1 Describe the general characteristics of lipids

2 Classify fatty acids and describe the relationship between melting point and the number of double bonds

3 Draw the structure of a wax and identify the carboxylic acid and alcohol components

4 Draw the structure of triacylglycerols and describe the difference between a fat and an oil

5 Draw the hydrolysis products of triacylglycerols

6 Identify the two major classes of phospholipids

7 Describe the structure of a cell membrane, as well as different mechanisms of transport across the membrane

8 Recognize the main structural features of steroids like cholesterol, and describe the relationship between blood cholesterol level and cardiovascular disease

9 Define what a hormone is and list several examples of steroid hormones

10 Identify fat-soluble vitamins

11 Discuss the general structural features and biological activity of prostaglandins and leukotrienes

664 **Chapter 19** Lipids

C hapter 19 is the first of four chapters that deal with the chemistry of *biomolecules,* **organic molecules found in biological systems.** Chapter 19 focuses on lipids, biomolecules that contain many carbon–carbon and carbon–hydrogen bonds, making them soluble in organic solvents and insoluble in water. Chapter 20 discusses carbohydrates, the largest group of biomolecules in nature, while Chapter 21 focuses on proteins and the amino acids that compose them. Finally, the properties of DNA, the polymer responsible for the storage of genetic information in the chromosomes of cells, is presented in Chapter 22. These compounds are all organic molecules, so many of the principles and chemical reactions that you have already learned will be examined once again. But, as you will see, each class of compound has its own unique features that we will discuss as well.

19.1 Introduction to Lipids

- *Lipids* are biomolecules that are soluble in organic solvents and insoluble in water.

Lipids are unique among organic molecules because their identity is defined on the basis of a *physical property* and not by the presence of a particular functional group. Because of this, lipids come in a wide variety of structures and they have many different functions. Common lipids include triacylglycerols in vegetable oils, cholesterol in egg yolk, and vitamin E in leafy greens.

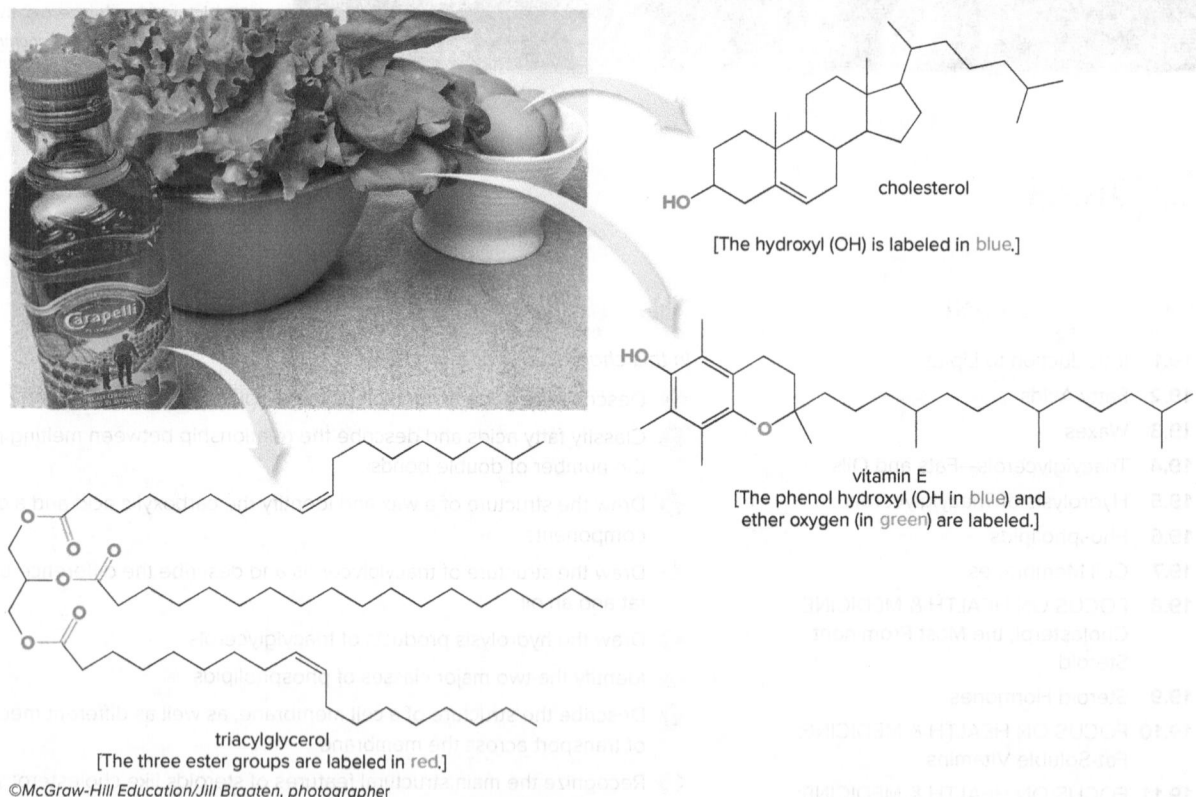

cholesterol
[The hydroxyl (OH) is labeled in blue.]

vitamin E
[The phenol hydroxyl (OH in blue) and ether oxygen (in green) are labeled.]

triacylglycerol
[The three ester groups are labeled in red.]
©McGraw-Hill Education/Jill Braaten, photographer

The word *lipid* comes from the Greek word *lipos* for "fat."

Lipids contain a large number of nonpolar carbon–carbon and carbon–hydrogen bonds. In addition, most lipids have a few polar bonds that may be found in a variety of functional groups. For example, a triacylglycerol contains three esters, cholesterol possesses a hydroxyl group, and vitamin E has both a phenol (an OH group on a benzene ring) and an ether. The size of these functional groups is small compared to the overall size of the molecules. As a result, lipids are nonpolar or weakly polar molecules that are very soluble in organic solvents like hexane (C_6H_{14}) and carbon tetrachloride (CCl_4), and insoluble in a polar medium like water.

SAMPLE PROBLEM 19.1 IDENTIFYING LIPIDS

Which compounds are likely to be lipids? Sorbitol is a sweetener used in sugar-free mints and gum. β-Carotene is the orange pigment in carrots, and the precursor of vitamin A.

a.

CH₂OH
H—C—OH
HO—C—H
H—C—OH
H—C—OH
CH₂OH
sorbitol

b.

β-carotene

Analysis

Lipids contain many nonpolar C—C and C—H bonds and few polar bonds.

Solution

a. Sorbitol is not likely to be a lipid because it contains six polar OH groups bonded to only six carbon atoms.

b. β-Carotene is likely to be a lipid because it contains only nonpolar C—C and C—H bonds.

PRACTICE PROBLEM 19.1

Which compounds are likely to be lipids?

a. mevalonic acid

b. menthol

c. estradiol

More Practice: **Try Problem 19.23.**

Table 19.1 Summary of Lipid Chemistry Prior to Chapter 19

Topic	Section
Vitamin A	11.7A
Fatty acids	13.3B
Oral contraceptives	13.5
Margarine and butter	13.7
Aspirin and prostaglandins	17.4B
Soap	17.6C
Olestra, a synthetic fat	17.9C

Because lipids share many properties with hydrocarbons, several features of lipid structure and properties have been discussed in previous chapters, as summarized in Table 19.1.

Lipids can be categorized as hydrolyzable or nonhydrolyzable.

1. *Hydrolyzable lipids* can be converted into smaller molecules by hydrolysis with water. We will examine three subgroups: waxes, triacylglycerols, and phospholipids.

```
                    Hydrolyzable
                       lipids
          ┌──────────────┼──────────────┐
        Waxes      Triacylglycerols   Phospholipids
```

Most hydrolyzable lipids contain an ester. In the presence of acid, base, or an enzyme, the C—O bond of the ester is cleaved, and a carboxylic acid and an alcohol are formed.

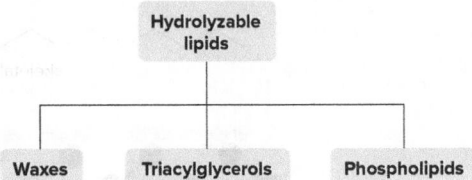

2. *Nonhydrolyzable lipids* cannot be cleaved into smaller units by aqueous hydrolysis. Nonhydrolyzable lipids tend to be more varied in structure. We will examine three different types: steroids, fat-soluble vitamins, and eicosanoids.

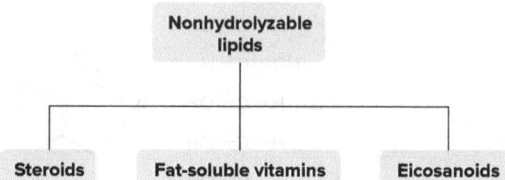

Lipids have many important roles in biological systems. Since lipids release over twice the amount of energy per gram than carbohydrates or proteins (9 kcal/g for lipids compared to 4 kcal/g for carbohydrates and proteins, Section 6.1), lipids are an excellent source of energy. Moreover, lipids are key components of the cell membrane, and they serve as chemical messengers in the body. A lipid coating protects a leaf's surface and keeps it from drying out. Ducks are insulated by a protective layer of lipids on their feathers.

PROBLEM 19.1

In which solvents or solutions will a lipid be soluble: (a) CH_2Cl_2; (b) 5% aqueous NaCl solution; (c) $CH_3CH_2CH_2CH_2CH_3$?

19.2 Fatty Acids

Hydrolyzable lipids are derived from **fatty acids,** carboxylic acids that were first discussed in Section 13.3B.

• *Fatty acids* are carboxylic acids (RCOOH) with long carbon chains of 12–20 carbon atoms.

Because they have many nonpolar C—C and C—H bonds and few polar bonds, fatty acids are lipids, making them soluble in organic solvents and insoluble in water. Palmitic acid is a common 16-carbon fatty acid whose structure is given in condensed, skeletal, and three-dimensional representations.

$$CH_3CH_2CH_2CH_2CH_2CH_2CH_2CH_2CH_2CH_2CH_2CH_2CH_2CH_2CH_2COOH$$
palmitic acid
$C_{16}H_{32}O_2$

The nonpolar part of the molecule (comprised of C—C and C—H bonds) is not attracted to water, so it is said to be ***hydrophobic*** (water fearing). The polar part of the molecule is attracted to water, so it is said to be ***hydrophilic*** (water loving). In a lipid, the hydrophobic portion is always much larger than the hydrophilic portion.

Naturally occurring fatty acids have an even number of carbon atoms. There are two types of fatty acids.

Recall from Section 13.3 that a **cis** alkene has two alkyl groups on the *same* side of the double bond, whereas a **trans** alkene has two alkyl groups on *opposite* sides of the double bond.

- *Saturated* fatty acids have no double bonds in their long hydrocarbon chains.
- *Unsaturated* fatty acids have one or more double bonds in their long hydrocarbon chains. Generally, double bonds in naturally occurring fatty acids are cis.

Three-dimensional models for stearic acid, a saturated fatty acid, and oleic acid, an unsaturated fatty acid with one cis double bond, are shown. Table 19.2 lists the structures of the most common saturated and unsaturated fatty acids.

cis double bond

stearic acid

a saturated fatty acid
no double bonds in the long chain

oleic acid

an unsaturated fatty acid
one cis double bond in the long chain

Table 19.2 Common Fatty Acids

Number of C's	Number of C=C's	Structure	Name	Mp (°C)
		Saturated Fatty Acids		
12	0	$CH_3(CH_2)_{10}COOH$	Lauric acid	44
14	0	$CH_3(CH_2)_{12}COOH$	Myristic acid	58
16	0	$CH_3(CH_2)_{14}COOH$	Palmitic acid	63
18	0	$CH_3(CH_2)_{16}COOH$	Stearic acid	71
20	0	$CH_3(CH_2)_{18}COOH$	Arachidic acid	77
		Unsaturated Fatty Acids		
16	1	$CH_3(CH_2)_5CH{=}CH(CH_2)_7COOH$	Palmitoleic acid	1
18	1	$CH_3(CH_2)_7CH{=}CH(CH_2)_7COOH$	Oleic acid	16
18	2	$CH_3(CH_2)_4CH{=}CHCH_2CH{=}CH(CH_2)_7COOH$	Linoleic acid	−5
18	3	$CH_3CH_2CH{=}CHCH_2CH{=}CHCH_2CH{=}CH(CH_2)_7COOH$	Linolenic acid	−11
20	4	$CH_3(CH_2)_4(CH{=}CHCH_2)_4(CH_2)_2COOH$	Arachidonic acid	−49

668   **Chapter 19** Lipids

The most common saturated fatty acids are palmitic and stearic acid. The most common unsaturated fatty acid is oleic acid. Linoleic and linolenic acids are called **essential fatty acids** because humans cannot synthesize them and must acquire them in our diets.

Oils formed from omega-3 fatty acids may provide health benefits to individuals with cardiovascular disease, as discussed in Section 19.4.

Unsaturated fatty acids are sometimes classified as **omega-*n* acids,** where *n* is the carbon at which the first double bond occurs in the carbon chain, beginning at the end of the chain that contains the CH_3 group. Thus, linoleic acid is an omega-6 acid and linolenic acid is an omega-3 acid.

first C=C at C6 ⟶ an **omega-6 acid**
linoleic acid

first C=C at C3 ⟶ an **omega-3 acid**

linolenic acid

As we learned in Section 13.3B, the presence of cis double bonds affects the melting point of these fatty acids greatly.

- As the number of double bonds in the fatty acid *increases,* the melting point *decreases.*

The cis double bonds introduce kinks in the long hydrocarbon chain, which makes it difficult for the molecules to pack closely together in a solid. **The larger the number of cis double bonds, the more kinks in the hydrocarbon chain, and the lower the melting point.**

SAMPLE PROBLEM 19.2 DETERMINING THE CHARACTERISTICS OF A FATTY ACID

(a) Draw a skeletal structure of gadoleic acid, $CH_3(CH_2)_9CH{=}CH(CH_2)_7COOH$, a 20-carbon fatty acid obtained from fish oils. (b) Label the hydrophobic and hydrophilic portions. (c) Predict how its melting point compares to the melting points of arachidic acid and arachidonic acid (Table 19.2).

Analysis

- Skeletal structures have a carbon at the intersection of two lines and at the end of every line. The double bond must have the cis arrangement in an unsaturated fatty acid.
- The nonpolar C—C and C—H bonds comprise the hydrophobic portion of a molecule, and the polar bonds comprise the hydrophilic portion.
- For the same number of carbons, increasing the number of double bonds decreases the melting point of a fatty acid.

Solution

a. and b. The skeletal structure for gadoleic acid is drawn below. The hydrophilic portion is the COOH group and the hydrophobic portion is the rest of the molecule.

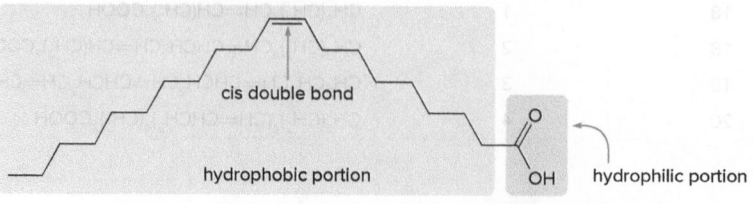

cis double bond

hydrophobic portion   OH   hydrophilic portion

Gadoleic acid (Sample Problem 19.2) and DHA (Problem 19.2) are two fatty acids derived from tuna fish oil.
©Tono Balaguer/123RF

c. Gadoleic acid has one cis double bond, giving it a lower melting point than arachidic acid (no double bonds) but a higher melting point than arachidonic acid (four double bonds).

PRACTICE PROBLEM 19.2

(a) Draw a skeletal structure for each fatty acid. (b) Label the hydrophobic and hydrophilic portions of each molecule. (c) Without referring to Table 19.2, which fatty acid has the higher melting point, **A** or **B**? Explain your choice.

$$CH_3(CH_2)_{16}COOH \qquad CH_3(CH_2)_4CH=CHCH_2CH=CH(CH_2)_7COOH$$
$$\textbf{A} \qquad\qquad\qquad\qquad \textbf{B}$$

More Practice: Try Problems 19.27–19.30, 19.31a–c, 19.32a–c.

PROBLEM 19.2

DHA (4,7,10,13,16,19-docosahexaenoic acid) is a common fatty acid present in tuna fish oil. (a) Draw a skeletal structure for DHA. (b) Give the omega-*n* designation for DHA.

$$CH_3CH_2CH=CHCH_2CH=CHCH_2CH=CHCH_2CH=CHCH_2CH=CHCH_2CH=CHCH_2CH_2COOH$$
$$DHA$$

PROBLEM 19.3

Give the omega-*n* designation for (a) oleic acid; (b) arachidonic acid (Table 19.2).

19.3   Waxes

Waxes are the simplest hydrolyzable lipids.

- *Waxes* are esters (RCOOR') formed from a fatty acid (RCOOH) and a high molecular weight alcohol (R'OH).

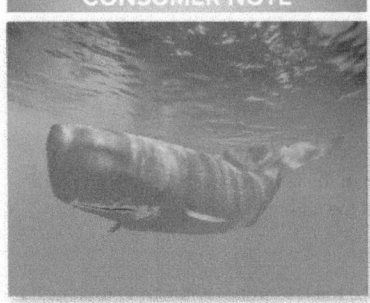

When commercial whaling was commonplace, spermaceti wax obtained from sperm whales was used extensively in cosmetics and candles. ©*Dennis Scott/ Corbis/Getty Images*

Water beads up on the surface of a leaf because of its waxy coating. ©*Daniel C. Smith*

For example, spermaceti wax, isolated from the heads of sperm whales, is largely cetyl palmitate, an ester with the structure $CH_3(CH_2)_{14}COO(CH_2)_{15}CH_3$. Cetyl palmitate is formed from a 16-carbon fatty acid [$CH_3(CH_2)_{14}COOH$] and a 16-carbon alcohol [$CH_3(CH_2)_{15}OH$].

Because of their long nonpolar carbon chains, **waxes are very hydrophobic.** They form a protective coating on the feathers of birds to make them water repellent, and on leaves to prevent water evaporation. Lanolin is a wax that coats the wool fibers of sheep. Beeswax, a complex mixture of over 200 different compounds, contains the wax myricyl palmitate as its major component. The three-dimensional structure of this compound shows how small the polar ester group is compared to the long hydrocarbon chains.

myricyl palmitate

$$CH_3(CH_2)_{14}\overset{\displaystyle O}{\overset{\|}{C}}O(CH_2)_{29}CH_3$$

hydrophobic region   hydrophobic region

(left): ©McGraw-Hill Education/Jill Braaten, photographer; (right): ©Ralf Hettler/Getty Images RF

SAMPLE PROBLEM 19.3 DRAWING THE STRUCTURE OF A WAX

Draw the structure of cetyl myristate, a minor component of spermaceti wax, formed from a 14-carbon fatty acid and a 16-carbon straight-chain alcohol.

Analysis

To draw the wax, arrange the carboxyl group of the fatty acid (RCOOH) next to the OH group of the alcohol (R'OH) with which it reacts. Then, replace the OH group of the fatty acid with the OR' group of the alcohol, forming an ester RCOOR' with a new C—O bond at the carbonyl carbon.

Solution

Draw the structures of the fatty acid and the alcohol, and replace the OH group of the 14-carbon acid with the $O(CH_2)_{15}CH_3$ group of the alcohol.

CH_3(CH_2)_12 — C — OH   +   H—O(CH_2)_15CH_3   ⟶   new C—O bond   CH_3(CH_2)_12 — C — O(CH_2)_15CH_3   +   H_2O

14-carbon fatty acid   16-carbon alcohol   cetyl myristate

PRACTICE PROBLEM 19.3

Draw the structure of a wax formed from stearic acid [$CH_3(CH_2)_{16}COOH$] and each alcohol.

a. $CH_3(CH_2)_9OH$ b. $CH_3(CH_2)_{11}OH$ c. $CH_3(CH_2)_{29}OH$

More Practice: Try Problems 19.33d, 19.34d, 19.35, 19.36.

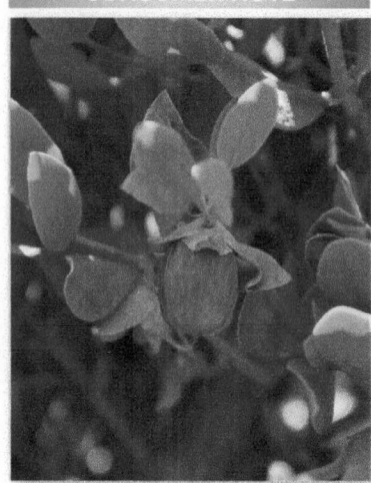

The seeds of the jojoba plant grown in the southwestern United States are rich in waxes used in cosmetics and personal care products. *Source: USDA, ARS, National Arid Land Plant Genetic Resources Unit*

PROBLEM 19.4

One component of jojoba oil is a wax formed from eicosenoic acid [$CH_3(CH_2)_7CH=CH(CH_2)_9CO_2H$] and $CH_3(CH_2)_7CH=CH(CH_2)_8OH$. Draw the structure of the wax, indicating the cis geometry that both carbon–carbon double bonds possess.

PROBLEM 19.5

Explain why beeswax is insoluble in water, slightly soluble in ethanol (CH_3CH_2OH), and very soluble in chloroform ($CHCl_3$).

Like other esters, **waxes (RCOOR') are hydrolyzed with water in the presence of acid or base to re-form the carboxylic acid (RCOOH) and alcohol (R'OH) from which they are prepared** (Section 17.9). Thus, hydrolysis of cetyl palmitate in the presence of H_2SO_4 forms a fatty acid and a long chain alcohol by cleaving the carbon–oxygen single bond of the ester.

The C—O bond is broken.

$$CH_3(CH_2)_{14}\overset{O}{\underset{}{C}}O(CH_2)_{15}CH_3 \;+\; H_2O \;\xrightarrow{H_2SO_4}\; CH_3(CH_2)_{14}\overset{O}{\underset{}{C}}OH \;+\; H{-}O(CH_2)_{15}CH_3$$

cetyl palmitate   fatty acid   alcohol

PROBLEM 19.6

What hydrolysis products are formed when cetyl laurate (shown in the ball-and-stick model) is treated with aqueous acid?

cetyl laurate

19.4 Triacylglycerols—Fats and Oils

Animal fats and vegetable oils, the most abundant lipids, are composed of **triacylglycerols.**

- *Triacylglycerols*, or triglycerides, are triesters formed from glycerol and three molecules of fatty acids.

glycerol   fatty acids   triacylglycerol   block diagram

R groups have 11–19 C's.   [Three ester groups are labeled in red.]

fatty acid

fatty acid

fatty acid

glycerol

672   **Chapter 19**   Lipids

19.4A   General Features

Simple triacylglycerols are composed of three identical fatty acid side chains, whereas **mixed triacylglycerols** have two or three different fatty acids. The fatty acids may be saturated or unsaturated. **Monounsaturated triacylglycerols** have a single carbon–carbon double bond, whereas **polyunsaturated triacylglycerols** have more than one carbon–carbon double bond.

Simple triacylglycerol

Mixed triacylglycerol

three identical saturated carbon chains

one unsaturated carbon chain

Fats and **oils** are triacylglycerols with different physical properties.

• Fats have higher melting points—they are *solids* at room temperature.
• Oils have lower melting points—they are *liquids* at room temperature.

The identity of the three fatty acids in the triacylglycerol determines whether it is a fat or an oil. *Increasing* the number of double bonds in the fatty acid side chains *decreases* the melting point of the triacylglycerol.

• Fats are derived from fatty acids having few double bonds.
• Oils are derived from fatty acids having a larger number of double bonds.

Table 19.3 lists the fatty acid composition of some common fats and oils. Solid fats have a relatively high percentage of saturated fatty acids and are generally animal in origin. Thus, lard (hog fat), butter, and whale blubber contain a high percentage of saturated fats. With no double bonds, the three side chains of the saturated lipid lie parallel with each other, making it possible for the triacylglycerol molecules to pack relatively efficiently in a crystalline lattice, thus leading to a higher melting point.

animal products
source of saturated fats

no double bonds in the long carbon chains

a saturated triacylglycerol

Table 19.3 Fatty Acid Composition of Some Fats and Oils

Substance	% Saturated	% Monounsaturated	% Polyunsaturated	% Trans[a]
Cooking Fat				
Lard	39	44	11	1
Butter	60	26	5	5
Shortening	22	29	29	18
Oils				
Canola	7	58	29	0
Safflower	9	12	24	0
Sunflower	10	20	66	0
Corn	13	24	60	0
Olive	13	72	8	0
Soybean	16	44	37	0
Peanut	17	49	32	0
Palm	50	37	10	0
Coconut	87	6	2	0
Margarine/Spreads				
70% Soybean oil, stick	18	2	29	23
60% Vegetable oil spread	18	22	54	5

[a]Trans double bonds are formed when triacylglycerols are partially hydrogenated, as described in Section 13.7.
[Source: Harvard School of Public Health, but similar data are available from many other sources.]

Oil in the coconuts from plantations like this one is high in saturated fats, which are believed to contribute to a greater risk of heart disease.
©Vachira Sat/Shutterstock RF

Liquid oils have a higher percentage of unsaturated fatty acids and are generally vegetable in origin. Thus, oils derived from corn, soybeans, and olives contain more unsaturated lipids. In the unsaturated lipid, a cis double bond places a kink in the side chain, making it more difficult to pack efficiently in the solid state, thus leading to a lower melting point.

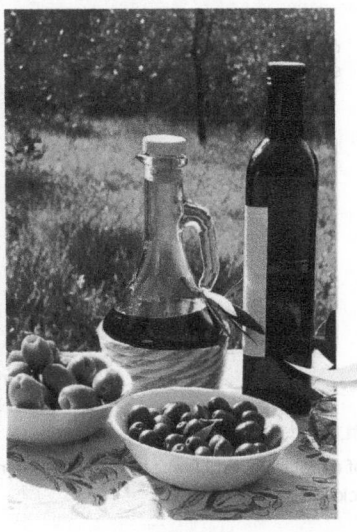

vegetable oil
source of unsaturated oils
©Image Source/Getty Images RF

one (or more) cis double bonds in the long carbon chains

an unsaturated triacylglycerol

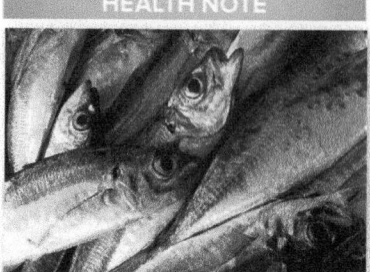

Fish oils are high in unsaturated triacylglycerols derived from omega-3 fatty acids. ©Ingram Publishing RF

Unlike other vegetable oils, oils from palm and coconut trees are very high in saturated fats. Considerable evidence currently suggests that diets high in saturated fats lead to a greater risk of heart disease (Sections 19.4B and 19.8). For this reason, the demand for coconut and palm oil has decreased considerably in recent years, and many coconut plantations previously farmed in the South Pacific are no longer in commercial operation.

Oils derived from fish such as salmon, herring, mackerel, and sardines are very rich in polyunsaturated triacylglycerols. These triacylglycerols pack so poorly that they have very low melting points, and they remain liquids even in very cold water. Fish oils derived from omega-3 fatty acids are thought to be especially beneficial for individuals at risk for developing coronary artery disease.

SAMPLE PROBLEM 19.4 DRAWING THE STRUCTURE OF A TRIACYLGLYCEROL

Draw the structure of a triacylglycerol formed from glycerol, one molecule of stearic acid, and two molecules of oleic acid. Bond the stearic acid to the 2° OH group (OH on the middle carbon atom) of glycerol.

Analysis

To draw the triacylglycerol, arrange each OH group of glycerol next to the carboxyl group of a fatty acid. Then join each O atom of glycerol to a carbonyl carbon of a fatty acid, to form three new C—O bonds.

Solution

Form three new ester bonds (RCOOR') from OH groups of glycerol and the three fatty acids (RCOOH).

oleic acid (R group in blue)
stearic acid (R group in red)

glycerol
2° OH

$+ 3 H_2O$

triacylglycerol

PRACTICE PROBLEM 19.4

Draw the structure of a triacylglycerol that contains (a) three molecules of stearic acid; (b) three molecules of oleic acid.

More Practice: Try Problems 19.41, 19.42.

In addition to triacylglycerols, the cocoa used to prepare chocolate contains antioxidants (Section 13.12) and caffeine (Section 18.4). ©Ingram Publishing/ SuperStock RF

PROBLEM 19.7

Unlike many fats and oils, the cocoa butter used to make chocolate is remarkably uniform in composition. All triacylglycerols contain oleic acid esterified to the 2° OH group of glycerol, and either palmitic acid or stearic acid esterified to the 1° OH groups. Draw the structure of a possible triacylglycerol that composes cocoa butter.

19.4B   FOCUS ON HEALTH & MEDICINE
Fats and Oils in the Diet

Fats and oils in our diet come from a variety of sources—meat, dairy products, seeds and nuts, salad dressing, fried foods, and any baked good or packaged food made with oil. Some fat is required in the diet. Fats are the building blocks of cell membranes, and stored body fat insulates an organism and serves as an energy source that can be used at a later time.

Currently, the United States Food and Drug Administration recommends that no more than 20–35% of an individual's calorie intake come from lipids. Moreover, a high intake of *saturated* triacylglycerols is linked to an increased incidence of heart disease. Saturated fats stimulate cholesterol synthesis in the liver and transport to the tissues, resulting in an increase in cholesterol concentration in the blood. An elevated cholesterol level in the blood can lead to cholesterol deposits or plaques on arteries, causing a narrowing of blood vessels, heart attack, and stroke (Section 19.8).

In contrast, *unsaturated* triacylglycerols lower the risk of heart disease by decreasing the amount of cholesterol in the blood. Unsaturated triacylglycerols from omega-3 fatty acids appear to reduce the risk of heart attack, especially in individuals who already have heart disease.

Dietary recommendations on fat intake must also take into account trans triacylglycerols, so-called *trans fats.* As we learned in Section 13.7, trans fats are formed when liquid oils are partially hydrogenated to form semi-solid triacylglycerols. The three-dimensional structure of a trans triacylglycerol shows its similarity to saturated triacylglycerols. Like saturated fats, trans fats also *increase* the amount of cholesterol in the bloodstream, thus increasing an individual's risk of developing coronary artery disease.

Nutrition Facts
Serving Size 11 Crackers (31g)
Servings Per Container About 7

Amount Per Serving	
Calories 150 Calories from Fat 50	

	% Daily Value*
Total Fat 6g	9%
Saturated Fat 1g	5%
Trans Fat 0g	
Polyunsaturated Fat 3g	
Monounsaturated Fat 1g	
Cholesterol 0mg	0%
Sodium 270mg	11%
Total Carbohydrate 21g	7%
Dietary Fiber 1g	4%
Sugars 4g	

©McGraw-Hill Education/Jill Braaten, photographer

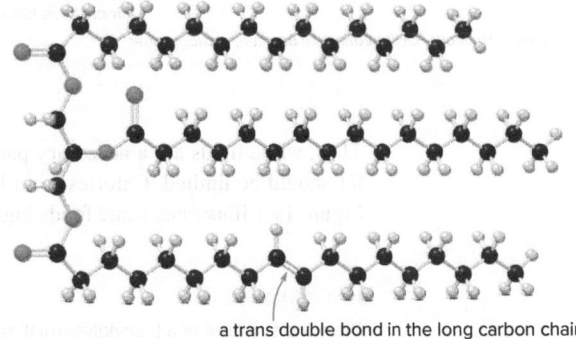

a trans double bond in the long carbon chain

a trans triacylglycerol

Figure 19.1   Saturated, Unsaturated, and Trans Triacylglycerols in the Diet

Food source   **Triacylglycerol**

Foods rich in saturated triacylglycerols:
fatty red meat, cheese, butter, fried foods,
ice cream

- no double bonds in the carbon chains
- solid at room temperature
- increases blood cholesterol level

Foods rich in unsaturated triacylglycerols:
plant oils, nuts, soybeans, fish (salmon,
herring, mackerel)

- one (or more) double bonds in the carbon chains
- liquid at room temperature
- decreases blood cholesterol level

Foods rich in trans triacylglycerols:
margarine, processed foods, fried foods,
some baked goods

- one (or more) trans double bonds in the carbon chains
- semi-solid at room temperature
- increases blood cholesterol level

(top to bottom): ©McGraw-Hill Education/Jill Braaten, photographer

Thus, while lipids are a necessary part of anyone's diet, the amount of saturated fat and trans fat should be limited. Calories from lipids should instead be obtained from unsaturated oils. Figure 19.1 illustrates some foods high in saturated, unsaturated, and trans triacylglycerols.

PROBLEM 19.8

Draw the structure of a triacylglycerol that fits each description:

a. a saturated triacylglycerol formed from three 12-carbon fatty acids

b. an unsaturated triacylglycerol that contains three cis double bonds

c. a trans triacylglycerol that contains a trans double bond in each hydrocarbon chain

19.5   Hydrolysis of Triacylglycerols

Like other esters, **triacylglycerols are hydrolyzed with water in the presence of acid, base, or enzymes (in biological systems) to form glycerol and three molecules of fatty acids.** Thus, hydrolysis of tristearin with aqueous sulfuric acid forms glycerol and three molecules of stearic acid.

tristearin

$+ \ 3 \ H\!-\!OH$

H_2SO_4

OH

OH   +   3 HO

stearic acid

OH

glycerol

Hydrolysis cleaves the three single bonds between the carbonyl carbons and the oxygen atoms of the esters (Section 17.9). Since tristearin contains three identical R groups on the carbonyl carbons, three molecules of a single fatty acid, stearic acid, are formed. Triacylglycerols that contain different R groups bonded to the carbonyl carbons form mixtures of fatty acids, as shown in Sample Problem 19.5.

SAMPLE PROBLEM 19.5 DRAWING THE PRODUCTS OF TRIACYLGLYCEROL HYDROLYSIS

Draw the products formed when the given triacylglycerol is hydrolyzed with water in the presence of sulfuric acid.

Analysis

To draw the products of ester hydrolysis, cleave the three C—O single bonds at the carbonyl carbons to form glycerol and three fatty acids (RCOOH).

Solution

Hydrolysis forms glycerol and stearic, palmitic, and palmitoleic acids. Bonds broken during hydrolysis are shown in red.

Bonds broken during hydrolysis

$3\,H{-}OH$ | H_2SO_4

glycerol + stearic acid

palmitic acid

palmitoleic acid

PRACTICE PROBLEM 19.5

Draw the products formed from hydrolysis of each triacylglycerol.

a.

b.

More Practice: Try Problems 19.49e, 19.50e, 19.51, 19.52.

19.5A FOCUS ON THE HUMAN BODY
Metabolism of Triacylglycerols

Humans store energy in the form of triacylglycerols, kept in a layer of fat cells, called **adipose cells,** below the surface of the skin, in bone marrow, in the breast area (of women), around the kidneys, and in the pelvis (Figure 19.2). Adipose tissue contains large groups of adipose cells,

Figure 19.2

The Storage and Metabolism of Triacylglycerols

triacylglycerol

metabolism

CO_2 + H_2O +   **Energy** 9 kcal/g

adipose cells

Triacylglycerols are stored in adipose cells below the skin and concentrated in some regions of the body. The average fat content of men and women is ~20% and ~25%, respectively. This stored fat provides two to three months of the body's energy needs.

©McGraw-Hill Education/Dennis Strete, photographer

some of which may be so laden with lipid molecules that the remainder of the cell—the cytoplasm and the nucleus—occupies only a small volume on one side. In adulthood, the number of adipose cells is constant. When weight is lost or gained the amount of stored lipid in each cell changes, but the number of adipose cells does not change.

Adipose tissue serves to insulate the organism, as well as provide energy for its metabolic needs for long periods of time. The first step in the metabolism of a triacylglycerol is hydrolysis of the ester bonds to form glycerol and three fatty acids. **This reaction is simply ester hydrolysis.** In cells, this reaction is carried out with enzymes called **lipases.**

ENVIRONMENTAL NOTE

When the price of crude oil is high, the use of **biofuels** such as biodiesel becomes economically attractive. Although biofuels are prepared from renewable resources such as vegetable oils and animal fats, they still burn to form CO_2, a gas that contributes to climate change. ©AP/Wide World Photos

triacylglycerol   glycerol   three fatty acids

$3 H—OH$ lipase

Complete metabolism of a triacylglycerol yields CO_2 and H_2O, and a great deal of energy (Section 24.7). This overall reaction is reminiscent of the combustion of alkanes in fossil fuels, a process that also yields CO_2 and H_2O and provides energy to heat homes and power automobiles (Section 12.8). Fundamentally, both processes convert C—C and C—H bonds to C—O and O—H bonds, a highly exothermic reaction. Carbohydrates provide an energy boost, but only for the short term, such as during strenuous exercise. Our long-term energy needs are provided by triacylglycerols, because they store 9 kcal/g, whereas carbohydrates and proteins store only 4 kcal/g.

Because triacylglycerols release heat on combustion, they can in principle be used as fuels for vehicles. In fact, coconut oil was used as a fuel during both World Wars I and II, when gasoline and diesel supplies ran short. Since coconut oil is more viscous than petroleum products and freezes at 24 °C, engines must be modified to use it and it can't be used in cold climates. Nonetheless, a limited number of trucks and boats can now use vegetable oils, sometimes blended with diesel—*biodiesel*—as a fuel source.

PROBLEM 19.9

Review Section 5.2 on balancing chemical equations. Then, write a balanced equation for the complete combustion (or metabolism) of tristearin to CO_2 and H_2O.

$$+ \quad O_2 \xrightarrow[\text{enzymes}]{} \quad CO_2 \quad + \quad H_2O$$

tristearin

19.5B Soap Synthesis

As we learned in Section 17.6, soaps are metal salts of carboxylic acids that contain many carbon atoms in a long hydrocarbon chain; that is, **soaps are metal salts of fatty acids.** For example, sodium stearate is the sodium salt of stearic acid, an 18-carbon saturated fatty acid.

sodium stearate

ionic end
polar head

long hydrocarbon chain
nonpolar tail

Soap is prepared by the basic hydrolysis (saponification) of a triacylglycerol. Heating an animal fat or vegetable oil with aqueous base hydrolyzes the three esters to form glycerol and sodium salts of three fatty acids.

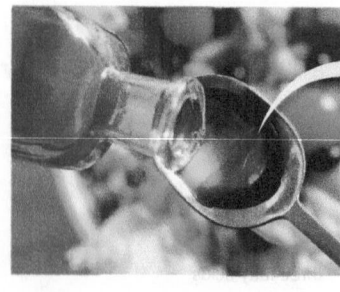

$+ \quad 3 \text{ NaOH}$

triolein

$\downarrow \text{H}_2\text{O}$

glycerol

$+ \quad 3 \text{ Na}^+ \text{ }^-\text{O}$

sodium oleate

soap

These carboxylate salts are **soaps,** which clean away dirt as we saw in Figure 17.3. The nonpolar tail dissolves grease and oil, and the polar head makes it soluble in water. Most triacylglycerols have two or three different R groups in their hydrocarbon chains, so soaps are usually mixtures of two or three different carboxylate salts.

Soaps are typically made from lard (from hogs), tallow (from cattle or sheep), coconut oil, or palm oil. All soaps work in the same way but have somewhat different properties depending on the lipid source. The length of the carbon chain in the fatty acids and the number of sites of unsaturation affect the properties of the soap to a limited extent.

PROBLEM 19.10

What is the composition of the soap formed by basic hydrolysis of each triacylglycerol?

a.

b.

19.6   Phospholipids

Phospholipids are lipids that contain a phosphorus atom. Two common types of phospholipids are **phosphoacylglycerols** and **sphingomyelins.** Both classes are found almost exclusively in the cell membranes of plants and animals as discussed in Section 19.7. Block diagrams that compare the general structural features of triacylglycerols, phosphoacylglycerols, and sphingomyelins are drawn.

glycerol — fatty acid	glycerol — fatty acid	sphingosine
— fatty acid	— fatty acid	— fatty acid
— fatty acid	— phosphate — alcohol	— phosphate — alcohol
triacylglycerol	**phosphoacylglycerol**	**sphingomyelin**

Phospholipids can be considered organic derivatives of phosphoric acid (H_3PO_4), formed by replacing two of the H atoms by R groups. This type of functional group is called a **phosphodiester.** In cells, the remaining OH group on phosphorus loses its proton, giving the phosphodiester a net negative charge.

phosphoric acid
H_3PO_4

phosphodiester

phosphodiester in cells

19.6A   Phosphoacylglycerols

Phosphoacylglycerols (or **phosphoglycerides**) are the most common type of phospholipid. They form the principal lipid component of most cell membranes. Their structure resembles the triacylglycerols of the preceding section with one important difference. Only *two* of the hydroxyl groups of glycerol are esterified with fatty acids. The third OH group is part of a phosphodiester, which is also bonded to an alkyl group (R") derived from a low molecular weight alcohol.

General structure of a phosphoacylglycerol

R" is typically one of two different groups.

There are two prominent types of phosphoacylglycerols. They differ in the identity of the R" group in the phosphodiester.

- When R" = $CH_2CH_2NH_3^+$, the compound is called a *cephalin* or phosphatidylethanolamine.
- When R" = $CH_2CH_2N(CH_3)_3^+$, the compound is called a *lecithin* or phosphatidylcholine.

cephalin
(phosphatidylethanolamine)

Derived from the alcohol: H—O—NH_3^+
ethanolamine

lecithin
(phosphatidylcholine)

Derived from the alcohol: H—O—$N(CH_3)_3^+$
choline

The phosphorus side chain of a phosphoacylglycerol makes it different from a triacylglycerol. **The two fatty acid side chains form two nonpolar "tails" that lie parallel to each other, while the phosphodiester end of the molecule is a charged or polar "head."** A three-dimensional structure of a phosphoacylglycerol is shown in Figure 19.3.

SAMPLE PROBLEM 19.6 DRAWING THE STRUCTURE OF A PHOSPHOACYLGLYCEROL

Draw the structure of a cephalin formed from two molecules of stearic acid.

Analysis

Substitute the 18-carbon saturated fatty acid stearic acid for the R and R' groups in the general structure of a cephalin molecule. In a cephalin, —$CH_2CH_2NH_3^+$ forms part of the phosphodiester.

Solution

from stearic acid

general structure

Answer

PRACTICE PROBLEM 19.6

Draw the structure of two different cephalins containing oleic acid and palmitic acid as fatty acid side chains.

More Practice: Try Problems 19.55, 19.56.

Figure 19.3

Three-Dimensional Structure
of a Phosphoacylglycerol

a lecithin molecule

fatty acid chains

charged atoms

two nonpolar tails

polar head

Often drawn as:

polar head   nonpolar tails

A phosphoacylglycerol has two distinct regions: two nonpolar tails due to the long-chain fatty acids, and a very polar head from the charged phosphodiester.

19.6B   Sphingomyelins

Sphingomyelins, the second major class of phospholipids, differ in two important ways from the triacylglycerols and the phosphoacylglycerols.

- Sphingomyelins do *not* contain a glycerol backbone. Instead, sphingomyelins are derived from sphingosine.
- Sphingomyelins do *not* contain an ester. Instead, their single fatty acid is bonded to the carbon backbone by an amide bond.

General structure of a sphingomyelin

sphingosine

sphingosine

fatty acid

phosphate — alcohol

amide bond

$R' = CH_2CH_2\overset{+}{N}H_3$ or
$CH_2CH_2\overset{+}{N}(CH_3)_3$

Like the phosphoacylglycerols in Section 19.6A, sphingomyelins contain a phosphodiester derived from ethanolamine or choline. As a result, sphingomyelins also contain a polar (ionic) head and two nonpolar tails. An example of a sphingomyelin is drawn.

amide formed with oleic acid

derived from choline

a sphingomyelin

The coating that surrounds and insulates nerve cells, the **myelin sheath,** is particularly rich in sphingomyelins, and is vital for proper nerve function (Figure 19.4). Deterioration of the myelin sheath, as seen in multiple sclerosis, leads to disabling neurological disorders.

Figure 19.4   Focus on Health & Medicine: Nerve Cells and Multiple Sclerosis

layers of healthy myelin sheath
surrounding a nerve fiber

neuron

myelinated
axons

nonpolar tails

The charged portion
makes up the polar head.

sphingomyelin molecule present in the myelin sheath

exposed nerve fiber

damaged myelin sheath present in
individuals with multiple sclerosis

Multiple sclerosis (MS) is a degenerative disease characterized by scarring of the myelin sheath, the insulating layer that surrounds a nerve fiber. Without the protective myelin sheath, normal nerve transmission is disrupted and a variety of effects—numbness, blindness, speech disorders, and tremors—can result.

699

Figure 19.5 A Comparison of a Triacylglycerol, a Phosphoacylglycerol, and a Sphingomyelin

R'' = H, CH₃

R'' = H, CH₃   R = C₁₃H₂₇

- A **triacylglycerol** has three nonpolar side chains.
- Glycerol is the backbone.
- There are three esters formed from three fatty acids.

- A **phosphoacylglycerol** has two nonpolar side chain tails and one ionic head.
- Glycerol is the backbone.
- There are two esters formed with the two fatty acids.
- A phosphodiester is located on a terminal carbon of glycerol.

- A **sphingomyelin** has two nonpolar side chain tails and one ionic head.
- Sphingosine is the backbone.
- A sphingomyelin contains an amide, not an ester.
- A phosphodiester is located on a terminal carbon of sphingosine.

Figure 19.5 compares the structural features of the most common hydrolyzable lipids: a triacylglycerol, a phosphoacylglycerol, and a sphingomyelin.

PROBLEM 19.11

Identify the components of each lipid and classify it as a triacylglycerol, a phosphoacylglycerol, or a sphingomyelin. Classify any phosphoacylglycerol as a cephalin or lecithin.

a.

b.

c.

19.7   Cell Membranes

The cell membrane is a beautifully complex example of how chemistry comes into play in a biological system.

19.7A   Structure of the Cell Membrane

The basic unit of living organisms is the **cell.** The cytoplasm is the aqueous medium inside the cell, separated from water outside the cell by the **cell membrane.** The cell membrane serves two apparently contradictory functions. It acts as a barrier to the passage of ions and molecules into and out of the cell, but it is also selectively permeable, allowing nutrients in and waste out.

Phospholipids, especially phosphoacylglycerols, are the major component of the cell membrane. **Phospholipids contain a hydrophilic polar head and two nonpolar tails composed of C—C and C—H bonds.** When phospholipids are mixed with water, they assemble in an arrangement called a **lipid bilayer,** with the ionic heads oriented on the outside and the nonpolar tails on the inside. The polar heads electrostatically interact with the polar solvent H_2O, while the nonpolar tails are held in close proximity by numerous London dispersion forces.

To review London dispersion forces, re-read Section 7.7A.

Cell membranes are composed of these lipid bilayers (Figure 19.6). The charged heads of the phospholipids are oriented toward the aqueous interior and exterior of the cell. The nonpolar tails form the hydrophobic interior of the membrane, thus serving as an insoluble barrier that protects the cell from the outside. The identity of the fatty acids in the phospholipid determines the rigidity of this bilayer. When the fatty acids are saturated, they pack well in the interior of the lipid bilayer, and the membrane is less fluid. When there are many unsaturated fatty acids, the nonpolar tails cannot pack as well and the bilayer is more fluid.

While the phospholipid bilayer forms the main fabric of the cell membrane, proteins and cholesterol (Section 19.8) are embedded in the membrane as well. **Peripheral proteins** are embedded within the

Figure 19.6

Composition of the Cell Membrane

carbohydrates

hydrophobic region

hydrophilic region

cholesterol

cytoplasm

peripheral protein

integral protein

nonpolar
polar

nucleus

cell membrane

cell

Cell membranes are composed of a lipid bilayer having the hydrophilic polar heads of phospholipids arranged on the exterior of the bilayer, where they can interact with the polar aqueous environment inside and outside the cell. The hydrophobic tails of the phospholipid are arranged in the interior of the bilayer, forming a "greasy" layer that is only selectively permeable to the passage of species from one side to the other.

membrane and extend outward on one side only. **Integral proteins** extend through the entire bilayer. Some lipids and proteins on the membrane surface are bonded to carbohydrates, forming **glycolipids** and **glycoproteins.** The polar carbohydrate chains extend into the surrounding aqueous environment.

PROBLEM 19.12

Why are phospholipids rather than triacylglycerols present in cell membranes?

PROBLEM 19.13

A cell membrane from one source **(A)** contains phospholipids formed from linoleic and oleic acids. A cell membrane from a second source **(B)** contains phospholipids formed from stearic and palmitic acids. How will these two cell membranes differ?

19.7B Transport Across a Cell Membrane

How does a molecule or ion in the water on one side of a cell membrane pass through the nonpolar interior of the cell membrane to the other side? A variety of transport mechanisms occur (Figure 19.7).

Figure 19.7

How Substances Cross
a Cell Membrane

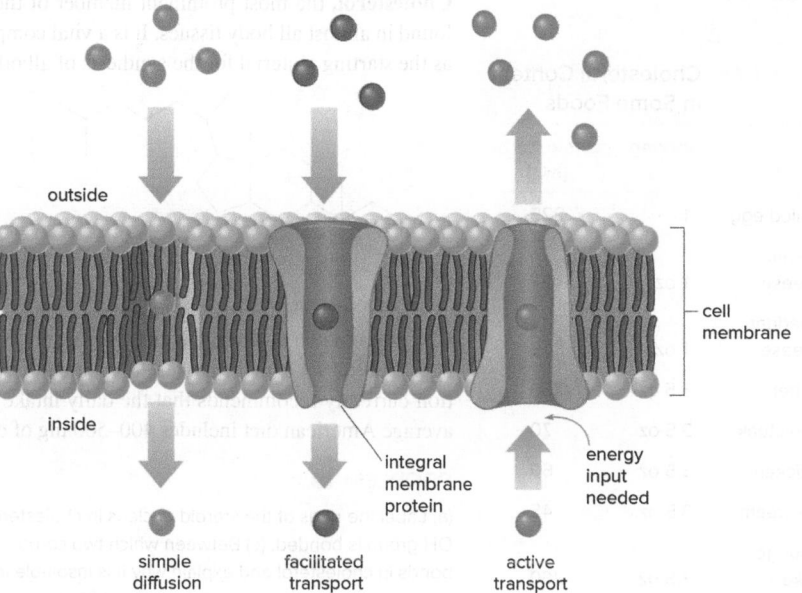

outside

inside

cell membrane

integral membrane protein

energy input needed

simple diffusion

facilitated transport

active transport

Small molecules like O_2 and CO_2 can simply diffuse through the cell membrane, traveling from the side of higher concentration to the side of lower concentration. With larger polar molecules and some ions, simple diffusion is too slow or not possible, so a process of **facilitated transport** occurs. Ions such as Cl^- or HCO_3^- and glucose molecules travel through the channels created by integral proteins.

Some ions, notably Na^+, K^+, and Ca^{2+}, must move across the cell membrane against the concentration gradient—that is, from a region of lower concentration to a region of higher concentration. To move an ion across the membrane in this fashion requires energy input, and the process is called **active transport.** Active transport occurs whenever a nerve impulse causes a muscle to contract. In this process, energy is supplied to move K^+ ions from outside to inside a cell, against a concentration gradient.

PROBLEM 19.14

Why don't ions readily diffuse through the interior of the cell membrane?

19.8   FOCUS ON HEALTH & MEDICINE
Cholesterol, the Most Prominent Steroid

The steroids are a group of lipids whose carbon skeletons contain three six-membered rings and one five-membered ring. This tetracyclic carbon skeleton is drawn below.

steroid skeleton

numbering the steroid skeleton

Many steroids also contain two methyl groups that are bonded to the rings. The steroid rings are lettered **A, B, C,** and **D,** and the 17 ring carbons are numbered as shown. The two methyl groups are numbered C18 and C19. Steroids differ in the identity and location of the substituents attached to the skeleton.

Cholesterol, the most prominent member of the steroid family, is synthesized in the liver and found in almost all body tissues. It is a vital component for healthy cell membranes, and it serves as the starting material for the synthesis of all other steroids and vitamin D.

cholesterol

Cholesterol is obtained in the diet from a variety of sources, including meat, cheese, butter, and eggs. Table 19.4 lists the cholesterol content in some foods. While the American Heart Association currently recommends that the daily intake of cholesterol should be less than 300 mg, the average American diet includes 400–500 mg of cholesterol each day.

PROBLEM 19.15

(a) Label the rings of the steroid nucleus in cholesterol. (b) Give the number of the carbon to which the OH group is bonded. (c) Between which two carbons is the double bond located? (d) Label the polar bonds in cholesterol and explain why it is insoluble in water.

HEALTH NOTE

Plants do not synthesize cholesterol, so fresh fruits and vegetables, nuts, and whole grains are cholesterol free.
©Purestock/SuperStock RF

Table 19.4 **Cholesterol Content in Some Foods**

Food	Serving Size	Cholesterol (mg)
Boiled egg	1	225
Cream cheese	1 oz	27
Cheddar cheese	1 oz	19
Butter	3.5 oz	250
Beefsteak	3.5 oz	70
Chicken	3.5 oz	60
Ice cream	3.5 oz	45
Sponge cake	3.5 oz	260

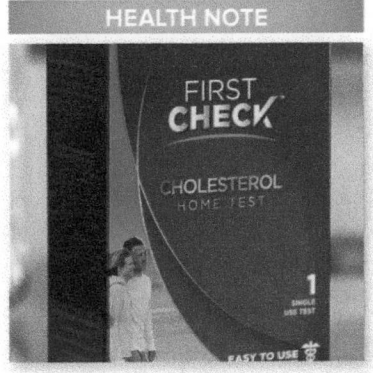

Cholesterol home test kits allow individuals to monitor their cholesterol levels without going to the doctor.
©Jill Braaten RF

While health experts agree that the amount of cholesterol in the diet should be limited, it is also now clear that elevated *blood* cholesterol (serum cholesterol) can lead to coronary artery disease. It is estimated that only 25% of the cholesterol in the blood comes from dietary sources, with the remainder synthesized in the liver. High blood cholesterol levels are associated with an increased risk of developing coronary artery disease, heart attack, and stroke. To understand the relationship between cholesterol and heart disease, we must learn about how cholesterol is transported through the bloodstream.

Like other lipids, cholesterol is insoluble in the aqueous medium of the blood, because it has only one polar OH group and many nonpolar C—C and C—H bonds. In order for it to be transported from the liver where it is synthesized, to the tissues, cholesterol combines with phospholipids and proteins to form small water-soluble spherical particles called **lipoproteins.**

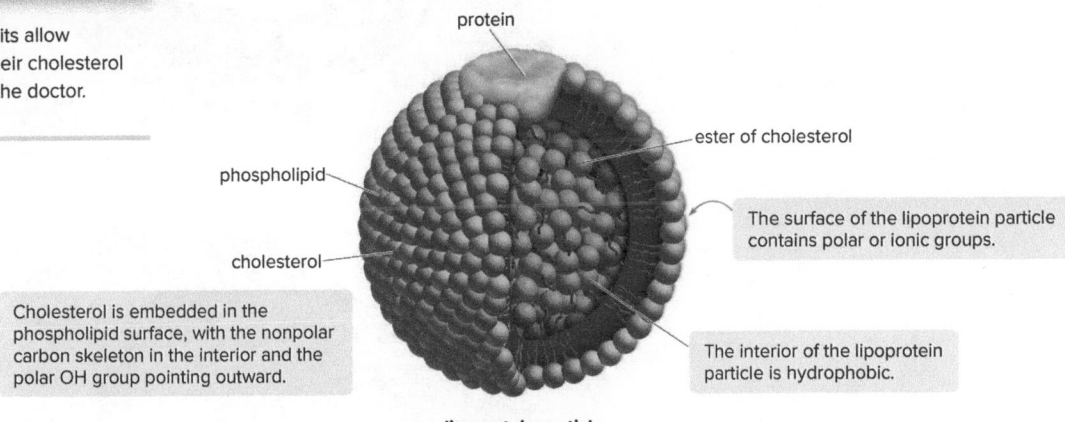

protein

ester of cholesterol

phospholipid

The surface of the lipoprotein particle contains polar or ionic groups.

cholesterol

Cholesterol is embedded in the phospholipid surface, with the nonpolar carbon skeleton in the interior and the polar OH group pointing outward.

The interior of the lipoprotein particle is hydrophobic.

lipoprotein particle

In a lipoprotein, the polar heads of phospholipids and the polar portions of protein molecules are arranged on the surface. The nonpolar molecules are buried in the interior of the particle. In this way, the nonpolar material is "dissolved" in an aqueous environment.

Lipoproteins are classified on the basis of their density, with two types being especially important in determining serum cholesterol levels.

- **Low-density lipoproteins (LDLs) transport cholesterol from the liver to the tissues.**
- **High-density lipoproteins (HDLs) transport cholesterol from the tissues back to the liver.**

Figure 19.8 shows a cross-section of both an HDL and LDL particle. HDL particles contain much more protein and much less cholesterol (and esters of cholesterol) than LDL particles.

Figure 19.8

Cross-Section of an HDL and LDL Particle

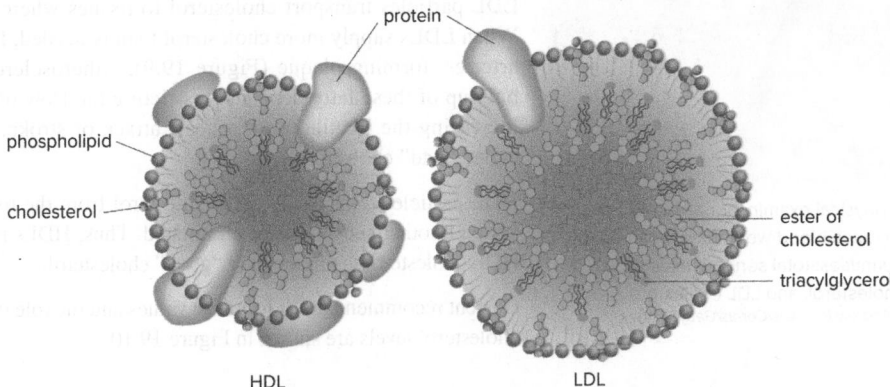

protein

phospholipid

cholesterol

ester of cholesterol

triacylglycerol

HDL   LDL

Figure 19.9   Plaque Formation in an Artery

a. Open artery

b. Blocked artery

a. Cross-section of a clear artery with no buildup of plaque

b. Artery almost completely blocked by the buildup of plaque

(a–b): ©Ed Reschke

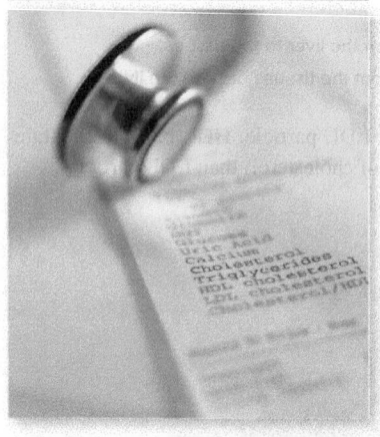

HEALTH NOTE

A physical examination by a physician includes blood work that measures three quantities: total serum cholesterol, HDL cholesterol, and LDL cholesterol.
©Andrew Brookes/Corbis/Getty Images

LDL particles transport cholesterol to tissues where it is incorporated in cell membranes. When LDLs supply more cholesterol than is needed, LDLs deposit cholesterol on the wall of arteries, forming plaque (Figure 19.9). Atherosclerosis is a disease that results from the buildup of these fatty deposits, restricting the flow of blood, increasing blood pressure, and increasing the likelihood of a heart attack or stroke. As a result, LDL cholesterol is often called "bad" cholesterol.

HDL particles transport excess cholesterol from the tissues back to the liver, where it is converted to other substances or eliminated. Thus, HDLs reduce the level of serum cholesterol, so HDL cholesterol is often called "good" cholesterol.

Current recommendations for these values and the role of HDLs and LDLs in determining serum cholesterol levels are shown in Figure 19.10.

> **Figure 19.10**   HDLs, LDLs, and Cholesterol Level
>
>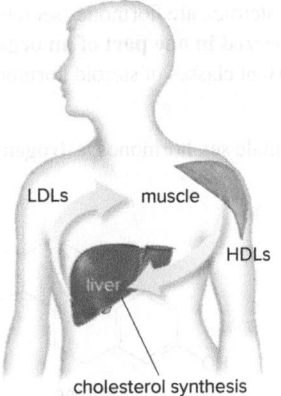
>
> LDLs   muscle
>
> HDLs
>
> liver
>
> cholesterol synthesis
>
> Current recommendations by the National Cholesterol Education Program:
>
> - Total serum cholesterol: < 200 mg/dL
> - HDL cholesterol: > 40 mg/dL
> - LDL cholesterol: < 100 mg/dL
>
> Cholesterol is synthesized in the liver. High HDL levels are considered desirable because HDL transports cholesterol back to the liver. Low LDLs are considered desirable to avoid the buildup of plaque in the arteries.

Several drugs called **statins** are now available to reduce the level of cholesterol in the bloodstream. These compounds act by blocking the synthesis of cholesterol at its very early stages. Two examples include atorvastatin (Lipitor) and simvastatin (Zocor).

Generic name atorvastatin
Trade name Lipitor

Generic name simvastatin
Trade name Zocor

PROBLEM 19.16

Would you expect triacylglycerols to be contained in the interior of a lipoprotein particle or on the surface with the phospholipids? Explain your choice.

PROBLEM 19.17

Lovastatin, which occurs naturally in oyster mushrooms, was the first statin to be marketed. Identify the functional groups in lovastatin.

lovastatin

19.9 Steroid Hormones

Many biologically active steroids are hormones secreted by the endocrine glands. **A *hormone* is a molecule that is synthesized in one part of an organism, which then elicits a response at a different site.** Two important classes of steroid hormones are the **sex hormones** and the **adrenal cortical steroids.**

There are two types of female sex hormones, **estrogens** and **progestins.**

estradiol   estrone   progesterone

Estradiol, progesterone, and oral contraceptives were discussed in Section 13.5.

- Estradiol and estrone are estrogens synthesized in the ovaries. They control the development of secondary sex characteristics in females and regulate the menstrual cycle.
- Progesterone is a progestin often called the "pregnancy hormone." It is responsible for the preparation of the uterus for implantation of a fertilized egg.

The male sex hormones are called **androgens.**

testosterone   androsterone

- Testosterone and androsterone are androgens synthesized in the testes. They control the development of secondary sex characteristics in males—growth of facial hair, increase in muscle mass, and deepening of the voice.

Synthetic androgen analogues, called **anabolic steroids,** promote muscle growth. They were first developed to help individuals whose muscles had atrophied from lack of use following surgery. They have since come to be used by athletes and bodybuilders, although their use is not permitted in competitive sports. Many physical and psychological problems result from their prolonged use.

Anabolic steroids, such as stanozolol, nandrolone, and tetrahydrogestrinone, have the same effect on the body as testosterone, but they are more stable, so they are not metabolized as quickly. Tetrahydrogestrinone (also called THG or The Clear), the performance-enhancing drug used by track star Marion Jones during the 2000 Sydney Olympics, was considered a "designer steroid" because it was initially undetected in urine tests for doping. After its chemical structure and properties were determined, it was added to the list of banned anabolic steroids in sports in 2004.

stanozolol   nandrolone   tetrahydrogestrinone

A second group of steroid hormones includes the **adrenal cortical steroids.** Three examples of these hormones are aldosterone, cortisone, and cortisol. All of these compounds are synthesized in the outer layer of the adrenal gland. Aldosterone regulates blood pressure and volume by controlling the concentration of Na^+ and K^+ in body fluids. Cortisone and cortisol serve as anti-inflammatory agents and they regulate carbohydrate metabolism.

aldosterone   cortisone   cortisol

Cortisone and related compounds are used to suppress organ rejection after transplant surgery and to treat many allergic and autoimmune disorders. Prolonged use of these steroids can have undesired side effects, including bone loss and high blood pressure. Prednisone, a widely used synthetic alternative, has similar anti-inflammatory properties but can be taken orally.

prednisone
(synthetic steroid)

©A.T. Willett/Alamy

PROBLEM 19.18

Compare the structures of estrone and progesterone. (a) Identify the differences in the A ring of these hormones. (b) How do these hormones differ in functionality at C17?

PROBLEM 19.19

The male sex hormone testosterone and the anabolic steroid nandrolone have very similar structures and, as you might expect, similar biological activity. Point out the single structural difference in these two compounds.

19.10   FOCUS ON HEALTH & MEDICINE
Fat-Soluble Vitamins

Vitamins are organic compounds required in small quantities for normal metabolism (Section 11.7). Since our cells cannot synthesize these compounds, they must be obtained in the diet. Vitamins can be categorized as fat soluble or water soluble. **The fat-soluble vitamins are lipids.**

The four fat-soluble vitamins—**A, D, E,** and **K**—are found in fruits and vegetables, fish, liver, and dairy products. Although fat-soluble vitamins must be obtained from the diet, they do not have to be ingested every day. Excess vitamins are stored in adipose cells, and then used when needed. Table 19.5 summarizes the dietary sources and recommended daily intake of the fat-soluble vitamins.

Vitamin A (Section 11.7) is obtained from liver, oily fish, and dairy products, and is synthesized from β-carotene, the orange pigment in carrots. In the body, vitamin A is converted to 11-*cis*-retinal, the light-sensitive compound responsible for vision in all vertebrates (Section 16.7). It is also needed for healthy mucous membranes. A deficiency of vitamin A causes night blindness, as well as dry eyes and skin.

vitamin A

©Pixtal/age fotostock RF

Vitamin D, strictly speaking, is not a vitamin because it can be synthesized in the body from cholesterol. Nevertheless, it is classified as such, and many foods (particularly milk) are fortified with vitamin D so that we get enough of this vital nutrient. Vitamin D helps regulate both calcium and phosphorus metabolism. A deficiency of vitamin D causes rickets, a bone disease characterized by knock-knees, spinal curvature, and other skeletal deformities.

Table 19.5   Fat-Soluble Vitamins

Vitamin	Food Source	Recommended Daily Intake
A	Liver, kidney, oily fish, dairy products, eggs, fortified breakfast cereals	900 µg (men) 700 µg (women)
D	Fortified milk and breakfast cereals	5 µg
E	Sunflower and safflower oils, nuts, beans, whole grains, leafy greens	15 mg
K	Cauliflower, soybeans, broccoli, leafy greens, green tea	120 µg (men) 90 µg (women)

Source: Data from Harvard School of Public Health.

vitamin D

©Stockbyte/Getty Images RF

Vitamin E is an antioxidant, and in this way it protects unsaturated side chains in fatty acids from unwanted oxidation (Section 13.12). A deficiency of vitamin E causes numerous neurological problems, although it is rare for vitamin E deficiency to occur.

vitamin E

©Polka Dot Images/Getty Images RF

Vitamin K regulates the synthesis of prothrombin and other proteins needed for blood to clot. A severe deficiency of vitamin K leads to excessive and sometimes fatal bleeding because of inadequate blood clotting.

vitamin K

©Design Pics Inc/Alamy

PROBLEM 19.20

Why is it much easier to overdose on a fat-soluble vitamin than a water-soluble vitamin?

19.11   FOCUS ON HEALTH & MEDICINE
Prostaglandins and Leukotrienes

Prostaglandins (Section 17.4) and **leukotrienes** are two types of **eicosanoids,** a group of biologically active compounds containing 20 carbon atoms derived from the fatty acid, arachidonic acid.

arachidonic acid
(four cis double bonds)

a fatty acid

$PGF_{2\alpha}$
a prostaglandin

LTC_4
a leukotriene

The word *eicosanoid* is derived from the Greek word *eikosi,* meaning "20."

All eicosanoids are very potent compounds present in low concentration in cells. Eicosanoids are not stored in cells; rather, they are synthesized from arachidonic acid in response to an external stimulus. They are **local mediators,** meaning that they perform their function in the environment in which they are synthesized. This distinguishes them from hormones, which are first synthesized and then transported to their site of action.

19.11A   Prostaglandins

Prostaglandins are a group of carboxylic acids that contain a five-membered ring and have a wide range of biological activities. $PGF_{2\alpha}$ and PGE_1 are two examples.

$PGF_{2\alpha}$

PGE_1

As we learned in Section 17.4, prostaglandins are responsible for inflammation. Aspirin and ibuprofen relieve pain and decrease inflammation because they block the synthesis of prostaglandins by inhibiting the cyclooxygenase enzyme needed for their synthesis.

Prostaglandins also decrease gastric secretions, inhibit blood platelet aggregation, stimulate uterine contractions, and relax the smooth muscles of the uterus. Because of these many biological functions, prostaglandins and their analogues have found several clinical uses. For example, dinoprostone, the generic name for PGE_2, is administered to relax the smooth muscles of the uterus when labor is induced, and to terminate early pregnancies. Misoprostol, a synthetic prostaglandin, prevents gastric ulcers in patients who are at high risk of developing them.

PGE$_2$
(dinoprostone)

misoprostol

More recently, it has been discovered that two *different* cyclooxygenase enzymes, called COX-1 and COX-2, are responsible for prostaglandin synthesis. COX-1 is involved with the usual production of prostaglandins, but COX-2 is responsible for the synthesis of additional prostaglandins in inflammatory diseases like arthritis. **NSAIDs—nonsteroidal anti-inflammatory drugs**—like aspirin and ibuprofen, inactivate both the COX-1 and COX-2 enzymes. This activity also results in an increase in gastric secretions, making an individual more susceptible to ulcer formation.

A group of anti-inflammatory drugs that block only the COX-2 enzyme was developed in the 1990s. These drugs—rofecoxib, valdecoxib, and celecoxib—do not cause an increase in gastric secretions, and thus were touted as an especially effective treatment for patients with arthritis, who need daily doses of these medications. Unfortunately, both rofecoxib and valdecoxib have been removed from the market, because their use has been associated with an increased risk of heart attack and stroke. Celecoxib, on the other hand, has fewer side effects, so it is still available and widely used.

Generic name rofecoxib
Trade name Vioxx

Generic name valdecoxib
Trade name Bextra

Generic name celecoxib
Trade name Celebrex

PROBLEM 19.21

(a) What functional groups are present in PGE$_2$? (b) Draw a skeletal structure for PGE$_2$. The double bond closest to the COOH group is cis and the remaining double bond is trans.

19.11B Asthma and Leukotrienes

Asthma is an obstructive lung disease that affects millions of Americans. Because it involves episodic constriction of small airways, bronchodilators such as albuterol (Section 15.3) are used to treat symptoms by widening airways. Since asthma is also characterized by chronic inflammation, inhaled steroids that reduce inflammation are also commonly used.

The **leukotrienes** are molecules that contribute to the asthmatic response by constricting smooth muscles, especially in the lungs. Leukotrienes, such as leukotriene C$_4$ (LTC$_4$), are synthesized in several steps from arachidonic acid. The first step involves an oxidation reaction catalyzed by an enzyme called a lipoxygenase.

arachidonic acid

lipoxygenase   several steps

LTC$_4$

New asthma drugs act by blocking the synthesis of leukotriene C$_4$ from arachidonic acid. For example, zileuton (trade name Zyflo CR) inhibits the lipoxygenase enzyme needed in the first step. By blocking the synthesis of leukotriene C$_4$, a compound responsible for the disease, zileuton treats the cause of asthma, not just its symptoms.

Generic name zileuton
Trade name Zyflo CR

PROBLEM 19.22

(a) A sulfur atom between two alkyl groups (RSR) is called a sulfide. Identify all other functional groups in LTC$_4$. (b) Label the double bonds in LTC$_4$ as cis or trans.

CHAPTER HIGHLIGHTS

KEY TERMS

Active transport (19.7)
Adrenal cortical steroid (19.9)
Anabolic steroid (19.9)
Androgen (19.9)
Cell membrane (19.7)
Cephalin (19.6)
Eicosanoid (19.11)
Estrogen (19.9)
Facilitated transport (19.7)
Fat (19.4)
Fat-soluble vitamin (19.10)
Fatty acid (19.2)
High-density lipoprotein (19.8)
Hormone (19.9)

Hydrolyzable lipid (19.1)
Hydrophilic (19.2)
Hydrophobic (19.2)
Lecithin (19.6)
Leukotriene (19.11)
Lipase (19.5)
Lipid (19.1)
Lipid bilayer (19.7)
Lipoprotein (19.8)
Low-density lipoprotein (19.8)
Nonhydrolyzable lipid (19.1)
Oil (19.4)
Omega-n acid (19.2)
Phosphatidylcholine (19.6)

Phosphatidylethanolamine (19.6)
Phosphoacylglycerol (19.6)
Phosphodiester (19.6)
Phospholipid (19.6)
Progestin (19.9)
Prostaglandin (19.11)
Saponification (19.5)
Saturated fatty acid (19.2)
Soap (19.5)
Sphingomyelin (19.6)
Steroid (19.8)
Triacylglycerol (19.4)
Unsaturated fatty acid (19.2)
Wax (19.3)

KEY REACTIONS

[1] Hydrolysis of waxes (19.3)

[2] Hydrolysis of triacylglycerols in the presence of acid or enzymes (19.5)

[3] Hydrolysis of triacylglycerols in the presence of base—saponification (19.5)

KEY CONCEPTS

❶ What are the general characteristics of lipids? (19.1)

- Lipids are biomolecules that contain many nonpolar C—C and C—H bonds, making them soluble in organic solvents and insoluble in water.
- Hydrolyzable lipids, including waxes, triacylglycerols, and phospholipids, can be converted to smaller molecules on reaction with water.
- Nonhydrolyzable lipids, including steroids, fat-soluble vitamins, and eicosanoids, cannot be cleaved into smaller units by hydrolysis.

❷ How are fatty acids classified, and what is the relationship between their melting points and the number of double bonds they contain? (19.2)

- Fatty acids are saturated if they contain no carbon–carbon double bonds and unsaturated if they contain one or more double bonds. Naturally occurring unsaturated fatty acids generally contain cis double bonds.
- As the number of double bonds in the fatty acid increases, its melting point decreases.

❸ What are waxes? (19.3)

- A wax is an ester (RCOOR') formed from a fatty acid (RCOOH) and a high molecular weight alcohol (R'OH). Since waxes contain many nonpolar C—C and C—H bonds, they are hydrophobic.
- Waxes (RCOOR') are hydrolyzed to fatty acids (RCOOH) and alcohols (R'OH).

❹ What are triacylglycerols, and how do the triacylglycerols in a fat and oil differ? (19.4)

- Triacylglycerols, or triglycerides, are triesters formed from glycerol and three molecules of fatty acids. A monounsaturated triacylglycerol contains one carbon–carbon double bond, whereas polyunsaturated triacylglycerols have more than one carbon–carbon double bond.
- Fats are triacylglycerols derived from fatty acids having few double bonds, making them solids at room temperature. Fats are generally obtained from animal sources.
- Oils are triacylglycerols derived from fatty acids having a larger number of double bonds, making them liquid at room temperature. Oils are generally obtained from plant sources.

700   **Chapter 19**   Lipids

5 **What hydrolysis products are formed from a triacylglycerol? (19.5)**

- Triacylglycerols are hydrolyzed in acid or with enzymes (in biological systems) to form glycerol and three molecules of fatty acids. Base hydrolysis of a triacylglycerol forms glycerol and sodium salts of fatty acids—soaps.

6 **What are the major types of phospholipids? (19.6)**

- All phospholipids contain a phosphorus atom, and have a polar (ionic) head and two nonpolar tails. Phosphoacylglycerols are derived from glycerol, two molecules of fatty acids, phosphate, and an alcohol (either ethanolamine or choline). Sphingomyelins are derived from sphingosine, a fatty acid (that forms an amide), a phosphate, and an alcohol (either ethanolamine or choline).

7 **Describe the structure of the cell membrane. How do molecules and ions cross the cell membrane? (19.7)**

- The main component of the cell membrane is phospholipids, arranged in a lipid bilayer with the ionic heads oriented towards the outside of the bilayer, and the nonpolar tails on the interior.
- Small molecules like O_2 and CO_2 diffuse through the membrane from the side of higher concentration to the side of lower concentration. Larger polar molecules and some ions (Cl^-, HCO_3^-, and glucose) travel through channels created by integral membrane proteins (facilitated diffusion). Some cations (Na^+, K^+, and Ca^{2+}) must travel against the concentration gradient, a process called active transport, which requires energy input.

8 **What are the main structural features of steroids? What is the relationship between the steroid cholesterol and cardiovascular disease? (19.8)**

- Steroids are tetracyclic lipids that contain three six-membered rings and one five-membered ring. Because cholesterol is insoluble in the aqueous medium of the blood, it is transported

through the bloodstream in water-soluble particles called lipoproteins.

- Low-density lipoprotein particles (LDLs) transport cholesterol from the liver to the tissues. If the blood cholesterol level is high, it forms plaque on the walls of arteries, increasing the risk of heart attack and stroke. High-density lipoprotein particles (HDLs) transport cholesterol from the tissues to the liver, where it is metabolized or eliminated.

9 **What is a hormone? Give examples of steroid hormones. (19.9)**

- A hormone is a molecule that is synthesized in one part of an organism, and elicits a response at a different site. Steroid hormones include estrogens and progestins (female sex hormones), androgens (male sex hormones), and adrenal cortical steroids such as cortisone, which are synthesized in the adrenal gland.

10 **Which vitamins are fat soluble? (19.10)**

- Fat-soluble vitamins are lipids required in small quantities for normal cell function, and which cannot be synthesized in the body. Vitamins A, D, E, and K are fat soluble.

11 **What are the general characteristics of prostaglandins and leukotrienes? (19.11)**

- Prostaglandins are a group of carboxylic acids that contain a five-membered ring and are derived from arachidonic acid. Prostaglandins cause inflammation, decrease gastric secretions, inhibit blood platelet aggregation, stimulate uterine contractions, and relax the smooth muscle of the uterus.
- Leukotrienes, acyclic molecules derived from arachidonic acid, contribute to the asthmatic response by constricting smooth muscles in the lungs.

PROBLEMS

Selected in-chapter and odd-numbered end-of-chapter problems have brief answers in Appendix B. The *Student Study Guide and Solutions Manual* contains detailed solutions to all in-chapter and odd-numbered end-of-chapter problems, as well as additional worked examples and a chapter self-test.

General Characteristics of Lipids

19.23 Which compounds could be lipids?

a.   ribose

c.   pyruvic acid

b.   farnesol
(lily of the valley)

19.24 Label each compound as a hydrolyzable or nonhydrolyzable lipid.

a. eicosanoid   e. wax
b. oleic acid   f. estrogen
c. phospholipid   g. PGE_1
d. cephalin

19.25 In which solvents might a wax be soluble: (a) H_2O; (b) CH_2Cl_2; (c) $CH_3CH_2OCH_2CH_3$?

19.26 In which solvents or solutions might a steroid be soluble: (a) blood plasma; (b) CCl_4; (c) 5% NaCl solution?

Fatty Acids, Waxes, and Triacylglycerols

19.27 Rank the fatty acids in order of increasing melting point: $CH_3(CH_2)_{16}COOH$, $CH_3(CH_2)_7CH=CH(CH_2)_7COOH$, and $CH_3(CH_2)_5CH=CH(CH_2)_7COOH$.

19.28 How does each of the following affect the melting point of a fatty acid: (a) increasing the number of carbon atoms; (b) increasing the number of double bonds?

19.29 Rank the fatty acids in order of increasing melting point.

A

B

C

19.30 How would you expect the melting points of the following unsaturated fatty acids to compare? Explain your choice.

A

B

19.31 Some fish oils contain triacylglycerols formed from the polyunsaturated fatty acid, 7,10,13,16,19-docosapentaenoic acid.

7,10,13,16,19-docosapentaenoic acid

a. Label the hydrophobic and hydrophilic portions of the fatty acid.
b. How does the melting point of this fatty acid compare to its all trans isomer?
c. Would you expect this fatty acid to be a solid or a liquid at room temperature?
d. What type of omega-*n* acid is this fatty acid?

19.32 Some marine plankton contain triacylglycerols formed from the polyunsaturated fatty acid, 3,6,9,12,15-octadecapentaenoic acid.

3,6,9,12,15-octadecapentaenoic acid

a. Label the hydrophobic and hydrophilic portions of the fatty acid.
b. How does the melting point of this fatty acid compare to the melting point of oleic acid?
c. Would you expect this fatty acid to be a solid or a liquid at room temperature?
d. What type of omega-*n* acid is this fatty acid?

19.33 Consider fatty acid **A** depicted in the ball-and-stick model.

A

a. Draw a skeletal structure for **A** and clearly show the cis double bond.
b. What type of omega-*n* acid is this fatty acid?
c. Draw a stereoisomer of **A**.
d. Draw the structure of the wax formed from **A** and $CH_3(CH_2)_{10}OH$.

19.34 Consider fatty acid **B** depicted in the ball-and-stick model.

B

a. Draw a skeletal structure for **B** and clearly show the cis double bond.
b. What type of omega-*n* acid is this fatty acid?
c. Draw a stereoisomer of **B**.
d. Draw the structure of the wax formed from **B** and $CH_3(CH_2)_8OH$.

19.35 Draw the structure of a wax formed from palmitic acid $[CH_3(CH_2)_{14}COOH]$ and each alcohol.
a. $CH_3(CH_2)_{21}OH$
b. $CH_3(CH_2)_{11}OH$
c. $CH_3(CH_2)_9OH$

19.36 Draw the structure of a wax formed from a 30-carbon straight chain alcohol and each carboxylic acid.
a. lauric acid
b. myristic acid
c. $CH_3(CH_2)_{22}COOH$

19.37 What hydrolysis products are formed when each wax is treated with aqueous sulfuric acid?
a. $CH_3(CH_2)_{16}COO(CH_2)_{17}CH_3$
b. $CH_3(CH_2)_{12}COO(CH_2)_{25}CH_3$
c. $CH_3(CH_2)_{14}COO(CH_2)_{27}CH_3$

19.38 What hydrolysis products are formed when each wax is treated with aqueous sulfuric acid?
a. $CH_3(CH_2)_{18}COO(CH_2)_{29}CH_3$
b. $CH_3(CH_2)_{24}COO(CH_2)_{23}CH_3$
c. $CH_3(CH_2)_{14}COO(CH_2)_{17}CH_3$

19.39 (a) Which food is high in unsaturated triacylglycerols? (b) Which food is high in saturated fat? (c) Which food likely contains trans fats?

A

B

C

(a–c): ©McGraw-Hill Education/Mark Dierker, photographer

19.40 Match the nutrition label to the type of food: (a) corn oil; (b) butter; (c) margarine.

A

B

C

(a–c): ©McGraw-Hill Education/Mark Dierker, photographer

19.41 Draw a triacylglycerol that fits each description:
   a. a triacylglycerol formed from lauric, myristic, and linoleic acids
   b. an unsaturated triacylglycerol that contains two cis double bonds in one fatty acid side chain
   c. a saturated triacylglycerol formed from three 14-carbon fatty acids

19.42 Draw a triacylglycerol that fits each description:
   a. a triacylglycerol formed from two molecules of lauric acid and one molecule of palmitic acid
   b. a polyunsaturated triacylglycerol formed from three molecules of linoleic acid
   c. a trans triacylglycerol that contains two trans double bonds

19.43 Draw the structure of a triacylglycerol that yields only the sodium carboxylate depicted in the ball-and-stick model when it is hydrolyzed in base.

Na^+

19.44 Draw the structure of a triacylglycerol that yields only the sodium carboxylate depicted in the ball-and-stick model when it is hydrolyzed in base.

Na^+

19.45 Consider the following four types of compounds: [1] fatty acids; [2] soaps; [3] waxes; [4] triacylglycerols. For each type of compound: (a) give the general structure; (b) draw the structure of a specific example; (c) label the compound as water soluble or water insoluble; (d) label the compound as soluble or insoluble in the organic solvent hexane $[CH_3(CH_2)_4CH_3]$.

19.46 How do fats and oils compare with respect to each of the following features?
   a. identity and number of functional groups present
   b. number of carbon–carbon double bonds present
   c. melting point
   d. natural source

19.47 For the food product shown in the accompanying photo, label each statement as true or false.

©TristanBM/Shutterstock RF

   a. It contains trans triacylglycerols.
   b. It contains saturated triacylglycerols.
   c. It is likely high in triacylglycerols that are derived from stearic acid.
   d. A diet high in this food is linked to an increased incidence of heart disease.

19.48 For the food product shown in the accompanying photo, label each statement as true or false.

©Bewaru/Shutterstock RF

a. It contains trans triacylglycerols.

b. It contains unsaturated triacylglycerols.

c. It is likely high in triacylglycerols that are derived from palmitic acid.

d. A diet high in this food is linked to an increased incidence of heart disease.

19.49 Answer the following questions about the given triacylglycerol.

a. What fatty acids are used to form this triacylglycerol?

b. Would you expect this triacylglycerol to be a solid or a liquid at room temperature?

c. What regions are hydrophobic?

d. What regions are hydrophilic?

e. What hydrolysis products are formed when the triacylglycerol is treated with aqueous sulfuric acid?

19.50 Answer the following questions about the given triacylglycerol.

a. What fatty acids are used to form this triacylglycerol?

b. Would you expect this triacylglycerol to be a solid or a liquid at room temperature?

c. What regions are hydrophobic?

d. What regions are hydrophilic?

e. What hydrolysis products are formed when the triacylglycerol is treated with aqueous sulfuric acid?

19.51 Draw the products formed when each triacylglycerol is hydrolyzed under each of the following conditions: [1] water and H_2SO_4; [2] water and NaOH.

a.

b.

19.52 Draw the products formed when each triacylglycerol is hydrolyzed under each of the following conditions: [1] water and H_2SO_4; [2] water and NaOH.

a.

b.

Phospholipids and Cell Membranes

19.53 Which of the following are phospholipids: (a) triacylglycerols; (b) leukotrienes; (c) sphingomyelins; (d) fatty acids?

19.54 Which of the following are phospholipids: (a) prostaglandins; (b) cephalins; (c) lecithins; (d) steroids?

19.55 Draw a phospholipid that fits each description.

a. a cephalin formed from two molecules of palmitoleic acid

b. a phosphatidylcholine formed from two molecules of lauric acid

c. a sphingomyelin formed from stearic acid and ethanolamine

19.56 Draw a phospholipid that fits each description.

a. a lecithin formed from two molecules of oleic acid

b. a phosphatidylethanolamine formed from two molecules of myristic acid

c. a sphingomyelin formed from palmitic acid and choline

19.57 In transporting molecules or ions across a cell membrane, what is the difference between diffusion and facilitated transport? Give an example of a molecule or ion that crosses the membrane by each method.

19.58 How would a cell membrane having phospholipids that contain a high percentage of oleic acid differ from a cell membrane having phospholipids that contain a high percentage of stearic acid?

Steroids

19.59 Draw the structure of the anabolic steroid 4-androstene-3,17-dione, also called "andro," from the following description. Andro contains the tetracyclic steroid skeleton with carbonyl groups at C3 and C17, a double bond between C4 and C5, and methyl groups bonded to C10 and C13.

19.60 Draw the structure of the anabolic steroid methenolone from the following description. Methenolone contains the tetracyclic steroid skeleton with a carbonyl group at C3, a hydroxyl at C17, a double bond between C1 and C2, and methyl groups bonded to C1, C10, and C13.

19.61 Why must cholesterol be transported through the bloodstream in lipoprotein particles?

19.62 Describe the role of HDLs and LDLs in cholesterol transport in the blood. What is the relationship of HDL and LDL levels to cardiovascular disease?

19.63 Fenofibrate, a drug used to lower cholesterol levels in patients at risk of cardiovascular disease, acts by breaking down lipoprotein particles, thereby lowering lipid levels in the blood. Fenofibrate is converted to the active drug, fenofibric acid, by hydrolysis of the labeled ester. What is the structure of fenofibric acid?

fenofibrate

19.64 Boldenone undecylenate (available under the brand names Boldane, Equipoise, and others) is an anabolic steroid banned by Major League Baseball and other competitive sports. Boldenone undecylenate can be prepared by the reaction of boldenone with 10-undecenoic acid to form an ester. What is the structure of boldenone undecylenate?

boldenone   +   10-undecenoic acid

19.65 (a) Draw the structure of an estrogen and an androgen. (b) What structural features are similar in the two steroids? (c) What structural features are different? (d) Describe the biological activity of each steroid.

19.66 (a) Draw the structure of an androgen and a progestin. (b) What structural features are similar in the two steroids? (c) What structural features are different? (d) Describe the biological activity of each steroid.

Prostaglandins and Leukotrienes

19.67 What are the similarities and differences between prostaglandins and leukotrienes?

19.68 Why aren't prostaglandins classified as hormones?

19.69 What two structural features characterize all prostaglandins?

19.70 List three biological functions of prostaglandins in the body.

19.71 Explain why aspirin and celecoxib differ in how they act as anti-inflammatory agents.

19.72 How does zileuton treat the cause of asthma, not just relieve its symptoms?

Vitamins

19.73 Answer each question with regard to vitamins A and D.
   a. How many tetrahedral carbons does the vitamin contain?
   b. How many trigonal planar carbons does the vitamin contain?
   c. Identify the functional groups.
   d. Label all polar bonds.
   e. What function does the vitamin serve in the body?
   f. What problems result when there is a deficiency of the vitamin?
   g. Give a dietary source.

19.74 Answer each question in Problem 19.73 for vitamins E and K.

General Questions

19.75 Give an example of each type of lipid.
   a. a monounsaturated fatty acid
   b. a wax that contains a total of 30 carbons
   c. a saturated triacylglycerol
   d. a sphingomyelin derived from ethanolamine

19.76 Give an example of each type of lipid.
   a. a polyunsaturated fatty acid
   b. a wax derived from a 12-carbon fatty acid
   c. a polyunsaturated triacylglycerol
   d. a cephalin

19.77 Consider each of the following components: [1] glycerol; [2] fatty acid; [3] phosphate; [4] ester; [5] carboxyl group; [6] five-membered ring; [7] steroid nucleus. Which of these components are found in each of the following types of lipids?
   a. prostaglandin   c. triacylglycerol
   b. androgen   d. wax

19.78 Consider each of the following components: [1] glycerol; [2] sphingosine; [3] phosphate; [4] ester; [5] carboxyl group; [6] hydroxyl group; [7] steroid nucleus. Which of these components are found in each of the following lipids?
   a. leukotriene C_4 c. lecithin
   b. estradiol   d. fatty acid

19.79 Block diagrams representing the general structures of three types of lipids are drawn. Which terms describe each diagram: (a) phospholipid; (b) triacylglycerol; (c) hydrolyzable lipid; (d) sphingomyelin; (e) phosphoacylglycerol? More than one term may apply to a diagram.

19.80 For each block diagram in Problem 19.79, label the portion of the molecule that is derived from each component: glycerol, sphingosine, fatty acid, phosphate, and choline.

19.81 Which "cartoon" represents a soap and which represents a phosphoacylglycerol? What structural features are present in the polar head and nonpolar tails of each compound?

19.82 Why are phosphoacylglycerols more water soluble than triacylglycerols?

Applications

19.83 The main fatty acid component of the triacylglycerols in coconut oil is lauric acid, $CH_3(CH_2)_{10}COOH$. Explain why coconut oil is a liquid at room temperature despite the fact that it contains a large fraction of this saturated fatty acid.

19.84 Drain cleaners that contain sodium hydroxide, NaOH, are especially effective at clearing drains clogged with fat molecules. What chemical reaction occurs when aqueous NaOH comes into contact with the fat present in the drain?

19.85 What is the difference between vegetable oil from plants and motor oil, obtained from crude oil (Section 12.6)?

19.86 Why do laboratory blood results now report the levels of cholesterol, HDLs, and LDLs? What are the current recommendations for these values?

19.87 Can an individual survive on a completely fat-free diet?

19.88 Can an individual survive on a cholesterol-free diet?

19.89 Why should saturated fats in the diet be avoided?

19.90 Why is it recommended that polyunsaturated oils be substituted for saturated fats in the diet?

19.91 Why do animals that live in cold climates have triacylglycerols that contain a higher percentage of unsaturated fatty acid side chains?

19.92 If the serum cholesterol level in an adult is 167 mg/dL, how much cholesterol is contained in 5.0 L of blood? (Recall from Chapter 1 that 1 L = 10 dL.)

CHALLENGE PROBLEMS

19.93 Sometimes it is possible to convert one lipid molecule to another by a simple organic reaction that you learned in previous chapters. What type of reaction converts each starting material to the given product?
  a. cortisone → cortisol (Section 19.9)
  b. estradiol → estrone (Section 19.9)
  c. PGE_2 → PGE_1 (Section 19.11)

19.94 How many triacylglycerols can be prepared from three different fatty acids? Draw all possible structures, excluding stereoisomers.

20

Table sugar contains **sucrose,** a
sweet-tasting carbohydrate
obtained from sugarcane.
*©Maximilian Stock Ltd./Photographer's
Choice/Getty Images*

Carbohydrates

CHAPTER OUTLINE

20.1 Introduction

20.2 Monosaccharides

20.3 The Cyclic Forms of
Monosaccharides

20.4 Reduction and Oxidation of
Monosaccharides

20.5 Disaccharides

20.6 Polysaccharides

20.7 FOCUS ON THE HUMAN BODY:
Useful Carbohydrate Derivatives

20.8 FOCUS ON THE HUMAN BODY:
Blood Type

CHAPTER GOALS

In this chapter you will learn how to:

1. Identify the three major types of carbohydrates

2. Recognize the major structural features of monosaccharides

3. Draw the cyclic forms of monosaccharides and classify them as
α or β anomers

4. Draw reduction and oxidation products of monosaccharides

5. Recognize the major structural features of disaccharides

6. Describe the characteristics of cellulose, starch, and glycogen

7. Give examples of some carbohydrate derivatives that contain amino groups,
amides, or carboxylate anions

8. Describe the role that carbohydrates play in determining blood type

Why Study Carbohydrates?

In Chapter 20, we turn our attention to **carbohydrates,** the largest group of organic molecules in nature, comprising approximately 50% of the earth's biomass. Carbohydrates can be simple or complex, having as few as three or as many as thousands of carbon atoms. The glucose metabolized for energy in cells, the sucrose of table sugar, and the cellulose of plant stems and tree trunks are all examples of carbohydrates. Carbohydrates on cell surfaces determine blood type, and carbohydrates form the backbone of DNA, the carrier of all genetic information in the cell. Unlike the lipids of Chapter 19, which are composed of mainly carbon–carbon and carbon–hydrogen bonds and few functional groups, carbohydrates have many polar functional groups, whose structure and properties can be understood by applying the basic principles of organic chemistry.

20.1 Introduction

Carbohydrates, commonly referred to as sugars and starches, are polyhydroxy aldehydes and ketones, or compounds that can be hydrolyzed to them. Historically, the word *carbohydrate* was given to this group of compounds because the molecular formula of simple carbohydrates could be written as $C_n(H_2O)_n$, making them *hydrates of carbon*.

Carbohydrates are classified into three groups:

- Monosaccharides (Sections 20.2–20.4)
- Disaccharides (Section 20.5)
- Polysaccharides (Sections 20.6–20.7)

Monosaccharides or simple sugars are the simplest carbohydrates. Glucose and fructose, the two major constituents of honey, are monosaccharides. Glucose contains an aldehyde at one end of a six-carbon chain, and fructose contains a ketone. Every other carbon atom has a hydroxyl group bonded to it. Monosaccharides cannot be converted to simpler compounds by hydrolysis.

honey
©Michelle Garrett/Corbis/Getty Images

aldehyde

glucose   fructose

ketone

common monosaccharides

Disaccharides are composed of two monosaccharides joined together. Lactose, the principal carbohydrate in milk, is a disaccharide. Disaccharides contain at least one acetal carbon—a carbon atom singly bonded to two OR (alkoxy) groups. Although disaccharides contain no carbonyl groups, they are hydrolyzed to simple monosaccharides that contain an aldehyde or ketone, as we will learn in Section 20.5.

lactose
a common disaccharide

©ImageSource/Corbis RF

Polysaccharides have three or more monosaccharides joined together. Starch, the main carbohydrate found in the seeds and roots of plants, is a polysaccharide composed of hundreds of glucose molecules joined together. Like disaccharides, polysaccharides contain acetals but no carbonyl groups, and they are hydrolyzed to simple monosaccharides that contain carbonyl groups. Pasta, bread, rice, and potatoes are foods that contain a great deal of starch.

Source: Scott Bauer/USDA

one form of starch
a polysaccharide
[Acetal carbons are labeled with *.]

Carbohydrates are storehouses of chemical energy. Carbohydrates are synthesized in green plants and algae through **photosynthesis,** a process that uses the energy from the sun to convert carbon dioxide and water into glucose and oxygen. Almost all of the oxygen in the atmosphere results from photosynthesis. Plants store glucose in the form of polysaccharides like starch and cellulose (Section 20.6).

Energy is stored in **photosynthesis.**

$$6\ CO_2\ +\ 6\ H_2O\ \xrightarrow[\text{chlorophyll}]{\text{sunlight}}\ \underset{\text{glucose}}{C_6H_{12}O_6}\ +\ 6\ O_2$$

Energy is released in **metabolism.**

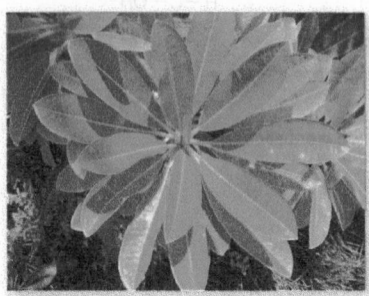

Chlorophyll in green leaves converts CO_2 and H_2O to glucose and O_2 during photosynthesis. ©Daniel C. Smith

The energy stored in glucose bonds is released when glucose is metabolized. The oxidation of glucose is a multistep process that forms carbon dioxide, water, and a great deal of energy. Although the metabolism of lipids provides more energy per gram than the metabolism of carbohydrates, glucose is the preferred source when a burst of energy is needed during exercise. Glucose is water soluble, so it can be quickly and easily transported through the bloodstream to tissues.

PROBLEM 20.1

Label the hemiacetal carbon—the carbon bonded to one OH and one OR group—in lactose (Section 16.8). Label all other hydroxyls as 1°, 2°, or 3°.

20.2 Monosaccharides

Monosaccharides, the simplest carbohydrates, generally have three to six carbon atoms in a chain, with a **carbonyl group** at either the terminal carbon, numbered C1, or the carbon adjacent to it, numbered C2. In most carbohydrates, each of the remaining carbon atoms has a **hydroxyl group.** Monosaccharides are drawn vertically, with the carbonyl group at (or near) the top.

- Monosaccharides with a carbonyl group at C1 are aldehydes called *aldoses.*
- Monosaccharides with a carbonyl group at C2 are ketones called *ketoses.*

Glyceraldehyde is the simplest aldose and dihydroxyacetone is the simplest ketose. Glyceraldehyde and dihydroxyacetone both have molecular formula $C_3H_6O_3$, so they are **constitutional isomers;** that is, they have the same molecular formula but a different arrangement of atoms. Glucose is the most prevalent aldose.

All carbohydrates have common names. The simplest aldehyde, glyceraldehyde, and the simplest ketone, dihydroxyacetone, are the only monosaccharides whose names do not end in the suffix *-ose.*

A monosaccharide is characterized by the number of carbons in its chain.

- A triose has three carbons.
- A tetrose has four carbons.
- A pentose has five carbons.
- A hexose has six carbons.

These terms are then combined with the words *aldose* and *ketose* to indicate both the number of carbon atoms in the monosaccharide and whether it contains an aldehyde or ketone. Thus, glyceraldehyde is an aldotriose (three carbons and an aldehyde), dihydroxyacetone is a ketotriose (three carbons and a ketone), and glucose is an aldohexose (six carbons and an aldehyde).

SAMPLE PROBLEM 20.1 CLASSIFYING A MONOSACCHARIDE

Classify each monosaccharide by the type of carbonyl group and the number of carbons in the chain.

a.
$$
\begin{array}{c}
\text{H} \\
\text{C}=\text{O} \\
\text{H}-\text{C}-\text{OH} \\
\text{H}-\text{C}-\text{OH} \\
\text{H}-\text{C}-\text{OH} \\
\text{CH}_2\text{OH}
\end{array}
$$
ribose

b.
$$
\begin{array}{c}
\text{CH}_2\text{OH} \\
\text{C}=\text{O} \\
\text{HO}-\text{C}-\text{H} \\
\text{H}-\text{C}-\text{OH} \\
\text{H}-\text{C}-\text{OH} \\
\text{CH}_2\text{OH}
\end{array}
$$
fructose

Analysis

Identify the type of carbonyl group to label the monosaccharide as an aldose or ketose. An aldose has the C=O at C1, so that a hydrogen atom is bonded to the carbonyl carbon. A ketose has two carbons bonded to the carbonyl carbon. Count the number of carbons in the chain to determine the suffix—namely, *-triose, -tetrose,* and so forth.

Solution

a.
$$
\begin{array}{c}
\text{H} \\
\text{C}=\text{O} \quad \text{aldehyde} \\
\text{H}-\text{C}-\text{OH} \\
\text{H}-\text{C}-\text{OH} \\
\text{H}-\text{C}-\text{OH} \\
\text{CH}_2\text{OH}
\end{array}
$$
ribose
5 C's in the chain
Answer: aldopentose

b.
$$
\begin{array}{c}
\text{CH}_2\text{OH} \\
\text{C}=\text{O} \quad \text{ketone} \\
\text{HO}-\text{C}-\text{H} \\
\text{H}-\text{C}-\text{OH} \\
\text{H}-\text{C}-\text{OH} \\
\text{CH}_2\text{OH}
\end{array}
$$
fructose
6 C's in the chain
Answer: ketohexose

PRACTICE PROBLEM 20.1

Classify each monosaccharide by the type of carbonyl group and the number of carbons in the chain.

a.
$$
\begin{array}{c}
\text{H} \\
\text{C}=\text{O} \\
\text{HO}-\text{C}-\text{H} \\
\text{H}-\text{C}-\text{OH} \\
\text{H}-\text{C}-\text{OH} \\
\text{CH}_2\text{OH}
\end{array}
$$
arabinose

b.
$$
\begin{array}{c}
\text{H} \\
\text{C}=\text{O} \\
\text{HO}-\text{C}-\text{H} \\
\text{H}-\text{C}-\text{OH} \\
\text{CH}_2\text{OH}
\end{array}
$$
threose

c.
$$
\begin{array}{c}
\text{CH}_2\text{OH} \\
\text{C}=\text{O} \\
\text{H}-\text{C}-\text{OH} \\
\text{CH}_2\text{OH}
\end{array}
$$
erythrulose

More Practice: Try Problems 20.23, 20.24, 20.25a, 20.26a, 20.27b, 20.28b.

PROBLEM 20.2

Classify the monosaccharide by the type of carbonyl group and the number of carbons in the chain.

PROBLEM 20.3

Draw the structure of (a) an aldotetrose; (b) a ketopentose; (c) an aldohexose.

Monosaccharides are all sweet tasting, but their relative sweetness varies a great deal. Monosaccharides are polar compounds with high melting points. The presence of so many polar functional groups capable of hydrogen bonding makes them very water soluble.

PROBLEM 20.4

Rank the following compounds in order of increasing water solubility: glucose, hexane [$CH_3(CH_2)_4CH_3$], and 1-decanol [$CH_3(CH_2)_9OH$]. Explain your choice.

20.2A Fischer Projection Formulas

A striking feature of carbohydrate structure is the presence of chirality centers. **All carbohydrates except for dihydroxyacetone contain one or more chirality centers.** The simplest aldose, glyceraldehyde, has one chirality center—one carbon atom bonded to four different groups. Thus, there are two possible enantiomers—mirror images that are not superimposable.

Chirality centers and enantiomers were first encountered in Section 15.2.

Two enantiomers of glyceraldehyde

chirality center

naturally occurring isomer
D-glyceraldehyde

OH on right

chirality center

unnatural isomer
L-glyceraldehyde

OH on left

Only one enantiomer of glyceraldehyde occurs in nature. When the carbon chain is drawn vertically with the aldehyde at the top, a convention used with carbohydrates, the naturally occurring enantiomer has the OH group drawn on the **right side** of the carbon chain. **To distinguish the two enantiomers, the prefixes D and L precede the name.** Thus, the naturally occurring enantiomer is labeled D-glyceraldehyde, while the unnatural isomer is L-glyceraldehyde.

Fischer projection formulas are commonly used to depict the chirality centers in monosaccharides. Recall from Section 15.6 that a Fischer projection formula uses a cross to represent a tetrahedral carbon in which the horizontal bonds come forward (on wedges) and vertical bonds go behind (on dashed wedges). In a Fischer projection formula:

- A carbon atom is located at the intersection of the two lines of the cross.
- The horizontal bonds come forward, on wedges.
- The vertical bonds go back, on dashed wedges.

Using a Fischer projection formula, D-glyceraldehyde becomes:

D-glyceraldehyde

Fischer projection formula

HEALTH NOTE

A 5% intravenous glucose (dextrose) solution provides a patient with calories and hydration. ©*Digital Vision/Alamy Rf*

PROBLEM 20.5

Draw L-glyceraldehyde using a Fischer projection formula.

20.2B   Monosaccharides with More Than One Chirality Center

Fischer projection formulas are also used for compounds like aldohexoses that contain several chirality centers. Glucose, for example, contains four chirality centers labeled in the structure below. To convert the molecule to a Fischer projection, the molecule is drawn with a vertical carbon skeleton with the aldehyde at the top, and the horizontal bonds are assumed to come forward (on wedges). In the Fischer projection, each chirality center is replaced by a cross.

glucose   Fischer projection formula

The letters D and L are used to label all monosaccharides, even those with many chirality centers. **The configuration of the chirality center *farthest* from the carbonyl group determines whether a monosaccharide is D or L.**

- A D monosaccharide has the OH group on the chirality center farthest from the carbonyl on the right (like D-glyceraldehyde).
- An L monosaccharide has the OH group on the chirality center farthest from the carbonyl on the left (like L-glyceraldehyde).

chirality center
farthest from the C=O

OH on the right   OH on the left
D sugar   L sugar

Glucose and all other naturally occurring sugars are D sugars. L-Glucose, a compound that does not occur in nature, is the enantiomer of D-glucose. L-Glucose has the opposite configuration at *every* chirality center.

D-glucose   L-glucose

The location of the H and OH is opposite at every chirality center in the enantiomer.

OH on the right   OH on the left

naturally occurring enantiomer   unnatural enantiomer

SAMPLE PROBLEM 20.2 DETERMINING THE STEREOCHEMICAL FEATURES OF A MONOSACCHARIDE

Consider the aldopentose ribose. (a) Label all chirality centers. (b) Classify ribose as a D or L monosaccharide. (c) Draw the enantiomer.

ribose

Analysis

- A chirality center has four different groups around a carbon atom.
- The labels D and L are determined by the position of the OH group on the chirality center farthest from the carbonyl group: a D sugar has the OH group on the right and an L sugar has the OH group on the left.
- To draw an enantiomer, draw the mirror image so that each group is a reflection of the group in the original compound.

Solution

a. The three carbons that contain both H and OH groups in ribose are chirality centers labeled in blue.

b. Ribose is a D sugar because the OH group on the chirality center farthest from the carbonyl is on the right.

c. The enantiomer of D-ribose, L-ribose, has all three OH groups on the left side of the carbon chain.

PRACTICE PROBLEM 20.2

For each monosaccharide: [1] label all chirality centers; [2] classify the monosaccharide as D or L; [3] draw the enantiomer.

More Practice: Try Problems 20.25b, 20.26b, 20.29, 20.30.

PROBLEM 20.6

For each type of monosaccharide, [1] give an example of a D sugar; [2] label each chirality center: (a) an aldopentose; (b) a ketohexose; (c) a ketotetrose.

Insulin injections taken by diabetic patients help to maintain a proper blood glucose level. ©*Keith Brofsky/Getty Images RF*

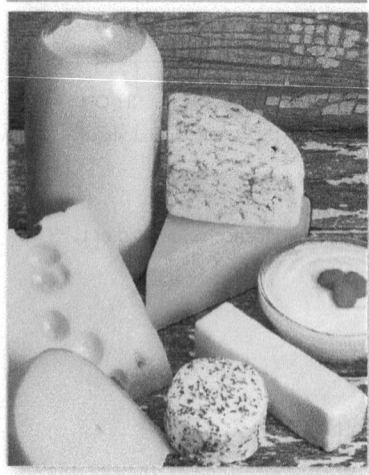

An individual with galactosemia must avoid cow's milk and all products derived from cow's milk. ©*Comstock/Getty Images RF*

20.2C   Common Monosaccharides

The most common monosaccharides in nature are the aldohexoses D-glucose and D-galactose, and the ketohexose D-fructose.

D-glucose   D-galactose   D-fructose

Glucose, also called dextrose, is the sugar referred to when blood sugar is measured. It is the most abundant monosaccharide. Glucose is the building block for the polysaccharides starch and cellulose. Glucose, the carbohydrate that is transported in the bloodstream, provides energy for cells when it is metabolized. Normal blood glucose levels are in the range of 70–110 mg/dL. Excess glucose is converted to the polysaccharide glycogen (Section 20.6) or fat.

Insulin, a protein produced in the pancreas, regulates blood glucose levels. When glucose concentration increases after eating, insulin stimulates the uptake of glucose in tissues and its conversion to glycogen. Patients with diabetes produce insufficient insulin to adequately regulate blood glucose levels, and the concentration of glucose rises. With close attention to diet and daily insulin injections or other medications, a normal level of glucose can be maintained in most diabetic patients. Individuals with poorly controlled diabetes can develop many other significant complications, including cardiovascular disease, chronic renal failure, and blindness.

Galactose is one of the two monosaccharides that form the disaccharide lactose (Section 20.5). Galactose is a stereoisomer of glucose, because the position of a hydrogen atom and hydroxyl group at a single chirality center is different in the two monosaccharides.

Only this chirality center is different.

D-glucose   D-galactose

Individuals with galactosemia, a rare inherited disease, lack an enzyme needed to metabolize galactose. Galactose accumulates, causing a variety of physical problems, including cataracts, cirrhosis, and mental retardation. Galactosemia can be detected in newborn screening, and affected infants must be given soy-based formula to avoid all milk products with lactose.

Fructose is one of two monosaccharides that form the disaccharide sucrose (Section 20.5). Fructose is a ketohexose found in honey and is almost twice as sweet as normal table sugar with about the same number of calories per gram.

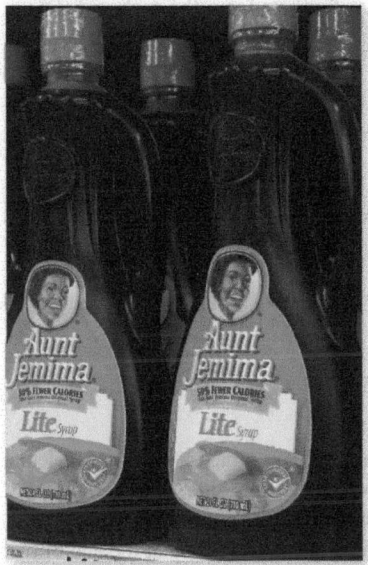

CONSUMER NOTE

Some "lite" food products have fewer calories because they use only half as much fructose as sucrose for the same level of sweetness. ©Jill Braaten RF

PROBLEM 20.7

D-Glucose and D-galactose are stereoisomers because they have the same molecular formula but a different three-dimensional geometry. How are D-glucose and D-fructose related? How are D-galactose and D-fructose related?

20.3 The Cyclic Forms of Monosaccharides

In Section 16.8 we learned that an aldehyde or ketone reacts with one equivalent of an alcohol to form a **hemiacetal,** a compound that contains a hydroxyl group (OH) and an alkoxy group (OR) on the same carbon.

aldehyde   alcohol

hemiacetal

OH and OR' on the same C

Generally, hemiacetals from acyclic reactants are unstable. When a compound contains *both* a hydroxyl group and an aldehyde or ketone, however, an intramolecular cyclization reaction forms a stable cyclic hemiacetal.

$HOCH_2CH_2CH_2CH_2$ re-draw

5-hydroxypentanal

hemiacetal

The C=O and OH groups react.

The carbon atom that is part of the hemiacetal is a new chirality center, called the *anomeric carbon*. Thus, two different products called **anomers** are formed.

new chirality center
the anomeric carbon

anomeric carbon

anomeric carbon

α anomer   β anomer

- The α anomer has the OH group drawn down, below the ring (shown in red).
- The β anomer has the OH group drawn up, above the ring (shown in blue).

PROBLEM 20.8

Locate the hemiacetal carbon in each compound and label the compound as an α or β anomer.

a.   b.   c.

CH_2OH CH_2OH CH_2OH

20.3A The Cyclic Forms of D-Glucose

Although the monosaccharides in Section 20.2 were drawn as acyclic carbonyl compounds, the hydroxyl and carbonyl groups of monosaccharides undergo intramolecular cyclization to form **hemiacetals.** Let's illustrate the process with D-glucose, and then learn a general method for drawing the cyclic forms of any aldohexose.

Which of the five OH groups in glucose is at the right distance from the carbonyl group to form a six-membered ring? The **O atom on the chirality center farthest from the carbonyl** (C5) is six atoms from the carbonyl carbon, placing it at the proper distance for cyclization to form a six-membered ring with a hemiacetal.

This OH group is the right distance away from the carbonyl for cyclization to a six-membered ring.

D-glucose

To convert this acyclic form (labeled **A**) into a cyclic hemiacetal, first rotate the carbon skeleton clockwise 90° to form **B**. Note that groups that were drawn on the right side of the carbon skeleton in **A** end up *below* the carbon chain in **B**. Then twist the chain to put the OH group on C5 close to the aldehyde carbonyl, forming **C**. In this process, the CH_2OH group at the end of the chain ends up *above* the carbon skeleton. Realize that **A**, **B**, and **C** are all different representations of D-glucose. The molecule has been rotated and twisted but the carbon skeleton and relative arrangement of the substituents have not changed.

We are now set to draw the cyclic hemiacetals formed by reaction of the OH group on C5 with the aldehyde carbonyl. Since cyclization creates a new chirality center, there are *two* **cyclic forms of D-glucose**, an **α anomer** and a **β anomer**.

- The α anomer, called α-D-glucose, has the OH group on the anomeric carbon drawn down (shown in red).
- The β anomer, called β-D-glucose, has the OH group on the anomeric carbon drawn up (shown in blue).

Figure 20.1   The Three Forms of D-Glucose

α-D-glucose   acyclic D-glucose   β-D-glucose

α anomer   aldehyde C=O   β anomer
37%   trace   63%

Although Haworth projections represent the six-membered ring of glucose as a flat hexagon, in reality, the ring is puckered as shown in the three-dimensional models (c.f. the ball-and-stick model of cyclohexane in Section 12.5).

These flat, six-membered rings used to represent the cyclic hemiacetals of glucose and other sugars are called **Haworth projections.**

Thus, D-glucose really exists in three different forms—an acyclic aldehyde and two cyclic hemiacetals—all of which are in equilibrium. Each cyclic hemiacetal can be isolated and crystallized separately, but when any one compound is placed in solution, an equilibrium mixture of all three forms results. This process is called **mutarotation.** At equilibrium, the mixture has 37% of the α anomer, 63% of the β anomer, and only a trace amount of the acyclic aldehyde. Three-dimensional models for the three forms of D-glucose are shown in Figure 20.1.

20.3B   Haworth Projections

All aldohexoses exist primarily as cyclic hemiacetals typically drawn in Haworth projections. To convert an acyclic monosaccharide to a Haworth projection, follow the stepwise *How To* procedure.

How To   Draw a Haworth Projection from an Acyclic Aldohexose

Example: Draw both anomers of D-mannose in a Haworth projection.

D-mannose

—Continued

How To, continued . . .

Step [1] **Place the O atom in the upper right corner of a hexagon, and add the CH$_2$OH group on the first carbon to the left of the O atom.**

- For naturally occurring D sugars, the CH$_2$OH group is drawn *up*, above the plane of the six-membered ring.

CH$_2$OH ← CH$_2$OH is above the plane of the six-membered ring.

D-mannose

Step [2] **Place the anomeric carbon on the first carbon clockwise from the O atom.**

- For an **α anomer**, the **OH** is drawn *down* in a D sugar.
- For a **β anomer**, the **OH** is drawn *up* in a D sugar.

anomeric carbon
α anomer

anomeric carbon
β anomer

Step [3] **Add the substituents (OH and H) to the three remaining carbons (C2–C4), clockwise around the ring.**

- The substituents on the *right* side of the carbon skeleton (shown in red) are drawn *down* in the Haworth projection.
- The substituents on the *left* side of the carbon skeleton (shown in blue) are drawn *up* in the Haworth projection.

Add groups on C2–C4.

α anomer   +   β anomer

SAMPLE PROBLEM 20.3 DRAWING A HAWORTH PROJECTION FROM AN ACYLIC ALDOHEXOSE

Draw the α anomer of D-galactose.

D-galactose

Analysis and Solution

[1] Draw a hexagon with an O atom in the upper right corner. Add the CH₂OH above the ring on the first carbon to the left of the O atom.

D-galactose

[2] Draw the anomeric carbon on the first carbon clockwise from the O atom.

- The α anomer has the OH group drawn down.

α anomer

[3] Add the OH groups and H atoms to the three remaining carbons (C2–C4).

- Groups on the *right* side in the acyclic form are drawn *down*, below the six-membered ring, and groups on the *left* side in the acyclic form are drawn *up*, above the six-membered ring.

α anomer of cyclic D-galactose

PRACTICE PROBLEM 20.3

Convert each aldohexose to the indicated anomer using a Haworth projection.

a.   b.   c.

α anomer   β anomer   α anomer

More Practice: Try Problems 20.33, 20.34.

20.3C   The Cyclic Forms of Fructose, a Ketohexose

Certain monosaccharides—notably aldopentoses and ketohexoses—form five-membered rings, *not* six-membered rings, in solution. The same principles apply to drawing these structures as for drawing six-membered rings, except the ring size is one atom smaller.

- Cyclization forms two anomers at the hemiacetal carbon. For a D sugar, the OH group is drawn down on the new chirality center in the α anomer and up in the β anomer.

For example, D-fructose forms a five-membered ring when it cyclizes to a hemiacetal because the carbonyl group is a ketone at C2, instead of an aldehyde at C1. Note that the cyclic structures of fructose contain two CH_2OH groups bonded to the five-membered ring, one of which is located at the anomeric carbon.

acyclic D-fructose

re-draw

α anomer
α-D-fructose

β anomer
β-D-fructose

The two cyclic forms of D-fructose contain a five-membered ring.

SAMPLE PROBLEM 20.4 LABELING ANOMERS IN FIVE-MEMBERED RINGS

Locate the anomeric carbon in each five-membered ring, and label the compound as an α or β anomer.

Analysis

- The anomeric carbon is bonded to an OH group and an O atom that is part of the ring.
- The α anomer has the OH group drawn down. The β anomer has the OH group drawn up.

Solution

In each part, the anomeric C is labeled in blue. In (a), the OH group is drawn up, making it a β anomer. In (b), the OH group is drawn down, making it an α anomer.

PRACTICE PROBLEM 20.4

Locate the anomeric carbon in each compound and label the compound as an α or β anomer.

More Practice: Try Problems 20.39b, 20.40b, 20.41, 20.42.

20.4 Reduction and Oxidation of Monosaccharides

The aldehyde carbonyl group of the acyclic form of a monosaccharide undergoes two common reactions—**reduction to an alcohol** and **oxidation to a carboxylic acid.** Even though the acyclic form may be present in only trace amounts, the equilibrium can be tipped in its favor by Le Châtelier's principle (Section 6.6). When the carbonyl group of the acyclic form reacts with a reagent, thus depleting its equilibrium concentration, the equilibrium will shift to compensate for the loss. More of the acyclic form will be produced, which can react further.

20.4A Reduction of the Aldehyde Carbonyl Group

Like other aldehydes, the **carbonyl group of an aldose is reduced to a 1° alcohol** using hydrogen (H_2) in the presence of palladium (Pd) metal (Section 16.6). This alcohol is called an **alditol,** sometimes referred to as a "sugar alcohol." For example, reduction of D-glucose with H_2 and Pd yields glucitol, commonly called sorbitol.

H_2 adds to the C=O.

β-D-glucose + α anomer

D-glucose (D-sorbose)

This form reacts.

+ H_2 → Pd →

glucitol (sorbitol)

The alditol contains an OH group on every C.

Sorbitol, which is 60% as sweet as table sugar (sucrose), is used as a sweetening agent in a variety of sugar-free candies and gum.

Xylitol (Sample Problem 20.5) is used as a substitute sweetener in sugar-free—that is, sucrose-free—products.
©McGraw-Hill Education/Mark Dierker, photographer

SAMPLE PROBLEM 20.5 DRAWING THE PRODUCT FROM REDUCTION OF AN ALDOSE WITH H_2

Draw the structure of the compound formed when D-xylose is treated with H_2 in the presence of a Pd catalyst. The product, xylitol, is a sweetener used in sugarless chewing gum and other products.

D-xylose

Analysis

- Locate the C=O and mentally break one bond in the double bond.
- Mentally break the H—H bond of the reagent and add one H atom to each atom of the C=O, forming new C—H and O—H bonds.

Solution

xylose → xylitol

PRACTICE PROBLEM 20.5

What compound is formed when each aldose is treated with H_2 in the presence of a Pd catalyst?

More Practice: Try Problems 20.45[1], 20.46[1], 20.67g, 20.68g.

20.4B   Oxidation of the Aldehyde Carbonyl Group

The aldehyde carbonyl of an aldose is easily oxidized with a variety of reagents to form a carboxyl group, yielding an **aldonic acid.** For example, D-glucose is oxidized with a Cu^{2+} reagent called **Benedict's reagent** to form gluconic acid. In the process, a characteristic color change occurs as the blue Cu^{2+} is reduced to Cu^+, forming brick-red Cu_2O.

This reaction is an oxidation because the product carboxylic acid has one more C—O bond than the starting aldehyde. Carbohydrates that are oxidized with Benedict's reagent are called **reducing sugars,** because the Cu^{2+} in Benedict's reagent is reduced to Cu^+ during the reaction. Those that do not react with Benedict's reagent are called **nonreducing sugars. All aldoses are reducing sugars.**

Perhaps surprisingly, **ketoses are also reducing sugars.** Although ketoses do not contain an easily oxidized aldehyde, they do contain a ketone carbonyl adjacent to a CH_2OH group that undergoes rearrangement under basic reaction conditions to form an aldose, which is then oxidized with Benedict's reagent. For example, fructose rearranges to an aldose, which is then oxidized to an aldonic acid. Thus, fructose is a reducing sugar.

fructose — rearrangement — aldose — 2 Cu^{2+} / OH$^-$ — aldonic acid + Cu$_2$O

SAMPLE PROBLEM 20.6 DRAWING THE PRODUCT FROM OXIDATION OF AN ALDOSE

Draw the product formed when each monosaccharide is oxidized with Benedict's reagent.

a. L-threose

b. D-erythrulose

Analysis

To draw the oxidation product of an aldose, convert the CHO group to COOH. To oxidize a ketose, first rearrange the ketose to an aldose by moving the carbonyl group to C1 to give an aldehyde. Then convert the CHO group to COOH.

Solution

L-Threose in part (a) is an aldose, so its oxidation product can be drawn directly. D-Erythrulose in part (b) is a ketose, so it undergoes rearrangement prior to oxidation.

a. L-threose — oxidation

b. D-erythrulose — rearrangement — oxidation

PRACTICE PROBLEM 20.6

What aldonic acid is formed by oxidation of each monosaccharide?

More Practice: Try Problems 20.45[2], 20.46[2], 20.47, 20.48, 20.67f, 20.68f.

PROBLEM 20.9

Label each compound as an aldonic acid or an alditol.

a.

b.

PROBLEM 20.10

What product is formed when D-arabinose is treated with each reagent: (a) H_2, Pd; (b) Benedict's reagent?

D-arabinose

Test strips that contain glucose oxidase are used to measure glucose concentration in urine. ©McGraw-Hill Education/Jill Braaten, photographer

20.4C   FOCUS ON HEALTH & MEDICINE
Monitoring Glucose Levels

In order to make sure that their blood glucose levels are in the proper range, individuals with diabetes frequently measure the concentration of glucose in their blood. A common method for carrying out this procedure today involves the oxidation of glucose to gluconic acid using the enzyme glucose oxidase.

D-glucose   + O_2 $\xrightarrow{\text{glucose oxidase}}$ gluconic acid   + H_2O_2

Figure 20.2

Monitoring Blood Glucose Levels

glucose meter

test strip

small pinprick for a
blood sample

A small drop of blood is placed on a disposable test strip that is inserted in an electronic blood
glucose meter, and the glucose concentration is read on a digital display.
©McGraw-Hill Education/Jill Braaten, photographer

In the presence of glucose oxidase, oxygen (O_2) in the air oxidizes the aldehyde of glucose to a
carboxyl group. The O_2, in turn, is reduced to hydrogen peroxide, H_2O_2. In the first generation of
meters for glucose monitoring, the H_2O_2 produced in this reaction was allowed to react with another organic compound to produce a colored product. The intensity of the colored product was
then correlated to the amount of glucose in the blood. Test strips used for measuring glucose
concentration in the urine are still based on this technology.

Modern glucose meters are electronic devices that measure the amount of oxidizing agent that
reacts with a known amount of blood (Figure 20.2). This value is correlated with blood glucose
concentration and the result is displayed digitally. A high blood glucose level may mean that an
individual needs more insulin, whereas a low level may mean that it is time to ingest some
calories.

20.5 Disaccharides

Disaccharides are carbohydrates composed of two monosaccharides. Disaccharides are
acetals, compounds that contain two alkoxy groups (OR groups) bonded to the same carbon.
Recall from Section 16.8 that reaction of a hemiacetal with an alcohol forms an **acetal.**

In a similar fashion, a disaccharide results when a hemiacetal of one monosaccharide reacts with
a hydroxyl group of a second monosaccharide to form an acetal. The new C—O bond that joins
the two rings together is called a **glycosidic linkage.**

[The acetal O's are labeled in red.]

The two monosaccharide rings may be five-membered or six-membered. All disaccharides contain at least one acetal that joins the rings together. Each ring is numbered beginning at the
anomeric carbon, the carbon in each ring bonded to two oxygen atoms.

The glycosidic linkage that joins the two monosaccharides in a disaccharide can be oriented in two different ways, shown with Haworth projections in structures **A** and **B**.

α glycoside

The glycoside bond is **down.**

1→4-α-glycosidic linkage

A

β glycoside

The glycoside bond is **up.**

1→4-β-glycosidic linkage

B

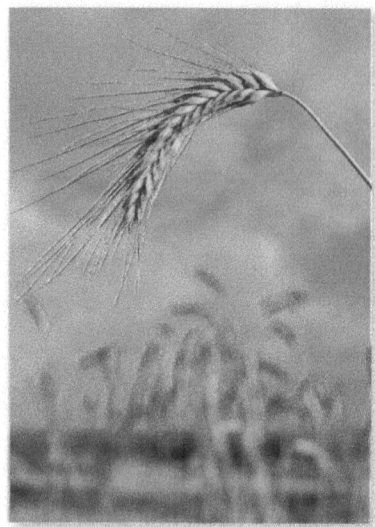

Maltose gets its name from malt, the liquid obtained from barley used in the brewing of beer. ©Sodapix AG, Switzerland/ Glow Images RF

- An α glycoside has the glycosidic linkage oriented down, below the plane of the ring that contains the acetal joining the monosaccharides.
- A β glycoside has the glycosidic linkage oriented up, above the plane of the ring that contains the acetal joining the monosaccharides.

Numbers are used to designate which ring atoms are joined in the disaccharide. Disaccharide **A** has a **1→4-α-glycosidic linkage** because the glycoside bond is oriented down and joins C1 of one ring to C4 of the other. Disaccharide **B** has a **1→4-β-glycosidic linkage** because the glycoside bond is oriented up and joins C1 of one ring to C4 of the other.

Sample Problem 20.7 illustrates these structural features in the disaccharide **maltose.** Maltose, which is formed by the hydrolysis of starch, is found in grains such as barley. Maltose is formed from two molecules of glucose.

glycosidic linkage

maltose

SAMPLE PROBLEM 20.7 LOCATING AND CLASSIFYING GLYCOSIDIC LINKAGES

(a) Locate the glycosidic linkage in maltose. (b) Number the carbon atoms in both rings. (c) Classify the glycosidic linkage as α or β, and use numbers to designate its location.

glucose CH_2OH CH_2OH glucose

maltose

Analysis and Solution

a. and b. The glycosidic linkage is the acetal C—O bond that joins the two monosaccharides, labeled in red. Each ring is numbered beginning at the anomeric carbon, the carbon bonded to two oxygen atoms.

acetal carbon

CH_2OH CH_2OH

c. Maltose has an α glycosidic linkage because the C—O bond is drawn down. The glycosidic linkage joins C1 of one ring to C4 of the other ring, so maltose contains a 1→4-α-glycosidic linkage.

PRACTICE PROBLEM 20.7

(a) Locate the glycosidic linkage in cellobiose. (b) Number the carbon atoms in both rings. (c) Classify the glycosidic linkage as α or β, and use numbers to designate its location.

cellobiose

More Practice: Try Problems 20.57b, c; 20.58b, c.

The hydrolysis of a disaccharide cleaves the C—O glycosidic linkage and forms two monosaccharides. For example, hydrolysis of maltose yields two molecules of glucose.

Cleave the glycosidic linkage.

maltose   +   H—OH   ⟶   glucose   +   glucose

Water is added in hydrolysis.

SAMPLE PROBLEM 20.8 DRAWING THE HYDROLYSIS PRODUCTS OF A DISACCHARIDE

Draw the products formed when the following disaccharide is hydrolyzed with water.

Analysis

Locate the glycosidic linkage, the acetal C—O bond that joins the two monosaccharides. Cleave the C—O bond by adding the elements of H_2O across the bond.

Solution

Two monosaccharides are formed by cleaving the glycosidic linkage.

PRACTICE PROBLEM 20.8

What monosaccharides are formed when cellobiose (Practice Problem 20.7) is hydrolyzed with water?

More Practice: Try Problems 20.49, 20.50, 20.57e, 20.58e.

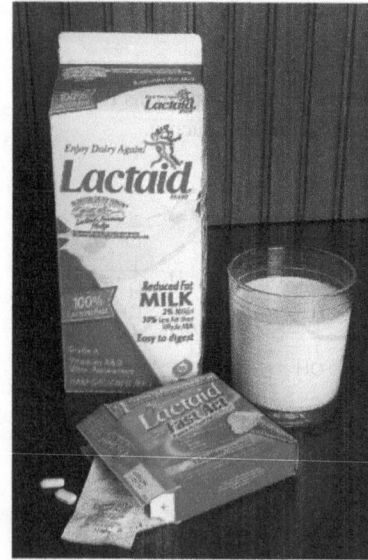

Individuals who are lactose intolerant can drink lactose-free milk. Tablets that contain the lactase enzyme can also be taken when ice cream or other milk products are ingested. ©McGraw-Hill Education/Jill Braaten, photographer

20.5A FOCUS ON HEALTH & MEDICINE
Lactose Intolerance

Lactose is the principal disaccharide found in milk from both humans and cows. Unlike many mono- and disaccharides, lactose is not appreciably sweet. Lactose consists of one galactose ring and one glucose ring, joined by a 1→4-β-glycoside bond from the anomeric carbon of galactose to C4 of glucose.

©D. Hurst/Alamy RF

Lactose is digested in the body by first cleaving the 1→4-β-glycoside bond using the enzyme *lactase*. **Individuals who are lactose intolerant no longer produce this enzyme,** and so lactose cannot be properly digested, causing abdominal cramps and diarrhea. Lactose intolerance is especially prevalent in Asian and African populations whose diets have not traditionally included milk beyond infancy.

PROBLEM 20.11

Lactose contains both an acetal and a hemiacetal. Label both functional groups. What products are formed when lactose is hydrolyzed with water?

Beano and similar products have the enzyme needed to digest raffinose, thus helping to reduce bloating and ease discomfort caused when foods that contain raffinose are ingested.
©Sara Stathas/Alamy

PROBLEM 20.12

Raffinose is a trisaccharide found in beans, cabbage, and broccoli. Because humans do not possess the enzyme needed to hydrolyze a glycosidic linkage in raffinose, it passes undigested to the large intestine, where it is fermented by bacteria, producing gas and causing flatulence. Label the acetals in raffinose.

raffinose

20.5B   FOCUS ON HEALTH & MEDICINE
Sucrose and Artificial Sweeteners

Sucrose, the disaccharide found in sugarcane and the compound generally referred to as "sugar," is the most common disaccharide in nature. It contains one glucose ring and one fructose ring. Unlike maltose and lactose, which contain only six-membered rings, sucrose contains one six-membered and one five-membered ring.

sugarcane

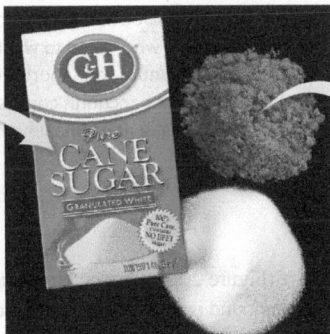

two varieties of refined sugar

sucrose

(left): ©Pixtal/age fotostock RF; (right): ©McGraw-Hill Education/Elite Images

Sucrose's pleasant sweetness has made it a widely used ingredient in baked goods, cereals, bread, and many other products. It is estimated that the average American ingests 100 lb of sucrose annually. Like other carbohydrates, however, sucrose contains many calories. To reduce caloric intake while maintaining sweetness, a variety of artificial sweeteners have been developed. These include aspartame,

Figure 20.3   Artificial Sweeteners

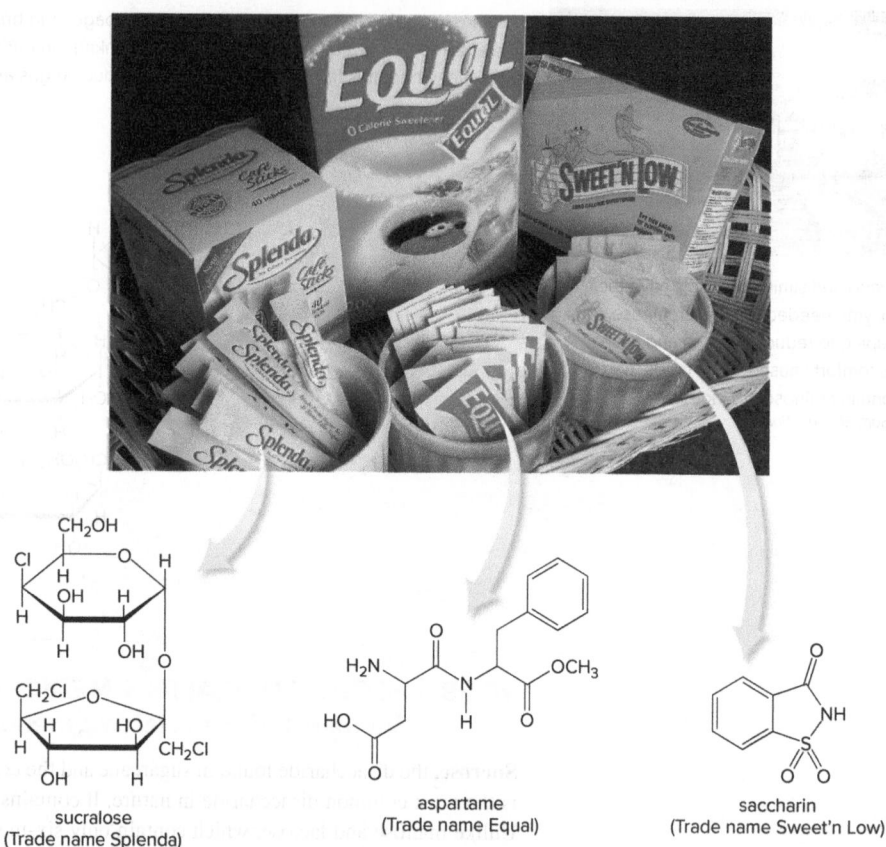

sucralose
(Trade name Splenda)

aspartame
(Trade name Equal)

saccharin
(Trade name Sweet'n Low)

The sweetness of these artificial sweeteners was discovered accidentally. The sweetness of sucralose was discovered in 1976 when a chemist misunderstood his superior, and so he *tasted* rather than *tested* his compound. Aspartame was discovered in 1965 when a chemist licked his dirty fingers in the lab and tasted its sweetness. Saccharin, the oldest known artificial sweetener, was discovered in 1879 by a chemist who failed to wash his hands after working in the lab. Saccharin was not used extensively until sugar shortages occurred during World War I. Although there were concerns in the 1970s that saccharin causes cancer, there is no proven link between cancer occurrence and saccharin intake at normal levels. *©McGraw-Hill Education/Jill Braaten, photographer*

Table 20.1 Relative Sweetness of Some Carbohydrates and Artificial Sweeteners

Compound	Relative Sweetness
Sorbitol	0.60
Glucose	0.75
Sucrose	1.00
Fructose	1.75
Aspartame	150
Saccharin	350
Sucralose	600

saccharin, and sucralose (Figure 20.3). These compounds are much sweeter than sucrose, so only a small amount of each compound is needed to achieve the same level of perceived sweetness.

A relative sweetness scale ranks the sweetness of carbohydrates and synthetic sweeteners, as shown in Table 20.1.

Aspartame (trade name NutraSweet) is used in the artificial sweetener Equal and many diet beverages. While harmless to most individuals, aspartame is hydrolyzed in the body to the amino acid phenylalanine (and other products). Infants afflicted with phenylketonuria cannot metabolize this amino acid, so it accumulates, causing mental retardation. When this condition is identified early, a diet limiting the consumption of phenylalanine (and compounds like aspartame that are converted to it) can make a normal life possible.

Rebaudioside A, a naturally occurring glycoside about 400 times sweeter than table sugar, is obtained from the leaves of the stevia plant, a shrub native to Central and South America. Rebaudioside A is sold as a natural, low-calorie sweetener under the trade name Truvia. ©*inga/Alamy*

PROBLEM 20.13

Sucralose is prepared from sucrose. Locate the acetals in sucralose. Label each alkyl halide as 1°, 2°, or 3°.

PROBLEM 20.14

Rebaudioside A is a sweet glycoside obtained from the stevia plant. Locate the three acetals in rebaudioside A.

rebaudioside A
(Trade name Truvia)
$R = C_{26}H_{39}O_6$

20.5C FOCUS ON HEALTH & MEDICINE
Human Milk Oligosaccharides

Although the benefits of breast milk to a newborn have been known for a long time, how individual components impact the health of a newborn has only recently been discovered.

Human milk oligosaccharides (HMOs), which contain three or four monosaccharides joined together, constitute a group of carbohydrates found in breast milk. 2'-Fucosyllactose is the most prevalent component, comprising about 30% of all HMOs. The two glycosidic linkages that join the three monosaccharides together are shown in red.

2'-fucosyllactose

HMOs, often called the fiber of breast milk, are not hydrolyzed by the gastric juices of the stomach, nor are they absorbed in the intestines. Nevertheless, they play a key role in the health of a

732   **Chapter 20**   Carbohydrates

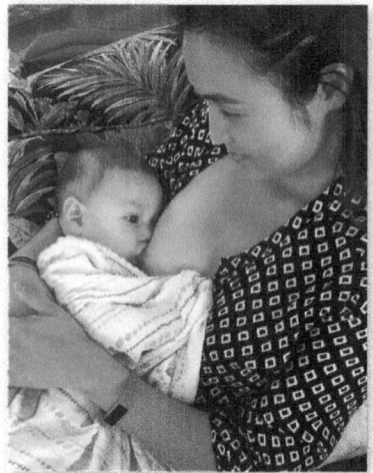

The World Health Organization recommends that children are exclusively breast fed until six months of age, and then nursed along with other forms of nutrition until a child is two years old.
©Daniel C. Smith

newborn, by helping to establish the presence of beneficial bacteria in the colon of an infant. Moreover, harmful pathogens attach to the surface of HMOs and are eliminated in the feces of the nursing infant.

Ongoing research continues to study the hundreds of unique components of human breast milk, in an effort to understand its benefits to both the mother and the child, even after infancy.

PROBLEM 20.15

Label all acetals and hemiacetals in 3-fucosyllactose, another HMO found in breast milk.

3-fucosyllactose

20.6   Polysaccharides

Polysaccharides contain three or more monosaccharides joined together. Three prevalent polysaccharides in nature are **cellulose, starch,** and **glycogen,** each of which consists of repeating glucose units joined by glycosidic bonds.

β glycosidic linkage

cellulose—repeating structure

α glycosidic linkage

starch and glycogen—repeating structure

- Cellulose contains glucose rings joined in 1→4-β-glycosidic linkages.
- Starch and glycogen contain glucose rings joined in 1→4-α-glycosidic linkages.

20.6A   Cellulose

Cellulose is found in the cell walls of nearly all plants, where it gives support and rigidity to wood, plant stems, and grass (Figure 20.4). Wood, cotton, and flax are composed largely of cellulose.

Figure 20.4   Cellulose

layers of microfibrils
in the plant cell wall

cell wall

cellulose fiber

plant cell

cellulose molecules

glucose

long chains of cellulose molecules hydrogen bonded together

©Biophoto Associates/Science Source

Cellulose is an unbranched polymer composed of repeating glucose units joined in a 1→4-β-glycosidic linkage. The β glycosidic linkages create long linear chains of cellulose molecules that stack in sheets, making an extensive three-dimensional array.

CH₂OH

CH₂OH

CH₂OH

CH₂OH

cellulose

β glycosidic linkage
(shown in blue)

In some cells, cellulose is hydrolyzed by an enzyme called a **β-glycosidase,** which cleaves all of the β glycoside bonds, forming glucose. **Humans do not possess this enzyme, and therefore *cannot* digest cellulose.** Ruminant animals, on the other hand, such as cattle, deer, and camels, have bacteria containing this enzyme in their digestive systems, so they can derive nutritional benefit from eating grass and leaves.

The outer bark of the cottonwood tree is largely the polysaccharide cellulose, while the inner bark also contains salicin (Section 17.7), a naturally occurring analgesic related to aspirin. Native Americans of the Pacific Northwest used cottonwood bark and leaves to treat wounds. Cottonwood seeds are embedded in cotton fluff that allows the seeds to be blown a large distance for dispersal. ©Daniel C. Smith

Much of the insoluble fiber in our diet is cellulose, which passes through the digestive system without being metabolized. Foods rich in cellulose include whole wheat bread, brown rice, and bran cereals. Fiber is an important component of the diet even though it gives us no nutrition; fiber adds bulk to solid waste, so that it is eliminated more readily.

20.6B   Starch

Starch is the main carbohydrate found in the seeds and roots of plants. Corn, rice, wheat, and potatoes are common foods that contain a great deal of starch. **Starch is a polymer composed of repeating glucose units joined in α glycosidic linkages.** The two common forms of starch are **amylose** and **amylopectin.**

α glycosidic linkage
(shown in red)

amylose
(the linear form of starch)

Two polysaccharide chains are connected at a branch point along one chain.

α glycosidic linkage
(shown in red)

amylopectin
(the branched form of starch)

Amylose, which comprises about 20% of starch molecules, has an unbranched skeleton of glucose molecules with **1→4-α-glycoside bonds.** Because of this linkage, an amylose chain adopts a helical arrangement, giving it a very different three-dimensional shape from the linear chains of cellulose (Figure 20.5).

Amylopectin, which comprises about 80% of starch molecules, consists of a backbone of glucose units joined in **α glycosidic bonds,** but it also contains considerable branching along the chain. The linear linkages of amylopectin are formed by **1→4-α-glycoside bonds,** similar to amylose.

Both forms of starch are water soluble. Since the OH groups in these starch molecules are not buried in a three-dimensional network, they are available for hydrogen bonding with water molecules, leading to greater water solubility than cellulose.

Both amylose and amylopectin are hydrolyzed to glucose with cleavage of the glycosidic bonds. The human digestive system has the necessary amylase enzymes needed to catalyze this process. Bread and pasta made from wheat flour, rice, and corn tortillas are all sources of starch that are readily digested.

Biodegradable foam packing peanuts can now be produced from starch obtained from grains. Since they are composed of water-soluble starch, they can be mixed with water and washed down the drain for disposal. ©StarchTech, Inc.

PROBLEM 20.16

Label all acetal carbons in the structure of amylopectin drawn at the beginning of Section 20.6B.

Figure 20.5   Starch—Amylose and Amylopectin

wheat kernels

wheat stalks

amylopectin

amylose

(left): ©anopdesignstock/Getty Images RF; (right): ©SafakOguz/Getty Images RF

20.6C Glycogen

Glycogen is the major form in which polysaccharides are stored in animals. Glycogen, a polymer of glucose containing **α glycosidic bonds,** has a branched structure similar to amylopectin, but the branching is much more extensive (Figure 20.6).

Figure 20.6   Glycogen

branching

glycogen in liver cells

glycogen

©Dennis Kunkel Microscopy, Inc./Science Source

Glycogen is stored principally in the liver and muscle. When glucose is needed for energy in the cell, glucose units are hydrolyzed from the ends of the glycogen polymer, and then further metabolized with the release of energy. Because glycogen has a highly branched structure, there are many glucose units at the ends of the branches that can be cleaved whenever the body needs them.

PROBLEM 20.17

Cellulose is water *in*soluble, despite its many OH groups. Based on its three-dimensional structure, why do you think this is so?

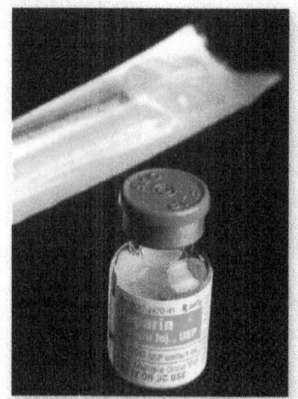

Injections of heparin in an intravenous line keep the line from clogging with blood.
©Jeffrey Sauger/Bloomberg/Getty Images

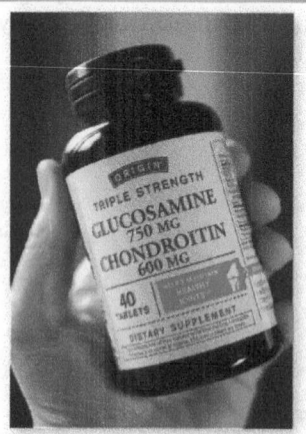

Both chondroitin and glucosamine are sold as dietary supplements for individuals suffering from osteoarthritis. Ongoing research is examining the role of these supplements in replacing and rebuilding lost joint cartilage in the hope of halting or reversing the progression of arthritis.
©McGraw-Hill Education/Jill Braaten, photographer

20.7 FOCUS ON THE HUMAN BODY
Useful Carbohydrate Derivatives

Many other simple and complex carbohydrates with useful properties exist in the biological world. Several are derived from monosaccharides that contain an amino (NH_2) or amide ($NHCOCH_3$) group in place of an OH group. Examples include D-glucosamine, the most abundant amino sugar in nature, and N-acetyl-D-glucosamine (NAG). Other carbohydrates are derived from D-glucuronate, which contains a carboxylate anion, COO^-, in place of the CH_2OH group of the typical monosaccharide skeleton.

D-glucosamine   N-acetyl-D-glucosamine   D-glucuronate

20.7A Glycosaminoglycans

Glycosaminoglycans (GAGs) are a group of unbranched carbohydrates derived from alternating amino sugar and glucuronate units. Glycosaminoglycans form a gel-like matrix that acts as a lubricant, making them key components in connective tissue and joints.

Examples include **hyaluronate,** which is found in the extracellular fluid that lubricates joints and the vitreous humor of the eye; **chondroitin,** a component of cartilage and tendons; and **heparin,** which is stored in the mast cells of the liver and other organs and prevents blood clotting (Figure 20.7). While the monosaccharide rings of hyaluronate and chondroitin are joined by β glycosidic linkages (shown in blue), those of heparin are joined by α glycosidic linkages (shown in red).

PROBLEM 20.18

Classify the glycosidic linkages in chondroitin and heparin (Figure 20.7) as α or β, and use numbers to designate their location.

Figure 20.7

Glycosaminoglycans

hyaluronate

heparin

chondroitin

Hyaluronates form viscous solutions that act as lubricants in the fluid around joints. They also give the vitreous humor of the eye its gelatin-like consistency. Chondroitin strengthens cartilage, tendons, and the walls of blood vessels. Heparin is an anticoagulant.

20.7B   Chitin

Chitin, the second most abundant carbohydrate polymer, is a polysaccharide formed from *N*-acetyl-D-glucosamine units joined together in **1→4-β-glycosidic linkages.** Chitin is identical in structure to cellulose, except that each OH group at C2 is now replaced by $NHCOCH_3$. The exoskeletons of lobsters, crabs, and shrimp are composed of chitin. Like cellulose, chitin chains are held together by an extensive network of hydrogen bonds, forming water-insoluble sheets.

β glycosidic linkage (shown in blue)

chitin

hydrolysis

D-glucosamine

The rigidity of a crab shell is due to chitin, a high molecular weight carbohydrate molecule. Much of the D-glucosamine sold in over-the-counter dietary supplements comes from shellfish. ©*Maskot/Image Source RF*

Chitin-based coatings have found several commercial applications, such as extending the shelf life of fruits. Processing plants now convert the shells of crabs, lobsters, and shrimp into chitin and various derivatives for use in many consumer products. Complete hydrolysis of the glycoside and amide bonds in chitin forms the dietary supplement D-glucosamine.

PROBLEM 20.19

Suppose that chitin contained α glycosidic linkages. Draw a portion of the resulting polysaccharide that contains four *N*-acetyl-D-glucosamine units joined together.

20.8   FOCUS ON THE HUMAN BODY
Blood Type

Human blood is classified into one of four types using the ABO system proposed in the early 1900s by Karl Landsteiner. There are four blood types—A, B, AB, and O. An individual's blood type is determined by three or four monosaccharides attached to a membrane protein of red blood cells. These monosaccharides include:

D-galactose   L-fucose   *N*-acetyl-D-glucosamine   *N*-acetyl-D-galactosamine

Each blood type is associated with a different carbohydrate structure, as shown in Figure 20.8. Three monosaccharides occur in all blood types—*N*-acetyl-D-glucosamine, D-galactose, and L-fucose. Type A blood contains a fourth monosaccharide, *N*-acetyl-D-galactosamine, and type B blood contains an additional D-galactose unit. Type AB blood has both type A and type B carbohydrates.

The short polysaccharide chains distinguish one type of red blood cell from another, and signal the cells about foreign viruses, bacteria, and other agents. When a foreign substance enters the blood, the body's immune system uses antibodies to attack and destroy the invading substance so that it does the host organism no harm.

Knowing an individual's blood type is necessary before receiving a blood transfusion. Because the blood of an individual may contain antibodies to another blood type, the types of blood that can be given to a patient are often limited. An individual with blood type A produces antibodies to type B blood, and an individual with blood type B produces antibodies to type A blood. Type AB blood contains no antibodies to other blood types, while type O blood contains antibodies to both types A and B. As a result:

- Individuals with type O blood are called *universal donors* because no antibodies to type O are produced by those with types A, B, and AB blood. Type O blood can be given to individuals of any blood type.

- Individuals with type AB blood are called *universal recipients* because their blood contains no antibodies to blood types A, B, or O. Individuals with type AB blood can receive blood of any type.

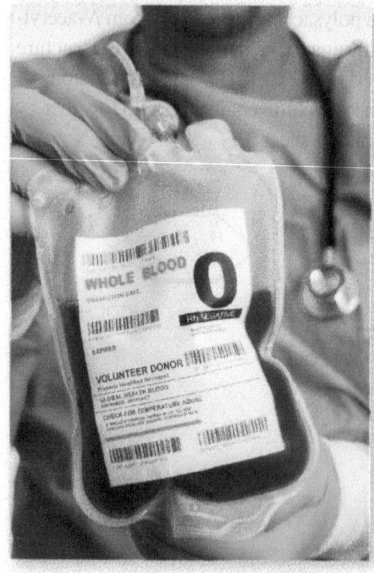

The blood type of a blood donor and recipient must be compatible, so donated blood is clearly labeled with the donor's blood type. ©DieterMeyrl/Getty ImagesRF

Figure 20.8 Carbohydrates and Blood Types

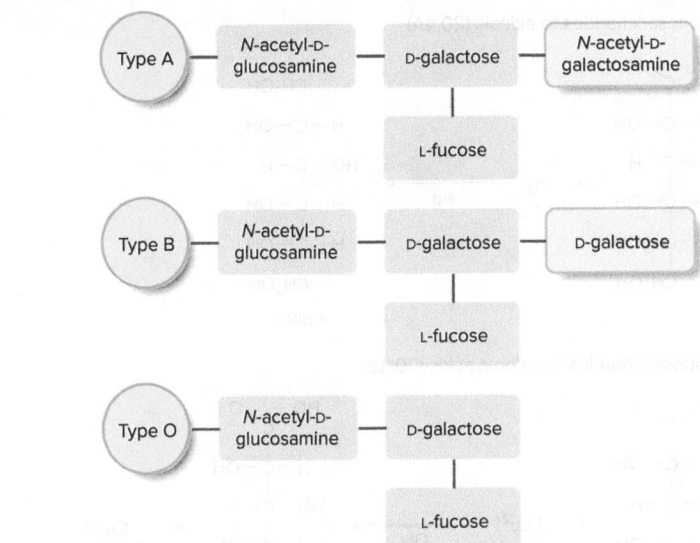

Each blood type is characterized by a different polysaccharide that is covalently bonded to a membrane protein of the red blood cell. There are three different carbohydrate sequences, one each for A, B, and O blood types. Blood type AB contains the sequences for both blood type A and blood type B.

Table 20.2 Compatibility Chart of Blood Types

Blood Type	Can Receive Blood Type:	Can Donate to Blood Type:
A	A, O	A, AB
B	B, O	B, AB
AB	A, B, AB, O	AB
O	O	A, B, AB, O

Table 20.2 lists what blood types can be safely given to an individual. Blood must be carefully screened to make sure that the blood types of the donor and recipient are compatible. Should the wrong blood type be administered, antibodies of the immune system will attack the foreign red blood cells, causing them to clump together, which can block blood vessels and even result in death.

PROBLEM 20.20

How do *N*-acetyl-D-glucosamine and *N*-acetyl-D-galactosamine differ in structure? Are these two compounds constitutional isomers or stereoisomers? Explain your choice.

CHAPTER HIGHLIGHTS

KEY TERMS

Alditol (20.4)
Aldonic acid (20.4)
Aldose (20.2)
α Anomer (20.3)
β Anomer (20.3)
Anomeric carbon (20.3)
Benedict's reagent (20.4)
Carbohydrate (20.1)
Disaccharide (20.1)

α Glycoside (20.5)
β Glycoside (20.5)
Glycosidic linkage (20.5)
Haworth projection (20.3)
Hexose (20.2)
Ketose (20.2)
Monosaccharide (20.1)
D Monosaccharide (20.2)
L Monosaccharide (20.2)

Mutarotation (20.3)
Nonreducing sugar (20.4)
Pentose (20.2)
Polysaccharide (20.1)
Reducing sugar (20.4)
Tetrose (20.2)
Triose (20.2)

KEY REACTIONS

[1] Reduction of monosaccharides to alditols (20.4A)

alditol

[2] Oxidation of monosaccharides to aldonic acids (20.4B)

aldonic acid

[3] Hydrolysis of disaccharides (20.5)

KEY CONCEPTS

❶ What are the three major types of carbohydrates? (20.1)

- Monosaccharides, which cannot be hydrolyzed to simpler compounds, generally have three to six carbons with a carbonyl group at either the terminal carbon or the carbon adjacent to it. Generally, all other carbons have OH groups bonded to them.
- Disaccharides are composed of two monosaccharides.
- Polysaccharides are composed of three or more monosaccharides.

❷ What are the major structural features of monosaccharides? (20.2)

- Monosaccharides with a carbonyl group at C1 are called aldoses, and those with a carbonyl at C2 are called ketoses. Generally, all other carbons have OH groups bonded to them. The terms triose, tetrose, and so forth are used to indicate the number of carbons in the chain.
- The acyclic form of monosaccharides is drawn with Fischer projection formulas. A D sugar has the OH group of the chirality

center farthest from the carbonyl on the right side. An L sugar has the OH group of the chirality center farthest from the carbonyl on the left side.

❸ How are the cyclic forms of monosaccharides drawn? (20.3)

- In aldohexoses the OH group on C5 reacts with the aldehyde carbonyl to give two cyclic hemiacetals called anomers. The acetal carbon is called the anomeric carbon. The α anomer has the OH group on the new chirality center drawn down for a D sugar, and the β anomer has the OH group drawn up.

α anomer   β anomer

4 **What reduction and oxidation products are formed from monosaccharides? (20.4)**

- Monosaccharides are reduced to alditols with H_2 and Pd.
- Monosaccharides are oxidized to aldonic acids with Benedict's reagent. Sugars that are oxidized with Benedict's reagent are called reducing sugars.

5 **What are the major structural features of disaccharides? (20.5)**

- Disaccharides contain two monosaccharide units joined by an acetal C—O bond called a glycosidic linkage. An α glycoside has the glycosidic linkage oriented down, and a β glycoside has the glycosidic linkage oriented up.
- Disaccharides are hydrolyzed to two monosaccharides by the cleavage of the glycosidic C—O bond with water.
- Lactose (the principal disaccharide in milk) and sucrose (table sugar) are common disaccharides.

6 **What are the differences in the polysaccharides cellulose, starch, and glycogen? (20.6)**

- Cellulose, starch, and glycogen are all polymers of the monosaccharide glucose.
- Cellulose is an unbranched polymer composed of repeating glucose units joined in 1→4-β-glycosidic linkages. Cellulose forms long chains that stack in three-dimensional sheets. The human digestive system does not contain the needed enzyme to metabolize cellulose.
- There are two forms of starch—amylose, which is an unbranched polymer; and amylopectin, which is a branched polysaccharide polymer. Both forms contain 1→4-α-glycosidic

linkages, and the polymer winds in a helical arrangement. Starch is digestible because the human digestive system has the needed amylase enzyme to catalyze hydrolysis.

- Glycogen resembles amylopectin but is more extensively branched. Glycogen is the major form in which polysaccharides are stored in animals.

7 **Give examples of some carbohydrate derivatives that contain amino groups, amides, or carboxylate anions. (20.7)**

- Glycosaminoglycans are a group of unbranched carbohydrates derived from amino sugar and glucuronate units. Examples include hyaluronate, which forms a gel-like matrix in joints and the vitreous humor of the eye; chondroitin, which is a component of cartilage and tendons; and heparin, an anticoagulant.
- Chitin, a polymer of N-acetyl-D-glucosamine, forms the hard exoskeletons of crabs, lobsters, and shrimp.

8 **What role do carbohydrates play in determining blood type? (20.8)**

- Human blood type—A, B, AB, or O—is determined by three or four monosaccharides attached to a membrane protein on the surface of red blood cells. There are three different carbohydrate sequences, one for each of the A, B, and O blood types. Blood type AB contains the sequences for both blood type A and blood type B. Since the blood of an individual may contain antibodies to another blood type, blood type must be known before receiving a transfusion.

PROBLEMS

Selected in-chapter and odd-numbered end-of-chapter problems have brief answers in Appendix B. The *Student Study Guide and Solutions Manual* contains detailed solutions to all in-chapter and odd-numbered end-of-chapter problems, as well as additional worked examples and a chapter self-test.

Monosaccharides

20.21 Draw the structure of each type of compound.
- a. an L-aldopentose
- b. a D-aldotetrose
- c. a five-carbon alditol

20.22 Draw the structure of each type of compound.
- a. a D-aldotriose
- b. an L-ketohexose
- c. a four-carbon aldonic acid

20.23 Classify each monosaccharide by the type of carbonyl group and the number of carbons in the chain.

a.
```
    H   O
     \ //
      C
      |
  HO—C—H
      |
  HO—C—H
      |
    CH₂OH
```

b.
```
    H   O
     \ //
      C
      |
  HO—C—H
      |
  HO—C—H
      |
  HO—C—H
      |
   H—C—OH
      |
    CH₂OH
```

c.
```
    CH₂OH
      |
      C=O
      |
   H—C—OH
      |
  HO—C—H
      |
    CH₂OH
```

20.24 Classify each monosaccharide by the type of carbonyl group and the number of carbons in the chain.

a.
```
    H   O
     \ //
      C
      |
  HO—C—H
      |
    CH₂OH
```

b.
```
    H   O
     \ //
      C
      |
   H—C—OH
      |
  HO—C—H
      |
  HO—C—H
      |
    CH₂OH
```

c.
```
    H   O
     \ //
      C
      |
   H—C—OH
      |
   H—C—OH
      |
  HO—C—H
      |
  HO—C—H
      |
    CH₂OH
```

20.25 (a) Classify each monosaccharide by the type of carbonyl group and number of carbons in the chain. (b) Locate the chirality centers in each compound.

A   B

742   **Chapter 20**   Carbohydrates

20.26 (a) Classify each monosaccharide by the type of carbonyl group and number of carbons in the chain. (b) Locate the chirality centers in each compound.

C   **D**

20.27 (a) Draw a Fischer projection of the monosaccharide depicted in the ball-and-stick model and label it as a D or L sugar. (b) Classify the monosaccharide by the type of carbonyl group and number of carbons it contains.

20.28 (a) Draw a Fischer projection of the monosaccharide depicted in the ball-and-stick model and label it as a D or L sugar. (b) Classify the monosaccharide by the type of carbonyl group and number of carbons it contains.

20.29 For each compound in Problem 20.23: [1] label all the chirality centers; [2] classify the compound as a D or L monosaccharide; [3] draw the enantiomer; [4] draw a Fischer projection.

20.30 For each compound in Problem 20.24: [1] label all the chirality centers; [2] classify the compound as a D or L monosaccharide; [3] draw the enantiomer; [4] draw a Fischer projection.

20.31 Consider monosaccharides **A**, **B**, and **C**.

$$
\begin{array}{ccc}
\text{H}\diagdown\!\!\diagup\!\!^{\text{O}}_{\text{C}} & \text{H}\diagdown\!\!\diagup\!\!^{\text{O}}_{\text{C}} & \text{CH}_2\text{OH} \\
\text{H}-\text{C}-\text{OH} & \text{H}-\text{C}-\text{OH} & \text{C}=\text{O} \\
\text{H}-\text{C}-\text{OH} & \text{HO}-\text{C}-\text{H} & \text{H}-\text{C}-\text{OH} \\
\text{CH}_2\text{OH} & \text{CH}_2\text{OH} & \text{CH}_2\text{OH} \\
\textbf{A} & \textbf{B} & \textbf{C}
\end{array}
$$

a. Which two monosaccharides are stereoisomers?
b. Identify two compounds that are constitutional isomers.
c. Draw the enantiomer of **B**.
d. Draw a Fischer projection for **A**.

20.32 Consider monosaccharides **D**, **E**, and **F**.

$$
\begin{array}{ccc}
\text{H}\diagdown\!\!\diagup\!\!^{\text{O}}_{\text{C}} & \text{CH}_2\text{OH} & \text{H}\diagdown\!\!\diagup\!\!^{\text{O}}_{\text{C}} \\
\text{H}-\text{C}-\text{OH} & \text{C}=\text{O} & \text{HO}-\text{C}-\text{H} \\
\text{H}-\text{C}-\text{OH} & \text{HO}-\text{C}-\text{H} & \text{HO}-\text{C}-\text{H} \\
\text{H}-\text{C}-\text{OH} & \text{HO}-\text{C}-\text{H} & \text{H}-\text{C}-\text{OH} \\
\text{CH}_2\text{OH} & \text{CH}_2\text{OH} & \text{CH}_2\text{OH} \\
\textbf{D} & \textbf{E} & \textbf{F}
\end{array}
$$

a. Which two monosaccharides are stereoisomers?
b. Identify two compounds that are constitutional isomers.
c. Draw the enantiomer of **F**.
d. Draw a Fischer projection for **D**.

20.33 Using Haworth projections, draw the α and β anomers of the following D monosaccharide.

$$
\begin{array}{c}
\text{H}\diagdown\!\!\diagup\!\!^{\text{O}}_{\text{C}} \\
\text{HO}-\text{C}-\text{H} \\
\text{H}-\text{C}-\text{OH} \\
\text{HO}-\text{C}-\text{H} \\
\text{H}-\text{C}-\text{OH} \\
\text{CH}_2\text{OH}
\end{array}
$$

20.34 Using Haworth projections, draw the α and β anomers of the following D monosaccharide.

$$
\begin{array}{c}
\text{H}\diagdown\!\!\diagup\!\!^{\text{O}}_{\text{C}} \\
\text{H}-\text{C}-\text{OH} \\
\text{H}-\text{C}-\text{OH} \\
\text{HO}-\text{C}-\text{H} \\
\text{H}-\text{C}-\text{OH} \\
\text{CH}_2\text{OH}
\end{array}
$$

20.35 (a) Label the hemiacetal carbon in the given monosaccharide, and identify the hydroxyl group on the anomeric carbon. (b) Label all other OH groups as 1°, 2°, or 3°.

20.36 (a) Label the hemiacetal carbon in the given monosaccharide, and identify the hydroxyl group on the anomeric carbon. (b) Label all other OH groups as 1°, 2°, or 3°.

20.37 Consider the following cyclic monosaccharide.

CH_2OH

a. Label the hemiacetal carbon.
b. Label the monosaccharide as an α or β anomer.
c. Draw the other anomer.
d. Draw a stereoisomer that differs in the arrangement of substituents at C2.

20.38 Consider the following cyclic monosaccharide.

CH_2OH

a. Label the hemiacetal carbon.
b. Label the monosaccharide as an α or β anomer.
c. Draw the other anomer.
d. Draw a stereoisomer that differs in the arrangement of substituents at C3.

20.39 For each monosaccharide: [1] label all acetal and hemiacetal carbons; [2] label the anomeric carbon; [3] designate the compound as an α or β anomer.

a. CH_2OH b. CH_2OH

20.40 For each monosaccharide: [1] label all acetal and hemiacetal carbons; [2] label the anomeric carbon; [3] designate the compound as an α or β anomer.

a. CH_2OH b. CH_2OH

20.41 Aldopentoses exist as five-membered rings in their cyclic forms. For each aldopentose: [1] label the hemiacetal carbon; [2] designate the monosaccharide as an α or β anomer.

a. CH_2OH b. CH_2OH

20.42 Aldopentoses exist as five-membered rings in their cyclic forms. For each aldopentose: [1] label the hemiacetal carbon; [2] designate the monosaccharide as an α or β anomer.

a. CH_2OH b. CH_2OH

Reactions of Carbohydrates

20.43 Label each compound as a monosaccharide, an aldonic acid, or an alditol.

a.

c.

b.

20.44 Label each compound as a monosaccharide, an aldonic acid, or an alditol.

a.

c.

b.

20.45 Draw the organic products formed when each monosaccharide is treated with each of the following reagents: [1] H_2, Pd; [2] Cu^{2+}, OH^-.

20.46 Draw the organic products formed when each monosaccharide is treated with each of the following reagents: [1] H_2, Pd; [2] Cu^{2+}, OH^-.

a. b. c.

20.47 What product is formed when each compound is treated with Benedict's reagent?

a.

b.

744   **Chapter 20**   Carbohydrates

20.48 What product is formed when each compound is treated with Benedict's reagent?

a.

```
      H   O
       \ //
        C
        |
  HO—C—H
        |
  HO—C—H
        |
   H—C—OH
        |
      CH₂OH
```

b.

```
      CH₂OH
        |
        C=O
        |
   H—C—OH
        |
  HO—C—H
        |
      CH₂OH
```

20.49 What monosaccharides are formed when each disaccharide is hydrolyzed?

a.
b.

20.50 What monosaccharides are formed when each disaccharide is hydrolyzed?

a.
b.

Disaccharides and Polysaccharides

20.51 Identify polysaccharides **A** and **B** as either amylopectin or glycogen. Then decide if each of the following statements refers to one, both, or neither of the polysaccharides.

a. This polysaccharide contains 1→4-α-glycosidic bonds.
b. This polysaccharide is stored in the liver.
c. This polysaccharide is found in bread and pasta.
d. This polysaccharide is composed of galactose units.

20.52 Identify polysaccharides **C** and **D** as either amylose or cellulose. Then decide if each of the following statements refers to one, both, or neither of the polysaccharides.

a. This polysaccharide contains 1→4-α-glycosidic bonds.
b. This polysaccharide is not digestible by humans.
c. This polysaccharide is stored in the liver and muscle.
d. This polysaccharide is composed of glucose units.

20.53 If a monosaccharide is represented by a single blue sphere, which of the following representations corresponds to (a) lactose; (b) cellulose; (c) amylopectin?

20.54 If a monosaccharide is represented by a single blue sphere, which of the following representations corresponds to (a) a disaccharide; (b) glycogen; (c) amylose?

20.55 Draw the structure of a disaccharide that contains two six-membered rings and an α glycosidic linkage.

20.56 Draw the structure of a disaccharide that contains one six-membered ring and one five-membered ring as well as a β glycosidic linkage.

20.57 Consider the disaccharide isomaltose.

isomaltose

a. Label any acetal and hemiacetal in isomaltose.
b. Number each monosaccharide ring.
c. Classify the glycosidic linkage as α or β, and use numbers to designate its location.
d. Is the hemiacetal drawn as an α or β anomer?
e. What monosaccharides are formed when isomaltose is hydrolyzed?

20.58 Consider the disaccharide sophorose.

sophorose

a. Label any acetal and hemiacetal in sophorose.
b. Number each monosaccharide ring.
c. Classify the glycosidic linkage as α or β, and use numbers to designate its location.
d. Is the hemiacetal drawn as an α or β anomer?
e. What monosaccharides are formed when sophorose is hydrolyzed?

20.59 Draw the structure of a disaccharide formed from two galactose units joined by a 1→4-β-glycosidic linkage. (The cyclic structure of galactose appears in Sample Problem 20.3.)

20.60 Draw the structure of a disaccharide formed from two mannose units joined by a 1→4-α-glycosidic linkage. (The cyclic structure of mannose appears in Section 20.3B.)

20.61 In what ways are cellulose and amylose similar? How do the structures of cellulose and amylose differ?

20.62 In what ways are amylopectin and glycogen similar? How do the structures of amylopectin and glycogen differ?

20.63 Draw a short segment of a polysaccharide that contains three galactose units joined together in 1→4-α-glycosidic linkages. (The cyclic structure of galactose appears in Sample Problem 20.3.)

20.64 Draw a short segment of a polysaccharide that contains three mannose units joined together in 1→4-β-glycosidic linkages. (The cyclic structure of mannose appears in Section 20.3B.)

General Questions

20.65 What is the major disaccharide or polysaccharide in each of the following items?

a.   b.   c.

(a): ©FoodCollection/StockFood RF; (b): ©Uppercut Images/SuperStock RF; (c): ©Rachel Weill/UpperCut Images/Getty Images RF

20.66 What is the major disaccharide or polysaccharide in each of the following items?

(a): ©McGraw-Hill Education/Andrew Resek, photographer; (b): ©McGraw-Hill Education/Mark Steinmetz, photographer; (c): ©Purestock/Getty Images RF

20.67 Consider the following monosaccharide.

a. Is the monosaccharide a D or L sugar?
b. Classify the monosaccharide by the type of carbonyl and the number of atoms in the chain.
c. Draw the enantiomer.
d. Label the chirality centers.
e. Draw the α anomer of the cyclic form.
f. What product is formed when the monosaccharide is treated with Benedict's reagent?
g. What product is formed when the monosaccharide is treated with H_2 and Pd?
h. Label the monosaccharide as a reducing or nonreducing sugar.

20.68 Consider the following monosaccharide.

a. Is the monosaccharide a D or L sugar?
b. Classify the monosaccharide by the type of carbonyl and the number of atoms in the chain.
c. Draw the enantiomer.
d. Label the chirality centers.
e. Draw the β anomer of the cyclic form.
f. What product is formed when the monosaccharide is treated with Benedict's reagent?
g. What product is formed when the monosaccharide is treated with H_2 and Pd?
h. Label the monosaccharide as a reducing or nonreducing sugar.

746   **Chapter 20**   Carbohydrates

Applications

20.69   Describe the difference between lactose intolerance and galactosemia.

20.70   Explain why cellulose is a necessary component of our diet even though we don't digest it.

20.71   Explain why fructose is called a reduced calorie sweetener while sucralose is called an artificial sweetener.

20.72   How do oxidation reactions help an individual with diabetes monitor blood glucose levels?

20.73   Why can an individual with type A blood receive only blood types A and O, but he or she can donate to individuals with either type A or AB blood?

20.74   Why can an individual with type B blood receive only blood types B and O, but he or she can donate to individuals with either type B or AB blood?

20.75   Would you predict chitin to be digestible by humans? Explain why or why not.

20.76   Why can horses derive nutritional value from eating grass but humans cannot?

20.77   Name three glycosaminoglycans and their roles in the body.

20.78   Why is chitin water insoluble but the *N*-acetyl-D-glucosamine from which it is made water soluble?

CHALLENGE PROBLEMS

20.79   In much the same way that aldoses are reduced with H_2 and Pd, 2-ketohexoses are also reduced. One difference occurs, however, in that two products are formed on reduction of 2-ketohexoses. Draw the two products formed when fructose (Section 20.2C) is reduced, and label the products as stereoisomers, constitutional isomers, or anomers. Explain your choice.

20.80   Convert each cyclic form to an acyclic monosaccharide.

a.   b.

21

Whales have a high concentration of the protein myoglobin in their muscles. Myoglobin binds oxygen, so it serves as an oxygen reservoir while the whale is submerged for long periods of time.
©Image Source/Alamy RF

Amino Acids, Proteins, and Enzymes

CHAPTER OUTLINE

21.1 Introduction

21.2 Amino Acids

21.3 Acid–Base Behavior of Amino Acids

21.4 Peptides

21.5 FOCUS ON THE HUMAN BODY: Biologically Active Peptides

21.6 Proteins

21.7 FOCUS ON THE HUMAN BODY: Common Proteins

21.8 Protein Hydrolysis and Denaturation

21.9 Enzymes—Characteristics and Classification

21.10 How Enzymes Work

21.11 FOCUS ON HEALTH & MEDICINE: Using Enzymes to Diagnose and Treat Diseases

CHAPTER GOALS

In this chapter you will learn how to:

1. Identify the general structural features of amino acids

2. Describe the acid–base properties of amino acids

3. Draw simple peptides from individual amino acids, and label the N- and C-terminal amino acids

4. Give examples of simple biologically active peptides

5. Describe the characteristics of the primary, secondary, tertiary, and quaternary structure of proteins

6. Describe the features of fibrous proteins like α-keratin and collagen

7. Describe the features of globular proteins like hemoglobin and myoglobin

8. Draw the products of protein hydrolysis

9. Describe protein denaturation

10. Describe the main features of enzymes and classify an enzyme into one of six categories

11. Discuss three types of enzyme inhibitors

12. Describe the use of enzymes to diagnose and treat disease

Why Study
Amino Acids, Proteins,
and Enzymes?

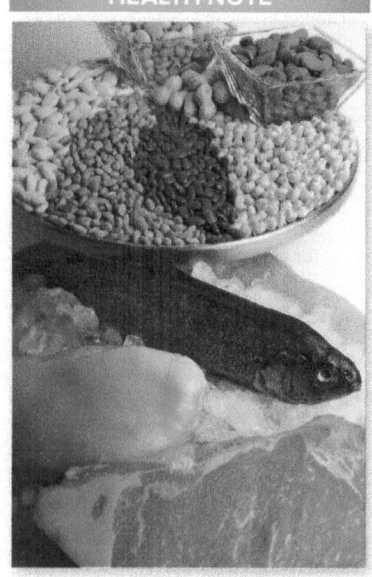

Meat, fish, beans, and nuts are all
high-protein foods. ©Jill Braaten RF

O f the four major groups of biomolecules—lipids, carbohydrates, proteins, and nucleic
acids—proteins have the widest array of functions. **Keratin** and **collagen,** for example,
form long insoluble fibers, giving strength and support to tissues. Hair, horns, hooves, and
fingernails are all made up of keratin. **Collagen** is found in bone, connective tissue, tendons,
and cartilage. **Membrane proteins** transport small organic molecules and ions across cell
membranes. **Insulin,** the hormone that regulates blood glucose levels, and **hemoglobin,** which
transports oxygen from the lungs to tissues, are proteins. **Enzymes** are proteins that catalyze
and regulate all aspects of cellular function. In Chapter 21 we discuss proteins and their
primary components, the amino acids.

21.1   Introduction

Proteins **are biomolecules that contain many amide bonds, formed by joining amino acids**
together.

$$
H_2N-\overset{\overset{\displaystyle H}{|}}{\underset{\underset{\displaystyle R}{|}}{C}}-\overset{\overset{\displaystyle O}{\|}}{C}-OH \longrightarrow \quad -N-CH-C-N-CH-C-N-CH-C-N-CH-C-
$$

amino acid   protein
[Amide bonds are shown in red.]

The word *protein* comes from the Greek *proteios* meaning "of first importance." Proteins occur
widely in the human body, accounting for approximately 50% of its dry weight (Figure 21.1).
Fibrous proteins, like keratin in hair, skin, and nails and collagen in connective tissue, give
support and structure to tissues and cells. Protein hormones and enzymes regulate the body's
metabolism. Transport proteins carry substances through the blood, and storage proteins store
elements and ions in organs. Contractile proteins control muscle movements, and immunoglobu-
lins are proteins that defend the body against foreign substances.

Figure 21.1   Proteins in the Human Body

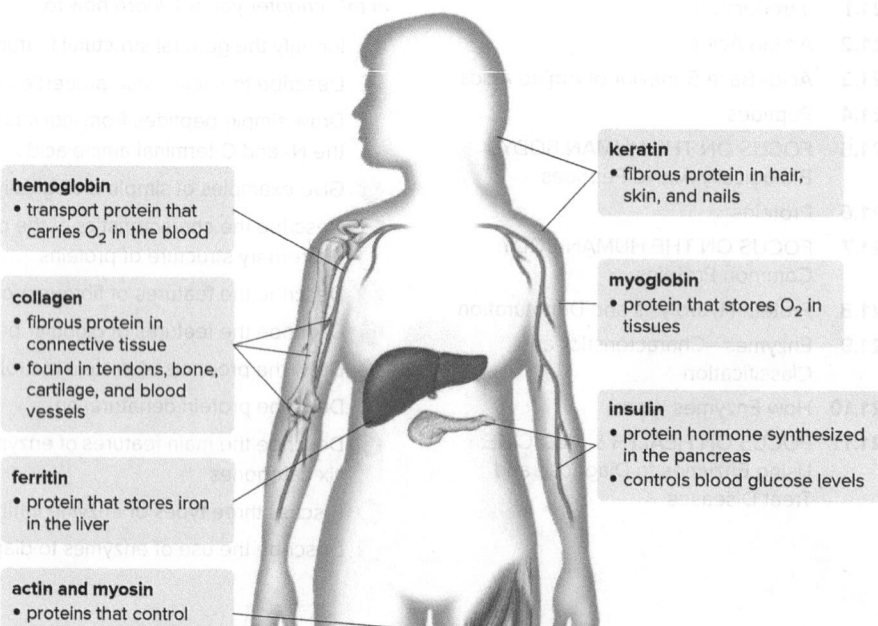

hemoglobin
• transport protein that
carries O$_2$ in the blood

collagen
• fibrous protein in
connective tissue
• found in tendons, bone,
cartilage, and blood
vessels

ferritin
• protein that stores iron
in the liver

actin and myosin
• proteins that control
muscle contractions

keratin
• fibrous protein in hair,
skin, and nails

myoglobin
• protein that stores O$_2$ in
tissues

insulin
• protein hormone synthesized
in the pancreas
• controls blood glucose levels

Unlike lipids and carbohydrates, which the body stores for use when needed, protein is not stored, so it must be consumed on a daily basis. The current recommended daily intake for adults is 0.8 g of protein per kg of body weight. Since children need protein for both growth and maintenance, the recommended daily intake is higher, as shown in Table 21.1. The average protein intake in the United States is often twice what is necessary.

21.2 Amino Acids

To understand protein properties and structure, we must first learn about the amino acids that compose them.

21.2A General Features of Amino Acids

Amino acids contain two functional groups—an amino group (NH$_2$) and a carboxyl group (COOH). In most naturally occurring amino acids, the amino group is bonded to the α carbon, the carbon adjacent to the carbonyl group (Section 17.2), making them **α-amino acids.**

α-amino acid

glycine
the simplest amino acid

The 20 amino acids that occur naturally in proteins differ in the identity of the R group bonded to the α carbon. The R group is called the **side chain** of the amino acid. The simplest amino acid, called **glycine,** has R = H. Other side chains may be simple alkyl groups, or have additional functional groups such as OH, SH, COOH, or NH$_2$. Table 21.2 lists the structures of the 20 common amino acids that occur in proteins.

- Amino acids with an additional COOH group in the side chain are called acidic amino acids.
- Those with an additional basic N atom in the side chain are called basic amino acids.
- All others are neutral amino acids.

All amino acids have common names, which are abbreviated by a three-letter or one-letter designation. For example, glycine is often written as the three-letter abbreviation **Gly,** or the one-letter abbreviation **G.** These abbreviations are also given in Table 21.2.

Amino acids never exist in nature as neutral molecules with all uncharged atoms. Because amino acids contain a base (NH$_2$ group) and an acid (COOH), proton transfer from the acid to the base forms a salt called a **zwitterion,** which contains both a positive and a negative charge. These salts have high melting points and are water soluble.

The acid–base chemistry of amino acids is discussed in greater detail in Section 21.3. The structures in Table 21.2 show the charged form of the amino acids at the physiological pH of the blood.

This neutral form of an amino acid does **not** exist.

proton transfer

(+) and (−) charges in the same compound

zwitterion

a **salt**

This salt is the neutral form of an amino acid.

Table 21.1 Recommended Daily Protein Intake

Group	Daily Protein Intake (g protein/kg body weight)
Children (1–3 years)	1.1
Children (4–13 years)	0.95
Children (14–18 years)	0.85
Adult	0.8

Source: Data from U.S. Food and Drug Administration.

Humans can synthesize only 10 of the 20 amino acids needed for proteins. The remaining 10, called **essential amino acids,** must be obtained from the diet and consumed on a regular, almost daily basis. Diets that include animal products readily supply all of the needed amino acids.

Table 21.2 The 20 Common Naturally Occurring Amino Acids

	Neutral Amino Acids				
Name	**Structure**	**Abbreviations**	**Name**	**Structure**	**Abbreviations**
Alanine	$H_3\overset{+}{N}-\underset{\underset{CH_3}{\vert}}{\overset{\overset{H}{\vert}}{C}}-COO^-$	Ala A	Phenylalanine*	$H_3\overset{+}{N}-\underset{\underset{CH_2}{\vert}}{\overset{\overset{H}{\vert}}{C}}-COO^-$	Phe F
Asparagine	$H_3\overset{+}{N}-\underset{\underset{CH_2CONH_2}{\vert}}{\overset{\overset{H}{\vert}}{C}}-COO^-$	Asn N	Proline	⌏$-COO^-$	Pro P
Cysteine	$H_3\overset{+}{N}-\underset{\underset{CH_2SH}{\vert}}{\overset{\overset{H}{\vert}}{C}}-COO^-$	Cys C	Serine	$H_3\overset{+}{N}-\underset{\underset{CH_2OH}{\vert}}{\overset{\overset{H}{\vert}}{C}}-COO^-$	Ser S
Glutamine	$H_3\overset{+}{N}-\underset{\underset{CH_2CH_2CONH_2}{\vert}}{\overset{\overset{H}{\vert}}{C}}-COO^-$	Gln Q	Threonine*	$H_3\overset{+}{N}-\underset{\underset{CH(OH)CH_3}{\vert}}{\overset{\overset{H}{\vert}}{C}}-COO^-$	Thr T
Glycine	$H_3\overset{+}{N}-\underset{\underset{H}{\vert}}{\overset{\overset{H}{\vert}}{C}}-COO^-$	Gly G	Tryptophan*	$H_3\overset{+}{N}-\underset{\underset{CH_2}{\vert}}{\overset{\overset{H}{\vert}}{C}}-COO^-$	Trp W
Isoleucine*	$H_3\overset{+}{N}-\underset{\underset{CH(CH_3)CH_2CH_3}{\vert}}{\overset{\overset{H}{\vert}}{C}}-COO^-$	Ile I	Tyrosine	$H_3\overset{+}{N}-\underset{\underset{CH_2}{\vert}}{\overset{\overset{H}{\vert}}{C}}-COO^-$	Tyr Y
Leucine*	$H_3\overset{+}{N}-\underset{\underset{CH_2CH(CH_3)_2}{\vert}}{\overset{\overset{H}{\vert}}{C}}-COO^-$	Leu L	Valine*	$H_3\overset{+}{N}-\underset{\underset{CH(CH_3)_2}{\vert}}{\overset{\overset{H}{\vert}}{C}}-COO^-$	Val V
Methionine*	$H_3\overset{+}{N}-\underset{\underset{CH_2CH_2SCH_3}{\vert}}{\overset{\overset{H}{\vert}}{C}}-COO^-$	Met M			

Essential amino acids are labeled with an asterisk (*).

(continued on next page)

Table 21.2 (continued)

Acidic Amino Acids			Basic Amino Acids		
Name	Structure	Abbreviations	Name	Structure	Abbreviations
Aspartic acid	$H_3\overset{+}{N}-\underset{CH_2COO^-}{\overset{H}{\underset{\|}{\overset{\|}{C}}}}-COO^-$	Asp D	Arginine*	$H_3\overset{+}{N}-\underset{(CH_2)_3-N-\underset{H}{\overset{NH_2}{\underset{\|}{C}}}-NH_2}{\overset{H}{\underset{\|}{\overset{\|}{C}}}}-COO^-$	Arg R
Glutamic acid	$H_3\overset{+}{N}-\underset{CH_2CH_2COO^-}{\overset{H}{\underset{\|}{\overset{\|}{C}}}}-COO^-$	Glu E	Histidine*	$H_3\overset{+}{N}-\underset{CH_2}{\overset{H}{\underset{\|}{\overset{\|}{C}}}}-COO^-$	His H
			Lysine*	$H_3\overset{+}{N}-\underset{(CH_2)_4\overset{+}{N}H_3}{\overset{H}{\underset{\|}{\overset{\|}{C}}}}-COO^-$	Lys K

Essential amino acids are labeled with an asterisk (*).

A diet of rice and tofu provides all essential amino acids. A peanut butter sandwich on wheat bread does the same. ©FoodCollection/StockFood RF

Since plant sources generally do not have sufficient amounts of all of the essential amino acids, vegetarian diets must be carefully balanced. Grains—wheat, rice, and corn—are low in lysine, and legumes—beans, peas, and peanuts—are low in methionine, but a combination of these foods provides all the needed amino acids.

PROBLEM 21.1

In addition to the amino and carboxyl groups, what other functional groups are present in each amino acid: (a) asparagine; (b) serine; (c) cysteine?

21.2B Stereochemistry of Amino Acids

Except for the simplest amino acid, glycine, **all other amino acids have a chirality center—a carbon bonded to four different groups—on the α carbon.** Thus, an amino acid like alanine (R = CH₃) has two possible enantiomers, drawn below in both three-dimensional representations, with wedges and dashed wedges, and Fischer projections.

L isomer = L-alanine
naturally occurring enantiomer

D-alanine = D isomer

Like monosaccharides, the prefixes D and L are used to designate the arrangement of groups on the chirality center of amino acids. When drawn with a vertical carbon chain having the −COO⁻ group at the top and the R group at the bottom,

- L Amino acids have the −NH₃⁺ group on the *left* side in the Fischer projection. Common naturally occurring amino acids are L isomers.
- D Amino acids have the −NH₃⁺ group on the *right* side in the Fischer projection. D Amino acids occur infrequently in nature.

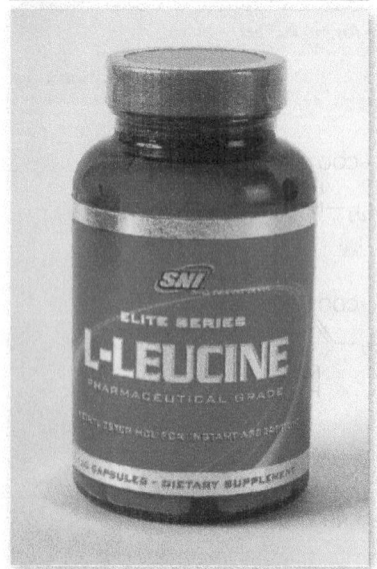

The essential amino acid leucine is sold as a dietary supplement that is used by body builders to help prevent muscle loss and heal muscle tissue after injury.
©Jill Braaten RF

MSG (monosodium glutamate), the sodium salt of glutamic acid (Table 21.2), is a common food additive used as a flavor enhancer in canned soups and other processed products.
©Comstock/Getty Images RF

SAMPLE PROBLEM 21.1 DRAWING FISCHER PROJECTIONS

Draw the Fischer projection for each amino acid: (a) L-leucine; (b) D-cysteine.

Analysis

To draw an amino acid in a Fischer projection, place the $-COO^-$ group at the top and the R group at the bottom. The L isomer has the $-NH_3^+$ on the left side and the D isomer has the $-NH_3^+$ on the right side.

Solution

a. For leucine, R = $CH_2CH(CH_3)_2$

H_3N^+ —H
$CH_2CH(CH_3)_2$
NH_3^+ on left
L isomer

b. For cysteine, R = CH_2SH

H— NH_3^+
CH_2SH
NH_3^+ on right
D isomer

PRACTICE PROBLEM 21.1

Draw both enantiomers of each amino acid in Fischer projections and label them as D or L:
(a) phenylalanine; (b) methionine.

More Practice: Try Problems 21.25[1], 21.26[1], 21.28.

PROBLEM 21.2

Which of the following amino acids is naturally occurring? By referring to the structures in Table 21.2, name each amino acid and include its D or L designation in the name.

a. H_3N^+—H
CH_2OH

b. H—NH_3^+
$CH_2CH_2COO^-$

c. H_3N^+—H
CH_2COO^-

21.3 Acid–Base Behavior of Amino Acids

As mentioned in Section 21.2, an amino acid contains both a basic amino group (NH_2) and an acidic carboxyl group (COOH). As a result, proton transfer from the acid to the base forms a **zwitterion,** a salt that contains both a positive and a negative charge. The zwitterion is *neutral;* that is, the net charge on the salt is zero.

The lone pair can bond to a proton.
H_2N—C—C
R   OH
The carboxyl group can donate a proton.

→ proton transfer →

H_3N^+—C—C
R O^-
zwitterion

In actuality, **an amino acid can exist in different forms, depending on the pH of the aqueous solution in which it is dissolved.** When the pH of a solution is around 6, alanine (R = CH_3) and other neutral amino acids exist in their zwitterionic form (**A**), having no net charge. In this form, the carboxyl group bears a net negative charge—it is a **carboxylate anion**—and the amino group bears a net positive charge (an **ammonium cation**).

ammonium cation

carboxylate anion

alanine
no net charge
A
pH ≈ 6

When strong acid is added to lower the pH to 2 or less, the carboxylate anion gains a proton and the **amino acid has a net positive charge** (form **B**).

Adding acid:

The carboxylate anion picks up a proton.

pH ≤ 2

overall +1 charge
B

When strong base is added to **A** to raise the pH to 10 or higher, the ammonium cation loses a proton and the **amino acid has a net negative charge** (form **C**).

Adding base:

The ammonium cation loses a proton.

overall −1 charge
C

Thus, **alanine exists in one of three different forms depending on the pH of the solution in which it is dissolved.** At the physiological pH of 7.4, neutral amino acids are primarily in their zwitterionic forms.

- The pH at which the amino acid exists primarily in its neutral form is called its *isoelectric point*, abbreviated as p*I*.

The isoelectric points of neutral amino acids are generally around 6. Acidic amino acids (Table 21.2), which have an additional carboxyl group that can lose a proton, have lower p*I* values (around 3). The three basic amino acids, which have an additional basic nitrogen atom that can accept a proton, have higher p*I* values (7.6–10.8).

SAMPLE PROBLEM 21.2 DETERMINING THE STRUCTURE OF AN AMINO ACID AT A GIVEN pH

Draw the structure of the amino acid glycine at each pH: (a) 6; (b) 2; (c) 11.

Analysis

- A neutral amino acid exists in its zwitterionic form (no net charge) at its isoelectric point, which is pH ≈ 6. The zwitterionic forms of neutral amino acids appear in Table 21.2.
- At low pH (≤ 2), the carboxylate anion is protonated and the amino acid has a net positive (+1) charge.
- At high pH (≥ 10), the ammonium cation loses a proton and the amino acid has a net negative (−1) charge.

Solution

a. At pH = 6, the neutral, zwitterionic form of glycine predominates.

neutral
pH = 6

b. At pH = 2, glycine has a net +1 charge.

+1 charge
pH = 2

c. At pH = 11, glycine has a net −1 charge.

−1 charge
pH = 11

PRACTICE PROBLEM 21.2

Draw the structure of the amino acid valine at each pH: (a) 6; (b) 2; (c) 11. Which form predominates at valine's isoelectric point?

More Practice: Try Problems 21.31c, 21.32c, 21.33, 21.34.

PROBLEM 21.3

Identify the amino acid shown with all uncharged atoms in the ball-and-stick model, and draw the neutral, positively charged, and negatively charged forms of the amino acid.

21.4 Peptides

When amino acids are joined together by amide bonds, they form larger molecules called **peptides** and **proteins**.

- A *dipeptide* has two amino acids joined together by *one* amide bond.
- A *tripeptide* has three amino acids joined together by *two* amide bonds.

dipeptide

tripeptide

[Amide bonds are shown in red.]

Polypeptides and **proteins** both have many amino acids joined together in long linear chains, but the term **protein** is usually reserved for polymers of more than 40 amino acids.

- The amide bonds in peptides and proteins are called *peptide bonds*.
- The individual amino acids are called *amino acid residues*.

To form a dipeptide, **the −NH₃⁺ group of one amino acid forms an amide bond with the carboxylate (−COO⁻) of another amino acid, and the elements of H₂O are removed.** Because each amino acid has both functional groups, two different dipeptides can be formed. This is illustrated with alanine (Ala) and serine (Ser) to form dipeptides **A** and **B**.

1. The −COO⁻ group of alanine can combine with the −NH₃⁺ group of serine.

Ala   Ser   new amide bond in red
reacting functional groups   **A**

2. The −COO⁻ group of serine can combine with the −NH₃⁺ group of alanine.

Ser   Ala   new amide bond in red
reacting functional groups   **B**

Dipeptides **A** and **B** are **constitutional isomers** of each other. Both have an ammonium cation (−NH₃⁺) at one end of their chains and a carboxylate anion (−COO⁻) at the other.

- The amino acid with the free −NH₃⁺ group on the α carbon is called the N-terminal amino acid.
- The amino acid with the free −COO⁻ group on the α carbon is called the C-terminal amino acid.

By convention, **the N-terminal amino acid is always written at the *left* end of the chain and the C-terminal amino acid at the *right*.**

N-terminal   C-terminal   N-terminal   C-terminal
amino acid   amino acid   amino acid   amino acid

[Alanine is drawn in blue. Serine is drawn in red.]

alanylserine   serylalanine
Ala–Ser   Ser–Ala

Peptides are named as derivatives of the C-terminal amino acid. To name a peptide:

- Name the C-terminal amino acid using the names in Table 21.2.
- Name all other amino acids from left to right as substituents of the C-terminal amino acid. Change the *-ine* or *-ic acid* ending of the amino acid name to the suffix *-yl.*

Thus, peptide **A,** which has serine as its C-terminal amino acid, is named as *alanylserine.* Peptide **B,** which has alanine as its C-terminal amino acid, is named as *serylalanine.*

The peptide can be abbreviated by writing the one- or three-letter symbols for the amino acids in the chain from the N-terminal to the C-terminal end. Thus, Ala–Ser has alanine at the N-terminal end and serine at the C-terminal end, whereas Ser–Ala has serine at the N-terminal end and alanine at the C-terminal end.

SAMPLE PROBLEM 21.3 IDENTIFYING THE N-TERMINAL AND C-TERMINAL AMINO ACIDS IN A PEPTIDE

Label the N-terminal and C-terminal amino acids in each peptide.

a.

$$CH(CH_3)_2$$
$$|$$
$$CH_2$$
$$\quad\quad O \quad\quad\quad\quad | \quad\quad O$$
$$\quad\quad \| \quad\quad\quad\quad\quad\quad \|$$
$$H_3\overset{+}{N}{-}CH{-}C{-}N{-}CH{-}C$$
$$\quad\quad | \quad\quad | \quad\quad\quad\quad\quad O^-$$
$$\quad\quad CH_2 \quad H$$
$$\quad\quad |$$
$$\quad\quad CH_2SCH_3$$

b. Tyr–Pro–Glu–His   c. TSFMMQNA

Analysis

- The amino acid with the free $-NH_3^+$ group on the α carbon is the N-terminal amino acid, drawn at the left end of the chain.
- The amino acid with the free $-COO^-$ group on the α carbon is the C-terminal amino acid, drawn at the right end of the chain.

Solution

The N-terminal amino acids are labeled in blue, and the C-terminal amino acids are labeled in red.

a.

$$CH(CH_3)_2$$
$$|$$
$$CH_2$$
$$\quad\quad O \quad\quad\quad\quad | \quad\quad O$$
$$\quad\quad \| \quad\quad\quad\quad\quad\quad \|$$
$$H_3\overset{+}{N}{-}CH{-}C{-}N{-}CH{-}C$$
$$\quad\quad | \quad\quad | \quad\quad\quad\quad\quad O^-$$
$$\quad\quad CH_2 \quad H$$
$$\quad\quad |$$
$$\quad\quad CH_2SCH_3$$

b. Tyr–Pro–Glu–His   c. TSFMMQNA

PRACTICE PROBLEM 21.3

Identify the N-terminal and C-terminal amino acid in each peptide.

a.

$$\quad\quad O \quad\quad\quad\quad\quad O$$
$$\quad\quad \| \quad\quad\quad\quad\quad\quad \|$$
$$H_3\overset{+}{N}{-}CH{-}C{-}N{-}CH{-}C$$
$$\quad\quad | \quad\quad | \quad | \quad\quad O^-$$
$$\quad\quad CH_2 \quad H \quad CH_3$$
$$\quad\quad |$$
$$\quad\quad CH(CH_3)_2$$

c.

$$\quad\quad O \quad\quad\quad\quad\quad O \quad\quad\quad\quad\quad O$$
$$\quad\quad \| \quad\quad\quad\quad\quad\quad \| \quad\quad\quad\quad\quad\quad \|$$
$$H_3\overset{+}{N}{-}CH{-}C{-}N{-}CH{-}C{-}N{-}CH{-}C$$
$$\quad\quad | \quad\quad | \quad | \quad | \quad | \quad\quad O^-$$
$$\quad\quad CH_2 \quad H \quad CH_3 \quad H \quad CH_2$$
$$\quad\quad | \quad\quad\quad\quad\quad\quad\quad\quad\quad\quad\quad | $$
$$\quad\quad\quad\quad\quad\quad\quad\quad\quad\quad\quad\quad\quad CH_2CONH_2$$

b. Arg–His–Asn–Tyr   d. Val–Thr–Pro–Phe

More Practice: Try Problems 21.37b, c; 21.38b, c; 21.41[3]; 21.42[3]; 21.43[2]; 21.44[2].

PROBLEM 21.4

(a) Identify the N-terminal amino acid in the tetrapeptide alanylglycylleucylmethionine. (b) What is the C-terminal amino acid? (c) Write the peptide using three-letter symbols for the amino acids.

Drawing a dipeptide from component amino acids is illustrated in the stepwise *How To* procedure.

How To Draw a Dipeptide from Two Amino Acids

Example: Draw the structure of the dipeptide Val–Gly, and label the N-terminal and C-terminal amino acids.

Step [1] **Draw the structures of the individual amino acids from left to right.**

- Use the three-letter symbols to identify the amino acids in the peptide. In this example, Val is valine and Gly is glycine.
- Draw the structures of the amino acids by placing the $-COO^-$ of one amino acid next to the $-NH_3^+$ group of the adjacent amino acid.

—Continued

How To, continued . . .

- Always draw the $-NH_3^+$ group on the left and the $-COO^-$ group on the right.

Place these two groups next to each other.

Draw valine on the left because its symbol appears first in the structure.

$$H_3\overset{+}{N}-CH-\overset{\overset{\displaystyle O}{\|}}{C}$$
$(CH_3)_2CH$ O^- + $H_3\overset{+}{N}-CH-\overset{\overset{\displaystyle O}{\|}}{\underset{H}{C}}-O^-$

Val   Gly

Step [2] Join the adjacent $-COO^-$ and $-NH_3^+$ groups together.

- Form a new amide bond by joining the carbonyl carbon of one amino acid to the N atom of the second amino acid.

N-terminal amino acid   new amide bond

$$H_3\overset{+}{N}-CH-\overset{\overset{\displaystyle O}{\|}}{C}$$
$(CH_3)_2CH$ O^- + $H_3\overset{+}{N}-CH-\overset{\overset{\displaystyle O}{\|}}{\underset{H}{C}}-O^-$ ⟶ $H_3\overset{+}{N}-CH-\overset{\overset{\displaystyle O}{\|}}{C}-\underset{H}{N}-CH-\overset{\overset{\displaystyle O}{\|}}{\underset{H}{C}}-O^-$

Val   Gly   Val–Gly

C-terminal amino acid

- Valine is the N-terminal amino acid because it contains a free $-NH_3^+$ group on the α carbon.
- Glycine is the C-terminal amino acid because it contains a free $-COO^-$ group on the α carbon.

SAMPLE PROBLEM 21.4 DRAWING THE STRUCTURE OF A DIPEPTIDE

Draw the structure of the dipeptide Ala–Gln.

Analysis and Solution

[1] Draw the structures of the individual amino acids from left to right.

- Use Table 21.2 to identify the structures that correspond to each three-letter abbreviation. Ala is alanine and Gln is glutamine.
- Arrange the $-COO^-$ of one amino acid (drawn on the right) next to the $-NH_3^+$ group of the adjacent amino acid (drawn on the left).

$$H_3\overset{+}{N}-CH-\overset{\overset{\displaystyle O}{\|}}{C}$$
    CH_3 O^-

$$H_3\overset{+}{N}-CH-\overset{\overset{\displaystyle O}{\|}}{C}$$
    CH_2 O^-
    CH_2CONH_2

Ala   Gln
alanine   glutamine

[2] Form an amide bond by joining the $-COO^-$ of one amino acid to the $-NH_3^+$ group of the other amino acid.

amide bond

$$H_3\overset{+}{N}-CH-\overset{\overset{\displaystyle O}{\|}}{C}$$
    CH_3 O^- + $H_3\overset{+}{N}-CH-\overset{\overset{\displaystyle O}{\|}}{C}-O^-$
    CH_2
    CH_2CONH_2 ⟶ $H_3\overset{+}{N}-CH-\overset{\overset{\displaystyle O}{\|}}{C}-\underset{H}{N}-CH-\overset{\overset{\displaystyle O}{\|}}{C}-O^-$
    CH_3 CH_2
        CH_2CONH_2

Ala   Gln   Ala–Gln

PRACTICE PROBLEM 21.4

Draw the structure of each dipeptide: (a) Gly–Phe; (b) Gln–Ile; (c) Leu–Cys.

More Practice: Try Problems 21.41[1], 21.42[1].

PROBLEM 21.5

(a) Draw the structures of the two possible dipeptides that can be formed by combining leucine and asparagine. (b) In each dipeptide, label the N- and C-terminal amino acids. (c) Name each peptide using three-letter abbreviations.

SAMPLE PROBLEM 21.5 IDENTIFYING AMINO ACIDS IN A PEPTIDE

Identify the individual amino acids used to form the following tripeptide. What is the name of the tripeptide?

Analysis

- Locate the amide bonds in the peptide. To draw the structures of the individual amino acids, break the amide bonds by adding water. Add O^- to the carbonyl carbon to form a carboxylate anion $-COO^-$ and 2 H's to the N atom to form $-NH_3^+$.
- Identify the amino acids by comparing with Table 21.2.
- To name the peptide: [1] Name the C-terminal amino acid. [2] Name the other amino acids as substituents by changing the *-ine* (or *-ic acid*) ending to the suffix *-yl*. Place the names of the substituent amino acids in order from left to right.

Solution

To determine the amino acids that form the peptide, work backwards. Break the amide bonds in red that join the amino acids together. This forms leucine, alanine, and tyrosine.

The tripeptide is named as a derivative of the C-terminal amino acid, tyrosine, with leucine and alanine as substituents; thus, the tripeptide is named **leucylalanyltyrosine.**

PRACTICE PROBLEM 21.5

Identify the individual amino acids in each dipeptide, and then name the dipeptide using three-letter abbreviations.

More Practice: Try Problems 21.43[1], [3]; 21.44[1], [3].

SAMPLE PROBLEM 21.6 IDENTIFYING THE AMINO ACIDS IN A PEPTIDE

Locate the peptide bond in the dipeptide shown in the ball-and-stick model, and identify the amino acids that form the dipeptide. Name the dipeptide using the three-letter abbreviations for the amino acids.

Analysis

- Convert the ball-and-stick model to a structural formula. The peptide bond is the amide bond that joins the two amino acids together.
- Identify the side chains of the amino acids and use Table 21.2 to determine the names.
- Name the dipeptide by writing the three-letter abbreviations for the amino acids with the N-terminal amino acid first, followed by the C-terminal amino acid.

Solution

The peptide bond is the amide bond that contains a carbon atom doubly bonded to oxygen and singly bonded to nitrogen.

The side chains of the two amino acids, the R groups that extend from the peptide backbone, identify them as alanine and cysteine (Table 21.2). The dipeptide is named with the N-terminal amino acid (alanine) first, followed by the C-terminal amino acid (cysteine), using the three-letter abbreviations: **Ala–Cys.**

PRACTICE PROBLEM 21.6

Locate the peptide bond in the dipeptide shown in the ball-and-stick model, and identify the amino acids that form the dipeptide. Name the dipeptide using the three-letter abbreviations for the amino acids.

More Practice: Try Problems 21.35, 21.36.

21.5   FOCUS ON THE HUMAN BODY
Biologically Active Peptides

Many relatively simple peptides have important biological functions.

21.5A   Neuropeptides—Enkephalins and Pain Relief

Enkephalins, pentapeptides synthesized in the brain, act as painkillers and sedatives by binding to pain receptors. Two enkephalins that differ in the identity of only one amino acid are known. Met-enkephalin contains a C-terminal methionine residue, whereas leu-enkephalin contains a C-terminal leucine.

Tyr–Gly–Gly–Phe–Met
met-enkephalin

Tyr–Gly–Gly–Phe–Leu
leu-enkephalin

The addictive narcotic analgesics morphine and heroin (Section 18.5) bind to the same receptors as the enkephalins and thus produce a similar physiological response. Enkephalins, however, produce only short-term pain-relieving effects because their peptide bonds are readily hydrolyzed by enzymes in the brain. Morphine and heroin, on the other hand, are not readily hydrolyzed, so they are biologically active for a much longer time period.

Enkephalins are related to a group of larger polypeptides called **endorphins** that contain 16–31 amino acids. Endorphins also block pain and are thought to produce the feeling of well-being experienced by an athlete after excessive or strenuous exercise.

21.5B   Peptide Hormones—Oxytocin and Vasopressin

Oxytocin and **vasopressin** are cyclic nonapeptide hormones secreted by the pituitary gland. Their sequences are identical except for two amino acids, yet this is enough to give them very different biological activities.

Cys — Tyr — Ile
| |
S   Gln
| |
S   Asn
   Cys
|
Pro — Leu — GlyNH$_2$

oxytocin

Cys — Tyr — Phe
| |
S   Gln
| |
S   Asn
   Cys
|
Pro — Arg — GlyNH$_2$

vasopressin

- The N-terminal amino acid is labeled in red.
- The amino acids that differ are labeled in blue.

Oxytocin stimulates the contraction of uterine muscles, and it initiates the flow of milk in nursing mothers (Figure 21.2). Oxytocin, sold under the trade names Pitocin and Syntocinon, is used to induce labor.

Figure 21.2   Physiological Effects of Oxytocin

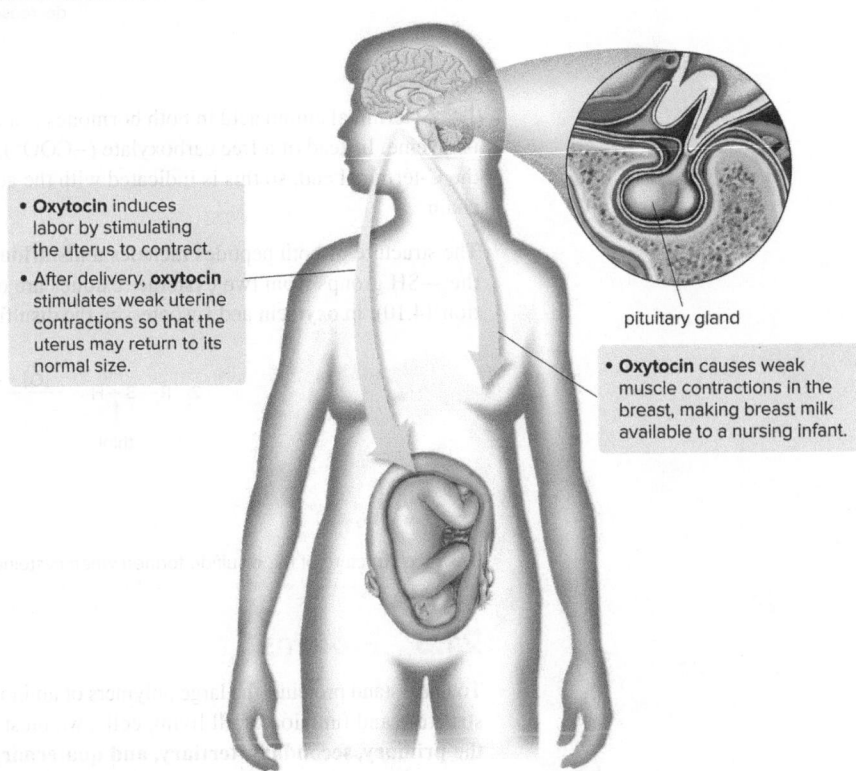

- **Oxytocin** induces labor by stimulating the uterus to contract.
- After delivery, **oxytocin** stimulates weak uterine contractions so that the uterus may return to its normal size.

pituitary gland

- **Oxytocin** causes weak muscle contractions in the breast, making breast milk available to a nursing infant.

Vasopressin, also called antidiuretic hormone (ADH), targets the kidneys and helps to keep the electrolytes in body fluids in the normal range. Vasopressin is secreted when the body is dehydrated and causes the kidneys to retain fluid, thus decreasing the volume of the urine (Figure 21.3).

Figure 21.3   Vasopressin—An Antidiuretic Hormone

pituitary
gland

• Secretion of **vasopressin** by the
pituitary gland causes the kidneys
to retain fluid, resulting in
decreased urine output.

decreased urine output

The N-terminal amino acid in both hormones is a cysteine residue, and the C-terminal residue is glycine. Instead of a free carboxylate ($-COO^-$), both peptides have an amide ($-CONH_2$) at the C-terminal end, so this is indicated with the additional NH_2 group drawn at the end of the chain.

The structure of both peptides includes a **disulfide bond,** a form of covalent bonding in which the —SH groups from two cysteine residues are oxidized to form a sulfur–sulfur bond (Section 14.10). In oxytocin and vasopressin, the disulfide bonds make the peptides cyclic.

$$2 \ \text{R}-\text{S}-\text{H} \xrightarrow{[O]} \text{R}-\text{S}-\text{S}-\text{R}$$

thiol   disulfide bond

PROBLEM 21.6

Draw the structure of the disulfide formed when cysteine is oxidized.

21.6 Proteins

To understand proteins, the large polymers of amino acids that are responsible for so much of the structure and function of all living cells, we must learn about four levels of structure, called the **primary, secondary, tertiary, and quaternary structure** of proteins.

21.6A   Primary Structure

The *primary structure* of a protein is the particular sequence of amino acids that is joined together by peptide bonds. The most important element of this primary structure is the amide bond that joins the amino acids.

The carbonyl carbon of the amide has **trigonal planar** geometry. All six atoms involved in the peptide bond lie in the same plane. All bond angles are 120° and the C=O and N—H bonds are oriented 180° from each other. As a result, the backbone of the protein adopts a zigzag arrangement as shown in the three-dimensional structure of a portion of a protein molecule.

peptide bond

[Amide bonds are shown in red.]

120°

120°

These six atoms lie in a plane.

The primary structure of a protein—the exact sequence of amino acids—determines all properties and function of a protein. As we will see in Section 21.7, substitution of a single amino acid by a different amino acid can result in very different properties.

PROBLEM 21.7

Can two *different* proteins be composed of the same number and type of amino acids?

21.6B   Secondary Structure

The three-dimensional arrangement of localized regions of a protein is called its secondary structure. These regions arise due to hydrogen bonding between the N—H proton of one amide and the C=O oxygen of another. Two arrangements that are particularly stable are called the **α-helix** and the **β-pleated sheet.**

α-Helix

The **α-helix** forms when a peptide chain twists into a right-handed or clockwise spiral, as shown in Figure 21.4. Several important features characterize an α-helix.

- Each turn of the helix has 3.6 amino acids.
- The N—H and C=O bonds point along the axis of the helix in opposite directions.
- The C=O group of one amino acid is hydrogen bonded to an N—H group four amino acid residues farther along the chain.
- The R groups of the amino acids extend outward from the core of the helix.

Both the myosin in muscle and the α-keratin in hair are proteins composed almost entirely of α-helices.

a. The right-handed α-helix

b. The backbone of the α-helix

hydrogen
bond

3.6 residues

All atoms of the α-helix are
drawn in this representation.
All C=O bonds are pointing
up and all N—H bonds are
pointing down.

Only the peptide backbone is
drawn in this representation.
The hydrogen bonds between
the C=O and N—H of amino
acids four residues away from
each other are shown.

β-Pleated Sheet

The **β-pleated sheet** forms when two or more peptide chains, called **strands,** line up side-by-side, as shown in Figure 21.5. All β-pleated sheets have the following characteristics:

- The C=O and N—H bonds lie in the plane of the sheet.
- Hydrogen bonding often occurs between the N—H and C=O groups of nearby amino acid residues.
- The R groups are oriented above and below the plane of the sheet, and alternate from one side to the other along a given strand.

The β-pleated sheet arrangement is favored by amino acids with small R groups, like alanine and glycine. With larger R groups, steric interactions prevent the chains from getting close together, so the sheet cannot be stabilized by hydrogen bonding.

Most proteins have regions of α-helix and β-pleated sheet, in addition to other regions that cannot be characterized by either of these arrangements. Shorthand symbols are often used to indicate these regions of secondary structure (Figure 21.6). In particular, a flat helical ribbon is used for the α-helix, while a flat wide arrow is used for the β-pleated sheet. These representations are often used in **ribbon diagrams** to illustrate protein structure.

Proteins are drawn in a variety of ways to show different aspects of their structure. Figure 21.7 illustrates three different representations of the protein lysozyme, an enzyme found in both plants and animals. Lysozyme catalyzes the hydrolysis of bonds in bacterial cell walls, weakening them, often causing the bacteria to burst.

Figure 21.5 Three-Dimensional Structure of the β-Pleated Sheet

hydrogen bond

The β-pleated sheet consists of extended strands of the peptide chains held together by hydrogen bonding. The C=O and N—H bonds lie in the plane of the sheet, while the R groups (shown as yellow balls) alternate above and below the plane.

Figure 21.6 Shorthand Symbols Representing Protein Structure

α-helix   β-sheet   random region

Figure 21.7 Lysozyme

a. Ball-and-stick model

b. Space-filling model

c. Ribbon diagram

(a) The ball-and-stick model of lysozyme shows the protein backbone with color-coded C, N, O, and S atoms. Individual amino acids are most clearly located using this representation. (b) The space-filling model uses color-coded balls for each atom in the backbone of the enzyme and illustrates how the atoms fill the space they occupy. (c) The ribbon diagram shows regions of α-helix and β-pleated sheet that are not clearly in evidence in the other two representations.

Figure 21.8

Spider Dragline Silk

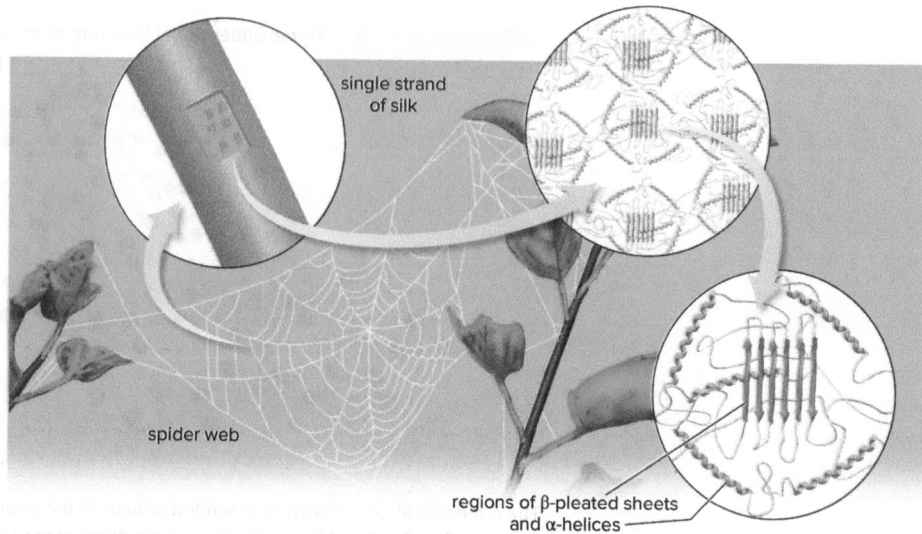

single strand
of silk

spider web

regions of β-pleated sheets
and α-helices

Spider dragline silk has regions of α-helix and β-pleated sheet that make it both elastic and strong. The green coils represent the α-helical regions, while the purple arrows represent the β-pleated sheet regions. The thin gray lines represent other areas of the protein that are neither α-helix nor β-pleated sheet.

Spider dragline silk is a strong yet elastic protein because it has regions of β-pleated sheet and regions of α-helix (Figure 21.8). α-Helical regions impart elasticity to the silk because the peptide chain is twisted (not fully extended), so it can stretch. β-Pleated sheet regions are almost fully extended, so they can't be stretched further, but their highly ordered three-dimensional structure imparts strength to the silk. Thus, spider silk suits the spider by having both types of secondary structure with beneficial properties.

21.6C Tertiary and Quaternary Structure

The three-dimensional shape adopted by the entire peptide chain is called its tertiary structure. A peptide generally folds into a shape that maximizes its stability. In the aqueous environment of the cell, proteins often fold in such a way as to place a large number of polar and charged groups on their outer surface, to maximize the dipole–dipole and hydrogen-bonding interactions with water. This generally places most of the nonpolar side chains in the interior of the protein, where **London dispersion forces** between these hydrophobic groups help stabilize the molecule, too.

In addition, polar functional groups **hydrogen bond** with each other (not just water), and amino acids with charged side chains like $-COO^-$ and $-NH_3^+$ can stabilize tertiary structure by **electrostatic interactions.**

Finally, **disulfide bonds are the only covalent bonds that stabilize tertiary structure.** As mentioned in Section 21.5, these strong bonds form by the oxidation of two cysteine residues on either the same polypeptide chain or another polypeptide chain of the same protein.

The many disulfide bonds in the proteins that compose fingernails make nails strong and hard. ©Diffused Productions/Alamy RF

Disulfide bonds can form in two different ways.

Between two SH groups on the same chain:

$-CH_2SH$ [O] $-CH_2-S$

$-CH_2SH$ $-CH_2-S$

intramolecular disulfide bond

Between two SH groups on different chains:

$-CH_2SH$ [O] $-CH_2S$

$HSCH_2-$ SCH_2

intermolecular disulfide bond

Insulin, for example, consists of two separate polypeptide chains (labeled the **A** and **B** chains) that are covalently linked by two intermolecular disulfide bonds, as shown in Figure 21.9. The **A** chain, which also has an intramolecular disulfide bond, has 21 amino acid residues, whereas the **B** chain has 30.

Figure 21.9   Insulin

Insulin is a small protein consisting of two polypeptide chains (designated as the **A** and **B** chains), held together by two disulfide bonds. An additional disulfide bond joins two cysteine residues within the **A** chain.

residue 1

A chain   Gly-Ile-Val-Glu-Gln-Cys-Cys-Thr-Ser-Ile-Cys-Ser-Leu-Tyr-Gln-Leu-Glu-Asn-Tyr-Cys-Asn 21

8 9 10

B chain   Phe-Val-Asn-Gln-His-Leu-Cys-Gly-Ser-His-Leu-Val-Glu-Ala-Leu-Tyr-Leu-Val-Cys-Gly

residue 1

Thr-Lys-Pro-Thr-Tyr-Phe-Phe-Gly-Arg-Glu

30

Synthesized by groups of cells in the pancreas called the islets of Langerhans, insulin is the protein that regulates blood glucose levels.

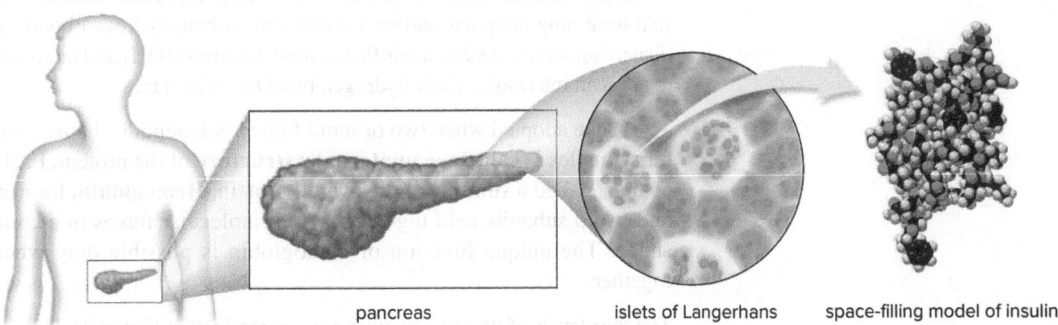

pancreas   islets of Langerhans   space-filling model of insulin

A relative or complete lack of insulin results in diabetes. Many of the abnormalities associated with this disease can be controlled by the injection of insulin. Until the recent availability of human insulin through genetic engineering techniques (Section 22.10), all insulin used by individuals with diabetes was obtained from pigs and cattle. The amino acid sequences of these insulin proteins are slightly different from that of human insulin. Pig insulin differs in one amino acid only, whereas bovine insulin has three different amino acids. This is shown in the accompanying table.

	Chain A			Chain B
Position of Residue →	8	9	10	30
Human insulin	Thr	Ser	Ile	Thr
Pig insulin	Thr	Ser	Ile	Ala
Bovine insulin	Ala	Ser	Val	Ala

Figure 21.10   The Stabilizing Interactions in Secondary and Tertiary Protein Structure

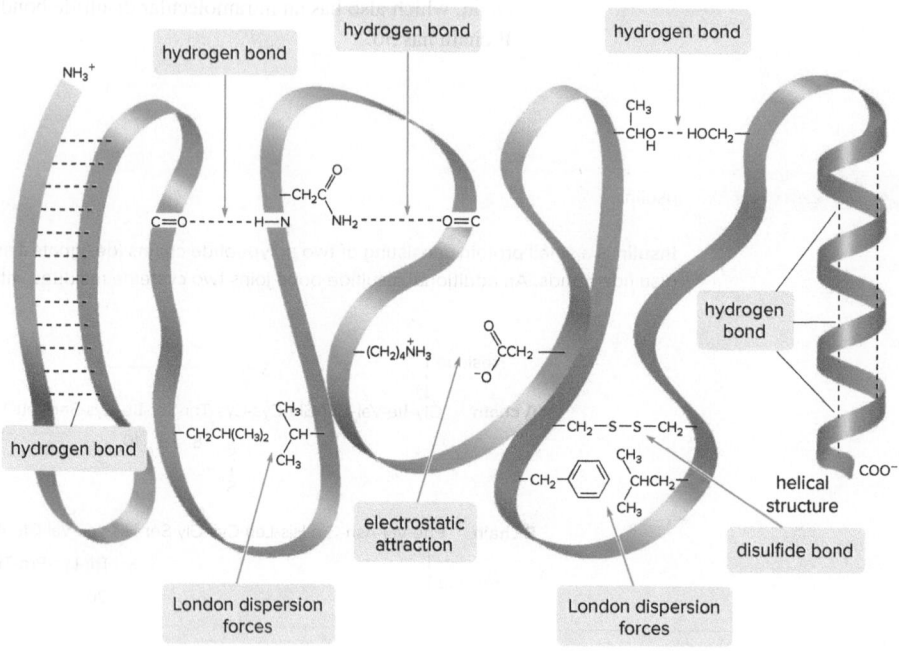

Figure 21.10 schematically illustrates the many different kinds of intramolecular forces that stabilize the secondary and tertiary structures of polypeptide chains. Nearby amino acid residues that have only nonpolar carbon–carbon and carbon–hydrogen bonds are stabilized by London dispersion forces. Amino acids that contain hydroxyl (OH) and amino groups (NH_2) in their side chains can intermolecularly hydrogen bond to each other.

The shape adopted when two or more folded polypeptide chains come together into one protein complex is called the **quaternary structure** of the protein. Each individual polypeptide chain is called a **subunit** of the overall protein. **Hemoglobin,** for example, consists of two α and two β subunits held together by intermolecular forces in a compact three-dimensional shape. The unique function of hemoglobin is possible only when all four subunits are together.

The four levels of protein structure are summarized in Figure 21.11.

PROBLEM 21.8

Draw the structures of each pair of amino acids and indicate what types of intermolecular forces are present between the side chains. Use Figure 21.10 as a guide.

a. Ser and Tyr

b. Val and Leu

c. 2 Phe residues

PROBLEM 21.9

The fibroin proteins found in silk fibers consist of large regions of β-pleated sheets stacked one on top of another. The polypeptide sequence in these regions has the amino acid glycine at every other residue. Explain how this allows the β-pleated sheets to stack on top of each other.

Figure 21.11   The Primary, Secondary, Tertiary, and Quaternary Structure of Proteins

amino acid sequence

β-pleated sheet

α-helix

3-D shape of a
polypeptide chain

protein complex of
polypeptide chains

| **Primary structure** | **Secondary structure** | **Tertiary structure** | **Quaternary structure** |

21.7   FOCUS ON THE HUMAN BODY
Common Proteins

Proteins are generally classified according to their three-dimensional shapes.

- *Fibrous proteins* are composed of long linear polypeptide chains that are bundled together to form rods or sheets. These proteins are insoluble in water and serve structural roles, giving strength and protection to tissues and cells.

- *Globular proteins* are coiled into compact shapes with hydrophilic outer surfaces that make them water soluble. Enzymes and transport proteins are globular to make them soluble in blood and other aqueous environments.

21.7A   α-Keratins

α-Keratins are the proteins found in hair, hooves, nails, skin, and wool. They are composed almost exclusively of long sections of α-helix units, having large numbers of alanine and leucine residues. These nonpolar amino acids extend outward from the α-helix, so these proteins are very insoluble in water. Two α-keratin helices coil around each other, forming a structure called a **supercoil** or **superhelix.** These, in turn, form larger and larger bundles of fibers, ultimately forming a strand of hair, as shown schematically in Figure 21.12.

α-Keratins also have a number of cysteine residues, and because of this, disulfide bonds are formed between adjacent helices. The number of disulfide bridges determines the strength of the material. Claws, horns, and fingernails have extensive networks of disulfide bonds, making them extremely hard.

Figure 21.12

Figure 21.12

Anatomy of a Hair

strand of hair

supercoil

A supercoil is formed from two
α-helices wound around each other.

Bundles of supercoils come
together to form a hair.

The α-keratin in hair is made up largely of α-helix.

©photosindia/Getty Images RF

21.7B　Collagen

Collagen, the most abundant protein in vertebrates, is found in connective tissues such as bone, cartilage, tendons, teeth, and blood vessels. Glycine and proline account for a large fraction of its amino acid residues. Collagen forms an elongated left-handed helix, and then three of these helices wind around each other to form a right-handed **superhelix** or **triple helix.** The side chain of glycine is only a hydrogen atom, so the high glycine content allows the collagen superhelices to lie compactly next to each other, thus stabilizing the superhelices via hydrogen bonding. Two views of the collagen superhelix are shown in Figure 21.13.

Vitamin C is required for a reaction that modifies the original amino acids incorporated into the collagen chain so that strong hydrogen bonds form between the helices. When there is a deficiency of vitamin C in the diet, the collagen fibers do not form properly and scurvy results. Weakened blood vessels and poorly formed cartilage lead to spongy and bloody gums and dark purple skin lesions.

Figure 21.13

Two Different Representations
for the Triple Helix of Collagen

In collagen, three polypeptide chains having an unusual left-handed helix wind around each other in a right-handed triple helix. The high content of small glycine residues allows the chains to lie close to each other, permitting hydrogen bonding between the chains.

21.7C Hemoglobin and Myoglobin

Hemoglobin and **myoglobin,** two globular proteins, are called **conjugated proteins** because they are composed of a protein unit and a nonprotein molecule. In hemoglobin and myoglobin, the nonprotein unit is called **heme,** a complex organic compound containing the Fe^{2+} ion complexed with a large nitrogen-containing ring system. The Fe^{2+} ion of hemoglobin and myoglobin binds oxygen. Hemoglobin, which is present in red blood cells, transports oxygen to wherever it is needed in the body, whereas myoglobin stores oxygen in tissues.

The high concentration of myoglobin in a whale's muscles allows it to remain underwater for long periods of time.
©*Daniel C. Smith*

heme

Myoglobin has 153 amino acid residues in a single polypeptide chain (Figure 21.14a). It has eight separate α-helical sections and a heme group held in a cavity inside the polypeptide. Myoglobin gives cardiac muscle its characteristic red color.

Hemoglobin consists of four polypeptide chains (two α subunits and two β subunits), each of which carries a heme unit (Figure 21.14b). Hemoglobin has more nonpolar amino acid residues than myoglobin. When each subunit is folded, some of these remain on the surface. The London dispersion forces between these hydrophobic groups are what stabilize the quaternary structure of the four subunits.

Carbon monoxide is poisonous because it binds to the Fe^{2+} of hemoglobin 200 times more strongly than does oxygen. Hemoglobin complexed with CO cannot carry O_2 from the lungs to the tissues. Without O_2 available to the tissues for metabolism, cells cannot function, and they die.

The properties of all proteins depend on their three-dimensional shape, and their shape depends on their primary structure—that is, their amino acid sequence. This is particularly well

Figure 21.14   Protein Ribbon Diagrams for Myoglobin and Hemoglobin

a. Myoglobin

b. Hemoglobin

heme

heme

Myoglobin consists of a single polypeptide chain with a heme unit shown in a ball-and-stick model.

Hemoglobin consists of two α and two β chains shown in red and blue, respectively, and four heme units shown in ball-and-stick models.

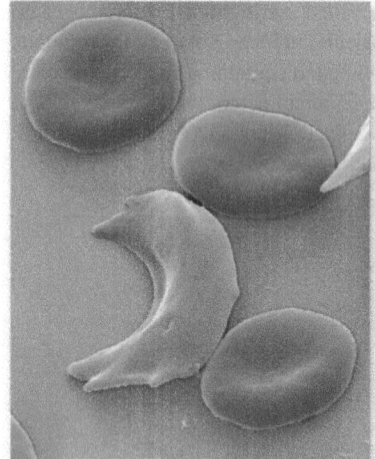

When red blood cells take on a "sickled" shape in persons with sickle cell disease, they block capillaries causing organ injury and they break easily leading to profound anemia. This devastating illness results from the change of a single amino acid in hemoglobin. Note the single sickled cell surrounded by three red cells with normal shape.
©Eye of Science/Science Source

exemplified by comparing normal hemoglobin with **sickle cell hemoglobin,** a mutant variation in which a single amino acid of both β subunits is changed from glutamic acid to valine. The replacement of one acidic amino acid (Glu) with one nonpolar amino acid (Val) changes the shape of hemoglobin, which has profound effects on its function. Red blood cells with sickle cell hemoglobin become elongated and crescent shaped, and they are unusually fragile. As a result, they rupture and occlude capillaries, causing pain and inflammation, leading to severe anemia and organ damage. The end result is often a painful and premature death.

This disease, called **sickle cell anemia,** is found almost exclusively among people originating from central and western Africa, where malaria is an enormous health problem. Sickle cell hemoglobin results from a genetic mutation in the DNA sequence that is responsible for the synthesis of hemoglobin. Individuals who inherit this mutation from both parents develop sickle cell anemia, whereas those who inherit it from only one parent are said to have the sickle cell trait. They do not develop sickle cell anemia and they are more resistant to malaria than individuals without the mutation. The relative benefit of this mutation apparently accounts for this detrimental gene being passed on from generation to generation.

PROBLEM 21.10

Why is hemoglobin more water soluble than α-keratin?

21.8   Protein Hydrolysis and Denaturation

The properties of a protein are greatly altered and often entirely destroyed when any level of protein structure is disturbed.

21.8A   Protein Hydrolysis

Like other amide bonds, the peptide bonds in proteins are hydrolyzed by treatment with aqueous acid, base, or certain enzymes.

- The hydrolysis of the amide bonds in a protein forms the individual amino acids that comprise the primary structure.

For example, hydrolysis of the amide bonds in the tripeptide Ile–Gly–Phe forms the amino acids isoleucine, glycine, and phenylalanine. When each amide bond is broken, the elements of H_2O are added, forming a carboxylate anion ($-COO^-$) in one amino acid and an ammonium cation ($-NH_3^+$) in the other.

The first step in the digestion of dietary protein is hydrolysis of the amide bonds of the protein backbone. The enzyme pepsin in the acidic gastric juices of the stomach cleaves some of the amide bonds to form smaller peptides, which pass into the small intestine and are further broken down into individual amino acids by the enzymes trypsin and chymotrypsin.

Proteins in the diet serve a variety of nutritional needs. Like carbohydrates and lipids, proteins can be metabolized for energy. Moreover, the individual amino acids formed by hydrolysis are used as starting materials to make new proteins that the body needs. Likewise, the N atoms in the amino acids are incorporated into other biomolecules that contain nitrogen.

SAMPLE PROBLEM 21.7 DRAWING THE PRODUCTS OF PEPTIDE HYDROLYSIS

Draw the structures of the amino acids formed by hydrolysis of the neuropeptide leu-enkephalin (Section 21.5).

Analysis

Locate each amide bond in the protein or peptide backbone. To draw the hydrolysis products, break each amide bond by adding the elements of H_2O to form a carboxylate anion ($-COO^-$) in one amino acid and an ammonium cation ($-NH_3^+$) in the other.

Solution

[1] Locate the amide bonds in the peptide backbone.
[2] Break each bond by adding H_2O.

leu-enkephalin

Tyr   Gly   Gly   Phe   Leu

PRACTICE PROBLEM 21.7

Draw the structure of the products formed by hydrolysis of each tripeptide: (a) Ala–Leu–Gly; (b) Ser–Thr–Phe; (c) Leu–Tyr–Asn.

More Practice: Try Problems 21.45–21.49.

21.8B   Protein Denaturation

When the secondary, tertiary, or quaternary structure of a protein is disturbed, the properties of a protein are also altered and the biological activity is often lost.

- *Denaturation* is the process of altering the shape of a protein without breaking the amide bonds that form the primary structure.

Cooking or whipping egg whites denatures the globular proteins they contain, forming insoluble protein.
©McGraw-Hill Education/Jill Braaten, photographer

High temperature, acid, base, and even agitation can disrupt the noncovalent interactions that hold a protein in a specific shape. Heat breaks up weak London forces between nonpolar amino acids. Heat, acid, and base disrupt hydrogen-bonding interactions between polar amino acids, which account for much of the secondary and tertiary structure. As a result, denaturation causes a globular protein to uncoil into an undefined randomly looped structure.

coiled globular protein

heat

loose coils and loops

Denaturation often makes globular proteins less water soluble. Globular proteins are typically folded with hydrophobic regions in the interior to maximize the interaction of polar residues on the outside surface with water. This makes them water soluble. When the protein is denatured, more hydrophobic regions are exposed and the protein often loses water solubility.

We witness many examples of protein denaturation in the kitchen. As milk ages it becomes sour from enzymes that produce lactic acid. The acid also denatures milk proteins, which precipitate as an insoluble curd. Ovalbumin, the major protein in egg white, is denatured when an egg is boiled or fried, forming a solid. Even vigorously whipping egg whites denatures its protein, forming the stiff meringue used to top a lemon meringue pie.

PROBLEM 21.11

Heating collagen, a water-insoluble fibrous protein, forms the jelly-like substance called gelatin. Explain how this process may occur.

21.9 Enzymes—Characteristics and Classification

***Enzymes* are proteins that serve as biological catalysts for reactions in all living organisms.** Like all catalysts (Section 6.4), enzymes increase the rate of reactions, but they themselves are not permanently changed in the process. Moreover, the position of equilibrium is not altered by an enzyme, nor are the relative energies of the starting material and product.

Enzymes are crucial to the biological reactions that occur in the body, which would otherwise often proceed too slowly to be of any use. In humans, enzymes must catalyze reactions under very specific physiological conditions, usually a pH around 7.4 and a temperature of 37 °C.

21.9A Characteristics of Enzymes

Enzymes are generally water-soluble, globular proteins that exhibit two characteristic features.

- **Enzymes greatly enhance reaction rates. An enzyme-catalyzed reaction can be 10^6 to 10^{12} times faster than a similar uncatalyzed reaction.**
- **Enzymes are very specific.**

The specificity of an enzyme varies. Some enzymes, such as catalase, catalyze a single reaction. Catalase catalyzes the conversion of hydrogen peroxide (H_2O_2) to O_2 and H_2O (Section 5.1).

$$2\ H_2O_2(l) \xrightarrow{\text{catalase}} 2\ H_2O(l) + O_2(g)$$

Other enzymes, such as carboxypeptidase A, catalyze a particular type of reaction with a variety of substrates. Carboxypeptidase A, a digestive enzyme that breaks down proteins, catalyzes the

When a bloody wound is cleaned with hydrogen peroxide, the enzyme catalase in the blood converts the H_2O_2 to H_2O and O_2, forming a white foam of oxygen bubbles. ©Daniel C. Smith

hydrolysis of a specific type of peptide bond—the amide bond closest to the C-terminal end of the protein.

Only this amide bond is broken.

The conversion of lactate to pyruvate is catalyzed by the enzyme lactate dehydrogenase. To carry out this reaction, a **cofactor** is also needed.

lactate
The 2 H's in red are removed.

coenzyme

pyruvate

formed from the coenzyme

> • A *cofactor* is a metal ion or a nonprotein organic molecule needed for an enzyme-catalyzed reaction to occur.

NAD^+ (nicotinamide adenine dinucleotide, Section 16.6) is the cofactor that oxidizes lactate to pyruvate. **An organic compound that serves as an enzyme cofactor is called a *coenzyme*.** While lactate dehydrogenase greatly speeds up this oxidation reaction, NAD^+ is the coenzyme that actually oxidizes the substrate, lactate. NAD^+ is a common biological oxidizing agent used as a coenzyme (Section 23.4).

The need for metal ions as enzyme cofactors explains why trace amounts of certain metals must be present in our diet. For example, enzymes that catalyze certain oxidation reactions require either Fe^{2+} or Cu^{2+} as a cofactor needed for transferring electrons.

21.9B Classification of Enzymes

Enzymes are classified into six categories by the type of reaction they catalyze.

> • Oxidoreductases catalyze oxidation–reduction reactions.

When a substrate is oxidized or reduced, a coenzyme is required. The coenzyme serves as the oxidizing or reducing agent. For example, the enzyme lactate dehydrogenase catalyzes the reduction of pyruvate to lactate with the coenzyme NADH, nicotinamide adenine dinucleotide. Lactate dehydrogenase catalyzes both the reduction of pyruvate to lactate as well as the oxidation of lactate to pyruvate (Section 21.9A).

pyruvate

substrate

coenzyme

enzyme

lactate

reduced product

Oxidoreductases are subclassified as **oxidases** when they catalyze oxidations, **reductases** when they catalyze reduction, or **dehydrogenases** when two hydrogen atoms are removed or added during the redox reaction.

• Transferases catalyze the transfer of a group from one molecule to another.

For example, a **transaminase** catalyzes the transfer of an amino group (NH₂, Section 24.9), and a **kinase** catalyzes the transfer of a phosphate (Section 24.2). Alanine transaminase catalyzes the transfer of an amino group from alanine to α-ketoglutarate to form pyruvate and glutamate. This process begins the metabolism of amino acids.

• Hydrolases catalyze hydrolysis reactions—the cleavage of bonds with water.

For example, the digestion of a triacylglycerol, which begins with the hydrolysis of its three esters to glycerol and fatty acids (Section 19.5), occurs with hydrolases called **lipases.**

CONSUMER NOTE

Meat tenderizers contain papain, an enzyme that hydrolyzes peptide bonds, making meat more tender by breaking down the protein in tough fibers. Papain is obtained from the fruit of the papaya tree. ©McGraw-Hill Education/David Moyer, photographer

In addition to lipases, which catalyze the hydrolysis of lipids, other subclasses of hydrolases include **proteases,** which catalyze protein hydrolysis, and **nucleases,** which catalyze the hydrolysis of phosphate bonds in nucleic acids (Chapter 22). Carboxypeptidase A (Section 21.9A) is a protease.

• Isomerases catalyze the conversion of one isomer to another.

One step in the metabolism of glucose involves the **isomerization**—conversion of one isomer to another—of dihydroxyacetone phosphate to glyceraldehyde 3-phosphate (Section 24.3) catalyzed by triose phosphate isomerase.

The ketone and 1° alcohol in dihydroxyacetone phosphate are isomerized to an aldehyde and 2° alcohol with the same molecular formula.

• Lyases catalyze the addition of a molecule to a double bond or the elimination of a molecule to give a double bond.

The addition of H₂O to fumarate in the citric acid cycle (Section 23.5) is catalyzed by the lyase fumarase.

Lyases are subclassified as **dehydrases** when they catalyze the removal of H_2O, **decarboxylases** when they catalyze the removal of CO_2, and **synthases** when they catalyze the addition of a small molecule such as H_2O to a double bond. Fumarase is a synthase.

> • Ligases catalyze bond formation accompanied by energy release from a hydrolysis reaction.

A ligase enzyme catalyzes the joining together of two molecules. Because this process is often energetically unfavorable, the energy released in a hydrolysis reaction is used to drive the reaction. The most common energetically favorable hydrolysis reaction is the conversion of adenosine 5'-triphosphate (ATP) to adenosine 5'-diphosphate (ADP) and HPO_4^{2-}. The two reactions are said to be coupled.

For example, the energy needed for the reaction of pyruvate with CO_2 to form oxaloacetate is provided by the hydrolysis of ATP to ADP. This reaction is catalyzed by pyruvate carboxylase.

$$CH_3\overset{\overset{O}{\|}}{C}-CO_2^- + CO_2 + ATP \xrightarrow[\text{carboxylase}]{\text{pyruvate}} {}^-O\overset{\overset{O}{\|}}{C}-CH_2-\overset{\overset{O}{\|}}{C}-CO_2^- + ADP + HPO_4^{2-}$$

pyruvate   oxaloacetate

enzyme

We will return to the chemistry of coupled reactions when we learn about the details of ATP and ADP in Chapter 23. Table 21.3 summarizes the common classes of enzymes.

Table 21.3 Classification of Enzymes

Enzyme Class or Subclass	Reaction Catalyzed
Oxidoreductases	**Oxidation–reduction**
• Oxidases	• Oxidation
• Reductases	• Reduction
• Dehydrogenases	• Addition or removal of 2 H's
Transferases	**Transfer of a group**
• Transaminases	• Transfer of an NH_2 group
• Kinases	• Transfer of a phosphate
Hydrolases	**Hydrolysis**
• Lipases	• Hydrolysis of lipid esters
• Proteases	• Hydrolysis of amide bonds in proteins
• Nucleases	• Hydrolysis of nucleic acids
Isomerases	**Isomerization**
Lyases	**Addition to a double bond or elimination to give a double bond**
• Dehydrases	• Removal of H_2O
• Decarboxylases	• Removal of CO_2
• Synthases	• Addition of a small molecule to a double bond
Ligases	**Bond formation accompanied by ATP hydrolysis**
• Carboxylases	• Bond formation between a substrate and CO_2

SAMPLE PROBLEM 21.8 CLASSIFYING ENZYMES

Classify the enzyme used in each of the following reactions.

a.

pyruvate → acetaldehyde + CO_2

b. $H_3\overset{+}{N}$—CH—C—N—CH_2—C + H_2O ⟶ $H_3\overset{+}{N}$—C—C + $H_3\overset{+}{N}$—CH_2—C

Analysis

Concentrate on the functional groups that change in the reaction, and use Table 21.3 to classify the enzyme.

Solution

a. The reaction involves the loss of a molecule (CO_2) from a double bond, so the enzyme is a lyase. Because CO_2 is removed, the lyase is subclassified as a decarboxylase.

b. The reaction involves hydrolysis—that is, cleavage of a bond with water—so the enzyme is a hydrolase. Because hydrolysis cleaves the amide bond in a dipeptide, the hydrolase is subclassified as a protease.

PRACTICE PROBLEM 21.8

What class of enzyme catalyzes each of the following reactions?

a. succinate ⟶ fumarate

b. malate ⟶ oxaloacetate

More Practice: Try Problems 21.71–21.74.

PROBLEM 21.12

What class of enzyme catalyzes the following reaction?

maleic acid ⟶ fumaric acid

21.9C Naming Enzymes

The name of an enzyme generally has two parts.

- **The first part identifies the substrate on which the enzyme acts.**
- **The second part identifies the class of reaction catalyzed (Table 21.3).**

Thus, *succinate dehydrogenase* catalyzes the removal of two hydrogen atoms from the substrate succinate, and *pyruvate decarboxylase* catalyzes the loss of CO_2 from the substrate pyruvate.

Some older names of enzymes are still in common use. The names are derived from the name of the substrate by adding the suffix -*ase*. Thus, hydrolysis of the disaccharide lact*ose* is catalyzed by the enzyme lact*ase*. In addition, some enzymes are still identified by names that are not related to the substrate or type of reaction they catalyze. Examples include the digestive enzymes trypsin, chymotrypsin, and pepsin, which catalyze the hydrolysis of proteins.

SAMPLE PROBLEM 21.9 NAMING AN ENZYME

Suggest a name for the enzyme that catalyzes the following reaction.

phenylalanine

Analysis

Determine the type of reaction that occurs by examining the functional groups that change. Add the name of the reaction type from Table 21.3 to the name of the substrate.

Solution

The reaction involves the transfer of an amino group from phenylalanine to another reactant, so the enzyme is a transferase, specifically a transaminase. Because the name of the substrate is phenylalanine, the enzyme can be called **phenylalanine transaminase.**

PRACTICE PROBLEM 21.9

Suggest a name for the enzyme that catalyzes each of the following reactions.

a. transfer of a phosphate from ATP to glycerol

b. addition of water to fumarate

c. isomerization of glucose 6-phosphate to fructose 6-phosphate

More Practice: Try Problems 21.75, 21.76.

PROBLEM 21.13

Describe the reaction catalyzed by each enzyme: (a) aspartate transaminase; (b) glyceraldehyde 3-phosphate dehydrogenase.

21.10   How Enzymes Work

An enzyme contains a region called the **active site** that binds the substrate, forming an **enzyme–substrate complex.** The active site is often a small cavity that contains amino acids that are attracted to the substrate with various types of intermolecular forces. Sometimes polar amino acids of the enzyme hydrogen bond to the substrate or nonpolar amino acids have stabilizing hydrophobic interactions.

substrate

active site

enzyme   enzyme–substrate complex   products

enzyme

21.10A   Enzyme Specificity

Two models have been proposed to explain the specificity of a substrate for an enzyme's active site: the **lock-and-key model** and the **induced-fit model.**

In the lock-and-key model, the shape of the active site is rigid. The three-dimensional geometry of the substrate must exactly match the shape of the active site for catalysis to occur. The lock-and-key model explains the high specificity observed in many enzyme reactions.

The shape of the active site exactly matches the shape of the substrates.

In the induced-fit model, the shape of the active site is more flexible. It is thought that when the substrate and the enzyme interact, the shape of the active site can adjust to fit the shape of the substrate.

The shape of the active site adjusts to fit the shape of the substrates.

This model is often used to explain why some enzymes catalyze reactions with a wider variety of substrates. The shape of the active site and the substrate must still be reasonably similar, but once bound, the shape of the active site is different from that of the active site in the unbound enzyme. A well-characterized example of the induced-fit model is seen in the binding of glucose to the enzyme hexokinase, shown in Figure 21.15.

Figure 21.15   Hexokinase—An Example of the Induced-Fit Model

a. Shape of the active site before binding   b. Shape of the active site after binding

active site   glucose

glucose in the active site

The open cavity of the active site of the enzyme closes around the substrate for a tighter fit.

(a) The free enzyme has a small open cavity that fits a glucose molecule. (b) Once bound, the cavity encloses the glucose molecule more tightly in the enzyme–substrate complex.

21.10B Factors That Affect Enzyme Activity

The activity of an enzyme is affected by both temperature and pH.

As we learned in Section 6.4, an increase in temperature increases the rate of most chemical reactions. **Enzyme-catalyzed reactions also exhibit an increase in rate with increasing temperature until a maximum activity occurs,** often around 37 °C, and then activity falls off rapidly. At higher temperatures the enzyme begins to denature, and at 50–60 °C its activity is usually destroyed. Figure 21.16a illustrates an example of how the rate of an enzyme-catalyzed reaction changes with temperature.

Figure 21.16 Factors Affecting Enzyme Activity

a. Temperature

b. pH

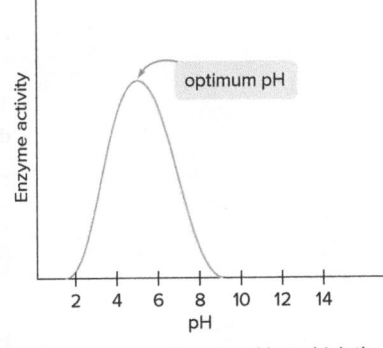

(a) An enzyme-catalyzed reaction increases in rate with increasing temperature until the enzyme begins to denature. Then, the reaction rate decreases rapidly. The maximum rate for the enzyme depicted in this graph occurs at approximately 37 °C.

(b) The optimum pH is the pH at which the catalytic activity of the enzyme is at its maximum. The enzyme depicted in this graph has maximum activity at pH 5.

Enzyme activity is also affected by pH. Each enzyme has an optimum pH at which catalysis occurs at a maximum rate. Although enzymes in cells have an optimum pH around 7.4, a digestive enzyme like pepsin, which is secreted in the gastric juices of the stomach, has an optimum pH of 2. Figure 21.16b illustrates how the activity of an enzyme with an optimum pH of 5 varies with pH.

PROBLEM 21.14

Estimate the optimum pH for the digestive enzyme trypsin, which hydrolyzes proteins in the small intestine, from the following graph.

PROBLEM 21.15

Using the graph in Figure 21.16a, determine which temperature in each pair gives the higher rate of reaction: (a) 25 °C or 35 °C; (b) 35 °C or 45 °C.

PROBLEM 21.16

Consider the enzyme pancreatic amylase, which has an optimum pH of 7.0. How is the rate of a pancreatic amylase-catalyzed reaction affected by each of the following changes: (a) lowering the pH from 7 to 4; (b) increasing the pH from 7 to 9; (c) decreasing the temperature from 37 °C to 28 °C; (d) increasing the temperature from 37 °C to 50 °C?

21.10C   Allosteric Control

Sometimes the activity of an enzyme is affected by the binding of a molecule called a regulator at a location other than the active site. Such an enzyme is called an **allosteric enzyme** and the process is called **allosteric control.**

- *Allosteric control* is the binding of a regulator to a site on an enzyme that affects the enzyme's ability to bind a substrate at its active site.

The binding of the regulator changes the shape of the protein, which can either increase or decrease the rate of the reaction.

- *Negative* allosteric control occurs when a regulator makes the active site less able to bind the substrate, and the rate of the reaction decreases.
- *Positive* allosteric control occurs when a regulator makes the active site more able to bind the substrate, and the rate of the reaction increases.

Figure 21.17 illustrates the difference between negative and positive allosteric control.

Figure 21.17   Allosteric Control

- With negative allosteric control, binding of the regulator to the enzyme triggers a change in shape (step [1]), making the active site less accessible or unavailable to bind the substrate, so no reaction occurs (step [2]).
- With positive allosteric control, binding of the regulator may cause the shape of the active site to more closely resemble the substrate (step [1]), thus allowing the substrate to bind (step [2]).

PROBLEM 21.17

X is an allosteric enzyme that converts a particular substrate to a product. When a regulator **Y** binds to **X**, the rate of the enzyme-catalyzed conversion of substrate to product increases. Is **Y** a positive or negative regulator of the enzyme **X**?

21.10D   Enzyme Inhibitors

Substances that bind to an enzyme and in the process greatly alter or destroy the enzyme's activity are called **inhibitors.** An inhibitor can bind to an enzyme reversibly or irreversibly.

- A *reversible* inhibitor binds to an enzyme but then enzyme activity is restored when the inhibitor is released.
- An *irreversible* inhibitor covalently binds to an enzyme, permanently destroying its activity.

Penicillin is an antibiotic that kills bacteria because it irreversibly binds to glycopeptide transpeptidase, an enzyme required for the synthesis of a bacterial cell wall (Section 17.11). Penicillin binds to a hydroxyl group (OH) of the enzyme, thus inactivating it, halting cell wall construction and killing the bacterium. Penicillin has no effect on human cells because they are surrounded by a flexible cell membrane and not a cell wall.

penicillin G

Penicillin is covalently bound to the enzyme, inactivating it.

enzyme   inactive enzyme

Reversible inhibition can be **competitive** or **noncompetitive.**

A *noncompetitive* **inhibitor binds to the enzyme but does not bind at the active site, thus exerting negative allosteric control.** The inhibitor causes the enzyme to change shape so that the active site can no longer bind the substrate. When the noncompetitive inhibitor is no longer bound to the enzyme, normal enzyme activity resumes.

The substrate no longer fits.

substrate

noncompetitive inhibitor

active site   enzyme   active site   bound inhibitor   active site

Without the inhibitor, the substrate fits into the active site.

When the inhibitor is bound, the active site changes shape and the substrate no longer fits.

A *competitive* **inhibitor has a shape and structure similar to that of the substrate, so it competes with the substrate for binding to the active site.** The antibiotic **sulfanilamide** (Section 13.13B) is a competitive inhibitor of the enzyme needed to synthesize the vitamin folic acid from *p*-aminobenzoic acid in bacteria. When sulfanilamide binds to the active site, *p*-aminobenzoic acid cannot be converted to folic acid, so a bacterium cannot grow and reproduce. Sulfanilamide does not affect human cells because humans do not synthesize folic acid and must obtain it in the diet.

sulfanilamide
a competitive inhibitor

p-aminobenzoic acid
PABA

folic acid

Both compounds can bind to the active site.

PROBLEM 21.18

The nerve gas sarin acts as a poison by covalently bonding to a hydroxyl group in the active site of the enzyme acetylcholinesterase. This binding results in a higher-than-normal amount of acetylcholine at a nerve synapse, resulting in muscle spasms. From this description, would you expect sarin to be a competitive, noncompetitive, or irreversible inhibitor?

PROBLEM 21.19

Use the given representations for an enzyme, substrate, and inhibitor to illustrate the process of competitive inhibition.

active site

enzyme   substrate   inhibitor

21.10E Zymogens

Sometimes an enzyme is synthesized in an inactive form, and then it is converted to its active form when it is needed. The inactive precursor of an enzyme is called a **zymogen** or **proenzyme.** Often the zymogen contains additional amino acids in its peptide chain, which are then cleaved when activation is desired.

cleavage
here

inactive zymogen

active enzyme

For example, the digestive enzymes trypsin and chymotrypsin are synthesized in the pancreas as the zymogens trypsinogen and chymotrypsinogen, respectively. As zymogens, these proteins are inactive and thus they do not digest the proteins that make up the pancreas. When they pass into the small intestine, however, some of the amino acids are removed from the peptide chain to form the active enzymes, which then catalyze the hydrolysis of peptide bonds during protein digestion.

PROBLEM 21.20

Explain why the proteins involved in blood clotting, fibrin and thrombin, are first synthesized as the zymogens fibrinogen and prothrombin, respectively.

21.11 FOCUS ON HEALTH & MEDICINE
Using Enzymes to Diagnose and Treat Diseases

Measuring enzyme levels in the blood and understanding the key role of enzymes in biological reactions have aided greatly in both diagnosing and treating diseases.

21.11A Enzyme Levels as Diagnostic Tools

Certain enzymes are present in a higher concentration in particular cells. When the cells are damaged by disease or injury, the cells rupture and die, releasing the enzymes into the bloodstream. Measuring the activity of the enzymes in the blood then becomes a powerful tool to diagnose the presence of disease or injury in some organs.

Measuring enzyme levels is now routine for many different conditions. For example, when a patient comes into an emergency room with chest pain, measuring the level of creatine phosphokinase (CPK) and other enzymes indicates whether a heart attack, which results in damage to some portion of the heart, has occurred. Common enzymes used for diagnosis are listed in Table 21.4.

Table 21.4 Common Enzymes Used for Diagnosis

Enzyme	Condition
Creatine phosphokinase	Heart attack
Alkaline phosphatase	Liver or bone disease
Acid phosphatase	Prostate cancer
Amylase, lipase	Diseases of the pancreas

21.11B Treating Disease with Drugs That Interact with Enzymes

Molecules that inhibit an enzyme can be useful drugs. The antibiotics penicillin and sulfanilamide are two examples discussed in Section 21.10. Drugs used to treat high blood pressure and acquired immune deficiency syndrome (AIDS) are also enzyme inhibitors.

ACE inhibitors are a group of drugs used to treat individuals with high blood pressure. Angiotensin is an octapeptide that narrows blood vessels, thus increasing blood pressure. Angiotensin is formed from the zymogen angiotensinogen by action of **ACE, the angiotensin-converting enzyme,** which cleaves two amino acids from the inactive decapeptide.

By blocking the conversion of angiotensinogen to angiotensin, blood pressure is decreased. Several effective ACE inhibitors are currently available, including captopril and enalapril.

Generic name captopril
Trade name Capoten

Generic name enalapril
Trade name Vasotec

Several enzyme inhibitors are also available to treat human immunodeficiency virus (HIV), the virus that causes AIDS. The most effective treatments are **HIV protease inhibitors.** These drugs inhibit the action of the HIV protease enzyme, an essential enzyme needed by HIV to make copies of itself that go on to infect other cells. Deactivating the HIV protease enzyme decreases the virus population, bringing the disease under control. Several protease inhibitors are currently available, and often an individual takes a "cocktail" of several drugs to keep the disease in check. Amprenavir (trade name Agenerase) is a protease inhibitor taken twice daily by individuals who are HIV positive. The three-dimensional structure of the HIV-1 protease enzyme is shown in Figure 21.18.

Generic name amprenavir
Trade name Agenerase

Figure 21.18   The HIV Protease Enzyme

a. Ball-and-stick model of the HIV protease enzyme

b. Ribbon diagram with the protease inhibitor amprenavir in the active site

CHAPTER HIGHLIGHTS

KEY TERMS

Active site (21.10)

Allosteric control (21.10)

Amino acid (21.2)

Coenzyme (21.9)

Cofactor (21.9)

Competitive inhibitor (21.10)

Conjugated protein (21.7)

C-Terminal amino acid (21.4)

Decarboxylase (21.9)

Dehydrase (21.9)

Dehydrogenase (21.9)

Denaturation (21.8)

Dipeptide (21.4)

Enzyme (21.9)

Enzyme–substrate complex (21.10)

Fibrous protein (21.7)

Globular protein (21.7)

α-Helix (21.6)

Heme (21.7)

Hydrolase (21.9)

Induced-fit model (21.10)

Inhibitor (21.10)

Irreversible inhibitor (21.10)

Isoelectric point (21.3)

Isomerase (21.9)

Kinase (21.9)

Ligase (21.9)

Lipase (21.9)

Lock-and-key model (21.10)

Lyase (21.9)

Noncompetitive inhibitor (21.10)

N-Terminal amino acid (21.4)

Nuclease (21.9)

Oxidase (21.9)

Oxidoreductase (21.9)

Peptide (21.4)

Peptide bond (21.4)

β-Pleated sheet (21.6)

Primary structure (21.6)

Protease (21.9)

Protein (21.1)

Quaternary structure (21.6)

Reductase (21.9)

Reversible inhibitor (21.10)

Secondary structure (21.6)

Synthase (21.9)

Tertiary structure (21.6)

Transaminase (21.9)

Transferase (21.9)

Tripeptide (21.4)

Zwitterion (21.2)

Zymogen (21.10)

KEY CONCEPTS

① What are the main structural features of an amino acid? (21.2)

- Amino acids contain an amino group (NH_2) on the α carbon to the carboxyl group (COOH). Because they contain both an acid and a base, amino acids exist in their neutral form as zwitterions having the general structure $^+H_3NCH(R)COO^-$. Because they are salts, amino acids are water soluble and have high melting points.

- All amino acids except glycine (R = H) have a chirality center on the α carbon. L Amino acids are naturally occurring.

- Amino acids are subclassified as neutral, acidic, or basic by the functional groups present in the R group, as shown in Table 21.2.

② Describe the acid–base properties of amino acids. (21.3)

- Neutral, uncharged amino acids exist as zwitterions containing an ammonium cation ($-NH_3^+$) and a carboxylate anion ($-COO^-$).

- When strong acid is added, the carboxylate anion gains a proton and the amino acid has a net +1 charge. When strong base is added, the ammonium cation loses a proton and the amino acid has a net −1 charge.

overall +1 charge
pH ≤ 2

pH ≈ 6

overall −1 charge
pH ≥ 10

③ What are the main structural features of peptides? (21.4)

- Peptides contain amino acids, called amino acid residues, joined together by amide (peptide) bonds. The amino acid that contains the free $-NH_3^+$ group on the α carbon is called the N-terminal amino acid, and the amino acid that contains the free $-COO^-$ group on the α carbon is the C-terminal amino acid.

- Peptides are written from left to right, from the N-terminal to the C-terminal end, using the one- or three-letter abbreviations for the amino acids listed in Table 21.2.

④ Give examples of simple biologically active peptides. (21.5)

- Enkephalins are pentapeptides that act as sedatives and painkillers by binding to pain receptors.

- Oxytocin is a nonapeptide hormone that stimulates the contraction of uterine muscles and initiates the flow of milk in nursing mothers.

- Vasopressin is a nonapeptide hormone that serves as an antidiuretic; that is, vasopressin causes the kidneys to retain water.

⑤ What are the general characteristics of the primary, secondary, tertiary, and quaternary structure of proteins? (21.6)

- The primary structure of a protein is the particular sequence of amino acids joined together by amide bonds.

- The two most common types of secondary structure are the α-helix and the β-pleated sheet. Both structures are stabilized by hydrogen bonds between the N—H and C=O groups.

- The tertiary structure is the three-dimensional shape adopted by the entire peptide chain. London dispersion forces stabilize hydrophobic interactions between nonpolar amino acids. Hydrogen bonding and ionic interactions occur between polar or charged amino acid residues. Disulfide bonds are covalent sulfur–sulfur bonds that occur between cysteine residues in different parts of the peptide chain.
- When a protein contains more than one polypeptide chain, the quaternary structure describes the shape of the protein complex formed by two or more chains.

6 **What are the basic features of fibrous proteins like α-keratin and collagen? (21.7)**

- Fibrous proteins are composed of long linear polypeptide chains that serve structural roles and are water insoluble.
- α-Keratin in hair is a fibrous protein composed almost exclusively of α-helix units that wind together to form a superhelix. Disulfide bonds between chains make the resulting bundles of protein chains strong.
- Collagen, found in connective tissue, is composed of a superhelix formed from three elongated left-handed helices.

7 **What are the basic features of globular proteins like hemoglobin and myoglobin? (21.7)**

- Globular proteins have compact shapes and are folded to place polar amino acids on the outside to make them water soluble. Hemoglobin and myoglobin are both conjugated proteins composed of a protein unit and a heme molecule. The Fe^{2+} ion of the heme binds oxygen. While myoglobin has a single polypeptide chain, hemoglobin contains four peptide chains that form a single protein molecule.

8 **What products are formed when a protein is hydrolyzed? (21.8)**

- Hydrolysis breaks up the primary structure of a protein to form the amino acids that compose it. All of the amide bonds are broken by the addition of water, forming a carboxylate anion ($-COO^-$) in one amino acid and an ammonium cation ($-NH_3^+$) in the other.

9 **What is denaturation? (21.8)**

- Denaturation is a process that alters the shape of a protein by disrupting the secondary, tertiary, or quaternary structure. High temperature, acid, base, and agitation can denature a protein. Compact water-soluble proteins uncoil and become less water soluble.

10 **What are the main structural features of enzymes and how are enzymes classified? (21.9, 21.10)**

- Enzymes are biological catalysts that greatly increase the rate of biological reactions and are highly specific for a substrate or a type of substrate. An enzyme binds a substrate at its active site, forming an enzyme–substrate complex by either the lock-and-key model or the induced-fit model.
- Enzymes are classified into six categories by the type of reaction they catalyze; oxidoreductases, transferases, hydrolases, isomerases, lyases, and ligases (Table 21.3).

11 **What are the three types of enzyme inhibitors? (21.10)**

- Enzyme inhibitors cause an enzyme to lose activity. Irreversible inhibition occurs when an inhibitor covalently binds the enzyme and permanently destroys its activity. Competitive reversible inhibition occurs when the inhibitor is structurally similar to the substrate and competes with it for occupation of the active site. Noncompetitive reversible inhibition occurs when an inhibitor binds to a location other than the active site, altering the shape of the active site.

12 **How are enzymes used in medicine? (21.11)**

- Measuring blood enzyme levels is used to diagnose heart attacks and diseases that cause higher-than-normal concentrations of certain enzymes to enter the blood.
- Drugs that inhibit the action of an enzyme can be used to kill bacteria. ACE inhibitors are used to treat high blood pressure. HIV protease inhibitors are used to treat HIV by binding to an enzyme needed by the virus to replicate itself.

PROBLEMS

Selected in-chapter and odd-numbered end-of-chapter problems have brief answers in Appendix B. The *Student Study Guide and Solutions Manual* contains detailed solutions to all in-chapter and odd-numbered end-of-chapter problems, as well as additional worked examples and a chapter self-test.

Amino Acids

21.21 The amino acid alanine is a solid at room temperature and has a melting point of 315 °C, whereas pyruvic acid (CH_3COCO_2H) has a similar molecular weight but is a liquid at room temperature with a boiling point of 165 °C. Account for the difference.

21.22 Why is phenylalanine water soluble but 4-phenylbutanoic acid ($C_6H_5CH_2CH_2CH_2COOH$), a compound of similar molecular weight, water insoluble?

21.23 Draw the structure of a naturally occurring amino acid that:
   a. contains a 1° alcohol
   b. contains an amide
   c. is an essential amino acid with an aromatic ring
   d. is a neutral amino acid with a 3° carbon atom in its side chain

21.24 Draw the structure of a naturally occurring amino acid that:
   a. contains a 2° alcohol
   b. contains a thiol
   c. is an acidic amino acid
   d. is a neutral amino acid with a phenol in the side chain

21.25 For each amino acid: [1] draw the L enantiomer in a Fischer projection; [2] classify the amino acid as neutral, acidic, or basic; [3] give the three-letter symbol; [4] give the one-letter symbol.

    a. leucine   c. lysine

    b. tryptophan   d. aspartic acid

21.26 For each amino acid: [1] draw the L enantiomer in a Fischer projection; [2] classify the amino acid as neutral, acidic, or basic; [3] give the three-letter symbol; [4] give the one-letter symbol.

    a. arginine   c. glutamic acid

    b. tyrosine   d. valine

21.27 Draw both enantiomers of each amino acid and label them as D or L: (a) methionine; (b) asparagine.

21.28 Which of the following Fischer projections represent naturally occurring amino acids? Name each amino acid and designate it as a D or L isomer.

    a. H_3N^+ — H   b. H — NH_3^+

         $CH_2CH(CH_3)_2$ CH_2COO^-

21.29 For each amino acid: [1] give the name; [2] give the three-letter abbreviation; [3] give the one-letter abbreviation; [4] classify the amino acid as neutral, acidic, or basic.

    a. H_3N^+ — H   b.

         $CH_2CH_2CONH_2$

21.30 For each amino acid: [1] give the name; [2] give the three-letter abbreviation; [3] give the one-letter abbreviation; [4] classify the amino acid as neutral, acidic, or basic.

    a. H_3N^+ — H   b. H_3N^+ — H

         $CH_2CH_2SCH_3$ CH_2

Acid–Base Properties of Amino Acids

21.31 (a) Identify the amino acid shown with all uncharged atoms in the ball-and-stick model. (b) Give the three-letter and one-letter abbreviations for the amino acid. (c) Draw the form present at the isoelectric point of the amino acid.

21.32 (a) Identify the amino acid shown with all uncharged atoms in the ball-and-stick model. (b) Give the three-letter and one-letter abbreviations for the amino acid. (c) Draw the form of the amino acid present at pH 11.

21.33 Draw the amino acid leucine at each pH: (a) 6; (b) 10; (c) 2. Which form predominates at leucine's isoelectric point?

21.34 Draw the structure of the neutral, positively charged, and negatively charged forms of the amino acid tyrosine. Which form predominates at pH 1? Which form predominates at pH 11? Which form predominates at the isoelectric point?

Peptides

21.35 Locate the peptide bond in the dipeptide shown in the ball-and-stick model, and identify the amino acids that form the dipeptide. Name the dipeptide using the three-letter abbreviations for the amino acids.

21.36 Label the N-terminal and C-terminal amino acids in the dipeptide shown in the ball-and-stick model. Name the dipeptide using the one-letter abbreviations for the amino acids.

21.37 Melittin, the principal toxin of bee venom, consists of a peptide with the sequence GIGAVLKVLTTGLPALISWIKRKRQQ (using one-letter abbreviations for the amino acids).

    a. How many amide bonds join the amino acids in the peptide chain?

    b. Give the name of the N-terminal amino acid.

    c. Give the name of the C-terminal amino acid.

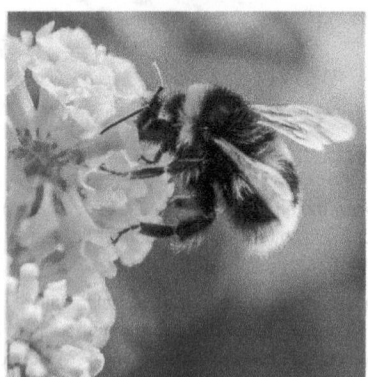

©bigemrg/Getty Images RF

21.38 α-Cobratoxin is a neurotoxin found in the venom of the Chinese cobra, *Naja atra*, a prevalent venomous snake that inhabits China and Taiwan. A partial sequence of its 71 amino acid chain is shown.

    a. How many amide bonds join the amino acids in the peptide chain?

    b. Give the name of the N-terminal amino acid.

    c. Give the name of the C-terminal amino acid.

IRCFITPDIT— **51 amino acids** —CNPFPTRKRP

©Mitja Derenda/Getty Images RF

21.39 (a) Draw the structure of the two possible dipeptides that can be formed by combining valine and phenylalanine. (b) In each dipeptide, label the N- and C-terminal amino acids. (c) Name each peptide using three-letter symbols.

21.40 (a) Draw the structure of the two possible dipeptides that can be formed by combining glycine and asparagine. (b) In each dipeptide, label the N- and C-terminal amino acids. (c) Name each peptide using three-letter symbols.

21.41 For each tripeptide: [1] draw the structure of the tripeptide; [2] label the amide bonds; [3] identify the N-terminal and

C-terminal amino acids; [4] name the peptide using three-letter symbols for the amino acids.

    a. leucylvalyltryptophan

    b. phenylalanylserylthreonine

21.42 For each tripeptide: [1] draw the structure of the tripeptide; [2] label the amide bonds; [3] identify the N-terminal and C-terminal amino acids; [4] name the peptide using three-letter symbols for the amino acids.

    a. tyrosylleucylisoleucine

    b. methionylisoleucylcysteine

21.43 For each tripeptide: [1] identify the amino acids that form the peptide; [2] label the N- and C-terminal amino acids; [3] name the tripeptide using three-letter symbols.

a. $H_3\overset{+}{N}$—CH—C—N—CH—C—N—CH—C—O$^-$
with groups CH(CH$_3$)$_2$, H, H, H, CH$_2$ (phenyl), O

b. $H_3\overset{+}{N}$—CH—C—N—CH—C—N—CH—C—O$^-$
with groups CH$_2$CH(CH$_3$)$_2$, H, CH$_2$ (phenol, OH), H, CH$_2$SCH$_3$

21.44 For each tripeptide: [1] identify the amino acids that form the peptide; [2] label the N- and C-terminal amino acids; [3] name the tripeptide using three-letter symbols.

a. $H_3\overset{+}{N}$—CH—C—N—CH—C—N—CH—C—O$^-$
with groups CH$_2$COO$^-$, H, CH$_3$, H, CHCH$_3$ / CH$_2$CH$_3$

b. $H_3\overset{+}{N}$—CH—C—N—CH—C—N—CH—C—O$^-$
with groups CH$_2$OH, H, CH$_2$ (phenyl), H, CH$_2$CONH$_2$

21.45 What amino acids are formed by hydrolysis of the tripeptide depicted in the ball-and-stick model?

21.46 Give the three-letter abbreviations for the amino acids formed by hydrolysis of the tripeptide depicted in the ball-and-stick model.

21.47 Draw the structures of the amino acids formed when the tripeptides in Problem 21.43 are hydrolyzed.

21.48 Draw the structures of the amino acids formed when the tripeptides in Problem 21.44 are hydrolyzed.

21.49 Bradykinin is a nonapeptide that stimulates smooth muscle contraction, dilates blood vessels, causes pain, and is a component of bee venom. Draw the structure of the amino acids formed on hydrolysis of one mole of bradykinin, and tell how many moles of each amino acid are formed.

Arg–Pro–Pro–Gly–Phe–Ser–Pro–Phe–Arg
bradykinin

21.50 Aspartame, the methyl ester of a dipeptide, is the common artificial sweetener NutraSweet (Section 20.5B). Draw the structure of the products formed when the amide and ester bonds are hydrolyzed. Which amino acid contains the carbonyl group of the peptide bond? Which amino acid contains the nitrogen atom of the amide bond?

aspartame

21.51 Chymotrypsin is a digestive enzyme that hydrolyzes only certain peptide bonds: the carbonyl group in the amide bond must come from phenylalanine, tyrosine, or tryptophan. Draw the structure of the amino acids and peptides formed by hydrolysis of the following peptide with chymotrypsin: Gly–Tyr–Gly–Ala–Phe–Val.

21.52 Trypsin is a digestive enzyme that hydrolyzes peptide bonds only when the carbonyl group in the amide bond comes from lysine or arginine. Draw the structure of the amino acids and peptides formed by hydrolysis of the following peptide with trypsin: Gly–Lys–Arg–Ala–Ala–Arg.

Proteins

21.53 What type of intermolecular forces exist between the side chains of each of the following pairs of amino acids?
   a. isoleucine and valine   c. Lys and Glu
   b. threonine and phenylalanine d. Arg and Asp

21.54 What type of interactions occur at each of the labeled sites in the portion of the protein ribbon shown?

21.55 Which peptide in each pair contains amino acids with side chains that exhibit predominantly London dispersion forces?
   a. Met–Gly–Leu–Phe–Gln–Ala or Lys–Gly–Arg–Tyr–Trp–Glu
   b. Tyr–Asp–Leu–Lys–His or Phe–Asn–Leu–Leu–Met

21.56 Decide if the side chains of the amino acid residues in the following peptides are nonpolar or polar, and label the hydrophobic and hydrophilic end of each peptide.
   a. VLLFGEDEK   b. RKYSFLGAA

21.57 Which type of protein structure is indicated in each region (**A–C**) of the following representation? Choose from primary structure, α-helix, β-pleated sheet, tertiary structure, or quaternary structure.

21.58 Label each of the following diagrams as representing the primary, secondary, tertiary, or quaternary structure of a protein.

21.59 Draw the structures of the amino acids asparagine and serine, and show how hydrogen bonding is possible between the two side chains.

21.60 Draw the structures of the amino acids tyrosine and threonine, and show how hydrogen bonding is possible between the two side chains.

21.61 Label the regions of secondary structure in the following protein ribbon diagram.

21.62 Label the regions of secondary structure in the following protein ribbon diagram.

21.63 Compare α-keratin and hemoglobin with regard to each of the following: (a) secondary structure; (b) water solubility; (c) function; (d) location in the body.

21.64 Compare collagen and myoglobin with regard to each of the following: (a) secondary structure; (b) water solubility; (c) function; (d) location in the body.

21.65 When a protein is denatured, how is its primary, secondary, tertiary, and quaternary structure affected?

21.66 Hydrogen bonding stabilizes both the secondary and tertiary structures of a protein. (a) What functional groups hydrogen bond to stabilize secondary structure? (b) What functional groups hydrogen bond to stabilize tertiary structure?

21.67 Describe the function or biological activity of each protein or peptide: (a) insulin; (b) myoglobin; (c) α-keratin; (d) chymotrypsin; (e) oxytocin.

21.68 Describe the function or biological activity of each protein or peptide: (a) collagen; (b) hemoglobin; (c) vasopressin; (d) pepsin; (e) met-enkephalin.

Enzymes

21.69 Using the given representations for an enzyme and substrate, which diagram represents (a) the enzyme–substrate complex; (b) competitive inhibition; (c) noncompetitive inhibition?

substrate

enzyme   **A**   **B**   **C**

21.70 What is the difference between a dehydrogenase and a dehydrase?

21.71 What class of enzyme catalyzes each of the following reactions?

21.72 What class of enzyme catalyzes each of the following reactions?
  a. hydrolysis of Val–Gly to Val and Gly
  b. transfer of a phosphate from ATP to fructose 6-phosphate
  c. conversion of CH_3CH_2OH to CH_3CHO with NAD^+

21.73 What class of enzyme catalyzes the following reaction?

21.74 What class of enzyme catalyzes the following reaction?

21.75 What kind of reaction is catalyzed by each of the following enzymes?
  a. citrate decarboxylase   c. serine transaminase
  b. oxalate reductase

21.76 What kind of reaction is catalyzed by each of the following enzymes?
  a. a protease   c. a lipase
  b. a reductase

21.77 Use the graph of enzyme activity versus pH for enzymes **A** and **B** to answer the questions.

a. What is the optimum pH for enzyme **A**?
b. What is the optimum pH for enzyme **B**?
c. Which enzyme has the higher activity at pH 4?
d. Which enzyme has the higher activity at pH 9?

21.78 How will each of the following changes affect the rate of an enzyme-catalyzed reaction whose optimum pH is 7.4?

a. decreasing the temperature from 37 °C to 5 °C

b. increasing the temperature from 37 °C to 90 °C

c. increasing the pH from 7.4 to 10

d. increasing the pH from 5 to 7.4

21.79 What is the difference between positive and negative allosteric control?

21.80 Explain the role of zymogens in (a) controlling blood pressure; (b) the action of digestive enzymes.

21.81 How are enzyme inhibitors used to treat high blood pressure? Give a specific example of a drug used and an enzyme inhibited.

21.82 How are enzyme inhibitors used to treat HIV? Give a specific example of a drug used and an enzyme inhibited.

21.83 Use the given representations for an enzyme, substrate, and inhibitor to illustrate the process of noncompetitive inhibition.

active site

enzyme   substrate   inhibitor

21.84 Use the given representations for an enzyme and substrate to illustrate the difference between the lock-and-key model and the induced-fit model of enzyme specificity.

active site

enzyme   substrate

Applications

21.85 What structural feature in α-keratin makes fingernails harder than skin?

21.86 Why does the α-keratin in hair contain many cysteine residues?

21.87 Why must vegetarian diets be carefully balanced?

21.88 Why does cooking meat make it easier to digest?

21.89 Sometimes an incision is cauterized (burned) to close the wound and prevent bleeding. What does cauterization do to protein structure?

21.90 Why is insulin administered by injection instead of taken in tablet form?

21.91 With reference to enzyme activity, why are surgical instruments sterilized by heating with steam in an autoclave?

21.92 The silk produced by a silkworm is a protein with a high glycine and alanine content. With reference to the structure, how does this make the silk fiber strong?

21.93 Explain the difference in the mechanism of action of penicillin and sulfanilamide. How is enzyme inhibition involved in both mechanisms? Why don't penicillin and sulfanilamide kill both human and bacterial cells?

21.94 How are blood enzyme levels used to diagnose certain diseases? Give an example of a specific condition and enzyme used for diagnosis.

CHALLENGE PROBLEMS

21.95 Explain why two amino acids—aspartic acid and glutamic acid—have a +1 net charge at low pH, but a −2 net charge at high pH.

21.96 Suggest a reason for the following observation. Proteins like collagen that are high in proline content do not contain an α-helix in their secondary structure.

22

Techniques to analyze DNA
samples are commonly utilized
in criminal investigations and to
screen for genetic diseases.
©Cultura Creative/Alamy RF

Nucleic Acids and Protein Synthesis

CHAPTER OUTLINE

22.1 Nucleosides and Nucleotides

22.2 Nucleic Acids

22.3 The DNA Double Helix

22.4 Replication

22.5 RNA

22.6 Transcription

22.7 The Genetic Code

22.8 Translation and Protein Synthesis

22.9 Mutations and Genetic Diseases

22.10 Recombinant DNA

22.11 FOCUS ON HEALTH & MEDICINE:
Viruses

CHAPTER GOALS

In this chapter you will learn how to:

1. Draw the structure of nucleosides and nucleotides

2. Draw short segments of the nucleic acids DNA and RNA

3. Describe the basic features of the DNA double helix

4. Outline the main steps of replication

5. List the three types and functions of RNA molecules

6. Explain the process of transcription

7. Describe the basic elements of the genetic code

8. Explain the process of translation

9. Define the terms "mutation" and "genetic disease"

10. Describe the basic features of recombinant DNA, the polymerase chain
reaction, and DNA fingerprinting

11. Describe the main characteristics of viruses

Why Study
**Nucleic Acids and
Protein Synthesis?**

Whether you are tall or short, fair-skinned or dark-complexioned, blue-eyed or brown-eyed, your unique characteristics are determined by the nucleic acid polymers that reside in the chromosomes of your cells. The nucleic acid **DNA** stores the genetic information of a particular organism, while the nucleic acid **RNA** translates this genetic information into the synthesis of proteins needed by cells for proper function and development. Even minor alterations in the nucleic acid sequence can have significant effects on an organism, sometimes resulting in devastating diseases like sickle cell anemia and cystic fibrosis. In Chapter 22, we study nucleic acids and learn how the genetic information stored in DNA is translated into protein synthesis.

22.1   Nucleosides and Nucleotides

Nucleic acids are unbranched polymers composed of repeating monomers called *nucleotides*. There are two types of nucleic acids.

- DNA, deoxyribonucleic acid, stores the genetic information of an organism and transmits that information from one generation to another.
- RNA, ribonucleic acid, translates the genetic information contained in DNA into proteins needed for all cellular functions.

The nucleotide monomers that compose DNA and RNA consist of three components—a **monosaccharide, a nitrogen-containing base, and a phosphate group.**

DNA molecules contain several million nucleotides while RNA molecules are much smaller, containing perhaps a few thousand nucleotides. DNA is contained in the chromosomes of the nucleus, each chromosome having a different type of DNA. The number of chromosomes differs from species to species. Humans have 46 chromosomes (23 pairs). An individual chromosome is composed of many genes. **A** *gene* **is a portion of the DNA molecule responsible for the synthesis of a single protein.**

We begin our study of nucleic acids with a look at the structure and formation of the nucleotide monomers.

22.1A   Nucleosides—Joining a Monosaccharide and a Base

The nucleotides of both DNA and RNA contain a five-membered ring monosaccharide, often called simply the *sugar* component.

- In RNA, the monosaccharide is the aldopentose D-ribose.
- In DNA the monosaccharide is D-2-deoxyribose, an aldopentose that lacks a hydroxyl group at C2.

The prefix *deoxy* means "without oxygen."

Only five common nitrogen-containing bases are present in nucleic acids. Three bases with one ring (**cytosine, uracil,** and **thymine**) are derived from the parent compound **pyrimidine.** Two bases with two rings (**adenine** and **guanine**) are derived from the parent compound **purine.** Each base is designated by a one-letter abbreviation as shown.

pyrimidine
(parent compound)

cytosine
C

uracil
U
(RNA only)

thymine
T
(DNA only)

purine
(parent compound)

adenine
A

guanine
G

Uracil (U) occurs only in RNA, while thymine (T) occurs only in DNA. As a result:

- DNA contains the bases A, G, C, and T.
- RNA contains the bases A, G, C, and U.

A *nucleoside* is formed by joining the anomeric carbon of the monosaccharide with a nitrogen atom of the base. A nucleoside is an *N*-glycoside, because it is a nitrogen derivative of the glycosides discussed in Chapter 20. Primes (') are used to number the carbons of the monosaccharide in a nucleoside, to distinguish them from the atoms in the rings of the base.

D-ribose

cytosine
C

join

cytidine
a ribonucleoside

N-glycoside

D-2-deoxyribose

adenine
A

join

deoxyadenosine
a deoxyribonucleoside

N-glycoside

With pyrimidine bases, the nitrogen atom at the 1 position bonds with the 1' carbon of the sugar. With purine bases, the nitrogen atom at the 9 position bonds with the 1' carbon of the sugar. Joining cytosine with ribose forms the ribonucleoside **cytidine.** Joining adenine with 2-deoxyribose forms the deoxyribonucleoside **deoxyadenosine.**

Nucleosides are named as derivatives of the bases from which they are formed.

- To name a nucleoside derived from a pyrimidine base, use the suffix *-idine* (cytosine → cy*tidine*).
- To name a nucleoside derived from a purine base, use the suffix *-osine* (adenine → aden*osine*).
- For deoxyribonucleosides, add the prefix *deoxy-*, as in *deoxy*adenosine.

SAMPLE PROBLEM 22.1 NAMING A NUCLEOSIDE

Identify the base and monosaccharide used to form the following nucleoside, and then name it.

Analysis

- The sugar portion of a nucleoside contains the five-membered ring. If there is an OH group at C2', the sugar is ribose, and if there is no OH group at C2', the sugar is deoxyribose.
- The base is joined to the five-membered ring as an *N*-glycoside. A pyrimidine base has one ring and is derived from either cytosine, uracil, or thymine. A purine base has two rings and is derived from either adenine or guanine.
- Nucleosides derived from pyrimidines end in the suffix *-idine*. Nucleosides derived from purines end in the suffix *-osine*.

Solution

- The sugar contains no OH at C2', so it is derived from deoxyribose.
- The base is thymine.
- To name the deoxyribonucleoside, change the suffix of the base to *-idine* and add the prefix *deoxy*; thus, thymine → deoxythymidine.

PRACTICE PROBLEM 22.1

Identify the base and monosaccharide used to form the following nucleosides, and then assign names.

More Practice: Try Problems 22.21–22.24.

PROBLEM 22.1

Draw the structure of guanosine. Number the carbon atoms in the monosaccharide. Classify the compound as a ribonucleoside or a deoxyribonucleoside.

PROBLEM 22.2

5-Fluorouracil is an anticancer drug that interferes with DNA synthesis because its structure resembles a DNA base that is needed for normal DNA replication. 5-Fluorouracil is sold as a cream to treat basal cell carcinoma, the most common form of skin cancer. What DNA base does 5-fluorouracil resemble?

22.1B   Nucleotides—Joining a Nucleoside with a Phosphate

Nucleotides are formed by adding a phosphate group to the 5'-OH of a nucleoside. Nucleotides are named by adding the term *5'-monophosphate* to the name of the nucleoside from which they are derived. **Ribonucleotides** are derived from ribose, while **deoxyribonucleotides** are derived from 2-deoxyribose.

phosphate

cytidine
a ribonucleoside

cytidine 5'-monophosphate
a ribonucleotide

CMP

Add phosphate here.

phosphate

deoxyadenosine
a deoxyribonucleoside

deoxyadenosine 5'-monophosphate
a deoxyribonucleotide

dAMP

Add phosphate here.

Because of the lengthy names of nucleotides, three- or four-letter abbreviations are commonly used instead. Thus, **c**ytidine 5'-**m**onophosphate is **CMP** and **d**eoxy**a**denosine 5'-**m**onophosphate is **dAMP**.

Figure 22.1 summarizes the information about nucleic acids and their components learned thus far. Table 22.1 summarizes the names and abbreviations used for the bases, nucleosides, and nucleotides needed in nucleic acid chemistry.

Figure 22.1

Summary of the Components
of Nucleosides, Nucleotides,
and Nucleic Acids

Type of Compound	Components
Nucleoside	• A monosaccharide + a base • A **ribo**nucleoside contains the monosaccharide **ribose.** • A **deoxy**ribonucleoside contains the monosaccharide 2-**deoxy**ribose.
Nucleotide	• A nucleoside + phosphate = a monosaccharide + a base + phosphate • A **ribo**nucleotide contains the monosaccharide **ribose.** • A **deoxy**ribonucleotide contains the monosaccharide 2-**deoxy**ribose.
DNA	• A polymer of **deoxy**ribonucleotides • The monosaccharide is 2-**deoxy**ribose. • The bases are **A, G, C,** and **T.**
RNA	• A polymer of **ribo**nucleotides • The monosaccharide is **ribose.** • The bases are **A, G, C,** and **U.**

Table 22.1   Names of Bases, Nucleosides, and Nucleotides in Nucleic Acids

Base	Abbreviation	Nucleoside	Nucleotide	Abbreviation
DNA				
Adenine	A	Deoxyadenosine	Deoxyadenosine 5'-monophosphate	dAMP
Guanine	G	Deoxyguanosine	Deoxyguanosine 5'-monophosphate	dGMP
Cytosine	C	Deoxycytidine	Deoxycytidine 5'-monophosphate	dCMP
Thymine	T	Deoxythymidine	Deoxythymidine 5'-monophosphate	dTMP
RNA				
Adenine	A	Adenosine	Adenosine 5'-monophosphate	AMP
Guanine	G	Guanosine	Guanosine 5'-monophosphate	GMP
Cytosine	C	Cytidine	Cytidine 5'-monophosphate	CMP
Uracil	U	Uridine	Uridine 5'-monophosphate	UMP

PROBLEM 22.3

Identify the base and monosaccharide in each nucleotide. Name the nucleotide and give its three- or four-letter abbreviation.

PROBLEM 22.4

Which nucleic acid (DNA or RNA) contains each of the following components?

a. the sugar ribose   c. the base T   e. the nucleotide GMP

b. the sugar deoxyribose   d. the base U   f. the nucleotide dCMP

PROBLEM 22.5

Label each statement about the compound deoxycytidine as true or false.

a. Deoxycytidine is a nucleotide.

b. Deoxycytidine is a nucleoside.

c. Deoxycytidine contains a phosphate at its 5'-OH group.

d. Deoxycytidine contains a pyrimidine base.

Di- and triphosphates can also be prepared from nucleosides by adding two and three phosphate groups, respectively, to the 5'-OH. For example, adenosine can be converted to adenosine 5'-diphosphate and adenosine 5'-triphosphate, abbreviated as ADP and ATP, respectively. We will learn about the central role of these phosphates, especially ATP, in energy production in Chapter 23.

adenosine 5'-diphosphate
ADP

adenosine 5'-triphosphate
ATP

SAMPLE PROBLEM 22.2 DRAWING THE STRUCTURES OF A NUCLEOTIDE

Draw the structure of the nucleotide GMP.

Analysis

Translate the abbreviation to a name; GMP is guanosine 5'-monophosphate. First, draw the sugar. Since there is no *deoxy* prefix in the name, GMP is a ribonucleotide and the sugar is ribose. Then draw the base, in this case guanine, bonded to C1' of the sugar ring. Finally, add the phosphate. GMP has one phosphate group bonded to the 5'-OH of the nucleoside.

Solution

Add phosphate here.

Add base here.

ribose

guanosine 5'-monophosphate
GMP

PRACTICE PROBLEM 22.2

Draw the structure of each nucleotide: (a) UMP; (b) dTMP; (c) AMP.

More Practice: Try Problems 22.27, 22.28.

PROBLEM 22.6

Give the name that corresponds to each abbreviation: (a) GTP; (b) dCDP; (c) dTTP; (d) UDP.

phosphodiester

22.2 Nucleic Acids

Nucleic acids—both DNA and RNA—are polymers of nucleotides, formed by joining the 3'-OH group of one nucleotide with the 5'-phosphate of a second nucleotide in a **phosphodiester** linkage (Section 19.6).

For example, joining the 3'-OH group of dCMP (deoxycytidine 5'-monophosphate) and the 5'-phosphate of dAMP (deoxyadenosine 5'-monophosphate) forms a dinucleotide that contains a 5'-phosphate on one end (called the **5' end**) and a 3'-OH group on the other end (called the **3' end**).

As additional nucleotides are added, the nucleic acid grows, each time forming a new phosphodiester linkage that holds the nucleotides together. Figure 22.2 illustrates the structure of a polynucleotide formed from four different nucleotides. Several features are noteworthy.

- A polynucleotide contains a backbone consisting of alternating sugar and phosphate groups. All polynucleotides contain the same sugar–phosphate backbone.
- The identity and order of the bases distinguish one polynucleotide from another.
- A polynucleotide has one free phosphate group at the 5' end.
- A polynucleotide has a free OH group at the 3' end.

Figure 22.2 Primary Structure of a Polynucleotide

In a polynucleotide, phosphodiester bonds join the 3'-carbon of one nucleotide to the 5'-carbon of another. The name of a polynucleotide is read from the 5' end to the 3' end, using the one-letter abbreviations for the bases it contains. Drawn is the structure of the polynucleotide CATG.

The **primary structure** of a polynucleotide is the sequence of nucleotides that it contains. This sequence, which is determined by the identity of the bases, is unique to a nucleic acid. **In DNA, the sequence of bases carries the genetic information of the organism.**

Polynucleotides are named by the sequence of the bases they contain, beginning at the 5' end and using the one-letter abbreviation for the bases. Thus, the polynucleotide in Figure 22.2 contains the bases cytosine, adenine, thymine, and guanine, in order from the 5' end; thus, it is named CATG.

SAMPLE PROBLEM 22.3 DRAWING AND NAMING A DINUCLEOTIDE

(a) Draw the structure of a dinucleotide formed by joining the 3'-OH group of AMP to the 5'-phosphate in GMP. (b) Label the 5' and 3' ends. (c) Name the dinucleotide.

Analysis

Draw the structure of each nucleotide, including the sugar, the phosphate bonded to C5', and the base at C1'. In this case the sugar is ribose because the names of the mononucleotides do not contain the prefix *deoxy.* Bond the 3'-OH group to the 5'-phosphate to form the phosphodiester bond. The name of the dinucleotide begins with the nucleotide that contains the free phosphate at the 5' end.

Solution

a. and b.

c. Polynucleotides are named beginning at the 5' end, so this dinucleotide is named AG.

PRACTICE PROBLEM 22.3

Draw the structure of a dinucleotide formed by joining the 3'-OH group of dTMP to the 5'-phosphate in dGMP.

More Practice: Try Problems 22.31–22.34.

PROBLEM 22.7

Draw the structure of each polynucleotide: (a) CU; (b) TAG.

PROBLEM 22.8

Label each statement about the polynucleotide ATGGCG as true or false.

a. The polynucleotide has six nucleotides.

b. The polynucleotide contains six phosphodiester linkages.

c. The nucleotide at the 5' end contains the base guanine.

d. The nucleotide at the 3' end contains the base guanine.

e. The polynucleotide could be part of a DNA molecule.

f. The polynucleotide could be part of an RNA molecule.

22.3   The DNA Double Helix

Our current understanding of the structure of DNA is based on the model proposed initially by James Watson and Francis Crick in 1953 (Figure 22.3).

- **DNA consists of two polynucleotide strands that wind into a right-handed double helix.**

The sugar–phosphate backbone lies on the outside of the helix and the bases lie on the inside, perpendicular to the axis of the helix. The two strands of DNA run in *opposite* directions; that is, one strand runs from the 5' end to the 3' end, while the other runs from the 3' end to the 5' end.

Figure 22.3   The Three-Dimensional Structure of DNA—A Double Helix

DNA consists of a double helix of polynucleotide chains. In view (a), the three-dimensional molecular model shows the sugar–phosphate backbone with the red (O), black (C), and white (H) atoms visible on the outside of the helix. In view (b), the bases on the interior of the helix are labeled.
©MOLEKUUL/SPL/age fotostock RF

Figure 22.4   Hydrogen Bonding in the DNA Double Helix

hydrogen bonding between base pairs

Hydrogen bonding of base pairs (A–T and C–G) holds the two strands of DNA together.

The double helix is stabilized by hydrogen bonding between the bases of the two DNA strands as shown in Figure 22.4. A purine base on one strand always hydrogen bonds with a pyrimidine base on the other strand. Two bases hydrogen bond together in a predictable manner, forming **complementary base pairs.**

- Adenine pairs with thymine using two hydrogen bonds, forming an A–T base pair.
- Cytosine pairs with guanine using three hydrogen bonds, forming a C–G base pair.

Because of this consistent pairing of bases, knowing the sequence of one strand of DNA allows us to write the sequence of the other strand, as shown in Sample Problem 22.4.

SAMPLE PROBLEM 22.4 WRITING THE SEQUENCE OF THE COMPLEMENTARY STRAND OF A DNA MOLECULE

Write the sequence of the complementary strand of the following portion of a DNA molecule:
5'–TAGGCTA–3'.

Analysis

The complementary strand runs in the opposite direction, from the 3' to the 5' end. Use base pairing to determine the corresponding sequence on the complementary strand: A pairs with T and C pairs with G.

Solution

Original strand: 5'–T A G G C T A–3'

Complementary strand: 3'–A T C C G A T–5'

PRACTICE PROBLEM 22.4

Write the complementary strand for each of the following strands of DNA.

  a. 5'–AAACGTCC–3'   c. 5'–ATTGCACCCGC–3'

  b. 5'–TATACGCC–3'   d. 5'–CACTTGATCGG–3'

More Practice: Try Problems 22.39, 22.40.

Figure 22.5 The Structure of a Chromosome

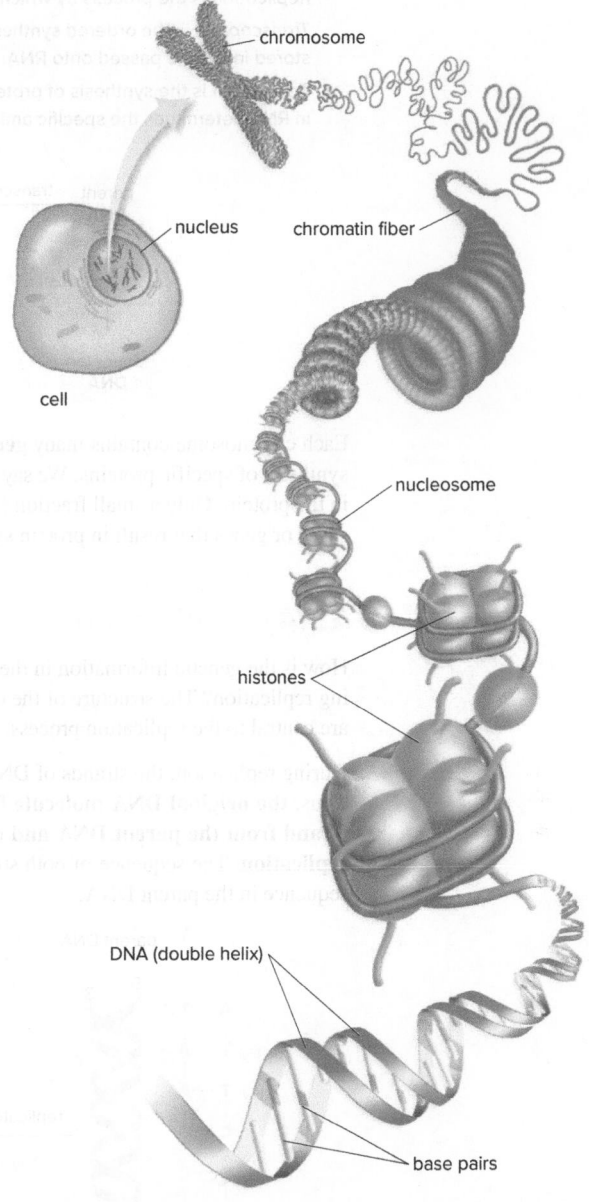

The enormously large DNA molecules that compose the **human genome**—the total DNA content of an individual—pack tightly into the nucleus of the cell. The double-stranded DNA helices wind around a core of protein molecules called **histones** to form a chain of **nucleosomes,** as shown in Figure 22.5. The chain of nucleosomes winds into a supercoiled fiber called **chromatin,** which composes each of the 23 pairs of chromosomes in humans.

In Section 22.2 we learned that the **genetic information of an organism is stored in the sequence of bases of its DNA molecules.** How is this information transferred from one generation to another? How, too, is the information stored in DNA molecules used to direct the synthesis of proteins?

Identical twins have the same genetic makeup, so that characteristics determined by DNA—such as hair color, eye color, or complexion—are also identical. ©Daniel C. Smith

To answer these questions, we must understand three key processes.

- *Replication* is the process by which DNA makes a copy of itself when a cell divides.
- *Transcription* is the ordered synthesis of RNA from DNA. In this process, the genetic information stored in DNA is passed onto RNA.
- *Translation* is the synthesis of proteins from RNA. In this process, the genetic message contained in RNA determines the specific amino acid sequence of a protein.

Each chromosome contains many **genes,** those portions of the DNA molecules that result in the synthesis of specific proteins. We say that the genetic message of the DNA molecule is *expressed* in the protein. Only a small fraction (1–2%) of the DNA in a chromosome contains genetic messages or genes that result in protein synthesis.

22.4   Replication

How is the genetic information in the DNA of a parent cell passed on to new daughter cells during replication? The structure of the double helix and the presence of complementary base pairs are central to the replication process.

During replication, the strands of DNA separate and each serves as a template for a new strand. Thus, **the original DNA molecule forms two DNA molecules, each of which contains one strand from the parent DNA and one new strand.** This process is called **semiconservative replication.** The sequence of both strands of the daughter DNA molecules exactly matches the sequence in the parent DNA.

Although the semiconservative nature of replication has been known since the elegant experiments of Matthew Meselson and Franklin Stahl were reported in 1958, the details of replication have only slowly been determined over the last 50 years. The first step in replication is the unwinding of the DNA helix to expose the bases on each strand. Unwinding occurs at many places simultaneously along the helix, creating "bubbles" where replication can occur. The point at which unwinding occurs is called the **replication fork.** Unwinding breaks the hydrogen bonds that hold the two strands of the double helix together.

Once bases have been exposed on the unwound strands of DNA, the enzyme DNA polymerase cata-lyzes the replication process using the four nucleoside triphosphates (derived from the bases A, T, G, and C) that are available in the nucleus. Three features are key and each is illustrated in Figure 22.6.

- The identity of the bases on the template strand determines the order of the bases on the new strand: A must pair with T, and G must pair with C.
- A new phosphodiester bond is formed between the 5'-phosphate of the nucleoside triphosphate and the 3'-OH group of the new DNA strand.
- Replication occurs in only one direction on the template strand, from the 3' end to the 5' end.

Figure 22.6

DNA Replication

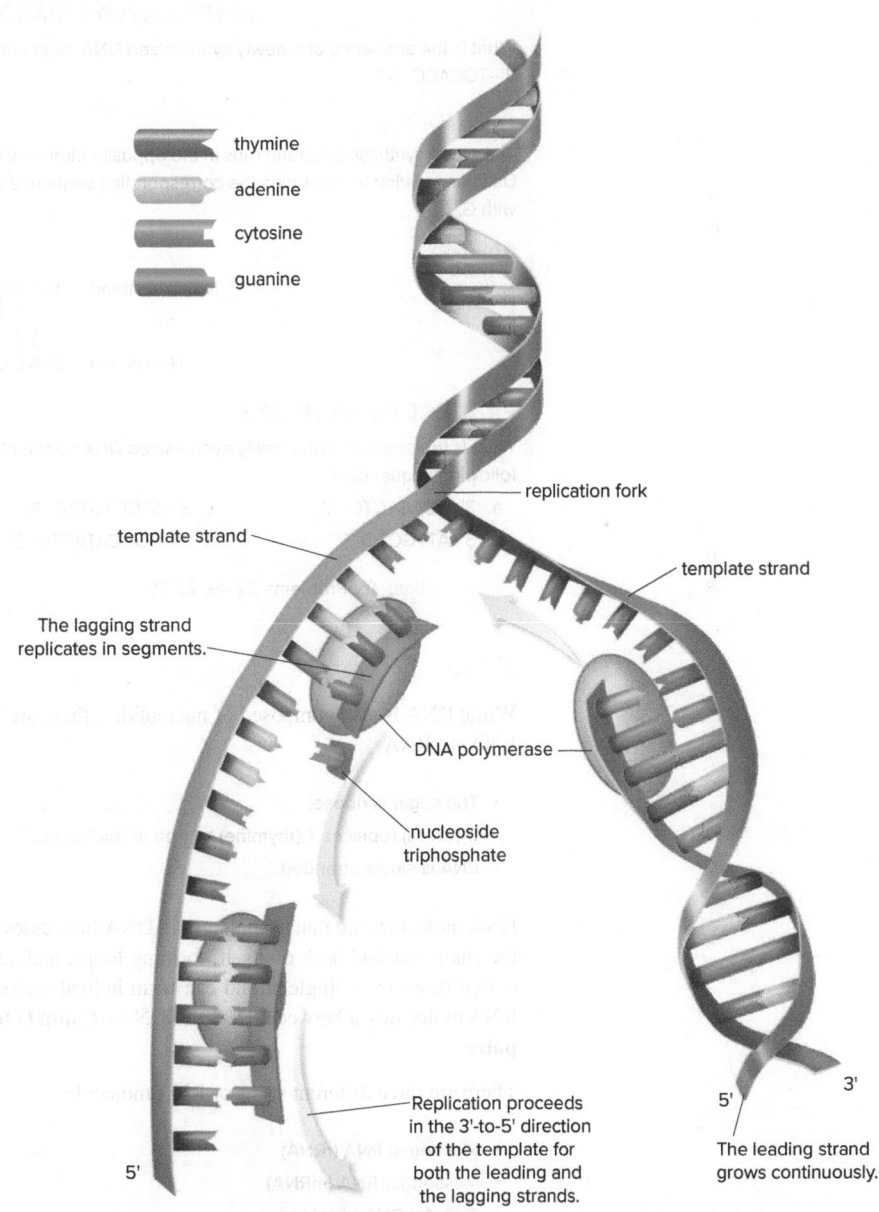

thymine
adenine
cytosine
guanine

replication fork

template strand

template strand

The lagging strand replicates in segments.

DNA polymerase

nucleoside triphosphate

Replication proceeds in the 3'-to-5' direction of the template for both the leading and the lagging strands.

5'

5'   3'

The leading strand grows continuously.

Replication proceeds along both strands of unwound DNA. Replication always occurs in the same direction, from the 3' to the 5' end of the template strand. The leading strand grows continuously, whereas the lagging strand must be synthesized in fragments that are joined together by a DNA ligase enzyme.

Because replication proceeds in only one direction—that is, from the 3' end to the 5' end of the template—the two new strands of DNA must be synthesized by somewhat different techniques. One strand, called the **leading strand,** grows continuously. Since its sequence is complementary to the template, its nucleotide sequence grows in the 5' to 3' direction. The other strand, called the **lagging strand,** is synthesized in small fragments, which are then joined together by a DNA ligase enzyme. The end result is two new strands of DNA, one in each of the daughter DNA molecules, both with complementary base pairs joining the two DNA strands together.

SAMPLE PROBLEM 22.5 DETERMINING THE SEQUENCE OF A NEWLY SYNTHESIZED STRAND OF DNA

What is the sequence of a newly synthesized DNA segment if the template strand has the sequence 3'–TGCACC–5'?

Analysis

The newly synthesized strand runs in the opposite direction, from the 5' end to the 3' end in this example. Use base pairing to determine the corresponding sequence on the new strand: A pairs with T, and C pairs with G.

Solution

Template strand: 3'–T G C A C C–5'

New strand: 5'–A C G T G G–3'

PRACTICE PROBLEM 22.5

What is the sequence of a newly synthesized DNA segment if the template strand has each of the following sequences?

a. 3'–AGAGTCTC–5'   c. 3'–ATCCTGTAC–5'

b. 5'–ATTGCTC–3'   d. 5'–GGCCATACTC–3'

More Practice: Try Problems 22.49, 22.50.

22.5   RNA

While RNA is also composed of nucleotides, there are important differences between DNA and RNA. In RNA,

- The sugar is ribose.
- U (uracil) replaces T (thymine) as one of the bases.
- RNA is single stranded.

RNA molecules are much smaller than DNA molecules. Although RNA contains a single strand, the chain can fold back on itself, forming loops, and intermolecular hydrogen bonding between paired bases on a single strand can form helical regions. When base pairing occurs within an RNA molecule (or between RNA and DNA), **C and G form base pairs,** and **A and U form base pairs.**

There are three different types of RNA molecules.

- Ribosomal RNA (rRNA)
- Messenger RNA (mRNA)
- Transfer RNA (tRNA)

Ribosomal RNA, the most abundant type of RNA, is found in the ribosomes in the cytoplasm of the cell. Each ribosome is composed of one large subunit and one small subunit that contain both

RNA and protein. rRNA provides the site where polypeptides are assembled during protein synthesis.

Messenger RNA is the carrier of information from DNA (in the cell nucleus) to the ribosomes (in the cytoplasm). Each gene of a DNA molecule corresponds to a specific mRNA molecule. The sequence of nucleotides in the mRNA molecule determines the amino acid sequence in a particular protein. mRNA is synthesized from DNA on an as-needed basis, and then rapidly degraded after a particular protein is synthesized.

Transfer RNA, the smallest type of RNA, interprets the genetic information in mRNA and brings specific amino acids to the site of protein synthesis in the ribosome. Each amino acid is recognized by one or more tRNA molecules, which contain 70–90 nucleotides. tRNAs have two important sites. The 3' end, called the **acceptor stem,** always contains the nucleotides ACC and has a free OH group that binds a specific amino acid. Each tRNA also contains a sequence of three nucleotides called an **anticodon,** which is complementary to three bases in an mRNA molecule, and identifies what amino acid must be added to a growing polypeptide chain.

tRNA molecules are often drawn in the cloverleaf fashion shown in Figure 22.7a. The acceptor stem and anticodon region are labeled. Folding creates regions of the tRNA in which nearby complementary bases hydrogen bond to each other. A model that more accurately depicts the three-dimensional structure of a tRNA molecule is shown in Figure 22.7b.

Table 22.2 summarizes the characteristics of the three types of RNAs.

Figure 22.7   Transfer RNA

a. tRNA–Cloverleaf representation

- amino acid
- acceptor stem
- hydrogen bonding between complementary base pairs
- anticodon

A
C
C
3'

5'

Folding of the tRNA molecule creates regions in which complementary base pairs hydrogen bond to each other. Each tRNA binds a specific amino acid to its 3' end and contains an anticodon that identifies that amino acid for protein synthesis.

b. tRNA–Three-dimensional representation

In the three-dimensional model of a tRNA, the binding site for the amino acid is shown in yellow and the anticodon is shown in red.
©Kenneth Eward/Science Source

Table 22.2 Three Types of RNA Molecules

Type of RNA	Abbreviation	Function
Ribosomal RNA	rRNA	The site of protein synthesis, found in the ribosomes
Messenger RNA	mRNA	Carries the information from DNA to the ribosomes
Transfer RNA	tRNA	Brings specific amino acids to the ribosomes for protein synthesis

22.6   Transcription

The conversion of the information in DNA to the synthesis of proteins begins with *transcription—that is, the synthesis of messenger RNA from DNA.*

RNA synthesis begins in the same manner as DNA replication: the double helix of DNA unwinds (Figure 22.8). Because RNA is single stranded, however, only one strand of DNA is needed for RNA synthesis.

- The *template* strand is the strand of DNA used for RNA synthesis.
- The *informational* strand (the non-template strand) is the strand of DNA not used for RNA synthesis.

Figure 22.8   Transcription

partially unwound
DNA double helix

gene that codes for
a specific protein

RNA polymerase

non-template
strand of DNA

5'

3' end

3'

RNA nucleotides

5'

template
strand of DNA

newly made RNA

re-formed
DNA helix

RNA

direction of transcription

In transcription, the DNA helix unwinds and RNA polymerase catalyzes the formation of mRNA along the DNA template strand. Transcription proceeds from the 3' end to the 5' end of the template, forming an mRNA molecule with base pairs complementary to the DNA template strand.

Each mRNA molecule corresponds to a small segment of a DNA molecule. Transcription begins at a particular sequence of bases on the DNA template using an RNA polymerase enzyme, and proceeds from the 3' end to the 5' end of the template strand. Complementary base pairing determines what RNA nucleotides are added to the growing RNA chain: C pairs with G, T pairs with A, and A pairs with U. Thus, the RNA chain grows from the 5' to 3' direction. Transcription is completed when a particular sequence of bases on the DNA template is reached. The new mRNA molecule is released and the double helix of the DNA molecule re-forms.

In bacteria, the new mRNA molecule is ready for protein synthesis immediately after it is prepared. In humans, the mRNA molecule first formed is modified before it is ready for protein synthesis. Portions of the mRNA molecule are removed and pieces of mRNA are spliced together by mechanisms that will not be discussed here.

- Transcription forms a messenger RNA molecule with a sequence that is *complementary* to the DNA template from which it is prepared.
- Since the informational strand of DNA is complementary to the template strand, the mRNA molecule is an *exact copy of the informational strand*, except that the base U replaces T on the RNA strand.

How the base sequence of an RNA molecule compares with the informational and template strands of a DNA molecule is shown in Sample Problem 22.6.

SAMPLE PROBLEM 22.6 DETERMINING THE SEQUENCE OF AN mRNA MOLECULE

If a portion of the template strand of a DNA molecule has the sequence 3'–CTAGGATAC–5', what is the sequence of the mRNA molecule produced from this template? What is the sequence of the informational strand of this segment of the DNA molecule?

Analysis

mRNA has a base sequence that is complementary to the template from which it is prepared. mRNA has a base sequence that is identical to the informational strand of DNA, except that it contains the base U instead of T.

Solution

		complementary
Template strand of DNA:	3'–C T A G G A T A C–5'	
mRNA sequence:	5'–G A U C C U A U G–3'	complementary
Informational strand of DNA:	5'–G A T C C T A T G–3'	

PRACTICE PROBLEM 22.6

For each DNA segment: [1] What is the sequence of the mRNA molecule synthesized from each DNA template? [2] What is the sequence of the informational strand of the DNA molecule?

a. 3'–TGCCTAACG–5'   c. 3'–TTAACGCGA–5'
b. 3'–GACTCC–5'   d. 3'–CAGTGACCGTAC–5'

More Practice: Try Problems 22.51, 22.53, 22.54.

PROBLEM 22.9

What is the sequence of the DNA template strand from which each of the following mRNA strands was synthesized?

a. 5'–UGGGGCAUU–3'   c. 5'–CCGACGAUG–3'
b. 5'–GUACCU–3'   d. 5'–GUAGUCACG–3'

22.7 The Genetic Code

Once the genetic information of DNA has been transcribed in a messenger RNA molecule, RNA can direct the synthesis of an individual protein. How can RNA, which is composed of only four different nucleotides, direct the synthesis of polypeptides that are formed from 20 different amino acids? The answer lies in the **genetic code.**

- A sequence of three nucleotides (a triplet) codes for a specific amino acid. Each triplet is called a *codon.*

For example, the codon UAC in an mRNA molecule codes for the amino acid serine, and the codon UGC codes for the amino acid cysteine. The same genetic code occurs in almost all organisms, from bacteria to whales to humans.

Given four different nucleotides (A, C, G, and U), there are 64 different ways to combine them into groups of three, so there are 64 different codons. Sixty-one codons code for specific amino acids, so many amino acids correspond to more than one codon, as shown in Table 22.3. For example, the codons GGU, GGC, GGA, and GGG all code for the amino acid glycine. Three codons—UAA, UAG, and UGA—do not correspond to any amino acids; they are called **stop codons** because they signal the termination of protein synthesis.

Table 22.3 The Genetic Code—Triplets in Messenger RNA

First Base (5' end)	Second Base								Third Base (3' end)
	U		C		A		G		
U	UUU	Phe	UCU	Ser	UAU	Tyr	UGU	Cys	U
	UUC	Phe	UCC	Ser	UAC	Tyr	UGC	Cys	C
	UUA	Leu	UCA	Ser	UAA	Stop	UGA	Stop	A
	UUG	Leu	UCG	Ser	UAG	Stop	UGG	Trp	G
C	CUU	Leu	CCU	Pro	CAU	His	CGU	Arg	U
	CUC	Leu	CCC	Pro	CAC	His	CGC	Arg	C
	CUA	Leu	CCA	Pro	CAA	Gln	CGA	Arg	A
	CUG	Leu	CCG	Pro	CAG	Gln	CGG	Arg	G
A	AUU	Ile	ACU	Thr	AAU	Asn	AGU	Ser	U
	AUC	Ile	ACC	Thr	AAC	Asn	AGC	Ser	C
	AUA	Ile	ACA	Thr	AAA	Lys	AGA	Arg	A
	AUG	Met	ACG	Thr	AAG	Lys	AGG	Arg	G
G	GUU	Val	GCU	Ala	GAU	Asp	GGU	Gly	U
	GUC	Val	GCC	Ala	GAC	Asp	GGC	Gly	C
	GUA	Val	GCA	Ala	GAA	Glu	GGA	Gly	A
	GUG	Val	GCG	Ala	GAG	Glu	GGG	Gly	G

PROBLEM 22.10

What amino acid is coded for by each codon?

a. GCC   b. AAU   c. CUA   d. AGC   e. CAA   f. AAA

PROBLEM 22.11

What codons code for each amino acid?

a. glycine   b. isoleucine   c. lysine   d. glutamic acid

Codons are written from the 5' to 3' end of mRNA. The 5' end of the mRNA molecule codes for the N-terminal amino acid in a protein, and the 3' end of the mRNA molecule codes for the C-terminal amino acid. Sample Problem 22.7 illustrates the conversion of a sequence of bases in mRNA to a sequence of amino acids in a peptide.

SAMPLE PROBLEM 22.7 DERIVING AN AMINO ACID SEQUENCE FROM mRNA

Derive the amino acid sequence that is coded for by the following mRNA sequence.

5' CAU AAA ACG GUG UUA AUA 3'

Analysis

Use Table 22.3 to identify the codons that correspond to each amino acid. Codons are written from the 5' to 3' end of an mRNA molecule and correspond to a peptide written from the N-terminal to C-terminal end.

Solution

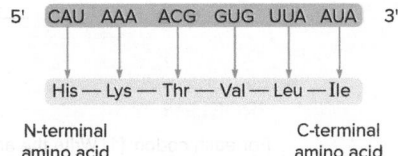

PRACTICE PROBLEM 22.7

Derive the amino acid sequence that is coded for by each mRNA sequence.

a. 5' CAA GAG GUA UCC UAC AGA 3'
b. 5' GUC AUC UGG AGG GGC AUU 3'
c. 5' CUA UGC AGU AGG ACA CCC 3'

More Practice: Try Problems 22.59, 22.60.

PROBLEM 22.12

Write a possible mRNA sequence that codes for each of the following peptides.

a. Met–Arg–His–Phe   c. Gln–Asn–Gly–Ile–Val
b. Gly–Ala–Glu–Gln   d. Thr–His–Asp–Cys–Trp

PROBLEM 22.13

Considering the given sequence of nucleotides in an mRNA molecule, (a) what is the sequence of the DNA template strand from which the RNA was synthesized? (b) What peptide is synthesized by this mRNA sequence?

5' GAG CCC GUA UAC GCC ACG 3'

22.8 Translation and Protein Synthesis

The translation of the information in messenger RNA to protein synthesis occurs in the ribosomes. Each type of RNA plays a role in protein synthesis.

- mRNA contains the sequence of codons that determines the order of amino acids in the protein.
- Individual tRNAs bring specific amino acids to add to the peptide chain.
- rRNA contains binding sites that provide the platform on which protein synthesis occurs.

Each individual tRNA contains an **anticodon** of three nucleotides that is complementary to the codon in mRNA and identifies individual amino acids (Section 22.5). For example, a codon of

UCA in mRNA corresponds to an anticodon of AGU in a tRNA molecule, which identifies serine as the amino acid. Other examples are shown in Table 22.4.

Table 22.4 Relating Codons, Anticodons, and Amino Acids

mRNA Codon		tRNA Anticodon		Amino Acid
ACA	$\longrightarrow$	UGU	$\longrightarrow$	threonine
GCG	$\longrightarrow$	CGC	$\longrightarrow$	alanine
AGA	$\longrightarrow$	UCU	$\longrightarrow$	arginine
UCC	$\longrightarrow$	AGG	$\longrightarrow$	serine

PROBLEM 22.14

For each codon: [1] Write the anticodon. [2] What amino acid does each codon represent?

a. CGG   b. GGG   c. UCC   d. AUA   e. CCU   f. GCC

There are three stages in translation: initiation, elongation, and termination. Figure 22.9 depicts the main features of translation.

[1] Initiation

Translation begins when an mRNA molecule binds to the smaller subunit of the ribosome and a tRNA molecule carries the first amino acid of the peptide chain to the binding site. Translation always begins at the codon AUG, which codes for the amino acid methionine. The arriving tRNA contains an anticodon with the complementary base sequence UAC. The large and small subunits of the ribosome combine to form a tight complex where protein synthesis takes place.

[2] Elongation

The next tRNA molecule containing an anticodon for the second codon binds to mRNA, delivering its amino acid, and a peptide bond forms between the two amino acids. The first tRNA molecule, which has delivered its amino acid and is no longer needed, dissociates from the complex. The ribosome shifts to the next codon along the mRNA strand and the process continues when a new tRNA molecule binds to the mRNA. Protein synthesis always occurs on two adjacent sites of the ribosome.

[3] Termination

Translation continues until a stop codon is reached. There is no tRNA that contains an anticodon complementary to any of the three stop codons (UAA, UAG, and UGA), so protein synthesis ends and the protein is released from the ribosome. Often the first amino acid in the chain, methionine, is not needed in the final protein and so it is removed after protein synthesis is complete.

Figure 22.10 shows a representative segment of DNA, and the mRNA, tRNA, and amino acid sequences that correspond to it.

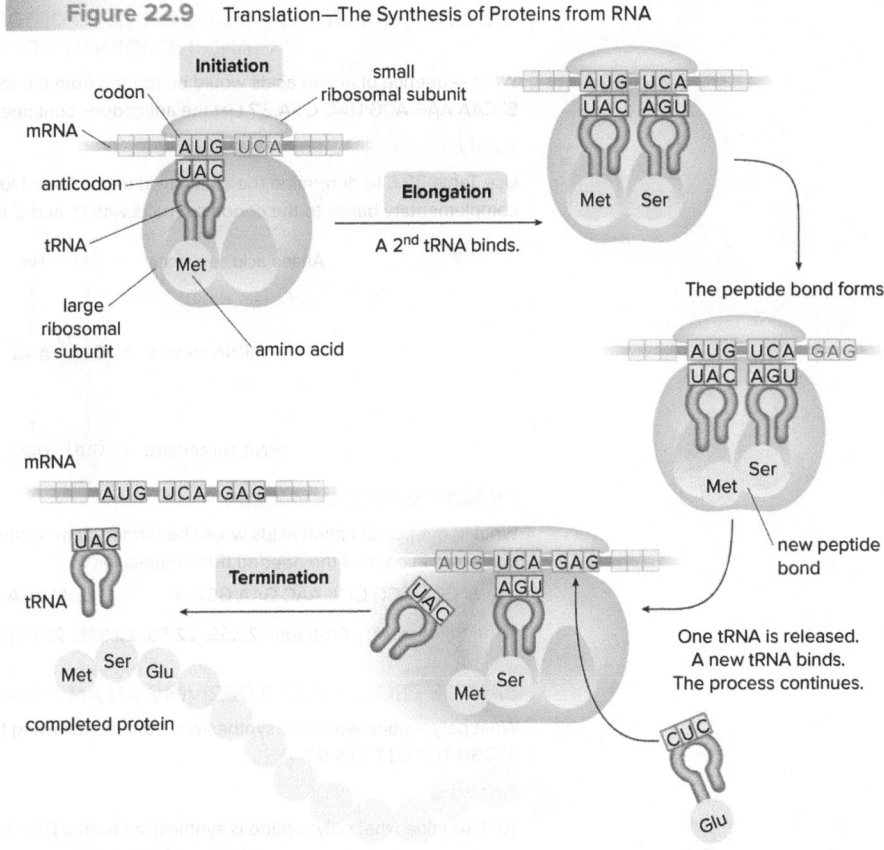

Figure 22.9 Translation—The Synthesis of Proteins from RNA

- **Initiation** consists of the binding of the ribosomal subunits to mRNA and the arrival of the first tRNA carrying its amino acid. Hydrogen bonding occurs between the complementary bases of the codon of mRNA and the anticodon of the tRNA.
- The protein is synthesized during **elongation.** One by one a tRNA with its designated amino acid binds to a site on the ribosome adjacent to the first tRNA. A peptide bond forms and a tRNA is released. The ribosome shifts to the next codon and the process continues.
- **Termination** occurs when a stop codon is reached. The synthesis is complete and the protein is released from the complex.

Figure 22.10 Comparing the Sequence of DNA, mRNA, tRNA, and a Polypeptide

General, Organic, and Biochemisty

SAMPLE PROBLEM 22.8 USING mRNA TO DETERMINE AN AMINO ACID SEQUENCE AND THE IDENTITY OF tRNA ANTICODONS

What sequence of amino acids would be formed from the following mRNA sequence:
5' CAA AAG ACG UAC CGA 3'? List the anticodons contained in each of the needed tRNA molecules.

Analysis

Use Table 22.3 to determine the amino acid that is coded for by each codon. The anticodons contain complementary bases to the codons: A pairs with U, and C pairs with G.

Solution

Amino acid sequence: Gln   Lys   Thr   Tyr   Arg

mRNA codons: 5' CAA AAG ACG UAC CGA 3'

tRNA anticodons: GUU UUC UGC AUG GCU

PRACTICE PROBLEM 22.8

What sequence of amino acids would be formed from each mRNA sequence? List the anticodons contained in each of the needed tRNA molecules.

   a. 5' CCA CCG GCA AAC GAA GCA 3'   b. 5' GCA CCA CUA AGA GAC 3'

More Practice: Try Problems 22.55, 22.56, 22.64b, 22.65[2], 22.66[2], 22.67a, 22.68a.

SAMPLE PROBLEM 22.9 DERIVING AN AMINO ACID SEQUENCE FROM DNA

What polypeptide would be synthesized from the following template strand of DNA:
3' CGG TGT CTT TTA 5'?

Analysis

To determine what polypeptide is synthesized from a DNA template, two steps are needed.

- Use the DNA sequence to determine the transcribed mRNA sequence: C pairs with G, T pairs with A, and A (on DNA) pairs with U (on mRNA).
- Use the codons in Table 22.3 to determine what amino acids are coded for by a given codon in mRNA.

Solution

DNA template strand: ⟶ 3' CGG TGT CTT TTA 5'

mRNA: ⟶ 5' GCC ACA GAA AAU 3'

Polypeptide: ⟶ Ala — Thr — Glu — Asn

PRACTICE PROBLEM 22.9

What polypeptide would be synthesized from each of the following template strands of DNA?
   a. 3' TCT CAT CGT AAT GAT TCG 5'   b. 3' GCT CCT AAA TAA CAC TTA 5'

More Practice: Try Problems 22.63, 22.69a, 22.70a.

22.9 Mutations and Genetic Diseases

Although replication provides a highly reliable mechanism for making an exact copy of DNA, occasionally an error occurs, thus producing a DNA molecule with a slightly different nucleotide sequence.

- A *mutation* is a change in the nucleotide sequence in a molecule of DNA.

If the mutation occurs in a nonreproductive cell, the mutation is passed on to daughter cells within the organism, but is not transmitted to the next generation. If the mutation occurs in an egg or sperm cell, it is passed on to the next generation of an organism. Some mutations are random events, while others are caused by **mutagens,** chemical substances that alter the structure of DNA. Exposure to high-energy radiation such as X-rays or ultraviolet light can also produce mutations.

Mutations can be classified according to the change that results in a DNA molecule.

- A *point* mutation is the *substitution* of one nucleotide for another.

Original DNA: ~~~~ G A **G** T T C ~~~~

replacement of **G** by **C**

Point mutation: ~~~~ G A **C** T T C ~~~~

- A *deletion* mutation occurs when one or more nucleotides is *lost* from a DNA molecule.

Original DNA: ~~~~ G A **G** T T C ~~~~

loss of **G**

Deletion mutation: ~~~~ G A T T C ~~~~

- An *insertion* mutation occurs when one or more nucleotides is *added* to a DNA molecule.

Original DNA: ~~~~ G A G T T C ~~~~

addition of **C**

Insertion mutation: ~~~~ G A G **C** T T C ~~~~

A mutation can have a negligible, minimal, or catastrophic effect on an organism. To understand the effect of a mutation, we must determine the mRNA sequence that is transcribed from the DNA sequence as well as the resulting amino acid for which it codes. A point mutation in the three-base sequence CTT in a gene that codes for a particular protein illustrates some possible outcomes of a mutation.

The sequence CTT in DNA is transcribed to the codon GAA in mRNA, and using Table 22.3, this triplet codes for the amino acid glutamic acid. If a point mutation replaces CTT by CTC in DNA, CTC is transcribed to the codon GAG in mRNA. Because GAG codes for the *same* amino acid—glutamic acid—this mutation does not affect the protein synthesized by this segment of DNA. Such a mutation is said to be **silent.**

Original: C T T ⟶ G A A ⟶ Glu
DNA   mRNA   same amino acid   The mutation has no effect.
Point mutation: C T C ⟶ G A G ⟶ Glu

Alternatively, suppose a point mutation replaces CTT by CAT in DNA. CAT is transcribed to the codon GUA in mRNA, and GUA codes for the amino acid valine. Now, the mutation produces a protein with one *different* amino acid—namely, valine instead of glutamic acid. In some proteins this alteration of the primary sequence may have little effect on the protein's secondary and tertiary structure. In other proteins, such as hemoglobin, the substitution of valine for glutamic acid produces a protein with vastly different properties, resulting in the fatal disease sickle cell anemia (Section 21.7).

Original: C T T ⟶ G A A ⟶ Glu
DNA   mRNA   different amino acid   The effect of the mutation
Point mutation: C A T ⟶ G U A ⟶ Val   varies with the protein.

Finally, suppose a point mutation replaces CTT by ATT in DNA. ATT is transcribed to the codon UAA in mRNA, and UAA is a stop codon. This terminates protein synthesis and no more amino acids are added to the protein chain. In this case, a needed protein is not synthesized, and depending on the protein's role, the organism may die.

Original: C T T ⟶ G A A ⟶ Glu
DNA   mRNA   Protein synthesis stops and the
Point mutation: A T T ⟶ U A A ⟶ Stop   effects may be catastrophic.

SAMPLE PROBLEM 22.10 DETERMINING THE RESULT OF A POINT MUTATION

(a) What dipeptide is produced from the following segment of DNA: AGAGAT? (b) What happens to the dipeptide when a point mutation occurs and the DNA segment contains the sequence ATAGAT instead?

Analysis

- Transcribe the DNA sequence to an mRNA sequence with complementary base pairs.
- Use Table 22.3 to determine what amino acids are coded for by each codon.

Solution

a. UCU codes for serine and CUA codes for leucine, so the dipeptide Ser–Leu results.

$$A\,G\,A\quad G\,A\,T \longrightarrow U\,C\,U\quad C\,U\,A \longrightarrow Ser\,-\,Leu$$

DNA	mRNA	dipeptide

b. UAU codes for tyrosine, so the point mutation results in the synthesis of the dipeptide Tyr–Leu.

$$A\,T\,A\quad G\,A\,T \longrightarrow U\,A\,U\quad C\,U\,A \longrightarrow Tyr\,-\,Leu$$

DNA	mRNA	dipeptide

PRACTICE PROBLEM 22.10

Consider the following sequence of DNA: AACTGA. (a) What dipeptide is formed from this DNA after transcription and translation? (b) How is the amino acid sequence affected when point mutations produce each of the following DNA sequences: [1] AACGGA; [2] ATCTGA; [3] AATTGA?

More Practice: Try Problems 22.69b–d, 22.70b–d.

PROBLEM 22.15

Suppose a deletion mutation occurs and the DNA segment TATGCACTT is converted to TAACTT. How do the peptides synthesized from each of these DNA segments compare?

A patient with cystic fibrosis must regularly receive chest physiotherapy, a procedure that involves pounding on the chest to dislodge thick mucus clogging the lungs. *Source: Cystic Fibrosis Trust*

When a mutation causes a protein deficiency or results in a defective protein and the condition is inherited from one generation to another, a **genetic disease** results. For example, cystic fibrosis, the most common genetic disease in Caucasians, is caused by a mutation resulting in the synthesis of a defective protein—cystic fibrosis transmembrane conductance regulator (CFTR)—needed for proper passage of ions across cell membranes. Individuals with cystic fibrosis have decreased secretions of pancreatic enzymes, resulting in a failure to thrive (poor growth), and they produce thick sticky mucus in the lungs that leads to devastating lung infections and a shortened life span. Other genetic diseases and their molecular bases are listed in Table 22.5.

Table 22.5 Genetic Diseases

Disease	Characteristics
Tay–Sachs disease	Mental retardation; caused by a defective hexosaminidase A enzyme
Sickle cell anemia	Anemia; occlusion and inflammation of blood capillaries, caused by defective hemoglobin
Phenylketonuria	Mental retardation; caused by a deficiency of the enzyme phenylalanine hydroxylase needed to convert the amino acid phenylalanine to tyrosine
Galactosemia	Mental retardation; caused by a deficiency of an enzyme needed for galactose metabolism
Huntington's disease	Progressive physical disability; caused by a defect in the gene that codes for the Htt protein, resulting in degeneration in the neurons in certain areas of the brain

22.10 Recombinant DNA

Laboratory techniques devised over the last 30 years allow scientists to manipulate DNA molecules and produce new forms of DNA that do not occur in nature.

> • *Recombinant DNA* is synthetic DNA that contains segments from more than one source.

The term **genetic engineering** is often used to describe the process of manipulating DNA in the laboratory that allows a gene (a segment of DNA) in one organism to be spliced (inserted) into the DNA of another organism, thus forming recombinant DNA.

22.10A   General Principles

Three key elements are needed to form recombinant DNA:

- **A DNA molecule into which a new DNA segment will be inserted**
- **An enzyme that cleaves DNA at specific locations**
- **A gene from a second organism that will be inserted in the original DNA molecule**

Forming recombinant DNA often begins with circular, double-stranded DNA molecules called **plasmids** in the bacterium *Escherichia coli* (*E. coli*) (Figure 22.11). Plasmid DNA is isolated from the bacteria and then cleaved (cut) at a specific site with an enzyme called a

Figure 22.11   Preparing Recombinant DNA

recombinant DNA

[1]   Bacterial plasmid DNA is cut by the restriction endonuclease EcoRI to form double-stranded linear DNA with two sticky ends.

[2]   A second sample of human DNA is cut with the same restriction endonuclease to form DNA segments having sticky ends that are complementary to those of the plasmid DNA.

[3]   Combining the two pieces of DNA in the presence of a DNA ligase enzyme forms DNA containing the new segment. The recombinant DNA is larger than the original plasmid because of the inserted segment of DNA.

Genetically modified crops contain DNA altered by various techniques, often resulting in increased disease resistance or improvement in shelf life or nutrition. In the 1990s, much of Hawaii's papaya industry was devastated by the papaya ringspot virus. The rainbow papaya was genetically engineered with resistance to the virus, thus allowing papaya production to resume on the Big Island of Hawaii. ©J C Clamp/Alamy

restriction endonuclease. Many different restriction endonucleases are known. Each enzyme recognizes a specific sequence of bases in a DNA molecule and cuts the double-stranded DNA at a particular position.

For example, the enzyme EcoRI recognizes the sequence GAATTC and cuts the DNA molecule between G and A on *both* strands. Because the plasmid DNA is circular to begin with, this forms linear double-stranded DNA with two ends of known sequence. These ends are called **sticky ends** because one strand contains unpaired bases that are ready to hydrogen bond with another DNA segment having the complementary base sequence.

If the same restriction endonuclease is now used to cut DNA from another source, say human DNA, a second segment of DNA is now available having the needed complementary base sequence. When the two segments of DNA are combined together in the presence of a DNA ligase enzyme, the DNA segment is joined to the open plasmid DNA and a recombinant DNA molecule is formed.

The newly engineered recombinant DNA molecule can then be re-inserted into a bacterial cell. Transcription converts the recombinant DNA into RNA and RNA directs the synthesis of the protein that corresponds to the inserted DNA sequence. Because bacteria rapidly grow and divide, large amounts of protein can be synthesized by this method in a short period of time.

Insulin, a hormone used by millions of individuals with diabetes, was the first genetically engineered protein available in significant quantities by these methods. Prior to its availability in 1983, individuals with diabetes used insulin isolated from cows or pigs. This insulin has a similar but not identical amino acid sequence to human insulin, as we learned in Section 21.6. These small differences can lead to allergic reactions in some individuals.

PROBLEM 22.16

The restriction endonuclease HindIII recognizes the DNA sequence AAGCTT and cuts the DNA between A and A. Given the following segment of double-stranded DNA, draw the sticky ends that result from cleavage with this enzyme.

5′ ∼∼∼∼ C C A A G C T T G G A T T ∼∼∼∼ 3′

3′ ∼∼∼∼ G G T T C G A A C C T A A ∼∼∼∼ 5′

22.10B   Polymerase Chain Reaction

In order to study a specific gene, such as the gene that causes the fatal inherited disorder cystic fibrosis, millions of copies of pure gene are needed. In fact, virtually an unlimited number of copies of any gene can be synthesized in just a few hours using a technique called the **polymerase chain reaction (PCR).** PCR *clones* a segment of DNA; that is, PCR produces exact copies of a fragment of DNA.

- In this way, PCR *amplifies* a specific portion of a DNA molecule, producing millions of copies of a single molecule.

Four elements are needed to amplify DNA by PCR:

- The **segment of DNA** that must be copied
- **Two primers**—short polynucleotides that are complementary to the two ends of the segment to be amplified
- **A DNA polymerase enzyme** that will catalyze the synthesis of a complementary strand of DNA from a template strand
- **Nucleoside triphosphates** that serve as the source of the nucleotides A, T, C, and G needed in the synthesis of the new strands of DNA

Each cycle of the polymerase chain reaction involves three steps, illustrated in the stepwise *How To* procedure.

How To   Use the Polymerase Chain Reaction to Amplify a Sample of DNA

Step [1]   Heat the DNA segment to unwind the double helix to form single strands.

Step [2]   Add primers that are complementary to the DNA sequence at either end of the DNA segment to be amplified.

- The primers must hydrogen bond to a single strand of DNA and thus they must have the complementary sequence to the template strand.
- The primers form a short segment of double-stranded DNA on each strand, to which the DNA polymerase can add new nucleotides to the 3' end.

Step [3]   Use a DNA polymerase and added nucleotides to lengthen the DNA segment.

- DNA polymerase catalyzes the synthesis of a new strand of DNA complementary to the existing strand using nucleoside triphosphates (dATP, dCTP, dGTP, and dTTP) available in the reaction mixture.
- After one three-step cycle, *one* molecule of double-stranded DNA has formed *two* molecules of double-stranded DNA. Each double-stranded DNA molecule contains one original strand and one newly synthesized strand.
- **After each cycle, the amount of DNA *doubles*.** After 20 cycles, about 1,000,000 copies have been made.

Each step of a PCR cycle is carried out at a different temperature. PCR is now a completely automated process using a **thermal cycler,** an apparatus that controls the heating and cooling needed for each step. A heat-tolerant DNA polymerase called **Taq polymerase** is also typically used, so that new enzyme need not be added as each new cycle begins.

22.10C FOCUS ON THE HUMAN BODY
DNA Fingerprinting

Because the DNA of each individual is unique, **DNA fingerprinting** is now routinely used as a method of identification.

Almost any type of cell—skin, saliva, semen, blood, and so forth—can be used to obtain a DNA fingerprint. After the DNA in a sample is amplified using PCR techniques, the DNA is cut into fragments with various restriction enzymes and the fragments are separated by size using a technique called gel electrophoresis. DNA fragments can be visualized on X-ray film after they react with a radioactive probe. The result is an image consisting of a set of horizontal bands, each band corresponding to a segment of DNA, sorted from low to high molecular weight.

To compare the DNA of different individuals, samples are placed next to each other on the same gel and the position of the horizontal bands compared. DNA fingerprinting is now routinely used in criminal cases to establish the guilt or innocence of a suspect (Figure 22.12). Only identical twins have identical DNA, but related individuals have several similar DNA fragments. Thus, DNA fingerprinting can be used to establish paternity by comparing the DNA of a child with that of each parent. DNA is also used to identify a body when no other means of identification is possible. DNA analysis was instrumental in identifying human remains found in the rubble of the World Trade Center after the towers collapsed on September 11, 2001.

Each band corresponds to a fragment of DNA.

Decreasing size of DNA fragments

Figure 22.12

DNA Fingerprinting in Forensic Analysis

Each vertical lane (numbered 1–13) corresponds to a DNA sample.

- Lanes 1, 3, 9, and 13 are called DNA ladders. They correspond to DNA fragments of known size and are used to show the approximate size of the DNA fragments of the fingerprints.
- Lane 4 is the DNA obtained from a female assault victim and lane 7 is the female DNA from the crime scene. The two lanes match, indicating that they are from the same individual.
- Two individuals (**A** and **B**), whose DNA appears in lanes 5 and 6, were considered suspects.
- The male DNA obtained at the crime scene is shown in lane 8. The horizontal bands correspond to those of suspect **A**, incriminating him and eliminating individual **B** as a suspect.

Source: Courtesy Genelex Corp., www.genelex.com

22.10D The Human Genome Project

Modern advances in DNA technology have yielded impressive results in the last 20 years.

The **Human Genome Project,** launched in 1990 and completed in 2003, was an international undertaking to identify and sequence all three billion nucleotide base pairs in the human genome. This project has yielded much vital information. We now know, for example, that only 2% of the base pairs constitute the 20,000 genes of the human genome, a much smaller fraction than originally assumed. A multinational research effort has been in place for over a decade to determine the role of the "junk" DNA—DNA that does not encode for a protein. Results have shown that this DNA is responsible for a variety of necessary functions in the cell.

Many medical advances have also resulted from this project. The genetic basis of thousands of genetic diseases is now known, and in the United States, all newborns are screened for numerous genetic disorders by a simple blood test shortly after birth. When genetic disorders are discovered within a family, parents can undergo genetic testing and learn how likely it is that their offspring will inherit an abnormality.

An enormous amount of DNA sequence information is now available, and as technology has improved, thousands of genomes in the plant and animal world have been sequenced. A genome that might have taken years to sequence in 1990 can now be determined in a matter of days. The cost of a partial genetic screen is no longer prohibitive, so individuals can learn more about their ancestry or their risk of developing certain genetic diseases by a blood test or saliva swab.

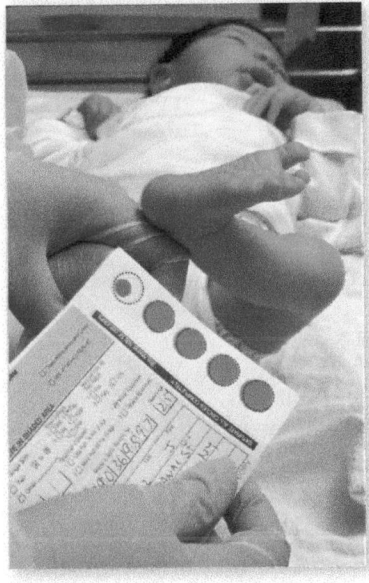

Newborn screening can detect life-threatening disorders that are treatable if detected early. ©Ted Horowitz/Corbis/Getty Images

22.11 FOCUS ON HEALTH & MEDICINE
Viruses

A *virus* is an infectious agent consisting of a DNA or RNA molecule that is contained within a protein coating. Since a virus contains no enzymes or free nucleotides of its own, it is incapable of replicating. When it invades a host organism, however, it takes over the biochemical machinery of the host.

A virus that contains DNA uses the materials in the host organism to replicate its DNA, transcribe DNA to RNA, and synthesize a protein coating, thus forming new virus particles. These new virus particles leave the host cell and infect new cells and the process continues. Many prevalent diseases, including the common cold, influenza, and herpes, are viral in origin.

A vaccine is an inactive form of a virus that causes an individual's immune system to produce antibodies to the virus to ward off infection. Many childhood diseases that were once very common, including mumps, measles, and chickenpox, are now prevented by vaccination. Polio has been almost completely eradicated, even in remote areas worldwide, by vaccination.

A virus that contains a core of RNA is called a **retrovirus.** Once a retrovirus invades a host organism, it must first make DNA by a process called **reverse transcription** (Figure 22.13). Once viral DNA has been synthesized, the DNA can transcribe RNA, which can direct protein synthesis. New retrovirus particles are thus synthesized and released to infect other cells.

AIDS (acquired immune deficiency syndrome) is caused by HIV (human immunodeficiency virus), a retrovirus that attacks lymphocytes central to the body's immune response against invading organisms. As a result, an individual infected with HIV becomes susceptible to life-threatening bacterial infections. HIV is spread by direct contact with the blood or other body fluids of an infected individual.

Major progress in battling the AIDS epidemic has occurred in recent years. HIV is currently best treated with a "cocktail" of drugs designed to destroy the virus at different stages of its reproductive cycle. One group of drugs, the protease inhibitors such as amprenavir (Section 21.11), act as enzyme inhibitors that prevent viral RNA from synthesizing needed proteins.

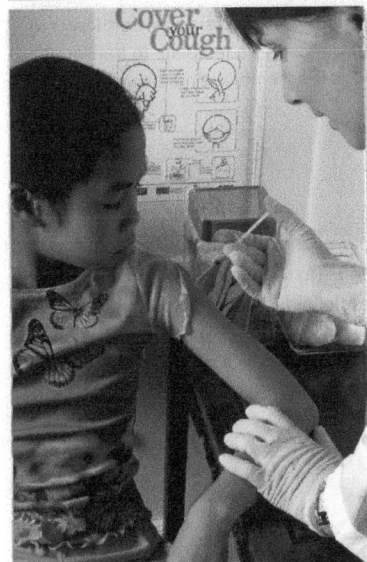

Childhood vaccinations have significantly decreased the incidence of once common diseases such as chickenpox, measles, and mumps. ©McGraw-Hill Education/Jill Braaten, photographer

Figure 22.13

How a Retrovirus Infects an Organism

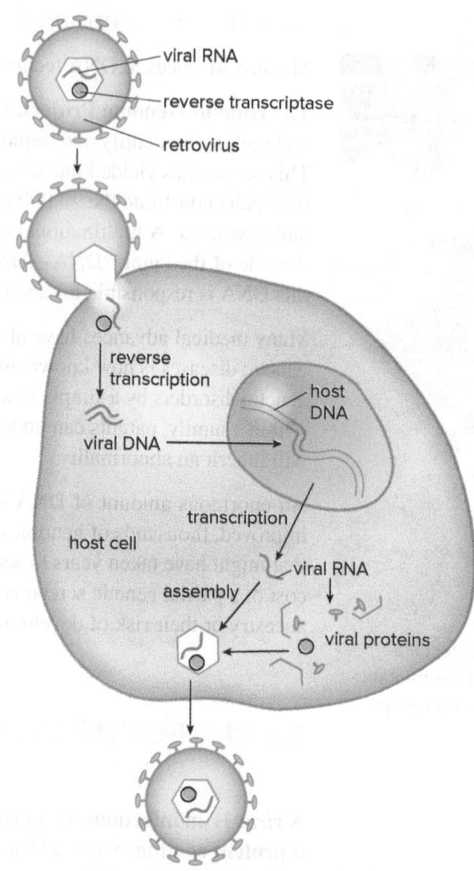

A retrovirus (containing viral RNA and a reverse transcriptase) binds and infects a host cell. Reverse transcription forms viral DNA from RNA. One strand of viral DNA becomes a template to transcribe viral RNA, which is then translated into viral proteins. A new virus is assembled and the virus leaves the host cell to infect other cells.

HEALTH NOTE

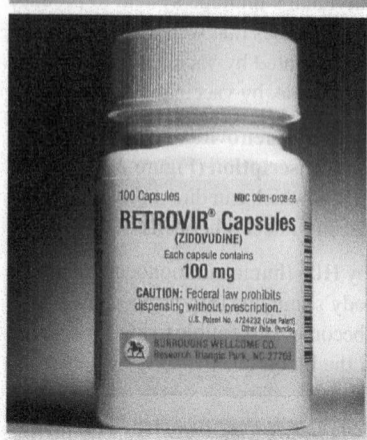

AZT, also called zidovudine and originally sold under the trade name Retrovir, has been available since the 1990s for the treatment of HIV. ©James Keyser/The LIFE Picture Collection/Getty Images

Other drugs are designed to interfere with reverse transcription, an essential biochemical process unique to the virus. Two drugs in this category are **AZT** (azidodeoxythymidine) and **ddI** (dideoxyinosine). These drugs are synthetic analogues of nucleosides. The structure of each drug closely resembles the nucleotides that must be incorporated in viral DNA, and thus they are inserted into a growing DNA strand after a phosphate is introduced at the 5'-OH. Each drug lacks a hydroxyl group at the 3' position, however, so no additional nucleotide can be added to the DNA chain, thus halting DNA synthesis.

Thus, HIV protease inhibitors and nucleoside analogues both disrupt the life cycle of HIV, but they do so by very different mechanisms.

CHAPTER HIGHLIGHTS

KEY TERMS

Anticodon (22.8)

Codon (22.7)

Complementary base pairs (22.3)

Deletion mutation (22.9)

Deoxyribonucleic acid (DNA, 22.1, 22.3)

Deoxyribonucleoside (22.1)

Deoxyribonucleotide (22.1)

DNA fingerprinting (22.10)

Gene (22.1)

Genetic code (22.7)

Genetic disease (22.9)

Genetic engineering (22.10)

Insertion mutation (22.9)

Lagging strand (22.4)

Leading strand (22.4)

Messenger RNA (mRNA, 22.5)

Mutation (22.9)

Nucleic acid (22.1, 22.2)

Nucleoside (22.1)

Nucleotide (22.1)

Plasmid (22.10)

Point mutation (22.9)

Polymerase chain reaction (PCR, 22.10)

Polynucleotide (22.2)

Recombinant DNA (22.10)

Replication (22.4)

Restriction endonuclease (22.10)

Retrovirus (22.11)

Reverse transcription (22.11)

Ribonucleic acid (RNA, 22.1, 22.5)

Ribonucleoside (22.1)

Ribonucleotide (22.1)

Ribosomal RNA (rRNA, 22.5)

Transcription (22.6)

Transfer RNA (tRNA, 22.5)

Translation (22.8)

Virus (22.11)

KEY CONCEPTS

① What are the main structural features of nucleosides and nucleotides? (22.1)

- A nucleoside contains a monosaccharide joined to a nitrogen-containing base at the anomeric carbon.
- A nucleotide contains a monosaccharide joined to a nitrogen-containing base, and a phosphate bonded to the 5'-OH group of the monosaccharide.
- The monosaccharide is either ribose or 2-deoxyribose, and the bases are abbreviated as A, G, C, T, and U.

② How do the nucleic acids DNA and RNA differ in structure? (22.2)

- DNA is a polymer of deoxyribonucleotides, where the sugar is 2-deoxyribose and the bases are A, G, C, and T. DNA is double stranded.
- RNA is a polymer of ribonucleotides, where the sugar is ribose and the bases are A, G, C, and U. RNA is single stranded.

③ Describe the basic features of the DNA double helix. (22.3)

- DNA consists of two polynucleotide strands that wind into a right-handed double helix. The sugar–phosphate backbone lies on the outside of the helix and the bases lie on the inside. The two strands run in opposite directions; that is, one strand runs from the 5' end to the 3' end and the other runs from the 3' end to the 5' end. The double helix is stabilized by hydrogen bonding between complementary base pairs; A pairs with T, and C pairs with G.

④ Outline the main steps in the replication of DNA. (22.4)

- Replication of DNA is semiconservative; an original DNA molecule forms two DNA molecules, each of which has one strand from the parent DNA and one new strand.
- In replication, DNA unwinds and the enzyme DNA polymerase catalyzes replication on both strands. The identity of the bases on the template strand determines the order of the bases on the new strand, with A pairing with T and C pairing with G. Replication occurs from the 3' end to the 5' end of each strand. One strand, the leading strand, grows continuously, while the other strand, the lagging strand, is synthesized in fragments and then joined together with a DNA ligase enzyme.

⑤ List the three types of RNA molecules and describe their functions. (22.5)

- Ribosomal RNA (rRNA), which consists of one large subunit and one small subunit, provides the site where proteins are assembled.
- Messenger RNA (mRNA) contains the sequence of nucleotides that determines the amino acid sequence in a protein. mRNA is transcribed from DNA such that each DNA gene corresponds to a different mRNA molecule.
- Transfer RNA (tRNA) contains an anticodon that identifies the amino acid that it carries on its acceptor stem and delivers that amino acid to a growing polypeptide.

826   **Chapter 22**   Nucleic Acids and Protein Synthesis

6 **What is transcription? (22.6)**

- Transcription is the synthesis of mRNA from DNA. The DNA helix unwinds and RNA polymerase catalyzes RNA synthesis from the 3' to 5' end of the template strand, forming mRNA with complementary bases.

7 **What are the main features of the genetic code? (22.7)**

- mRNAs contain sequences of three bases called codons that code for individual amino acids. There are 61 codons that correspond to the 20 amino acids, as well as three stop codons that signal the end of protein synthesis.

8 **How are proteins synthesized by the process of translation? (22.8)**

- Translation begins with initiation, the binding of the ribosomal subunits to mRNA and the arrival of the first tRNA with an amino acid. During elongation, tRNAs bring individual amino acids to the ribosome one after another, and new peptide bonds are formed. Termination occurs when a stop codon is reached.

9 **What is a mutation and how are mutations related to genetic diseases? (22.9)**

- Mutations are changes in the nucleotide sequence in a DNA molecule. A point mutation results in the substitution of one nucleotide for another. Deletion and insertion mutations result in the loss or addition of nucleotides, respectively. A mutation that causes an inherited condition may result in a genetic disease.

10 **What are the principal features of three techniques using DNA in the laboratory—recombinant DNA, the polymerase chain reaction (PCR), and DNA fingerprinting? (22.10)**

- Recombinant DNA is synthetic DNA formed when a segment of DNA from one source is inserted into the DNA of another source. When inserted into a bacterium, recombinant DNA can be used to prepare large quantities of useful proteins.
- The polymerase chain reaction (PCR) is used to amplify a portion of a DNA molecule to produce millions of copies of a single gene.
- DNA fingerprinting is used to identify an individual by cutting DNA with restriction endonucleases to give a unique set of fragments.

11 **What are the main characteristics of viruses? (22.11)**

- A virus is an infectious agent that contains either DNA or RNA within a protein coat. When the virus invades a host cell, it uses the biochemical machinery of the host to replicate. A retrovirus contains RNA and a reverse transcriptase that allow the RNA to synthesize viral DNA, which then transcribes RNA that directs protein synthesis.

PROBLEMS

Selected in-chapter and odd-numbered end-of-chapter problems have brief answers in Appendix B. The *Student Study Guide and Solutions Manual* contains detailed solutions to all in-chapter and odd-numbered end-of-chapter problems, as well as additional worked examples and a chapter self-test.

Nucleosides, Nucleotides, and Nucleic Acids

22.17 Label each statement as pertaining to DNA, RNA, or both.
- a. The polynucleotide is double stranded.
- b. The polynucleotide may contain adenine.
- c. The polynucleotide may contain dGMP.
- d. The polynucleotide is a polymer of ribonucleotides.

22.18 Label each statement as pertaining to DNA, RNA, or both.
- a. The polynucleotide is single stranded.
- b. The polynucleotide may contain guanine.
- c. The polynucleotide may contain UMP.
- d. The polynucleotide is a polymer of deoxyribonucleotides.

22.19 (a) Give the name of each compound shown as a ball-and-stick model. (b) Classify the compound as a base, nucleoside, or nucleotide. (c) Would the compound be a component of DNA, RNA, or both?

A   B

22.20 (a) Give the name of each compound shown as a ball-and-stick model. (b) Classify the compound as a base, nucleoside, or nucleotide. (c) Would the compound be a component of DNA, RNA, or both?

C   D

22.21 Identify the base and monosaccharide in each compound and then name it.

a.

b.

22.22 Identify the base and monosaccharide in each compound and then name it.

a.

b.

22.23 (a) Identify the base and monosaccharide in the following nucleotide. (b) Give the name and three- or four-letter abbreviation for the compound.

22.24 (a) Identify the base and monosaccharide in the following nucleotide. (b) Give the name and three- or four-letter abbreviation for the compound.

22.25 Draw the structure of each of the following:
   a. a purine base
   b. a nucleoside that contains 2-deoxyribose and a pyrimidine base
   c. a nucleotide that contains ribose and a purine base
   d. a triphosphate of guanosine

22.26 Draw the structure of each of the following:
   a. a pyrimidine base
   b. a nucleoside that contains 2-deoxyribose and a purine base
   c. a nucleotide that contains ribose and a pyrimidine base
   d. a diphosphate of uridine

22.27 Draw the structure of each nucleoside or nucleotide.
   a. adenosine   c. GDP
   b. deoxyguanosine   d. dTDP

22.28 Draw the structure of each nucleoside or nucleotide.
   a. uridine   c. dGMP
   b. deoxycytidine   d. UTP

22.29 Consider the given dinucleotide.

   a. Identify the bases present in the dinucleotide.
   b. Label the 5' and 3' ends.
   c. Give the three- or four-letter abbreviations for the two nucleotides.
   d. Is this dinucleotide a ribonucleotide or a deoxyribonucleotide? Explain your choice.
   e. Name the dinucleotide.

22.30 Answer Problem 22.29 for the following dinucleotide.

22.31 Draw the structures of the two possible dinucleotides formed from uridine 5'-monophosphate and adenosine 5'-monophosphate.

22.32 Draw the structures of the two possible dinucleotides formed from deoxythymidine 5'-monophosphate and deoxycytidine 5'-monophosphate.

22.33 Draw the structure of each dinucleotide and identify the 5' and 3' ends.
   a. the deoxyribonucleotide formed by joining the 3'-OH group of dTMP with the 5'-phosphate of dAMP
   b. the ribonucleotide formed by joining the 5'-phosphate of GMP with the 3'-OH of CMP

22.34 Draw the structure of each dinucleotide and identify the 5' and 3' ends.

    a. the deoxyribonucleotide formed by joining two deoxyguanosine 5'-phosphates together

    b. the ribonucleotide formed by joining the 5'-phosphate of UMP with the 3'-OH of AMP

22.35 Draw the deoxyribonucleotide TGA. Label the 5' and 3' ends.

22.36 Draw the ribonucleotide CGU. Label the 5' and 3' ends.

22.37 Describe in detail the DNA double helix with reference to each of the following features: (a) the sugar–phosphate backbone; (b) the functional groups at the end of each strand; (c) the hydrogen bonding between strands.

22.38 Describe in detail the DNA double helix with reference to each of the following features: (a) the location of the bases; (b) the complementary base pairing; (c) the phosphodiester linkages.

22.39 Write the sequence of the complementary strand of each segment of a DNA molecule.

    a. 5'–AAATAAC–3'   c. 5'–CGATATCCCG–3'

    b. 5'–ACTGGACT–3'   d. 5'–TTCCCGGGATA–3'

22.40 Fill in the complementary bases at the labeled sites of the portion of DNA shown.

22.41 If 27% of the nucleotides in a sample of DNA contain the base adenine (A), what are the percentages of bases T, G, and C?

22.42 If 19% of the nucleotides in a sample of DNA contain the base cytosine (C), what are the percentages of bases G, A, and T?

22.43 Complementary base pairing occurs between two strands of DNA, between two different sites on an RNA molecule, and between one strand of DNA and one strand of RNA. Which base pairs are the same in all three settings?

22.44 Complementary base pairing occurs between two strands of DNA, and between one strand of DNA and one strand of RNA. Give an example of a base pair that is unique to each setting.

22.45 Figure 22.4 shows the hydrogen-bonding interactions that occur in an A–T base pair. Using the given structures, draw the hydrogen-bonding interaction(s) that are possible between thymine and guanine. Explain why T–A base pairing occurs instead of T–G base pairing.

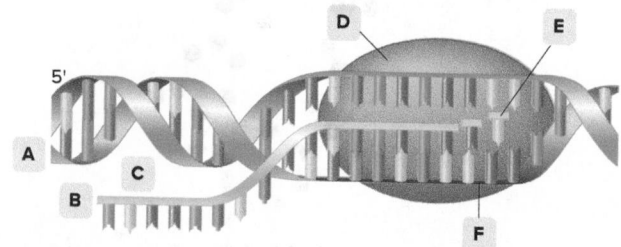

cytosine   adenine

thymine   guanine

22.46 Figure 22.4 shows the hydrogen-bonding interactions that occur in a C–G base pair. Using the given structures, draw the hydrogen-bonding interaction(s) that are possible between cytosine and adenine. Explain why C–G base pairing occurs instead of C–A base pairing.

Replication, Transcription, Translation, and Protein Synthesis

22.47 Consider the following simple graphic that illustrates the main features of DNA replication. Label each of the letters (**A–G**) with one of the following terms: leading strand, lagging strand, template strand, 5' end, or 3' end. A term may be used more than once.

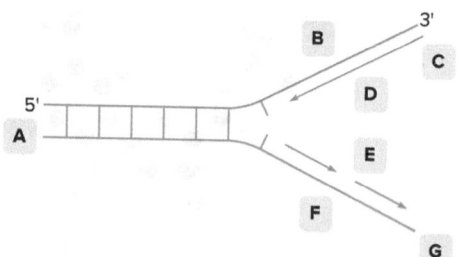

22.48 Consider the following graphic that illustrates the transcription of DNA to RNA. Label each of the letters (**A–F**) with one of the following terms: nucleotide, RNA, template strand, RNA polymerase, 5' end, or 3' end.

22.49 What is the sequence of a newly synthesized DNA segment if the template strand has the sequence 3'–ATGGCCTATGCGAT–5'?

22.50 What is the sequence of a newly synthesized DNA segment if the template strand has the sequence 3'–CGCGATTAGATATTGCCGC–5'?

22.51 What mRNA is transcribed from each DNA sequence in Problem 22.39?

22.52 Explain the roles of messenger RNA and transfer RNA in converting the genetic information coded in DNA into protein synthesis.

22.53 For each DNA segment: [1] What is the sequence of the mRNA molecule synthesized from each DNA template? [2] What is the sequence of the informational strand of the DNA molecule?

    a. 3'–ATGGCTTA–5'   c. 3'–GGTATACCG–5'

    b. 3'–CGGCGCTTA–5'   d. 3'–TAGGCCGTA–5'

22.54 For each DNA segment: [1] What is the sequence of the mRNA molecule synthesized from each DNA template? [2] What is the sequence of the informational strand of the DNA molecule?

    a. 3'–GGCCTATA–5'   c. 3'–CTACTG–5'

    b. 3'–GCCGAT–5'   d. 3'–ATTAGAGC–5'

22.55 For each codon, give its anticodon and the amino acid for which it codes.

    a. CUG   b. UUU   c. AAG   d. GCA

22.56 For each codon, give its anticodon and the amino acid for which it codes.

    a. GUU   b. AUA   c. CCC   d. GCG

22.57 Fill in the missing information in the schematic of a tRNA during the elongation phase of translation.

22.58 Fill in the missing information in the schematic of a tRNA during the elongation phase of translation.

22.59 Derive the amino acid sequence that is coded for by each mRNA sequence.

    a. 5' CCA ACC UGG GUA GAA 3'

    b. 5' AUG UUU UUA UGG UGG 3'

    c. 5' GUC GAC GAA CCG CAA 3'

22.60 Derive the amino acid sequence that is coded for by each mRNA sequence.

    a. 5' AAA CCC UUU UGU 3'

    b. 5' CCU UUG GAA GUA CUU 3'

    c. 5' GGG UGU AUG CAC CGA UUG 3'

22.61 Write a possible mRNA sequence that codes for each peptide.

    a. Ile–Met–Lys–Ser–Tyr

    b. Pro–Gln–Glu–Asp–Phe

    c. Thr–Ser–Asn–Arg

22.62 Write a possible mRNA sequence that codes for each peptide.

    a. Phe–Phe–Leu–Lys

    b. Val–Gly–Gln–Asp–Asn

    c. Arg–His–Ile–Ser

22.63 Using the given DNA template strand in the following representation, fill in the transcribed mRNA sequence and the polypeptide that would be synthesized from this template.

22.64 Using the given mRNA sequence in the following representation, (a) fill in the DNA template strand from which this mRNA was synthesized. (b) What polypeptide would be synthesized from this mRNA sequence?

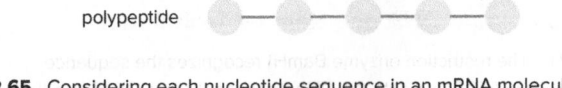

22.65 Considering each nucleotide sequence in an mRNA molecule: [1] write the sequence of the DNA template strand from which the mRNA was synthesized; [2] give the peptide synthesized by the mRNA.

    a. 5' UAU UCA AUA AAA AAC 3'

    b. 5' GAU GUA AAC AAG CCG 3'

22.66 Considering each nucleotide sequence in an mRNA molecule: [1] write the sequence of the DNA template strand from which the mRNA was synthesized; [2] give the peptide synthesized by the mRNA.

    a. 5' UUG CUC AAC CAA 3'

    b. 5' AUU GUA CCA CAA CCC 3'

Mutations

22.67 Consider the following mRNA sequence: 5'–CUU CAG CAC–3'.

    a. What amino acid sequence is coded for by this mRNA?

    b. What is the amino acid sequence if a mutation converts CAC to AAC?

    c. What is the amino acid sequence if a mutation converts CUU to CUC?

    d. What occurs when a mutation converts CAG to UAG?

    e. What occurs if CU is deleted from the beginning of the chain?

22.68 Consider the following mRNA sequence: 5'–ACC UUA CGA–3'.

    a. What amino acid sequence is coded for by this mRNA?

    b. What is the amino acid sequence if a mutation converts ACC to ACU?

    c. What is the amino acid sequence if a mutation converts UUA to UCA?

    d. What is the amino acid sequence if a mutation converts CGA to AGA?

    e. What occurs if C is added to the beginning of the chain?

22.69 Consider the following sequence of DNA: 3'–TTA CGG–5'.
a. What dipeptide is formed from this DNA after transcription and translation?
b. If a mutation converts CGG to CGT in DNA, what dipeptide is formed?
c. If a mutation converts CGG to CCG in DNA, what dipeptide is formed?
d. If a mutation converts CGG to AGG in DNA, what dipeptide is formed?

22.70 Consider the following sequence of DNA: 3'–ATA GGG–5'.
a. What dipeptide is formed from this DNA after transcription and translation?
b. If a mutation converts ATA to ATG in DNA, what dipeptide is formed?
c. If a mutation converts ATA to AGA in DNA, what dipeptide is formed?
d. What occurs when a mutation converts ATA to ATT in DNA?

Recombinant DNA and Related Techniques

22.71 The restriction enzyme BamHI recognizes the sequence GGATCC and cuts the DNA between the two G's. Given the following segment of double-stranded DNA, draw the sticky ends that result from cleavage with this enzyme.

5' ⌇⌇⌇ C C G G T T G G A T C C T T ⌇⌇⌇ 3'

3' ⌇⌇⌇ G G C C A A C C T A G G A A ⌇⌇⌇ 5'

22.72 The restriction enzyme PstI recognizes the sequence GACGTC and cuts the DNA between the G and A. Given the following segment of double-stranded DNA, draw the sticky ends that result from cleavage with this enzyme.

5' ⌇⌇⌇ G G A T G A C G T C A A T T ⌇⌇⌇ 3'

3' ⌇⌇⌇ C C T A C T G C A G T T A A ⌇⌇⌇ 5'

22.73 Describe the main steps in preparing recombinant DNA from plasmid DNA.

22.74 Describe the main steps in using the polymerase chain reaction to amplify a small amount of DNA.

22.75 The given gel contains the DNA fingerprint of a mother (lane 1), father (lane 2), and four children (lanes 3–6). One child is adopted, two children are the offspring of both parents, and one child is the offspring of one parent only.

a. Which lanes, if any, represent a biological child of both parents? Explain your choice.
b. Which lanes, if any, represent an adopted child? Explain your choice.

22.76 With reference to the gel in Problem 22.75: (a) which lanes (if any) represent a biological child of the mother only; (b) which lanes (if any) represent a biological child of the father only; (c) which lanes (if any) represent twins? Explain each choice.

22.77 The lanes in the given gel show the DNA of a father and three children. Which lane represents the DNA of the father?

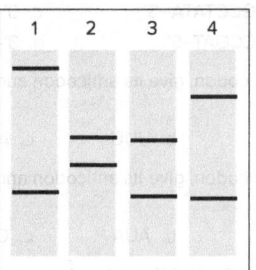

22.78 Which lane in the given gel represents an identical twin of the individual whose DNA is shown in lane 1?

Viruses

22.79 Lamivudine, also called 3TC, is a nucleoside analogue used in the treatment of HIV and the virus that causes hepatitis B. (a) What nucleoside does lamivudine resemble? (b) How does lamivudine inhibit reverse transcription?

lamivudine
3TC

22.80 What is reverse transcription?

General Questions

22.81 Consider a template strand of DNA with the following sequence: 3'–CAA TGT ATT TTT GCT–5'. (a) What is the informational strand of DNA that corresponds to this template? (b) What mRNA is prepared from this template? (c) What polypeptide is prepared from the mRNA?

22.82 Consider a template strand of DNA with the following sequence: 3'–ATT AAA GCC TTC TGT–5'. (a) What is the informational strand of DNA that corresponds to this template? (b) What mRNA is prepared from this template? (c) What polypeptide is prepared from the mRNA?

22.83 Fill in the base, codon, anticodon, or amino acid needed to complete the following table that relates the sequences of DNA, mRNA, tRNA, and the resulting polypeptide.

DNA informational strand:	5' end							3' end
DNA template strand:	3' end	TTG	ATA	GGT	TGC	TTC	TAC	5' end
mRNA codons:	5' end							3' end
tRNA anticodons:								
Polypeptide:								

22.84 Fill in the base, codon, anticodon, or amino acid needed to complete the following table that relates the sequences of DNA, mRNA, tRNA, and the resulting polypeptide.

DNA informational strand:	5' end						3' end
DNA template strand:	3' end	TCC	GAC	TTG	TGC	CAT	CAC	5' end
mRNA codons:	5' end						3' end
tRNA anticodons:							
Polypeptide:							

22.85 Fill in the base, codon, anticodon, or amino acid needed to complete the following table that relates the sequences of DNA, mRNA, tRNA, and the resulting polypeptide.

DNA informational strand:	5' end	AAC					3' end
DNA template strand:	3' end		CAT				5' end
mRNA codons:	5' end			UCA		AUG	3' end
tRNA anticodons:					GUG		
Polypeptide:				Thr			

22.86 Fill in the base, codon, anticodon, or amino acid needed to complete the following table that relates the sequences of DNA, mRNA, tRNA, and the resulting polypeptide.

DNA informational strand:	5' end		ACA			3' end
DNA template strand:	3' end	CAA			GTC	5' end
mRNA codons:	5' end		UAC			3' end
tRNA anticodons:				ACA		
Polypeptide:				Lys		

22.87 If there are 325 amino acids in a polypeptide, how many bases are present in a single strand of the gene that codes for it, assuming that every base is transcribed and then translated to polypeptide?

22.88 If a single strand of a gene contains 678 bases, how many amino acids result in the polypeptide prepared from it, assuming every base of the gene is transcribed and then translated?

22.89 Met-enkephalin (Tyr–Gly–Gly–Phe–Met) is a painkiller and sedative (Section 21.5). What is a possible nucleotide sequence in the template strand of the gene that codes for met-enkephalin, assuming that every base of the gene is transcribed and then translated?

22.90 Leu-enkephalin (Tyr–Gly–Gly–Phe–Leu) is a painkiller and sedative (Section 21.5). What is a possible nucleotide sequence in the template strand of the gene that codes for leu-enkephalin, assuming that every base of the gene is transcribed and then translated?

CHALLENGE PROBLEMS

22.91 Give a possible nucleotide sequence in the template strand of the gene that codes for the following tripeptide.

22.92 Give a possible nucleotide sequence in the template strand of the gene that codes for the following tripeptide.

23

The immediate energy needs of a sprinter are supplied by ATP and creatine phosphate, two reactive molecules that release energy by cleaving a bond during hydrolysis.
©Image Source RF

Metabolism and Energy Production

CHAPTER OUTLINE

23.1 Introduction
23.2 An Overview of Metabolism
23.3 ATP and Energy Production
23.4 Coenzymes in Metabolism
23.5 The Citric Acid Cycle
23.6 The Electron Transport Chain and Oxidative Phosphorylation
23.7 FOCUS ON HEALTH & MEDICINE: Hydrogen Cyanide

CHAPTER GOALS

In this chapter you will learn how to:

1. Define metabolism and explain where energy production occurs in cells
2. Describe the main characteristics of the four stages of catabolism
3. Explain the role of ATP in energy production and how coupled reactions drive energetically unfavorable reactions
4. Describe the roles of the main coenzymes used in metabolism
5. List the main features of the citric acid cycle
6. Describe the main components of the electron transport chain and oxidative phosphorylation
7. Explain why compounds such as cyanide that disrupt the electron transport chain are poisons

Despite the wide diversity among life forms, virtually all organisms contain the same types of biomolecules—lipids, carbohydrates, proteins, and nucleic acids—and use the same biochemical reactions. Chapter 23 is the first of two chapters that deal with the complex biochemical pathways that convert one molecule into another in cells. In Chapter 23 we concentrate on the fundamental reactions that produce energy, while in Chapter 24 we examine specific pathways for the metabolism of lipids, carbohydrates, and proteins. Although the pathways often involve many steps, individual reactions can be understood by applying the same chemical principles you have already learned.

23.1 Introduction

Each moment thousands of reactions occur in a living cell: large molecules are broken down into smaller components, small molecules are converted into larger molecules, and energy changes occur.

- *Metabolism* is the sum of all of the chemical reactions that take place in an organism.

There are two types of metabolic processes called **catabolism** and **anabolism.**

- *Catabolism* is the breakdown of large molecules into smaller ones. Energy is generally released during catabolism.
- *Anabolism* is the synthesis of large molecules from smaller ones. Energy is generally absorbed during anabolism.

The oxidation of glucose ($C_6H_{12}O_6$) to carbon dioxide (CO_2) and water (H_2O) is an example of catabolism, whereas the synthesis of a protein from component amino acids is an example of anabolism. Often the conversion of a starting material to a final product occurs by an organized series of consecutive reactions called a **metabolic pathway.** A metabolic pathway may be **linear** or **cyclic.**

Cyclic metabolic pathway

Linear metabolic pathway

A ⟶ B ⟶ C ⟶ D

- A *linear* pathway is a series of reactions that generates a final product different from any of the reactants.
- A *cyclic* pathway is a series of reactions that regenerates the first reactant.

In this chapter we concentrate on energy changes that occur during metabolism. The human body needs energy to move, think, talk, laugh, and breathe. It also requires energy to maintain a constant temperature and to synthesize new cells and tissues.

While the reactions in living organisms follow the same principles as reactions in the laboratory, the energy needs of the body come with some special requirements. The body usually can't use the calories of a big meal all at once, so the energy must be stored and then gradually released. Moreover, energy must be stored in molecules that are readily accessible for use anywhere in the body at any time the energy is needed.

Figure 23.1   The Mitochondrion in a Typical Animal Cell

- mitochondrion
- cytoplasm
- inner membrane
- outer membrane
- intermembrane space
- matrix

A mitochondrion is a small organelle located in the cytoplasm of the cell. Cellular energy production occurs in the mitochondria.

Where does energy production occur in cells? A typical animal cell, such as the one shown in Figure 23.1, is surrounded by a cell membrane (Section 19.7) and has a nucleus that contains DNA in chromosomes (Section 22.3). The **cytoplasm,** the region of the cell between the cell membrane and the nucleus, contains various specialized structures called **organelles,** each of which has a specific function. **Mitochondria** are small sausage-shaped organelles in which energy production takes place. Mitochondria contain an outer membrane and an inner membrane with many folds. The area between these two membranes is called the **intermembrane space.** Energy production occurs within the **matrix,** the area surrounded by the inner membrane of the mitochondrion. The number of mitochondria in a cell varies depending on its energy needs. Cells in the heart, brain, and muscles of the human body typically contain many mitochondria.

Mitochondrion is the singular form of the plural mitochondria.

23.2   An Overview of Metabolism

Just as gasoline is the fuel that powers automobiles, so, too, food is the fuel that is metabolized by the body to provide energy. Catabolism breaks down the carbohydrates, proteins, and lipids in food into smaller molecules, releasing energy to supply the body's needs. This process involves numerous catabolic pathways that can be organized into four stages, as shown in Figure 23.2.

23.2A   Stage [1]—Digestion

The catabolism of food begins with **digestion,** which is catalyzed by enzymes in the saliva, stomach, and small intestine (Figure 23.3). Digestion converts large molecules into smaller components. The hydrolysis of carbohydrates to monosaccharides begins with amylase enzymes in the saliva, and continues in the small intestine. Protein digestion begins in the stomach, where acid denatures the protein, and the protease pepsin begins to cleave the protein backbone into smaller polypeptides and amino acids. Digestion continues in the small intestine, where trypsin and chymotrypsin further cleave the protein backbone to form amino acids. Triacylglycerols, the most common lipids, are first emulsified by bile secreted by the liver, and then hydrolyzed to glycerol and fatty acids by lipases in the small intestine.

Figure 23.2   The Four Stages in Biochemical Catabolism and Energy Production

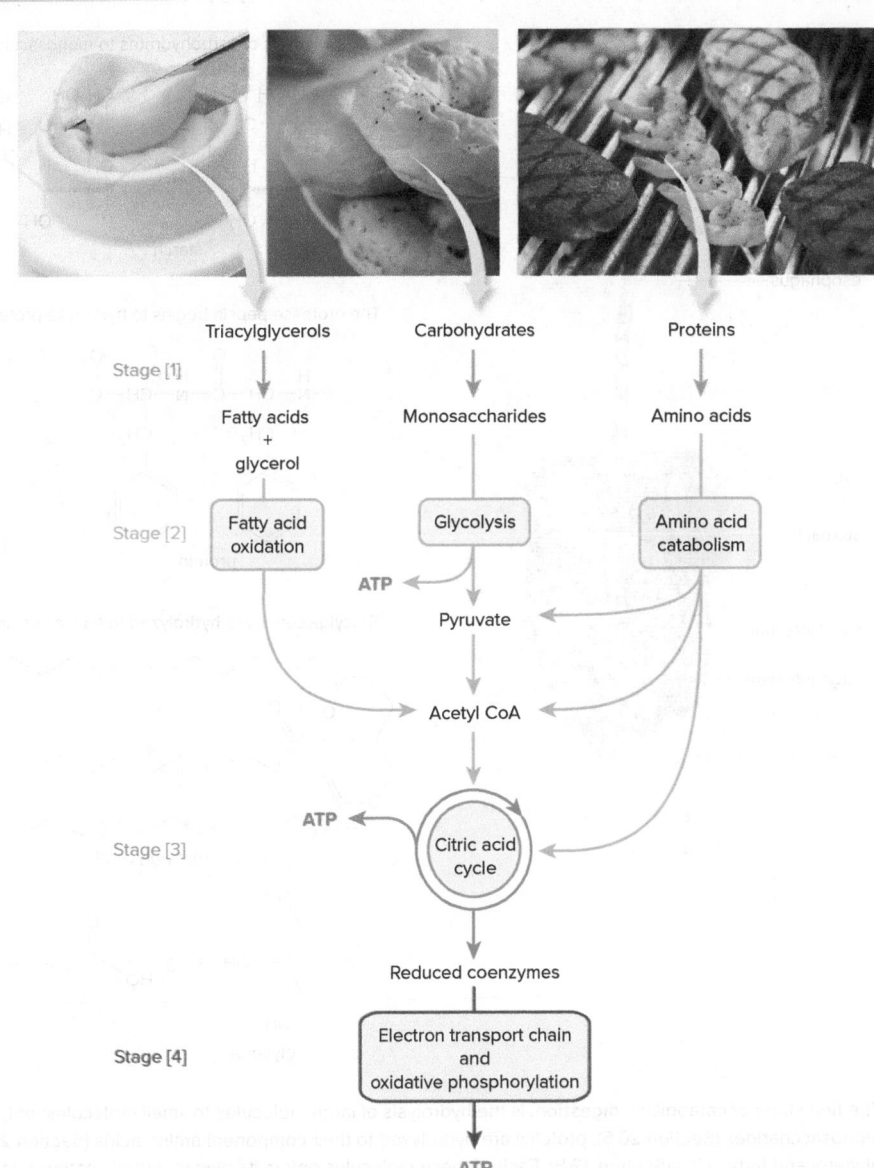

(left): ©Fuse/Getty Images RF; (middle): ©anopdesignstock/Getty Images RF;
(right): ©Lew Robertson/Brand X Pictures/Getty Images RF

Once these small molecules are formed during digestion, they are each absorbed through the intestinal wall into the bloodstream and transported to other cells in the body. Some substances such as cellulose are not metabolized as they travel through the digestive tract. When these materials can't be absorbed, they pass into the large intestine and are excreted.

23.2B   Stages [2]–[4] of Catabolism

Once small molecules are formed, catabolism continues to break down each type of molecule to smaller units, releasing energy in the process.

Figure 23.3   Digestion of Carbohydrates, Proteins, and Triacylglycerols

The first stage of catabolism, **digestion,** is the hydrolysis of large molecules to small molecules: polysaccharides such as starch are hydrolyzed to monosaccharides (Section 20.6), proteins are hydrolyzed to their component amino acids (Section 21.8), and triacylglycerols are hydrolyzed to glycerol and fatty acids (Section 19.5). Each of these molecules enters its own metabolic pathway to be further broken down into smaller components, releasing energy.

Stage [2]—Formation of Acetyl CoA

Monosaccharides, amino acids, and fatty acids are degraded into **acetyl groups (CH_3CO—),** two-carbon units that are bonded to coenzyme A (a coenzyme), forming **acetyl CoA.** Details of the structure of acetyl CoA are given in Section 23.4.

The product of the catabolic pathways is the *same* for all three types of molecules. As a result, a common catabolic pathway, the **citric acid cycle,** continues the processing of all types of biomolecules to generate energy.

Stage [3]—The Citric Acid Cycle

The citric acid cycle is based in the mitochondria. In this biochemical cycle, the acetyl groups of acetyl CoA are oxidized to carbon dioxide. Some energy produced by this process is stored in the bonds of a nucleoside triphosphate (Section 22.1) and reduced coenzymes, whose structures are shown in Section 23.4.

Stage [4]—The Electron Transport Chain and Oxidative Phosphorylation

Within the mitochondria, the electron transport chain and oxidative phosphorylation produce **ATP**—adenosine 5'-triphosphate—the primary energy-carrying molecule in metabolic pathways. Oxygen combines with hydrogen ions and electrons from the reduced coenzymes to form water. The result of catabolism is that biomolecules are converted to CO_2 and H_2O and energy is produced and stored in ATP molecules.

Since all catabolic pathways converge in the citric acid cycle, we begin our discussion of catabolism with this central common pathway. In order to understand the details, however, we must first learn about the structure and properties of some of the molecules involved. In particular, Section 23.3 is devoted to a discussion of ATP and how it is used to supply energy in reactions. In Section 23.4 we examine the structure and reactions of the key coenzymes nicotinamide adenine dinucleotide (NAD^+), flavin adenine dinucleotide (FAD), and coenzyme A.

PROBLEM 23.1

What advantage might there be to funneling all catabolic pathways into a single common pathway, the citric acid cycle?

23.3 ATP and Energy Production

As we learned in Section 22.1, **ATP,** adenosine 5'-triphosphate, is a nucleoside triphosphate formed by adding three phosphates to the 5'-OH group of adenosine, a nucleoside composed of the sugar ribose and the base adenine. Similarly, **ADP,** adenosine 5'-diphosphate, is a nucleoside diphosphate formed by adding two phosphates to the 5'-OH group of adenosine.

23.3A   General Features of ATP Hydrolysis and Formation

In metabolic pathways, the interconversion of ATP and ADP is the most important process for the storage and release of energy.

- Hydrolysis of ATP cleaves one phosphate group, forming ADP and hydrogen phosphate, HPO_4^{2-}, often abbreviated as P_i (inorganic phosphate). This reaction *releases* 7.3 kcal/mol of energy.

Any process, such as walking, running, swallowing, or breathing, is fueled by the release of energy from the hydrolysis of ATP to ADP. ATP is the most prominent member of a group of "high-energy" molecules, reactive molecules that release energy by cleaving a bond during hydrolysis. Because ATP contains four negatively charged oxygen atoms in close proximity, the electronic repulsion of the like charges drives the hydrolysis to ADP, which has fewer negatively charged oxygens and therefore less electronic repulsion.

- The reverse reaction, phosphorylation, adds a phosphate group to ADP, forming ATP. Phosphorylation *requires* 7.3 kcal/mol of energy.

By way of these reactions, ATP is a transporter of energy.

- Energy is absorbed and stored in ATP when it is synthesized from ADP.
- Energy is released when ATP is hydrolyzed to ADP.

Figure 23.4 summarizes the reactions and energy changes that occur when ATP is synthesized and hydrolyzed. As we learned in Section 6.2, when energy is *released* in a reaction, the energy change is reported as a *negative* (−) value, so the energy change for ATP hydrolysis is −7.3 kcal/mol. When energy is *absorbed* in a reaction, the energy change is reported as a *positive* (+) value, so the energy change for the phosphorylation of ADP is +7.3 kcal/mol. The synthesis of ATP with HPO_4^{2-} is the reverse of ATP hydrolysis, and the energy changes for such reactions are *equal* in value but *opposite* in sign.

Figure 23.4	ATP Hydrolysis and Synthesis					
						Energy change
ATP Hydrolysis	ATP	+	H_2O	$\longrightarrow$	ADP + HPO_4^{2-}	−7.3 kcal/mol
ATP Synthesis	ADP	+	HPO_4^{2-}	$\longrightarrow$	ATP + H_2O	+7.3 kcal/mol

Energy is released.   Energy is absorbed.

ATP is constantly synthesized and hydrolyzed. It is estimated that each ATP molecule exists for about a minute before it is hydrolyzed and its energy released.

PROBLEM 23.2

GTP, guanosine 5′-triphosphate, is another high-energy molecule that releases 7.3 kcal of energy when it is hydrolyzed to GDP. Convert the ball-and-stick model of GTP to a structural formula, and write the equation for the hydrolysis of GTP to GDP.

GTP

23.3B   Coupled Reactions in Metabolic Pathways

As we learned in Section 6.5, a reaction that releases energy is a favorable process because it forms products that are lower in energy than the reactants. On the other hand, a reaction that absorbs energy is an unfavorable process because it forms products that are higher in energy than the reactants.

The hydrolysis of ATP to ADP is a favorable reaction: energy is released and some of the electronic repulsion due to many closely situated negative charges is relieved. The energy released in ATP hydrolysis can be used to drive a reaction that has an unfavorable energy change by **coupling** the two reactions together.

- Coupled reactions are pairs of reactions that occur together. The energy released by one reaction provides the energy to drive the other reaction.

Let's consider the catabolism of glucose to CO_2 and H_2O, a process that requires a large number of steps in various biochemical pathways. Although the overall conversion releases a great deal of energy, the energy change associated with each individual step is much smaller. In some reactions energy is released, whereas in others energy is absorbed. The hydrolysis of ATP provides the energy to drive the reactions that require energy.

In the first step in the metabolism of glucose, for example, glucose reacts with hydrogen phosphate (HPO_4^{2-}) to form glucose 6-phosphate, a process that requires 3.3 kcal/mol of energy. This process is energetically unfavorable because energy is absorbed (+3.3 kcal/mol). However, by coupling this reaction with ATP hydrolysis, an energetically favorable reaction (−7.3 kcal/mol of energy released), the coupled reaction becomes an energetically favorable process (−4.0 kcal/mol of energy released).

						Energy change	
Phosphorylation	glucose + HPO_4^{2-} ⟶		glucose 6-phosphate + H_2O			+3.3 kcal/mol ⟵	energy required
Hydrolysis	ATP + H_2O ⟶		ADP +		HPO_4^{2-}	−7.3 kcal/mol ⟵	energy released
Coupled reaction	glucose + ATP ⟶		glucose 6-phosphate +		ADP	−4.0 kcal/mol	

Energy is released.

- The coupled reaction is the net reaction, written by summing the substances in both equations and eliminating those compounds that appear on both sides of the reaction arrows.
- The overall energy change is found by summing the energies for the individual steps.

Thus, in this example:

- The hydrolysis of ATP provides the energy for the phosphorylation of glucose.

Although the coupled reactions are written as two separate equations for emphasis in the preceding example, in reality, a single reaction takes place. ATP transfers a phosphate to glucose, forming glucose 6-phosphate and ADP, while both molecules are held in close proximity at the active site of hexokinase, as shown in Figure 23.5.

- Coupling an energetically unfavorable reaction with an energetically favorable reaction that releases *more* energy than the amount required is a common phenomenon in biochemical reactions.

Coupled reactions explain how ATP can be synthesized by the energetically unfavorable process of phosphorylation. Phosphorylation must be coupled with a reaction that releases *more*

Figure 23.5   A Coupled Reaction—Phosphorylation of Glucose by ATP

ADP

ADP

glucose

glucose
6-phosphate

enzyme

The enzyme hexokinase binds glucose at its active site and ATP is also bound in close proximity. ATP transfers a phosphate directly to the glucose molecule to form ADP and glucose 6-phosphate. This coupled reaction is energetically favorable.

than 7.3 kcal/mol of energy. Such a reaction is the hydrolysis of phosphoenolpyruvate to form pyruvate.

								Energy change	

Phosphorylation   ADP   + HPO_4^{2-} $\longrightarrow$ ATP   + H_2O +7.3 kcal/mol $\longleftarrow$ energy required

Hydrolysis

$$CH_2{=}\overset{\overset{\displaystyle OPO_3^{2-}}{|}}{C}{-}COO^- \; + \; H_2O \; \longrightarrow \; CH_3{-}\overset{\overset{\displaystyle O}{\|}}{C}{-}COO^- \; + \; HPO_4^{2-}$$

phosphoenolpyruvate   pyruvate   −14.8 kcal/mol $\longleftarrow$ energy released

Coupled reaction

$$CH_2{=}\overset{\overset{\displaystyle OPO_3^{2-}}{|}}{C}{-}COO^- \; + \; ADP \; \longrightarrow \; CH_3{-}\overset{\overset{\displaystyle O}{\|}}{C}{-}COO^- \; + \; ATP$$

−7.5 kcal/mol

Energy is released.

Because the hydrolysis of phosphoenolpyruvate releases more energy than the phosphorylation of ADP (−14.8 kcal versus +7.3 kcal), the coupled reaction becomes energetically favorable (−7.5 kcal/mol of energy released).

SAMPLE PROBLEM 23.1 CALCULATING ENERGY CHANGES IN A COUPLED REACTION

The phosphorylation of fructose to fructose 6-phosphate requires 3.8 kcal/mol of energy. This unfavorable reaction can be driven by the hydrolysis of ATP to ADP. (a) Write the equation for the coupled reaction. (b) How much energy is released in the coupled reaction?

					Energy change

fructose   + HPO_4^{2-} $\longrightarrow$ fructose 6-phosphate   + H_2O +3.8 kcal/mol

Analysis

Write the equation for the hydrolysis of ATP to ADP (Section 23.3A). Add together the substances in this equation and the given equation to give the net equation—that is, the equation for the coupled reaction. To determine the overall energy change, add together the energy changes for each step.

Solution

a. The coupled equation shows the overall reaction that combines the phosphorylation of fructose and the hydrolysis of ATP.

Cross out compounds that appear on both sides of the reaction arrows.

[1]   fructose   + $HP\cancel{O}_4^{2-}$ $\longrightarrow$ fructose 6-phosphate   + $\cancel{H_2O}$

[2]   ATP   + $\cancel{H_2O}$ $\longrightarrow$ ADP   + $HP\cancel{O}_4^{2-}$

Coupled reaction: fructose   +   ATP $\longrightarrow$ fructose 6-phosphate   +   ADP

b. The overall energy change is the sum of the energy changes for each step:
+3.8 kcal/mol + (−7.3) kcal/mol = −3.5 kcal/mol.

PRACTICE PROBLEM 23.1

The phosphorylation of glucose to glucose 1-phosphate requires 5.0 kcal/mol of energy. This unfavorable reaction can be driven by the hydrolysis of ATP to ADP. (a) Write the equation for the coupled reaction. (b) How much energy is released in the coupled reaction?

glucose + HPO_4^{2-} $\longrightarrow$ glucose 1-phosphate + H_2O

More Practice: Try Problems 23.25–23.32.

Coupled reactions that use ATP or coenzymes are often drawn using a combination of horizontal and curved arrows. The principal organic reactants and products are drawn from left to right with a reaction arrow as usual, but additional compounds like ATP and ADP are drawn on a curved arrow. This technique is meant to emphasize the organic substrates of the reaction, while making it clear that other materials are needed for the reaction to occur.

$$CH_2=\overset{\overset{\displaystyle OPO_3{}^{2-}}{|}}{C}-COO^- \quad \xrightarrow{\underset{ADP \qquad ATP}{}} \quad CH_3-\overset{\overset{\displaystyle O}{||}}{C}-COO^-$$

phosphoenolpyruvate   pyruvate

PROBLEM 23.3

Write each of the following reactions using curved arrow symbolism.

a. reaction of fructose with ATP to form fructose 6-phosphate and ADP (Sample Problem 23.1)

b. reaction of glucose with ATP to form glucose 6-phosphate and ADP

23.3C   FOCUS ON THE HUMAN BODY
Creatine and Athletic Performance

Many athletes take creatine supplements to boost their performance. Creatine is synthesized in the body from the amino acid arginine, and is present in the diet in meat and fish. Creatine is stored in muscles as creatine phosphate, a high-energy molecule that releases energy by cleavage of its P—N bond on hydrolysis.

This bond is broken.

$$^-O-\overset{\overset{\displaystyle O}{||}}{\underset{\underset{\displaystyle O^-}{|}}{P}}-\overset{\displaystyle H}{N}-\overset{\overset{\displaystyle \overset{+}{N}H_2}{||}}{C}-N-CH_2COO^- \ + \ H_2O \ \longrightarrow \ H_2N-\overset{\overset{\displaystyle \overset{+}{N}H_2}{||}}{\underset{\underset{\displaystyle CH_3}{|}}{C}}-N-CH_2COO^- \ + \ HPO_4{}^{2-}$$

		Energy change
creatine phosphate	creatine	−10.3 kcal/mol

Energy is released.

Because more energy is released from the hydrolysis of creatine phosphate than is needed for the phosphorylation of ADP, the coupling of these two reactions results in the formation of ATP from ADP.

$$creatine\ phosphate \quad \xrightarrow{\underset{ADP \qquad ATP}{}} \quad creatine$$

Creatine phosphate is stored in muscles. When existing ATP supplies are depleted during strenuous exercise, creatine phosphate reacts with ADP to form a new supply of ATP as a source of more energy. Once existing supplies of both ATP and creatine phosphate have been depleted—which occurs in as little as 10 seconds—other catabolic processes must supply more ATP to continue an activity. Energy-generating pathways that need oxygen input—**aerobic reactions**—are discussed in Sections 23.5–23.6. Energy-generating pathways that do not need oxygen input—**anaerobic reactions**—are discussed in Sections 24.3–24.4.

Do creatine supplements increase athletic performance? Some evidence suggests that in athletic events that require short bursts of intense energy, increased creatine intake increases the amount of creatine phosphate in the muscle. This, in turn, allows an athlete to maintain a high rate of activity for a longer period of time. It is questionable whether creatine alone adds body mass. It

CONSUMER NOTE

Since the 1990s, creatine supplements have been used by some athletes who wish to increase muscle mass and strength. ©Jill Braaten RF

is thought, however, that since an athlete has a greater energy reserve, an individual can train harder and longer, resulting in greater muscle mass.

PROBLEM 23.4

Use the values for the hydrolysis of creatine phosphate to creatine (−10.3 kcal/mol) and the phosphorylation of ADP to ATP (+7.3 kcal/mol) to calculate the energy change in the following reaction. Is energy released or required in this reaction?

creatine phosphate   creatine

23.4   Coenzymes in Metabolism

Many reactions in metabolic pathways involve coenzymes. As we learned in Section 21.9, a *coenzyme* **is an organic compound needed for an enzyme-catalyzed reaction to occur.** Some coenzymes serve as important oxidizing and reducing agents (Sections 23.4A and 23.4B), whereas coenzyme A activates acetyl groups (CH_3CO^-), resulting in the transfer of a two-carbon unit to other substrates (Section 23.4C).

23.4A   Coenzymes NAD$^+$ and NADH

Many coenzymes are involved in oxidation and reduction reactions. As we learned in Section 5.4, oxidation and reduction can be defined in terms of changes in electrons, hydrogen atoms, or oxygen atoms.

- Oxidation results in . . .   a loss of electrons, *or*
                              a loss of hydrogen, *or*
                              a gain of oxygen.
- Reduction results in . . . a gain of electrons, *or*
                              a gain of hydrogen, *or*
                              a loss of oxygen.

A coenzyme may serve as an oxidizing agent or a reducing agent in a biochemical pathway.

- An oxidizing agent causes an oxidation reaction to occur, so the oxidizing agent is reduced.
- A reducing agent causes a reduction reaction to occur, so the reducing agent is oxidized.

In examining what happens to a coenzyme during oxidation and reduction, it is convenient to think in terms of hydrogen atoms being composed of protons (H^+) and electrons (e^-).

- When a coenzyme gains hydrogen atoms—that is, H^+ and e^-—the coenzyme is reduced; thus, the coenzyme is an *oxidizing* agent.
- When a coenzyme loses hydrogen atoms—that is, H^+ and e^-—the coenzyme is oxidized; thus, the coenzyme is a *reducing* agent.

The coenzyme **nicotinamide adenine dinucleotide, NAD⁺,** is a common biological oxidizing agent. Although its structure is complex, it is the six-membered ring containing the positively charged nitrogen atom (shown in red) that participates in oxidation reactions. When NAD⁺ reacts with two hydrogen atoms, this ring gains one proton and two electrons and one proton is left over. Thus, the ring is reduced and a new C—H bond is formed in the product, written as **NADH,** and referred to as the *reduced form* of nicotinamide adenine dinucleotide.

Add 2 H⁺ and 2 e⁻.

NAD⁺
nicotinamide adenine dinucleotide

new C—H bond

NADH
(reduced form of NAD⁺)

Curved arrow symbolism is often used to depict reactions with coenzymes.

1 C—O bond

$$^-OOCCH_2CH-\overset{OH}{\underset{COO^-}{\underset{|}{C}}}-COO^- \quad \xrightarrow{NAD^+ \quad NADH + H^+} \quad ^-OOCCH_2CH-\overset{O}{\underset{COO^-}{\underset{\|}{C}}}-COO^-$$

2 C—O bonds

isocitrate

oxalosuccinate

The conversion of isocitrate to oxalosuccinate is an **oxidation** because the number of C—O bonds in the substrate *increases*. **NAD⁺ serves as the oxidizing agent and, in the process, is reduced to NADH.** The reduced form of the coenzyme, NADH, is a biological reducing agent, as we learned in Section 16.6. When NADH reacts, it forms NAD⁺ as a product. Thus, **NAD⁺ and NADH are interconverted by oxidation and reduction reactions.**

SAMPLE PROBLEM 23.2 DETERMINING THE COENZYME NEEDED FOR AN OXIDATION OR REDUCTION

Label each reaction as an oxidation or reduction, and give the reagent, NAD⁺ or NADH, that would be used to carry out the reaction.

a.

$$CH_3-\overset{H}{\underset{H}{\overset{|}{\underset{|}{C}}}}-OH \longrightarrow \overset{O}{\overset{\|}{\underset{}{C}}} \underset{CH_3 \quad H}{}$$

ethanol   acetaldehyde

b.

$$CH_3-\overset{O}{\overset{\|}{C}}-\overset{O}{\overset{\|}{C}}-O^- \longrightarrow CH_3-\overset{H}{\underset{}{\overset{|}{C}}}\overset{OH}{\underset{}{}}-\overset{O}{\overset{\|}{C}}-O^-$$

pyruvate   lactate

Analysis

Count the number of C—O bonds in the starting material and product. Oxidation increases the number of C—O bonds and reduction decreases the number of C—O bonds. NAD⁺ is the coenzyme needed for an oxidation, and NADH is the coenzyme needed for a reduction.

Solution

a. The conversion of ethanol to acetaldehyde is an oxidation, because the product has two C—O bonds and the reactant has only one. To carry out the oxidation, the oxidizing agent NAD^+ could be used.

ethanol   acetaldehyde

b. The conversion of pyruvate to lactate is a reduction, because the product has one fewer C—O bond than the reactant. To carry out the reduction, the reducing agent NADH could be used.

pyruvate   lactate

PRACTICE PROBLEM 23.2

Label each reaction as an oxidation or reduction, and give the reagent, NAD^+ or NADH, that would be used to carry out the reaction.

More Practice: Try Problems 23.39, 23.40.

23.4B Coenzymes FAD and FADH$_2$

Flavin adenine dinucleotide, FAD, is another common biological oxidizing agent. Although its structure is complex, just four atoms of the tricyclic ring system (2 N's and 2 C's shown in red) participate in redox reactions. When it acts as an oxidizing agent, FAD is reduced by adding two hydrogen atoms, forming **FADH$_2$**, the *reduced form* of flavin adenine dinucleotide.

Add 2 H$^+$ and 2 e$^-$.

FAD
flavin adenine dinucleotide

FADH$_2$
(reduced form of FAD)

Table 23.1 summarizes the common coenzymes used in oxidation and reduction reactions.

Table 23.1 Coenzymes Used for Oxidation and Reduction

Coenzyme Name	Abbreviation	Role
Nicotinamide adenine dinucleotide	NAD$^+$	Oxidizing agent
Nicotinamide adenine dinucleotide (reduced form)	NADH	Reducing agent
Flavin adenine dinucleotide	FAD	Oxidizing agent
Flavin adenine dinucleotide (reduced form)	FADH$_2$	Reducing agent

Leafy green vegetables, soybeans, and almonds are good sources of riboflavin, vitamin B₂. Since this vitamin is light sensitive, riboflavin-fortified milk contained in glass or clear plastic bottles should be stored in the dark. ©McGraw-Hill Education/Jill Braaten, photographer

FAD is synthesized in cells from vitamin B₂, **riboflavin.** Riboflavin is a yellow, water-soluble vitamin obtained in the diet from leafy green vegetables, soybeans, almonds, and liver. When large quantities of riboflavin are ingested, excess amounts are excreted in the urine, giving it a bright yellow appearance.

riboflavin
vitamin B₂

PROBLEM 23.5

Convert the ball-and-stick model of riboflavin to a structural formula, and explain why riboflavin is a water-soluble vitamin.

PROBLEM 23.6

Which reagent, FAD or FADH₂, would be used to carry out the following reaction?

23.4C   Coenzyme A

Coenzyme A differs from other coenzymes in this section because it is not an oxidizing or a reducing agent. In addition to many other functional groups, coenzyme A contains a **sulfhydryl group (SH group),** making it a **thiol (RSH).** To emphasize this functional group, we sometimes abbreviate the structure as **HS–CoA.**

$$HS-CH_2CH_2NH-\overset{\displaystyle O}{\overset{\displaystyle \|}{C}}-CH_2CH_2-\overset{H}{\underset{}{N}}-\overset{\displaystyle O}{\overset{\displaystyle \|}{C}}-\overset{OH}{\underset{}{CH}}-\overset{CH_3}{\underset{CH_3}{\overset{|}{\underset{|}{C}}}}-CH_2-O-\overset{\displaystyle O}{\overset{\displaystyle \|}{\underset{O^-}{P}}}-O-\overset{\displaystyle O}{\overset{\displaystyle \|}{\underset{O^-}{P}}}-O-CH_2$$

thiol

coenzyme A

= HS—CoA

The sulfhydryl group of coenzyme A reacts with acetyl groups (CH₃CO—) or other acyl groups (RCO—) to form **thioesters, RCOSR'.** When an acetyl group is bonded to coenzyme A, the

Figure 23.6

Acetyl Coenzyme A

thioester

acetyl CoA

Acetyl CoA is a thioester that delivers a two-carbon acetyl group in a variety of metabolic pathways.

product is called **acetyl coenzyme A,** or simply **acetyl CoA.** The skeletal structure and a ball-and-stick model of acetyl CoA are shown in Figure 23.6.

$$CH_3-\overset{\overset{\displaystyle O}{\|}}{C}- \quad + \quad HS-CoA \quad \longrightarrow \quad CH_3-\overset{\overset{\displaystyle O}{\|}}{C}-S-CoA \qquad R-\overset{\overset{\displaystyle O}{\|}}{C}-S-R'$$

acetyl CoA　　　　　　　**General structure of a thioester**

Thioesters such as acetyl CoA are another group of high-energy compounds that release energy on reaction with water. In addition, acetyl CoA reacts with other substrates in metabolic pathways to deliver its two-carbon acetyl group, as in the citric acid cycle in Section 23.5.

This bond is broken.

Energy change

$$CH_3-\overset{\overset{\displaystyle O}{\|}}{C}-S-CoA \quad + \quad H_2O \quad \longrightarrow \quad CH_3-\overset{\overset{\displaystyle O}{\|}}{C}-O^- \quad + \quad HS-CoA \qquad -7.5 \text{ kcal/mol}$$

acetyl CoA　　　　　　　　　　　　　　　　coenzyme A

Coenzyme A is synthesized in cells from **pantothenic acid, vitamin B$_5$,** which is obtained in the diet from a variety of sources, especially whole grains and eggs.

pantothenic acid
vitamin B$_5$

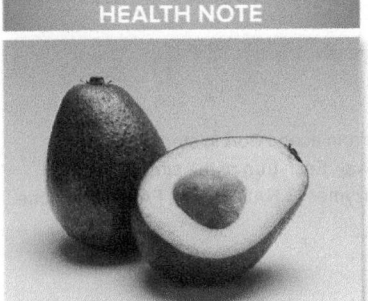

HEALTH NOTE

Avocados are an excellent dietary source of pantothenic acid, vitamin B$_5$. ©Digital Vision/Getty Images RF

PROBLEM 23.7

Convert the ball-and-stick model of pantothenic acid to a structural formula, and predict its water solubility.

PROBLEM 23.8

What products are formed when the thioester $CH_3CH_2CH_2COSCoA$ is hydrolyzed with water?

23.5   The Citric Acid Cycle

The **citric acid cycle,** a series of enzyme-catalyzed reactions that occur in mitochondria, comprises the third stage of the catabolism of biomolecules—carbohydrates, lipids, and amino acids—to carbon dioxide, water, and energy.

- The citric acid cycle is a cyclic metabolic pathway that begins with the addition of acetyl CoA to a four-carbon substrate and ends when the same four-carbon compound is formed as a product eight steps later.
- The citric acid cycle produces high-energy compounds for ATP synthesis in stage [4] of catabolism.

23.5A   Overview of the Citric Acid Cycle

The citric acid cycle is also called the tricarboxylic acid cycle (TCA cycle) or the **Krebs cycle,** named for Hans Krebs, a German chemist and Nobel Laureate who worked out the details of these reactions in 1937. A general scheme of the citric acid cycle, shown in Figure 23.7, illustrates the key features. All intermediates in the citric acid cycle are carboxylate anions derived from di- and tricarboxylic acids.

- The citric acid cycle begins when two carbons of acetyl CoA ($CH_3COSCoA$) react with a four-carbon organic substrate to form a six-carbon product (step [1]).
- Two carbon atoms are removed to form two molecules of CO_2 (steps [3] and [4]).
- Four molecules of reduced coenzymes (NADH and $FADH_2$) are formed in steps [3], [4], [6], and [8]. These molecules serve as carriers of electrons to the electron transport chain in stage [4] of catabolism, which ultimately results in the synthesis of a great deal of ATP.
- One mole of GTP is synthesized in step [5]. GTP is a high-energy nucleoside triphosphate similar to ATP.

Glycolysis, fatty acid oxidation, and amino acid catabolism—three processes that generate acetyl CoA—are discussed in detail in Chapter 24.

Figure 23.7   General Features of the Citric Acid Cycle

The citric acid cycle begins with the addition of two carbons from acetyl CoA in step [1] to a four-carbon organic substrate, drawn at the top of the cyclic pathway. Each turn of the citric acid cycle forms two molecules of CO_2, four molecules of reduced coenzymes (3 NADH and 1 $FADH_2$), and one high-energy GTP molecule.

23.5B   Specific Steps of the Citric Acid Cycle

The eight reactions of the citric acid cycle, which can be conceptually divided into two parts, are shown in Figure 23.8. The first part of the cycle includes the addition of acetyl CoA to oxaloacetate to form the six-carbon product citrate, which undergoes two separate

Figure 23.8   Steps in the Citric Acid Cycle

Each step of the citric acid cycle is enzyme catalyzed. The net result of the eight-step cycle is the conversion of the two carbons added to oxaloacetate to two molecules of CO_2. Reduced coenzymes (NADH and $FADH_2$) are also formed, which carry electrons to the electron transport chain to synthesize ATP. One molecule of high-energy GTP is synthesized in step [5]. Gray boxes highlight the atoms that are changed at each step of the cycle.

decarboxylations—reactions that give off CO_2. In part [2], functional groups are added and oxidized to re-form oxaloacetate, the substrate needed to begin the cycle again.

Part [1] of the Citric Acid Cycle

As shown in Figure 23.8, acetyl CoA enters the cycle by reaction with oxaloacetate at step [1] of the pathway. This reaction, catalyzed by citrate synthase, adds two carbons to oxaloacetate, forming citrate. In step [2], the 3° alcohol of citrate is isomerized to the 2° alcohol isocitrate using aconitase. These first two steps add carbon atoms and rearrange functional groups.

Loss of two carbon atoms begins in step [3], by decarboxylation of isocitrate using isocitrate dehydrogenase. The oxidizing agent NAD^+ also converts the 2° alcohol to a ketone to form α-ketoglutarate, which now contains one fewer carbon atom. This reaction forms NADH and H^+, which will carry electrons and protons gained in this reaction to the electron transport chain. In step [4], decarboxylation releases a second molecule of CO_2. Also, oxidation with NAD^+ in the presence of coenzyme A forms the thioester succinyl CoA using the enzyme α-ketoglutarate dehydrogenase. **By the end of step [4], two carbons are lost as CO_2 and two molecules of NADH are formed.**

Although it might be convenient to think of the two molecules of CO_2 as originating in the acetyl CoA added in step [1], the carbon atoms in CO_2 were *not* added during this cycle of the pathway.

The overall result of steps [1]–[4] of the citric acid cycle:

$$CH_3-\overset{\overset{\displaystyle O}{\|}}{C}-SCoA \;+\; \underset{\substack{\text{oxaloacetate}}}{\overset{\displaystyle CO_2^-}{\underset{\displaystyle CO_2^-}{\overset{|}{\underset{|}{\overset{\displaystyle C=O}{\underset{\displaystyle CH_2}{|}}}}}} \xrightarrow{\;\;\text{1}-\text{4}\;\;} \underset{\substack{\text{succinyl CoA}}}{\overset{\displaystyle CO_2^-}{\underset{\displaystyle SCoA}{\overset{|}{\underset{|}{\overset{\displaystyle CH_2}{\underset{\displaystyle C=O}{|}}}}}} \;+\; 2\,CO_2$$

- The C's from acetyl CoA in step [1] are shown in blue.
- Two C's of oxaloacetate (shown in green) are lost as CO_2.

Part [2] of the Citric Acid Cycle

Part [2] consists of four reactions that manipulate the functional groups of succinyl CoA to re-form oxaloacetate. In step [5], the thioester bond of succinyl CoA is hydrolyzed to form succinate, releasing energy to convert GDP to GTP. GTP, guanosine 5'-triphosphate, is similar to ATP: GTP is a high-energy molecule that releases energy when a P—O bond is hydrolyzed. This is the only step of the citric acid cycle that directly generates a triphosphate.

In step [6], succinate is converted to fumarate with FAD and succinate dehydrogenase. This reaction forms the reduced coenzyme $FADH_2$, which will carry electrons and protons to the electron transport chain. Addition of water in step [7] forms malate and oxidation of the 2° alcohol in malate with NAD^+ forms oxaloacetate in step [8]. Another molecule of NADH is also formed in step [8]. By the end of step [8], two more molecules of reduced coenzymes ($FADH_2$ and NADH) are formed. **Since the product of step [8] is the starting material of step [1], the cycle can continue as long as additional acetyl CoA is available for step [1].**

The overall result of steps [5]–[8] of the citric acid cycle:

$$\underset{\substack{\text{succinyl CoA}}}{\overset{\displaystyle CO_2^-}{\underset{\displaystyle SCoA}{\overset{|}{\underset{|}{\overset{\displaystyle CH_2}{\underset{\displaystyle C=O}{\overset{|}{\underset{|}{CH_2}}}}}}}} \xrightarrow{\;\;\text{Steps 5}-\text{8}\;\;} \underset{\substack{\text{oxaloacetate}}}{\overset{\displaystyle CO_2^-}{\underset{\displaystyle CO_2^-}{\overset{|}{\underset{|}{\overset{\displaystyle C=O}{\underset{\displaystyle CH_2}{|}}}}}}$$

- The C's from acetyl CoA in step [1] are shown in blue.
- The number of C's stays the same.
- A CH_2 group is oxidized to a C=O.
- The thioester is hydrolyzed to CO_2^-.

Overall, the citric acid cycle results in formation of

- **two molecules of CO_2**
- **four molecules of reduced coenzymes (3 NADH and 1 $FADH_2$)**
- **one molecule of GTP**

The net equation for the citric acid cycle can be written as shown. The ultimate fate of each product is also indicated.

$$CH_3-\overset{O}{\overset{\|}{C}}-SCoA \ + \ 2\,H_2O \ + \ 3\,NAD^+ \ + \ FAD \ + \ GDP \ + \ HPO_4^{2-}$$

overall reaction

$$2\,CO_2 \ + \ HSCoA \ + \ 3\,NADH \ + \ 3\,H^+ \ + \ FADH_2 \ + \ GTP$$

exhaled gas | The coenzyme re-enters the cycle. | The reduced coenzymes enter the electron transport chain. | energy source

- **The main function of the citric acid cycle is to produce reduced coenzymes that enter the electron transport chain and ultimately produce ATP.**

The rate of the citric acid cycle depends on the body's need for energy. When energy demands are high and the amount of available ATP is low, the cycle is activated. When energy demands are low and NADH concentration is high, the cycle is inhibited.

Although the citric acid cycle is complex, many individual reactions can be understood by applying the basic principles of organic chemistry learned in previous chapters.

SAMPLE PROBLEM 23.3 ANALYZING AN INDIVIDUAL STEP OF THE CITRIC ACID CYCLE

(a) Write out the reaction that converts succinate to fumarate with FAD using curved arrow symbolism.
(b) Classify the reaction as an oxidation, reduction, or decarboxylation.

Analysis

Use Figure 23.8 to draw the structures for succinate and fumarate. Draw the organic reactant and product on the horizontal arrow and the oxidizing reagent FAD, which is converted to $FADH_2$, on the curved arrow. Oxidation reactions result in a loss of electrons, a loss of hydrogen, or a gain of oxygen. Reduction reactions result in a gain of electrons, a gain of hydrogen, or a loss of oxygen. A decarboxylation results in the loss of CO_2.

Solution

a. Equation:

b. Since succinate contains four C—H bonds and fumarate contains only two C—H bonds, hydrogen atoms have been lost, making this reaction an oxidation. In the process FAD is reduced to $FADH_2$.

PRACTICE PROBLEM 23.3

(a) Draw out the structures for the reaction that converts malate to oxaloacetate with NAD^+ using curved arrow symbolism. (b) Classify the reaction as an oxidation, reduction, or decarboxylation.

More Practice: Try Problems 23.43; 23.44; 23.47a, b.

PROBLEM 23.9

Convert the ball-and-stick model of the given intermediate in the citric acid cycle to a skeletal structure, and name the compound.

PROBLEM 23.10

Convert the ball-and-stick model of the given intermediate in the citric acid cycle to a skeletal structure, and name the compound. Identify the carbon atoms that are converted to CO_2 later in the cycle.

PROBLEM 23.11

Suggest a name for the enzyme that converts malate to oxaloacetate in step [8] of the citric acid cycle.

23.6   The Electron Transport Chain and Oxidative Phosphorylation

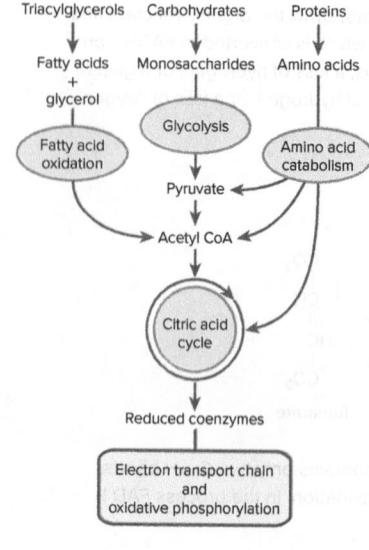

Most of the energy generated during the breakdown of biomolecules is formed during stage [4] of catabolism. Because oxygen is required, this process is called **aerobic respiration.** There are two facets to this stage:

- the electron transport chain, or the respiratory chain
- oxidative phosphorylation

The reduced coenzymes formed in the citric acid cycle enter the **electron transport chain,** and the electrons they carry are transferred from one molecule to another by a series of oxidation–reduction reactions. Each reaction releases energy until electrons and protons react with oxygen to form water. Electron transfer also causes H^+ ions to be pumped across the inner mitochondrial cell membrane, creating an energy reservoir that is used to synthesize ATP by the **phosphorylation** of ADP.

In contrast to the combustion of gasoline, which releases energy all at once in a single reaction, the energy generated during metabolism is released in small portions as the result of many reactions.

23.6A   The Electron Transport Chain

The electron transport chain is a multistep process that relies on four enzyme systems, called **complexes I, II, III, and IV,** as well as mobile electron carriers. Each complex is composed of enzymes, additional protein molecules, and metal ions that can gain and lose electrons in oxidation and reduction reactions. The complexes are situated in the inner membrane of the mitochondria, arranged so that electrons can be passed to progressively stronger oxidizing agents (Figure 23.9).

Figure 23.9   The Electron Transport Chain and ATP Synthesis in a Mitochondrion

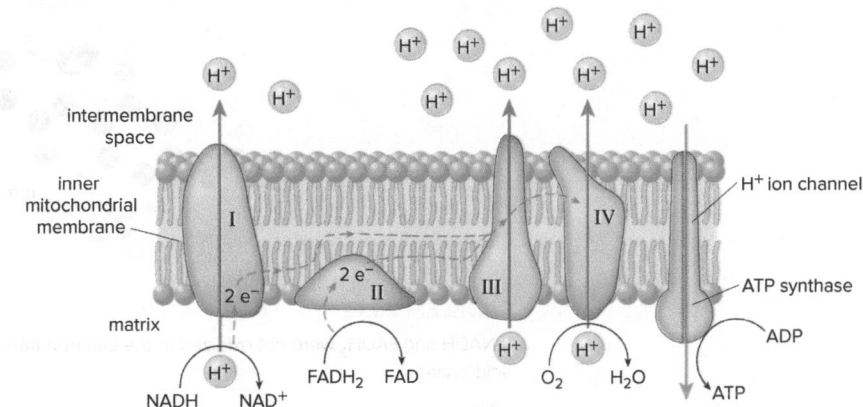

The four enzyme complexes (I–IV) of the electron transport chain are located within the inner membrane of a mitochondrion, between the matrix and the intermembrane space. Electrons enter the chain when NADH and $FADH_2$ are oxidized and then transported through a series of complexes along the pathway shown in red. The electrons ultimately combine with O_2 to form H_2O. Protons (H$^+$) are pumped across the inner membrane into the intermembrane space at three locations shown by blue arrows. The energy released when protons return to the matrix by traveling through a channel (in green) in the ATP synthase enzyme is used to convert ADP to ATP.

The electron transport chain begins with the reduced coenzymes—3 NADH and 1 $FADH_2$— formed during the citric acid cycle. These reduced coenzymes are electron rich and as such, they are capable of donating electrons to other species. Thus, **NADH and $FADH_2$ are *reducing agents* and when they donate electrons, they are oxidized.** When NADH donates two electrons, it is oxidized to NAD$^+$, which can re-enter the citric acid cycle. Likewise, when $FADH_2$ donates two electrons, it is oxidized to FAD, which can be used as an oxidant in step [6] of the citric acid cycle once again.

Once in the electron transport chain, the electrons are passed down from complex to complex in a series of redox reactions, and small packets of energy are released along the way. At the end of the chain, **the electrons and protons (obtained from the reduced coenzymes or the matrix of the mitochondrion) react with inhaled oxygen to form water** and this facet of the process is complete.

Because oxygen is needed for the final stage of electron transport, this process is **aerobic.**

Because the electron transport chain is crucial for energy production in cells, substances that disrupt the chain are often toxic. Rotenone, an organic compound isolated from jicama seeds and other plant sources, is a pesticide and insecticide that blocks electron transport at complex I.

CONSUMER NOTE

Although the seeds of the jicama plant contain the toxin rotenone, the edible root is crisp and sweet and consumed raw or cooked in some Mexican dishes.
©*Arco Images GmbH/Alamy*

Because it is mildly toxic to humans, rotenone use is being phased out in the United States. Disruption of electron transport by hydrogen cyanide is discussed in Section 23.7.

rotenone

PROBLEM 23.12

If NADH and $FADH_2$ were not oxidized in the electron transport chain, what would happen to the citric acid cycle?

PROBLEM 23.13

At several points in the electron transport chain, iron cations gain or lose electrons by reactions that interconvert Fe^{2+} and Fe^{3+} cations. (a) When Fe^{3+} is converted to Fe^{2+}, is the reaction an oxidation or a reduction? (b) Is Fe^{3+} an oxidizing agent or a reducing agent?

23.6B ATP Synthesis by Oxidative Phosphorylation

Although the electron transport chain illustrates how electrons carried by reduced coenzymes ultimately react with oxygen to form water, we have still not learned how ATP, the high-energy triphosphate needed for energy transport, is synthesized. The answer lies in what happens to the H^+ ions in the mitochondrion.

H^+ ions generated by reactions in the electron transport chain, as well as H^+ ions present in the matrix of the mitochondria, are pumped across the inner mitochondrial membrane into the inter-membrane space at three different sites (Figure 23.9). This process requires energy, because it moves protons against the concentration gradient. The energy comes from redox reactions in the electron transport chain. Since the concentration of H^+ ions is then higher on one side of the membrane, this creates a potential energy gradient, much like the potential energy of water that is stored behind a dam.

To return to the matrix, the H^+ ions travel through a channel in the ATP synthase enzyme. ATP synthase is the enzyme that catalyzes the phosphorylation of ADP to form ATP. The energy re-leased as the protons return to the matrix converts ADP to ATP. This process is called **oxidative phosphorylation,** because the energy that results from the oxidation of the reduced coenzymes is used to transfer a phosphate group.

> **Energy released from H^+ movement fuels phosphorylation.**

$$ADP + HPO_4^{2-} \longrightarrow ATP + H_2O$$

PROBLEM 23.14

In which region of the mitochondrion—the matrix or the intermembrane space—would the pH be lower? Explain your choice.

23.6C ATP Yield from Oxidative Phosphorylation

How much ATP is generated during stage [4] of catabolism?

- Each NADH enters the electron transport chain at complex I in the inner mitochondrial membrane, and the resulting cascade of reactions produces enough energy to synthesize 2.5 ATPs.
- $FADH_2$ enters the electron transport chain at complex II, producing energy for the synthesis of 1.5 ATPs.

How much ATP is generated for each acetyl CoA fragment that enters the entire common catabolic pathway—that is, stages [3] and [4] of catabolism?

For each turn of the citric acid cycle, three NADH molecules and one $FADH_2$ molecule are formed. In addition, one GTP molecule is produced directly during the citric acid cycle (step [5]); one GTP molecule is equivalent in energy to one ATP molecule. These facts allow us to calculate the total number of ATP molecules formed for each acetyl CoA.

$$3 \text{ NADH} \times 2.5 \text{ ATP/NADH} = 7.5 \text{ ATP}$$
$$1 \text{ FADH}_2 \times 1.5 \text{ ATP/FADH}_2 = 1.5 \text{ ATP}$$
$$1 \text{ GTP} = \underline{1 \text{ ATP}}$$
$$10 \text{ ATP}$$

- Complete catabolism of each acetyl CoA molecule that enters the citric acid cycle forms **10 ATP** molecules.

Each ATP molecule can now provide the energy to drive energetically unfavorable reactions.

23.7 FOCUS ON HEALTH & MEDICINE
Hydrogen Cyanide

The reactions detailed in the electron transport chain and oxidative phosphorylation are so crucial for the health of an organism that disruption of even a single step can have disastrous consequences. When any one step is inhibited, energy production ceases, and an organism cannot survive.

Hydrogen cyanide (HCN, Section 4.6) is a lethal gas used as a chemical weapon during World War I and in the gas chambers of Nazi Germany during World War II. HCN is a poison because it produces cyanide (CN^-), which irreversibly binds to the Fe^{3+} ion of cytochrome oxidase. Cytochrome oxidase is the key enzyme in complex IV of the electron transport chain. When bonded to cyanide, Fe^{3+} cannot be reduced to Fe^{2+} and the transfer of electrons to oxygen to form water cannot occur. ATP synthesis is halted and cell death ensues.

A few naturally occurring compounds that contain CN groups form HCN when they are hydrolyzed in the presence of certain enzymes. As an example, **amygdalin** is present in the seeds and pits of apricots, peaches, and wild cherries. Amygdalin, and its close relative laetrile, were once touted as anticancer drugs, and are still available in some countries for this purpose. Amygdalin's effectiveness in targeting cancer cells is unproven, and the HCN produced by hydrolysis kills all types of cells in the body.

©McGraw-Hill Education/Jill Braaten, photographer

ENVIRONMENTAL NOTE

The golden bamboo lemur of Madagascar subsists primarily on giant bamboo, despite the high levels of toxic cyanide it contains. ©Connie Brainsilver/ Science Source

The side effects that result from taking amygdalin resemble those of chronic exposure to cyanide and include headache, vomiting, coma, and in some cases, death.

Interestingly, the diet of the golden bamboo lemur, a critically endangered species that inhabits Madagascar, contains shoots of giant bamboo as its main component. Giant bamboo contains such high levels of cyanide that most mammals would die after ingesting it. Evidently, the golden bamboo lemur has developed a mechanism for detoxifying cyanide, although that mechanism is currently unknown.

CHAPTER HIGHLIGHTS

KEY TERMS

Acetyl CoA (23.4)	Coenzyme A (23.4)	Mitochondrion (23.1)
Adenosine 5'-diphosphate (ADP, 23.3)	Coupled reactions (23.3)	NADH (23.4)
Adenosine 5'-triphosphate (ATP, 23.3)	Electron transport chain (23.6)	Nicotinamide adenine dinucleotide
Anabolism (23.1)	$FADH_2$ (23.4)	(NAD$^+$, 23.4)
Catabolism (23.1)	Flavin adenine dinucleotide (FAD, 23.4)	Oxidative phosphorylation (23.6)
Citric acid cycle (23.5)	Metabolism (23.1)	Phosphorylation (23.3)

KEY CONCEPTS

① What is metabolism and where is energy produced in cells? (23.1)

- Metabolism is the sum of all of the chemical reactions that take place in an organism. Catabolic reactions break down large molecules and release energy, whereas anabolic reactions synthesize larger molecules and require energy.
- Energy is produced in the mitochondria, sausage-shaped organelles that contain an outer and inner cell membrane. Energy is produced in the matrix, the area surrounded by the inner membrane.

② What are the four stages of metabolism? (23.2)

- Metabolism begins with digestion in stage [1], in which large molecules—polysaccharides, proteins, and triacylglycerols—are hydrolyzed to smaller molecules—monosaccharides, amino acids, fatty acids, and glycerol.
- In stage [2], biomolecules are degraded into two-carbon acetyl units.
- The citric acid cycle comprises stage [3]. The citric acid cycle converts two carbon atoms to two molecules of CO_2, and forms reduced coenzymes, NADH and $FADH_2$, which carry electrons and energy to the electron transport chain.
- In stage [4], the electron transport chain and oxidative phosphorylation produce ATP, and oxygen is converted to water.

③ What is ATP and how do coupled reactions with ATP drive energetically unfavorable reactions? (23.3)

- ATP is the primary energy-carrying molecule in metabolic pathways. The hydrolysis of ATP cleaves one phosphate group and releases 7.3 kcal/mol of energy.
- The hydrolysis of ATP provides the energy to drive a reaction that requires energy. A pair of reactions of this sort is said to be coupled.

④ List the main coenzymes in metabolism and describe their roles. (23.4)

- Nicotinamide adenine dinucleotide (NAD^+) is a biological oxidizing agent that accepts electrons and protons, thus generating its reduced form NADH. NADH is a reducing agent that donates electrons and protons, re-forming NAD^+.
- Flavin adenine dinucleotide (FAD) is a biological oxidizing agent that accepts electrons and protons, thus yielding its reduced form, $FADH_2$. $FADH_2$ is a reducing agent that donates electrons and protons, re-forming FAD.

- Coenzyme A reacts with acetyl groups (CH_3CO—) to form high-energy thioesters that deliver two-carbon acetyl groups to other substrates.

⑤ What are the main features of the citric acid cycle? (23.5)

- The citric acid cycle is an eight-step cyclic pathway that begins with the addition of acetyl CoA to a four-carbon substrate. In the citric acid cycle, two carbons are converted to CO_2 and four molecules of reduced coenzymes are formed. One molecule of a high-energy nucleoside triphosphate is also formed.

⑥ What are the main components of the electron transport chain and oxidative phosphorylation? (23.6)

- The electron transport chain is a multistep process that takes place in the inner membrane of mitochondria. Electrons from reduced coenzymes enter the chain and are passed from one molecule to another in a series of redox reactions, releasing energy along the way. At the end of the chain, electrons and protons react with inhaled oxygen to form water.
- H^+ ions are pumped across the inner membrane of the mitochondrion, forming a high concentration of H^+ ions in the intermembrane space, thus creating a potential energy gradient. When the H^+ ions travel through the channel in the ATP synthase enzyme, this energy is used to convert ADP to ATP—a process called oxidative phosphorylation.

⑦ Why do compounds such as cyanide act as poisons when they disrupt the electron transport chain? (23.7)

- Since all catabolic pathways converge at the electron transport chain, these steps are needed to produce energy for normal cellular processes. Compounds that disrupt a single step can halt ATP synthesis so that an organism cannot survive.
- Cyanide from HCN irreversibly binds to the Fe^{3+} ion of the enzyme cytochrome oxidase and, as a result, Fe^{3+} cannot be reduced to Fe^{2+} and water cannot be formed from oxygen. Since the electron transport chain is disrupted, energy is not generated for oxidative phosphorylation, ATP is not synthesized, and cell death often follows.

PROBLEMS

Selected in-chapter and odd-numbered end-of-chapter problems have brief answers in Appendix B. The *Student Study Guide and Solutions Manual* contains detailed solutions to all in-chapter and odd-numbered end-of-chapter problems, as well as additional worked examples and a chapter self-test.

Metabolism

23.15 Describe the main features of a mitochondrion. Where does energy production occur in a mitochondrion?

23.16 Explain why mitochondria are called the powerhouses of the cell.

23.17 Place the following steps in the catabolism of carbohydrates in order: the electron transport chain, the conversion of glucose to acetyl CoA, the hydrolysis of starch, oxidative phosphorylation, and the citric acid cycle.

23.18 Describe the main features of the four stages of catabolism.

23.19 In what stage of catabolism does each of the following processes occur?

   a. cleavage of a protein with chymotrypsin

   b. oxidation of a fatty acid to acetyl CoA

   c. oxidation of malate to oxaloacetate with NAD^+

   d. conversion of ADP to ATP with ATP synthase

   e. hydrolysis of starch to glucose with amylase

23.20 In what stage of catabolism does each of the following processes occur?

   a. conversion of a monosaccharide to acetyl CoA

   b. hydrolysis of a triacylglycerol with lipase

   c. reaction of oxygen with protons and electrons to form water

   d. conversion of succinate to fumarate with FAD

   e. degradation of a fatty acid to acetyl CoA

ATP and Coupled Reactions

23.21 What are coupled reactions and why does coupling occur?

23.22 Explain why ATP and GTP are called "high-energy" compounds.

23.23 Acetyl phosphate is another example of a high-energy phosphate. What products would be formed when acetyl phosphate is hydrolyzed with water?

$$CH_3-\overset{\overset{\displaystyle O}{\|}}{C}-O-\overset{\overset{\displaystyle O}{\|}}{\underset{\underset{\displaystyle O^-}{|}}{P}}-O^-$$

acetyl phosphate

23.24 ADP undergoes hydrolysis in a similar manner to ATP; that is, a P—O bond is cleaved. Draw the structure of the product of ADP hydrolysis.

23.25 The reaction of succinate with coenzyme A to form succinyl CoA requires energy, and the hydrolysis of ATP releases energy as shown in the given equations.

	Energy change
succinate + HSCoA $\longrightarrow$ succinyl CoA + H_2O	+9.4 kcal/mol
ATP + H_2O $\longrightarrow$ ADP + HPO_4^{2-}	−7.3 kcal/mol

   a. Combine the equations and write the coupled reaction.

   b. Is the coupled reaction energetically favorable? Explain.

23.26 The hydrolysis of succinyl CoA to succinate and coenzyme A releases energy, and the phosphorylation of ADP requires energy as shown in the given equations.

	Energy change
succinyl CoA + H_2O $\longrightarrow$ succinate + HSCoA	−9.4 kcal/mol
ADP + HPO_4^{2-} $\longrightarrow$ ATP + H_2O	+7.3 kcal/mol

   a. Combine the equations and write the coupled reaction.

   b. Is the coupled reaction energetically favorable? Explain.

23.27 The phosphorylation of glucose with HPO_4^{2-} forms glucose 1-phosphate and water and requires 5.0 kcal/mol of energy.

   a. Write the equation for this reaction.

   b. This unfavorable reaction can be driven by the hydrolysis of ATP to ADP. Write an equation for the coupled reaction.

   c. Calculate the energy change for the coupled reaction.

23.28 Write an equation for the reverse reaction described in Problem 23.27—that is, the hydrolysis of glucose 1-phosphate to form glucose and HPO_4^{2-}. What is the energy change in this reaction?

23.29 The phosphorylation of fructose 6-phosphate to form fructose 1,6-bisphosphate and water requires 3.9 kcal/mol of energy.

fructose 6-phosphate + HPO_4^{2-} $\longrightarrow$ fructose 1,6-bisphosphate + H_2O

   a. What is the energy change for the reverse reaction—that is, the hydrolysis of fructose 1,6-bisphosphate to form fructose 6-phosphate?

   b. Write a coupled reaction that shows how the energy from ATP hydrolysis (−7.3 kcal/mol) can be used to drive the given reaction.

   c. What is the energy change for the coupled reaction?

23.30 a. Use the values in Problem 23.29 to calculate the energy change in the following reaction.

fructose 1,6-bisphosphate + ADP $\longrightarrow$ fructose 6-phosphate + ATP

   b. Is this reaction energetically favorable or unfavorable?

   c. Write this reaction using curved arrow symbolism.

   d. Can this reaction be used to synthesize ATP from ADP? Explain.

23.31 Refer to the following equations to answer the questions.

	Energy change
1,3-bisphosphoglycerate + H_2O $\longrightarrow$	
3-phosphoglycerate + HPO_4^{2-}	−11.8 kcal/mol
ATP + H_2O $\longrightarrow$ ADP + HPO_4^{2-}	−7.3 kcal/mol

   a. Write the equation for the coupled reaction of 1,3-bisphosphoglycerate with ADP to form 3-phosphoglycerate and ATP.

   b. Calculate the energy change for this coupled reaction.

   c. Can this reaction be used to synthesize ATP from ADP? Explain.

23.32 Refer to the equations in Problem 23.31 to answer the following questions.

   a. Write the equation for the coupled reaction of 3-phosphoglycerate with ATP to form 1,3-bisphosphoglycerate and ADP.

   b. Calculate the energy change for this coupled reaction.

   c. Is this reaction energetically favorable? Explain.

23.33 (a) Draw the structure of the high-energy nucleoside triphosphate GTP. (b) Draw the structure of the hydrolysis product formed when one phosphate is removed.

23.34 If the phosphorylation of GDP to form GTP requires 7.3 kcal/mol of energy, how much energy is released when GTP is hydrolyzed to GDP?

Coenzymes

23.35 Classify each substance as an oxidizing agent, a reducing agent, or neither: (a) $FADH_2$; (b) ATP; (c) NAD^+.

23.36 Classify each substance as an oxidizing agent, a reducing agent, or neither: (a) NADH; (b) ADP; (c) FAD.

23.37 When a substrate is oxidized, is NAD^+ oxidized or reduced? Is NAD^+ an oxidizing agent or a reducing agent?

23.38 When a substrate is reduced, is FADH₂ oxidized or reduced? Is FADH₂ an oxidizing agent or a reducing agent?

23.39 Label the reaction as an oxidation or reduction and give the coenzyme, NAD⁺ or NADH, which might be used to carry out the transformation. Write the reaction using skeletal structures with curved arrow symbolism.

23.40 Label the reaction as an oxidation or reduction and give the coenzyme, NAD⁺ or NADH, which might be used to carry out the transformation. Write the reaction using skeletal structures with curved arrow symbolism.

Citric Acid Cycle

23.41 What steps in the citric acid cycle have each of the following characteristics?
   a. The reaction generates NADH.
   b. CO₂ is removed.
   c. The reaction utilizes FAD.
   d. The reaction forms a new carbon–carbon single bond.

23.42 What steps in the citric acid cycle have each of the following characteristics?
   a. The reaction generates FADH₂.
   b. The organic substrate is oxidized.
   c. The reaction utilizes NAD⁺.
   d. The reaction breaks a carbon–carbon bond.

23.43 (a) Convert the ball-and-stick model of **A**, one of the eight synthetic intermediates in the citric acid cycle, to a structural formula, and name the compound. (b) What is the immediate precursor of **A** in the citric acid cycle; that is, what compound forms **A** as a reaction product? (c) What compound is formed from **A** in the citric acid cycle?

A

23.44 (a) Convert the ball-and-stick model of **B**, one of the eight synthetic intermediates in the citric acid cycle, to a structural formula, and name the compound. (b) What is the immediate

precursor of **B** in the citric acid cycle; that is, what compound forms **B** as a reaction product? (c) What compound is formed from **B** in the citric acid cycle?

B

23.45 (a) Which intermediate(s) in the citric acid cycle contain two chirality centers? (b) Which intermediate(s) contain a 2° alcohol?

23.46 (a) Which intermediate(s) in the citric acid cycle contain one chirality center? (b) Which intermediate(s) contain a 3° alcohol?

23.47 The conversion of isocitrate to α-ketoglutarate in step [3] of the citric acid cycle actually occurs by a two-step process: isocitrate is converted first to oxalosuccinate, which then goes on to form α-ketoglutarate.

isocitrate   oxalosuccinate   α-ketoglutarate

   a. Classify reaction [3a] as an oxidation, reduction, or decarboxylation.
   b. Classify reaction [3b] as an oxidation, reduction, or decarboxylation.
   c. For which step is NAD⁺ necessary?
   d. Why is the enzyme that catalyzes this reaction called isocitrate dehydrogenase?

23.48 The conversion of citrate to isocitrate in step [2] of the citric acid cycle actually occurs by a two-step process (steps [2a] and [2b]) with aconitate formed as an intermediate.

citrate   aconitate   isocitrate

   a. What atoms are added or removed in each step?
   b. Steps [2a] and [2b] are not considered oxidation or reduction reactions despite the fact that the number of C—H and C—O bonds changes in these reactions. Explain why this is so.
   c. From your knowledge of organic chemistry learned in previous chapters, what type of reaction occurs in step [2a]? In step [2b]?

23.49 In what step does a hydration reaction occur in the citric acid cycle?

23.50 What products of the citric acid cycle are funneled into the electron transport chain?

Electron Transport Chain and Oxidative Phosphorylation

23.51 Why are the reactions that occur in stage [4] of catabolism sometimes called aerobic respiration?

23.52 What is the role of each of the following in the electron transport chain: (a) NADH; (b) O_2; (c) complexes I–IV; (d) H^+ ion channel?

23.53 What is the role of each of the following in the electron transport chain: (a) $FADH_2$; (b) ADP; (c) ATP synthase; (d) the inner mitochondrial membrane?

23.54 Explain the importance of the movement of H^+ ions across the inner mitochondrial membrane and then their return passage through the H^+ ion channel in ATP synthase.

23.55 What are the final products of the electron transport chain?

23.56 What product is formed from each of the following compounds during the electron transport chain: (a) NADH; (b) $FADH_2$; (c) ADP; (d) O_2?

23.57 Why does one NADH that enters the electron transport chain ultimately produce 2.5 ATPs, while one $FADH_2$ produces 1.5 ATPs?

23.58 How does the energy from the proton gradient result in ATP synthesis?

General Questions and Applications

23.59 Label each statement about the citric acid cycle as true or false.
   a. The citric acid cycle is a cyclic metabolic pathway that involves eight steps.
   b. Four molecules of NADH and one molecule of $FADH_2$ are formed in the cycle.
   c. The cycle is activated when the amount of available ATP is low and energy demands are high.
   d. The cycle is inhibited when the concentration of NADH is low.

23.60 Label each statement about the electron transport chain and oxidative phosphorylation as true or false.
   a. NADH and $FADH_2$ are oxidized in the electron transport chain.

   b. The electron transport chain involves four enzyme complexes found in the mitochondria.
   c. HCN is a poison that binds to the ATP synthase enzyme, thus inhibiting oxidative phosphorylation.
   d. During electron transport, H^+ is pumped across the inner mitochondrial membrane into the matrix.

23.61 What reaction or process in metabolism is catalyzed by each of the following enzymes: (a) pepsin; (b) succinate dehydrogenase; (c) ATP synthase?

23.62 What reaction or process in metabolism is catalyzed by each of the following enzymes: (a) lipase; (b) α-ketoglutarate dehydrogenase; (c) amylase?

23.63 How does the metabolism of the two carbons of acetyl CoA form 10 molecules of ATP?

23.64 What is the difference between phosphorylation and oxidative phosphorylation?

23.65 What is the structural difference between ATP and ADP?

23.66 What is the structural difference between coenzyme A and acetyl CoA?

23.67 From what you learned about monosaccharides in Chapter 20 and phosphates in Chapter 23: (a) Draw the structure of glucose 1-phosphate. (b) Using structures, write the equation for the hydrolysis of glucose 1-phosphate to glucose and HPO_4^{2-}.

23.68 From what you learned about monosaccharides in Chapter 20 and phosphates in Chapter 23: (a) Draw the structure of glucose 6-phosphate. (b) Using structures, write the equation for the hydrolysis of glucose 6-phosphate to glucose and HPO_4^{2-}.

23.69 How are the citric acid cycle and the electron transport chain interrelated?

23.70 Why is the citric acid cycle considered to be part of the aerobic catabolic pathways, even though oxygen is not directly involved in any step in the cycle?

23.71 In which tissue would a cell likely have more mitochondria, the heart or the bone? Explain your choice.

23.72 What is the fate of an acetyl CoA molecule after several turns of the citric acid cycle?

23.73 What is the role of stored creatine phosphate in muscles?

23.74 Explain how HCN acts as a poison by interfering with the synthesis of ATP.

CHALLENGE PROBLEMS

23.75 How many moles of ATP can be synthesized from ADP using the 500. Calories ingested during a fast-food lunch? How many molecules of ATP does this correspond to?

23.76 With reference to the structure of amygdalin (Section 23.7): (a) Locate each acetal. (b) How many chirality centers are present? (c) What monosaccharide is used to form amygdalin?

24

The stored fat in penguins and other marine animals insulates them in icy waters and serves as an energy source when they are unable to regularly search for food. ©*Daniel C. Smith*

Carbohydrate, Lipid, and Protein Metabolism

CHAPTER OUTLINE

24.1 Introduction
24.2 Understanding Biochemical Reactions
24.3 Glycolysis
24.4 The Fate of Pyruvate
24.5 The ATP Yield from Glucose
24.6 Gluconeogenesis
24.7 The Catabolism of Triacylglycerols
24.8 Ketone Bodies
24.9 Amino Acid Metabolism

CHAPTER GOALS

In this chapter you will learn how to:

1. Understand the basic features of biochemical reactions
2. Describe the main aspects of glycolysis
3. List the pathways for pyruvate metabolism
4. Calculate the energy yield from glucose metabolism
5. Describe the main features of gluconeogenesis
6. Summarize the process of the β-oxidation of fatty acids
7. Calculate the energy yield from fatty acid oxidation
8. Identify the structures of ketone bodies and describe their role in metabolism
9. Describe the main components of amino acid catabolism

862   **Chapter 24**   Carbohydrate, Lipid, and Protein Metabolism

Why Study
Carbohydrate, Lipid, and Protein Metabolism?

A complex set of biochemical pathways converts ingested carbohydrates, lipids, and proteins to usable materials and energy to meet the body's needs.
©Dennis Gray/Cole Group/Getty Images RF

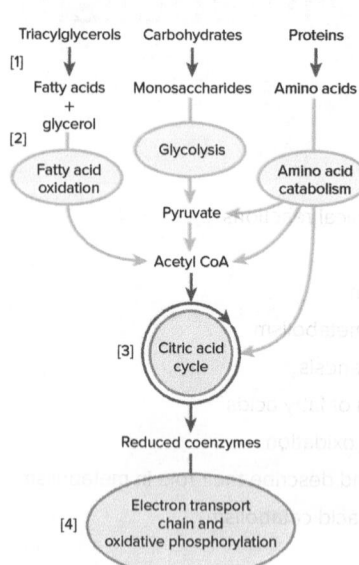

The metabolism of ingested food begins with the hydrolysis of large biomolecules into small compounds that can be absorbed through the intestinal wall. In Chapter 23 we learned that the last stages of catabolism, which produce energy from acetyl coenzyme A (acetyl CoA) by means of the citric acid cycle, electron transport chain, and oxidative phosphorylation, are the same for all types of biomolecules. The catabolic pathways that form acetyl CoA are different, however, depending on the particular type of biomolecule. In Chapter 24 we examine the specific metabolic pathways for carbohydrates, lipids, and proteins.

24.1   Introduction

Recall from Section 23.2 that we can conceptually consider catabolism as the sum of four stages. Catabolism begins with digestion in stage [1] in which polysaccharides, triacylglycerols, and proteins are hydrolyzed to smaller compounds that can be absorbed by the bloodstream and delivered to individual cells. Each type of biomolecule is then converted to acetyl CoA by different pathways in stage [2]. Acetyl CoA enters the citric acid cycle and produces reduced coenzymes, whose energy is stored in ATP (stages [3] and [4]). Since we already learned many important facts about stages [1], [3], and [4] of catabolism, we now consider the metabolic pathways that convert monosaccharides, fatty acids and glycerol, and amino acids to acetyl CoA in stage [2].

- **Carbohydrates:** Glycolysis converts glucose, the most common monosaccharide, to pyruvate, which is then metabolized to acetyl CoA (Sections 24.3–24.4).

$$\text{glucose} \xrightarrow{\text{glycolysis}} 2\ CH_3-\overset{O}{\underset{}{C}}-\overset{O}{\underset{}{C}}-O^- \longrightarrow 2\ CH_3-\overset{O}{\underset{}{C}}-SCoA$$

pyruvate   acetyl CoA

- **Lipids:** Fatty acids are converted to thioesters, which are oxidized by a stepwise procedure that sequentially cleaves two-carbon units from the carbonyl end to form acetyl CoA (Section 24.7).

$$CH_3(CH_2)_{16}-\overset{O}{\underset{}{C}}-OH \longrightarrow CH_3(CH_2)_{16}-\overset{O}{\underset{}{C}}-SCoA \longrightarrow 9\ CH_3-\overset{O}{\underset{}{C}}-SCoA$$

fatty acid   thioester   acetyl CoA

- **Amino acids:** The amino acids formed from protein hydrolysis are often assembled into new proteins without any other modification. Since excess amino acids are not stored in the body, they are catabolized for energy as discussed in Section 24.9. The amino groups (NH_2) of amino acids are converted to urea [$(NH_2)_2C{=}O$], which is excreted in urine.

24.2   Understanding Biochemical Reactions

Before examining the specific reactions of glycolysis, let's pause to consider some principles that will help us better understand these processes.

The biochemical reactions we learned in Chapter 23 and those we will examine in Chapter 24 are often challenging for a student to tackle. On the one hand, cells use the basic principles of organic chemistry in oxidation, reduction, acid–base, and other reactions. On the other hand, the use of enzymes and coenzymes allows cells to carry out transformations that are not easily replicated or even possible in the lab, so many reactions take on a new and different appearance. Moreover, many substrates have several functional groups and these reactions often proceed with complete selectivity at just one of them.

While it is often difficult to predict the exact product of some reactions, it should be possible to *understand* and *analyze* a reaction by examining the reactants and products, the reagents (coenzymes and other materials), and the enzymes. The name of an enzyme is often a clue as to the type of reaction. Common types of enzymes were listed in Table 21.3.

As an example, consider the conversion of fructose 6-phosphate to fructose 1,6-bisphosphate, step [3] in glycolysis (Section 24.3). In this reaction, a phosphate group is transferred from ATP to fructose 6-phosphate. Recall from Section 21.9 that a **kinase** is a transferase that catalyzes the transfer of a phosphate.

It would probably be hard for you to predict that this reaction converts only the OH group at C1 to a phosphate, given that the substrate has four OH groups. Nonetheless, it is possible to *understand* the reaction by looking at all of its components.

- A phosphate is added to fructose 6-phosphate to form fructose 1,6-bisphosphate, a product with two phosphate groups.
- The new phosphate in the product comes from ATP, a high-energy nucleoside triphosphate that transfers a phosphate to other compounds—in this case, fructose 6-phosphate.
- Loss of a phosphate from ATP forms ADP.
- The reaction is catalyzed by a kinase enzyme, also indicating that a phosphate is transferred.

Sample Problems 24.1 and 24.2 illustrate the process in other examples.

SAMPLE PROBLEM 24.1 ANALYZING A BIOCHEMICAL REACTION

Analyze the following reaction by considering the functional groups that change and the name of the enzyme.

Analysis

- Consider the functional groups that are added or removed as a clue to the type of reaction.
- Classify the reagent (when one is given) as to the type of reaction it undergoes.
- Use the name of the enzyme as a clue to the reaction type.

Solution

The —COO^- of pyruvate is lost as CO_2, meaning that a **decarboxylation** has occurred. This is supported by the type of enzyme, a *decarboxylase,* which typically catalyzes decarboxylations (Table 21.3). A carbon–carbon bond is broken in the process, giving CO_2 as one of the products. No coenzyme is used here; the reaction does not involve oxidation, reduction, or thioester synthesis.

PRACTICE PROBLEM 24.1

Analyze the following reaction by considering the functional groups that change and the name of the enzyme.

dihydroxyacetone phosphate   glyceraldehyde 3-phosphate

More Practice: Try Problem 24.23.

SAMPLE PROBLEM 24.2 ANALYZING A BIOCHEMICAL REACTION

Analyze the following reaction by considering the functional groups that change, the coenzyme utilized, and the name of the enzyme.

1,3-bisphosphoglycerate   3-phosphoglycerate

Analysis

- Consider the functional groups that are added or removed as a clue to the type of reaction.
- Classify the reagent—that is, any coenzyme or other reactant—as to the type of reaction it undergoes. For example, NAD^+ is an oxidizing agent, whereas NADH is a reducing agent. ATP transfers phosphate groups to substrates, whereas ADP accepts phosphate groups from substrates.
- Use the name of the enzyme as a clue to the reaction type.

Solution

A phosphate group is removed from the reactant to give 3-phosphoglycerate. This phosphate is transferred to the nucleoside diphosphate ADP to form the nucleoside triphosphate ATP. Because kinase enzymes catalyze the addition or removal of phosphates, the enzyme used for the reaction is phosphoglycerate *kinase*. No coenzyme is used here; the reaction does not involve oxidation, reduction, or thioester synthesis.

PRACTICE PROBLEM 24.2

Analyze the following reaction by considering the functional groups that change, the coenzyme utilized, and the name of the enzyme.

glyceraldehyde 3-phosphate   3-phosphoglycerate

More Practice: Try Problem 24.24.

24.3   Glycolysis

The metabolism of monosaccharides centers around glucose. Whether it is obtained by the hydrolysis of ingested polysaccharides or stored glycogen (Section 20.6), glucose is the principal monosaccharide used for energy in the human body.

- *Glycolysis* is a linear, 10-step pathway that converts glucose, a six-carbon monosaccharide, to two molecules of pyruvate ($CH_3COCO_2^-$).

Figure 24.1

An Overview of Glycolysis

CH$_2$OH

glucose

This bond is broken at step [4].

① ATP → ADP

②

③ ATP → ADP

④

Energy-investment phase

dihydroxyacetone phosphate   +   glyceraldehyde 3-phosphate

⑤

⑥ NAD$^+$ → **NADH + H$^+$**

⑦ ADP → **ATP**

⑧

⑨

⑩ ADP → **ATP**

Energy-generating phase

Two molecules of pyruvate are formed from each molecule of glucose. ⟶ CH$_3$—C—C—O$^-$

pyruvate

In the energy-investment phase of glycolysis, ATP supplies energy needed for steps [1] and [3]. In the energy-generating phase, each three-carbon product from step [5] forms one NADH and two ATP molecules. Because two glyceraldehyde 3-phosphate molecules are formed from each glucose molecule, a total of two NADH and four ATP molecules are formed in the energy-generating phase.

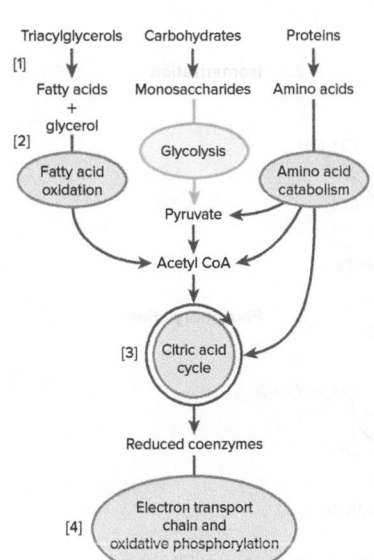

Glycolysis is an anaerobic (without air) pathway that takes place in the cytoplasm and can be conceptually divided into two parts (Figure 24.1).

- Steps [1]–[5] comprise the *energy-investment phase*. The addition of two phosphate groups requires the energy stored in two ATP molecules. Cleavage of a carbon–carbon bond forms two three-carbon products.

- Steps [6]–[10] comprise the *energy-generating phase*. Each of the three-carbon products is ultimately oxidized, forming **NADH**, and two high-energy phosphate bonds are broken to form two ATP molecules.

The specific reactions of glycolysis are discussed in Section 24.3A. To better understand these reactions, recall a few facts from Chapter 23.

- Coenzyme NAD$^+$ is a biological *oxidizing* agent that converts C—H bonds to C—O bonds. In the process, NAD$^+$ is reduced to NADH + H$^+$.

- The phosphorylation of ADP *requires* energy and forms ATP, a high-energy nucleoside triphosphate.

- The hydrolysis of ATP *releases* energy and forms ADP.

24.3A   The Steps in Glycolysis

The specific steps and all needed enzymes in glycolysis are shown in Figures 24.2–24.4.

Glycolysis: Steps [1]–[3]

Glycolysis begins with the phosphorylation of glucose to form glucose 6-phosphate (Figure 24.2). This energetically unfavorable reaction is coupled with the hydrolysis of ATP to ADP to make the reaction energetically favorable. Isomerization of glucose 6-phosphate to fructose 6-phosphate takes place with an isomerase enzyme in step [2]. Phosphorylation in step [3], an energy-absorbing reaction, can be driven by the hydrolysis of ATP, yielding fructose 1,6-bisphosphate.

- Overall, the first three steps of glycolysis add two phosphate groups and isomerize a six-membered glucose ring to a five-membered fructose ring.
- The energy stored in two ATP molecules is utilized to modify the structure of glucose for the later steps that generate energy.

Figure 24.2   Glycolysis: Steps [1]–[3]

- All $-PO_3^{2-}$ groups in glycolysis are abbreviated as $-$(P).
- The energy from two ATP molecules is used for phosphorylation in steps [1] and [3].

PROBLEM 24.1

Use Figure 24.2 to name **A** and **B**, two intermediates in glycolysis. What type of isomers—constitutional isomers or stereoisomers—do **A** and **B** represent?

A   **B**

Glycolysis: Steps [4]–[5]

Cleavage of the six-carbon chain of fructose 1,6-bisphosphate forms two three-carbon products—dihydroxyacetone phosphate and glyceraldehyde 3-phosphate—as shown in Figure 24.3. These two products have the same molecular formula but a different arrangement of atoms; that is, they are *constitutional isomers* of each other. Since only glyceraldehyde 3-phosphate continues on in glycolysis, dihydroxyacetone phosphate is isomerized to glyceraldehyde 3-phosphate in step [5], completing the energy-investment phase of glycolysis.

In summary:

- The first phase of glycolysis converts glucose to *two* molecules of glyceraldehyde 3-phosphate.
- The energy from two ATP molecules is utilized.

PROBLEM 24.2

As we learned in Section 23.3, the hydrolysis of ATP to ADP releases 7.3 kcal/mol of energy. If the coupled reaction, fructose 6-phosphate + ATP → fructose 1,6-bisphosphate + ADP, releases 3.4 kcal/mol of energy, how much energy is required for the phosphorylation of fructose 6-phosphate?

$$\text{fructose 6-phosphate} + HPO_4^{2-} \longrightarrow \text{fructose 1,6-bisphosphate} + H_2O$$

Figure 24.3

Glycolysis: Steps [4] and [5]

fructose 1,6-bisphosphate

This bond is broken.

aldolase   (4)   **Cleavage**

dihydroxyacetone phosphate   +   glyceraldehyde 3-phosphate

Two molecules of glyceraldehyde 3-phosphate are formed from **one** glucose molecule.

triose phosphate isomerase

(5)   **Isomerization**

Cleavage of a carbon–carbon bond and isomerization form two molecules of glyceraldehyde 3-phosphate from glucose, completing the energy-investment phase of glycolysis.

Glycolysis: Steps [6]–[10]

Each three-carbon aldehyde (glyceraldehyde 3-phosphate) produced in step [5] of glycolysis is carried through a series of five reactions that ultimately form pyruvate (Figure 24.4).

In step [6], oxidation of the –CHO group of glyceraldehyde 3-phosphate and phosphorylation with HPO_4^{2-} form 1,3-bisphosphoglycerate. In this process, the oxidizing agent NAD^+ is reduced to NADH. Transfer of a phosphate group from 1,3-bisphosphoglycerate to ADP

Figure 24.4   Glycolysis: Steps [6]–[10]

In the energy-generating phase of glycolysis, NADH is formed in step [6] and ATP is formed in steps [7] and [10]. Since one glucose molecule yields two molecules of glyceraldehyde that begin the sequence, **2 $CH_3COCO_2^-$, 2 NADH,** and **4 ATP** are ultimately formed in steps [6]–[10].

forms 3-phosphoglycerate and generates ATP in step [7]. Isomerization of the phosphate group in step [8] and loss of water in step [9] form phosphoenolpyruvate. Finally, transfer of a phosphate to ADP forms ATP and pyruvate in step [10]. Thus, **one NADH molecule is produced in step [6] and two ATPs are formed in steps [7] and [10] for each glyceraldehyde 3-phosphate.**

- Because each glucose molecule yielded *two* glyceraldehyde 3-phosphate molecules in step [5], overall *two* NADH molecules and *four* ATP molecules are formed in the energy-generating phase of glycolysis.

PROBLEM 24.3

Identify all of the reactions of glycolysis that utilize kinases. What species is phosphorylated in each reaction?

PROBLEM 24.4

Identify the three reactions in glycolysis that involve the conversion of one constitutional isomer to another. Name the enzymes involved in each reaction.

24.3B The Net Result of Glycolysis

Three major products are formed in glycolysis—**ATP, NADH,** and **pyruvate.**

- Two ATP molecules are used in the energy-investment phase (steps [1] and [3]), and four molecules of ATP are formed in the energy-generating phase (steps [7] and [10]). The net result is the *synthesis of two molecules of ATP from glycolysis.*

- Two molecules of NADH are formed from two glyceraldehyde 3-phosphate molecules in step [6]. The NADH formed in glycolysis must be transported from the cytoplasm to the mitochondria for use in the electron transport chain to generate more ATP.

- Two three-carbon molecules of pyruvate ($CH_3COCO_2^-$) are formed from the six carbon atoms of glucose. The fate of pyruvate depends on oxygen availability, as discussed in Section 24.4.

Thus, the ATP production of glycolysis is small compared to that produced from the electron transport chain and oxidative phosphorylation. The overall process of glycolysis can be summarized in the following equation.

$$C_6H_{12}O_6 + 2\,NAD^+ \xrightarrow[\text{2 ADP} \quad \text{2 ATP}]{} 2\,CH_3-\overset{\overset{O}{\|}}{C}-\overset{\overset{O}{\|}}{C}-O^- + 2\,NADH + 2\,H^+$$

glucose   pyruvate

Although glycolysis is an ongoing pathway in cells, the rate of glycolysis depends on the body's need for the products it forms—that is, pyruvate, ATP, and NADH. When ATP levels are high, glycolysis is inhibited at various stages. When ATP levels are depleted, such as during strenuous exercise, glycolysis is activated so that more ATP is synthesized.

PROBLEM 24.5

The level of citrate, one intermediate in the citric acid cycle, also regulates the rate of glycolysis. How might a high level of citrate affect the rate of glycolysis?

24.3C   Glycolysis and Other Hexoses

Although glucose is the major monosaccharide obtained by the hydrolysis of ingested carbohydrates, three other six-carbon monosaccharides are also obtained in lesser amounts in the diet.

(left): ©Corbis/VCG/Getty Images RF; (middle): ©Pixtal/SuperStock RF; (right): ©Brand X Pictures/Getty Images RF

- **Fructose is obtained by the hydrolysis of the disaccharide sucrose, found in sugar beets and sugarcane.**
- **Galactose is obtained by the hydrolysis of the disaccharide lactose in milk.**
- **Mannose is obtained from polysaccharides in fruits such as cranberries and currants.**

These hexoses enter glycolysis at various points along the metabolic pathway. Fructose enters glycolysis in two different ways. In the muscle and kidneys, it is phosphorylated with ATP to form fructose 6-phosphate, the substrate for step [3]. In the liver, fructose is converted by a multistep route to glyceraldehyde 3-phosphate, which enters the pathway at step [6].

Galactose is phosphorylated with ATP to form galactose 1-phosphate, which is converted to glucose 6-phosphate in several steps. Individuals with **galactosemia** lack one of the necessary enzymes required for this process, resulting in an abnormally high galactose concentration, with disabling and sometimes fatal results (Section 20.2). Galactosemia can be detected in newborn screening, and is treated by eliminating galactose from the diet.

Mannose is converted to mannose 6-phosphate and is then isomerized to fructose 6-phosphate, the substrate in step [3] of glycolysis. In this way, all of the other common hexoses are converted to intermediates in the glycolytic pathway, and as a result, they are metabolized to pyruvate.

PROBLEM 24.6

(a) Are galactose and mannose constitutional isomers or stereoisomers? (b) Draw the structure of galactose 1-phosphate and mannose 6-phosphate. (c) Are these two phosphates constitutional isomers or stereoisomers?

24.3D   FOCUS ON HEALTH & MEDICINE
Glycolysis and Cancer Cells

It has been known for a long time that many cancerous tumors depend largely on glycolysis to supply their energy needs, even though the yield of ATP from glycolysis is small—only two molecules of ATP for each glucose molecule. This occurs in part because glycolysis is an anaerobic pathway and often tumor cells are not located in proximity to oxygen-carrying blood vessels. As a result, glycolysis often proceeds ten times faster in cancer cells compared to healthy cells.

Although many cancer chemotherapies target derailing DNA synthesis as a method of killing fast-growing cancer cells, some recent research has aimed at attacking specific points on the glycolytic pathway. This strategy was pinned on the theory that without the ATP generated from glycolysis, cancer cells would be energy starved and unable to survive. In fact, promising results have been obtained by shutting down glycolysis in breast cancer cells by targeting a specific enzyme, thus opening the way for new therapies with perhaps fewer side effects than traditional chemotherapy.

24.4   The Fate of Pyruvate

Although pyruvate is the end product of glycolysis, it is not the final product of glucose metabolism. What happens to pyruvate depends on the existing conditions and the organism. In particular, there are three possible products:

$$CH_3-\overset{\overset{\displaystyle O}{\|}}{C}-\overset{\overset{\displaystyle O}{\|}}{C}-O^- \longrightarrow CH_3-\overset{\overset{\displaystyle O}{\|}}{C}-SCoA \quad or \quad CH_3-\overset{\overset{\displaystyle OH}{|}}{\underset{\underset{\displaystyle H}{|}}{C}}-\overset{\overset{\displaystyle O}{\|}}{C}-O^- \quad or \quad CH_3CH_2OH$$

pyruvate   acetyl CoA   lactate   ethanol

- **Acetyl CoA, $CH_3COSCoA$, is formed under aerobic conditions.**
- **Lactate, $CH_3CH(OH)CO_2^-$, is formed under anaerobic conditions.**
- **Ethanol, CH_3CH_2OH, is formed in fermentation.**

24.4A   Conversion to Acetyl CoA

When oxygen is plentiful, oxidation of pyruvate by NAD^+ in the presence of coenzyme A forms acetyl CoA and carbon dioxide. For this process to occur, pyruvate must diffuse across the outer membrane of a mitochondrion, and then be transported across the inner mitochondrial membrane into the matrix.

$$CH_3-\overset{\overset{\displaystyle O}{\|}}{C}-\overset{\overset{\displaystyle O}{\|}}{C}-O^- + HS-CoA \xrightarrow[]{NAD^+ \quad NADH + H^+} CH_3-\overset{\overset{\displaystyle O}{\|}}{C}-SCoA + CO_2$$

pyruvate   acetyl CoA

Although oxygen is not needed for this specific reaction, oxygen is needed to oxidize NADH back to NAD^+. Without an adequate supply of NAD^+, this pathway cannot occur. The acetyl CoA formed in this process then enters the common metabolic pathways—the citric acid cycle, the electron transport chain, and oxidative phosphorylation—to generate a great deal of ATP.

24.4B   FOCUS ON HEALTH & MEDICINE
Conversion to Lactate

When oxygen levels are low, the metabolism of pyruvate must follow a different course. Oxygen is needed to oxidize the NADH formed in step [6] of glycolysis back to NAD^+. If there is not enough O_2 to re-oxidize NADH, cells must get NAD^+ in a different way. The conversion of pyruvate to lactate provides the solution.

Reduction of pyruvate with NADH forms lactate and NAD^+, which can now re-enter glycolysis and oxidize glyceraldehyde 3-phosphate at step [6].

$$CH_3-\overset{\overset{\displaystyle O}{\|}}{C}-\overset{\overset{\displaystyle O}{\|}}{C}-O^- \xrightarrow[]{NADH + H^+ \quad NAD^+} CH_3-\overset{\overset{\displaystyle OH}{|}}{\underset{\underset{\displaystyle H}{|}}{C}}-\overset{\overset{\displaystyle O}{\|}}{C}-O^-$$

NAD$^+$ can re-enter glycolysis at step [6].

pyruvate   lactate

HEALTH NOTE

Muscle fatigue is caused by lactate buildup due to the anaerobic metabolism of glucose. Deep breaths after exercise replenish O_2 in oxygen-depleted tissues and allow the re-oxidation of lactate to pyruvate. ©*Radius Images/Alamy RF*

At rest, the O_2 level in cells is sufficient for the aerobic oxidation of pyruvate to acetyl CoA in humans, so lactate production occurs regularly only in red blood cells, which have no mitochondria and therefore no machinery of aerobic catabolism. During periods of strenuous exercise, when ATP needs are high, however, there is an inadequate level of oxygen to re-oxidize NADH in the electron transport chain. At these times, pyruvate is reduced to lactate for the sole purpose of re-oxidizing NADH to NAD^+ to maintain glycolysis. Under anaerobic conditions, therefore, lactate becomes the main product of glucose metabolism and only two ATP molecules are formed per glucose.

$$\text{Anaerobic conditions} \quad C_6H_{12}O_6 \xrightarrow{\;\;\overset{\text{2 ADP}\;\;\;\text{2 ATP}}{\quad\quad}\;\;} 2\ CH_3-\underset{\underset{H}{|}}{\overset{\overset{OH}{|}}{C}}-CO_2^-$$

glucose   lactate

Anaerobic metabolism leads to an increase in lactate levels in muscles, which in turn is associated with soreness and cramping. During these periods an "oxygen debt" is created. When vigorous activity ceases, an individual inhales deep breaths of air to repay the oxygen debt caused by heavy exercise. Lactate is then gradually re-oxidized to pyruvate, which can once again be converted to acetyl CoA, and muscle soreness, fatigue, and shortness of breath resolve.

In any tissue deprived of oxygen, pyruvate is converted to lactate rather than acetyl CoA. The pain produced during a heart attack, for example, is caused by an increase in lactate concentration that results when the blood supply to part of the heart muscle is blocked (Figure 24.5). The lack of oxygen delivery to heart tissue results in the anaerobic metabolism of glucose to lactate rather than acetyl CoA.

Measuring lactate levels in the blood is a common diagnostic tool used by physicians to assess how severely ill an individual is. **A higher-than-normal lactate concentration generally indicates inadequate oxygen delivery to some tissues.** Lactate levels increase transiently during exercise but can remain elevated because of lung disease, congestive heart failure, or the presence of a serious infection.

Figure 24.5

Lactate Production During a Heart Attack

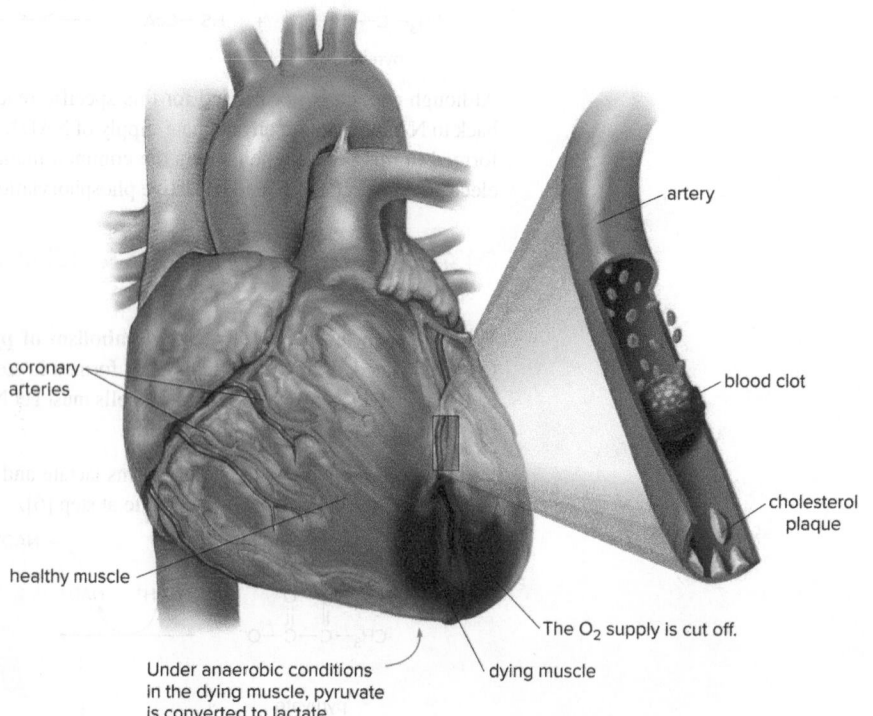

artery

blood clot

coronary arteries

cholesterol plaque

healthy muscle

The O_2 supply is cut off.

Under anaerobic conditions in the dying muscle, pyruvate is converted to lactate.

dying muscle

24.4C FOCUS ON HEALTH & MEDICINE
Conversion to Ethanol

In yeast and other microorganisms, pyruvate is converted to ethanol (CH_3CH_2OH) and carbon dioxide (CO_2) by a two-step process: decarboxylation (loss of CO_2) to acetaldehyde followed by reduction to ethanol.

$$CH_3-\overset{O}{\underset{}{C}}-\overset{O}{\underset{}{C}}-O^- \xrightarrow[\text{decarboxylase}]{\text{pyruvate}} CH_3-\overset{O}{\underset{}{C}}-H \xrightarrow[\text{dehydrogenase}]{\text{alcohol}} CH_3CH_2OH$$

pyruvate

pyruvate

$+$

ethanol

CO_2

NADH + H⁺   →   NAD⁺

The NAD⁺ generated during reduction can enter glycolysis as an oxidizing agent in step [6]. As a result, glucose can be metabolized by yeast under anaerobic conditions: glycolysis forms pyruvate, which is further metabolized to ethanol and carbon dioxide. Two molecules of ATP are generated during glycolysis.

• *Fermentation* is the anaerobic conversion of glucose to ethanol and CO_2.

Fermentation $C_6H_{12}O_6$ → $2 CH_3CH_2OH$ + $2 CO_2$

glucose

ethanol

2 ADP   2 ATP

Fermentation plays a key role in the production of bread, beer, and cheese.
©*Tony Robbins/Photolibrary/Getty Images*

The ethanol in beer, wine, and other alcoholic beverages is obtained by the fermentation of sugar, quite possibly the oldest example of chemical synthesis. The carbohydrate source determines the type of alcoholic beverage formed. The sugars in grapes are fermented to form wine, barley malt is used for beer, and the carbohydrates in corn or rye form whiskey. When the fermented ethanol reaches a concentration of about 12%, the yeast cells that provide the enzymes for the process die and fermentation stops. Any alcoholic beverage with an ethanol concentration of greater than 12% must be distilled to increase the ethanol content. While ethanol consumption is considered socially acceptable in most societies, the irresponsible consumption of alcoholic beverages is a major health and social problem in many parts of the world (Section 14.6).

Fermentation plays a role in forming other food products. Cheese is produced by fermenting curdled milk, whereas yogurt is prepared by fermenting fresh milk. When yeast is mixed with flour, water, and sugar, the enzymes in yeast carry out fermentation to produce the CO_2 that causes bread to rise. Some of the characteristic and "intoxicating" odor associated with freshly baked bread is due to the ethanol that has evaporated during the baking process.

PROBLEM 24.7

What role does NADH play in the conversion of pyruvate to lactate? What role does NADH play in the conversion of pyruvate to ethanol?

PROBLEM 24.8

(a) In what way(s) is the conversion of pyruvate to acetyl CoA similar to the conversion of pyruvate to ethanol? (b) In what way(s) are the two processes different?

PROBLEM 24.9

(a) In what way(s) is the conversion of pyruvate to lactate similar to the conversion of pyruvate to ethanol? (b) In what way(s) are the two processes different?

24.5   The ATP Yield from Glucose

How much ATP is generated from the complete catabolism of glucose ($C_6H_{12}O_6$) to carbon dioxide (CO_2)? To answer this question we must take into account the number of ATP molecules formed in the following sequential pathways:

- the glycolysis of glucose to two pyruvate molecules
- the oxidation of two pyruvate molecules to two molecules of acetyl CoA
- the citric acid cycle
- the electron transport chain and oxidative phosphorylation

To calculate how much ATP is generated, we must consider both the ATP formed directly in reactions, as well as the ATP produced from reduced coenzymes after oxidative phosphorylation.

As we learned in Section 23.6, each NADH formed in the mitochondrial matrix provides the energy to yield 2.5 ATPs, whereas each $FADH_2$ yields 1.5 ATPs. In contrast, the NADH formed during glycolysis is generated in the cytoplasm *outside* the mitochondria. Although it cannot pass through the mitochondrial membrane, its electrons and energy can be transferred to other molecules—NADH or $FADH_2$—ultimately yielding 1.5 or 2.5 ATPs for each NADH. To simplify calculations, we will use the value 2.5 ATP/NADH consistently in calculations.

Finally, any calculation must also take into account that glucose is split into *two* three-carbon molecules at step [4] of glycolysis, so the **ATP yield in each reaction must be *doubled* after this step.** With this information and Figure 24.6 in hand, we can now determine the total yield of ATP from the complete catabolism of glucose.

Figure 24.6   The ATP Yield from the Aerobic Metabolism of Glucose to CO_2

The complete catabolism of glucose forms six CO_2 molecules and 32 ATP molecules.

- Glycolysis yields a net of two ATP molecules. The two molecules of NADH formed during step [6] of glycolysis yield five additional ATPs.

$$C_6H_{12}O_6 \longrightarrow 2\ CH_3COCO_2^- + \textbf{2 ATP} + 2\ NADH$$

glucose   pyruvate

$2 \times (2.5\ ATP/NADH) = \textbf{5 ATP}$

- Oxidation of two molecules of pyruvate to acetyl CoA in the mitochondria forms two NADH molecules that yield five ATP molecules.

$$2\ CH_3COCO_2^- \longrightarrow 2\ CH_3COSCoA + 2\ CO_2 + 2\ NADH$$

pyruvate   acetyl CoA

$2 \times (2.5\ ATP/NADH) = \textbf{5 ATP}$

- Beginning with two acetyl CoA molecules, the citric acid cycle (Figure 23.7) forms two GTP molecules, the energy equivalent of two ATPs, in step [5]. The six NADH molecules and two FADH$_2$ molecules also formed yield an additional 18 ATPs from the electron transport chain and oxidative phosphorylation. Thus, 20 ATPs are formed from two acetyl CoA molecules.

$2 \times (1.5\ ATP/FADH_2) = \textbf{3 ATP}$

$$2\ CH_3COSCoA \longrightarrow 4\ CO_2 + 2\ GTP + 6\ NADH + 2\ FADH_2$$

acetyl CoA

2 ATP

$6 \times (2.5\ ATP/NADH) = \textbf{15 ATP}$

Adding up the ATP formed in each pathway gives a **total of 32 molecules of ATP for the complete catabolism of each glucose molecule.** Most of the ATP generated from glucose metabolism results from the citric acid cycle, electron transport chain, and oxidative phosphorylation.

Glucose is the main source of energy for cells and the only source of energy used by the brain. When energy demands are low, glucose is stored as the polymer glycogen in the liver and muscles. When blood levels of glucose are low, glycogen is hydrolyzed to keep adequate blood glucose levels to satisfy the body's energy needs.

Blood glucose levels are carefully regulated by two hormones. When blood glucose concentration rises after a meal, **insulin** stimulates the passage of glucose into cells for metabolism. When blood glucose levels are low, the hormone **glucagon** stimulates the conversion of stored glycogen to glucose.

PROBLEM 24.10

How much ATP results from each transformation?

a. glucose → 2 pyruvate

b. pyruvate → acetyl CoA

c. glucose → 2 acetyl CoA

d. 2 acetyl CoA → 4 CO$_2$

PROBLEM 24.11

What three reactions form CO$_2$ when glucose is completely catabolized?

PROBLEM 24.12

What is the difference in ATP generation between the aerobic oxidation of glucose to CO$_2$ and the anaerobic conversion of glucose to lactate?

24.6 Gluconeogenesis

Now that we have learned how glucose is converted to CO$_2$ and energy, we can also consider one other metabolic pathway that involves glucose.

- *Gluconeogenesis* is the synthesis of glucose from noncarbohydrate sources—lactate, amino acids, or glycerol.

As such, **gluconeogenesis is an *anabolic* pathway rather than a catabolic pathway because it results in the synthesis of glucose from smaller molecules.** Gluconeogenesis occurs in the liver when the body has depleted both available glucose and stored glycogen reserves. Such a condition results during sustained vigorous exercise or fasting.

For example, the lactate that builds up in muscles as a result of vigorous exercise can be transported to the liver where it is oxidized to pyruvate, which is then converted to glucose by means of gluconeogenesis. The newly synthesized glucose is then utilized for energy or stored in the muscle as glycogen.

$$2\ CH_3\!-\!\underset{\underset{H}{|}}{\overset{\overset{OH}{|}}{C}}\!-\!CO_2^- \xrightarrow{\text{oxidation}} 2\ CH_3\!-\!\underset{}{\overset{\overset{O}{\|}}{C}}\!-\!CO_2^- \xrightarrow{\text{gluconeogenesis}} C_6H_{12}O_6$$

lactate   pyruvate   glucose

Conceptually, gluconeogenesis is the reverse of glycolysis; that is, **two molecules of pyruvate are converted to glucose by a stepwise pathway that passes through all of the same intermediates encountered in glycolysis.** In fact, 7 of the 10 steps of gluconeogenesis use the same enzymes as glycolysis. Three steps in glycolysis (steps [1], [3], and [10]), however, must use different enzymes to be energetically feasible for gluconeogenesis to occur. As a result, **gluconeogenesis provides a mechanism for synthesizing new glucose molecules from other substrates.**

- Glycolysis is a catabolic process that converts glucose to pyruvate.
- Gluconeogenesis is an anabolic process that synthesizes glucose from pyruvate.

Cycling compounds from the muscle to the liver and back to the muscle is called the **Cori cycle.** The Cori cycle involves the four operations shown in Figure 24.7.

Because the brain relies solely on glucose as an energy source, gluconeogenesis is a mechanism that ensures that the brain has a supply of glucose even when a diet is low in carbohydrates and glycogen reserves are low. Gluconeogenesis is not a commonly used metabolic pathway when carbohydrate intake is high. On the other hand, a low carbohydrate diet makes gluconeogenesis an important pathway that converts noncarbohydrate substrates—fats and amino acids—to needed glucose.

Figure 24.7

The Cori Cycle—Glycolysis and Gluconeogenesis

[1] Glycolysis in muscle

$C_6H_{12}O_6 \longrightarrow 2\ CH_3COCO_2^- \longrightarrow 2\ CH_3CH(OH)CO_2^-$
glucose   pyruvate   lactate

[4] Transport to the muscle   [2] Transport to the liver

$C_6H_{12}O_6 \longleftarrow 2\ CH_3COCO_2^- \longleftarrow 2\ CH_3CH(OH)CO_2^-$
glucose   pyruvate   lactate

[3] Gluconeogenesis in the liver

Steps in the Cori cycle:
[1] The catabolism of glucose in muscle forms pyruvate, which is reduced to lactate when the oxygen supply is limited.
[2] Lactate is transported to the liver.
[3] Oxidation of lactate forms pyruvate, which is then converted to glucose by the 10-step process of gluconeogenesis.
[4] Glucose is transported back to the muscle.

From what you learned about glycolysis in Section 24.3, what is the starting material and product of each of the following steps in gluconeogenesis: (a) step [1]; (b) step [3]; (c) step [10]?

24.7   The Catabolism of Triacylglycerols

The first step in the catabolism of triacylglycerols, the most common lipids, is the hydrolysis of the three ester bonds to form glycerol and fatty acids, which are then metabolized in separate pathways.

24.7A   Glycerol Catabolism

The glycerol formed from triacylglycerol hydrolysis is converted in two steps to dihydroxyacetone phosphate. Phosphorylation of glycerol with ATP forms glycerol 3-phosphate, which is then oxidized with NAD^+.

Since dihydroxyacetone phosphate is an intermediate in both glycolysis and gluconeogenesis, two pathways are available, depending on the energy needs of the organism.

Analyze the phosphorylation of glycerol in step [1] of glycerol metabolism by looking at the functional groups, the reagent, and the name of the enzyme, as discussed in Section 24.2.

24.7B   Fatty Acid Catabolism by β-Oxidation

Fatty acids are catabolized by **β-oxidation,** a process in which two-carbon acetyl CoA units are sequentially cleaved from the fatty acid. Key to this process is the oxidation of the β carbon to the carbonyl group of a thioester (RCOSR'), which then undergoes cleavage between the α and β carbons.

Fatty acid oxidation begins with conversion of the fatty acid to a thioester with coenzyme A. This process requires energy, which comes from the hydrolysis of two P—O bonds in ATP to form AMP, adenosine *mono*phosphate. Much like the beginning of glycolysis requires an energy investment, so, too, the initial step of fatty acid oxidation requires energy input.

Once the product, an **acyl CoA,** is inside the mitochondrion, the process of β-oxidation is set to begin. β-Oxidation requires four steps to cleave a two-carbon acetyl CoA unit from the acyl CoA, as shown with the 18-carbon fatty acid stearic acid in Figure 24.8.

In step [1], FAD removes two hydrogen atoms to form $FADH_2$ and a double bond between the α and β carbons of the thioester. Water is added to the double bond in step [2] to place an OH group on the β carbon to the carbonyl group, which is then oxidized in step [3] to form a carbonyl group. The NAD^+ oxidizing agent is reduced to NADH in step [3] as well. Finally, cleavage of the bond between the α and β carbons forms acetyl CoA and a 16-carbon acyl CoA in step [4].

- As a result, a new acyl CoA having two carbons fewer than the original acyl CoA is formed.

Figure 24.8   β-Oxidation of a Fatty Acid

- Atoms involved in each reaction are labeled in gray.

The following equation summarizes the important components of β-oxidation for a general acyl CoA, RCH$_2$CH$_2$COSCoA. **Each four-step sequence forms one molecule each of acetyl CoA, NADH, and FADH$_2$.**

Once the 16-carbon acyl CoA is formed in step [4], it becomes the substrate for a new four-step β-oxidation sequence. This type of metabolic pathway is called a **spiral pathway,** because the same set of reactions is repeated on increasingly smaller substrates. The process continues until a four-carbon acyl CoA is cleaved to form *two* acetyl CoA molecules. As a result:

- An 18-carbon acyl CoA is cleaved to *nine* two-carbon acetyl CoA molecules.
- A total of *eight* cycles of β-oxidation are needed to cleave the eight carbon–carbon bonds.

All bonds in red are cleaved, one at a time, beginning near the carbonyl end of the acyl CoA.

Thus, complete β-oxidation of the acyl CoA derived from stearic acid forms:

- **9 CH$_3$COSCoA molecules (from the 18-carbon fatty acid)**
- **8 NADH (from eight cycles of β-oxidation)**
- **8 FADH$_2$ (from eight cycles of β-oxidation)**

β-Oxidation of unsaturated fatty acids proceeds in a similar fashion, although an additional step is required. **Ultimately every carbon in the original fatty acid ends up as a carbon atom of acetyl CoA.**

SAMPLE PROBLEM 24.3 DETERMINING THE OUTCOME OF β-OXIDATION OF A FATTY ACID

Consider lauric acid, CH$_3$(CH$_2$)$_{10}$CO$_2$H. (a) How many molecules of acetyl CoA are formed from complete β-oxidation? (b) How many cycles of β-oxidation are needed for complete catabolism?

Analysis

The number of carbons in the fatty acid determines the number of molecules of acetyl CoA formed and the number of times β-oxidation occurs.

- The number of molecules of acetyl CoA equals one-half the number of carbons in the original fatty acid.
- Because the final turn of the cycle forms *two* molecules of acetyl CoA, the number of cycles is one fewer than the number of acetyl CoA molecules formed.

Solution

Lauric acid has 12 carbons, so it forms six molecules of acetyl CoA from five cycles of β-oxidation.

PRACTICE PROBLEM 24.3

For each fatty acid: [1] How many molecules of acetyl CoA are formed from complete catabolism?
[2] How many cycles of β-oxidation are needed for complete oxidation?

   a. arachidic acid ($C_{20}H_{40}O_2$)   b. palmitoleic acid ($C_{16}H_{30}O_2$)

More Practice: Try Problems 24.55–24.58.

24.7C   The Energy Yield from Fatty Acid Oxidation

How much energy—in terms of the number of molecules of ATP formed—results from the complete catabolism of a fatty acid? To determine this quantity, we must take into account the ATP cost for the conversion of the fatty acid to the acyl CoA, as well as the ATP production from the coenzymes (NADH and $FADH_2$) and acetyl CoA formed during β-oxidation. The steps are shown in the accompanying *How To* procedure.

***How To*   Determine the Number of Molecules of ATP Formed from a Fatty Acid**

Example: How much ATP is formed by the complete catabolism of stearic acid, $C_{18}H_{36}O_2$?

Step [1]   Determine the amount of ATP required to synthesize the acyl CoA from the fatty acid.

- Since the conversion of stearic acid ($C_{17}H_{35}COOH$) to an acyl CoA ($C_{17}H_{35}COSCoA$) requires the hydrolysis of two P—O bonds, this is equivalent to the energy released when 2 ATPs are converted to 2 ADPs.
- Thus, the first step in catabolism costs the equivalent of 2 ATPs—that is, **−2 ATPs.**

Step [2]   Add up the ATP generated from the coenzymes produced during β-oxidation.

- As we learned in Section 24.7B, each cycle of β-oxidation produces one molecule each of NADH and $FADH_2$. To cleave **eight** carbon–carbon bonds in stearic acid requires **eight** cycles of β-oxidation, so **8** NADH and **8** $FADH_2$ are produced.

$$8\ NADH\ \times\ 2.5\ ATP/NADH\ =\ 20\ ATP$$
$$8\ FADH_2\ \times\ 1.5\ ATP/FADH_2\ =\ \underline{12\ ATP}$$
$$\text{From reduced coenzymes:}\ \ \ \textbf{32 ATP}$$

- Thus, 32 ATPs would be produced from oxidative phosphorylation after the reduced coenzymes enter the electron transport chain.

Step [3]   Determine the amount of ATP that results from each acetyl CoA, and add the results for steps [1]–[3].

- From Section 24.7B, stearic acid generates nine molecules of acetyl CoA, which then enter the citric acid cycle and go on to produce ATP by the electron transport chain and oxidative phosphorylation. As we learned in Section 23.6, each acetyl CoA results in **10** ATPs.

$$9\ \text{acetyl CoA}\ \times\ 10\ ATP/\text{acetyl CoA}\ =\ \textbf{90 ATP}$$

- Totaling the values obtained in steps [1]–[3]:

$$(-2) + 32 + 90 = \textbf{120 ATP}\ \text{molecules from stearic acid}$$

Answer

Palmitic acid is the main constituent of palm oil, an edible oil obtained from the fruit of oil palms native to west and southwest Africa. ©KhunJompol/Getty Images RF

A grizzly bear uses stored body fat as its sole energy source during its many months of hibernation. β-Oxidation of fatty acids releases sufficient energy to maintain a constant body temperature between 32 and 35 °C and operate all necessary cellular processes. ©Daniel C. Smith

PROBLEM 24.15

Calculate the number of molecules of ATP formed by the complete catabolism of palmitic acid, shown in the ball-and-stick model.

palmitic acid

PROBLEM 24.16

Calculate the number of molecules of ATP formed by the complete catabolism of arachidic acid, $C_{20}H_{40}O_2$.

How does the energy generated in fatty acid catabolism compare to the energy generated from glucose catabolism? In Section 24.5, we determined that one molecule (or one mole) of glucose generates 32 molecules (or moles) of ATP, while the *How To* calculation demonstrates that one molecule (or one mole) of stearic acid generates 120 molecules (or moles) of ATP.

To compare these values, we need to compare the amount of ATP generated *per gram* of each material. To carry out a calculation of this sort, we need to use the molar masses of glucose (180 g/mol) and stearic acid (284 g/mol).

molar mass conversion factor

For glucose: $\dfrac{32\ \text{ATP}}{\text{mol glucose}} \times \dfrac{1\ \text{mol}}{180\ \text{g}} = \dfrac{0.18\ \text{mol ATP}}{\text{g glucose}}$

For stearic acid: $\dfrac{120\ \text{ATP}}{\text{mol stearic acid}} \times \dfrac{1\ \text{mol}}{284\ \text{g}} = \dfrac{0.42\ \text{mol ATP}}{\text{g stearic acid}}$ over twice as much energy per gram

This calculation demonstrates that **a fatty acid produces over *twice as much energy per gram* (in terms of moles of ATP generated) than glucose.** This is why lipids are so much more effective as energy-storing molecules than carbohydrates.

PROBLEM 24.17

Use the number of molecules of ATP formed from the complete catabolism of palmitic acid, $C_{16}H_{32}O_2$, in Problem 24.15 to calculate the molecules (or moles) of ATP formed per gram of palmitic acid (molar mass 256 g/mol).

PROBLEM 24.18

Another way to compare the energy content of molecules is to compare the number of ATPs they generate *per carbon* atom they contain. (a) How many ATPs are formed per carbon when glucose is completely catabolized? (b) How many ATPs are formed per carbon when stearic acid is completely catabolized? (c) Do these data support or refute the fact that lipids are more effective energy-storing molecules than carbohydrates?

24.8   Ketone Bodies

When carbohydrates do not meet energy needs, the body turns to catabolizing stored triacylglycerols, which generate acetyl CoA by β-oxidation of fatty acids. Normally the acetyl CoA is metabolized in the citric acid cycle. When acetyl CoA levels exceed the capacity of the citric acid cycle, however, acetyl CoA is converted to three compounds that are collectively called **ketone bodies**—acetoacetate, β-hydroxybutyrate, and acetone.

$$2\ CH_3-\overset{\overset{\displaystyle O}{\|}}{C}-SCoA \xrightarrow[\text{several steps}]{} \underset{\text{acetoacetate}}{CH_3-\overset{\overset{\displaystyle O}{\|}}{C}-CH_2-\overset{\overset{\displaystyle O}{\|}}{C}-O^-} \xrightarrow[]{NADH + H^+ \quad NAD^+} \underset{\text{β-hydroxybutyrate}}{CH_3-\overset{\overset{\displaystyle OH}{|}}{\underset{\displaystyle H}{C}}-CH_2-\overset{\overset{\displaystyle O}{\|}}{C}-O^-}$$

$$\downarrow CO_2$$

$$\underset{\text{acetone}}{CH_3-\overset{\overset{\displaystyle O}{\|}}{C}-CH_3}$$

- *Ketogenesis* is the synthesis of ketone bodies from acetyl CoA.

Acetoacetate is first formed from two molecules of acetyl CoA by a multistep process. Acetoacetate is either reduced to β-hydroxybutyrate with NADH or undergoes decarboxylation to form acetone. Ketone bodies are produced in the liver, and since they are small molecules that can hydrogen bond with water, they are readily soluble in blood and urine. Once they reach tissues, β-hydroxybutyrate and acetoacetate can be re-converted to acetyl CoA and metabolized for energy.

PROBLEM 24.19

Are any structural features common to the three ketone bodies?

PROBLEM 24.20

Why is the term "ketone body" a misleading name for β-hydroxybutyrate?

Ketostix are a brand of test strips that detect ketone bodies in urine.
©McGraw-Hill Education/Jill Braaten, photographer

Low carbohydrate diets such as the Atkins plan induce the use of stored fat for energy production to assist weight loss. ©McGraw-Hill Education/Jill Braaten, photographer

Under some circumstances—notably starvation, vigorous dieting, and uncontrolled diabetes—when glucose is unavailable or cannot pass into a cell for use as fuel, ketone bodies accumulate, a condition called **ketosis.** As a result, ketone bodies are eliminated in urine and the sweet odor of acetone can be detected in exhaled breath. Sometimes the first indication of diabetes in a patient is the detection of excess ketone bodies in a urine test.

An abnormally high concentration of ketone bodies can lead to **ketoacidosis**—that is, a lowering of the blood pH caused by the increased level of β-hydroxybutyrate and acetoacetate. Although the carbonic acid/bicarbonate buffer in the blood prevents drastic pH changes (Section 9.11), even a small drop in pH can alter many critical biochemical processes.

Low carbohydrate diets, popularized by Dr. Robert Atkins in a series of diet books published in the 1990s, restrict carbohydrate intake to induce the utilization of the body's stored fat as its main energy source. This increased level of fatty acid metabolism leads to an increased concentration of ketone bodies in the blood. Increased levels of ketone bodies in the urine—which can be detected using ketone test strips—can be used as an indicator that the body has switched to metabolic machinery that relies on fat rather than carbohydrates as its principal energy source. Some physicians recommend that the level of ketone bodies be monitored to avoid the risk of ketoacidosis.

PROBLEM 24.21

How is the concentration of acetyl CoA related to the production of ketone bodies?

24.9   Amino Acid Metabolism

After proteins are hydrolyzed in the stomach and intestines, the individual amino acids are reassembled to new proteins or converted to intermediates in other metabolic pathways. The catabolism of amino acids provides energy when the supply of carbohydrates and lipids is exhausted.

The catabolism of amino acids can be conceptually divided into two parts: the fate of the amino group and the fate of the carbon atoms. As shown in Figure 24.9, amino acid carbon skeletons are converted to pyruvate, acetyl CoA, or various carbon compounds that are part of the citric acid cycle.

Figure 24.9   An Overview of the Catabolism of Amino Acids

The breakdown of amino acids forms NH_4^+, which enters the urea cycle to form urea, and a carbon skeleton that is metabolized to either pyruvate, acetyl CoA, or an intermediate in the citric acid cycle.

24.9A   Degradation of Amino Acids—The Fate of the Amino Group

The catabolism of carbohydrates and triacylglycerols deals with the oxidation of carbon atoms only. With amino acids, an **amino group (—NH₂)** must be metabolized, as well. The catabolism of amino acids begins with the removal of the amino group from the carbon skeleton and the formation of ammonium (NH_4^+) by a two-step pathway: **transamination followed by oxidative deamination.**

- *Transamination* is the transfer of an amino group from an amino acid to an α-keto acid, usually α-ketoglutarate.

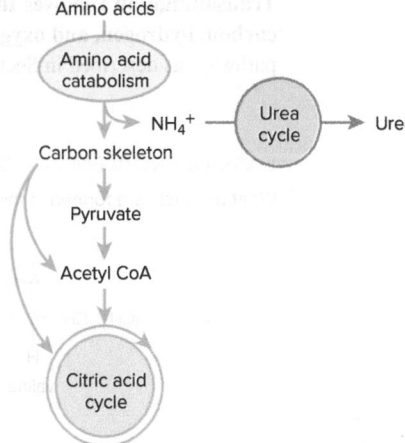

The C–H and C–NH₃⁺ groups are replaced by a C=O.

amino acid   α-keto acid   →(transaminase)→   α-keto acid   amino acid

The C=O is replaced by C–H and C–NH₃⁺ groups.

In transamination, the amino group of the amino acid and the ketone carbonyl oxygen of the α-keto acid are interchanged to form a new amino acid and a new α-keto acid. As an example, transfer of an amino group from alanine to α-ketoglutarate forms pyruvate and glutamate, the completely ionized form of the amino acid glutamic acid.

Transamination removes the amino group to form a carbon skeleton that contains only carbon, hydrogen, and oxygen atoms. These products are then degraded along other catabolic pathways as described in Section 24.9B.

SAMPLE PROBLEM 24.4 DRAWING THE PRODUCTS OF TRANSAMINATION

What products are formed in the following transamination reaction?

Analysis

To draw the products of transamination, convert the C—H and C—NH₃⁺ groups of the amino acid to a C=O, forming an α-keto acid.

Solution

PRACTICE PROBLEM 24.4

Draw the products formed when each amino acid undergoes transamination with α-ketoglutarate.

More Practice: Try Problems 24.75, 24.76.

The glutamate formed by transamination is then degraded by oxidative deamination using NAD⁺.

- In oxidative deamination, the C—H and C—NH₃⁺ bonds on the α carbon of glutamate are converted to C=O and an ammonium ion, NH₄⁺.

glutamate

In oxidative deamination, glutamate is re-converted to α-ketoglutarate, which can undergo trans-amination with another molecule of an amino acid and the cycle repeats. In this way, α-ketoglutarate removes an amino group from an amino acid and then loses that amino group as NH₄⁺ in a second step.

The ammonium ion then enters the **urea cycle,** where it is converted by a multistep pathway to **urea, (NH₂)₂C=O,** in the liver. Urea is then transported to the kidneys and excreted in urine.

urea

- The overall result of transamination and oxidative deamination is to remove an amino group from an amino acid and form an ammonium ion, NH₄⁺.

SAMPLE PROBLEM 24.5 DRAWING THE PRODUCTS OF TRANSAMINATION AND OXIDATIVE DEAMINATION

What final products are formed when leucine is subjected to transamination followed by oxidative deamination?

$$(CH_3)_2CHCH_2-\overset{\overset{+}{N}H_3}{\underset{H}{C}}-CO_2^-$$

leucine

Analysis

To draw the organic product, replace the C—H and C—NH₃⁺ on the α carbon of the amino acid by C=O. NH₄⁺ is formed from the amino group.

Solution

α carbon
$$(CH_3)_2CHCH_2-\overset{\overset{+}{N}H_3}{\underset{H}{C}}-CO_2^- \xrightarrow[\text{[2] oxidative deamination}]{\text{[1] transamination}} (CH_3)_2CHCH_2-\overset{O}{\overset{\|}{C}}-CO_2^- + NH_4^+$$

PRACTICE PROBLEM 24.5

What products are formed when each amino acid is subjected to transamination followed by oxidative deamination: (a) threonine; (b) glycine; (c) isoleucine? Use the structures in Table 21.2.

More Practice: Try Problems 24.79, 24.80.

24.9B   Degradation of Amino Acids—The Fate of the Carbon Skeleton

Once the nitrogen has been removed from an amino acid, the carbon skeletons of individual amino acids are catabolized in a variety of ways. There are three common fates of the carbon skeletons of amino acids, shown in Figure 24.10:

- conversion to pyruvate, $CH_3COCO_2^-$
- conversion to acetyl CoA, $CH_3COSCoA$
- conversion to an intermediate in the citric acid cycle

Figure 24.10   Amino Acid Catabolism

Glucogenic amino acids are highlighted in blue, while ketogenic amino acids are highlighted in gray. Amino acids that appear more than once in the scheme can be degraded by multiple routes.

Some amino acids such as alanine (Section 24.9A) are catabolized to pyruvate. Since pyruvate is an intermediate in both glycolysis and gluconeogenesis, pyruvate can be broken down for energy or used to synthesize glucose. In considering catabolism, amino acids are often divided into two groups.

- *Glucogenic* amino acids are catabolized to pyruvate or an intermediate in the citric acid cycle. Since these catabolic products can be used for gluconeogenesis, glucogenic amino acids can be used to synthesize glucose.

- *Ketogenic* amino acids are converted to acetyl CoA, or the related thioester acetoacetyl CoA, $CH_3COCH_2COSCoA$. These catabolic products cannot be used to synthesize glucose, but they can be converted to ketone bodies and yield energy by this path.

We will not examine the specific pathways that convert the carbon skeletons of individual amino acids into other products. Figure 24.10 illustrates where each amino acid feeds into the metabolic pathways we have already discussed.

PROBLEM 24.22

What metabolic intermediate is produced from the carbon atoms of each amino acid?

a. cysteine   b. aspartic acid   c. valine   d. threonine

CHAPTER HIGHLIGHTS

KEY TERMS

Acyl CoA (24.7)

Cori cycle (24.6)

Decarboxylation (24.2)

Fermentation (24.4)

Glucogenic amino acid (24.9)

Gluconeogenesis (24.6)

Glycolysis (24.3)

Ketogenesis (24.8)

Ketogenic amino acid (24.9)

Ketone bodies (24.8)

Ketosis (24.8)

β-Oxidation (24.7)

Oxidative deamination (24.9)

Transamination (24.9)

Urea cycle (24.9)

KEY CONCEPTS

① What are the main elements that provide clues to the outcome of a biochemical reaction? (24.2)

- To understand the course of a biochemical reaction, examine the functional groups that are added or removed, the reagents (coenzymes or other materials), and the enzyme. The name of an enzyme is often a clue as to the type of reaction.

② What are the main aspects of glycolysis? (24.3)

- Glycolysis is a linear, 10-step pathway that converts glucose to two three-carbon pyruvate molecules. In the energy-investment phase, steps [1]–[5], the energy from two ATP molecules is used for phosphorylation and two three-carbon products are formed. In the energy-generating phase, steps [6]–[10], the following species are generated: two pyruvate molecules ($CH_3COCO_2^-$), 2 NADHs, and 4 ATPs.
- The net result of glycolysis, considering both phases, is 2 $CH_3COCO_2^-$, 2 NADHs, and 2 ATPs.

③ What are the major pathways for pyruvate metabolism? (24.4)

- When oxygen is plentiful, pyruvate is converted to acetyl CoA, which can enter the citric acid cycle.
- When the oxygen level is low, the anaerobic metabolism of pyruvate forms lactate and NAD^+.
- In yeast and other microorganisms, pyruvate is converted to ethanol and CO_2 by fermentation.

④ How much ATP is formed by the complete catabolism of glucose? (24.5)

- To calculate the amount of ATP formed in the catabolism of glucose, we must take into account the ATP yield from glycolysis, the oxidation of two molecules of pyruvate to two molecules of acetyl CoA, the citric acid cycle, and oxidative phosphorylation.
- As shown in Figure 24.6, the complete catabolism of glucose forms six CO_2 molecules and 32 molecules of ATP.

⑤ What are the main features of gluconeogenesis? (24.6)

- Gluconeogenesis is the synthesis of glucose from noncarbohydrate sources—lactate, amino acids, or glycerol. Gluconeogenesis converts two molecules of pyruvate to glucose. Conceptually, gluconeogenesis is the reverse of glycolysis, but three steps in gluconeogenesis require different enzymes.

- Gluconeogenesis occurs when the body has depleted its supplies of glucose and stored glycogen, and takes place during sustained physical exercise and fasting.

⑥ Describe the main features of the β-oxidation of fatty acids. (24.7)

- β-Oxidation is a spiral metabolic pathway that sequentially cleaves two-carbon acetyl CoA units from an acyl CoA derived from a fatty acid. Each cycle of β-oxidation consists of a four-step sequence that forms one molecule each of acetyl CoA, NADH, and $FADH_2$.

⑦ How much ATP is formed from complete fatty acid oxidation? (24.7)

- To determine the ATP yield from the complete catabolism of a fatty acid, we must consider the ATP used up in the synthesis of the acyl CoA, the ATP generated from coenzymes produced during β-oxidation, and the ATP that results from the catabolism of each acetyl CoA.
- As an example, the complete catabolism of stearic acid, $C_{18}H_{36}O_2$, yields 120 ATPs.

⑧ What are ketone bodies and how do they play a role in metabolism? (24.8)

- Ketone bodies—acetoacetate, β-hydroxybutyrate, and acetone—are formed when acetyl CoA levels exceed the capacity of the citric acid cycle. Ketone bodies can be re-converted to acetyl CoA and metabolized for energy. When the level of ketone bodies is high, the pH of the blood can be lowered, causing ketoacidosis.

⑨ What are the main features of amino acid catabolism? (24.9)

- The catabolism of amino acids involves two parts. First, the amino group is removed by transamination followed by oxidative deamination. The NH_4^+ ion formed enters the urea cycle where it is converted to urea and eliminated in urine. The carbon skeletons of the amino acids are then catabolized by a variety of pathways to yield pyruvate, acetyl CoA, or an intermediate in the citric acid cycle.

PROBLEMS

Selected in-chapter and odd-numbered end-of-chapter problems have brief answers in Appendix B. The *Student Study Guide and Solutions Manual* contains detailed solutions to all in-chapter and odd-numbered end-of-chapter problems, as well as additional worked examples and a chapter self-test.

Analyzing Biochemical Reactions

24.23 Analyze each reaction by considering the functional groups that change, the coenzyme or other reactant, and the name of the enzyme.

a.

$$\underset{\text{OH}}{\text{CH}_3}-\overset{\text{OH}}{\underset{|}{\text{CH}}}-\text{CH}_2-\overset{\text{O}}{\underset{||}{\text{C}}}-\text{SCoA} \xrightarrow[\substack{\beta\text{-hydroxyacyl CoA}\\ \text{dehydrogenase}}]{\text{NAD}^+ \quad \text{NADH + H}^+} \text{CH}_3-\overset{\text{O}}{\underset{||}{\text{C}}}-\text{CH}_2-\overset{\text{O}}{\underset{||}{\text{C}}}-\text{SCoA}$$

b.

$$^-\text{O}_2\text{CCH}_2-\overset{\text{O}}{\underset{||}{\text{C}}}-\text{CO}_2^- \xrightarrow[\substack{\text{phosphoenolpyruvate}\\ \text{carboxykinase}}]{\text{GTP} \quad \text{GDP}} \text{CH}_2{=}\overset{\overset{\displaystyle \text{PO}_3{}^{2-}}{|}}{\underset{}{\text{C}}}-\overset{\text{O}}{\underset{||}{\text{C}}}-\text{O}^- \; + \; \text{CO}_2$$

24.24 Analyze each reaction by considering the functional groups that change, the coenzyme or other reactant, and the name of the enzyme.

a.

$$\underset{\text{3-phosphoglycerate}}{\overset{\text{PO}_3{}^{2-}}{\underset{|}{\text{O}}}-\text{CH}_2-\overset{\text{OH}}{\underset{|}{\text{CH}}}-\overset{\text{O}}{\underset{||}{\text{C}}}-\text{O}^-} \xrightarrow[\substack{\text{phosphoglycerate}\\ \text{kinase}}]{\text{ATP} \quad \text{ADP}} \underset{\text{1,3-bisphosphoglycerate}}{\overset{\text{PO}_3{}^{2-}}{\underset{|}{\text{O}}}-\text{CH}_2-\overset{\text{OH}}{\underset{|}{\text{CH}}}-\overset{\text{O}}{\underset{||}{\text{C}}}-\text{O}-\text{PO}_3{}^{2-}}$$

b.

$$\text{CH}_3-\overset{\text{O}}{\underset{||}{\text{C}}}-\text{CO}_2^- \; + \; \text{CO}_2 \xrightarrow[\text{pyruvate carboxylase}]{\text{ATP} \quad \text{ADP + HPO}_4{}^{2-}} {}^-\text{O}_2\text{CCH}_2-\overset{\text{O}}{\underset{||}{\text{C}}}-\text{CO}_2^-$$

24.25 In the conversion of glucose to stored glycogen, glucose 6-phosphate is converted to glucose 1-phosphate by the enzyme phosphoglucomutase. Suggest a reason for the name of this enzyme.

24.26 When mannose is metabolized to an intermediate in glycolysis, mannose 6-phosphate is converted to fructose 6-phosphate by phosphomannose isomerase. (a) Why is an isomerase enzyme used for this reaction? (b) What type of isomers do mannose 6-phosphate and fructose 6-phosphate represent?

$$\underset{\text{mannose 6-phosphate}}{\text{(structure)}} \xrightarrow[\text{isomerase}]{\text{phosphomannose}} \underset{\text{fructose 6-phosphate}}{\text{(structure)}}$$

Glucose Metabolism

24.27 (a) Convert the ball-and-stick model of **A,** one of the intermediates in glycolysis, to a structural formula, and name the compound. (b) What is the immediate precursor of **A** in glycolysis; that is, what compound forms **A** as a

reaction product? (c) What compound is formed from **A** in glycolysis?

A

24.28 (a) Convert the ball-and-stick model of **B,** one of the intermediates in glycolysis, to a structural formula, and name the compound. (b) What is the immediate precursor of **B** in glycolysis; that is, what compound forms **B** as a reaction product? (c) What compound is formed from **B** in glycolysis?

B

24.29 Compare the energy-investment phase and the energy-generating phase of glycolysis with regard to each of the following: (a) the reactant that begins the phase and the final product formed; (b) the amount of ATP used or formed; (c) the number of reduced coenzymes used or formed.

24.30 Compare glycolysis and gluconeogenesis with regard to the reactant that begins the pathway and the product formed at the end of the pathway.

24.31 Considering the individual steps in glycolysis:
a. Which steps form ATP?
b. Which steps use ATP?
c. Which steps form a reduced coenzyme?
d. Which step breaks a C—C bond?

24.32 Explain the role of the coenzymes NAD^+ and NADH in each reaction.
a. pyruvate $\longrightarrow$ acetyl CoA
b. pyruvate $\longrightarrow$ lactate
c. pyruvate $\longrightarrow$ ethanol

24.33 Glucose is completely metabolized to six molecules of CO_2. What specific reactions generate each molecule of CO_2?

24.34 Why is glycolysis described as an anaerobic process?

24.35 Write the overall equation with key coenzymes for each process.
a. glucose $\longrightarrow$ pyruvate
b. glucose $\longrightarrow$ ethanol

24.36 Write the overall equation with key coenzymes for each process.
a. glucose $\longrightarrow$ lactate
b. pyruvate $\longrightarrow$ acetyl CoA

24.37 Convert the ball-and-stick models to structural formulas and write the overall equation with key coenzymes for the following reaction.

24.38 Convert the ball-and-stick models to structural formulas and write the overall equation with key coenzymes for the following reaction.

24.39 Consider the aerobic and anaerobic avenues of pyruvate metabolism in the human body.
a. Where do the carbon atoms of pyruvate end up in each pathway?
b. What coenzymes are used and formed?

24.40 What is the main purpose for the conversion of pyruvate to lactate under anaerobic conditions?

24.41 What is the difference between glycolysis and gluconeogenesis?

24.42 Why is it incorrect to say that gluconeogenesis is simply the reverse of glycolysis?

24.43 What effect is observed on the rate of glycolysis under each of the following conditions?
a. low ATP concentration
b. low ADP concentration
c. high carbohydrate diet
d. low carbohydrate diet

24.44 What effect is observed on the rate of gluconeogenesis under each of the following conditions?
a. low ATP concentration
b. low ADP concentration
c. high carbohydrate diet
d. low carbohydrate diet

24.45 Describe the steps in the Cori cycle. In what organs do key reactions of the cycle occur?

24.46 How does a defect in monosaccharide metabolism result in galactosemia?

24.47 What metabolic products are formed from pyruvate in each case: (a) anaerobic conditions in the body; (b) anaerobic conditions in yeast; (c) aerobic conditions?

24.48 Why must the NADH produced in glycolysis be re-oxidized to NAD^+? How is this accomplished aerobically? How is this accomplished anaerobically?

24.49 Fill in the boxes with the number of moles of each substance formed during the aerobic metabolism of glucose.

24.50 What are the starting material and product of each step of gluconeogenesis: (a) step [2]; (b) step [5]; (c) step [8]?

24.51 In fermentation, where do the six carbon atoms of glucose end up?

24.52 Which compound(s) are formed during the fermentation of glucose to ethanol?

A   **B**   **C**

Triacylglycerol Metabolism

24.53 How much ATP is used or formed when a fatty acid is converted to an acyl CoA? Explain your reasoning.

24.54 How much ATP is ultimately generated from each cycle of β-oxidation of a fatty acid?

24.55 Myristic acid is an abundant fatty acid in the triacylglycerols of coconut oil. For myristic acid, $C_{13}H_{27}CO_2H$: (a) How many molecules of acetyl CoA are formed from complete β-oxidation? (b) How many cycles of β-oxidation are needed for complete oxidation?

©mypokcik/Shutterstock RF

24.56 Oleic acid is the most common fatty acid in the triacylglycerols of olive oil. For oleic acid, $C_{17}H_{33}CO_2H$: (a) How many molecules of acetyl CoA are formed from complete β-oxidation? (b) How many cycles of β-oxidation are needed for complete oxidation?

©Dasha Petrenko/Shutterstock RF

24.57 (a) How many molecules of acetyl CoA are formed from complete β-oxidation of the fatty acid depicted in the ball-and-stick model? (b) How many cycles of β-oxidation are needed for complete oxidation?

24.58 (a) How many molecules of acetyl CoA are formed from complete β-oxidation of the fatty acid depicted in the ball-and-stick model? (b) How many cycles of β-oxidation are needed for complete oxidation?

24.59 How much ATP is generated by the complete catabolism of myristic acid in Problem 24.55?

24.60 How much ATP is generated by the complete catabolism of oleic acid in Problem 24.56?

24.61 Draw the structure of the acyl CoA formed from palmitic acid, $C_{15}H_{31}CO_2H$. Use this acyl CoA to write out the four steps of β-oxidation.

24.62 Fill in the boxes with the number of moles of each substance formed during the metabolism of $CH_3(CH_2)_{20}CO_2H$.

$$CH_3(CH_2)_{20}CO_2H \xrightarrow{\text{β-oxidation}} \boxed{a.}\ CH_3COSCoA + \boxed{b.}\ NADH + \boxed{c.}\ FADH_2$$

24.63 Consider decanoic acid, $C_9H_{19}CO_2H$.
   a. Label the α and β carbons.
   b. Draw the acyl CoA derived from this fatty acid.
   c. How many acetyl CoA molecules are formed by complete β-oxidation?
   d. How many cycles of β-oxidation are needed for complete oxidation?
   e. How many molecules of ATP are formed from the complete catabolism of this fatty acid?

24.64 Consider docosanoic acid, $C_{21}H_{43}CO_2H$.
   a. Label the α and β carbons.
   b. Draw the acyl CoA derived from this fatty acid.
   c. How many acetyl CoA molecules are formed by complete β-oxidation?
   d. How many cycles of β-oxidation are needed for complete oxidation?
   e. How many molecules of ATP are formed from the complete catabolism of this fatty acid?

24.65 How many moles of ATP per gram of fatty acid are formed from the complete catabolism of decanoic acid (molar mass 172 g/mol) in Problem 24.63?

24.66 How many moles of ATP per gram of fatty acid are formed from the complete catabolism of docosanoic acid (molar mass 341 g/mol) in Problem 24.64?

Ketone Bodies

24.67 Which ball-and-stick models represent ketone bodies formed from acetyl CoA?

A   B   C

24.68 How is the production of ketone bodies related to ketoacidosis?

24.69 Why are more ketone bodies produced in an individual whose diabetes is poorly managed?

24.70 Why do some individuals use test strips to measure the presence of ketone bodies in their urine?

Amino Acid Metabolism

24.71 What is the difference between ketogenic and glucogenic amino acids?

24.72 What is the difference between transamination and oxidative deamination?

24.73 Draw the structure of the α-keto acid formed by the transamination of each amino acid: (a) glycine; (b) phenylalanine.

24.74 Draw the structure of the α-keto acid formed by the transamination of each amino acid: (a) tyrosine; (b) asparagine.

24.75 Draw the products formed in each transamination reaction.

a. $CH_3-\overset{\overset{+}{N}H_3}{\underset{H}{C}}-CO_2^-$ + $^-O_2CCH_2-\overset{O}{C}-CO_2^-$

b. $(CH_3)_2CHCH_2-\overset{\overset{+}{N}H_3}{\underset{H}{C}}-CO_2^-$ + $^-O_2CCH_2-\overset{O}{C}-CO_2^-$

24.76 Draw the products formed in each transamination reaction.

a. $(CH_3)_2CH-\overset{\overset{+}{N}H_3}{\underset{H}{C}}-CO_2^-$ + $^-O_2CCH_2-\overset{O}{C}-CO_2^-$

b. $CH_3CH_2CH(CH_3)-\overset{\overset{+}{N}H_3}{\underset{H}{C}}-CO_2^-$ + $^-O_2CCH_2CH_2-\overset{O}{C}-CO_2^-$

24.77 What amino acid yields the given α-keto acid after it undergoes transamination?

$CH_3-\overset{H}{\underset{OH}{C}}-\overset{O}{C}-CO_2^-$

24.78 What amino acid yields the given α-keto acid after it undergoes transamination?

$^-O_2CCH_2-\overset{O}{C}-CO_2^-$

24.79 What products are formed when each amino acid undergoes oxidative deamination with NAD$^+$ and a dehydrogenase enzyme: (a) leucine; (b) phenylalanine?

24.80 What products are formed when each amino acid undergoes oxidative deamination with NAD$^+$ and a dehydrogenase enzyme: (a) tyrosine; (b) tryptophan?

24.81 What metabolic intermediate is formed from the carbon skeleton of each amino acid?
a. phenylalanine   c. asparagine
b. glutamic acid   d. glycine

24.82 What metabolic intermediate is formed from the carbon skeleton of each amino acid?
a. lysine   c. methionine
b. tryptophan   d. serine

24.83 Using Table 21.2, name each amino acid, and identify what metabolic intermediate is formed from its carbon skeleton.

a. $H_3\overset{+}{N}-\overset{\overset{}{\underset{CH_2}{CH}}}{C}-\overset{O}{\underset{O^-}{C}}$ $\overset{}{\underset{CH_2CONH_2}{}}$

b. $H_3\overset{+}{N}-\overset{\overset{}{\underset{CH_3}{CH}}}{C}-\overset{O}{\underset{O^-}{C}}$

24.84 Using Table 21.2, name each amino acid, and identify what metabolic intermediate is formed from its carbon skeleton.

a. $H_3\overset{+}{N}-CH-\overset{O}{\underset{O^-}{C}}$ with CH_2 and benzene ring bearing OH

b. $H_3\overset{+}{N}-\overset{H}{C}-\overset{O}{\underset{O^-}{C}}$ with CH_2 and CO_2^-

24.85 Can an amino acid be considered both glucogenic and ketogenic? Explain your choice.

24.86 Which amino acids are classified as only glucogenic?

General Questions and Applications

24.87 What is the difference between a spiral and a cyclic metabolic pathway? Give an example of each.

24.88 What is the cause of the pain and cramping in a runner's muscles?

24.89 Explain the reaction that occurs during the baking of bread that causes the bread to rise.

24.90 Why is the concentration of ethanol in wine typically 12% or less?

24.91 How might pyruvate be metabolized in the cornea, tissue that has little blood supply?

24.92 How is pyruvate metabolized in red blood cells, which contain no mitochondria?

24.93 Why is the Atkins low carbohydrate diet called a ketogenic diet?

24.94 What metabolic conditions induce ketogenesis?

24.95 What type of enzyme would catalyze the conversion of hydroxyacetone (CH_3COCH_2OH) to each compound?

a. $CH_3-\overset{\overset{O}{\|}}{C}-CH_2OPO_3{}^{2-}$

b. $CH_3-\overset{\overset{O}{\|}}{C}-CHO$

c. $HO_2CCH_2-\overset{\overset{O}{\|}}{C}-CH_2OH$

24.96 What coenzyme would convert 6-hydroxy-2-hexanone ($CH_3COCH_2CH_2CH_2CH_2OH$) to each compound?

a. $CH_3-\overset{\overset{OH}{|}}{CH}(CH_2)_4OH$

b. $CH_3-\overset{\overset{O}{\|}}{C}-(CH_2)_3CHO$

c. $CH_3-\overset{\overset{O}{\|}}{C}-CH{=}CHCH_2CH_2OH$

CHALLENGE PROBLEMS

24.97 How much ATP is produced from the complete catabolism of one molecule of glycerol, $HOCH_2CH(OH)CH_2OH$?

24.98 How much ATP is produced from the complete catabolism of one molecule of the given triacylglycerol?

$$CH_2-O-\overset{\overset{O}{\|}}{C}-(CH_2)_4CH_3$$
$$CH-O-\overset{\overset{O}{\|}}{C}-(CH_2)_4CH_3$$
$$CH_2-O-\overset{\overset{O}{\|}}{C}-(CH_2)_4CH_3$$

24.99 Determine the amount of ATP generated per gram of glucose (molar mass 180.2 g/mol) compared to the amount of ATP generated per gram of arachidic acid (312.5 g/mol) during catabolism. Does your result support or refute the fact that lipids are more effective energy-storing molecules than carbohydrates?

24.100 Examine the nutrition label of a favorite breakfast cereal. Determine the number of grams of digestible carbohydrates in a serving by subtracting the number of grams of dietary fiber (due to indigestible cellulose) from the total carbohydrate content. Assume this value gives the number of grams of glucose per serving. How many moles of ATP are formed from the glucose (molar mass = 180.2 g/mol) in one serving of cereal?

25

The blood obtained from a donation is used to provide patients who need a transfusion with this important body fluid and its components.
©Keith Brofsky/Getty Images RF

Body Fluids

CHAPTER OUTLINE

25.1 Types of Body Fluids

25.2 Composition of the Blood

25.3 The Transport of Oxygen and Carbon Dioxide

25.4 Buffers in the Body

25.5 The Blood–Brain Barrier

25.6 The Role of the Kidneys

CHAPTER GOALS

In this chapter you will learn how to:

1. Describe and compare the composition of the major body fluids
2. Describe the major components of blood, as well as the function of each component
3. Understand how a blood clot forms
4. Explain how oxygen and carbon dioxide are transported in the bloodstream
5. Explain how buffers maintain a narrow pH range in the blood
6. Understand how the blood–brain barrier protects the brain
7. Understand the role of the kidneys in removing waste
8. List the main constituents in urine
9. Describe the role of the kidneys in pH, fluid, and electrolyte balance

Why Study Body Fluids?

Almost two-thirds of the total mass of the average human body is composed of body fluids. We have already learned about some facets of the chemistry of body fluids in prior chapters. For example, how the carbonic acid/bicarbonate buffer keeps the blood in a very narrow pH range was discussed in Chapter 9, and we were introduced to the role of the kidneys in filtering waste material from the blood in Chapter 8. In Chapter 25, we examine in detail the components and chemistry of the blood and other common body fluids.

25.1 Types of Body Fluids

Complex organisms that are composed of many different types of cells must rely on a mechanism that provides individual cells with what they need and a means to eliminate waste. In the human body, **body fluids** comprise the aqueous medium that provides nutrients, carries away waste, and brings chemicals that allow cells to communicate with each other. Body fluids are characterized by their location inside or outside of the cell.

- Intracellular fluid is the aqueous medium *within* a cell.
- Extracellular fluid is the aqueous medium *outside* of a cell.

Figure 25.1 shows the approximate distribution of the 42 L of water in an average human body. Almost two-thirds of the water in the body is intracellular. The metabolic reactions in Chapters 23 and 24 occur in the intracellular fluid. The remaining one-third is extracellular. The two most prevalent extracellular fluids are **interstitial fluid** and **plasma.**

- Interstitial fluid is the fluid that fills the space between cells.
- Plasma is the liquid portion of the blood.

Other types of extracellular fluids that occur in lesser amounts include urine, digestive juices, lymph, cerebrospinal fluid, and the synovial fluid that lubricates joints.

What is dissolved in the aqueous medium that constitutes body fluids? By the general solubility rule "Like dissolves like" (Section 8.3), most ions and small polar molecules capable of intermolecular hydrogen bonding are water soluble. Gases, such as O_2 and CO_2, are also soluble, as well

Figure 25.1   The Distribution of Body Fluids

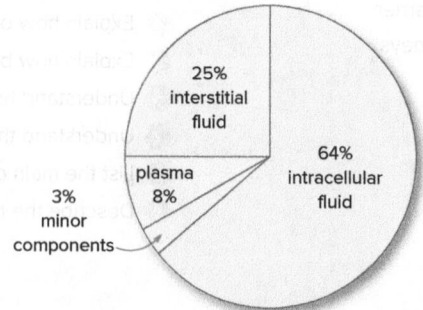

Intracellular fluid is the most abundant body fluid, comprising about 64% of the water in the body. Interstitial fluid (25% of body water) and plasma (8% of body water) are the most common extracellular fluids.

as large molecules that have many polar or charged functional groups. The most abundant dissolved species are inorganic ions, referred to as electrolytes.

How does the composition of the three main types of body fluids—intracellular fluid, interstitial fluid, and plasma—compare? As shown in Figure 25.2, the composition of the interstitial fluid and plasma is quite similar, with sodium (Na^+) the major cation and chloride (Cl^-) the major anion. The main difference in these extracellular fluids is that plasma contains more protein.

The composition of the intracellular fluid differs markedly from these extracellular fluids in both the identity of the ions and the amount of protein present. The principal cation in intracellular fluid is potassium (K^+), whereas the principal anion is hydrogen phosphate (HPO_4^{2-}). Moreover, intracellular fluid contains much more protein. Although the identity of the components is different in different body fluids, each type of fluid contains the same number of dissolved particles per unit volume.

Figure 25.2 Components of the Three Major Body Fluids

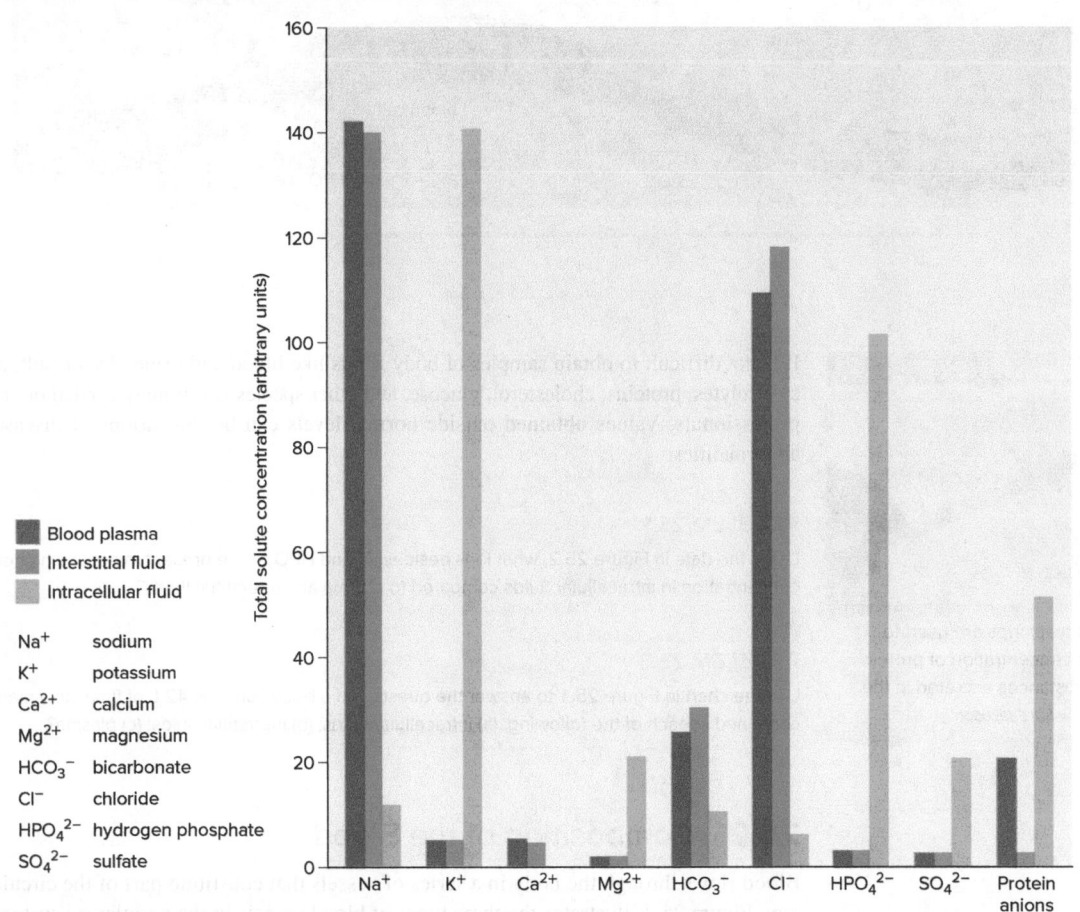

The ion profile shows that the composition of both extracellular fluids—interstitial fluid and plasma—is quite similar, but different from the composition of the intracellular fluid. Blood plasma and interstitial fluid contain a high concentration of Na^+ and Cl^-, whereas intracellular fluid contains a high concentration of K^+ and HPO_4^{2-}. Protein is most abundant in intracellular fluid, and little protein is present in interstitial fluid.

For substances to be transported in the body, materials must be exchanged from one body fluid to another, as shown in Figure 25.3. Oxygen and nutrients in the bloodstream must pass through the capillary walls of blood vessels into the interstitial fluid, and then pass from the interstitial fluid into tissue cells by crossing the cell membrane. The process is reversed to remove waste and carbon dioxide from inside the cell to the bloodstream.

Figure 25.3 Exchange of Materials Among Body Fluids

It is not difficult to obtain samples of body fluids like blood and urine. As a result, analysis of electrolytes, proteins, cholesterol, glucose, and other species is routinely carried out by medical professionals. Values obtained outside normal levels can be indications of disease or other abnormalities.

HEALTH NOTE

Color-coded test strips are used to measure the concentration of protein and other substances excreted in the urine. ©McGraw-Hill Education

PROBLEM 25.1

Using the data in Figure 25.2, what ions besides K^+ and HPO_4^{2-} are present in a much higher concentration in intracellular fluids compared to plasma and interstitial fluids?

PROBLEM 25.2

Use the chart in Figure 25.1 to answer the question. If a body contains 42 L of fluid, how many liters are contained in each of the following: (a) intracellular fluids; (b) interstitial fluids; (c) plasma?

25.2 Composition of the Blood

Blood flows through the body in a series of vessels that constitute part of the circulatory system. Figure 25.4 illustrates the three types of blood vessels in the circulatory system and how they are connected. Blood vessels that carry blood from the heart to the tissues are called **arteries,** whereas blood vessels that carry blood from the tissues to the heart are called **veins.** Arteries and veins are connected by a series of extremely small blood vessels called **capillaries.** Capillaries have very thin walls composed of single cells. The exchange of gases, nutrients, and waste from the blood to the interstitial fluid occurs across the walls of the capillaries.

Figure 25.4

Blood Vessels in the
Circulatory System

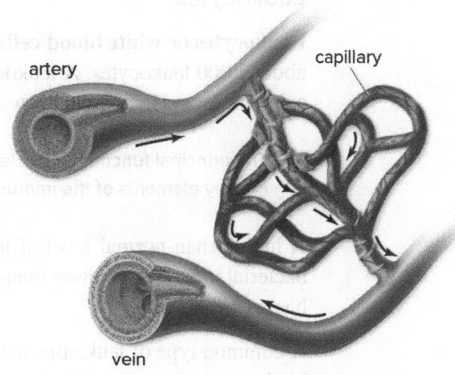

The blood serves three types of functions.

> [1] **Transport.** The blood carries gases (O_2 and CO_2), nutrients, waste, and hormones to or from tissues.
>
> [2] **Regulation.** The blood maintains a constant body temperature, and it helps to maintain both the pH and proper electrolyte concentrations in the body.
>
> [3] **Defense.** The blood contains the cells needed to fight infections and the factors needed for clotting.

25.2A Types of Blood Cells

Whole blood is a complex suspension of water containing dissolved electrolytes and organic compounds, together with insoluble blood cells. Of the 5 L of blood in an average human body, 55% is plasma and 45% is composed of three types of cells: erythrocytes (red blood cells), leukocytes (white blood cells), and platelets (thrombocytes).

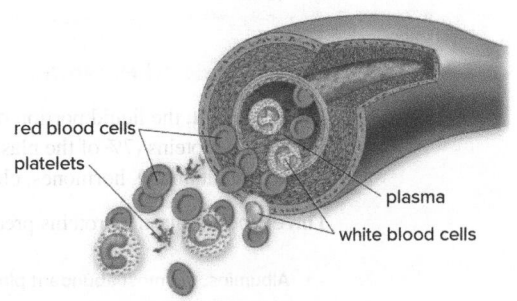

red blood cells

platelets

plasma

white blood cells

Erythrocytes

Erythrocytes or red blood cells are small, oval-shaped, flexible disks and the most numerous cells in the blood. An individual has on average five million erythrocytes per microliter. An erythrocyte has no nucleus, no DNA, no ribosomes, and no mitochondria. Erythrocytes are formed in bone marrow and survive for about 120 days.

> • Erythrocytes contain the protein hemoglobin (Section 21.7), which is used to transport oxygen to and carbon dioxide from tissues.

Anemia occurs when the number of erythrocytes is abnormally low. This condition can arise when too few erythrocytes are produced, or too many are destroyed or lost (as when a hemorrhage occurs).

Leukocytes

Leukocytes or white blood cells are minor components of the blood. Each microliter contains about 7,000 leukocytes. A leukocyte has a nucleus, as well as glucose, lipids, and proteins. They are synthesized in bone marrow and survive for three or four days in the bloodstream.

- The principal function of the leukocytes is to destroy bacteria and other foreign species, so they are key elements of the immune system.

A higher-than-normal level of leukocytes is observed when an individual is fighting an acute bacterial infection. A lower-than-normal level of leukocytes may be observed when an individual has a viral disease.

A common type of leukemia, a cancer that occurs in the blood or bone marrow, is characterized by the overproduction of leukocytes that do not mature and are unable to destroy invading foreign substances. An individual with leukemia has a lowered resistance to infections.

Platelets

Platelets or thrombocytes are more numerous than leukocytes, but considerably less numerous than erythrocytes. Each microliter of blood contains about 350,000 platelets. A platelet has no nucleus but it does contain protein and phospholipids. Platelets are formed in the bone marrow and spleen, and survive for five to nine days in the bloodstream.

- Platelets contain the machinery needed to initiate blood clot formation.

A low platelet count can result in excessive bleeding, whereas a high platelet count can lead to clot formation that can block key blood vessels, causing a heart attack or stroke.

PROBLEM 25.3

Compare erythrocytes, leukocytes, and platelets with regard to each of the following: (a) prevalence in the blood; (b) chief function; (c) presence or absence of a nucleus; (d) life span; (e) organ in which they are synthesized.

25.2B   Blood Plasma

Blood plasma, the liquid portion of the blood, is 92% water. The major dissolved substances in plasma are proteins (7% of the plasma volume), plus minor amounts of nutrients (carbohydrates, lipids, and vitamins), hormones, electrolytes, enzymes, and waste products such as urea.

Three types of plasma proteins predominate.

- Albumins, the most abundant plasma proteins, are the major contributors to the osmotic pressure of the plasma.
- Globulins play an important role in combating infections. Globulins complex with lipids, forming HDL and LDL particles (Section 19.8).
- Fibrinogen is a large protein needed for blood coagulation.

When a sample of whole blood is centrifuged, the plasma forms a light-colored liquid above the blood cells. The erythrocytes occupy a red layer at the bottom of the tube, and the leukocytes and platelets occupy a narrow band on top of the erythrocytes. Figure 25.5 summarizes the constituents of whole blood.

PROBLEM 25.4

Which of the following substances are present in whole blood? Which substances are present in blood plasma? (a) albumin; (b) leukocytes; (c) water; (d) electrolytes; (e) platelets.

Figure 25.5 The Components of Whole Blood

Plasma
Water
Proteins
• albumins
• globulins
• fibrinogen
Electrolytes
• sodium   • magnesium
• potassium   • chloride
• calcium   • bicarbonate
Other organic compounds
• nutrients (glucose, fatty acids, vitamins)
• gases (O_2 and CO_2)
• waste (urea)
• hormones

Cellular Components
Platelets (Thrombocytes)
White blood cells (Leukocytes)
Red blood cells (Erythrocytes)

Centrifuged whole blood contains a top layer with plasma, a bottom layer of red blood cells, and a narrow band in between with white blood cells and platelets.

25.2C Blood Serum and Clotting

When both the fibrinogen and blood cells are removed from whole blood, the liquid that remains is called **blood serum.** Because blood serum contains no fibrinogen, it is unable to clot.

A **blood clot** is a mesh of protein that traps blood cells, forming a plug that stops the flow of blood. Clotting is a life-saving mechanism. If blood did not clot when any blood vessel was injured, excessive blood loss would occur.

Clotting is a multistep mechanism that involves 12 clotting factors. When a blood vessel is injured, nearby blood vessels constrict and platelets collect at the site of injury. The enzyme thrombin converts the soluble protein fibrinogen, an inactive zymogen (Section 21.10), to the insoluble protein fibrin. Fibrin forms a mesh around a group of blood cells resulting in a clot that stops the flow of blood, as shown in Figure 25.6.

Vitamin K (Section 19.10) is needed for the synthesis of certain clotting factors, so a deficiency of vitamin K causes excessive bleeding.

Figure 25.6 Platelets and Blood Clotting

1. A blood vessel is injured.

2. Platelets form a plug.

platelet plug

3. The seal is reinforced by a clot of fibrin.

fibrin clot

red blood cell

thrombin

fibrinogen ⟶ **fibrin**

©Science Photo Library/Getty Images RF

Anticoagulants are compounds that inhibit clotting by interfering with one or more steps in the multistep clotting mechanism. **Heparin,** a polysaccharide derivative (Section 20.7), is a naturally occurring anticoagulant. **Warfarin** is a drug given to patients with certain heart ailments to minimize the possibility of abnormal clot formation that could block arteries. **Hemophilia** is a genetic disease in which an individual lacks one or more of the clotting factors.

PROBLEM 25.5

What is the difference between blood serum and blood plasma?

PROBLEM 25.6

What are the characteristics and causes of anemia, leukemia, and hemophilia, three diseases of the blood described in Section 25.2?

PROBLEM 25.7

What is the difference between fibrin and fibrinogen? Why is fibrinogen, and not fibrin, stored in the blood?

25.3 The Transport of Oxygen and Carbon Dioxide

The principal function of red blood cells is to transport gases—oxygen and carbon dioxide—using the protein **hemoglobin.** Blood that is rich in oxygen flows from the heart and lungs to capillaries. Capillaries have thin walls composed of a single layer of loosely spaced cells that allows the passage of water, gases, and other small molecules. The blood in capillaries also picks up waste carbon dioxide from the tissues and transports it to the lungs where it is expelled.

25.3A Hemoglobin

As we learned in Section 21.7, hemoglobin is a globular protein that consists of four polypeptide chains—two α subunits and two β subunits. Each polypeptide chain contains a heme unit, a complex organic compound that contains four nitrogen atoms complexed to an Fe^{2+} cation (Figure 25.7).

- Each Fe^{2+} cation reversibly complexes with O_2, so that hemoglobin can carry a maximum of four oxygen molecules.

Figure 25.7 Hemoglobin

heme

hemoglobin

Fe^{2+}

heme

The protein ribbon diagram for hemoglobin shows the two α and two β subunits in red and blue. Each subunit contains a heme with four N atoms complexed to an Fe^{2+} cation, depicted in the ball-and-stick model. A skeletal structure for heme appears in Section 21.7.

Figure 25.8 shows an end-on view of an oxygenated heme. The Fe cation and heme ring system occupy a plane, and the Fe atom is complexed above and below the plane with O_2 and an additional N atom from a histidine unit in the hemoglobin backbone. When one of the heme units binds oxygen, the quaternary structure of the protein changes somewhat, and the **remaining hemes have an *increased* affinity for binding oxygen.** This cooperative effect makes it easier for all four hemes to carry oxygen. Hemoglobin complexed with four oxygen molecules is bright red, in contrast to hemoglobin carrying fewer oxygens, which is darker red.

Figure 25.8   End-On View of a Heme Unit Bound to Oxygen

A nitrogen atom of a histidine ring in hemoglobin complexes with the Fe^{2+} as well.

Protein

When oxygen binds to hemoglobin, each Fe cation is complexed with six atoms—four N atoms in the heme, O_2, and an N atom of the amino acid histidine in the protein.

The amount of O_2 bound to hemoglobin depends on a variety of factors, including the partial pressure of oxygen in the environment. When the partial pressure of O_2 is high, as it is in inhaled air in the lungs, hemoglobin molecules are completely saturated with O_2 and all binding sites are occupied. In contrast, at lower partial pressures, only a fraction of heme units carry oxygen.

The amount of oxygen bound to hemoglobin is also affected by pH and CO_2 concentration. When muscles are actively working, H^+ ions and CO_2 are formed, decreasing the pH and increasing the amount of CO_2 present. Both factors increase the amount of O_2 *released* by hemoglobin, so that an active muscle has more O_2 available for metabolism than an inactive muscle.

PROBLEM 25.8

What color—bright red or dark red—is the blood withdrawn from a vein of a patient for a blood test? Explain your color choice.

25.3B   Delivering O_2 and Removing CO_2

To understand respiration, we must compare the partial pressures of O_2 and CO_2 in the blood and surrounding tissues. Gas transfer from one medium to another occurs by **diffusion,** a process in which the gas flows from a region of high concentration to a region of low concentration. The delivery of O_2 from the lungs to the tissues can thus be explained by examining the partial pressures of O_2 in various environments in the body (Figure 25.9).

Inhaled air is 21% O_2, thus giving it a partial pressure of 160 mm Hg (step [1]). Since the partial pressure of O_2 in the alveoli, small air sacs in the lungs, is less (100 mm Hg), O_2 flows from the inhaled air to the alveoli (step [2]). Blood flowing through capillaries that surround the alveoli arrives from the tissues with a lower partial pressure of O_2 (40 mm Hg), so O_2 flows from the alveoli to oxygenate the hemoglobin in the capillaries, raising the partial pressure of O_2 to 100 mm Hg.

When this blood is pumped by the heart to the tissues (step [3]), its partial pressure of O_2 is higher than the partial pressure of O_2 in the tissues (40 mm Hg), so O_2 flows across the capillary walls to the tissues. Blood leaving the capillaries has released a great deal of O_2, so the partial

Figure 25.9   Respiration and Partial Pressures of O$_2$ and CO$_2$

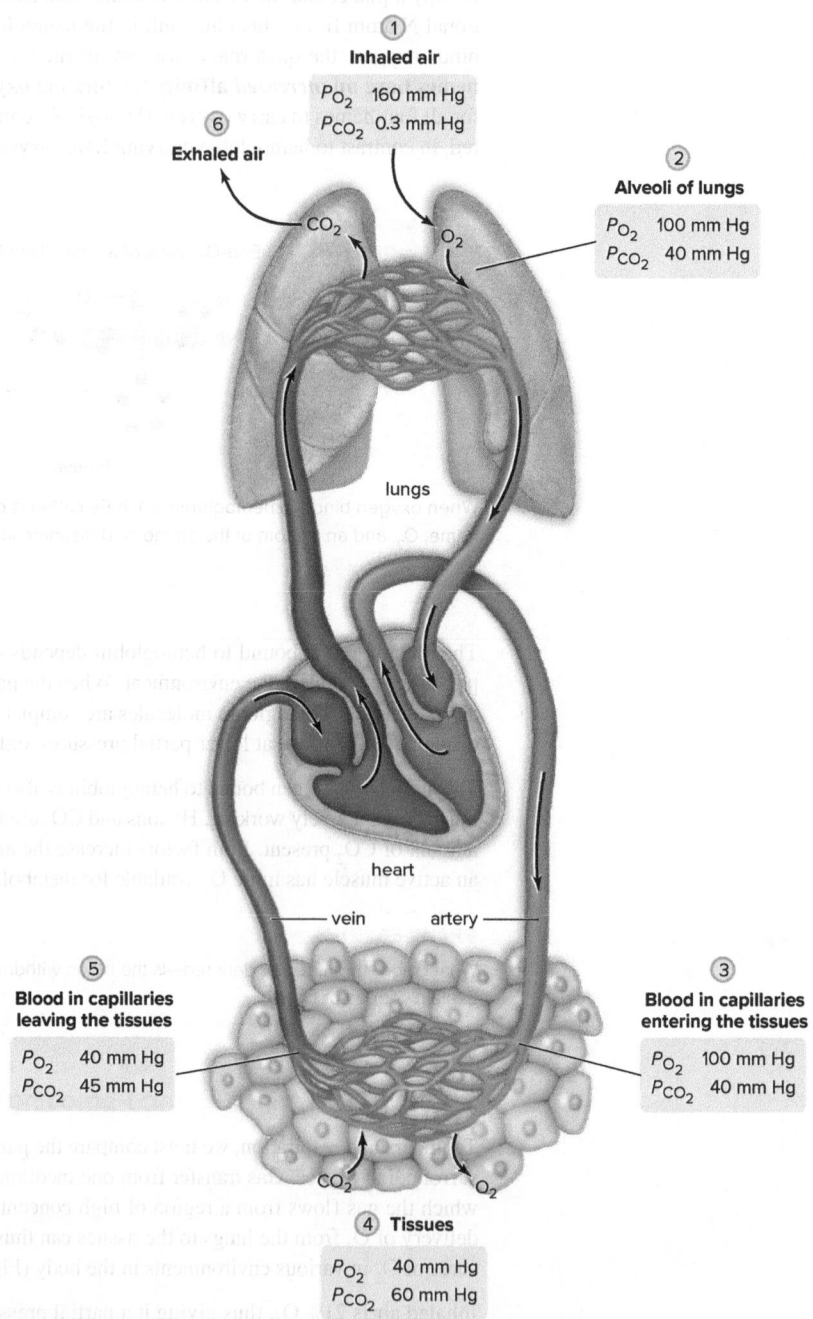

① **Inhaled air**

P_{O_2} 160 mm Hg
P_{CO_2} 0.3 mm Hg

② **Alveoli of lungs**

P_{O_2} 100 mm Hg
P_{CO_2} 40 mm Hg

⑥ **Exhaled air**

lungs

heart

vein   artery

⑤ **Blood in capillaries leaving the tissues**

P_{O_2} 40 mm Hg
P_{CO_2} 45 mm Hg

③ **Blood in capillaries entering the tissues**

P_{O_2} 100 mm Hg
P_{CO_2} 40 mm Hg

④ **Tissues**

P_{O_2} 40 mm Hg
P_{CO_2} 60 mm Hg

- O$_2$ flows from inhaled air → the alveoli → the capillaries → the tissues, from regions of higher partial pressure to regions of lower partial pressure (steps [1]–[4]).
- CO$_2$ flows from the tissues → the capillaries → the alveoli → exhaled air (steps [4]–[6]).

pressure of O_2 has decreased (40 mm Hg). When this blood is pumped to the alveoli of the lungs, O_2 from the alveoli flows into the blood in the capillaries and the process repeats (step [2]).

- O_2 always flows from a region of higher partial pressure to a region of lower partial pressure.

The diffusion of CO_2 proceeds in the opposite direction. Because CO_2 is released in metabolism, the partial pressure of CO_2 in the tissues is higher than the partial pressure of CO_2 in the capillaries, so CO_2 flows from the tissues to the capillaries (step [4]), increasing the partial pressure of CO_2 to 45 mm Hg (step [5]). When this blood is pumped to the lungs, the CO_2 first flows to the alveoli, and is then expelled to the atmosphere (step [6]), where its partial pressure is very low (0.3 mm Hg).

The partial pressure of O_2 in the air at high altitude is much lower than the partial pressure of O_2 at sea level. As a result, individuals who live at high altitude have less oxygen to deliver to tissues because the hemoglobin leaving the lungs is not completely saturated with oxygen. To counteract this effect, these individuals often have an increase in the number of erythrocytes, and thus more hemoglobin molecules that can pick up oxygen.

SAMPLE PROBLEM 25.1 UNDERSTANDING GAS FLOW DURING RESPIRATION

Which environment does **A** represent in the following diagram, the lungs or the tissues?

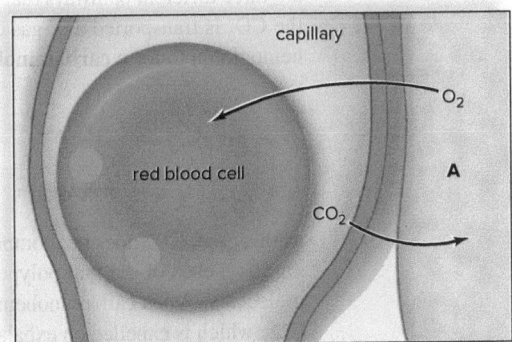

Analysis

Determine the direction of gas flow to identify **A.** In diffusion, a gas flows from a region of higher pressure to a region of lower pressure.

Solution

In the diagram, O_2 flows from **A** into the capillary while CO_2 flows in the opposite direction. Because the partial pressure of O_2 must be higher in **A** than the partial pressure of O_2 in the capillary, **A** represents the lungs, which are rich in O_2 from inhaled air.

PRACTICE PROBLEM 25.1

Which environment does **B** represent in the following diagram, the lungs or the tissues?

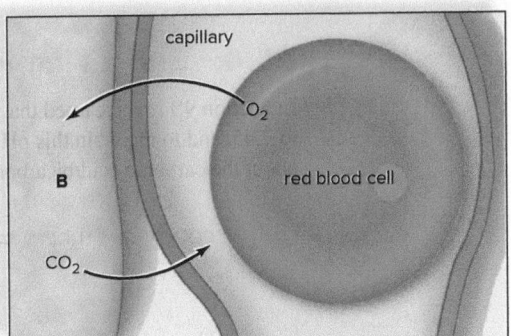

More Practice: Try Problem 25.36.

PROBLEM 25.9

Fill in the missing pressures (labeled **A** and **B**) in the following representation. Choose from 97 mm Hg or 38 mm Hg.

25.3C   How CO_2 Is Transported in the Blood

Unlike O_2 transport in the blood, which consists of a major pathway utilizing hemoglobin, there are three different pathways that remove the CO_2 produced metabolically in tissues. About 5% of the CO_2 is transported as a gas dissolved in blood plasma. A larger fraction of CO_2 reacts with hemoglobin to form **carbaminohemoglobin.**

$$Hb-NH_2 \;+\; CO_2 \;\rightleftharpoons\; Hb-\underset{H}{N}-\overset{O}{\underset{O^-}{C}} \;+\; H^+$$

hemoglobin   carbaminohemoglobin

In this case, CO_2 does not complex with the Fe^{2+} of hemoglobin; instead, it reacts with an NH_2 group on each of the four polypeptide chains. As a result, hemoglobin can carry up to four CO_2 molecules. When carbaminohemoglobin reaches the lungs it is re-converted to hemoglobin and CO_2, which is expelled on exhalation.

Finally, much of the CO_2 is converted to carbonic acid with the enzyme **carbonic anhydrase.** When carbonic acid reaches the lungs, it is re-converted to CO_2 and exhaled.

$$CO_2 \;+\; H_2O \;\underset{\text{carbonic anhydrase}}{\rightleftharpoons}\; H_2CO_3$$

carbonic acid

PROBLEM 25.10

How is each of the following involved in the transport of gases in the body: (a) diffusion; (b) carbaminohemoglobin; (c) alveoli; (d) carbonic anhydrase?

25.4   Buffers in the Body

In Section 9.11, we learned that the blood pH of a healthy individual lies in a narrow range, 7.35 to 7.45, and to maintain this pH range, the blood and other tissues are buffered. We also learned about the carbonic acid/bicarbonate (H_2CO_3/HCO_3^-) buffer in the blood.

$$CO_2(g) \;+\; H_2O(l) \;\rightleftharpoons\; H_2CO_3(aq) \;\overset{H_2O}{\rightleftharpoons}\; H_3O^+(aq) \;+\; HCO_3^-(aq)$$

carbonic acid   bicarbonate

principal buffer in the blood

Since carbonic acid is in equilibrium with CO_2 dissolved in the bloodstream, the amount of CO_2 is directly related to the H_3O^+ concentration and therefore the pH of the blood.

Two other buffers help to maintain a healthy pH range in the body—the phosphate buffer system and proteins. The phosphate buffer system occurs in intracellular fluid, and relies on the equilibrium between dihydrogen phosphate ($H_2PO_4^-$) and its conjugate base, hydrogen phosphate (HPO_4^{2-}). To maintain pH, hydrogen phosphate reacts with excess acid, and dihydrogen phosphate reacts with excess base.

$$H_2PO_4^- \; + \; H_2O \; \rightleftharpoons \; HPO_4^{2-} \; + \; H_3O^+$$

dihydrogen phosphate   hydrogen phosphate

Proteins in intracellular fluid and the blood can also act as buffers. The carboxylate anions (—COO^-) and ammonium cations (—NH_3^+) bonded to a protein backbone can react with excess acid and base, respectively, and thus maintain pH in the desired range (Figure 25.10).

Figure 25.10   Proteins as Buffers

COO⁻ → Acids react with the anionic carboxylates.

NH₃⁺ → Bases react with the cationic ammonium ions.

a protein buffer

We can use Le Châtelier's principle and the equation that shows the equilibrium between CO_2 and HCO_3^- to determine the effect of $[CO_2]$ and $[HCO_3^-]$ on the pH of the blood. As we learned in Section 9.11, when $[CO_2]$ increases due to a lower respiratory rate, equilibrium shifts to the right, $[H_3O^+]$ increases, and pH decreases. Alternatively, during heavy exercise, HCO_3^- reacts with the acids produced in metabolism, so $[HCO_3^-]$ decreases, $[H_3O^+]$ increases, and pH decreases. When the pH of the blood is lower than 7.35, **acidosis** results.

$$CO_2(g) \; + \; 2\,H_2O(g) \; \rightleftharpoons \; H_3O^+(aq) \; + \; HCO_3^-(aq)$$

Increasing $[CO_2]$...   ...or decreasing $[HCO_3^-]$...

...drives the equilibrium to the right, *increasing* $[H_3O^+] \longrightarrow$ *decreasing* pH.

When $[CO_2]$ decreases and more CO_2 is expelled, the equilibrium shifts to the left, $[H_3O^+]$ decreases, and pH increases. Also, when $[HCO_3^-]$ is elevated such as with excessive intake of antacids, $[H_3O^+]$ decreases, and pH increases. When the pH of the blood is greater than 7.45, **alkalosis** results.

$$CO_2(g) \; + \; 2\,H_2O(g) \; \rightleftharpoons \; H_3O^+(aq) \; + \; HCO_3^-(aq)$$

Decreasing $[CO_2]$...   ...or increasing $[HCO_3^-]$...

...drives the equilibrium to the left, *decreasing* $[H_3O^+] \longrightarrow$ *increasing* pH.

Table 25.1 lists some causes of acidosis and alkalosis.

Table 25.1 Acidosis and Alkalosis

Causes of Acidosis	Causes of Alkalosis
Decreased respiratory rate	Hyperventilation due to panic, excitement, or high fever
Advanced congestive heart failure	Excessive vomiting with loss of stomach acid
Advanced lung disease	Antacid overdose
Starvation	Excess aldosterone
Diabetes in poor control	
Excessive exercise	
Kidney failure	

PROBLEM 25.11

Using the diagram in Figure 25.10: (a) draw the product that results when a protein comes in contact with excess acid; (b) draw the product that results when a protein comes in contact with excess base.

PROBLEM 25.12

In what range would the blood pH of a heavy smoker with advanced emphysema fall: (a) less than 7.35; (b) 7.35–7.45; (c) greater than 7.45? Explain your choice.

25.5 The Blood–Brain Barrier

In contrast to the ready flow of many substances across membranes comprised of a single layer of loosely spaced cells of the capillaries in most of the body, the flow of materials into and out of the brain is much more restricted. The **blood–brain barrier** protects the brain from fluctuations in concentration of compounds in the blood, as well as the passage of unwanted substances into the brain.

> • **The blood–brain barrier is a tight layer of cells that forms the walls of the capillaries in the brain.**

In contrast to the walls of other capillaries that allow material to pass through the spaces between the cells, nothing can pass between the cells of the capillaries in the brain. As a result, all substances must pass through the cell membrane of the blood capillaries (Figure 25.11).

What can penetrate the blood–brain barrier? Small, uncharged molecules like O_2, CO_2, and H_2O can diffuse through the cell membrane. Glucose and certain amino acids are polar or ionic and these substances are transported across the membrane by specific transport proteins. Uncharged organic molecules that are readily soluble in the lipid bilayer of the cell membrane also can pass into the brain. Compounds in this category include caffeine, nicotine, heroin, and certain hormones. General anesthetics such as halothane ($CF_3CHClBr$) and sevoflurane [$(CF_3)_2CHOCH_2F$] are also weakly polar compounds that can penetrate the blood–brain barrier and pass into the brain.

halothane

sevoflurane

Figure 25.11

The Blood–Brain Barrier

Because ions are not soluble in the nonpolar lipids of the cell membrane, the blood–brain barrier is only slightly permeable to ions.

Some substances can cross the blood–brain barrier and flow both into and out of the brain, whereas other substances can be transported in one direction only. For example, L-dopa (Figure 15.3), a drug used to treat Parkinson's disease, can cross the blood–brain barrier in both directions.

L-dopa $\xrightarrow[\text{blood–brain barrier}]{\textcircled{1}\ \text{Travel across the}}$ $\xrightarrow[\text{Loss of } CO_2]{\textcircled{2}}$ dopamine

L-Dopa can enter and leave the brain.   Dopamine cannot enter the brain.

Once it crosses into the brain, it is converted to the neurotransmitter dopamine, which controls movement and emotions and is a key molecule for maintaining an individual's mental and physical health. Parkinson's disease is caused by the degeneration of the dopamine-producing neurons in the brain, and L-dopa thus serves as a supply of this essential neurotransmitter. Dopamine itself cannot be administered, because it can leave the brain, but it cannot cross the blood–brain barrier to enter the brain.

PROBLEM 25.13

(a) Which compound, morphine or heroin, is more polar? (b) Which compound can cross the blood–brain barrier more readily? (c) Explain why heroin is a more potent pain reliever than morphine.

morphine   heroin

PROBLEM 25.14

Explain why the noble gas xenon acts as a general anesthetic.

25.6 The Role of the Kidneys

The kidneys are vital organs that eliminate waste from body fluids and help to regulate fluid balance and electrolyte concentration. When blood flows to the kidneys, they filter away unwanted metabolic products, which are excreted in urine, and reabsorb water and essential nutrients such as glucose and amino acids (Figure 25.12). About 100 L of blood flows through the kidneys each day, and 1.5 L of urine is produced.

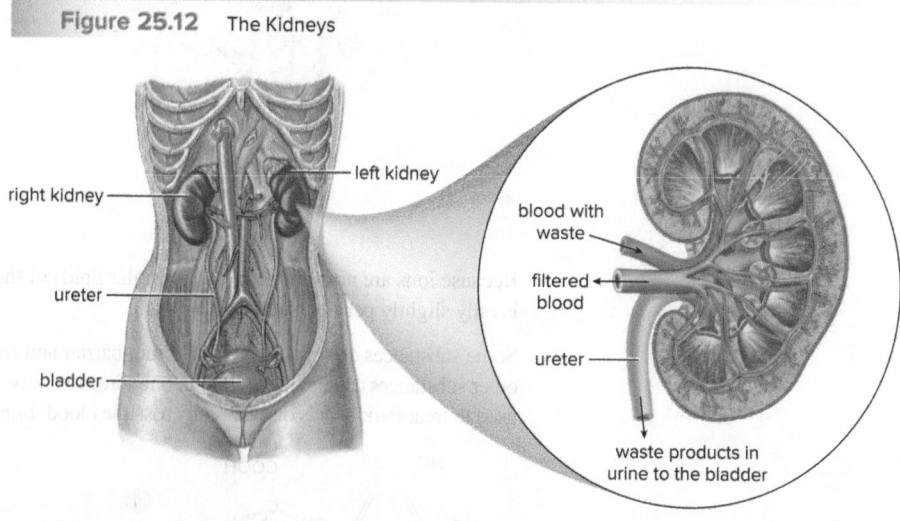

Figure 25.12   The Kidneys

25.6A How the Kidneys Filter the Blood

Each kidney is composed of about one million **nephrons** (Figure 25.13), which contain the machinery to purify the blood by a series of operations that involve filtration and reabsorption.

Blood is first pumped into a **glomerulus,** a group of tiny capillaries contained in **Bowman's capsule,** the head of a nephron. All of the water, electrolytes, and small molecules pass through the walls of the capillaries and are filtered into the urinary tubules. Only blood cells and large proteins are retained within the capillaries and remain in the blood.

Figure 25.13

Anatomy of a Nephron

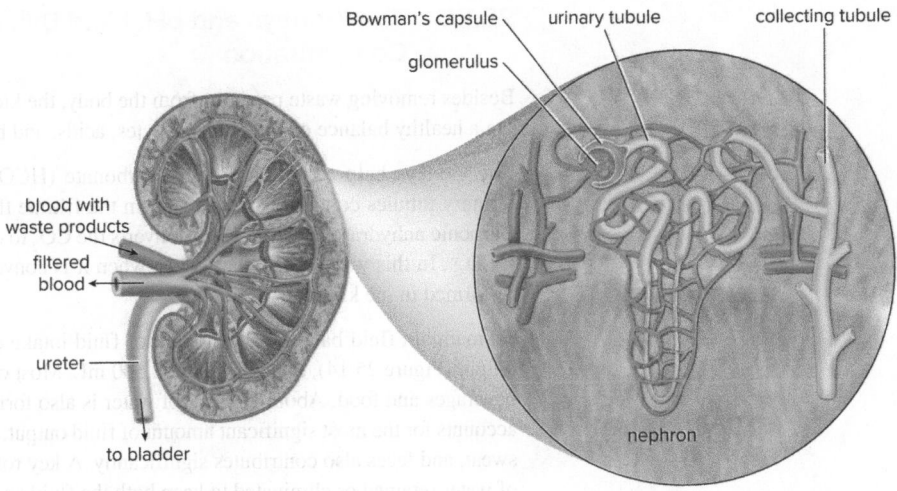

blood with
waste products

filtered
blood

ureter

to bladder

Bowman's capsule   urinary tubule   collecting tubule

glomerulus

nephron

The filtrate contains water and vital nutrients such as glucose and electrolytes in addition to waste products. The water and nutrients are then reabsorbed into the blood vessels surrounding the tubules. The remaining water and waste products form urine, which passes into the collecting tubule and is transported to the bladder by way of the ureter.

PROBLEM 25.15

Which of the following substances are contained in the filtrate that enters the urinary tubules of a nephron: (a) K^+; (b) erythrocytes; (c) glucose; (d) water; (e) waste products?

25.6B   Composition of Urine

About 96% of the urine excreted by the kidneys is water. The remaining 4% is composed of ions (Na^+, Ca^{2+}, Cl^-, HCO_3^-) and nitrogen-containing waste. The main organic waste product is **urea,** which is formed by the metabolism of amino acids (Section 24.9). Typically urine contains about 50 g of solutes—20 g of electrolytes and 30 g of nitrogen-containing waste.

The composition and volume of urine produced by an individual vary with fluid intake and exercise. In contrast to the blood, which has a very constant pH, the pH of urine can be anywhere between 4.6 and 8.0. The pH of the urine is related in part to the types of food in the diet. Eating more fruits and vegetables causes the urine to have a higher pH, whereas eating more protein causes the urine to have a lower pH.

The presence of other substances in the urine can be used to diagnose underlying conditions. For example, a higher-than-normal concentration of glucose and ketone bodies can indicate that an individual has diabetes.

PROBLEM 25.16

Creatine and creatinine are nitrogen-containing wastes present in low concentration in the urine. Why is each compound water soluble?

$(H_2N)_2C\!=\!O$
urea

creatine

creatinine

25.6C   The Kidneys and pH, Fluid Balance, and Electrolyte Concentration

Besides removing waste products from the body, the kidneys play an important role in maintaining a healthy balance of water, electrolytes, acids, and bases.

The kidneys help to maintain the bicarbonate (HCO_3^-) concentration in the blood buffers. Urinary tubules contain dissolved CO_2 in the filtrate that has passed through each glomerulus. Carbonic anhydrase (Section 25.3) converts the CO_2 to carbonic acid that dissociates into H^+ and HCO_3^-. In this way HCO_3^- that is lost when it is converted to CO_2 in the lungs and exhaled, is re-formed in the kidneys.

To maintain fluid balance, the amount of fluid intake each day must equal the amount of fluid output (Figure 25.14), typically about 2,500 mL. Most of the fluid ingested each day comes from beverages and food. About 250 mL of water is also formed from metabolism. Urine (1,500 mL) accounts for the most significant amount of fluid output. Loss of water through the skin and lungs, sweat, and feces also contributes significantly. A key role of the kidneys is to control the amount of water retained or eliminated to keep both the fluid and electrolyte concentration in balance.

Figure 25.14   Average Fluid Intake and Output

metabolism 10% (250 mL)
foods 30% (750 mL)
beverages 60% (1,500 mL)

2,500 mL

feces 4% (100 mL)
sweat 8% (200 mL)
via skin and lungs 28% (700 mL)
urine 60% (1,500 mL)

Average intake per day   Average output per day

Vasopressin (Figure 21.3), a hormone secreted by the pituitary gland, regulates the output of water from the body. When the concentration of solutes in the blood increases, indicating a shortage of water, more vasopressin is secreted. Vasopressin *increases* the amount of water retained and *decreases* the amount of urine output. Vasopressin is called the **antidiuretic hormone (ADH),** a hormone that reduces the volume of urine.

Aldosterone (Section 19.9) is a hormone responsible for proper Na^+ levels in the blood. Aldosterone causes an increase in the Na^+ concentration in the blood. As Na^+ concentration increases, more water is also absorbed, fluid is retained, and urine output *decreases*. In this way, the amount of urine excreted regulates both the water and electrolyte balance of an individual.

PROBLEM 25.17

What effect does a diuretic have on urine output?

PROBLEM 25.18

Individuals with a rare condition called diabetes insipidus do not produce vasopressin. How would urine output of an individual with diabetes insipidus compare with that of a healthy individual?

CHAPTER HIGHLIGHTS

KEY TERMS

Acidosis (25.4)

Albumins (25.2)

Aldosterone (25.6)

Alkalosis (25.4)

Anticoagulant (25.2)

Antidiuretic hormone (25.6)

Artery (25.2)

Blood–brain barrier (25.5)

Blood clot (25.2)

Blood plasma (25.2)

Blood serum (25.2)

Body fluids (25.1)

Bowman's capsule (25.6)

Capillary (25.2)

Carbaminohemoglobin (25.3)

Carbonic anhydrase (25.3)

Diffusion (25.3)

Erythrocyte (25.2)

Extracellular fluid (25.1)

Fibrin (25.2)

Fibrinogen (25.2)

Globulins (25.2)

Glomerulus (25.6)

Hemoglobin (25.3)

Hemophilia (25.2)

Heparin (25.2)

Interstitial fluid (25.1)

Intracellular fluid (25.1)

Kidneys (25.6)

Leukocyte (25.2)

Nephron (25.6)

Plasma (25.1)

Platelet (25.2)

Urea (25.6)

Vasopressin (25.6)

Vein (25.2)

Warfarin (25.2)

KEY CONCEPTS

1 **What are the major types of body fluids and how do their compositions compare? (25.1)**

- Body fluids are composed of intracellular fluids within cells and extracellular fluids outside cells.
- The most prevalent extracellular fluids are interstitial fluid between cells and plasma, the liquid portion of the blood. Both fluids contain Na^+ as the major cation and Cl^- as the major anion, but plasma has more protein.
- Intracellular fluid contains K^+ and HPO_4^{2-} as the major cation and anion, respectively, and more protein than plasma.

2 **What are the major components of the blood? (25.2)**

- Blood is composed of liquid plasma and insoluble blood cells.
- Plasma contains water, dissolved proteins, nutrients, hormones, electrolytes, enzymes, and wastes.
- There are three types of blood cells: erythrocytes (red blood cells), leukocytes (white blood cells), and platelets (thrombocytes).

3 **How does a blood clot form? (25.2)**

- When a blood vessel is injured, platelets collect at the site of injury and fibrinogen is converted to fibrin, which forms a mesh around the blood cells. The mechanism consists of many steps that include 12 clotting factors.

4 **How are oxygen and carbon dioxide transported in the bloodstream? (25.3)**

- Oxygen is transported from the lungs to the tissues by the heme units in the protein hemoglobin. Gas transfer occurs by the process of diffusion in a series of steps from regions of high partial pressure of O_2 to regions of low partial pressure.

- Carbon dioxide is transported in one of three ways. Some CO_2 travels from the tissues to the alveoli of the lungs as dissolved CO_2. A larger fraction reacts with hemoglobin to form carbaminohemoglobin. The largest fraction of CO_2 is converted to carbonic acid, which is converted to CO_2 with the enzyme carbonic anhydrase and expelled from the lungs.

5 **What role do buffers play in maintaining a narrow pH range in the blood? (25.4)**

- Three buffers help to maintain a healthy pH range in the body: the carbonic acid/bicarbonate buffer, the phosphate buffer system, and proteins.
- The principal buffer in the blood is the carbonic acid/ bicarbonate buffer. An increase in $[CO_2]$ or a decrease in $[HCO_3^-]$ causes an increase in $[H_3O^+]$, thus decreasing pH.
- A decrease in $[CO_2]$ or an increase in $[HCO_3^-]$ causes a decrease in $[H_3O^+]$, thus increasing pH.

6 **How does the blood–brain barrier protect the brain? (25.5)**

- The blood–brain barrier forms a tight layer of cells on the walls of brain capillaries.
- To cross the blood–brain barrier, a substance must pass through the nonpolar lipid membrane of the capillaries. Small molecules like O_2, CO_2, and H_2O as well as uncharged organic molecules can pass through the membrane. Specific transport proteins move glucose and certain amino acids across the membrane.

7 **How do the kidneys remove waste from the blood? (25.6)**

- The nephrons in the kidneys remove waste products from the blood. Water, electrolytes, and small molecules are filtered into the urinary tubules. Water and vital nutrients are reabsorbed into the bloodstream. Of the 100 L of liquid that passes through the kidneys each day, only 1.5 L ends up in urine.

8 **What are the main constituents of urine? (25.6)**
- Urine is mostly water (96%). The remaining 4% consists of about 50 g of solutes—primarily ions and nitrogen-containing waste. The main organic waste product is urea.

9 **How do the kidneys help to maintain a healthy pH, as well as achieve fluid and electrolyte balance in the body? (25.6)**
- The kidneys supply HCO_3^- to replace the HCO_3^- that is converted to CO_2 and expelled from the lungs.
- The kidneys control the amount of water retained or eliminated to keep both the fluid and electrolyte concentration in balance.

PROBLEMS

Body Fluids

25.19 List the three principal body fluids and the approximate percentage of body water contained in each type.

25.20 List the major ions present inside and outside of cells.

25.21 The bar graphs illustrate the concentrations of a cation and an anion in a body fluid. Which graph corresponds to interstitial fluid and which corresponds to intracellular fluid?

25.22 The bar graphs illustrate the concentration of a particular ion in either blood plasma or intracellular fluid. Indicate which of these fluids is shown in each column of the graphs.

Composition of the Blood

25.23 Consider the representations **A, B,** and **C** for the three types of blood cells. (a) Identify each type of blood cell. (b) Which type is present in the highest concentration? (c) Which type is present in the lowest concentration?

25.24 Fill in each box with the appropriate component of the blood.

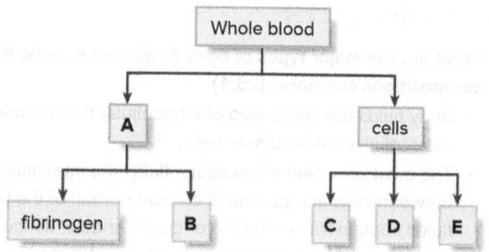

25.25 What type(s) of blood cells is (are) described with each statement? Choose from erythrocytes, leukocytes, or platelets.
- a. This type of blood cell has no nucleus.
- b. This type of blood cell survives in the bloodstream for the longest period of time.
- c. This type of blood cell is a key element in the immune system.
- d. This type of blood cell carries hemoglobin.
- e. This type of blood cell contains the machinery needed for clot formation.

25.26 What types of blood cells are involved in each of the following diseases: (a) excessive bleeding; (b) leukemia; (c) anemia?

25.27 For each substance, indicate if it is present in [1] whole blood, [2] blood plasma, or [3] blood serum. One or more answers may apply.
  a. globulins   c. erythrocytes
  b. fibrinogen   d. urea

25.28 What role is exhibited by each type of plasma protein: (a) fibrinogen; (b) globulins; (c) albumins?

25.29 Answer each question with a type of blood vessel: [1] artery; [2] vein; [3] capillary. (a) Which type of blood vessel carries blood from the tissues to the heart? (b) Which type carries blood that is rich in oxygen? (c) Which type contains a thin cell wall that allows the passage of water and small molecules?

25.30 What is the purpose of flushing an IV line with heparin after administering a medication intravenously?

25.31 How does each of the following substances play a role in blood clotting: (a) vitamin K; (b) fibrinogen; (c) platelets; (d) thrombin?

25.32 What advantages does the dimpled shape of a red blood cell offer over a completely spherical cell?

Oxygen and Carbon Dioxide Transport

25.33 Where does O_2 bind to hemoglobin? Where does CO_2 bind to hemoglobin?

25.34 How is the amount of O_2 bound to hemoglobin affected by each of the following: (a) the partial pressure of O_2; (b) the partial pressure of CO_2; (c) pH?

25.35 What three mechanisms are used for CO_2 transport from the tissues to the lungs?

25.36 Which of the following locations corresponds to each set of partial pressures of O_2 and CO_2: [1] inhaled air; [2] capillaries at the arterial end; [3] capillaries at the venous end; [4] tissues?

	P_{O_2} (mm Hg)	P_{CO_2} (mm Hg)
a.	40	60
b.	100	40
c.	160	0.3
d.	40	45

25.37 How does diffusion play a role in the transfer of O_2 from the air to the tissues?

25.38 How does living at high altitude affect both the number of O_2 molecules carried by each hemoglobin and the number of erythrocytes in the blood?

Buffers

25.39 Describe the three main buffer systems in the body.

25.40 What effect is observed on the pH of the blood in each of the following cases?
  a. $[HCO_3^-]$ decreases.   c. $[CO_2]$ increases.
  b. $[HCO_3^-]$ increases.   d. $[CO_2]$ decreases.

25.41 (a) List two causes that might decrease blood pH below 7.35. (b) List two causes that might increase blood pH greater than 7.45.

25.42 If an individual has decreased acid secretion in urine due to renal failure, how is the pH of the blood affected?

25.43 Explain how abnormally fast respiration—that is, hyperventilation—affects the pH of the blood.

25.44 The dihydrogen phosphate/hydrogen phosphate ($H_2PO_4^-$/HPO_4^{2-}) buffer helps to maintain the pH of body fluids. Write the equations that illustrate how this buffer reacts with excess acid (H_3O^+) and excess base (OH^-).

The Blood–Brain Barrier

25.45 Which of the following compounds is more likely to be a general anesthetic? Explain your choice.

a.   b.

25.46 Explain why nicotine can cross the blood–brain barrier.

25.47 Why can't an individual with Parkinson's disease be given dopamine to relieve his or her symptoms?

The Kidneys and Urine Formation

25.48 What are three important functions of the kidneys?

25.49 When blood flows through the glomerulus, which substances are retained in the capillaries and which become part of the filtrate: (a) sodium; (b) sulfate; (c) leukocytes; (d) platelets; (e) urea?

25.50 How does vasopressin affect the volume of urine excreted?

25.51 How does aldosterone affect the volume of urine excreted?

25.52 Why does the pH of urine vary greatly, but the pH of the blood in a healthy individual is always in a narrow range?

Index

Page numbers followed by *f* and *t* indicate figures and tables, respectively.

A

Acidosis, 13–14, 14*t*
ADH (antidiuretic hormone), 18
Albumins, 6, 7*f*
Aldosterone, 18
Alkalosis, 13–14, 14*t*
Altitude, 11
Anemia, 5
Anions, in body fluids, 3
Anticoagulants, 8
Antidiuretic hormone (ADH), 18
Arteries, 4, 5*f*

B

Bicarbonate, in body fluids, 3*f*
Bicarbonate/carbonate buffer, 12
Blood
    buffers in, 12–14
    composition of, 4–8, 7*f*
    flow of, 4
    functions of, 5
    gas transport in, 8–12
    pH of, 12–14
    renal filtration of, 16–17
Blood–brain barrier, 14–16, 15*f*
Blood cells, 5–6, 7*f*
Blood clot, 7
Blood clotting, 7–8, 7*f*
Blood plasma, 2–4, 2*f*, 3*f*, 6, 7*f*
Blood serum, 7
Blood transfusion, 1
Blood vessels, 4, 5*f*
Body fluids, 1–21. *See also* Blood
    components of, 3, 3*f*
    definition of, 2
    dissolved substances in, 2–3
    distribution of, 2, 2*f*
    intracellular versus extracellular, 2
    renal regulation of, 16–18
    samples and analysis, 4
    transport and exchange, 4, 4*f*
    types of, 2–4
Bowman's capsule, 16, 17*f*
Brain, blood–brain barrier and, 14–16, 15*f*
Buffers, 12–14, 13*f*

C

Caffeine, 14
Calcium ions, in body fluids, 3*f*
Capillaries, 4, 5*f*
Carbaminohemoglobin, 12
Carbonate, in buffer, 12
Carbon dioxide
    blood/blood gases, 8, 12
    partial pressure of, 9–12, 10*f*
    respiratory exchange of, 9–12, 10*f*
    transport in blood, 8, 12
Carbonic acid, in blood, 12
Carbonic anhydrase, 12
Cations, in body fluids, 3, 3*f*
Chloride ion, 3, 3*f*
Clotting, 7–8, 7*f*
Creatine, 17
Creatinine, 17

D

Diffusion, 9–12
Dihydrogen phosphate, 13
L-Dopa, 15
Dopamine, 15

E

Electrolytes
    in body fluids, 3
    in plasma, 3, 7*f*
    renal regulation of, 18
Erythrocytes, 5, 7*f*
Extracellular fluid, 2–4, 3*f*

F

Fibrin, 7, 7*f*
Fibrinogen, 6, 7, 7*f*
Filtration, renal, 16–17
Fluid balance, 18, 18*f*

G

Gas(es)
    partial pressure of, 9–12, 10*f*
    respiratory exchange of, 9–12, 10*f*
    solubility of, 2–3
    transport in blood, 8–12
Globulins, 6, 7*f*
Glomerulus, 16, 17*f*
Glucose
    transport across blood–brain barrier, 14
    in urine, 17

H

Halothane, 14
Heme, 8–9, 8*f*, 9*f*
Hemoglobin, 5, 8–9
    carbon dioxide and, 12
    structure of, 8, 8*f*
Hemophilia, 8
Heparin, 8
Heroin, 14, 16
Hydrogen phosphate, 3, 3*f*, 13

I

Interstitial fluid, 2–4, 2*f*, 3*f*
Intracellular fluid, 2–4, 2*f*, 3*f*
Ions, in body fluids, 3, 3*f*
Iron, in hemoglobin, 8–9, 8*f*, 9*f*

K

Ketone bodies, 17
Kidney(s)
    anatomy of, 16*f*
    blood filtration by, 16–17
    body fluid regulation by, 16–18

L

Le Châtelier's principle, 13
Leukemia, 6
Leukocytes, 5–6, 7*f*
"Like dissolves like," 2

M

Magnesium ions, in body fluids, 3*f*
Morphine, 16

N

Nephron, 16–17, 17*f*
Nicotine, 14
Nitrogen-containing waste, 17

O

Oxygen
    partial pressure of, 9–12, 10*f*
    respiratory exchange of, 9–12, 10*f*
    transport in blood, 8–12

P

Parkinson's disease, 15
Partial pressure, 9–12, 10*f*
pH
    of blood, 12–14
    renal regulation of, 18
    of urine, 17
Phosphate buffer, 13
Plasma, 2–4, 2*f*, 3*f*, 6, 7*f*
Platelets, 5–6, 7*f*
Potassium ions, in body fluids, 3, 3*f*
Proteins
    as buffers, 13, 13*f*
    in human body, 3
    plasma, 3, 6, 7*f*

R

Red blood cells, 5, 7*f*
Respiration, gas exchange in, 9–12, 10*f*

S

Serum, 7
Sevoflurane, 14
Sodium
    in body fluids, 3, 3*f*
    renal regulation of, 18
Solubility
    in body fluids, 2–3
    "like dissolves like," 2
Sulfate ions, 3*f*

T

Thrombin, 7, 7*f*
Thrombocytes, 5–6, 7*f*

U

Urea, 17
Urinalysis, 4, 4*mn*
Urine, 16–18
    composition of, 17–18
    pH of, 17

V

Vasopressin, 18
Veins, 4, 5*f*
Vitamin K, 7

W

Warfarin, 8
Water, renal regulation of, 18
White blood cells, 5–6, 7*f*
Whole blood, 5, 6, 7*f*

Appendix A

Useful Mathematical Concepts

Three common mathematical concepts are needed to solve many problems in chemistry:

- Using scientific notation
- Determining the number of significant figures
- Using a scientific calculator

Scientific Notation

To write numbers that contain many leading zeros (at the beginning) or trailing zeros (at the end), scientists use **scientific notation.**

- In scientific notation, a number is written as $y \times 10^x$, where y (the coefficient) is a number between 1 and 10, and x is an exponent, which can be any positive or negative whole number.

To convert a standard number to scientific notation:

1. Move the decimal point to give a number between 1 and 10.
2. Multiply the result by 10^x, where x is the number of places the decimal point was moved.
   - If the decimal point is moved to the **left,** x **is positive.**
   - If the decimal point is moved to the **right,** x **is negative.**

$$2822. \quad = \quad 2.822 \times 10^3 \qquad \text{the number of places the decimal point was moved to the left}$$

Move the decimal point three places to the left.

$$0.000\,004\,5 \quad = \quad 4.5 \times 10^{-6} \qquad \text{the number of places the decimal point was moved to the right}$$

Move the decimal point six places to the right.

To convert a number in scientific notation to a standard number, use the value of x in 10^x to indicate the number of places to move the decimal point in the coefficient.

- Move the decimal point to the right when x is positive.
- Move the decimal point to the left when x is negative.

$$2.521 \times 10^2 \qquad 2.521 \quad \dashrightarrow \quad 252.1$$

Move the decimal point two places to the right.

$$2.68 \times 10^{-2} \qquad 002.68 \quad \dashrightarrow \quad 0.0268$$

Move the decimal point two places to the left.

Table A.1 shows how several numbers are written in scientific notation.

Table A.1 Numbers in Standard Form and Scientific Notation

Number	Scientific Notation
26,200	2.62×10^4
0.006 40	6.40×10^{-3}
3,000,000	3×10^6
0.000 000 139	1.39×10^{-7}
2,000.20	2.00020×10^3

Often, numbers written in scientific notation must be multiplied or divided.

- To multiply two numbers in scientific notation, *multiply* the coefficients and *add* the exponents in the powers of 10.

Add exponents.
$(8 + 3)$

$$(3.0 \times 10^8) \quad \times \quad (2.0 \times 10^3) \quad = \quad 6.0 \times 10^{11}$$

Multiply coefficients.
(3.0×2.0)

- To divide two numbers in scientific notation, *divide* the coefficients and *subtract* the exponents in the powers of 10.

Divide coefficients. $\dfrac{6.0 \times 10^6}{2.0 \times 10^{10}}$ Subtract exponents. $= 3.0 \times 10^{-4}$
$(6.0 \div 2.0)$ $(6 - 10)$

Table A.2 shows the result of multiplying or dividing several numbers written in scientific notation.

Table A.2 Calculations Using Numbers Written in Scientific Notation

Calculation	Answer
$(3.5 \times 10^3) \times (2.2 \times 10^{22}) =$	7.7×10^{25}
$(3.5 \times 10^3) \div (2.2 \times 10^{22}) =$	1.6×10^{-19}
$(3.5 \times 10^3) \times (2.2 \times 10^{-10}) =$	7.7×10^{-7}
$(3.5 \times 10^3) \div (2.2 \times 10^{-10}) =$	1.6×10^{13}

Significant Figures

Whenever we measure a number, there is a degree of uncertainty associated with the result. The last number (farthest to the right) is an estimate. **Significant figures** are all of the digits in a measured number including one estimated digit. How many significant figures are contained in a number?

- All nonzero digits are always significant.
- A zero *counts* as a significant figure when it occurs between two nonzero digits, or at the end of a number with a decimal point.
- A zero does *not* count as a significant figure when it occurs at the beginning of a number, or at the end of a number that does not have a decimal point.

Table A.3 lists the number of significant figures in several quantities.

Table A.3 Examples Illustrating Significant Figures

Quantity	Number of Significant Figures	Quantity	Number of Significant Figures
1,267 g	Four	203 L	Three
24,345 km	Five	6.10 atm	Three
1.200 mg	Four	0.3040 g	Four
0.000 001 mL	One	1,200 m	Two

The number of significant figures must also be taken into account in calculations. To avoid reporting a value with too many digits, we must often **round off the number** to give the correct number of significant figures. Two rules are used in rounding off numbers.

- If the first number that must be dropped is 4 or fewer, drop it and all remaining numbers.
- If the first number that must be dropped is 5 or greater, *round the number up* by adding 1 to the last digit that will be retained.

To round 63.854 to two significant figures:

These digits must be retained.

63.854   first digit to be dropped

These digits must be dropped.

- Since the first digit to be dropped is 8 (5 or greater), add 1 to the first digit to its left.
- The number 63.854 rounded to two digits is **64**.

Table A.4 gives other examples of rounding off numbers.

Table A.4 Rounding Off Numbers

Original Number	Rounded to	Rounded Number
15.2538	Two places	15
15.2538	Three places	15.3
15.2538	Four places	15.25
15.2538	Five places	15.254

The first number to be dropped is indicated in red in each original number.

The number of significant figures in the answer of a problem depends on the type of mathematical calculation—multiplication (and division) or addition (and subtraction).

> • In multiplication and division, the answer has the same number of significant figures as the original number with the *fewest* significant figures.

five significant figures — 5.5067 × 2.6 = 14.31742 rounded to **14**

two significant figures ⤴   first digit to be dropped ⤴

The answer must contain only **two** significant figures.

> • In addition and subtraction, the answer has the same number of decimal places as the original number with the *fewest* decimal places.

two digits after the decimal point ⤵   10.17 + 3.5 = 13.67 rounded to **13.7**

one digit after the decimal point ⤴

last significant digit   The answer can have only **one** digit after the decimal point.

Table A.5 lists other examples of calculations that take into account the number of significant figures.

Table A.5 Calculations Using Significant Figures

Calculation	Answer
3.2 × 699 =	2,236.8 rounded to **2,200**
4.66892 ÷ 2.13 =	2.191981221 rounded to **2.19**
25.3 + 3.668 + 29.1004 =	58.0684 rounded to **58.1**
95.1 − 26.335 =	68.765 rounded to **68.8**

Using a Scientific Calculator

A scientific calculator is capable of carrying out more complicated mathematical functions than simple addition, subtraction, multiplication, and division. For example, these calculators allow the user to convert a standard number to scientific notation, as well as readily determine the logarithm (log) or antilogarithm (antilog) of a value. Carrying out these operations is especially important in determining pH or hydronium ion concentration in Chapter 9.

Described in this section are the steps that can be followed in calculations with some types of calculators. Consult your manual if these steps do not produce the stated result.

Converting a Number to Scientific Notation

To convert a number, such as 1,200, from its standard form to scientific notation:

- Enter 1200.
- Press 2nd and then SCI.
- The number will appear as 1.2^{03}, indicating that $1,200 = 1.2 \times 10^3$.

Entering a Number Written in Scientific Notation

To enter a number written in scientific notation with a positive exponent, such as 1.5×10^8:

- Enter 1.5.
- Press EE.
- Enter 8.
- The number will appear as 1.5^{08}, indicating that it is equal to 1.5×10^8.

To enter a number written in scientific notation with a negative exponent, such as 3.5×10^{-4}:

- Enter 3.5.
- Press EE.
- Enter 4.
- Press CHANGE SIGN $(+ \rightarrow -)$.
- The number will appear as 3.5^{-04}, indicating that it is equal to 3.5×10^{-4}.

Taking the Logarithm of a Number: Calculating pH from a Known [H₃O⁺]

Since $pH = -\log [H_3O^+]$, we must learn how to calculate logarithms on a calculator in order to determine pH values. To determine the pH from a known hydronium ion concentration, say $[H_3O^+] = 1.8 \times 10^{-5}$, carry out the following steps:

- Enter 1.8×10^{-5} (Enter 1.8; press EE; enter 5; press CHANGE SIGN). The number 1.8^{-05} will appear.
- Press LOG.
- Press CHANGE SIGN $(+ \rightarrow -)$.
- The number 4.744 727 495 will appear. Because the coefficient, 1.8, contains two significant figures, round the logarithm to 4.74, which has two digits to the right of the decimal point. Thus, the pH of the solution is 4.74.

Taking the Antilogarithm of a Number: Calculating [H₃O⁺] from a Known pH

Since $[H_3O^+] = \text{antilog}(-pH)$, we must learn how to calculate an antilogarithm—that is, the number that has a given logarithm value—using a calculator. To determine the hydronium ion concentration from a given pH, say 3.91, carry out the following steps:

- Enter 3.91.
- Press CHANGE SIGN $(+ \rightarrow -)$.
- Press 2nd and then LOG.
- The number 0.000 123 027 will appear. To convert this number to scientific notation, press 2nd and SCI.
- The number $1.230\,268\,771^{-04}$ will appear, indicating that $[H_3O^+] = 1.230\,268\,771 \times 10^{-4}$. Because the original pH (a logarithm) has two digits to the right of the decimal point, the answer must have two significant figures in the coefficient in scientific notation. As a result, $[H_3O^+] = 1.2 \times 10^{-4}$.

Table A.6 lists pH values that correspond to given [H$_3$O$^+$] values. You can practice using a calculator to determine pH or [H$_3$O$^+$] by entering a value in one column, following the listed steps, and then checking to see if you obtain the corresponding value in the other column.

Table A.6 The pH of a Solution from a Given Hydronium Ion Concentration [H$_3$O$^+$]

[H$_3$O$^+$]	pH	[H$_3$O$^+$]	pH
1.8×10^{-10}	9.74	4.0×10^{-13}	12.40
3.8×10^{-2}	1.42	6.6×10^{-4}	3.18
5.0×10^{-12}	11.30	2.6×10^{-9}	8.59
4.2×10^{-7}	6.38	7.3×10^{-8}	7.14

Appendix B

Answers to Selected In-Chapter and End-of-Chapter Problems

CHAPTER 1 PRACTICE PROBLEMS

1.1 a. pure substance   b. mixture
1.2 a. megaliter   b. millisecond   c. centigram   d. deciliter
1.3 a. 4   c. 2   e. 3   g. 7   i. 4
     b. 5   d. 4   f. 3   h. 2   j. 5
1.4 a. 1.3   b. 0.0025   c. 3,800
1.5 a. 37   b. 0.000 007 93   c. 32   d. 3,100
1.6 a. 28.0 cm   b. 127.5 mL   c. 30. mg   d. 2.08 s
1.7 a. 9.32×10^4 c. 6.78×10^6 e. 4.52×10^{12}
     b. 7.25×10^{-4} d. 3.0×10^{-5} f. 2.8×10^{-11}
1.8 a. 6,500   c. 0.037 80   e. 2,221,000
     b. 0.000 032 6   d. 104,000,000   f. 0.000 000 000 45
1.9 a. $\dfrac{0.621 \text{ mi}}{1 \text{ km}}$ $\dfrac{1 \text{ km}}{0.621 \text{ mi}}$ c. $\dfrac{454 \text{ g}}{1 \text{ lb}}$ $\dfrac{1 \text{ lb}}{454 \text{ g}}$
     b. $\dfrac{1000 \text{ mm}}{1 \text{ m}}$ $\dfrac{1 \text{ m}}{1000 \text{ mm}}$ d. $\dfrac{1000 \text{ μg}}{1 \text{ mg}}$ $\dfrac{1 \text{ mg}}{1000 \text{ μg}}$
1.10 a. 250 dL   b. 1,130 L   c. 81 cm   d. 100 mm
1.11 a. 1.91 km   b. 0.7 L   c. 140 cm
1.12 4 tablets
1.13 a. 13 mL   b. 420 mg
1.14 83.3 °F or 302 K
1.15 a,b,c: **B**
1.16 7.13 g

CHAPTER 1 PROBLEMS

1.1 Naturally occurring: ice, blood; synthetic: gloves, mask, plastic syringe, stainless steel needle
1.3 This is a chemical change because the particles on the left and right are different.
1.5 a,b,c: mixture   d. pure substance
1.7 1,000,000,000 nm
1.9 a. 3 cL   b. 1 μg   c. 5 km   d. 2 mL
1.11 9.8×10^{-5} g/dL
1.13 a. 0.46 mL   b. 460 μL
1.15 a. 68 °F   b. 66 °C   c. 77 °F   d. 348 K
1.17 7.61 L
1.19 a. element   b. compound   c,d: mixture
1.21

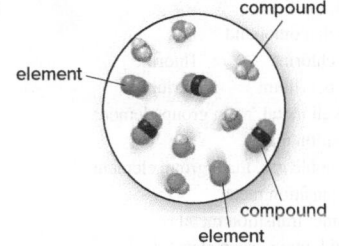

1.23 a. **D**   b. **B**
1.25 a. physical   b. chemical   c. physical
1.27 This is a physical change, because the compound CO_2 is unchanged in this transition. The same "particles" exist at the beginning and end of the process.
1.29 a. 76.5 °F   b. three   c. 24.7 °C
1.31 a. 10 cloves: exact number   b. 5 puppies: exact number
     2 tablespoons: inexact number   10 1b: inexact number
1.33 a. 5 dL   b. 10 mg   c. 5 cm   d. 10 Ms
1.35 a. 4   b. 2   c. 3   d. 2   e. 3   f. 4   g. 4   h. 2
1.37 a. 25,400   d. 0.123
     b. 1,250,000   e. 195
     c. 0.001 27   f. 197
1.39 a. 22   b. 21.97   c. 5.4   d. 50.1   e. 100   f. 1,044
1.41 a. 1.234×10^3 g   c. 5.244×10^6 L   e. 4.4×10^4 km
     b. 1.62×10^{-5} m   d. 5.62×10^{-3} g
1.43 a. 340,000,000   b. 0.000 058 22   c. 300   d. 0.000 000 068 6
1.45 a. 4.44×10^3 b. 5.6×10^{-5} c. 1.3×10^8 d. 9.8×10^{-4}
1.47 a. 4.00×10^{-4} g   c. 8.0×10^{-5} g
     b. 2×10^{-3} g   d. 3.4×10^3 mg
1.49 52.3 kg
1.51 a. 1,500 g   b. 3.3 lb   c. 53 oz
1.53 0.060 mg mercury
1.55 a. 130 cm   b. 1.4 L   c. 99.9 °F
1.57 $190 U.S.
1.59 a. 127 °F or 326 K   b. 177 °C or 450. K
1.61 a. −10 °C   b. −50 °F
1.63 a. **A** = corn oil; **B** = water; **C** = corn syrup
     b. **A** 28 g; **B** 50. g; **C** 137 g
1.65 a.   b.

1.67 1.01 g/mL
1.69 0.974 kg
1.71 a. heptane   b. olive oil   c. water   d. water
1.73 a. 0.186 g/dL   b. 1,860 mg/L
1.75 3 tablets
1.77 a. 1.9 kg   b. 4.2 lb
1.79 a. $0.67   b. $1.00
1.81 784.6 doses, so 784 full doses
1.83 16 tablets

1.85 1.0×10^2 mg
1.87 23, normal range
1.89 2 tablets (2.4)
1.91 0.15 g

CHAPTER 2 PRACTICE PROBLEMS

2.1 a. 4 hydrogens, 1 carbon   c. 6 hydrogens, 2 carbons, 1 oxygen
    b. 3 hydrogens, 1 nitrogen
2.2 $C_8H_{10}N_4O_2$
2.3 a. 9   b. 9   c. fluorine
2.4

Atomic Number	Element	Protons	Electrons
a. 2	Helium	2	2
b. 11	Sodium	11	11
c. 20	Calcium	20	20
d. 47	Silver	47	47
e. 78	Platinum	78	78

2.5 a. 4 protons and 5 neutrons
    b. atomic number = 4, mass number = 9
    c. beryllium
2.6

	Protons	Neutrons $(A - Z)$	Electrons
a.	17	18 (35 − 17)	17
b.	14	14 (28 − 14)	14
c.	92	146 (238 − 92)	92

2.7

	Atomic Number	Mass Number	Protons	Neutrons	Electrons
a.	6	13	6	7	6
b.	51	121	51	70	51

2.8

		Protons	Electrons	Atomic Number	Mass Number
With 12 neutrons:	$^{24}_{12}$Mg	12	12	12	12 + 12 = 24
With 13 neutrons:	$^{25}_{12}$Mg	12	12	12	12 + 13 = 25
With 14 neutrons:	$^{26}_{12}$Mg	12	12	12	12 + 14 = 26

2.9 a. [3]
    b. [1] eight electrons; [2] seven electrons; [3] eight electrons
    c. [1] $^{16}_{8}$O   [2] $^{16}_{7}$N   [3] $^{17}_{8}$O
2.10 a. 24.31 amu   b. 50.94 amu
2.11 sodium (Na, group 1A or 1, period 3)
    potassium (K, group 1A or 1, period 4)
    calcium (Ca, group 2A or 2, period 4)
    magnesium (Mg, group 2A or 2, period 3)
    phosphorus (P, group 5A or 15, period 3)
    sulfur (S, group 6A or 16, period 3)
    chlorine (Cl, group 7A or 17, period 3)

2.12 a. magnesium

    b. aluminum
    c. bromine

2.13 a. 12 electrons, 2 valence electrons, magnesium
    b. 15 electrons, 5 valence electrons, phosphorus
    c. 40 electrons, 2 valence electrons, zirconium
    d. 26 electrons, 2 valence electrons, iron
2.14 a. 7 valence electrons: $2s^22p^5$
    b. 8 valence electrons: $4s^24p^6$
    c. 2 valence electrons: $3s^2$
    d. 4 valence electrons: $4s^24p^2$
2.15 a. :B̈r: b. Li·   c. A̧l·   d. ·S̈:   e. :N̈e:
2.16 a. arsenic   b. silicon   c. phosphorus
2.17 a. **A**   b. **A**   c. **B**
2.18 a. [1]   b. [2]   c. [1] F; [2] Mg

CHAPTER 2 PROBLEMS

2.1 a. Ca   b. Rn   c. N   d. Au
2.3 a,d,f,h: metals   b,c,g: nonmetals   e. metalloid
2.5 a. 1 sodium, 1 carbon, 1 nitrogen
    b. 2 hydrogens, 1 sulfur
    c. 2 carbons, 6 hydrogens
    d. 1 tin, 2 fluorines
    e. 1 carbon, 1 oxygen
    f. 3 carbons, 8 hydrogens, 3 oxygens
2.7 a. 95   b. 52
2.9 a. 18   b. 6
2.11 a. titanium, Ti, group 4B (or 4), period 4, transition metal
    b. phosphorus, P, group 5A (or 15), period 3, main group element
    c. dysprosium, Dy, no group number, period 6, inner transition element
2.13 a. silicon   b. scandium   c. zinc
2.15 a. $1s^22s^22p^63s^1$ [Ne]$3s^1$
    b. $1s^22s^22p^63s^23p^2$ [Ne]$3s^23p^2$
    c. $1s^22s^22p^63s^23p^64s^23d^{10}4s^{10}6s^24d^{10}5p^5$ [Kr]$5s^24d^{10}5p^5$
2.17 a. carbon (black), oxygen (red)
    b. carbon (black), hydrogen (gray), chlorine (green)
2.19 a. gold, astatine, silver
    b. nitrogen, sodium, nickel
    c. sulfur, silicon, tin
    d. calcium, chromium, chlorine
    e. phosphorus, lead, platinum
    f. titanium, tantalum, thallium
2.21 a,c,e: element   b,d: compound
2.23 a. cesium   c. chlorine   e. fluorine
    b. ruthenium   d. beryllium   f. cerium
2.25 a. sodium: metal, alkali metal, main group element
    b. silver: metal, transition metal
    c. xenon: nonmetal, noble gas, main group element
    d. platinum: metal, transition metal
    e. uranium: metal, inner transition metal
    f. tellurium: metalloid, main group element
2.27 a. 5 protons and 6 neutrons   b. 5   c. 11   d. 5   e. B

2.29

	Element Symbol	Atomic Number	Mass Number	Number of Protons	Number of Neutrons	Number of Electrons
a.	C	6	12	6	6	6
b.	P	15	31	15	16	15
c.	Zn	30	65	30	35	30
d.	Mg	12	24	12	12	12
e.	I	53	127	53	74	53
f.	Be	4	9	4	5	4
g.	Zr	40	91	40	51	40
h.	S	16	32	16	16	16

2.31   a. **E** and **G**   b. **A, E,** and **J**   c. **G**   d. **A, E,** and **J**

2.33

s block elements

noble gases

group 4A

group 10

period 3

s block element

alkaline earth elements

transition metals

f block elements

2.35   hydrogen

2.37   K, Ca, Sc, Ti, V, Cr, Mn, Fe, Co, Ni, Cu, Zn, Ga: metals
Ge, As: metalloids
Se, Br, Kr: nonmetals

2.39   For ^{58}Ni: a. 28   b. 58   c. 28   d. 30
For ^{60}Ni: a. 28   b. 60   c. 28   d. 32

2.41

	Protons	Neutrons	Electrons
a.	13	14	13
b.	17	18	17
c.	16	18	16

2.43   a. $^{127}_{53}$I   b. $^{79}_{35}$Br   c. $^{107}_{47}$Ag

2.45   107.9 amu

2.47   a. 1   b. 4   c. 9   d. 16

2.49   a. B

1s   2s   2p

b. K

1s   2s   2p   3s   3p   4s

c. Se

1s   2s   2p   3s   3p

4s   3d   4p

d. Ar

1s   2s   2p   3s   3p

e. Zn

1s   2s   2p   3s   3p

4s   3d

2.51   a. B: $1s^22s^22p^1$ [He]$2s^22p^1$
b. K: $1s^22s^22p^63s^23p^64s^1$ [Ar]$4s^1$
c. Se: $1s^22s^22p^63s^23p^64s^23d^{10}4p^4$ [Ar]$4s^23d^{10}4p^4$
d. Ar: $1s^22s^22p^63s^23p^6$ [Ar]
e. Zn: $1s^22s^22p^63s^23p^64s^23d^{10}$ [Ar]$4s^23d^{10}$

2.53   a. 1   b. 3   c. 1

2.55   a. 38 electrons, 2 valence electrons, strontium
b. 16 electrons, 6 valence electrons, sulfur
c. 11 electrons, 1 valence electron, sodium
d. 17 electrons, 7 valence electrons, chlorine

2.57

	Electrons	Group Number	Valence Electrons	Period	Valence Shell
a. Carbon	6	4A (or 14)	4	2	2
b. Calcium	20	2A (or 2)	2	4	4
c. Krypton	36	8A (or 18)	8	4	4

2.59   a. carbon: $1s^22s^22p^2$; $2s^22p^2$
b. calcium: $1s^22s^22p^63s^23p^64s^2$; $4s^2$
c. krypton: $1s^22s^22p^63s^23p^64s^23d^{10}4p^6$; $4s^24p^6$

2.61   a. Not possible; the unpaired electron must be in a higher-energy orbital.
b. possible

2.63   a. sulfur: 6, $3s^23p^4$
b. chlorine: 7, $3s^23p^5$
c. barium: 2, $6s^2$
d. titanium: 2, $4s^2$
e. tin: 4, $5s^25p^2$

2.65   a. Be·   b. ·Ṡi·   c. :Ï: d. ·Mg·   e. :Är·

2.67   a. [3]   b. [1]   c. [3]

2.69   a. iodine   b. carbon   c. potassium   d. selenium

2.71   a. bromine   b. nitrogen   c. silicon   d. chlorine

2.73   a. neon < carbon < boron
b. beryllium < magnesium < calcium
c. sulfur < silicon < magnesium
d. neon < krypton < xenon
e. oxygen < sulfur < silicon
f. fluorine < sulfur < aluminum

2.75   fluorine, oxygen, sulfur, silicon, magnesium

2.77   sodium, magnesium, phosphorus, nitrogen, fluorine

2.79   a. $C_{13}H_{18}ClNO$ b. chlorine

2.81

	a. Type	b. Block	c,d: Radius	e,f: Ionization E	g. Valence Electrons
Sodium	Metal	s			1
Potassium	Metal	s	Largest	Lowest	1
Chlorine	Nonmetal	p	Smallest	Highest	7

2.83   Carbon-11 has the same number of protons and electrons as carbon-12—that is, six. Carbon-11 has only five neutrons, whereas carbon-12 has six neutrons. The symbol for carbon-11 is $^{11}_{6}$C.

2.85   0.80 kg

CHAPTER 3 PRACTICE PROBLEMS

3.1   a,d,e,f: covalent   b,c: ionic
3.2   a. compound: **A, C, D, E**   element: **B, F**   b. all
3.3 N^{3-}
3.4   a. K^+ b. Br^- c. V^{2+}
3.5   a. 28 protons, 26 electrons
        b. 34 protons, 36 electrons
        c. 26 protons, 26 electrons
3.6   a. +2   b. −1   c. −2   d. +1
3.7   a. NaBr   b. BaO   c. MgI_2 d. Li_2O

3.8   a.   b.

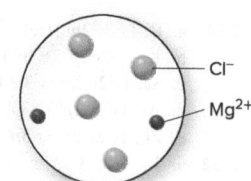

3.9   a. sodium fluoride   d. lithium oxide
        b. magnesium oxide   e. titanium oxide
        c. strontium bromide   f. aluminum chloride
3.10 a. chromium(III) chloride, chromic chloride
        b. lead(II) sulfide
        c. tin(IV) fluoride, stannic fluoride
        d. lead(IV) oxide
        e. iron(II) bromide, ferrous bromide
        f. gold(III) chloride
3.11 a. $CaBr_2$ c. $FeBr_3$ e. $CrCl_2$
        b. CuI   d. MgS
3.12 a. $MgSO_4$ c. $NiSO_4$ e. Li_2SO_4
        b. Na_2SO_4 d. $Al_2(SO_4)_3$
3.13 a. sodium carbonate   d. manganese acetate
        b. calcium hydroxide   e. iron(III) hydrogen sulfite, ferric bisulfite
        c. magnesium nitrate   f. magnesium phosphate

CHAPTER 3 PROBLEMS

3.1   compound: a,b,c,d,f
        element: e
        molecule: a,b,e
3.3   a. **A = S**   **B = S^{2-}**
        b. **C = Li^+**   **D = Li**
3.5   a. 79 protons, 78 electrons
        b. 79 protons, 76 electrons
        c. 50 protons, 48 electrons
        d. 50 protons, 46 electrons
3.7   a. 25 protons, 25 electrons
        b. 25 protons, 23 electrons
        c. $1s^2 2s^2 2p^6 3s^2 3p^6 4s^2 3d^5$ The two $4s^2$ valence electrons would
                                        be lost to form Mn^{2+}.
3.9   a. sulfide   d. aluminum
        b. copper(I), cuprous   e. tin(IV), stannic
        c. cesium
3.11 a. copper(I) oxide, cuprous oxide
        b. copper(II) oxide, cupric oxide
        c. copper(I) chloride, cuprous chloride
        d. copper(II) chloride, cupric chloride
3.13 Ionic compounds have high melting points and high boiling points.
        They usually dissolve in water. Their solutions conduct electricity and
        they form crystalline solids.
3.15 a. KOH   c. K_2SO_4 e. K_3PO_4
        b. KNO_2 d. $KHSO_3$ f. KCN

3.17 a,b,d: covalent   c. ionic
3.19 a. ionic   b,c,d: covalent
3.21 Be^{2+}
3.23 a. Ti^{2+} b. S^{2-} c. Al^{3+} d. Cl^- e. Ca^{2+}
3.25 a. Ba^{2+} b. P^{3-}
3.27 a. Be   b. Cl^- c. Rb^+
3.29 a. Na^+ c. Mn^{2+} e. Sn^{4+}
        b. Se^{2-} d. Au^{3+} f. Hg_2^{2+}
3.31 a,b,c,e: Ne   d. Ar   f. He
3.33 a. lose one electron   c. gain two electrons
        b. gain one electron   d. lose two electrons
3.35

	Number of Valence Electrons	Group Number	Number of Electrons Gained or Lost	Charge	Example
a.	1	1A	Lose 1	1+	Li
b.	7	7A	Gain 1	1−	Cl

3.37 a. 2A   b. +2   c. QF_2 d. QO
3.39 a. OH^-, hydroxide   b. NH_4^+, ammonium
3.41 a. sulfate, SO_4^{2-} b. nitrite, NO_2^- c. sulfide, S^{2-}
3.43 a. 9 protons, 10 electrons   c. 47 protons, 50 electrons
        b. 11 protons, 10 electrons
3.45 a. ClO_2^-, 33 protons, 34 electrons
        b. OCN^-, 21 protons, 22 electrons
3.47 a. CaS   b. $AlBr_3$ c. LiI   d. $NiCl_2$ e. Na_2Se
3.49 a. $LiNO_2$ c. $NaHSO_3$ e. $Mg(HSO_3)_2$
        b. $Ca(CH_3COO)_2$ d. $Mn_3(PO_4)_2$
3.51

	Y^-	Y^{2-}	Y^{3-}
X^+	XY	X_2Y	X_3Y
X^{2+}	XY_2	XY	X_3Y_2
X^{3+}	XY_3	X_2Y_3	XY

3.53 a. +1   b. +3   c. +2   d. +4
3.55

	Br^-	OH^-	HCO_3^-	SO_3^{2-}	PO_4^{3-}
Na^+	NaBr	NaOH	$NaHCO_3$	Na_2SO_3	Na_3PO_4
Co^{2+}	$CoBr_2$	$Co(OH)_2$	$Co(HCO_3)_2$	$CoSO_3$	$Co_3(PO_4)_2$
Al^{3+}	$AlBr_3$	$Al(OH)_3$	$Al(HCO_3)_3$	$Al_2(SO_3)_3$	$AlPO_4$

3.57 a. $KHSO_4$ b. $Ba(HSO_4)_2$ c. $Al(HSO_4)_3$ d. $Zn(HSO_4)_2$
3.59 a. $Ba(CN)_2$ b. $Ba_3(PO_4)_2$ c. $BaHPO_4$ d. $Ba(H_2PO_4)_2$
3.61 a. sodium oxide   e. cobalt(II) bromide
        b. barium sulfide   f. rubidium bromide
        c. lead(IV) sulfide   g. lead(II) bromide
        d. silver chloride
3.63 a. iron(II) chloride, ferrous chloride
        b. iron(III) bromide, ferric bromide
        c. iron(II) sulfide, ferrous sulfide
        d. iron(III) sulfide, ferric sulfide
3.65 a. Na_2S Na_2SO_4
        b. MgO $Mg(OH)_2$
        c. $MgSO_4$ $Mg(HSO_4)_2$
3.67 a. ammonium chloride
        b. lead(II) sulfate
        c. copper(II) nitrate, cupric nitrate
        d. calcium bicarbonate, calcium hydrogen carbonate
        e. iron(II) nitrate, ferrous nitrate
3.69 a. $Ca_3(PO_4)_2$ b. KOH   c. $ZnSO_4$ d. $FeSO_4$ e. $MnSO_4$

3.71 a. $MgCO_3$ e. $Au(NO_3)_3$
b. $NiSO_4$ f. Li_3PO_4
c. $Cu(OH)_2$ g. $Al(HCO_3)_3$
d. K_2HPO_4 h. $Cr(CN)_2$

3.73 a. $Pb(OH)_4$ lead(IV) hydroxide
b. $Pb(SO_4)_2$ lead(IV) sulfate
c. $Pb(HCO_3)_4$ lead(IV) bicarbonate
d. $Pb(NO_3)_4$ lead(IV) nitrate
e. $Pb_3(PO_4)_4$ lead(IV) phosphate
f. $Pb(CH_3CO_2)_4$ lead(IV) acetate

3.75 a. True.
b. False—ionic compounds are solids at room temperature.
c. False—most ionic compounds are soluble in water.
d. False—ionic solids exist as crystalline lattices with the ions arranged to maximize the electrostatic interactions of anions and cations.

3.77 NaCl

3.79 a. 30 protons, 30 electrons
b. 30 protons, 28 electrons
c. $1s^2 2s^2 2p^6 3s^2 3p^6 4s^2 3d^{10}$ The $4s^2$ electrons are lost to form Zn^{2+}.

3.81

Cation	a. Number of Protons	b. Number of Electrons	c. Noble Gas	d. Role
Na^+	11	10	Ne	Major cation in extracellular fluids and blood; maintains blood volume and blood pressure
K^+	19	18	Ar	Major intracellular cation
Ca^{2+}	20	18	Ar	Major cation in solid tissues like bone and teeth; required for normal muscle contraction and nerve function
Mg^{2+}	12	10	Ne	Required for normal muscle contraction and nerve function

3.83 $AgNO_3$

3.85 NH_4NO_3

3.87 a. MgO, KI
b. calcium hydrogen phosphate
c. iron(III) phosphate, ferric phosphate
d. Na_2SeO_3
e. The name chromium chloride is ambiguous. Without a designation as chromium(II) or chromium(III), one does not know the ratio of chromium cations to chloride anions.

CHAPTER 4 PRACTICE PROBLEMS

4.1 a. 1   b. 4   c. 1   d. 2   e. 3   f. 2

4.2 a. $H—\ddot{B}\ddot{r}:$ c. $H—\ddot{O}—\ddot{O}—H$ e. (ethane structure)

b. (H—C—F structure)   d. H—N—N—H   f. (H—C—Cl structure)

4.3 (H—C—O—C—H structure)

4.4 a. $H—C\equiv N$ b. $H—C=\ddot{O}$

4.5 a. (resonance structures for acetate-type anion) $\longleftrightarrow$

b. (resonance structures for H—C—N—H anion) $\longleftrightarrow$

4.6 a. SiO_2 b. PCl_3 c. SO_3 d. N_2O_3

4.7 a. bent   c. trigonal pyramidal
b. tetrahedral   d. trigonal planar

4.8 a. polar   c. nonpolar   e. polar
b. ionic   d. polar   f. polar

4.9 a. $H—Cl$ polar   c. (polar structure)   e. (nonpolar structure)
b. (nonpolar ethane structure)   d. $H—C\equiv N$ polar

4.10 a. (polar structure) polar C–O, O–H All C's are tetrahedral.
b. (trigonal planar / tetrahedral structure)

4.11 a. 7
b. 7
c. polar bonds: **A, C, D**   nonpolar bond: **B**

CHAPTER 4 PROBLEMS

4.1 $H\cdot \; + \; \cdot\ddot{C}\ddot{l}: \longrightarrow H\!:\!\ddot{C}\ddot{l}:$
H is surrounded by two electrons, giving it the noble gas configuration of He. Cl is surrounded by eight electrons, giving it the noble gas configuration of Ar.

4.3 a. (H—C—Cl structure)   c. (H—C—O—H structure)
b. (H—N—O—H structure)   d. (Br—C—Br structure)

4.5 (H—C—O—H with O structure)

4.7 $:\ddot{B}\ddot{r}—B—\ddot{B}\ddot{r}:$
Boron has only six electrons around it, so it does not follow the octet rule.

4.9 a. (resonance structures for nitrite ion) $\longleftrightarrow$
b. (resonance structures for formate-type ion) $\longleftrightarrow$

4.11 a. carbon disulfide   c. phosphorus pentachloride
b. sulfur dioxide   d. boron trifluoride

4.13 a. two   b. one

4.15 a. LiCl: ionic; the metal Li donates electrons to chlorine.
HCl: covalent; H and Cl share electrons because both are nonmetals and the electronegativity difference is not large enough for electron transfer to occur.

b. KBr: ionic; the metal K donates electrons to bromine.
HBr: covalent; H and Br share electrons because the electronegativity difference is not large enough for electron transfer to occur.

4.17 a. 4 bonds, 0 lone pairs   c. 1 bond, 3 lone pairs
b. 2 bonds, 2 lone pairs   d. 3 bonds, 1 lone pair

4.19 a. H—C=C—C≡N: b. H—S̈—C—C—Ö—H

4.21 H—Ö—C—C—Ö—H

4.23 a. H—Ï: c. H—S̈e—H
b. H—C—F̈:   d. :C̈l—C—C—C̈l:

4.25 a. H—C—N̈—H   b. H—Ö—N̈=Ö   c. H—C—C≡C—H

4.27 C=C (with :F̈: groups)

4.29 a. [H—Ö:]⁻   b. [H—Ö—H]⁺

4.31 (ring structure)

4.33 A resonance structure is one representation of an electron arrangement with a given placement of atoms. A resonance hybrid is a composite of two or more resonance structures.

4.35 [H—C—C=C—H]⁻

4.37 a. resonance structures   b. not resonance structures

4.39
[Ö=C—Ö:]²⁻ ⟷ [:Ö—C—Ö:]²⁻ ⟷ [:Ö—C=Ö]²⁻

4.41 a. phosphorus tribromide   c. nitrogen trichloride
b. sulfur trioxide   d. diphosphorus pentasulfide

4.43 a. SeO_2 b. CCl_4 c. N_2O_5

4.45 a. H—C—Ö—H   c. H—C—C=C—C—H
tetrahedral   bent   trigonal planar   tetrahedral
b.   N̈F_3
trigonal pyramidal

4.47 a. **A**   b. **B**   c. **B**

4.49 a. H—N—Ö—H   c. [H—C—N—H]⁺
trigonal pyramidal   bent   tetrahedral
b. H—C—C—H
tetrahedral   trigonal planar

4.51 a. [1] A linear geometry means two groups, so no lone pairs. [2] $BeCl_2$
b. [1] A bent geometry generally means four groups, so two lone pairs. [2] H_2O

4.53 a. H—Ö—C—C—C—Ö—H
b. **A**, trigonal planar
B, bent
C, tetrahedral

4.55 a. H—C—F̈:   b. H—C≡C—C—Ö—H   c. H—C=C=Ö:
both 109.5°   180° 109.5°   120° 180°
109.5°   120°

4.57 :C̈l—C—C̈l: C=C
CCl₄ is tetrahedral because carbon has four substituents. Each C in C₂Cl₄ has trigonal planar geometry because each carbon has three substituents.

4.59 a. Se < S < O   b. Na < P < Cl   c. Na < Li < Be

4.61 **B** < **C** < **A**
sulfur   chlorine   fluorine

4.63 a,b,c: covalent   d. ionic

4.65 a. nonpolar   b. polar   c. polar   d. polar   e. nonpolar

4.67 a. C—O   b. C—F   c. Si—C

4.69 δ+ δ−   δ+ δ−   δ+ δ−   δ+ δ−   δ+ δ−
C—O   C—N   C—F   C—Cl   Si—C   P—H
no dipole

4.71 a.   C=C (with Cl groups)
polar bonds, nonpolar compound
b.   H—C—C
polar bonds, polar compound

4.73 CHCl₃ has a net dipole, making it polar. CCl₄ has four polar bonds but no net dipole because the four bonds have dipoles that cancel one another.

4.75 **A** a.   C=C
b. one polar C—Cl bond
c. polar molecule
B a. :C̈l—C≡C—C̈l:
b. two polar C—Cl bonds
c. nonpolar molecule

4.77 a. 20 valence electrons   d. bent

b,c:

e. The compound is polar because the two bond dipoles do not cancel.

4.79 a–c.

d. Glycine is a polar molecule because the many bond dipoles do not cancel.

4.81

a. six lone pairs

b. seven trigonal planar C's, labeled with (*)

c. nonpolar bonds: **A, D**
   polar bonds: **B, C**

4.83 One possibility:

4.85 a,c:

polar

polar

b. C's with x, trigonal planar
   C with °, linear
   C with *, tetrahedral

4.87 a. The predicted shape around each carbon is tetrahedral.

b. 60°

c. The 60° bond angle deviates greatly from the theoretical tetrahedral bond angle, making the molecule unstable.

4.89 $:\ddot{O}-\ddot{S}=\ddot{O}: \longleftrightarrow :\ddot{O}=\ddot{S}-\ddot{O}: \longleftrightarrow :O=\ddot{S}=O:$

The S atom in each structure is surrounded by three groups, so the bond angle is similar to a trigonal planar arrangement (120°).

CHAPTER 5 PRACTICE PROBLEMS

5.1 The process is a chemical reaction because the reactants contain two gray spheres joined (indicating H_2) and two red spheres joined (indicating O_2), while the product (H_2O) contains a red sphere joined to two gray spheres (indicating O—H bonds).

5.2   reactants   products

a. $2\ H_2O_2(aq) \longrightarrow 2\ H_2O(l) + O_2(g)$ (4 H, 4 O)

b. $2\ C_8H_{18} + 25\ O_2 \longrightarrow 16\ CO_2 + 18\ H_2O$
   (16 C, 50 O, 36 H)

c. $2\ Na_3PO_4(aq) + 3\ MgCl_2(aq) \longrightarrow Mg_3(PO_4)_2(s) + 6\ NaCl(aq)$
   (3 Mg, 2 P, 8 O, 6 Na, 6 Cl)

5.3 a. $2\ H_2 + O_2 \longrightarrow 2\ H_2O$

b. $2\ NO + O_2 \longrightarrow 2\ NO_2$

c. $CH_4 + 2\ Cl_2 \longrightarrow CH_2Cl_2 + 2\ HCl$

5.4 $2\ C_2H_6 + 7\ O_2 \longrightarrow 4\ CO_2 + 6\ H_2O$

5.5 a. $2\ Al + 3\ H_2SO_4 \longrightarrow Al_2(SO_4)_3 + 3\ H_2$

b. $3\ Na_2SO_3 + 2\ H_3PO_4 \longrightarrow 3\ H_2SO_3 + 2\ Na_3PO_4$

5.6 decomposition

$2\ NCl_3 \longrightarrow N_2 + 3\ Cl_2$

5.7 a,d: single replacement   b,c: double replacement

5.8 (oxidized) (reduced)

a. $Zn(s) + 2\ H^+(aq) \longrightarrow Zn^{2+}(aq) + H_2(g)$
   $Zn \longrightarrow Zn^{2+} + 2\ e^-$
   $2\ H^+ + 2\ e^- \longrightarrow H_2$
   (reduced) (oxidized)

b. $Fe^{3+}(aq) + Al(s) \longrightarrow Al^{3+}(aq) + Fe(s)$
   $Al \longrightarrow Al^{3+} + 3\ e^-$
   $Fe^{3+} + 3\ e^- \longrightarrow Fe$
   (oxidized) (reduced)

c. $2\ I^- + Br_2 \longrightarrow I_2 + 2\ Br^-$
   $2\ I^- \longrightarrow I_2 + 2\ e^-$
   $Br_2 + 2\ e^- \longrightarrow 2\ Br^-$

d. $2\ AgBr \longrightarrow 2\ Ag + Br_2$
   $2\ Br^-$ (oxidized) $2\ Ag^+$ (reduced)
   $2\ Br^- \longrightarrow Br_2 + 2\ e^-$
   $2\ Ag^+ + 2\ e^- \longrightarrow 2\ Ag$

5.9 a. 1.20×10^{24} C atoms   c. 3.01×10^{23} C atoms
b. 3.61×10^{24} C atoms   d. 1.51×10^{25} C atoms

5.10 a. 100. mol   b. 0.0500 mol   c. 15 mol

5.11 424.4 g/mol

5.12 a. 29.2 g   b. 332 g   c. 101 g   d. 26.3 g

5.13 a. 1.71 mol   b. 1.59 mol   c. 1.39×10^{-3} mol   d. 1.39 mol

5.14 1.80×10^{21} molecules

5.15 a. 6.6 mol   b. 1.0 mol   c. 1.2 mol

5.16 a. 51 g   b. 22 g   c. 90. g

5.17 a. 72.4 g   b. 24.1 g   c. 7.24 g

5.18 88.0%

5.19 a. 154 g   b. 34.7%

5.20 a. 111 g   b. 59.0%

5.21 H_2 is the limiting reactant.

5.22 a. 1.0 mol   b. 0.67 mol   c. 1.3 mol   d. 4.0 mol

5.23 a. N_2 b. O_2

5.24 a. 26.8 g   b. 24.4 g

CHAPTER 5 PROBLEMS

5.1 The process is a physical change (freezing), because the particles in the reactants are the same as the particles in the products.

5.3 $2\ CO + O_2 \longrightarrow 2\ CO_2$

5.5 a,c: combination   b,d: decomposition

5.7 a. $C + O_2 \longrightarrow CO_2$

b. $MgCO_3 \longrightarrow MgO + CO_2$

c. $2\ Ag + Li_2CO_3 \longrightarrow 2\ Li + Ag_2CO_3$

d. $Na_2CO_3 + BaBr_2 \longrightarrow 2\ NaBr + BaCO_3$

5.9 a. $HCO_2H + 2\ H_2 \longrightarrow CH_3OH + H_2O$

b. HCO_2H is reduced. H_2 is oxidized.

5.11 a,b,c,d: 6.02×10^{23}

5.13 a. 100.09 amu   b. 166.0 amu

5.15 5.679×10^{-3} mol vitamin C

5.17 a. 44 g   b. 130 g   c. 24 g

5.19 a. 323 g   b. 37.8%

5.21 a,b,d: H_2 c: O_2

5.23 $2 CO + 2 O_3 \longrightarrow 2 CO_2 + 2 O_2$ (not balanced)

5.25 a. 2 H, 2 Cl, 1 Ca on both sides; therefore balanced

    b. 1 Ti, 4 Cl, 4 H, 2 O on left side, and 1 Ti, 1 Cl, 1 H, 2 O on right side; therefore NOT balanced

    c. 1 Al, 1 P, 7 O, 6 H on both sides; therefore balanced

5.27 $H_2 + Cl_2 \longrightarrow 2 HCl$

5.29 $CH_4 + 3 Br_2 \longrightarrow CHBr_3 + 3 HBr$

5.31 a. $Ni(s) + 2 HCl(aq) \longrightarrow NiCl_2(aq) + H_2(g)$

    b. $CH_4(g) + 4 Cl_2(g) \longrightarrow CCl_4(g) + 4 HCl(g)$

    c. $2 KClO_3 \longrightarrow 2 KCl + 3 O_2$

    d. $Al_2O_3 + 6 HCl \longrightarrow 2 AlCl_3 + 3 H_2O$

    e. $2 Al(OH)_3 + 3 H_2SO_4 \longrightarrow Al_2(SO_4)_3 + 6 H_2O$

5.33

5.35 a. $2 C_6H_6 + 15 O_2 \longrightarrow 12 CO_2 + 6 H_2O$

    b.

5.37 a. The reactants are CO and O_2 and the product is CO_2.

    b. $2 CO + O_2 \longrightarrow 2 CO_2$

    c. combination

5.39 a. The reactant is C_2H_6O and the products are $H_2C{=}CH_2$ and H_2O.

    b. $C_2H_6O \longrightarrow H_2C{=}CH_2 + H_2O$

    c. decomposition

5.41 double replacement

5.43 a. decomposition   c. combination

    b. single replacement   d. double replacement

5.45 a. $2 Na + Cl_2 \longrightarrow 2 NaCl$

    b. $2 NI_3 \longrightarrow N_2 + 3 I_2$

    c. $Cl_2 + 2 KI \longrightarrow 2 KCl + I_2$

    d. $KOH + HI \longrightarrow KI + H_2O$

5.47 a. Fe (oxidized) Cu^{2+} (reduced)

    $Fe \longrightarrow Fe^{2+} + 2 e^-$

    $Cu^{2+} + 2 e^- \longrightarrow Cu$

    b. Cl_2 (reduced) $2 I^-$ (oxidized)

    $2 I^- \longrightarrow I_2 + 2 e^-$

    $Cl_2 + 2 e^- \longrightarrow 2 Cl^-$

    c. 2 Na (oxidized) Cl_2 (reduced)

    $2 Na \longrightarrow 2 Na^+ + 2 e^-$

    $Cl_2 + 2 e^- \longrightarrow 2 Cl^-$

5.49   Zn Ag^+

    oxidized   reduced

    reducing agent   oxidizing agent

5.51 Acetylene is reduced because it gains hydrogen atoms.

5.53 a. 69.00 amu, 69.00 g/mol   c. 176.12 amu, 176.12 g/mol

    b. 342.2 amu, 342.2 g/mol

5.55 a. $C_9H_{11}NO_4$ b. 197.2 amu   c. 197.2 g/mol

5.57 a. 1 mol Sn   c. 1 mol N_2 molecules

    b. 6.02×10^{23} N atoms   d. 1 mol CO_2

5.59 a. $C_{11}H_{17}NO_3$ c. 0.0355 mol

    b. molar mass = 211.3 g/mol

5.61 a. 182 g   b. 710. g   c. 130. g   d. 390. g

5.63 a. 0.485 mol   b. 2.92×10^{23}

5.65 a. 1.46×10^{-3} mol   c. 0.0730 mol

    b. 0.0146 mol   d. 7.30×10^{-5} mol

5.67 a. 1.20×10^{24} c. 1.60×10^{25} e. 3.01×10^{29}

    b. 1.51×10^{23} d. 1.34×10^{26}

5.69 a. 2.38×10^{-4} mol   b. 1.43×10^{20} molecules

5.71 a. 324 g   b. 52.2 g   c. 1.1×10^3 g   d. 9.82 g

5.73 a. 12.5 mol   b. 12 mol   c. 0.50 mol   d. 0.40 mol

5.75 a. 220 g   b. 44 g   c. 4.5 g   d. 240 g

5.77 75%

5.79 a. 23.9 g   b. 62.8%

5.81 a. **B** limiting reactant   **A** in excess

    b. **A** limiting reactant   **B** in excess

    c. **B** limiting reactant   **A** in excess

5.83 a. O_2 is the limiting reactant.

    b. 2 N_2 molecules are left over.

    c.

5.85 a. NO   b. O_2 c. NO   d. NO

5.87

	Reactants		Products	
Equation	C_2H_4 +	$3 O_2 \longrightarrow$	$2 CO_2$ +	$2 H_2O$
Initial molecules	8	15	0	0
Molecules used or formed	-5	-15	10	10
Molecules remaining	3	0	10	10

5.89 a. 0.285 mol ethylene and 0.329 mol HCl

    b. ethylene

    c. 0.285 mol

    d. 18.4 g

    e. 57.6%

5.91 a. 342.3 g/mol

    b. $C_{12}H_{22}O_{11}(s) + H_2O(l) \longrightarrow 4 C_2H_6O(l) + 4 CO_2(g)$

    c. 8 mol   e. 101 g   g. 9.21 g

    d. 10 mol   f. 18.4 g   h. 13.6%

5.93 6.3×10^{22} ions

5.95 a. 354.5 g/mol   b. 18 g   c. 17.8 g   d. 84.3%

5.97 a. 2.1×10^{-3} g   b. 3.9×10^{18} molecules

CHAPTER 6 PRACTICE PROBLEMS

6.1 a. 10. cal   b. 55,600 cal   c. 1,360 kJ   d. 107,000 J

6.2 126 Cal, rounded to 100 Cal

6.3 a. +88 kcal/mol; endothermic   c. +119 kcal/mol; endothermic

    b. −136 kcal/mol; exothermic

6.4 The indicated bond has the higher bond dissociation energy, making it the stronger bond.

a. $H{-}\underset{\underset{\displaystyle H}{|}}{\overset{\overset{\displaystyle H}{|}}{C}}{-}\ddot{\ddot{Br}}$ b. $H{-}OH$

6.5   106 kcal
6.6   a. 96 kcal   b. 8.0 kcal   c. 1.8 kcal
6.7

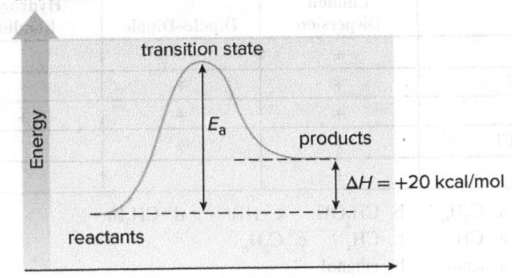

6.8   a. $\dfrac{[PCl_5]}{[PCl_3][Cl_2]}$ c. $\dfrac{[HBr]^2}{[Br_2][H_2]}$

b. $\dfrac{[SO_3]^2}{[SO_2]^2[O_2]}$ d. $\dfrac{[HCl]^3[CHCl_3]}{[CH_4][Cl_2]^3}$

6.9

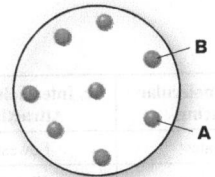

6.10   4
6.11   a. 4.75   b. 218
6.12   a. The system is not at equilibrium.
          b. The reaction proceeds to the left.
6.13   a,d: right   b,c: left
6.14   endothermic
6.15   a. right   b. left
6.16   a. right   b. left

CHAPTER 6 PROBLEMS

6.1   48.1 kJ or 48,100 J
6.3   a. absorbed   c. reactants
          b. reactants   d. endothermic
6.5

6.7   a. reactants favored   c. products favored
          b. products favored   d. reactants and products present
6.9   a. left   b. right
6.11   Potential energy is stored energy, whereas kinetic energy is the energy
          of motion. A stationary object on a hill has potential energy, but as it
          moves down the hill this potential energy is converted to kinetic
          energy.
6.13   a. 563,000 cal/h   c. 2.36×10^6 J/h
          b. 563 kcal/h   d. 2,360 kJ/h
6.15   a. 0.05 kcal   b. 0.23 kJ   c. 230 cal   d. 1.01×10^6 cal
6.17   236 Calories, rounded to 200 Calories

6.19   ice cream, 225 Cal, rounded to 200 Cal
          yogurt, 175 Cal, rounded to 200 Cal
6.21   148 Calories, rounded to 100 Calories
6.23   a. Cl_2 b. Cl_2 c. HF
6.25   a,d: exothermic   b,c: endothermic
6.27   a. 240 kcal   b. 280 kcal   c. 2.0×10^2 kcal
6.29   a. stronger bonds in products
          b. 2,710 kcal
          c. 339 kcal
          d. 37.6 kcal
6.31   a. X   b. Z   c. Y   d. X,Y   e. X,Z   f. Y   g. Z
6.33   a.

b.

c.

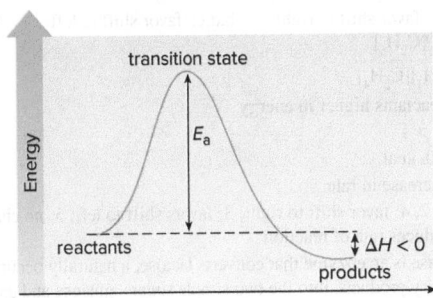

6.35   The reaction is exothermic.

6.37   Increasing temperature increases the number of collisions. Since the
          average kinetic energy of the colliding molecules is larger, more
          collisions are effective at causing reaction.

6.39 a. The reaction with $E_a = 1$ kcal will proceed faster because the energy of activation is lower.

b. K doesn't affect the reaction rate, so we cannot predict which reaction is faster.

c. One cannot predict which reaction will proceed faster from the ΔH.

6.41 b and c

6.43 A catalyst increases the reaction rate (a) and lowers the E_a (c). It has no effect on ΔH (b), K (d), or the relative energies of the reactants and products (e).

6.45 a. The system is not at equilibrium.

b. The reaction proceeds to the right.

6.47 a,b: products favored   c,d: reactants favored

6.49 a. [1]   b. [3]   c. [2]

6.51 a. [2]   b. [3]

6.53 a. $\dfrac{[NO_2]^2}{[NO]^2[O_2]}$ b. $\dfrac{[HBr]^2[CH_2Br_2]}{[CH_4][Br_2]^2}$

6.55 a. $2\,A \rightleftharpoons A_2$ b. $A_2 + 3\,B_2 \rightleftharpoons 2\,AB_3$

6.57 a. $\dfrac{[Br_2][H_2]}{[HBr]^2}$

b. reactants favored

c. ΔH positive

d. reactants lower in energy

e. You can't predict the reaction rate from the value of K.

6.59 [2] and [3]

6.61 a. $\dfrac{[CO_2][H_2]}{[CO][H_2O]}$ b. $K = 4.2$

6.63 The reaction is driven to the right.

6.65 a. increases NO and O_2, decreases N_2

b. increases N_2, NO, and O_2

6.67 [1] 200 °C [2] 100 °C

6.69 a,f: favor shift to right

b,c,d: favor shift to left

e. no change

6.71 a,c,f: favor shift to right   b,d,e: favor shift to left

6.73 a. $\dfrac{[C_2H_6]}{[H_2][C_2H_4]}$

b. reactants higher in energy

c. $K > 1$

d. 20. kcal

e. increase in rate

f. 1, 2, 4: favor shift to right; 3: favors shift to left; 5: no change, but reduces rate of reaction

6.75 Lactase is an enzyme that converts lactose, a naturally occurring sugar in dairy products, into the two simple sugars, glucose and galactose.

6.77 400 Calories

6.79 1.9 h, rounded to 2 h

6.81 8.8 cookies

6.83 30,200 kcal

CHAPTER 7 PRACTICE PROBLEMS

7.1 a. 2,300 mm Hg   b. 14 psi   c. 0.558 atm

7.2 a. 1.6 L   b. 3.2 L   c. 0.80 L   d. 16 L

7.3 0.44 L

7.4 392 K or 119 °C

7.5 290 mm Hg

7.6 a. 1.8 L   b. 2.6 L   c. 15 L

7.7 a. 1.0×10^2 L   b. 7.8 L   c. 12.6 L

7.8 36 mol

7.9 O_2: 2.5 atm CO_2: 1.5 atm

7.10 a. N_2: 62.5% O_2: 37.5%

b. N_2: 2,200 psi O_2: 1,300 psi

7.11

	London Dispersion	Dipole–Dipole	Hydrogen Bonding
a. Cl_2	+		
b. HCN	+	+	
c. HF	+	+	+
d. CH_3Cl	+	+	
e. H_2	+		

7.12 a. C_2H_6 b. CH_3OH c. HBr   d. CH_3Br

7.13 a. CH_4 b. CH_4 c. C_2H_6

7.14 a. sand   b. ethanol

7.15 392 cal, 1,640 J

7.16 Cu: 37 °C, Hg: 75 °C

7.17 a. 3,990 cal   b. 2,790 cal   c. 2.79 kcal   d. 1,440 cal

7.18 a. 23,000 cal   b. 23,000 cal   c. 9.7 kcal   d. 34 kcal

7.19 exothermic

7.20 5,300 cal

CHAPTER 7 PROBLEMS

7.1

	a. Density	b. Intermolecular Spacing	c. Intermolecular Attraction
Gas	Lowest	Greatest	Lowest
Liquid	Higher	Smaller	Higher
Solid	Highest	Smallest	Highest

7.3 a. 250 L   b. 24 mL

7.5 a. 0.067 mol   b. 0.38 mol   c. 1.1×10^{-3} mol

7.7 370 mm Hg

7.9 $\overset{\longrightarrow}{\underset{\delta+ \quad \delta-}{H-Cl}}$ $\overset{\longrightarrow}{\underset{\delta+ \quad \delta-}{H-Cl}}$

7.11 a. **A**   b. **D**

7.13 a. ionic   c. molecular

b. metallic   d. molecular

7.15 8,600 cal, 8.6 kcal

7.17 a. heating curve   c. 77 °C   e. liquid

b. 40 °C   d. solid and liquid

7.19 a. 2,600 psi   b. 1.3×10^5 mm Hg

7.21 a. 41 psi   b. 0.68 atm   c. 15,200 torr   d. 13,300 Pa

7.23 a. [3]   b. [2]

7.25 a. increases   b. decreases   c. increases

7.27 a,b,c: Volume increases.

7.29 a. Volume increases as outside atmospheric pressure decreases.

b. Volume decreases at the lower temperature.

c. Volume decreases as external pressure increases.

d. Volume increases as temperature increases.

7.31 a. 0.75 L   b. 1.1 L   c. 99.7 mm Hg

7.33 35 mL

7.35 a. 4.0 L   b. 1.1 L   c. 820 K

7.37 1.4 L

7.39 a. 4.34 atm   b. 350 mm Hg   c. 1,300 K

7.41 1.1 atm

7.43 a. 1.4 atm   b. 110 L   c. 740 K

7.45 a. 0.22 mol   b. 0.500 mol   c. 0.002 23 mol

7.47 a. 94 L   b. 1.8 L   c. 1.7 L

7.49 0.017 mol

7.51 0.19 mol or 1.1×10^{23} molecules

7.53 O_2 has more moles and more mass.

7.55 **A:** 210 mm Hg   **B:** 420 mm Hg

7.57 97 mm Hg for O_2 360 mm Hg for N_2

7.59 1,780 mm Hg

7.61 Water is capable of hydrogen bonding and these strong intermolecular forces give it a higher boiling point than H_2S.

7.63 a. London forces, dipole–dipole
b. London forces, dipole–dipole

7.65 d.

7.67 No, $H_2C=O$ has no H on the O atom.

7.69 Undecane has the higher melting point because it is larger in size.

7.71 butane, acetaldehyde, Freon-113

7.73 a. **B**   b. **A**   c. **A**

7.75 Glycerol is more viscous than water because it has three OH groups and has many opportunities for hydrogen bonding. Acetone cannot hydrogen bond, so its intermolecular forces are weaker and thus it has low viscosity.

7.77 a. ionic   c. metallic   e. amorphous
b. molecular   d. network

7.79 **Y**

7.81 a. 1.8×10^3 cal or 7.5×10^3 J   b. 4.0×10^3 cal or 1.7×10^4 J

7.83 a.

7.85 vaporization; energy absorbed

7.87 a,d: absorbed   b,c: released

7.89 a. [1] **W ⟶ X**; [2] **Y ⟶ Z**   b. 10 °C   c. 85 °C

7.91

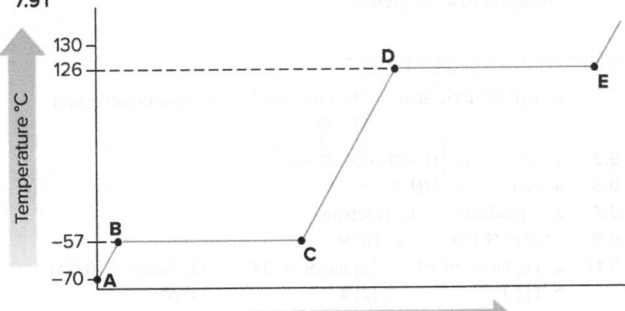

7.93 a. 6,100 cal   b. 6,100 cal   c. 25 kcal

7.95 Water is one of the few substances that expands as it enters the solid phase. This causes the bottle to crack when the water occupies a larger volume as it freezes.

7.97 a. As a person breathes faster, he eliminates more CO_2 from the lungs; therefore, the measured value of CO_2 is lower than the normal value of 40 mm Hg.
b. Many people with advanced lung disease have lost lung tissue over time and therefore cannot exchange adequate amounts of oxygen through the lungs and into the blood, leading to a lower-than-normal partial pressure of oxygen. In addition, they often breathe more slowly and with lower volumes than normal, so they cannot eliminate enough CO_2 and therefore the partial pressure of CO_2 climbs.

7.99 The molar mass is 4 g/mol and the gas is helium.

CHAPTER 8 PRACTICE PROBLEMS

8.1 a. 1 Eq Na^+ b. 2 Eq Mg^{2+} c. 0.5 Eq K^+ d. 1.5 Eq PO_4^{3-}

8.2 22 mEq

8.3 a,c,d,e: water soluble

8.4 a,c,e,f: water soluble   b,d: water insoluble

8.5 14% (w/v) ethanol
0.070% (w/v) antiseptic

8.6 81%

8.7 a. 2%
b. 250 mg (rounded to 300 mg)
c. The medicine is a suspension, so it settles out.

8.8 2.0×10^2 mL

8.9 a. 0.030 ppm   b. 0.5 ppm   c. 2.0 ppm   d. 0.23 ppm

8.10 a. 2.0 M   c. 10. M   e. 1.2 M
b. 8.0 M   d. 0.10 M   f. 1.4 M

8.11 a. 1.0×10^2 mL   c. 2.0 mL
b. 13 mL   d. 2.0×10^3 mL

8.12 a. 4.0 moles   c. 0.050 mole
b. 0.63 mole   d. 0.063 mole

8.13 a. 7.3 g   b. 150 g   c. 40. g   d. 3.7 g

8.14 0.35 M

8.15 a. 220 mL   b. 5.0×10^2 mL   c. 7.5 mL   d. 15 mL

8.16 a. 101.0 °C   b. 102.0 °C   c. 103.1 °C   d. 100.4 °C

8.17 a. **A**   b. **C**

8.18 a. −3.7 °C   b. −7.4 °C   c. −11 °C   d. −1.27 °C

8.19 a. 5.0% sugar solution   b. 4.0 M NaCl   c. 0.75 M NaCl

CHAPTER 8 PROBLEMS

8.1 a. heterogeneous mixture   b. colloid   c,d,e: solution

8.3 a. weak electrolyte   b. nonelectrolyte   c. strong electrolyte

8.5 29 mEq/L

8.7 a, b

8.9 A soft drink becomes "flat" when CO_2 escapes from the solution. CO_2 comes out of solution faster at room temperature than at the cooler temperature of the refrigerator, because the solubility of gases in liquids decreases as the temperature increases.

8.11 3.5%

8.13 0.833 M acetic acid

8.15 **F**

8.17 −7.4 °C

8.19 **C**

8.21 a. colloid   b. suspension   c. solution

8.23 **A.** The K^+ and I^- ions are separated when KI is dissolved in water. The solution contains ions, so it conducts an electric current.

8.25 a,b,d,e,h: solution   c. suspension   f,g: colloid

8.27 a. weak electrolyte   b. strong electrolyte

8.29 2.5 Eq K^+ 5.0 Eq Ca^{2+}
2.5 Eq Cl^- 5.0 Eq SO_4^{2-}

8.31 a. 130 mEq   b. 260 mEq   c. 58 mEq

8.33 a,b: **A**   c,d: **B**

8.35 a. unsaturated   b,c: saturated   d. supersaturated

8.37 a, c

8.39

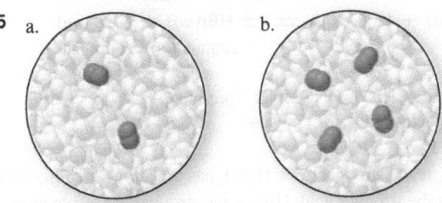
hydrogen bond

8.41 Water-soluble compounds are ionic or are small polar molecules that can hydrogen bond with the water solvent, but nonpolar compounds, such as oil, are soluble in nonpolar solvents.

8.43 Cholesterol is not water soluble because it is a large nonpolar molecule with a single OH group.

8.45 a.   b.

8.47 a. increased   b. decreased   c,d: no change

8.49 a,b,d,e,g: water soluble

8.51 a. 3.2%   b. 3.8 g

8.53 a. 1.3% (w/v)   b. 17% (w/v)   c. 8.00% (w/v)

8.55 24 mL

8.57 a. 2.3 M   b. 0.51 M   c. 0.66 M   d. 0.036 M

8.59 a. Add 12 g of acetic acid to the flask and then water to bring the volume to 250 mL.

     b. Add 55 mL of ethyl acetate to the flask and then water to bring the volume to 250 mL.

     c. Add 37 g of NaCl to the flask and then water to bring the volume to 250 mL.

8.61 a. 0.038 mol   b. 0.090 mol   c. 3.8 mol

8.63 a. 3.2 g   b. 5.7 g   c. 140 g

8.65 83 mL

8.67 a. 0.08 ppm   b. 0.7 ppm

8.69 B

8.71 a. 0.05 M   b. 50.0 mL

8.73 a. 15.0% (w/v)   b. 6.00% (w/v)   c. 5.0% (w/v)   d. 14% (w/v)

8.75 a. 10. mL   b. 450 mL   c. 1.5 mL   d. 2.5 mL

8.77 a. **B**   b. **A**   c. **B**

8.79 a. 101.5 °C   b. 101.2 °C   c. 103.1 °C

8.81 −4.5 °C

8.83 a. NaCl   b. glucose   c. NaCl   d. glucose

8.85 a. 0.10 M glucose   c. 0.10 M Na_2SO_4
     b. 0.20 M NaCl   d. 0.10 M glucose

8.87 a. **A > B**   c. no change   e. no change
     b. **B > A**   d. **A > B**

8.89 hypotonic

8.91 At warmer temperatures, CO_2 is less soluble in water and more is in the gas phase and escapes as the can is opened and pressure is reduced.

8.93 0.09% (w/v)   0.005 M

8.95 a. 280 mL would have to be given.

     b. The hypertonic mannitol draws water out of swollen brain cells and thus reduces the pressure on the brain.

8.97 Water moves out of the cells of the cucumber to the hypertonic salt solution, so the cucumber shrinks and loses its crispness.

8.99 6.3% (w/v)

8.101 7.3 g

8.103 a. yes   b. 0.000 50 mol

CHAPTER 9 PRACTICE PROBLEMS

9.1 a, c

9.2 a, b, d

9.3 a. $HCl(g) + NH_3(g)$ c. $OH^-(aq) + HSO_4^-(aq)$
        acid   base   base   acid

     b. $CH_3COOH(l) + H_2O(l)$
            acid   base

9.4 a. H_3O^+ b. HI   c. H_2CO_3

9.5 a. HS^- b. CN^- c. SO_4^{2-}

9.6 a. $H_2O(l) + HI(g) \rightleftharpoons I^-(aq) + H_3O^+(aq)$
       base   acid   conjugate   conjugate
                        base   acid

     b. $Br^-(aq) + HNO_3(aq) \rightleftharpoons HBr(aq) + NO_3^-(aq)$
       base   acid   conjugate   conjugate
                        acid   base

9.7 **A:** weak acid; H_3O^+, HNO_2, NO_2^- present
     B: strong acid; H_3O^+, Br^- present

9.8 **D < F < E**

9.9 a. H_2SO_4 is the stronger acid; H_3PO_4 has the stronger conjugate base.
     b. HCl is the stronger acid; HF has the stronger conjugate base.
     c. H_2CO_3 is the stronger acid; NH_4^+ has the stronger conjugate base.
     d. HF is the stronger acid; HCN has the stronger conjugate base.

9.10 a. $HPO_4^{2-} < H_2PO_4^- < H_3PO_4$
     b. $HCN < CH_3COOH < HF$

9.11 reactants

9.12 a. 10^{-11} M acidic   c. 3.6×10^{-5} M basic
     b. 10^{-3} M basic   d. 1.8×10^{-11} M acidic

9.13

	$[H_3O^+]$	$[OH^-]$
a.	10^{-11} M	10^{-3} M
b.	10^{-3} M	10^{-11} M
c.	1.5 M	6.7×10^{-15} M
d.	3.3×10^{-14} M	3.0×10^{-1} M

9.14 a. 6   b. 12   c. 5   d. 11

9.15 a. 1×10^{-13} M basic
     b. 1×10^{-7} M neutral
     c. 1×10^{-3} M acidic

9.16 a. 6×10^{-11} M   b. 2×10^{-8} M   c. 5×10^{-5} M

9.17 a. 5.74   b. 11.036   c. 4.06   d. 10.118

9.18 $H_2SO_4(aq) + CaCO_3(s) \longrightarrow CaSO_4(aq) + \underline{H_2O(l) + CO_2(g)}$
                                            from H_2CO_3

9.19 a,c,e: neutral   b,f: basic   d. acidic

9.20 0.41 M

9.21 a,b,c: pH 7.21
     The pH remains the same if equal amounts of the weak acid and conjugate base are present.

CHAPTER 9 PROBLEMS

9.1 a. hydrofluoric acid   b. nitric acid   c. hydrocyanic acid

9.3 a. Br^- b. $\left[H-O-\overset{\overset{O}{\|}}{C}-\overset{\overset{O}{\|}}{C}-O \right]^-$

9.5 a. NH_4^+ b. NH_2^-

9.7 a,c: products   b. reactants

9.9 a,b,d,e: H_2CO_3 c. HCN

9.11 a. [1] factor of 10   [2] factor of 100   [3] factor of 10,000
     b. [1] 4   [2] 4   [3] 6

9.13 a. $HNO_3(aq) + NaOH(aq) \longrightarrow H_2O(l) + NaNO_3(aq)$
     b. $H_2SO_4(aq) + 2\,KOH(aq) \longrightarrow 2\,H_2O(l) + K_2SO_4(aq)$

9.15 a. $HNO_3(aq) + NaHCO_3(aq) \longrightarrow NaNO_3(aq) + \underline{H_2O(l) + CO_2(g)}$
                                              from H_2CO_3

     b. $2\,HNO_3(aq) + MgCO_3(s) \longrightarrow Mg(NO_3)_2(aq) + \underline{H_2O(l) + CO_2(g)}$
                                              from H_2CO_3

9.17 30. mL

9.19 a. HCO_3^- and CO_3^{2-} are both needed to keep the ratio of their concentrations from changing very much when acid or base is added.
     b. $[HCO_3^-]$ increases and $[CO_3^{2-}]$ decreases.
     c. $[HCO_3^-]$ decreases and $[CO_3^{2-}]$ increases.

9.21 a, d, f

9.23 a, d, e, f

9.25 a. H_2S b. HCO_3^- c. HNO_2 d. $\left[H-\overset{\overset{\displaystyle H}{\,}}{\underset{\underset{\displaystyle H}{\,}}{C}}-\overset{\overset{\displaystyle H}{\,}}{\underset{\underset{\displaystyle H}{\,}}{N}}-H \right]^+$

9.27 a. NO_2^- b. NH_3 c. HO_2^-

9.29 a. NO_2^- b. CO_3^{2-}

9.31 a.

     acid   base   conjugate base   conjugate acid

     b.

     base   acid   conjugate acid   conjugate base

9.33 a. HI(g) acid $\qquad$ I$^-$(aq) conjugate base

$\qquad$ NH$_3$(g) base $\qquad$ NH$_4^+$(aq) conjugate acid

$\qquad$ b. HCOOH(l) acid $\qquad$ HCOO$^-$(aq) conjugate base

$\qquad$ H$_2$O(l) base $\qquad$ H$_3$O$^+$(aq) conjugate acid

$\qquad$ c. HSO$_4^-$(aq) base $\qquad$ H$_2$SO$_4$(aq) conjugate acid

$\qquad$ H$_2$O(l) acid $\qquad$ OH$^-$(aq) conjugate base

9.35 a. H$_2$CO$_3$ $\qquad$ b. CO$_3^{2-}$

9.37 a. H$_2$O $\qquad$ b. (CH$_3$NH$_3$)$^+$

9.39 HNO$_3$(aq) + H$_2$O(l) $\longrightarrow$ H$_3$O$^+$(aq) + NO$_3^-$(aq)

9.41 **A** represents HCl because it shows a fully dissociated acid.

$\qquad$ **B** represents HF because it is only partially dissociated.

9.43 a. **B** $\qquad$ b. **A**

9.45 a. CH$_3$COOH (stronger acid)

$\qquad$ H$_2$O (stronger conjugate base)

$\qquad$ b. H$_3$PO$_4$ (stronger acid)

$\qquad$ HCO$_3^-$ (stronger conjugate base)

$\qquad$ c. H$_2$SO$_4$ (stronger acid)

$\qquad$ HSO$_4^-$ (stronger conjugate base)

9.47 a. **A** $\qquad$ b. **B** $\qquad$ c. **B**

9.49

	Acid	Formula	Conjugate Base	Formula
a.	strong	H$_2$SO$_4$	weak	HSO$_4^-$
b.	weak	HOBr	strong	OBr$^-$
c.	strong	HNO$_3$	weak	NO$_3^-$
d.	weak	HCO$_2$H	strong	HCO$_2^-$

9.51 a. HSO$_4^-$ $\qquad$ stronger acid

$\qquad$ SO$_4^{2-}$ $\qquad$ conjugate base

$\qquad$ H$_2$PO$_4^-$

$\qquad$ HPO$_4^{2-}$ $\qquad$ conjugate base, stronger base

$\qquad$ b. CH$_3$COOH $\qquad$ stronger acid

$\qquad$ CH$_3$COO$^-$ $\qquad$ conjugate base

$\qquad$ CH$_3$CH$_2$COOH

$\qquad$ CH$_3$CH$_2$COO$^-$ $\qquad$ conjugate base, stronger base

9.53 a. **B** $\qquad$ b. **B** $\qquad$ c. **A**

9.55 0.14

9.57 a. H$_3$PO$_4$(aq) + CN$^-$(aq) $\rightleftharpoons$ H$_2$PO$_4^-$(aq) + HCN(aq)

$\qquad$ acid $\qquad\qquad\qquad\qquad\qquad$ conjugate acid

$\qquad\qquad\qquad\qquad\qquad\qquad$ products favored

$\qquad$ b. Br$^-$(aq) + HSO$_4^-$(aq) $\rightleftharpoons$ SO$_4^{2-}$(aq) + HBr(g)

$\qquad\qquad\qquad$ acid $\qquad\qquad\qquad$ conjugate acid

$\qquad$ reactants favored

$\qquad$ c. CH$_3$COO$^-$(aq) + H$_2$CO$_3$(aq) $\rightleftharpoons$ CH$_3$COOH(aq) + HCO$_3^-$(aq)

$\qquad\qquad\qquad$ acid $\qquad\qquad\qquad$ conjugate acid

$\qquad$ reactants favored

9.59 a. True

$\qquad$ b. False. A solution with a pH of 2 is 100 times more acidic than a solution with a pH of 4.

9.61 a. 9.1×10^{-6} M acidic $\qquad$ b. 2.5×10^{-3} M acidic

9.63 a. 10^{-6} M basic $\qquad$ c. 3.3×10^{-11} M acidic

$\qquad$ b. 10^{-4} M basic $\qquad$ d. 4.0×10^{-4} M basic

9.65 a. 10^{-12} M basic $\qquad$ c. 1.6×10^{-8} M basic

$\qquad$ b. 2.5×10^{-7} M acidic $\qquad$ d. 1.2×10^{-2} M acidic

9.67 a. 12 $\qquad$ b. 6.60 $\qquad$ c. 7.80 $\qquad$ d. 1.92

9.69

[H$_3$O$^+$]	[OH$^-$]	pH	Classification
5.3×10^{-3}	1.9×10^{-12}	2.28	acidic
5.0×10^{-7}	2.0×10^{-8}	6.30	acidic
4×10^{-5}	2.5×10^{-10}	4.4	acidic
1.5×10^{-5}	6.8×10^{-10}	4.82	acidic

9.71 a. 1×10^{-12} M $\qquad$ c. 1.6×10^{-2} M

$\qquad$ b. 1×10^{-1} M $\qquad$ d. 1.3×10^{-9} M

9.73 [H$_3$O$^+$] = 1.3×10^{-6} M $\qquad$ [OH$^-$] = 7.7×10^{-9} M

9.75 [H$_3$O$^+$] = 3×10^{-9} M $\qquad$ [OH$^-$] = 3×10^{-6} M

9.77 a. 2.60 $\qquad$ b. 12.17

9.79 HCl is fully dissociated to H$_3$O$^+$ and Cl$^-$ and CH$_3$COOH is not fully dissociated.

9.81 a. HBr(aq) + KOH(aq) $\longrightarrow$ KBr(aq) + H$_2$O(l)

$\qquad$ b. 2 HNO$_3$(aq) + Ca(OH)$_2$(aq) $\longrightarrow$ 2 H$_2$O(l) + Ca(NO$_3$)$_2$(aq)

$\qquad$ c. HCl(aq) + NaHCO$_3$(aq) $\longrightarrow$ NaCl(aq) + H$_2$O(l) + CO$_2$(g)

$\qquad$ d. H$_2$SO$_4$(aq) + Mg(OH)$_2$(aq) $\longrightarrow$ 2 H$_2$O(l) + MgSO$_4$(aq)

9.83 2 HNO$_3$(aq) + CaCO$_3$(s) $\longrightarrow$ Ca(NO$_3$)$_2$(aq) + CO$_2$(g) + H$_2$O(l)

9.85 a,e: neutral $\qquad$ b,d,f: basic $\qquad$ c. acidic

9.87 0.14 M

9.89 0.12 M

9.91 25 mL

9.93 **B** is a buffer because it contains equal amounts of the acid and its conjugate base.

9.95 c

9.97 a. HNO$_2$ is a proton donor that will react with added base and NO$_2^-$ is a proton acceptor that will react with added acid.

$\qquad$ b. The concentration of HNO$_2$ increases and that of NO$_2^-$ decreases when a small amount of acid is added to the buffer.

$\qquad$ c. The concentration of HNO$_2$ decreases and that of NO$_2^-$ increases when a small amount of base is added to the buffer.

9.99 a. 12.66 $\qquad$ b. 10.25

9.101 a. 4.74 $\qquad$ b. 5.05 $\qquad$ c. 4.44

9.103 CO$_2$ combines with rainwater to form H$_2$CO$_3$, which is acidic, lowering the pH.

9.105 By breathing into a bag, the individual breathes in air with a higher CO$_2$ concentration. Thus, the CO$_2$ concentration in the lungs and the blood increases, thereby lowering the pH.

9.107 A rise in CO$_2$ concentration leads to an increase in H$^+$(aq) concentration by the following equilibria:

$\qquad$ CO$_2$(g) + H$_2$O(l) $\rightleftharpoons$ H$_2$CO$_3$(aq) $\rightleftharpoons$ HCO$_3^-$(aq) + H$^+$(aq)

9.109 OCl$^-$(aq) + H$_2$O(l) $\longrightarrow$ HOCl(aq) + OH$^-$(aq)

$\qquad$ OH$^-$ is formed by this reaction, so the water is basic.

CHAPTER 10 PRACTICE PROBLEMS

10.1

	Atomic Number	Mass Number	Number of Protons	Number of Neutrons	Isotope Symbol
Cobalt-59	27	59	27	32	$^{59}_{27}$Co
Cobalt-60	27	60	27	33	$^{60}_{27}$Co

10.2 $^{131}_{53}$I $\longrightarrow$ $^{0}_{-1}$e + $^{131}_{54}$Xe

10.3 a. $^{74}_{33}$As $\longrightarrow$ $^{0}_{+1}$e + $^{74}_{32}$Ge

$\qquad$ b. $^{15}_{8}$O $\longrightarrow$ $^{0}_{+1}$e + $^{15}_{7}$N

10.4 a. 2 half-lives $\qquad$ b. 44 min

10.5 4.4 mL

10.6 30. mCi

10.7 $^{235}_{92}$U + $^{1}_{0}$n $\longrightarrow$ $^{133}_{51}$Sb + $^{100}_{41}$Nb + 3 $^{1}_{0}$n

10.8 a. $^{1}_{1}$H $\qquad$ b. $^{3}_{2}$He $\qquad$ c. $^{0}_{+1}$e

CHAPTER 10 PROBLEMS

10.1

	Atomic Number	Mass Number	Number of Protons	Number of Neutrons
a. $^{85}_{38}$Sr	38	85	38	47
b. $^{67}_{31}$Ga	31	67	31	36
c. Selenium-75	34	75	34	41

10.3   An α particle has no electrons around the nucleus.

10.5 $^{222}_{86}Rn \longrightarrow \, ^{4}_{2}He + \, ^{218}_{84}Po$

10.7   a. $^{218}_{84}Po \longrightarrow \, ^{4}_{2}He + \, ^{214}_{82}Pb$

       b. $^{230}_{90}Th \longrightarrow \, ^{4}_{2}He + \, ^{226}_{88}Ra$

       c. $^{252}_{99}Es \longrightarrow \, ^{4}_{2}He + \, ^{248}_{97}Bk$

10.9 $^{192}_{77}Ir \longrightarrow \, ^{192}_{78}Pt + \, ^{0}_{-1}e + \gamma$

10.11

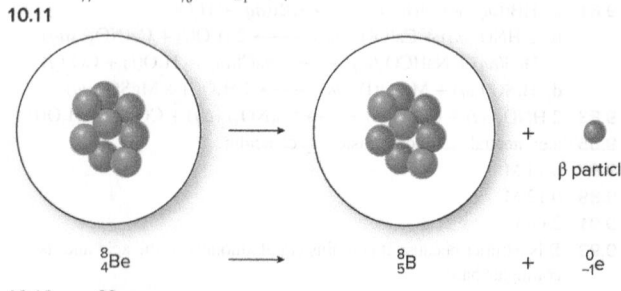

10.13   a. 80. mg

       b. 20.0 mg

       c. 10.0 mg

       d. 8 half-lives

10.15   a. 0.2 rem

       b. 14 mrem

       c. "a" is the higher dose.

10.17   a. 62 protons, 91 neutrons, 62 electrons

       b. $^{153}_{62}Sm \longrightarrow \, ^{153}_{63}Eu + \, ^{0}_{-1}e$

       c. 9.4 mCi

10.19

	a. Atomic Number	b. Mass Number	c. Number of Protons	d. Number of Neutrons	Isotope Symbol
A	9	18	9	9	$^{18}_{9}F$
B	9	19	9	10	$^{19}_{9}F$

10.21

	Atomic Number	Mass Number	Number of Protons	Number of Neutrons	Isotope Symbol
a. Chromium-51	24	51	24	27	$^{51}_{24}Cr$
b. Palladium-103	46	103	46	57	$^{103}_{46}Pd$
c. Potassium-42	19	42	19	23	$^{42}_{19}K$
d. Xenon-133	54	133	54	79	$^{133}_{54}Xe$

10.23

	Change in Mass	Change in Charge
a. α particle	−4	−2
b. β particle	0	+1
c. γ ray	0	0
d. Positron	0	−1

10.25

	Mass	Charge
a. α	4	+2
b. n	1	0
c. γ	0	0
d. β	0	−1

10.27   a. β particle, $^{60}_{27}Co \longrightarrow \, ^{60}_{28}Ni + \, ^{0}_{-1}e$

       b. positron, $^{55}_{27}Co \longrightarrow \, ^{55}_{26}Fe + \, ^{0}_{+1}e$

       c. α particle, $^{220}_{86}Rn \longrightarrow \, ^{216}_{84}Po + \, ^{4}_{2}He$

10.29

10.31

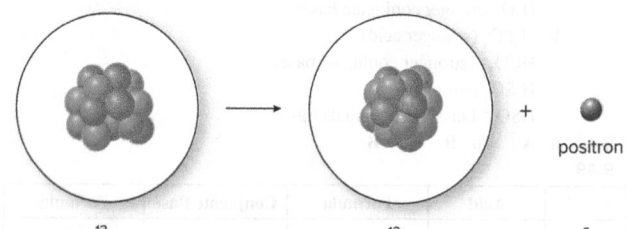

10.33   a. $^{59}_{26}Fe \longrightarrow \, ^{59}_{27}Co + \, ^{0}_{-1}e$ c. $^{178}_{80}Hg \longrightarrow \, ^{178}_{79}Au + \, ^{0}_{+1}e$

       b. $^{190}_{78}Pt \longrightarrow \, ^{186}_{76}Os + \, ^{4}_{2}He$

10.35   a. $^{90}_{39}Y \longrightarrow \, ^{90}_{40}Zr + \, ^{0}_{-1}e$ c. $^{210}_{83}Bi \longrightarrow \, ^{206}_{81}Tl + \, ^{4}_{2}He$

       b. $^{135}_{60}Nd \longrightarrow \, ^{135}_{59}Pr + \, ^{0}_{+1}e$

10.37 $^{214}_{83}Bi \longrightarrow \, ^{214}_{84}Po + \, ^{0}_{-1}e$

       $^{214}_{83}Bi \longrightarrow \, ^{210}_{81}Tl + \, ^{4}_{2}He$

10.39   a. $^{232}_{90}Th \longrightarrow \, ^{4}_{2}He + \, ^{228}_{88}Ra$

       b. $^{25}_{11}Na \longrightarrow \, ^{25}_{12}Mg + \, ^{0}_{-1}e$

       c. $^{118}_{54}Xe \longrightarrow \, ^{118}_{53}I + \, ^{0}_{+1}e$

       d. $^{243}_{96}Cm \longrightarrow \, ^{4}_{2}He + \, ^{239}_{94}Pu$

10.41 $^{228}_{89}Ac$

10.43   two

10.45   a. 4.4 g **A**   b. 2.2 g **A**, 2.2 g **B**   c. 0.55 g **A**, 3.9 g **B**

10.47   a. 16   b. 8

10.49   4.0 days

10.51

	Iodine-131	Xenon-131
a.	32 mg	32 mg
b.	16 mg	48 mg
c.	8.0 mg	56 mg
d.	4.0 mg	60. mg

10.53 1.9×10^{8} disintegrations/s

10.55   2.3 mL

10.57   2.6 mL

10.59   a. 10 mCi   b. 5 mCi   c. 1 mCi

10.61   20 Sv = 2,000 rem

       This represents a fatal dose because 600 rem is uniformly fatal.

10.63   a. fusion   b. fission   c. both   d. fusion

10.65   a. $^{235}_{92}U + \, ^{1}_{0}n \longrightarrow \, ^{137}_{50}Sn + \, ^{97}_{42}Mo + 2 \, ^{1}_{0}n$

       b. $^{235}_{92}U + \, ^{1}_{0}n \longrightarrow \, ^{93}_{36}Kr + \, ^{140}_{56}Ba + 3 \, ^{1}_{0}n$

10.67

10.69 tritium; $_1^3H$

10.71 a. $_{33}^{74}As \longrightarrow _{+1}^{0}e + _{32}^{74}Ge$ b. 3.8 mg   c. 1.5 mL

10.73 a. 38 protons, 51 neutrons, 38 electrons

b. $_{38}^{89}Sr \longrightarrow _{39}^{89}Y + _{-1}^{0}e$

c. 0.625 µg

10.75 a. $_{77}^{192}Ir \longrightarrow _{78}^{192}Pt + _{-1}^{0}e + \gamma$

b. 30. mg

c. 2.3 Ci

10.77 $_6^{12}C$

10.79 $_{83}^{209}Bi + _{26}^{58}Fe \longrightarrow _{109}^{266}Mt + _0^1n$
   meitnerium-266

10.81 a. used for the treatment and diagnosis of thyroid diseases

b. used for the treatment of breast cancer

c. used for the diagnosis of heart disease

10.83 a. Iodine-125, with its longer half-life, is used for the treatment of prostate cancers using implanted radioactive seeds.

b. Iodine-131, with its shorter half-life, is used for the diagnostic and therapeutic treatment of thyroid diseases and tumors. A patient is administered radioactive iodine-131, which is then incorporated into the thyroid hormone, thyroxine. Since its half-life is short, the radioactive iodine isotope decays so that little remains after a month or so.

10.85 Radiology technicians must be shielded to avoid exposure to excessive and dangerous doses of radiation.

10.87 High doses of stable iodine will prevent the absorption and uptake of the radioactive iodine-131.

10.89 370 kcal

CHAPTER 11 PRACTICE PROBLEMS

11.1 a. (structure)   b. (structure)   c. (structure)   d. (structure)   e. (structure)

11.2 a. (1), (2) both trigonal planar

b. (1) linear; (2) tetrahedral; (3) bent

c. (1) trigonal planar; (2) bent

d. (1) trigonal planar; (2) linear

11.3 (1) bent; (2) linear; (3), (4) trigonal planar; (5) bent; (6) tetrahedral

11.4 a. $CH_3(CH_2)_3CH_3$ c. $CH_3CH_2O(CH_2)_2OH$

b. $Br(CH_2)_2Br$ d. $CH_3CH_2C(CH_3)_3$

11.5 a. (structure)

b. (structure)

c. (structure)

11.6 a. (structure)   b. (structure)   c. (structure)

11.7 C1: 1 H   C3: 3 H's   C5: 2 H's   C7: 1 H

C2: 1 H   C4: 0 H's   C6: 2 H's   C8: 3 H's

11.8 a. (structure)

aldehyde

b. (structure)

carboxylic acid

c. (structure)

ketone

d. (structure)

ester

e. (structure)

amide

11.9 amide, aromatic ring, ether, hydroxyl, amine

11.10 a. $CH_3CH_2OCH_2CH_3$, ether

b. $CH_3CH_2CH=CHCH_2CHO$, alkene, aldehyde

11.11 a. nonpolar; all nonpolar bonds

b. polar; one polar $C=O$ bond

c. Nonpolar; the four bond dipoles cancel.

d. Polar; the polar $C-N$ and $N-H$ bond dipoles don't cancel.

11.12 a. insoluble

b. soluble

c. insoluble

CHAPTER 11 PROBLEMS

11.1 a,e: organic

b,c,d,f: inorganic

11.3 a. [structure: C bonded to H, H, H, Cl]

b. [structure: two carbons each bonded to H's and Br]

11.5 a. [structure: branched six-carbon chain]

b. [structure: ring with O and OH]

c. [structure: chain with C=C double bond and Br]

11.7 a. alcohol

b. aromatic ring, alkene

c. two amines

11.9 Both a carboxylic acid (RCO_2H) and an alcohol contain OH groups, but a carboxylic acid has a $C=O$ bonded to the OH group, whereas an alcohol does not. **A** = alcohol; **B** = carboxylic acid.

11.11 An amide has a carbonyl bonded to N, and an amine has as N bonded to only R's and H's. **C** amine; **D** amide

11.13 ester, amide, carboxylic acid

11.15 a. [structure: $Cl-C-H$ with $\delta-$ Cl labels and $\delta+$]

b. [structure: $C=O$ with $\delta+$ $\delta-$]

c. [structure: H bonded to C with O, F, Cl with partial charges]

d. [structure: aromatic ring attached to chain with N and CH_3, partial charges]

11.17 DDT is a weakly polar, fat-soluble compound that is soluble in tissues. Therefore, once it is ingested by birds, it stays in their tissues for long periods of time, making it detectable.

11.19 Niacin is soluble in water.

11.21 inorganic: (a), (b) organic: (c)

11.23 a. [structure: $H-C-C=C-C\equiv C-H$]

b. [structure: $H-C=C-C-O-H$]

c. [structure: $H-C\equiv C-C-C-H$ with Cl]

d. [structure: $H-C=C-C-C-N-H$ with O]

11.25 a. (1) trigonal planar; (2) linear

b. (1) tetrahedral; (2) bent; (3) tetrahedral

11.27 a. (1) and (2) 180°   c. (1) and (2) 109.5°

b. (1) and (2) 120°

11.29 (1) bent; (2) trigonal planar; (3) tetrahedral; (4) trigonal pyramidal

11.31 Each C is surrounded by three groups, so each carbon is trigonal planar giving 120° bond angles.

11.33 a. $CH_3(CH_2)_2C(CH_3)_3$ c. $CH_3(CH_2)_2CHO$

b. $(CH_3)_2CHCH_2O(CH_2)_2CH_3$

11.35 a. [structure: cyclohexane ring with H_2N and O methoxy]

b. [structure: cyclopentane ring with two Cl and methyl]

11.37 a. [structure: branched nine-carbon chain]

b. [structure: chain with O-H]

c. [structure: ester chain with O and O]

d. [structure: cyclohexane-type ring with Cl, Cl, O and chains]

11.39 a. [structure: branched chain]

b. [structure: chain with O-H and ether O]

11.41 a.

A   **B**

b.

A   **B**

⌐ Five bonds to C

11.43 a. (CH₃)₃CHCH₂CH₃

⌐ Five bonds to C

b. CH₃(CH₂)₄CH₂OH

⌐ Five bonds to C

c. (CH₃)₂C=CH₃

d.   Five bonds to C

e.   Five bonds to C

11.45 H—O—C

11.47 a. two alkenes
       b. ketone
       c. ester

11.49 a. ester
       b. two alkenes, two alkynes, one hydroxyl
       c. hydroxyl, ether, aldehyde, aromatic ring

11.51 two hydroxyl groups, aromatic ring, amine

11.53 (CH₃)₂C=CHCH₂CH₂C(CH₃)=CHCHO, two alkenes, aldehyde

11.55 a. HC≡C—CH₃
       b. CH₃CH₂CH₂OH
       c. CH₃CH₂CHO
       d. CH₃CH₂CCH₃

11.57 alkane   CH₃CH₂CH₂CH₂CH₃   C₅H₁₂

       alkene   CH₃—C—C=C—CH₃   C₅H₁₀

       alkyne   CH₃—C—C≡C—CH₃   C₅H₈

11.59 NaCl dissolves in water but not in dichloromethane and cholesterol dissolves in dichloromethane but not in water.

11.61 a.

b.

c.

11.63 Net dipoles and molecular geometry will determine whether a molecule is polar or nonpolar. When a molecule has polar bonds, we must determine whether the bond dipoles cancel or reinforce.

11.65 a.   b.

11.67 a. nonpolar   b. polar   c. polar

11.69 Ethylene glycol is more water soluble because it contains two polar hydroxyl groups capable of hydrogen bonding.

11.71 Sucrose has multiple OH groups and this makes it water soluble. 1-Dodecanol has a long hydrocarbon chain and a single OH group, so it is not water soluble.

11.73 Fat-soluble vitamins will persist in tissues and accumulate, whereas any excess of water-soluble vitamins will be excreted in the urine.

11.75 Vitamin E is a fat-soluble vitamin, making it soluble in organic solvents and insoluble in water.

11.77 a. Yes, there are just enough H's to give each C four bonds.
       b. No, there are too many H's.
       c. Yes, if you put the three C's in a ring, each C gets two H's.

11.79 a. CH₃CH₂CH₂NHCH₃
       b. CH₃CH₂CH₂—N—CH₃
       c. trigonal pyramidal around N
       d. This is a polar molecule. The bond dipoles don't cancel.

11.81 a. C₉H₁₁NO₂   c. seven   d. water soluble
       b,e: Polar bonds are in **bold.**

11.83

a. functional groups:
   (a) ketone   (d) aldehyde
   (b) alkene   (e) ketone
   (c) hydroxyl   (f) hydroxyl
b. Each O needs two lone pairs.
c. 21 C's
d. number of H's at atom:
   1'–0 H's
   2'–0 H's
   3'–1 H
   4'–2 H's
   5'–1 H
   6'–1 H
e. shape at each atom:
   1–tetrahedral
   2–tetrahedral
   3–bent
   4–trigonal planar
   5–tetrahedral

f.

11.85 The waxy coating will prevent loss of water from leaves and will keep leaves crisp.

11.87 THC is not water soluble. THC is fat soluble and will therefore persist in tissues for an extended period of time. Ethanol is water soluble and will be quickly excreted in the urine.

CHAPTER 12 PRACTICE PROBLEMS

12.1 a. not isomers   b. isomers   c. isomers   d. not isomers

12.2

12.3 a. $CH_3CH_2CH_2CH_3$ c.

   b. $(CH_3)_3CH$ d.

12.4 a. 3-methylpentane
   b. 4-methyl-5-propylnonane
   c. 2,4-dimethylhexane

12.5 a. 2,3-dimethylpentane
   b. 4-ethyloctane

12.6

12.7 a. methylcyclobutane   c. 1-ethyl-3-propylcyclopentane
   b. 1,1-dimethylcyclohexane   d. 1-ethyl-4-methylcyclohexane

CHAPTER 12 PROBLEMS

12.1 a. 8   b. 8   c. 18   d. 16
12.3 d.

12.5 a.   b.

12.7 a.

   b.

   c.

12.9 a. **A** and **B**   b. **C**
12.11 a. 2,3-dimethylbutane
   b. 4-ethyldecane
   c. 4-ethyl-3,4-dimethyloctane
12.13 four alkenes, ketone, ester
12.15 a.   c.

   b.   d.

12.17 Vaseline is nonpolar, so it is insoluble in a polar solvent like water, and soluble in a weakly polar solvent like dichloromethane.
12.19 a. $CH_3CH_2CH_3 + 5\ O_2 \longrightarrow 3\ CO_2 + 4\ H_2O$
   b. $2\ CH_3CH_2CH_2CH_3 + 13\ O_2 \longrightarrow 8\ CO_2 + 10\ H_2O$
12.21 $CH_3CH_2CH_2CH_2Cl + CH_3CH(Cl)CH_2CH_3$
12.23 64
12.25 $C_{27}H_{56}$

12.27 a. $CH_3(CH_2)_3CH_3$

c. $(CH_3)_3CC(CH_3)_3$

b. $CH_3CH_2CHCHCH_3$ with CH_3 and CH_3 substituents

d. structure with CH_3, CH_3, CH_3

12.29 a,c,d: constitutional isomers   b. identical

12.31 a. identical   b. constitutional isomers   c. constitutional isomers

12.33 a,d: constitutional isomers   b,c,e: identical

12.35 a. cyclohexane–CH_3 ;   cyclopentane–CH_2CH_3

b. $CH_3CH_2CH_2CH_2CH_2OH$ $CH_3OCH_2CH_2CH_2CH_3$

c. $CH_3CH_2CH_2Cl$ CH_3CHCH_3 with Cl

12.37 a. 9   b. 7

12.39 cyclopentane; cyclobutane; bicyclopropyl structure; methylcyclopropane; methylenecyclopropane structures

12.41 hexane; 2-methylpentane; 3-methylpentane; 2,2-dimethylbutane; 2,3-dimethylbutane

12.43 a. 4-methylheptane   b. ethylcyclopentane

12.45 a. 3-methylheptane   d. 4-ethyl-2,6-dimethyloctane
b. 3,5-dimethyloctane   e. 6-ethyl-2-methyloctane
c. 3,3-diethylhexane   f. 2,2,8,8-tetramethyldecane

12.47 a. cyclooctane   c. 1,1,2,2-tetramethylcyclobutane
b. methylcyclopropane   d. 1,3-diethylcyclohexane

12.49 a. $CH_3CH_2CHCH_2CH_2CH_3$ with CH_2CH_3

b. $CH_3CH_2CCH_2CH_2CH_2CH_3$ with CH_3 and CH_2CH_3

c. $CH_3CHCHCHCHCH_2CH_2CH_2CH_2CH_3$ with CH_3, CH_3, CH_3, CH_3

d. cyclooctane

e. cyclohexane with H_3C, CH_3, CH_3

f. cyclopentane with CH_2CH_3, CH_3, CH_3

12.51 a. 2-methylbutane: Number to give CH_3 the lower number, 2 not 3.
b. methylcyclopentane: no number assigned if only one substituent
c. 2-methylpentane: five-carbon chain
d. 2,5-dimethylheptane: longest chain not chosen
e. 1,3-dimethylcyclohexane: Number to give the second substituent the lower number.
f. 1-ethyl-2-propylcyclopentane: lower number assigned alphabetically

12.53

cyclopentane with CH_3 and CH_3
1,2-dimethylcyclopentane

cyclopentane with CH_3 and CH_3
1,3-dimethylcyclopentane

cyclopentane with CH_3 and CH_3
1,1-dimethylcyclopentane

12.55 a. chain structure

b. cyclopentane with CH_3 and CH_3

c. branched chain structure

12.57 a. H–C–C–C–C–C–C–C–C–C–C–H (10-carbon chain with H's)

b. 6-carbon chain structure with branches

c. cyclobutane structure with H's

12.59 a. ball-and-stick model   b. ball-and-stick model

12.61 a. $(CH_3)_4C$, $(CH_3)_2CHCH_2CH_3$, $CH_3CH_2CH_2CH_2CH_3$
b. $(CH_3)_2CHCHCH(CH_3)_2$, $CH_3CH_2CH_2CH(CH_3)_2$, $CH_3(CH_2)_4CH_3$

12.63 Hexane is a nonpolar hydrocarbon and is soluble in organic solvents but not in water.

12.65 a. $2\,CH_3CH_3 + 7\,O_2 \longrightarrow 4\,CO_2 + 6\,H_2O$
b. $(CH_3)_2CHCH_2CH_3 + 8\,O_2 \longrightarrow 5\,CO_2 + 6\,H_2O$

12.67 a. $2\,CH_3CH_2CH_3 + 7\,O_2 \longrightarrow 6\,CO + 8\,H_2O$
b. $2\,CH_3CH_2CH_2CH_3 + 9\,O_2 \longrightarrow 8\,CO + 10\,H_2O$

12.69 $C_6H_{12}O_6 + 6 O_2 \longrightarrow 6 CO_2 + 6 H_2O$

12.71 a. CH_3Br b.   c.

12.73 a. $CO_2 + H_2O$
b. $(CH_3)_3CC(CH_3)_2CH_2Cl$
c. $(CH_3)_3CC(CH_3)_2CH_2Br$

12.75 Higher molecular weight alkanes in warmer weather means less evaporation. Lower molecular weight alkanes in colder weather means the gasoline won't freeze.

12.77 The mineral oil can prevent the body's absorption of important fat-soluble vitamins, which are expelled with the mineral oil.

12.79 c. The nonpolar asphalt will be most soluble in the paint thinner because "like dissolves like."

12.81 a. 3-ethyl-4,4-dimethylheptane
b.
c. not water soluble
d. soluble in organic solvents
e. $C_{11}H_{24} + 17 O_2 \longrightarrow 11 CO_2 + 12 H_2O$

f.

12.83. a. propylcyclopentane
b.
c. not water soluble
d. soluble in organic solvents
e. $C_8H_{16} + 12 O_2 \longrightarrow 8 CO_2 + 8 H_2O$

f.

12.85 $C_{10}H_{18}$

12.87 Cyclopentane has a more rigid structure. The rings can get closer together because they are not floppy, resulting in an increased force of attraction.

CHAPTER 13 PRACTICE PROBLEMS

13.1 a.

b.

c.

13.2 a. 3-methyl-1-pentene
b. 3-ethyl-3-heptene
c. 2,4-heptadiene
d. 3-ethylcyclopentene

13.3 a. 4,5-dimethyl-1-octene
b. 2,3-dimethyl-2-hexene

13.4 a.
b.
c.
d.
e.
f. $CH_3CH_2CH_2CH_2CH_2CH_2CHCH_2C{\equiv}CH$ with CH_2CH_3 branch

13.5 a.
b.
c.

13.6 a. constitutional isomers
b. stereoisomers
c. constitutional isomers

13.7 a. $CH_3CH_2CH_2CH_2CH_2CH_3$ c.
b. $CH_3CHCH_2CH_2CH(CH_3)_2$ with CH_3 branch

13.8 a.   c.
b.   d.

13.9 a. $CH_3CH(OH)CH_2CH_3$
b. $CH_3CH_2CH(OH)CH_3$
c.

13.10 a.

b.

c.

13.11 a. propylbenzene
b. *p*-ethyliodobenzene
c. *m*-butylphenol
d. 2-bromo-5-chlorotoluene

CHAPTER 13 PROBLEMS

13.1 a. C_4H_8 b. C_6H_{14} c. C_7H_{12} d. C_5H_{10}

13.3 a. 2-methyl-3-nonyne
b. 6,6-dimethyl-3-octyne

13.5 a. cis   b.   cis

13.7 palmitic acid, 63 °C
palmitoleic acid, 1 °C

13.9 a.   b.

13.11 a.

+

b.

13.13 $CH_2=CHOCCH_3$

13.15 Compound (a) might be found in a sunscreen because it contains two aromatic rings.

13.17 a.   b.   c.

13.19 a. $C_{10}H_{12}O$
b. aromatic ring, alkene, ether
c. trans
d.

All other C's are trigonal planar.

13.21 a. $C_{10}H_{22}$ b. $C_{10}H_{20}$ c. $C_{10}H_{18}$

13.23 $HC{\equiv}CCH_2CH_2CH_3$ $CH_3C{\equiv}CCH_2CH_3$

13.25 a.

b.

all trigonal planar

c. tetrahedral trigonal planar

13.27 a. 2-ethyl-1-butene   b. 2-hexyne
13.29 a. 5,5-dimethyl-1-hexene   d. 5,5-dimethyl-2-hexyne
b. 3-ethyl-5,7-dimethyl-3-octene   e. 6-ethyl-5,6-dimethyl-2-octyne
c. 2-ethyl-1-heptene   f. 3,3-dimethyl-1,5-hexadiene
13.31 a. 5-ethyl-2-methyl-2-heptene   b. 3,4-diethyl-5-methyl-3-octene
13.33 a. 4-methylcyclohexene   b. 3,3-diethylcyclobutene

13.35 a.

b.

c.

d.

e. $CH_2=CH-CH=CHCH_2CH_2CH_3$

f.

13.37 a. Assign lower number to alkene: 2-methyl-2-hexene.
b. five-carbon chain: 2-pentene
c. Number to put the C=C between C1 and C2, and then give the first substituent the lower number: 1,6-dimethylcyclohexene.
d. seven-carbon chain: 3-methyl-1-heptyne

13.39   trans

13.41

13.43   cis alkene, *cis*-4-methyl-2-pentene

13.45   a.

cis-2-nonene

trans-2-nonene

b.

cis-2-methyl-3-heptene

trans-2-methyl-3-heptene

13.47

13.49   a. identical
         b. constitutional isomers

13.51   a. constitutional isomers   c. constitutional isomers
         b. stereoisomers

13.53   a. $CH_3CH_2CH_2CH_2CH_2CH_3$
         b. $(CH_3)_2CHCH_2CH_2CH_2CH_3$

         c.

         d.

13.55   a.

         b. $(CH_3)_2C-C(CH_3)_2$

         c. $CH_3CHCH_2CH(CH_3)_2$

         d.

13.57   a.

         b.

         c.

         d.

         e.

         f.

13.59 $CH_2\!=\!CH_2$ reagent: HBr

reagent: HCl

$-CH_3$ reagent: Cl_2

$CH_2\!=\!CHCH_2CH(CH_3)_2$ reagent: Br_2

13.61

13.63   a.

         b.

13.65

13.67

13.69   a. *p*-chloroethylbenzene   b. *o*-bromofluorobenzene

13.71   a. *m*-chloronitrobenzene   c. *o*-butylethylbenzene
         b. *p*-nitroaniline   d. 2,5-dichlorophenol

13.73

o-chloroaniline   *p*-chloroaniline

m-chloroaniline

13.75   a.

         b.

         c.

         d.

         e.

13.77 a.

b.

c.

13.79

13.81 four phenols (OH's bonded to a benzene ring), one carboxylic acid (OH bonded to a C=O)

13.83 Methoxychlor is more water soluble. The OCH_3 groups can hydrogen bond to water. This increase in water solubility makes methoxychlor more biodegradable.

13.85 a.

$CH_3CH_2CH_2CH_2CH_2CH_2CH_2$ $CH_2CH_2CH_2CH_2CH_2CH_2CH_2COOH$

$CH_3CH_2CH_2CH_2$ $CH_2CH_2CH_2CH_2CH_2CH_2CH_2CH_2CH_2COOH$

b.
$CH_3CH_2CH_2CH_2CH_2CH_2CH_2CH_2CH_2CH_2CH_2CH_2CH_2CH_2CH_2CH_2COOH$

c.
one possibility:

$CH_2CH_2CH_2CH_2CH_2CH_2CH_2COOH$

$CH_3CH_2CH_2CH_2CH_2CH_2CH_2CH_2$ H

13.87 c.

13.89 Benzene is converted to a more water-soluble compound that can then be excreted in the urine.

13.91 a.

$CH_3(CH_2)_5$ $(CH_2)_7COOH$

b.

$CH_3(CH_2)_5$ H $(CH_2)_7COOH$

c.

$CH_3(CH_2)_4$ $(CH_2)_8COOH$ (one possibility)

13.93 All the carbons in benzene are trigonal planar with 120° bond angles, resulting in a flat ring. In cyclohexane, all the carbons are tetrahedral so the ring is puckered.

13.95 a. $CH_2=CH(CH_2)_4CH_3$ 1-heptene

b. $CH_3(CH_2)_5CH_3$

c. $CH_3CH(OH)CH_2CH_2CH_2CH_2CH_3$

d.

$R = (CH_2)_4CH_3$

13.97 a.

8-methyl-1-nonene

b.

c.

13.99 a. HDPE: [1] high-density polyethylene
[2] no functional group
[3] HDPE is a rigid polymer used in milk jugs.

b. PS: [1] polystyrene
[2] aromatic ring
[3] PS is used in molded trays.

c. PAH: [1] polycyclic aromatic hydrocarbon
[2] aromatic ring
[3] PAHs are produced when organic compounds are burned.

13.101 They are constitutional isomers because the double bond is located in a different place on the carbon chain.

CHAPTER 14 PRACTICE PROBLEMS

14.1 a. 3°   b. 1°   c. 2°

14.2 a. 2-heptanol   c. 2-methylcyclohexanol
b. 4-ethyl-3-hexanol   d. 5-ethyl-6-methyl-3-nonanol

14.3 a.

b.

c.

14.4 a. $CH_3CCH_2CH_2CH_3$ c.

b. $(CH_3)_3CCH_2C-OH$ d. no reaction

14.5 a. $CH_3(CH_2)_5OCH_3$ c. $CH_3(CH_2)_6OH$

b.

d. $CH_3(CH_2)_5OCH_3$

14.6 a. 1-methoxybutane (or butyl methyl ether)
b. methoxycyclohexane
c. dipropyl ether

14.7 a. 3-pentanethiol
b. cyclohexanethiol
c. 5-ethyl-1-heptanethiol

CHAPTER 14 PROBLEMS

14.1 a.

b. The OH on the benzene ring of salmeterol is part of a phenol.

14.3 a.   b. $(CH_3)_3C—OH$

14.5 a. $CH_3CH_2CH_2CHCH_2CH_2C(CH_3)_3$
            |
            OH

b. $CH_3CH_2CHCHCH(CH_3)CH_2CH_3$
       | |
       OH CH_2CH_2CH_3

c.   d.

14.7 **B** has no H on the carbon adjacent to the carbon with the OH group, so H_2O cannot be lost.

14.9 $CH_3OCH_2CH_2CH_3$
          $CH_3CH_2OCH_2CH_3$
          $(CH_3)_2CHOCH_3$

14.11 a. $CH_3CH_2CH_2CH_2OCH_2CH_2CH_2CH_3$
           b. $CH_3CH_2CH_2OCH_2CH_3$
           c. $CH_3CH_2CH_2CH_2CH_2OCH_3$
           d. $CH_3CH_2CHCH_2CH_2CH_3$
                      |
                      OCH_2CH_3

14.13

14.15 a. 3°
           b. 2° OH on six-membered ring, 3° OH on five-membered ring, 1° OH bonded to CH_2 group

14.17 a. 2-bromohexane   c. 1-bromo-2-methylcyclohexane
           b. 3-chloro-2-methylpentane

14.19 The alcohol is 2°. The F on the six-membered ring is 2°. The F on the C that is part of two six-membered rings is 3°.

14.21 a. $CH_3CH_2CH_2SSCH_2CH_2CH_3$
           b. $CH_3CH_2CH_2CH_2SH + CH_3CH_2SH$

14.23 a. 1°   b. 3°   c. 2°   d. 2°

14.25 a. 2°   b. 3°   c. 2°   d. 1°

14.27 a. $CH_3CH_2CHCH_2CH_2CH_3$ c. $CH_3CH_2C—Br$
                      | |
                      OH   (with CH_3 groups)

b. $CH_3—O—CH_2CH_2CH_2CH_2CH_3$

14.29

14.31 $CH_3CH_2CH_2SH$

14.33 a. 2-methyl-3-pentanol   b. 1-chloro-2-methylcyclopentane

14.35 a. $CH_3CH_2C(CH_3)_2CH(OH)CH_3$
           b. 2°
           c. 3,3-dimethyl-2-pentanol

14.37 a. 2-pentanol   d. 4-butylcyclohexanol
           b. 3,3-dimethyl-2-hexanol   e. 2,2-dimethylcyclobutanol
           c. 4-ethyl-6-methyl-1-heptanol   f. 2,5-diethylcyclopentanol

14.39 a. $CH_3CH_2CHCH_2CH_2CH_3$
                      |
                      OH
           b. $CH_3CH_2CH_2OH$
           c.
           d. $CH_2CHCH_2CH_3$
               | |
               OH OH
           e.
           f. $HOCH_2CH_2CCH_2CCH_2CH_3$

14.41 a. 1-ethoxybutane (or butyl ethyl ether)
           b. 2-ethoxypentane
           c. ethoxycyclopentane

14.43 $CH_3CH_2CH_2CH_2CH_2CH_2CH_2OH$ 1-heptanol

$CH_3CH_2CH_2CH_2CH_2CHCH_3$ 2-heptanol
                     |
                     OH

$CH_3CH_2CH_2CH_2CHCH_2CH_3$ 3-heptanol
                   |
                   OH

$CH_3CH_2CH_2CHCH_2CH_2CH_3$ 4-heptanol
                  |
                  OH

14.45 a. 4-bromoheptane

b. 1-chloro-3-methylcyclobutane

c. 1-pentanethiol

14.47 a. (CH₃ with OCH₃, CH₃, H)

b.

c.

d. $CH_3CH_2CH_2CH_2Cl$

e.

f.

14.49 a. $CH_3CH_2CH_2I$ b. $HOCH_2CH_2OH$ c. $CH_3CH_2CH_2OH$

14.51 B < A < C

14.53 Ethanol is a polar molecule capable of hydrogen bonding with itself and water. The greater intermolecular forces make its boiling point higher. Both ethanol and dimethyl ether have only two carbons and can hydrogen bond to H_2O, so both are water soluble.

14.55 **A:** bp = 98 °C
B: bp = 118 °C

14.57 a.

b. —CH=CHCH₃

c.
$CH_3CH=CHCH_2CH_2CH_3$ (major product)   + $CH_2=CH(CH_2)_3CH_3$

d.
$CH_3CH=CCH_2CH_3$ (with CH₃) (major product)   + $CH_3CH_2CCH_2CH_3$ (with CH₂)

14.59 a. $CH_3CH=CHCH_2CH_2CH_3$ and $CH_3CH_2CH=CHCH_2CH_3$

b. The carbons of both double bonds are bonded to an equal number of H's; therefore, roughly equal amounts of both isomers are formed.

14.61 a.   b.

14.63 a. $CH_3(CH_2)_6COH$ c.

b. $CH_3CH_2CCH_2CH_3$ d. no reaction

14.65

14.67 a.   b.

14.69 a. $CH_3CH_2CH_2CH=CHCH_2CH_3$ b. $CH_3CH_2CH_2CCH_2CH_2CH_3$

14.71 $CH_3CH_2CH_2CH_2CH_2CH_2CH_2OH$

14.73 $(CH_3)_3COH$

14.75 a.   b. $CH_3(CH_2)_4S - S(CH_2)_4CH_3$

14.77 a. CH_3SH and $HSCH_2CH_2CH_3$

b. $CH_2=CHCH_2SH$ and $HSCH_2CH_2CH_3$

14.79 $C_4H_{10}O + 6 O_2 \longrightarrow 4 CO_2 + 5 H_2O$

14.81 a. CFCs are chlorofluorocarbons with a general formula of CF_xCl_{4-x}, HCFCs have fluorine, chlorine, and hydrogen bonded to carbons, and HFCs have only hydrogen and fluorine bonded to carbon.

b. CFCs interact and destroy the ozone layer, whereas HCFCs and HFCs decompose before ascending to the ozone layer.

14.83 PEG is capable of hydrogen bonding with water and this makes it water soluble. PVC cannot hydrogen bond to water, so it is water insoluble.

14.85

CH_3CH_2OH + $K_2Cr_2O_7$ $\longrightarrow$ CH_3COH + Cr^{3+} (green color)
              (orange)

The greater the blood alcohol level, the greater the color change from red-orange to green on the Breathalyzer.

14.87 CH_3C-COH (two C=O)

pyruvic acid

14.89

$CH_3CH_2OH \longrightarrow$ acetaldehyde $\xrightarrow{}$ acetic acid

Antabuse
(blocks conversion)

Antabuse blocks the conversion of acetaldehyde to acetic acid and the accumulation of acetaldehyde makes people ill.

14.91 Ether molecules have no H's on O's capable of hydrogen bonding to other ether molecules, but the hydrogens in water can hydrogen bond to the oxygen of the ether.

14.93 a. 3-ethylcyclopentanol

b. 2°

c. —CH₂CH₃   and   —CH₂CH₃

d. —CH₂CH₃

e. —CH₂CH₃

f. —OCH₂CH₃

14.95 a. $CH_3CH_2CCH_2OH$ (with CH₃, H) **A**   b. $CH_3CH=C-CH_3$ (with CH₃)

$CH_3CH_2CCH_3$ (with CH₃, OH) **B**

CHAPTER 15 PRACTICE PROBLEMS

15.1   a. constitutional isomers
b. identical
c. stereoisomers

15.2   a. $CH_3CHCH_2CH_3$ (with Cl)   c. CH_2=$CHCHCH_3$ (with OH)

b. none   d. phenyl-C(H)(CH₃)(Br)

15.3

chirality center

15.4   a.   b.

15.5   a. (CH₃, H—Br, Cl)   b. (COOH, H—OH, CH₂Cl)

15.6   a. levorotatory
b. +32

15.7   a. **Z**   b. **Y**   c. **Z** and **W**   d. **Y** and **X**

CHAPTER 15 PROBLEMS

15.1   a. constitutional isomers
b. stereoisomers
c. identical
d. constitutional isomers

15.3   a,d: achiral   b,c: chiral

15.5 $HOCH_2$—C(=O)—C(H)(OH)—CH_2OH
chirality center

15.7

two chirality centers

15.9

15.11 CH_3NH—

15.13   a.

chirality center

b.

15.15   a. H—(CH₃)—OH ; $CH_2CH_2CH_3$ | HO—(CH₃)—H ; $CH_2CH_2CH_3$

CH_2Cl | CH_2Cl

b. Cl—H ; CH_2CH_3 | H—Cl ; CH_2CH_3

15.17   optically inactive

15.19   a,c: diastereomers   b. enantiomers

15.21   a,c: achiral   b. chiral

15.23   a. (CF₃, Cl, Br, H)   b. H—C—Cl (CH₃, Cl)
chiral   achiral

15.25   **B** enantiomer; **C** identical

15.27

15.29   a. none   c.

b. $CH_3CCH_2CHCH_3$ (CH₃, Cl, H)   d. none

15.31   a. none   b.
chirality center

15.33   a. CH_3CH_2—C(CH₃)(H)—$CH_2CH_2CH_3$

b. CH_3CH_2—C(OH)(H)—$CH_2CH_2CH_3$

15.35

15.37 a. identical
b. enantiomers

15.39 a. constitutional isomers   c. identical
b. enantiomers   d. diastereomers
chirality center

15.41

CHO
|
CH₃—C—CH₃
|
CH₃

CHO
|
CH₃—C—CH₂CH₃
|
H

CH₃CH₂CH₂CH₂CHO

CH₃CHCH₂CHO
|
CH₃

15.43

CHO
|
Br—|—H
|
CH₃

15.45 a.

CHO
|
H—|—OH
|
CH₃

b.

OCH₃
|
CH₃—|—H
|
CH₂CH₃

15.47 a.

CH₃
|
H►C◄F
|
CH(CH₃)₂

b.

COOH
|
H►C◄NH₂
|
CH₃—C►H
|
CH₂CH₃

15.49 a. identical   b,c: enantiomers

15.51 a. An optically active compound rotates the plane of polarized light. An optically inactive compound does not rotate the plane of polarized light.
b. one possibility: CH₃CH₂CH₂CH₂OH
c. one possibility:

CH₃
|
CH₃CH₂—C‴H
|
OH

chiral and optically active

15.53 a. optically active
b. optically inactive

15.55 a. dextrorotatory
b. −52
c. 22 g

15.57 a. 1,2,5,6: diastereomers   3,4: enantiomers
b.

CH₂OH
|
C=O
|
H—C—OH
|
CH₂OH

15.59 They are diastereomers because they are not mirror images of one another.

15.61 a. CH₃CHCO₂H
|
OH

b.

H
|
CH₃—C◄COOH
|
OH

H
|
HOOC►C—CH₃
|
OH

c.

H
|
CH₃—|—COOH
|
OH

H
|
HOOC—|—CH₃
|
OH

15.63 a.

OH   CH₃
| |
CH₃CCH₂CH₂CH₂CH—CH₂CHO
|
CH₃

b.

HO   CH₃
| |
CH₃CCH₂CH₂CH₂—C◄CH₂CHO
| |
CH₃   H

CH₃   OH
| |
OHCCH₂—C◄CH₂CH₂CH₂CCH₃
| |
H   CH₃

c.

HO   CH₃
| |
CH₃CCH₂CH₂CH₂—|—CH₂CHO
| |
CH₃

CH₃   OH
| |
OHCCH₂—|—CH₂CH₂CH₂CCH₃
| |
H   CH₃

15.65 a.

CH₂
|
CH₃CH₂CO₂—C—
|
CH₃—C►H
|
CH₂N(CH₃)₂

d.

CH₂
|
CH₃—C—
|
CH₃CH₂CO₂—C◄H
|
CH₂N(CH₃)₂

b.

CH₂
|
—C—O₂CCH₂CH₃
|
H—C►CH₃
|
CH₂N(CH₃)₂

e.

CH₂
|
CH₃CH₂CO₂—
|
CH₃—|—H
|
CH₂N(CH₃)₂

c.

CH₂
|
CH₃CH₂CO₂—C—
|
H—C►CH₃
|
CH₂N(CH₃)₂

15.67 * = chirality center

CHAPTER 16 PRACTICE PROBLEMS

16.1 a. 5-methylhexanal
b. 3,3,4,4-tetramethylpentanal
c. 2,5,6-trimethyloctanal

16.2 a. 4-methyl-3-heptanone
b. 2 methylcyclopentanone
c. 2,2-dimethyl-3-heptanone

16.3 a.

O
‖
CH₃CH₂C—OH

b. no reaction

c.

CH₃   CH₃ O
| | ‖
CH₃C=CHCH₂CH₂CHCH₂C—OH

16.4 a. $CH_3(CH_2)_6\overset{O}{\overset{\|}{C}}-OH$ c.

b,d: no reaction

16.5 a. $CH_3CH_2CH_2CH_2\overset{OH}{|}$ c. $CH_3\overset{OH}{\underset{|}{C}}HCH_2CH_3$

b. d.

16.6 a. $(CH_3CH_2)_2\overset{OCH_3}{\underset{|}{C}}OH$ $(CH_3CH_2)_2\overset{OCH_3}{\underset{|}{C}}OCH_3$

hemiacetal acetal

b.

hemiacetal acetal

16.7 a. ether
b. acetal
c. hemiacetal
d. acetal

16.8

ether acetal oleandrin

16.9

solanine

Acetal carbons are labeled with (*).

16.10 a. + 2 CH₃OH

b. + 2 CH₃CH₂OH

c. + 2 CH₃OH

CHAPTER 16 PROBLEMS

16.1 a. aldehyde

b. ketone

c. ketone

d. aldehyde

16.3 a. $CH_3\overset{}{\underset{\underset{Cl}{|}}{C}}HCHO$ c. $CH_3(CH_2)_2CH(CH_2)_2\overset{\overset{CH_2CH_3}{|}}{C}HCH_2CHO$

b. $CH_3CH_2\overset{\overset{CH_3CH_2}{|}}{C}H\overset{\overset{CH_2CH_3}{|}}{C}HCH_2CHO$ $\underset{CH_2CH_3}{}$ d.

16.5 a. $CH_3CH_2CH_2CH_2\overset{O}{\overset{\|}{C}}CH_2CH_3$ c. $CH_3CH_2-$$-\overset{O}{\overset{\|}{C}}-CH_3$

b. $CH_3CH_2\overset{O}{\overset{\|}{C}}CH(CH_3)_2$ d.

16.7 Acetone and progesterone are both soluble in organic solvents. Only acetone is small enough to be soluble in water.

16.9 a. $(CH_3CH_2CH_2)_2C=O$
b. $CH_3(CH_2)_5CHO \xrightarrow[\text{reagent}]{\text{Tollens}} CH_3(CH_2)_5COOH$

16.11

16.13 a. acetal b. two ethers

16.15 a. $CH_3CH_2CH_2\overset{\overset{CH_2CH_3}{|}}{C}HCH_2CHO$ c.

b. $CH_3CH_2\overset{O}{\overset{\|}{C}}\overset{}{\underset{\underset{CH_3}{|}}{C}}HCH_3$ d.

16.17 a. Both are trigonal planar.
b. C=O is polar and C=C is not.
c. Both functional groups undergo addition reactions.

16.19 a. 2-methylpentanal b. 3-ethylcyclohexanone

16.21 a. 3-methylhexanal d. 6,6-diethyl-2,2-dimethyloctanal
b. 3,5-dimethylheptanal e. *p*-chlorobenzaldehyde
c. 3-propylhexanal

16.23 a. $CH_3CH_2\overset{\overset{Cl}{|}}{\underset{\underset{Cl}{|}}{C}}CH_2CHO$ c.

b. $CH_3CH_2\overset{}{\underset{\underset{CH_3}{|}}{C}}HCHCH_2CHO$ d. $CH_3CH_2CH_2\overset{\overset{OH}{|}}{C}HCH_2CHO$

16.25 a. 4-methyl-2-pentanone
b. 2,6-dimethylcyclohexanone
c. *o*-butylacetophenone
d. 2,4-dimethyl-3-hexanone
e. 3-chlorocyclopentanone

16.27 a.   c.

b.   d.

16.29

2,2-dimethylbutanal   3,3-dimethylbutanal

2,3-dimethylbutanal   2-ethylbutanal

16.31 a. $CH_3CH_2CH_2CH_2\overset{\text{O}}{\overset{\|}{C}}H$ c. $CH_3CH_2CH_2\overset{\text{CH}_3}{\underset{|}{C}}\overset{\text{O}}{\overset{\|}{C}}CH_3$

pentanal   3-methyl-2-hexanone

b. $CH_3CH_2CH_2\overset{\text{O}}{\overset{\|}{C}}CH_2CH_3$ d. $CH_3CH_2CH_2CH_2CH_2CH_2\overset{\text{O}}{\underset{\text{CH}_3}{\overset{\|}{C}}H}CH$

3-hexanone   2-methyloctanal

16.33

16.35 a. $(CH_3)_3CCH_2CHO$

b.

16.37 **C < A < B**
16.39 a. insoluble   b. soluble   c. insoluble
16.41 a. $CH_3(CH_2)_4COOH$ c. no reaction

b.   d. $CH_3(CH_2)_4COOH$

16.43 a. $CH_3(CH_2)_4COOH$ c. no reaction

b.   d. no reaction

16.45 a,b:

c. no reaction

d. $HO_2C-\overset{\text{O}}{\overset{\|}{C}}-\overset{\text{O}}{\overset{\|}{C}}-CO_2H$

16.47 a. $CH_3CH_2\overset{\text{CH}_3}{\underset{|}{C}H}CH_2CHO$

b.

16.49 a.   c. $CH_3CH_2\overset{\text{OH}}{\underset{|}{C}H}CH_2CH(CH_3)_2$

b.   d. $CH_3(CH_2)_7OH$

16.51

16.53 a.

b.

16.55 1-Methylcyclohexanol is a 3° alcohol and cannot be produced from the reduction of a carbonyl compound.

16.57 a.

b.

c.

d.

16.59 a. hemiacetal   b. two ethers
16.61 a,b:

16.63 a.

b. $CH_2(OCH_3)_2$

c.

d.

16.65 a.

b.

16.67 a.

hemiacetal carbon

b.

c.

16.69

16.71 a. + 2 $HOCH_2CH_2CH_3$

b. + 2 $HOCH_3$

16.73 a.   c. seven

b. *p*-methylacetophenone

d.

16.75 a.

b.

c.

d.

e.

f. + 2 CH_3CH_2OH

16.77 a.

b,c: no reaction

d.

e.

f. + 2 CH_3CH_2OH

16.79

$CH_2=CHCH_2CH_2CHO$ $CH_3CH=CHCH_2CHO$ $CH_3CH_2CH=CHCHO$

16.81 a.

b.

c.

d.

16.83

16.85

hemiacetal

alcohol

16.87 The cis double bond in 11-*cis*-retinal produces crowding, making the molecule unstable. Light energy converts this to the more stable trans isomer, and with this conversion an electrical impulse is generated in the optic nerve.

16.89

CHAPTER 17 PRACTICE PROBLEMS

17.1 a. 3,3-dimethylhexanoic acid   c. 2,4-diethylhexanoic acid
b. 4-chloropentanoic acid

17.2 a. methyl hexanoate   c. propyl pentanoate
b. ethyl benzoate

17.3 a.

b.

17.4 a. $CH_3(CH_2)_3CO_2H$
b. $CH_3(CH_2)_6CO_2^-Li^+$
c. CH_3CO_2H

17.5 a. sodium butanoate
b. lithium benzoate

17.6 a. $(CH_3)_2CH$ c. $CH_3(CH_2)_6$

b.   d.

17.7 a. $CH_3CH_2CH_2CH_2$

b. $CH_3CH_2CH_2CH_2$

c. $CH_3CH_2CH_2CH_2$

d. $CH_3CH_2CH_2CH_2$

17.8 a. $CH_3(CH_2)_8$ $+ CH_3OH$

b. CH_3CHCH_2 $+ CH_3CH_2OH$

c. $+ CH_3CH_2CH_2OH$

17.9 a. $CH_3(CH_2)_8$ $+ NH_4^+ HSO_4^-$

b. CH_3CHCH_2 $+ (CH_3NH_3)^+ HSO_4^-$

c. $+ [(CH_3CH_2CH_2)_2NH_2]^+HSO_4^-$

17.10 $H_2N-(CH_2)_6-NH_2 +$

CHAPTER 17 PROBLEMS

17.1 a. CH_3CH_2 OCH_2CH_3
ester

b. CH_3 $N-CH_3$
amide

c. $(CH_3)_3C$ OH
carboxylic acid

d. $(CH_3)_2CH$ $N(CH_3)_2$
amide

17.3 a. aromatic ring, two carboxyl groups, two amines, one amide
b. nine

17.5 valeric acid = pentanoic acid
isovaleric acid = 3-methylbutanoic acid

17.7

17.9 a. $CH_3CH_2-C(=O)-NH_2$

b. $CH_3CH_2CH_2CH_2CH_2-C(=O)-N(H)-CH_2CH_3$

c. $CH_3-C(=O)-N(CH_3)(CH_3)$

d. $CH_3CH_2CH_2-C(=O)-N(CH_3)-CH_2CH_2CH_2CH_3$

17.11 a.

17.13 a. $C_6H_5-CO_2^-Na^+ \; + \; H_2O$

b. $C_6H_5-CO_2^-Na^+ \; + \; Na^+HCO_3^-$

c. $C_6H_5-CO_2^-Na^+ \; + \; H_2CO_3$

17.15

$CH_3CH_2CH_2CH_2CH_2CH_2CH_2CH_2CH_2CH_2CH_2CH_2CH_2CH_2CH_2-C(=O)-O^-K^+$

17.17 (dimethoxybenzyl isovalerate structure with two OCH_3 groups, $CH_2O-C(=O)-CH_2CH(CH_3)_2$)

17.19 $CH_3CH_2O-C_6H_4-NH_2 \; + \; HO-C(=O)-CH_3$

17.21 (salicylic acid: benzene with COOH and OH) $\; + \; CH_3C(=O)OH$

17.23 a. $CH_3(CH_2)_8-C(=O)-O^-Na^+ \; + \; NH_3$

b. $CH_3CH(CH_3)CH_2-C(=O)-O^-Na^+ \; + \; CH_3NH_2$

c. (cyclohexyl)$-C(=O)-O^-Na^+ \; + \; (CH_3CH_2CH_2)_2NH$

17.25 $\{-OCH_2-(cyclohexyl)-CH_2O-C(=O)-C_6H_4-C(=O)-\}$

17.27 a. $CH_3CH(CH_3)CH_2CH_2CH_2-C(=O)-OH$ c. (cyclobutyl)$-C(=O)-OCH_3$

b. $CH_3CH_2CH_2CH_2-C(=O)-OCH_3$

17.29 a. $CH_3CH_2CH_2CH_2-C(=O)-NH_2$ c. $CH_3CH_2-C(=O)-N(CH_3)-CH_3$

b. $CH_3CH_2-C(=O)-N(H)-CH_2CH_3$

17.31 a. 4-methylpentanamide b. ethyl formate c. *o*-chlorobenzoic acid
17.33 a. 4-methylpentanoic acid c. 2-ethylheptanoic acid
b. 4,5-diethyloctanoic acid
17.35 a. propyl butanoate b. butyl benzoate
17.37 a. hexanamide b. *N*-ethyl-*N*-methylbenzamide
17.39 a. formamide c. 2-hydroxybutanoic acid
b. lithium acetate d. propyl propanoate
17.41 octyl acetate

17.43 a. $CH_3CH_2CH_2CH_2CH_2-CH(OH)-C(=O)-OH$

b. $CH_3CH_2CH_2CH_2CH_2-CH(Cl)-CH_2CH_2-C(=O)-OH$

c. (3,4-dibromobenzoic acid) e. $CH_3CH_2-C(Br)(Br)-C(=O)-OH$

d. $CH_3CH_2-C(=O)-O^-Li^+$ f. $CH_3CH(CH_3)-C(=O)-O-CH_2CH_3$

17.45 a. $H-C(=O)-OCH_2CH_2CH_3$

b. $CH_3CH_2CH_2-C(=O)-OCH_2CH_2CH_2CH_3$

c. $C_6H_5-C(=O)-OCH_2CH_2CH_2CH_2CH_2CH_2CH_3$

d. $CH_3CH_2CH_2CH_2CH_2-C(=O)-NHCH_2CH_3$

e. $CH_3CH_2CH_2CH_2CH_2CH_2-C(=O)-N(CH_3)-CH_2CH_3$

17.47 a. HCO_2CH_3 can hydrogen bond to water.
  b. CH_3CH_2COOH can hydrogen bond to itself and to water.
17.49 $CH_3CH_2CH(CH_3)_2 < CH_3CH_2COCH_3 < CH_3CH_2CO_2H$
17.51 $CH_3CH_2CONH_2$ can intermolecularly hydrogen bond, so it has stronger intermolecular forces.

17.53 a. $CH_3(CH_2)_3C(=O)O^-K^+$ + H_2O

  b. $(CH_3)_2CHCH_2CH_2CO^-Na^+$ + $NaHCO_3$

17.55 a. $CH_3CH_2CH_2C(=O)OCH_3$

  b. $CH_3CH_2CH_2C(=O)OCH_2CH_2CH_3$

  c. $CH_3CH_2CH_2C(=O)O-$cyclohexyl

  d. $CH_3CH_2CH_2C(=O)O-CH_2CH_2-$phenyl

17.57 $HO-$C$_6H_4-CO_2H$ and CH_3OH

17.59 a. $CH_3CH_2CH_2C(=O)NH_2$
  b. $CH_3CH_2CH_2C(=O)N(H)-CH_2CH_3$
  c. $CH_3CH_2CH_2C(=O)N(-CH_2CH_3)-CH_2CH_3$
  d. $CH_3CH_2CH_2C(=O)N(-CH_3)-CH_2CH_3$

17.61 a. cyclohexyl$-C(=O)OH$ + CH_3OH
  b. $HO-C(=O)CH_3$ +   cyclohexyl$-OH$

17.63 $HO-C_6H_4-NH_2$ + $HO-C(=O)CH_3$

17.65 phenyl$-CH_2-C(=O)OH$ + CH_3CH_2OH

17.67 a. $CH_3CH_2CH_2-C(=O)OH$ + $HOCH(CH_3)_2$
  b. decahydronaphthalenyl$-OH$ + $HO-C(=O)CH_3$

c. cyclohexyl$-CH_2CH_2-OH$ + $HO-C(=O)H$

17.69 a. $C_6H_4(CO_2H)(OCH_3)$ + $NH_4^+Cl^-$
  b. $(CH_3)_3C-C(=O)OH$ + $[(CH_3)_2NH_2]^+Cl^-$
  c. $[$cyclohexyl$-NH_3]^+Cl^-$ + $HO-C(=O)CH_3$

17.71 $HO-C(=O)-C_6H_4-C(=O)-OH$ $NH_2-(CH_2)_4-NH_2$

17.73
$-O-C(=O)-C_6H_4-C(=O)-OCH_2CH_2CH_2O-C(=O)-C_6H_4-C(=O)-O-CH_2CH_2CH_2-$

17.75 a. $CH_3-C(=O)-OCH_3$
  b. $(CH_3)_2CHOH$ + $HO-C(=O)CH_3$
  c. $Na^+O^--C(=O)-CH(CH_3)_2$ + $(CH_3)_2CHCH_2OH$
  d. $CH_3(CH_2)_4-C(=O)-O^-Na^+$ + H_2O

17.77 a. 5-methylhexanoic acid
  b. $CH_3CH_2CHCH_2CH_2-C(=O)-OH$ with CH_3 branch
  c. $CH_3CH_2CH_2CH_2CH_2-C(=O)-OCH_3$
  d. $CH_3CHCH_2CH_2CH_2-C(=O)-O^-Na^+$ + H_2O with CH_3 branch
  e. **A** is insoluble in H_2O, but soluble in organic solvent.
  f. $CH_3CHCH_2CH_2CH_2-C(=O)-OCH_2CH_3$ with CH_3 branch
  g. $CH_3CHCH_2CH_2CH_2-C(=O)-NHCH_2CH_3$ with CH_3 branch

17.79 b. This is a sodium salt of a long-chain carboxylic acid.

17.81 a.

   b. In the stomach naproxen exists as the neutral carboxylic acid.
   c. In the intestine naproxen exists as the ionized carboxylate anion.

17.83 Aspirin inhibits the production of prostaglandins.

17.85 The nonpolar end of a soap binds to dirt and hydrocarbons while the polar end then hydrogen bonds with water, thereby rendering the dirt soluble in water.

17.87

17.89 a.   b.

CHAPTER 18 PRACTICE PROBLEMS

18.1 a. $H_2N(CH_2)_3NH(CH_2)_4NH(CH_2)_3NH_2$

   b. CH_3CH_2O...

18.2 a. 2-butanamine
   b. *N*-methyl-1-propanamine
   c. *N,N*-dimethylcyclohexanamine
   d. dibutylamine

18.3 a. $(CH_3)_2CHCH_2NH_2$
   b. $(CH_3)_2CHCH_2OH$

18.4 a. $(CH_3CH_2NH_3)^+ + Cl^-$
   b. $[(CH_3CH_2)_2NH_2]^+ + Cl^-$
   c. $[(CH_3CH_2)_3NH]^+ + Cl^-$

18.5 a. methylammonium chloride
   b. dipropylammonium bromide
   c. ethyldimethylammonium acetate

18.6 a. insoluble
   b,c,d: soluble

CHAPTER 18 PROBLEMS

18.1 3° amine, 1° hydroxyl group

18.3 a. 2° amine
   b. (1) trigonal planar
       (2) tetrahedral
       (3) trigonal pyramidal

18.5 a. $CH_3CH_2CHCH_2CH_2CH_3$
              $\,$ |
              $\quad$ NH_2

   b. $CH_3CH_2CH_2CH_2CH_2NHCH_3$

   c. O_2N—〈 〉—NH_2

   d.

   e. $CH_3CH_2N(CH_3)_2$

   f.

   g.

   h.

18.7 pyridine and pyrrolidine rings

18.9 a. 3° amine
   b. Heroin contains two esters and an alkene in a ring. Naloxone contains a phenol, an alcohol, a ketone, and an alkene in an alkyl group bonded to the N atom.
   c. naloxone

18.11

18.13 A quaternary ammonium salt has four R groups bonded to N, so there is no proton available that can be removed.

18.15 a. 2° amine
   b. aromatic ring, alkyne
   c.

18.17 COOH must be removed and OH must be added.

18.19 This would require addition of a methyl group and removal of two OH groups.

18.21 albuterol: 1° and 2° alcohols, 2° amine
         salmeterol: 1° and 2° alcohols, 2° amine

18.23 2° amide and 3° amine

18.25

18.27 a. 2°   b. 3°

18.29 a. **C**
   b. **D**
   c. **B**
   d. **A**

18.31 a. **H**
   b. **F**
   c. **E**
   d. **G**

18.33 a. cyclohexanamine
  b. *N*-ethyl-*N*-methylaniline
18.35 a. diethylamine
  b. 3-octanamine
  c. *N*-methyl-3-hexanamine
  d. *N*-ethyl-2-heptanamine
18.37 a. $CH_3CH_2CH_2CH_2CH_2CH_2CH_2CH_2CH_2CH_2NH_2$

  b.

  c.

  d. CH_3CHCH_2COOH
         NH_2

  e. $CH_3CH_2CH_2CH_2CH_2CH_2CHCH_3$
                     $N(CH_2CH_2CH_3)_2$

  f. $CH_3CH_2NHCH_2CH_2CH_2CH_2CH_2CH_3$

18.39 a. $\left[(CH_3CH_2CH_2)_2NH_2 \right]^+$ Cl^-

  b. $(CH_3CH_2CH_2CH_2NH_3)^+$ Br^-

  c. $\left[CH_3CH_2N(CH_3)_2 \atop H \right]^+$ OH^-

18.41

trimethylamine   1-propanamine   *N*-methylethanamine   2-propanamine

18.43 Pyridine is capable of hydrogen bonding with water, so it is more water soluble. Pyridine has a higher boiling point than benzene.
18.45 a. $CH_3(CH_2)_5NH_2$
  b. $CH_3(CH_2)_9NH_2$

18.47

18.49 Primary amines can hydrogen bond to each other, whereas 3° amines cannot. Therefore, 1° amines will have higher boiling points than 3° amines of similar size. Any amine can hydrogen bond to water, so both 1° and 3° amines have similar solubility properties.
18.51 a. $CH_3CH_2NH_2 + H_2O \longrightarrow (CH_3CH_2NH_3)^+ + OH^-$
  b. $(CH_3CH_2)_2NH + H_2O \longrightarrow [(CH_3CH_2)_2NH_2]^+ + OH^-$
  c. $(CH_3CH_2)_3N + H_2O \longrightarrow [(CH_3CH_2)_3NH]^+ + OH^-$
18.53 a. $\left[CH_3CH_2CH_2NH(CH_3)_2 \right]^+$ + Cl^-

  b. $\left[CH_3CH_2CHCH_2CH_3 \atop NH_3 \right]^+$ + HSO_4^-

  c.

  d. $CH_3CH_2{-}N{-}CH_2CH_3$ + H_2O + Na^+
                  CH_2CH_3

18.55 a.

  b.

18.57 piperidine
18.59 Caffeine is a mild stimulant, imparting a feeling of alertness after consumption. It also increases heart rate, dilates airways, and stimulates the secretion of stomach acid. These effects are observed because caffeine increases glucose production, making an individual feel energetic.
18.61 An alkaloid solution is slightly basic because its amine pulls off a proton from water, forming OH^-.
18.63 Dopamine affects brain processes that control movement, emotions, and pleasure. Normal dopamine levels give an individual a pleasurable, satisfied feeling. Increased levels result in an intense "high." Drugs such as heroin, cocaine, and alcohol increase dopamine levels. When there is too little dopamine in the brain, an individual loses control of fine motor skills and Parkinson's disease results.
18.65 Serotonin plays an important role in mood, sleep, perception, and temperature regulation. We get sleepy after eating a turkey dinner on Thanksgiving because the unusually high level of tryptophan in turkey is converted to serotonin. A deficiency of serotonin causes depression.

18.67 a.

  c.

18.69

18.71 Chlorpheniramine is an example of an antihistamine. Antihistamines bind to the H1 histamine receptor, but they evoke a different response. An antihistamine like chlorpheniramine or diphenhydramine, for example, inhibits vasodilation, so it is used to treat the symptoms of the common cold and environmental allergies.

18.73 a,b:

3° amine
chirality center

c.

d.

e.

f.

g.

18.75 a,b,c,d:

aromatic ring   chirality centers   2° amine
ester
2-phenylethylamine in bold

e.

18.77

18.79 A vasodilator dilates blood vessels and a bronchodilator dilates airways in the lungs. Histamine is a vasodilator and albuterol is a bronchodilator.

18.81 Albuterol will exist in the ionic form in the stomach and as the neutral form in the intestine.

18.83 Heroin has two esters, which can be made from the two OH groups in morphine. Add acetic acid (CH_3COOH) and H_2SO_4 to make the two esters in heroin.

CHAPTER 19 PRACTICE PROBLEMS

19.1 b and c

19.2 a,b:

A =

hydrophilic portion
hydrophobic portion

B =

hydrophilic portion
hydrophobic portion

c. **A** will have the higher melting point because **A** is a saturated fatty acid and the molecules can pack together better.

19.3 a. $CH_3(CH_2)_{16}CO(CH_2)_9CH_3$ c. $CH_3(CH_2)_{16}CO(CH_2)_{29}CH_3$

b. $CH_3(CH_2)_{16}CO(CH_2)_{11}CH_3$

19.4

19.5 a.

b.

19.6

CHAPTER 19 PROBLEMS

19.1 a and c

19.3 a. omega-9   b. omega-6

19.5 Because beeswax is hydrophobic, it will be insoluble in a very polar solvent like water, only slightly soluble in the less polar solvent ethanol, and very soluble in the weakly polar solvent chloroform.

19.7

19.9 $2 C_{57}H_{110}O_6 + 163 O_2 \longrightarrow 114 CO_2 + 110 H_2O$

19.11 a. phosphoacylglycerol, cephalin

b. triacylglycerol

c. sphingomyelin

19.13 Membrane **A** will be more fluid or pliable because it contains unsaturated fatty acids.

19.15 a,b,c:

OH at C3   double bond between C5 and C6

19.17 two esters, one hydroxyl, two alkenes

19.19 Testosterone has a methyl group at C10 that nandrolone lacks.

19.21 a.

b.

19.23 b.

19.25 b and c

19.27 $CH_3(CH_2)_5CH=CH(CH_2)_7COOH$, $CH_3(CH_2)_7CH=CH(CH_2)_7COOH$, $CH_3(CH_2)_{16}COOH$

19.29 **B < A < C**

19.31 a.

hydrophobic   hydrophilic

b. The melting point would be lower than the melting point of the trans isomer.

c. liquid

d. omega-3 fatty acid

19.33 a.

b. omega-3 acid

c.

d.

19.35 a. $CH_3(CH_2)_{14}\overset{\overset{\displaystyle O}{\|}}{C}O(CH_2)_{21}CH_3$

b. $CH_3(CH_2)_{14}\overset{\overset{\displaystyle O}{\|}}{C}O(CH_2)_{11}CH_3$

c. $CH_3(CH_2)_{14}\overset{\overset{\displaystyle O}{\|}}{C}O(CH_2)_9CH_3$

19.37 a. $CH_3(CH_2)_{16}COOH + HO(CH_2)_{17}CH_3$
b. $CH_3(CH_2)_{12}COOH + HO(CH_2)_{25}CH_3$
c. $CH_3(CH_2)_{14}COOH + HO(CH_2)_{27}CH_3$

19.39 a. **B**   b. **C**   c. **A**

19.41 a.

b.

c.

19.43

19.45

Compound	a. General Structure	b. Example	c. Water Soluble (Y/N)	d. Hexane Soluble (Y/N)
[1] Fatty acid	RCOOH	$CH_3(CH_2)_{10}CO_2H$	N	Y
[2] Soap	$RCOO^-Na^+$	$CH_3(CH_2)_{10}CO_2^-Na^+$	Y	N
[3] Wax	RCOOR'	$CH_3(CH_2)_6CO_2(CH_2)_7CH_3$	N	Y
[4] Triacylglycerol			N	Y

19.47 a. false   b,c,d: true
19.49 a. arachidic acid, stearic acid, and lauric acid
b. solid
c. The long hydrocarbon chains are hydrophobic.
d. The ester linkages are hydrophilic.
e.

19.51 a.   [1] water and H_2SO_4

[2] water and NaOH

b.   [1] water and H_2SO_4

[2] water and NaOH

19.53 c.

19.55 a.

$CH_2-O-\overset{O}{\overset{\|}{C}}-(CH_2)_7CH=CH(CH_2)_5CH_3$

$CH-O-\overset{O}{\overset{\|}{C}}-(CH_2)_7CH=CH(CH_2)_5CH_3$

$CH_2-O-\overset{O}{\overset{\|}{P}}-O-CH_2CH_2\overset{+}{N}H_3$
$\overset{|}{O^-}$

b.

$CH_2-O-\overset{O}{\overset{\|}{C}}-(CH_2)_{10}CH_3$

$CH-O-\overset{O}{\overset{\|}{C}}-(CH_2)_{10}CH_3$

$CH_2-O-\overset{O}{\overset{\|}{P}}-O-CH_2CH_2\overset{+}{N}(CH_3)_3$
$\overset{|}{O^-}$

c.

$HO-CH-CH=CH(CH_2)_{12}CH_3$

$CH-NH-\overset{O}{\overset{\|}{C}}-(CH_2)_{16}CH_3$

$CH_2-O-\overset{O}{\overset{\|}{P}}-O-CH_2CH_2\overset{+}{N}H_3$
$\overset{|}{O^-}$

19.57 Diffusion is the movement of small molecules through a membrane along a concentration gradient. Facilitated transport is the transport of molecules through channels in a cell membrane. O_2 and CO_2 move by diffusion, whereas glucose and Cl^- move by facilitated transport.

19.59

19.61 Cholesterol is insoluble in the aqueous medium of the bloodstream. By being bound to a lipoprotein particle, it can be transported in the aqueous solution.

19.63

19.65 a.

estrone   testosterone

b. The estrogen (left) and androgen (right) both contain the four rings of the steroid skeleton. Both contain a methyl group bonded to C13.

c. The estrogen has an aromatic A ring and a hydroxyl group on this ring. The androgen has a carbonyl on the A ring but does not contain an aromatic ring. The androgen also contains a C=C in the A ring and an additional CH_3 group at C10. The D rings are also different. The estrogen contains a carbonyl at C17 and the androgen has an OH group.

d. Estrogens, synthesized in the ovaries, control the menstrual cycle and secondary sexual characteristics of females. Androgens, synthesized in the testes, control the development of male secondary sexual characteristics.

19.67 Prostaglandins and leukotrienes are two types of eicosanoids, a group of biologically active compounds containing 20 carbon atoms derived from the fatty acid arachidonic acid. Prostaglandins are a group of carboxylic acids that contain a five-membered ring. Leukotrienes do not contain a ring. They both mediate biological activity at the site where they are formed. Prostaglandins mediate inflammation and uterine contractions. Leukotrienes stimulate smooth muscle contraction in the lungs and lead to the narrowing of airways in individuals with asthma.

19.69 Prostaglandins contain a five-membered ring and a carboxyl group (COOH).

19.71 Aspirin inhibits the activity of both COX-1 and COX-2 enzymes, whereas celecoxib inhibits the activity of only COX-2.

19.73

	Vitamin A	Vitamin D
a.	10	21
b.	10	6
e.	Required for normal vision	Regulates calcium and phosphorus metabolism
f.	Night blindness	Rickets and skeletal deformities
g.	Liver, kidney, oily fish, dairy	Milk and breakfast cereals

c. and d.

vitamin A

vitamin D

19.75 a.

b. $CH_3(CH_2)_{12}COO(CH_2)_{15}CH_3$

c. $CH_2-O-\overset{O}{\overset{\|}{C}}-(CH_2)_{12}CH_3$

$CH-O-\overset{O}{\overset{\|}{C}}-(CH_2)_{12}CH_3$

$CH_2-O-\overset{O}{\overset{\|}{C}}-(CH_2)_{12}CH_3$

d. $HO-CH-CH=CH(CH_2)_{12}CH_3$

$CH-NH-\overset{O}{\overset{\|}{C}}-(CH_2)_{12}CH_3$

$CH_2-O-\overset{O}{\overset{\|}{P}}-O-CH_2CH_2\overset{+}{N}H_3$
$\overset{|}{O^-}$

19.77   a. [5], [6]   b. [6], [7]   c. [1], [2], [4]   d. [2], [4]

19.79   **A:** a, c, e   **B:** a, c, d   **C:** b, c

19.81   **A** represents a soap, and **B** represents a phosphoacylglycerol. Both compounds have ionic polar heads and nonpolar tails with many C—C and C—H bonds derived from fatty acids.

19.83   The hydrocarbon chains have only 12 carbons in them, making them short enough so that the triacylglycerol remains a liquid at room temperature.

19.85   Vegetable oils are composed of triacylglycerols, whereas motor oil, derived from petroleum, is mostly alkanes and other long-chain hydrocarbons.

19.87   No, certain fatty acids and fat-soluble vitamins are required in the diet.

19.89   Saturated fats are more likely to lead to atherosclerosis and heart disease.

19.91   The unsaturated triacylglycerols have lower melting points, thus remaining liquid at low temperatures. These unsaturated triacylglycerols allow the cells to remain more fluid with less rigid cell membranes than saturated triacylglycerols would allow for.

19.93   a. reduction   b. oxidation   c. reduction

CHAPTER 20 PRACTICE PROBLEMS

20.1   a. aldopentose   b. aldotetrose   c. ketotetrose

20.2

a.

b.

* chirality center

20.3   a.   c.   b.

20.4   a.   c.   b.

α anomer   β anomer

α anomer
* anomeric C

20.5   a.   b.   c.

20.6   a.   b.   c.

20.7   1⟶ 4-β-disaccharide

glycosidic linkage

20.8

CHAPTER 20 PROBLEMS

20.1

hemiacetal carbon

20.3   a.   b.   c.

20.5

20.7   D-Glucose and D-fructose are constitutional isomers.
D-Galactose and D-fructose are also constitutional isomers.

20.9   a. alditol
b. aldonic acid

20.11

20.13

20.15

3-fucosyllactose

20.17   Cellulose is water insoluble because the many OH groups are already hydrogen bonded to other OH groups in the three-dimensional structure. The OH groups are therefore less available for hydrogen bonding to water.

20.19

20.21   a., b., c.

20.23   a. aldotetrose   b. aldohexose   c. ketopentose

20.25

A
aldotetrose
* chirality center

B
aldohexose

20.27   a., b. aldotriose

20.29   a.

L-tetrose   enantiomer   Fischer projection

b.

D-hexose   enantiomer   Fischer projection

c.

L-pentose   enantiomer   Fischer projection

* chirality center

20.31 a. **A** and **B**
b. **B** and **C** (or **A** and **C**)

c.
CHO
HO—C—H
H—C—OH
CH₂OH

d.
CHO
H——OH
H——OH
CH₂OH

20.33

β anomer   α anomer

20.35 Using a skeletal structure:

1° HO—
2° HO—   hemiacetal C
                 OH ← OH on the anomeric C
HO   OH
2°   2°

20.37
CH₂OH
a. hemiacetal carbon
b. β anomer

c.

d.

20.39 a.
hemiacetal
anomeric carbon
β anomer

b.
CH₂OH   CH₂OH
hemiacetal
anomeric carbon
α anomer

20.41 a.
CH₂OH   OH
hemiacetal
β anomer

b.
CH₂OH   H
hemiacetal
α anomer

20.43 a. aldonic acid   b. alditol   c. monosaccharide

20.45 a. [1]
CH₂OH
HO—C—H
H—C—OH
CH₂OH

[2]
COOH
HO—C—H
H—C—OH
CH₂OH

b. [1]
CH₂OH
H—C—OH
HO—C—H
HO—C—H
CH₂OH

[2]
COOH
H—C—OH
HO—C—H
HO—C—H
CH₂OH

c. [1]
CH₂OH
H—C—OH
H—C—OH
HO—C—H
HO—C—H
CH₂OH

[2]
COOH
H—C—OH
H—C—OH
HO—C—H
HO—C—H
CH₂OH

20.47 a.
COOH
H—C—OH
H—C—OH
HO—C—H
CH₂OH

b.
COOH
H—C—OH
H—C—OH
H—C—OH
CH₂OH

20.49 a.

+

b.

+

20.51 **A** = glycogen   **B** = amylopectin
a. both   b. **A**   c. **C**   d. neither

20.53 a. **A**   b. **C**   c. **B**

20.55

20.57 a,b:
6
CH₂OH
5
4   acetal
1
OH
3   2
H   OH
6
CH₂
5
4   hemiacetal
1
OH
3   2
H   OH

c. 1→6-α-glycosidic linkage
d. β anomer

e.

α anomer + β anomer

20.59

20.61 Cellulose and amylose are both composed of repeating glucose units. In cellulose the glucose units are joined by a 1→4-β-glycosidic linkage, but in amylose they are joined by an α-(1→4) linkage. This leads to very different three-dimensional shapes, with cellulose forming sheets and amylose forming helices.

20.63

20.65 a. starch
       b. cellulose
       c. lactose

20.67 a. D sugar

d.
* chirality center

b. aldohexose

e.

g.

h. a reducing sugar

c.

f.

enantiomer

20.69 Lactose intolerance results from a lack of the enzyme lactase. It results in abdominal cramping and diarrhea. Galactosemia results from the inability to metabolize galactose. Therefore, it accumulates in the liver, causing cirrhosis, and in the brain, leading to mental retardation.

20.71 Fructose is a naturally occurring sugar with more perceived sweetness per gram than sucrose. Sucralose is a synthetic sweetener; that is, it is not naturally occurring.

20.73 An individual with type A blood can receive only blood types A and O, because he or she will produce antibodies and an immune response to B or AB blood. He or she can donate to individuals with either type A or AB blood because the type A polysaccharides are common to both and no immune response will be generated.

20.75 The long sheets of polysaccharides in chitin, similar to cellulose, have β glycosidic linkages and will not be digestible.

20.77 Hyaluronate is found in the extracellular fluid that lubricates joints and the vitreous humor of the eye. Chondroitin is a component of cartilage and tendons. Heparin is stored in the mast cells of the liver and other organs and prevents blood clotting.

20.79

fructose   reduction   stereoisomers
They differ in configuration at a single carbon.

CHAPTER 21 PRACTICE PROBLEMS

21.1 a.
L   D

b.
L   D

21.2 a.
predominant at pI

c.

b.

21.3 a. N-terminal: leucine   C-terminal: alanine
      b. N-terminal: arginine   C-terminal: tyrosine
      c. N-terminal: phenylalanine C-terminal: glutamine
      d. N-terminal: valine   C-terminal: phenylalanine

21.4 a. H₃N⁺—C(H)(H)—C(O)—N(H)—C(H)—COO⁻ with CH₂-phenyl side chain

b. H₃N⁺—C(H)(H)—C(O)—N(H)—C(H)—COO⁻ with CH₂CONH₂ and CH(CH₃)CH₂CH₃ side chains

c. H₃N⁺—C(H)(H)—C(O)—N(H)—C(H)—COO⁻ with CH₂CH(CH₃)₂ and CH₂SH side chains

21.5 a. alanine and isoleucine: Ala–Ile   b. tyrosine and valine: Tyr–Val

21.6

peptide bond

serine   glycine   Ser–Gly

21.7 a.
H₃N⁺—C(H)—COO⁻ with CH₃; H₃N⁺—C(H)—COO⁻ with CH₂CH(CH₃)₂; H₃N⁺—C(H)—COO⁻ with H

b.
H₃N⁺—C(H)—COO⁻ with CH₂OH; H₃N⁺—C(H)—COO⁻ with CH(OH)CH₃; H₃N⁺—C(H)—COO⁻ with CH₂-phenyl

c.
H₃N⁺—C(H)—COO⁻ with CH₂CH(CH₃)₂; H₃N⁺—C(H)—COO⁻ with CH₂-phenyl-OH; H₃N⁺—C(H)—COO⁻ with CH₂CONH₂

21.8 a,b: dehydrogenase

21.9 a. glycerol kinase   c. glucose 6-phosphate isomerase
b. fumarate synthase

CHAPTER 21 PROBLEMS

21.1 a. amide   b. alcohol   c. thiol

21.3 The amino acid is serine.

COO⁻ / H₃N⁺—C—H / CH₂OH   COOH / H₃N⁺—C—H / CH₂OH   COO⁻ / H₂N—C—H / CH₂OH

neutral form   positively charged form   negatively charged form

21.5
a. H₃N⁺—C(H)—C(O)—N(H)—C(H)—COO⁻ with CH₂CH(CH₃)₂ and CH₂CONH₂;   H₃N⁺—C(H)—C(O)—N(H)—C(H)—COO⁻ with CH₂CONH₂ and CH₂CH(CH₃)₂

b. N-terminal: leucine   N-terminal: asparagine
C-terminal: asparagine   C-terminal: leucine
c. Leu–Asn   Asn–Leu

21.7 Yes, the amino acids may be ordered differently.

21.9 Glycine has no large side chain and this allows for the β-sheets to stack well together.

21.11 Heating collagen disrupts the hydrogen bonding and other intermolecular forces. The superhelix unwinds, making it less ordered, turning it into the jelly-like substance gelatin.

21.13 a. Aspartate transaminase catalyzes the transfer of an NH₂ from aspartate to another compound.
b. Glyceraldehyde 3-phosphate dehydrogenase catalyzes the addition (or removal) of 2 H's from glyceraldehyde 3-phosphate.

21.15 a. 35 °C
b. 35 °C

21.17 positive

21.19 substrate

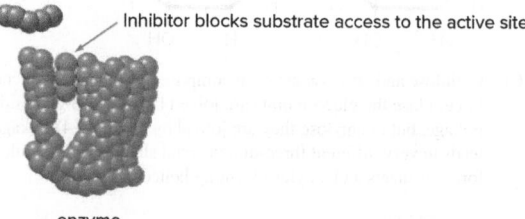
Inhibitor blocks substrate access to the active site.

enzyme

21.21 Alanine is an ionic salt with strong electrostatic forces, leading to its high melting point and making it a solid at room temperature. Pyruvic acid has much weaker intermolecular forces, so it is a liquid at room temperature.

21.23 a. H₃N⁺—C(H)—COO⁻ with CH₂OH   c. H₃N⁺—C(H)—COO⁻ with CH₂-phenyl

b. H₃N⁺—C(H)—COO⁻ with CH₂CONH₂   d. H₃N⁺—C(H)—COO⁻ with CH(CH₃)₂

	[1]	[2]	[3]	[4]
21.25 a. H₃N⁺—C(H)(COO⁻)—CH₂CH(CH₃)₂		neutral	Leu	L
b. H₃N⁺—C(H)(COO⁻)—CH₂-indole		neutral	Trp	W
c. H₃N⁺—C(H)(COO⁻)—(CH₂)₄NH₃⁺		basic	Lys	K
d. H₃N⁺—C(H)(COO⁻)—CH₂COO⁻		acidic	Asp	D

21.27 a.
$$\underset{\text{L}}{\overset{\text{COO}^-}{H_3\overset{+}{N}-\underset{\text{CH}_2\text{CH}_2\text{SCH}_3}{|}-H}}$$
$$\underset{\text{D}}{\overset{\text{COO}^-}{H-\underset{\text{CH}_2\text{CH}_2\text{SCH}_3}{|}-\overset{+}{N}H_3}}$$

b.
$$\underset{\text{L}}{\overset{\text{COO}^-}{H_3\overset{+}{N}-\underset{\text{CH}_2\text{CONH}_2}{|}-H}}$$
$$\underset{\text{D}}{\overset{\text{COO}^-}{H-\underset{\text{CH}_2\text{CONH}_2}{|}-\overset{+}{N}H_3}}$$

21.29

	[1]	[2]	[3]	[4]
a.	glutamine	Gln	Q	neutral
b.	tyrosine	Tyr	Y	neutral

21.31 a,b,c:

$$H_3\overset{+}{N}-\overset{\text{COO}^-}{\underset{\text{CH}_2\text{CH}_2\text{SCH}_3}{\overset{|}{C}}}-H$$

Met
M
methionine
neutral form present at the isoelectric point

21.33 a.
$$H_3\overset{+}{N}-\overset{H}{\underset{\text{CH}_2\text{CH}(\text{CH}_3)_2}{\overset{|}{C}}}-\text{COO}^-$$

predominant form at p*I*

b.
$$H_2N-\overset{H}{\underset{\text{CH}_2\text{CH}(\text{CH}_3)_2}{\overset{|}{C}}}-\text{COO}^-$$

c.
$$H_3\overset{+}{N}-\overset{H}{\underset{\text{CH}_2\text{CH}(\text{CH}_3)_2}{\overset{|}{C}}}-\text{COOH}$$

21.35

Phe–Ala
alanine
peptide bond
phenylalanine

21.37 a. 25
b. glycine
c. glutamine

21.39 a,b,c:

N-terminal amino acid

$$H_3\overset{+}{N}-\overset{H}{\underset{\text{CH}(\text{CH}_3)_2}{\overset{|}{C}}}-\overset{O}{\overset{||}{C}}-\overset{H}{\underset{\text{CH}_2}{\overset{|}{N}}}-\overset{H}{\underset{\text{}}{\overset{|}{C}}}-\text{COO}^-$$

Val–Phe

$$H_3\overset{+}{N}-\overset{H}{\underset{\text{CH}_2}{\overset{|}{C}}}-\overset{O}{\overset{||}{C}}-\overset{H}{N}-\overset{H}{\underset{\text{CH}(\text{CH}_3)_2}{\overset{|}{C}}}-\text{COO}^-$$

Phe–Val

C-terminal amino acid

21.41 a. [1]
$$H_3\overset{+}{N}-\overset{H}{\overset{|}{C}}-\overset{O}{\overset{||}{C}}\overset{*}{-}\overset{H}{N}-\overset{H}{\overset{|}{C}}-\overset{O}{\overset{||}{C}}\overset{*}{-}\overset{H}{N}-\overset{H}{\overset{|}{C}}-\text{COO}^-$$

with side chains $CH_2CH(CH_3)_2$, $CH(CH_3)_2$, and CH_2 (indole ring)

[2] * amide bonds labeled

[3] N-terminal: leucine
C-terminal: tryptophan

[4] Leu–Val–Trp

b. [1]
$$H_3\overset{+}{N}-\overset{H}{\overset{|}{C}}-\overset{O}{\overset{||}{C}}\overset{*}{-}\overset{H}{N}-\overset{H}{\overset{|}{C}}-\overset{O}{\overset{||}{C}}\overset{*}{-}\overset{H}{N}-\overset{H}{\overset{|}{C}}-\text{COO}^-$$

with side chains CH_2 (phenyl), CH_2OH, and $CH(OH)CH_3$

[2] * amide bonds labeled

[3] N-terminal: phenylalanine
C-terminal: threonine

[4] Phe–Ser–Thr

21.43 a. [1], [2] valine: N-terminal, glycine, phenylalanine: C-terminal
[3] Val–Gly–Phe
b. [1], [2] leucine: N-terminal, tyrosine, methionine: C-terminal
[3] Leu–Tyr–Met

21.45 alanine, cysteine, glycine

21.47 a.

$$H_3\overset{+}{N}-\overset{H}{\underset{\text{CH}(\text{CH}_3)_2}{\overset{|}{C}}}-\text{COO}^-$$
$$H_3\overset{+}{N}-\overset{H}{\underset{\text{H}}{\overset{|}{C}}}-\text{COO}^-$$
$$H_3\overset{+}{N}-\overset{H}{\underset{\text{CH}_2(\text{phenyl})}{\overset{|}{C}}}-\text{COO}^-$$

b.

$$H_3\overset{+}{N}-\overset{H}{\underset{\text{CH}_2\text{CH}(\text{CH}_3)_2}{\overset{|}{C}}}-\text{COO}^-$$
$$H_3\overset{+}{N}-\overset{H}{\underset{\text{CH}_2(\text{phenol})}{\overset{|}{C}}}-\text{COO}^-$$
$$H_3\overset{+}{N}-\overset{H}{\underset{\text{CH}_2\text{CH}_2\text{SCH}_3}{\overset{|}{C}}}-\text{COO}^-$$

21.49

$$\overset{\text{COO}^-}{\underset{\text{proline ring}}{}}$$ 3 moles Pro

$$H_3\overset{+}{N}-\overset{H}{\underset{(\text{CH}_2)_3-N-\overset{+}{C}-NH_2}{\overset{|}{C}}}-\text{COO}^-$$
$$H_3\overset{+}{N}-\overset{H}{\underset{\text{CH}_2}{\overset{|}{C}}}-\text{COO}^-$$ 2 moles each, Arg and Phe

$$H_3\overset{+}{N}-\overset{H}{\underset{\text{H}}{\overset{|}{C}}}-\text{COO}^-$$
$$H_3\overset{+}{N}-\overset{H}{\underset{\text{CH}_2\text{OH}}{\overset{|}{C}}}-\text{COO}^-$$ 1 mole each, Gly and Ser

21.51

Gly–Tyr

Val

Gly–Ala–Phe

21.53 a. London dispersion forces   c. electrostatic
 b. London dispersion forces   d. electrostatic

21.55 a. Met–Gly–Leu–Phe–Gln–Ala
 b. Phe–Asn–Leu–Leu–Met

21.57 **A** = primary structure
 B = β-pleated sheet
 C = α-helix

21.59

21.61

α-helix

random

β-sheet

random

α-helix

β-sheet   random

21.63

	a. Secondary Structure	b. H₂O Solubility	c. Function	d. Location
Hemoglobin	Globular with much α-helix	Soluble	Carries oxygen to tissues	Blood
Keratin	α-Helix	Insoluble	Firm tissues	Nail, hair

21.65 When heated, a protein's primary structure is unaffected. The 2°, 3°, and 4° structures may be altered.

21.67 a. Insulin is a hormone that controls glucose levels.
 b. Myoglobin stores oxygen in muscle.
 c. α-Keratin forms hard tissues such as hair and nails.
 d. Chymotrypsin is a protease that hydrolyzes peptide bonds.
 e. Oxytocin is a hormone that stimulates uterine contractions and induces the release of breast milk.

21.69 a. **B**   b. **C**   c. **A**

21.71 a. dehydrase
 b. isomerase

21.73 synthase

21.75 a. loss of CO_2 from citrate
 b. reduction of oxalate
 c. transfer of NH_2 from serine to another compound

21.77 a. 6   c. **A**
 b. 10   d. **B**

21.79 In positive allosteric control, a regulator makes the active site more able to bind the substrate, and the reaction rate increases. In negative allosteric control, a regulator makes the active site less able to bind the substrate, and the reaction rate decreases.

21.81 Captopril inhibits the angiotensin-converting enzyme, blocking the conversion of angiotensinogen to angiotensin. This reduces the concentration of angiotensin, which in turn lowers blood pressure.

21.83

active site

substrate

enzyme

inhibitor

The inhibitor alters active site configuration and the substrate cannot enter.

21.85 The α-keratin in nails has more cysteine residues to form disulfide bonds. The larger the number of disulfide bonds, the harder the substance.

21.87 Humans cannot synthesize the amino acids methionine and lysine. Diets that include animal products readily supply all the needed amino acids, but plant sources generally do not have sufficient amounts of all the essential amino acids. Grains—wheat, rice, and corn—are low in lysine, and legumes—beans, peas, and peanuts—are low in methionine, but a combination of these foods provides all the needed amino acids.

21.89 Cauterization denatures the proteins in a wound.

21.91 The high temperature causes bacterial enzymes to be denatured and inactive, so surgical instruments are sterilized.

21.93 Penicillin inhibits the formation of the bacterial cell wall by irreversibly binding to an enzyme needed for its construction. It does not affect humans because human cells have a cell membrane, but not a rigid cell wall. Sulfanilamide inhibits the production of folic acid and therefore reproduction in bacteria, but humans do not synthesize folic acid (they must ingest it instead), so it does not affect humans.

21.95 Both aspartic acid and glutamic acid have two carboxylic acid groups. At low pH they have a +1 charge with both acid groups protonated, but at a high pH both acid groups are ionized, leading to a net charge of −2.

Form of Asp at low pH

Form of Asp at high pH

CHAPTER 22 PRACTICE PROBLEMS

22.1 a. base = uracil, sugar = D-ribose, nucleoside = uridine

b. base = guanine, sugar = D-2-deoxyribose, nucleoside = deoxyguanosine

22.2 a.

UMP

b.

dTMP

c.

AMP

22.3

22.4 a. 3'-TTTGCAGG-5'   c. 3'-TAACGTGGGCG-5'

b. 3'-ATATGCGG-5'   d. 3'-GTGAACTAGCC-5'

22.5 a. 5'-TCTCAGAG-3'   c. 5'-TAGGACATG-3'

b. 3'-TAACGAG-5'   d. 3'-CCGGTATGAG-5'

22.6 a. [1] 5'-ACGGAUUGC-3'   [2] 5'-ACGGATTGC-3'

b. [1] 5'-CUGAGG-3'   [2] 5'-CTGAGG-3'

c. [1] 5'-AAUUGCGCU-3'   [2] 5'-AATTGCGCT-3'

d. [1] 5'-GUCACUGGCAUG-3'   [2] 5'-GTCACTGGCATG-3'

22.7 a. Gln–Glu–Val–Ser–Tyr–Arg

b. Val–Ile–Trp–Arg–Gly–Ile

c. Leu–Cys–Ser–Arg–Thr–Pro

22.8 a. Pro–Pro–Ala–Asn–Glu–Ala

GGU GGC CGU UUG CUU CGU

b. Ala–Pro–Leu–Arg–Asp

CGU GGU GAU UCU CUG

22.9 a. Arg–Val–Ala–Leu–Leu–Ser

b. Arg–Gly–Phe–Ile–Val–Asn

22.10 a. Leu–Thr

b. [1] Leu–Pro

[2] Stop codon, so no dipeptide is formed.

[3] Leu–Thr

CHAPTER 22 PROBLEMS

22.1

guanosine, a ribonucleoside

22.3 a. base = uracil, sugar = ribose, uridine 5'-monophosphate, UMP

b. base = thymine, sugar = D-2-deoxyribose, deoxythymidine 5'-monophosphate, dTMP

22.5 a,c: false   b,d: true

22.7 a.

b.

22.9 a. 3'-ACCCCGTAA-5'   c. 3'-GGCTGCTAC-5'

b. 3'-CATGGA-5'   d. 3'-CATCAGTGC-5'

22.11 a. GGU, GGC, GGA, GGG   c. AAA, AAG

b. AUU, AUC, AUA   d. GAA, GAG

22.13 a. 3'-CTC GGG CAT ATG CGG TGC-5'

b. Glu–Pro–Val–Tyr–Ala–Thr

22.15 Before deletion, the peptide contains the sequence Ile–Arg–Glu. After deletion, the peptide contains the sequence Ile–Glu.

22.17 a,c: DNA
   b. both
   d. RNA

22.19 **A:** a. deoxyadenosine   **B:** a. cytosine
         b. nucleoside   b. base
         c. DNA only   c. both DNA and RNA

22.21 a. base: cytosine
         monosaccharide: 2'-deoxyribose
         deoxycytidine
      b. base: guanine
         monosaccharide: ribose
         guanosine 5'-monophosphate

22.23 a.

      b. deoxythymidine 5'-monophosphate, dTMP

22.25 a.

      b.

      c.

      d.

22.27 a. HO—CH₂

22.29 a. uracil, adenine
      b. The 5' end has the free phosphate and the 3' end has two OH
         groups on the five-membered sugar ring.
      c. UMP, AMP
      d. This dinucleotide is a ribonucleotide because the sugar rings
         contain an OH group on C2'.
      e. UA

22.31

22.33 a.

5' end

3' end

b.

5' end

3' end

22.35

5' end

3' end

22.37 a. The DNA double helix has 2-deoxyribose as the only sugar. The sugar–phosphate groups are on the outside of the helix.

b. The 5' end has a phosphate and the 3' end has an OH group.

c. Hydrogen bonding occurs in the interior of the helix between base pairs: A pairs with T and G pairs with C.

22.39 a. 3'–TTTATTG–5'

b. 3'–TGACCTGA–5'

c. 3'–GCTATAGGGC–5'

d. 3'–AAGGGCCCTAT–5'

22.41 27% T, 23% G, 23% C

22.43 G and C

22.45

thymine   guanine

Only one hydrogen bond can form between T and G compared to two between T and A.

22.47 **A:** 3' end   **D:** leading strand   **G:** 5' end
B: template strand   **E:** lagging strand
C: 5' end   **F:** template strand

22.49 5'–TACCGGATACGCTA–3'

22.51 a. 3'–UUUAUUG–5'   c. 3'–GCUAUAGGGC–5'
b. 3'–UGACCUGA–5'   d. 3'–AAGGGCCCUAU–5'

22.53 a. [1] 5'–UACCGAAU–3'   [2] 5'–TACCGAAT–3'
b. [1] 5'–GCCGCGAAU–3'   [2] 5'–GCCGCGAAT–3'
c. [1] 5'–CCAUAUGGC–3'   [2] 5'–CCATATGGC–3'
d. [1] 5'–AUCCGGCAU–3'   [2] 5'–ATCCGGCAT–3'

22.55 a. GAC: Leu   c. UUC: Lys
b. AAA: Phe   d. CGU: Ala

22.57 anticodon: CGC; amino acid: alanine

22.59 a. Pro–Thr–Trp–Val–Glu
b. Met–Phe–Leu–Trp–Trp
c. Val–Asp–Glu–Pro–Gln

22.61 a. AUU AUG AAA AGU UAU
b. CCU CAA GAA GAU UUU
c. ACU AGU AAU CGU

22.63 mRNA: UUGCAGGAGUGCUAA
polypeptide: Leu–Gln–Glu–Cys

22.65 a. [1] 3' ATA AGT TAT TTT TTG 5'
[2] Tyr–Ser–Ile–Lys–Asn
b. [1] 3' CTA CAT TTG TTC GGC 5'
[2] Asp–Val–Asn–Lys–Pro

22.67 a. Leu–Gln–His
b. Leu–Gln–Asn
c. Leu–Gln–His, no change
d. This is a stop codon, so the chain is terminated.
e. A dipeptide, Ser–Ala, is synthesized.

22.69 a. Asn–Ala   b. Asn–Ala   c. Asn–Gly   d. Asn–Ser

22.71

5' ∿∿ C C G G T T G ⌐‾‾⌐ ⟶ G A T C C T T ∿∿ 3'
3' ∿∿ G G C C A A C T A G ⌐__⌐ G A A ∿∿ 5'
                           sticky ends

22.73 Circular plasmid DNA is isolated from bacteria and cleaved at a specific site with a restriction endonuclease. This forms "sticky ends" of DNA that are then combined with another DNA source, perhaps human, with complementary "sticky ends" to the plasmid DNA. These DNA strands come together and then a DNA ligase is used to re-form a circular DNA that is then reproduced by the bacteria.

22.75 a. Lanes 3 and 5 represent DNA of children who share both parents because they both have DNA fragments common to both parents.

b. Lane 4 represents DNA from an adopted child because the DNA fragments have little relationship to the parental DNA fragments.

22.77 lane 3

22.79 a. cytidine

b. Lamivudine is a nucleoside analogue that gets incorporated into a DNA chain, but since it does not contain a 3' hydroxyl group, synthesis is terminated.

22.81 a. 5' GTT ACA TAA AAA CGA 3'
b. 5' GUU ACA UAA AAA CGA 3'
c. Val–Thr

22.83

DNA informational strand:	5' end	AAC	TAT	CCA	ACG	AAG	ATG	3' end
DNA template strand:	3' end	TTG	ATA	GGT	TGC	TTC	TAC	5' end
mRNA codons:	5' end	AAC	UAU	CCA	ACG	AAG	AUG	3' end
tRNA anticodons:		UUG	AUA	GGU	UGC	UUC	UAC	
Polypeptide:		Asn	Tyr	Pro	Thr	Lys	Met	

22.85

DNA informational strand:	5' end	AAC	GTA	TCA	ACT	CAC	ATG	3' end
DNA template strand:	3' end	TTG	CAT	AGT	TGA	GTG	TAC	5' end
mRNA codons:	5' end	AAC	GUA	UCA	ACU	CAC	AUG	3' end
tRNA anticodons:		UUG	CAU	AGU	UGA	GUG	UAC	
Polypeptide:		Asn	Val	Ser	Thr	His	Met	

22.87 975

22.89 ATA CCA CCA AAA TAC

22.91 TAA CCT AAA

CHAPTER 23 PRACTICE PROBLEMS

23.1 a. glucose + ATP ⟶ glucose 1-phosphate + ADP
  b. −2.3 kcal/mol

23.2 a. reduction using NADH   b. oxidation using NAD⁺

23.3 a.

  b. oxidation

CHAPTER 23 PROBLEMS

23.1 This makes it possible to use the same reactions and the same enzyme systems to metabolize all types of biomolecules.

23.3 a. fructose ⟶ fructose 6-phosphate

  b. glucose ⟶ glucose 6-phosphate

23.5 Riboflavin has numerous polar groups (OH and NH) that can hydrogen bond to water, making it water soluble.

riboflavin

23.7 The many polar groups in vitamin B₅ make it water soluble.

pantothenic acid

23.9

malate

23.11 malate dehydrogenase

23.13 a. reduction   b. oxidizing agent

23.15 Mitochondria contain an outer membrane and an inner membrane with many folds. The area between these two membranes is called the intermembrane space. Energy production occurs within the matrix, the area surrounded by the inner membrane.

23.17 hydrolysis of starch, the conversion of glucose to acetyl CoA, the citric acid cycle, electron transport chain, oxidative phosphorylation

23.19 a. stage [1]   c. stage [3]   e. stage [1]
  b. stage [2]   d. stage [4]

23.21 Coupled reactions are pairs of reactions that occur together. The energy released by one reaction provides the energy to drive the other reaction.

23.23 CH_3CO^- + HPO_4^{2-}

23.25 a.

	Energy change
ATP + succinate + HSCoA ⟶ succinyl CoA + ADP + HPO_4^{2-}	+ 2.1 kcal/mol

  b. The reaction is not energetically favored because an input of energy is required.

23.27 a. glucose + HPO_4^{2-} ⟶ glucose 1-phosphate + H_2O
  b. glucose + ATP ⟶ glucose 1-phosphate + ADP
  c. −2.3 kcal/mol

23.29 a. −3.9 kcal/mol
  b. fructose 6-phosphate + HPO_4^{2-} ⟶ fructose 1,6-bisphosphate + H_2O
  ATP + H_2O ⟶ ADP + HPO_4^{2-}
  _____
  fructose 6-phosphate + ATP ⟶ fructose 1,6-bisphosphate + ADP
  c. +3.9 + (−7.3) = −3.4 kcal/mol

23.31 a. 1,3-bisphosphoglycerate + ADP ⟶ 3-phosphoglycerate + ATP
  b. −4.5 kcal/mol
  c. Yes, this is an energetically favorable coupled reaction that could be used to synthesize ATP from ADP.

23.33 a.

GTP

  b.

GDP

23.35 a. reducing agent
  b. neither
  c. oxidizing agent

23.37 When a substrate is oxidized, NAD⁺ is reduced. NAD⁺ is an oxidizing agent.

23.39

NAD^+ $NADH + H^+$ oxidation

23.41 a. steps [3], [4], and [8]   c. step [6]
b. steps [3] and [4]   d. step [1]

23.43 a.

fumarate   b. succinate   c. malate

23.45 a. isocitrate   b. malate, isocitrate

23.47 a. oxidation   b. decarboxylation   c. step [3a]
d. The elements of H_2 (hydrogen) are removed in converting isocitrate to oxalosuccinate.

23.49 step [7]

23.51 They require oxygen.

23.53 a. $FADH_2$ donates electrons to the electron transport chain.
b. ADP is a substrate for the formation of ATP.
c. ATP synthase catalyzes the formation of ATP from ADP.
d. The inner mitochondrial membrane contains the four complexes for the electron transport chain. ATP synthase is also embedded in the membrane and contains the H^+ ion channel that allows H^+ to return to the matrix.

23.55 NAD^+, FAD, and H_2O

23.57 $FADH_2$ enters the electron transport chain at complex II, whereas NADH enters at complex I.

23.59 a,c: true   b,d: false

23.61 a. Pepsin catalyzes the hydrolysis of proteins to amino acids in the stomach.
b. Succinate dehydrogenase catalyzes the conversion of succinate to fumarate in step [6] of the citric acid cycle.
c. ATP synthase catalyzes the oxidative phosphorylation of ADP to ATP.

23.63 Each two-carbon fragment of acetyl CoA that enters the citric acid cycle produces three molecules of NADH and one molecule of $FADH_2$. These then enter the electron transport chain and serve as reducing agents. For each NADH that enters the electron transport chain, there are 2.5 ATPs produced, and for each $FADH_2$, there are 1.5 ATPs produced. In addition, there is one GTP (an ATP equivalent) produced in the citric acid cycle.

In total: 3 NADH × 2.5 ATP/NADH =   7.5 ATP
1 $FADH_2$ × 1.5 ATP/$FADH_2$ =   1.5 ATP

1 GTP (ATP equivalent) = $\dfrac{1}{10}\ \dfrac{ATP}{ATP}$

23.65 ATP has three phosphate groups and ADP has two.

23.67 a. and b.

glucose 1-phosphate

23.69 The citric acid cycle generates the reducing agents NADH and $FADH_2$ that then enter the electron transport chain.

23.71 There would be more mitochondria in the heart because it has far more metabolic needs than bone.

23.73 Creatine phosphate, stored in muscles, is a high-energy phosphate that generates energy upon hydrolysis.

23.75 68 moles, 4.1×10^{25} molecules of ATP

CHAPTER 24 PRACTICE PROBLEMS

24.1 The reactant and product are constitutional isomers that differ in the location of a carbonyl and hydroxyl group. Thus, an isomerase enzyme converts one isomer to another.

24.2 The aldehyde (CHO) in the reactant is oxidized to a carboxylate anion (COO^-). NAD^+ is the oxidizing agent, which gets reduced to NADH. A dehydrogenase enzyme removes hydrogen from the reactant in the oxidation.

24.3 a. [1] 10; [2] 9 cycles   b. [1] 8; [2] 7 cycles

24.4 a.

b.

c.

24.5 a.

b.

c.

CHAPTER 24 PROBLEMS

24.1 **A** is glucose 6-phosphate and **B** is fructose 6-phosphate. **A** and **B** are constitutional isomers with a different arrangement of atoms but the same molecular formula.

24.3 step [1]: glucose; step [3]: fructose 6-phosphate; step [7]: ADP; step [10]: ADP

24.5 The rate of glycolysis would decrease.

24.7 NADH serves as the reducing agent for the conversion of pyruvate to both lactate and ethanol. The NAD^+ formed in the process can then be used as the oxidant in step [6] of glycolysis, making the process anaerobic.

24.9 a. Both use NADH to generate a reduced compound.
b. Ethanol is a two-carbon product formed by decarboxylation, whereas lactate is a three-carbon compound.

24.11 the conversion of pyruvate to acetyl CoA and steps [3] and [4] of the citric acid cycle

24.13

	Starting Material	Product
a.	Pyruvate	Phosphoenolpyruvate
b.	2-Phosphoglycerate	3-Phosphoglycerate
c.	Glucose 6-phosphate	Glucose

24.15 106

24.17 0.414 mol ATP/g palmitic acid

24.19 All three compounds contain at least one carbonyl group.

24.21 An increased concentration of acetyl CoA increases the production of ketone bodies.

24.23 a. Oxidation occurs with loss of hydrogen by a dehydrogenase enzyme. The coenzyme NAD^+ serves as an oxidant.

b. Transfer of phosphate from GTP to the reactant occurs, forming GDP. The loss of carbon dioxide takes place with the carboxykinase enzyme.

24.25 This reaction converts one isomer to another, so there is a change in position of the phosphate; thus, the enzyme is called a "mutase."

24.27 a.

$$^-O-\overset{\overset{\displaystyle O^-}{|}}{\underset{\underset{\displaystyle O^-}{|}}{P}}=O$$

b. 2-phosphoglycerate   c. pyruvate

$$CH_2=\overset{\overset{\displaystyle O}{\|}}{\underset{\underset{\displaystyle}{}}{C}}-\overset{\overset{\displaystyle O}{\|}}{C}-O^-$$

phosphoenolpyruvate

24.29 Energy-investment phase:

a. glucose, glyceraldehyde 3-phosphate

b. 2 ATP utilized

c. no coenzymes used or formed

Energy-generating phase:

a. glyceraldehyde 3-phosphate, pyruvate

b. 4 ATP/glucose produced

c. 2 NAD^+ used and 2 NADH produced per glucose

24.31 a. 7, 10

b. 1, 3

c. 6

d. 4

24.33 The conversion of pyruvate to acetyl CoA forms one CO_2 for each pyruvate. The conversion of isocitrate to α-ketoglutarate and α-ketoglutarate to succinyl CoA in the citric acid cycle forms one CO_2 for each acetyl CoA.

24.35 a.

$$C_6H_{12}O_6 + 2\ NAD^+ \xrightarrow[\text{2 ADP} \quad \text{2 ATP}]{} 2\ CH_3COCO_2^- + 2\ NADH + 2\ H^+$$

glucose   pyruvate

b.

$$C_6H_{12}O_6 \xrightarrow[\text{2 ADP} \quad \text{2 ATP}]{} 2\ CH_3CH_2OH + 2\ CO_2$$

glucose   ethanol

24.37

$$CH_3-\overset{\overset{\displaystyle O}{\|}}{C}-\overset{\overset{\displaystyle O}{\|}}{C}-O^- \xrightarrow[\quad]{NADH+H^+ \quad NAD^+} CH_3-\overset{\overset{\displaystyle OH}{|}}{\underset{\underset{\displaystyle H}{|}}{C}}-\overset{\overset{\displaystyle O}{\|}}{C}-O^-$$

pyruvate   lactate

24.39 a. aerobic: CO_2

anaerobic: lactate

b. aerobic: NAD^+ and FAD are used and NADH and $FADH_2$ are formed.

anaerobic: NADH is used to convert pyruvate to lactate and NAD^+ is formed.

24.41 Glycolysis takes glucose and breaks it into smaller units, producing pyruvate. Gluconeogenesis is the synthesis of glucose from lactate, amino acids, and glycerol.

24.43 a. increased   c. increased

b. decreased   d. decreased

24.45 In the Cori cycle, glucose in muscle is catabolized to pyruvate and then converted to lactate, which is transported to the liver. In the liver, lactate is converted to glucose by gluconeogenesis and then transported back to the muscle.

24.47 a. lactate

b. ethanol

c. CO_2

24.49 a. 2   b. 2   c. 2   d. 5   e. 6   f. 3   g. 4

24.51 two carbons in two molecules of CO_2 and four in two molecules of CH_3CH_2OH

24.53 Two phosphate bonds of ATP are hydrolyzed forming AMP; therefore, 2 ATP equivalents are used.

24.55 a. 7   b. 6

24.57 a. 3   b. 2

24.59 92

24.61

$$C_{15}H_{31}CO_2H \longrightarrow CH_3(CH_2)_{12}-CH_2-CH_2-\overset{\overset{\displaystyle O}{\|}}{C}-SCoA$$

C_{16} acyl CoA

acyl CoA dehydrogenase ⎡ FAD → $FADH_2$ ① **Oxidation**

$$CH_3(CH_2)_{12}-CH=CH-\overset{\overset{\displaystyle O}{\|}}{C}-SCoA$$

enoyl CoA hydratase ⎡ H_2O ② **Hydration**

$$CH_3(CH_2)_{12}-\overset{\overset{\displaystyle OH}{|}}{CH}-\overset{\overset{\displaystyle H}{|}}{CH}-\overset{\overset{\displaystyle O}{\|}}{C}-SCoA$$

β-hydroxyacyl CoA dehydrogenase ⎡ NAD^+ → $NADH + H^+$ ③ **Oxidation**

$$CH_3(CH_2)_{12}-\overset{\overset{\displaystyle O}{\|}}{C}-CH_2-\overset{\overset{\displaystyle O}{\|}}{C}-SCoA$$

acyl CoA acyltransferase ⎡ HSCoA ④ **Cleavage**

$$CH_3(CH_2)_{12}-\overset{\overset{\displaystyle O}{\|}}{C}-SCoA + CH_3-\overset{\overset{\displaystyle O}{\|}}{C}-SCoA$$

C_{14} acyl CoA   2 C's

24.63 a. $CH_3(CH_2)_6-\underset{\beta}{CH_2}-\underset{\alpha}{CH_2}-\overset{\overset{\displaystyle O}{\|}}{C}-OH$

b. $CH_3(CH_2)_6-\underset{\beta}{CH_2}-\underset{\alpha}{CH_2}-\overset{\overset{\displaystyle O}{\|}}{C}-SCoA$

c. 5   d. 4   e. 64

24.65 0.37 mol ATP/g decanoic acid

24.67 A, C

24.69 In poorly controlled diabetes, glucose cannot be metabolized. Fatty acids are used for metabolism and ketone bodies are formed to a greater extent.

24.71 Ketogenic amino acids are converted to acetyl CoA or a related thioester and can be converted to ketone bodies. Glucogenic amino acids are catabolized to pyruvate or another intermediate in the citric acid cycle.

24.73 a. $H-\overset{\overset{\displaystyle O}{\|}}{C}-CO_2^-$ b. ⌬$-CH_2-\overset{\overset{\displaystyle O}{\|}}{C}-CO_2^-$

24.75 a. $CH_3-\overset{\overset{\displaystyle O}{\|}}{C}-CO_2^-$ + $^-O_2CCH_2-\overset{\overset{\displaystyle +NH_3}{|}}{\underset{\underset{\displaystyle H}{|}}{C}}-CO_2^-$

b. $(CH_3)_2CHCH_2-\overset{\overset{\displaystyle O}{\|}}{C}-CO_2^-$ + $^-O_2CCH_2-\overset{\overset{\displaystyle +NH_3}{|}}{\underset{\underset{\displaystyle H}{|}}{C}}-CO_2^-$

24.77 threonine

24.79 a. $(CH_3)_2CHCH_2-\overset{\overset{\displaystyle O}{\|}}{C}-CO_2^-$ + NH_4^+

b. $\underset{\text{(benzene ring)}}{\bigcirc}-CH_2-\overset{\overset{\displaystyle O}{\|}}{C}-CO_2^-$ + NH_4^+

24.81 a. acetoacetyl CoA, fumarate   c. oxaloacetate
      b. α-ketoglutarate   d. pyruvate

24.83 a. amino acid: glutamine
        metabolic intermediate: α-ketoglutarate
      b. amino acid: alanine
        metabolic intermediate: pyruvate

24.85 Yes, phenylalanine, for example, can be degraded by multiple routes and can be both ketogenic and glucogenic.

24.87 A spiral pathway involves the same set of reactions repeated on increasingly smaller substrates; example: β-oxidation of fatty acids. A cyclic pathway is a series of reactions that regenerates the first reactant; example: citric acid cycle.

24.89 Glucose is metabolized anaerobically to form CO_2 and ethanol. The CO_2 causes bread to rise.

24.91 Pyruvate is metabolized anaerobically to lactate.

24.93 The diet calls for ingestion of protein and fat, so in the absence of carbohydrates to be metabolized, ketone bodies are formed.

24.95 a. kinase
      b. dehydrogenase
      c. carboxylase

24.97 18.5 ATP

24.99 One gram of arachidic acid produces more ATP than one gram of glucose (0.429 mol/g compared to 0.18 mol/g). This result supports the fact that lipids are more efficient at storing energy than carbohydrates.

Glossary

A

Acetal (16.8) A compound that contains two OR groups (alkoxy groups) bonded to the same carbon; general formula $R_2C(OR)_2$.

Acetyl CoA (23.4) A compound formed when an acetyl group ($CH_3CO–$) is bonded to coenzyme A (HS–CoA); $CH_3COSCoA$.

Achiral (15.2) Superimposable on a mirror image.

Acid (9.1) In the Arrhenius definition, a substance that contains a hydrogen atom and dissolves in water to form a hydrogen ion, H^+.

Acid dissociation constant, K_a (9.4) A constant, K_a, related to acid strength. The stronger the acid (HA), the larger the value of K_a; $K_a = [H_3O^+][A:^-]/[HA]$.

Acidic solution (9.5) A solution in which $[H_3O^+] > [OH^-]$; thus, $[H_3O^+] > 10^{-7}$ M.

Actinides (2.4) A group of elements in the periodic table beginning with thorium ($Z = 90$), and immediately following the element actinium (Ac).

Active site (6.4, 21.10) The region in an enzyme that binds a substrate, which then undergoes a very specific reaction with an enhanced rate.

Active transport (19.7) The process of moving an ion across a cell membrane that requires energy input.

Actual yield (5.9) The amount of product formed in a reaction, determined by weighing the product on a balance.

Acyclic alkane (12.1) An alkane with molecular formula C_nH_{2n+2}, which contains a chain of carbon atoms but no rings. An acyclic alkane is also called a saturated hydrocarbon.

Acyl CoA (24.7) The thioester formed from a fatty acid and coenzyme A that undergoes β-oxidation in mitochondria; general structure RCOSCoA.

Acyl group (17.1) A substituent having the formula RCO–.

Addition reaction (13.6) A reaction in which elements are added to a compound.

Adenosine 5'-diphosphate (ADP, 23.3) A nucleoside diphosphate formed by adding two phosphates to the 5'-OH group of adenosine.

Adenosine 5'-triphosphate (ATP, 23.3) A nucleoside triphosphate formed by adding three phosphates to the 5'-OH group of adenosine. ATP is the most prominent member of a group of "high-energy" molecules that release energy by cleavage of a P—O bond during hydrolysis.

Adrenal cortical steroid (19.9) A steroid hormone synthesized in the outer layer of the adrenal gland.

Alcohol (11.5) A compound containing a hydroxyl group (OH) bonded to a tetrahedral carbon atom; general formula ROH.

Aldehyde (11.5) A compound that has a hydrogen atom bonded directly to a carbonyl carbon; general formula RCHO.

Alditol (20.4) A compound produced when the carbonyl group of an aldose is reduced to a 1° alcohol.

Aldonic acid (20.4) A compound produced when the aldehyde carbonyl of an aldose is oxidized to a carboxyl group.

Aldose (20.2) A monosaccharide with an aldehyde carbonyl group at C1.

Alkali metal (2.4) An element located in group 1A (group 1) of the periodic table. Alkali metals include lithium (Li), sodium (Na), potassium (K), rubidium (Rb), cesium (Cs), and francium (Fr).

Alkaline earth element (2.4) An element located in group 2A (group 2) of the periodic table. Alkaline earth elements include beryllium (Be), magnesium (Mg), calcium (Ca), strontium (Sr), barium (Ba), and radium (Ra).

Alkaloid (18.4) A naturally occurring amine derived from a plant source.

Alkane (11.5) A compound having only C—C and C—H single bonds.

Alkene (11.5) A compound having a carbon–carbon double bond.

Alkoxy group (14.7) An OR group. An alkoxy group is named by changing the -yl ending of an alkyl group to -oxy.

Alkyl group (12.4) A group formed by removing one hydrogen from an alkane.

Alkyl halide (11.5) A compound with the general structure R—X that contains a halogen atom (X = F, Cl, Br, or I) bonded to a tetrahedral carbon.

Alkyne (11.5) A compound with a carbon–carbon triple bond.

Allosteric control (21.10) The binding of a regulator to a site on an enzyme that affects the enzyme's ability to bind a substrate at the active site.

Alpha (α) carbon (17.2) The carbon adjacent to a carbonyl group.

Alpha (α) particle (10.1) A high-energy particle that is emitted from a radioactive nucleus and contains two protons and two neutrons.

Amide (11.5) A compound that contains a nitrogen atom bonded directly to a carbonyl carbon; general structure $RCONR'_2$, where R' = H or alkyl.

Amine (11.5) An organic compound that contains a nitrogen atom bonded to one, two, or three alkyl groups; general structure RNH_2, R_2NH, or R_3N.

Amino acid (21.2) A compound that contains two functional groups—an amino group (NH_2) and a carboxyl group (COOH) bonded to the same carbon.

Amino group (11.5) An —NH_2 group.

Ammonium ion (3.6) An NH_4^+ ion.

Ammonium salt (18.6) An ionic compound that contains a positively charged ammonium ion and an anion. $(CH_3CH_2CH_2NH_3)^+Cl^-$ is an ammonium salt.

Amorphous solid (7.9) A solid with no regular arrangement of its particles.

Amphoteric compound (9.2) A compound that contains both a hydrogen atom and a lone pair of electrons, so that it can be either an acid or a base.

Anabolic steroid (19.9) A synthetic androgen analogue that promotes muscle growth.

Anabolism (23.1) The synthesis of large molecules from smaller ones in a metabolic pathway.

Androgen (19.9) A hormone that controls the development of secondary sex characteristics in males.

Anion (3.2) A negatively charged ion with more electrons than protons.

α Anomer (20.3) The cyclic form of a monosaccharide that contains a hemiacetal with the OH group drawn down, below the ring.

β Anomer (20.3) The cyclic form of a monosaccharide that contains a hemiacetal with the OH group drawn up, above the ring.

Anomeric carbon (20.3) The carbon atom that is part of the hemiacetal in a cyclic monosaccharide.

Anticodon (22.8) Three nucleotides in a tRNA molecule that are complementary to the codon in mRNA and identify an individual amino acid.

Antihistamine (18.10) A compound that binds to the H1 histamine receptor and prevents the action of histamine.

Antioxidant (13.4) A compound that prevents an unwanted oxidation reaction from occurring.

Anti-ulcer drug (18.10) A drug that binds to the H2 histamine receptor, thus reducing acid secretion in the stomach.

Aqueous solution (8.1) A solution with water as the solvent.

Aromatic compound (11.5) A compound that contains a benzene ring, a six-membered ring with three double bonds.

Aryl halide (13.13) An organic halide with the halogen bonded directly to a benzene ring.

Atmosphere (7.2) A unit used to measure pressure; 1 atm = 760 mm Hg.

Atom (2.2) The basic building block of matter composed of a nucleus and an electron cloud.

Atomic mass unit (2.2) A unit abbreviated as amu, which equals one-twelfth the mass of a carbon atom that has six protons and six neutrons; 1 amu = 1.661×10^{-24} g.

Atomic number (2.2) The number of protons in the nucleus of an atom; symbolized as Z.

Atomic weight (2.3) The weighted average of the mass of all naturally occurring isotopes of a particular element, reported in atomic mass units.

Avogadro's law (7.4) A gas law that states that the volume of a gas is proportional to the number of moles present when the pressure and temperature are held constant.

Avogadro's number (5.3) A quantity that contains 6.02×10^{23} items—usually atoms, molecules, or ions.

Axon (18.8) The long stem that protrudes from the cell body of a neuron.

B

Balanced chemical equation (5.2) An equation written so that an equal number of atoms of each element is present on both sides.

Barometer (7.2) A device for measuring atmospheric pressure.

Base (9.1) In the Arrhenius definition, a substance that contains hydroxide and dissolves in water to form OH^-.

Basic solution (9.5) A solution in which $[OH^-] > [H_3O^+]$; thus, $[OH^-] > 10^{-7}$ M.

Becquerel (10.4) An SI unit used to measure radioactivity, abbreviated as Bq; 1 Bq = 1 disintegration/s.

Benedict's reagent (20.4) A Cu^{2+} reagent that oxidizes the aldehyde carbonyl of an aldose to a carboxyl group, yielding an aldonic acid.

Beta (β) carbon (17.2) The carbon bonded to the α (alpha) carbon and located two carbons from a carbonyl group.

Beta (β) particle (10.1) A high-energy electron emitted from a radioactive nucleus.

Boiling point (bp, 7.7) The temperature at which a liquid is converted to the gas phase.

Boiling point elevation (8.8) The increase in the boiling point of a liquid solution due to the presence of a dissolved nonvolatile solute.

Bond dissociation energy (6.2) The energy needed to break a covalent bond by equally dividing the electrons between the two atoms in the bond.

Bonding (3.1) The joining of two atoms in a stable arrangement.

Boyle's law (7.3) A gas law that relates pressure and volume. Boyle's law states that for a fixed amount of gas at constant temperature, the pressure and volume of the gas are inversely related.

Branched-chain alkane (12.2) An alkane that contains one or more carbon branches bonded to a carbon chain.

Brønsted–Lowry acid (9.1) A proton donor.

Brønsted–Lowry base (9.1) A proton acceptor.

Buffer (9.10) A solution whose pH changes very little when acid or base is added. Most buffers are solutions composed of approximately equal amounts of a weak acid and the salt of its conjugate base.

Building-block element (2.1) One of the four nonmetals—oxygen, carbon, hydrogen, and nitrogen—that comprise 96% of the mass of the human body.

C

Calorie (6.1) A unit of energy that equals the amount of energy needed to raise the temperature of 1 g of water by 1 °C; abbreviated as cal, where 1 cal = 4.184 J.

Carbohydrate (20.1) A polyhydroxy aldehyde or ketone, or a compound that can be hydrolyzed to a polyhydroxy aldehyde or ketone.

Carbonate (3.6) A polyatomic anion with the structure CO_3^{2-}.

Carbonyl group (11.5) A carbon–oxygen double bond (C=O).

Carboxylate anion (17.6) The conjugate base of a carboxylic acid; general structure $RCOO^-$.

Carboxyl group (17.1) A COOH group.

Carboxylic acid (11.5) A compound that contains an OH group bonded directly to the carbonyl carbon; general structure RCOOH or RCO_2H.

Catabolism (23.1) The breakdown of large molecules into smaller ones during metabolism.

Catalyst (6.4) A substance that increases the rate of a reaction but is recovered unchanged at the end of the reaction.

Cation (2.8) A positively charged particle with fewer electrons than protons.

Cell membrane (19.7) The semipermeable membrane that surrounds the cell, composed of a lipid bilayer.

Celsius scale (1.9) One of three temperature scales in which water freezes at 0 °C and boils at 100 °C.

Cephalin (19.6) A phosphoacylglycerol in which the identity of the R group esterified to the phosphodiester is —$CH_2CH_2NH_3^+$. A cephalin is also called a phosphatidylethanolamine.

Chain reaction (10.6) The process by which each neutron produced during fission can go on to bombard another nucleus to produce more nuclei and more neutrons.

Charles's law (7.3) A gas law that states that for a fixed amount of gas at constant pressure, the volume of the gas is proportional to its Kelvin temperature.

Chemical equation (5.1) An expression that uses chemical formulas and other symbols to illustrate what reactants constitute the starting materials in a reaction and what products are formed.

Chemical formula (2.1) A representation that uses element symbols to show the identity of elements in a compound, and subscripts to show the number of atoms of each element contained in the compound.

Chemical properties (1.2) Those properties that determine how a substance can be converted to another substance by a chemical reaction.

Chemistry (1.1) The study of matter—its composition, properties, and transformations.

Chiral (15.2) Not superimposable on a mirror image.

Chirality center (15.2) A carbon atom bonded to four different groups.

Chlorination (13.13) A reaction with chlorine in which a Cl atom substitutes for a hydrogen atom.

Chlorofluorocarbon (14.9) A halogen-containing compound having the general molecular formula CF_xCl_{4-x}.

Cis isomer (13.3) An alkene with two R groups on the same side of the double bond.

Citric acid cycle (23.5) A cyclic metabolic pathway that begins with the addition of acetyl CoA to a four-carbon substrate and ends when the same four-carbon compound is formed as a product eight steps later.

Codon (22.7) A sequence of three nucleotides (triplet) in mRNA that codes for a specific amino acid.

Coenzyme (14.6, 21.9) An organic molecule needed for an enzyme-catalyzed reaction to occur.

Coenzyme A (23.4) A coenzyme that contains a sulfhydryl group (SH group) making it a thiol (RSH), and abbreviated as HS–CoA.

Cofactor (21.9) A metal ion or a nonprotein organic molecule needed for an enzyme-catalyzed reaction to occur.

Colligative properties (8.8) The properties of a solution that depend on the concentration of the solute but not its identity.

Colloid (8.1) A homogeneous mixture with large particles, often having an opaque appearance.

Combination reaction (5.3) A reaction in which two or more reactants are joined to form a single product.

Combined gas law (7.3) A gas law that relates pressure, volume, and temperature. For a constant number of moles, the product of pressure and volume divided by temperature is a constant.

Combustion (12.8) An oxidation reaction in which carbon-containing compounds react with oxygen to form carbon dioxide (CO_2) and water.

Competitive inhibitor (21.10) An enzyme inhibitor that has a shape and structure similar to that of the substrate, and competes with the substrate for binding to the active site.

Complementary base pairs (22.3) The predictable pairing of bases between two strands of DNA. Adenine pairs with thymine using two hydrogen bonds, forming an A–T base pair, and cytosine pairs with guanine using three hydrogen bonds, forming a C–G base pair.

Compound (1.3) A pure substance formed by chemically combining two or more elements.

Concentration (8.5) The amount of solute dissolved in a given amount of solution.

Condensation (7.8, 7.11) The conversion of a gas to a liquid.

Condensation polymer (17.10) A polymer formed when monomers containing two functional groups come together with loss of a small molecule such as water.

Condensed structure (11.4) A representation used for a compound having a chain of atoms bonded together. The atoms are drawn in, but the two-electron bond lines and lone pairs on heteroatoms are generally omitted.

Conjugate acid (9.2) The product formed by the gain of a proton by a base.

Conjugate acid–base pair (9.2) Two species that differ by the presence of a proton.

Conjugate base (9.2) The product formed by loss of a proton from an acid.

Conjugated protein (21.7) A compound composed of a protein unit and a nonprotein molecule.

Constitutional isomers (12.2) Isomers that differ in the way the atoms are connected to each other.

Conversion factor (1.7) A term that converts a quantity in one unit to a quantity in another unit.

Cooling curve (7.12) A graph that shows how the temperature of a substance changes as heat is removed.

Cori cycle (24.6) The cycling of lactate from the muscle to the liver, where it is re-oxidized to pyruvate and converted to glucose. Glucose is then transported back to the muscle, where it undergoes glycolysis.

Coupled reactions (23.3) Pairs of reactions that occur together. The energy released by an energetically favorable reaction drives an energetically unfavorable reaction.

Covalent bond (3.1) A chemical bond that results from the sharing of electrons between two atoms.

Critical mass (10.6) The amount of a radioactive element required to sustain a chain reaction.

Cross formula (15.6) A Fischer projection formula that replaces a chirality center with a cross. The horizontal lines represent wedged bonds and the vertical lines represent dashed wedges.

Crystalline solid (7.9) A solid with a regular arrangement of particles—atoms, molecules, or ions—with a repeating structure.

C-Terminal amino acid (21.4) In a peptide, the amino acid with the free —COO^- group on the α carbon.

Cubic centimeter (1.4) A unit of volume equal to one milliliter; one cubic centimeter = 1 cm^3 = 1 cc.

Curie (10.4) A unit used to measure radioactivity and equal to 3.7×10^{10} disintegrations/s. A curie corresponds to the decay rate of one gram of the element radium.

Cyclic hemiacetal (16.8) A compound formed by an intramolecular reaction of a hydroxyl group and an aldehyde or ketone.

Cycloalkane (12.1) A compound with the general formula C_nH_{2n} that contains carbons joined in one or more rings.

D

Dalton's law (7.6) A law that states that the total pressure (P_{total}) of a gas mixture is equal to the sum of the partial pressures of its component gases.

d Block (2.6) A group of elements consisting of the 10 columns of transition metals in the periodic table. The d subshell is filled last in these elements.

Decarboxylase (21.9) An enzyme that catalyzes the removal of CO_2.

Decarboxylation (24.2) The loss of carbon dioxide (CO_2) from a compound.

Decomposition reaction (5.3) A reaction in which a single reactant is converted to two or more products.

Dehydrase (21.9) An enzyme that catalyzes the removal of water.

Dehydration (14.5) The loss of water (H_2O) from a starting material.

Dehydrogenase (21.9) An enzyme that catalyzes the addition or removal of two hydrogen atoms.

Deletion mutation (22.9) The loss of one or more nucleotides from a DNA molecule.

Denaturation (21.8) The process of altering the shape of a protein without breaking the amide bonds that form the primary structure.

Dendrites (18.8) Numerous small filaments at the end of a neuron.

Density (1.10) A physical property that relates the mass of a substance to its volume; density = g/(mL or cc).

Deoxyribonucleic acid (DNA, 22.1, 22.3) A polymer of deoxyribo-nucleotides that stores the genetic information of an organism and transmits that information from one generation to another.

Deoxyribonucleoside (22.1) A compound that contains the monosaccharide 2-deoxyribose and a purine or pyrimidine base.

Deoxyribonucleotide (22.1) A compound that contains the monosaccharide 2-deoxyribose bonded to a purine or pyrimidine base, as well as a phosphate at the 5'-OH group.

Deposition (7.11) The conversion of a gas directly to a solid.

Deuterium (2.3) A hydrogen atom having one proton and one neutron, giving it a mass number of two.

Dextrorotatory (15.7) Rotating plane-polarized light in the clockwise direction. The rotation is labeled (+).

Dialysis (8.9) A process that involves the selective passage of substances across a semipermeable membrane, called a dialyzing membrane.

Diastereomers (15.8) Stereoisomers that are not mirror images of each other.

Diatomic molecule (4.1) A molecule that contains two atoms. Hydrogen (H_2) is a diatomic molecule.

Dilution (8.7) The addition of solvent to a solution to decrease the concentration of solute.

Diol (14.3) A compound with two hydroxyl groups, also called a glycol.

Dipeptide (21.4) A peptide formed from two amino acids joined together by one amide bond.

Dipole (4.7) The partial separation of charge in a bond or molecule.

Dipole–dipole interactions (7.7) The attractive intermolecular forces between the permanent dipoles of two polar molecules.

Diprotic acid (9.1) An acid that contains two acidic protons.

Disaccharide (20.1) A carbohydrate composed of two monosaccharides joined together.

Dissociation (9.3) The splitting apart of a covalent molecule (or an ionic compound) into individual ions.

Disulfide (14.10) A compound that contains a sulfur–sulfur bond.

DNA fingerprinting (22.10) A technique in which DNA is amplified using PCR and cut into fragments that are separated by size using gel electrophoresis. This forms a set of horizontal bands, each band corresponding to a segment of DNA, sorted from low to high molecular weight.

Double bond (4.2) A multiple bond that contains four electrons—that is, two two-electron bonds.

Double-headed arrow (13.9) An arrow drawn between resonance structures.

Double replacement reaction (5.3) A reaction in which two compounds exchange "parts"—atoms or ions—to form two new compounds.

E

Eicosanoids (19.11) A group of biologically active compounds containing 20 carbon atoms derived from arachidonic acid.

Electrolyte (8.2) A substance that conducts an electric current in water.

Electron (2.2) A negatively charged subatomic particle.

Electron cloud (2.2) The space surrounding the nucleus of an atom, which contains electrons and comprises most of the volume of an atom.

Electron-dot symbol (2.7) A symbol that shows the number of valence electrons around an atom.

Electronegativity (4.7) A measure of an atom's attraction for electrons in a bond.

Electronic configuration (2.6) The arrangement of electrons in an atom's orbitals.

Electron transport chain (23.6) A series of reactions that transfers electrons from reduced coenzymes to progressively stronger oxidizing agents, ultimately converting oxygen to water.

Element (1.3) A pure substance that cannot be broken down into simpler substances by a chemical reaction.

Elimination (14.5) A reaction in which elements of the starting material are "lost" and a new multiple bond is formed.

Enantiomers (15.2) Mirror images that are not superimposable.

Endothermic reaction (6.2) A chemical reaction where ΔH is positive (+) and energy is absorbed.

Energy (6.1) The capacity to do work.

Energy diagram (6.3) A schematic representation of the energy changes in a reaction, which plots energy on the vertical axis and the progress of the reaction—the reaction coordinate—on the horizontal axis.

Energy of activation (6.3) The difference in energy between the reactants and the transition state; symbolized by E_a.

English system of measurement (1.4) A system of measurement used primarily in the United States in which units are not systematically related to each other and require memorization.

Enthalpy change (6.2) The energy absorbed or released in any reaction—also called the heat of reaction and symbolized by ΔH.

Enzyme (6.4, 21.9) A biological catalyst composed of one or more chains of amino acids in a very specific three-dimensional shape.

Enzyme–substrate complex (21.10) A structure composed of a substrate bonded to the active site of an enzyme.

Epoxide (14.7) A cyclic ether containing an oxygen atom in a three-membered ring.

Equilibrium (6.5) A reaction that consists of forward and reverse reactions that have equal reaction rates, so the concentration of each species does not change.

Equilibrium constant (6.5) A characteristic value for a reaction at a given temperature and equal to the ratio of the concentrations of the products multiplied together to the concentrations of the reactants multiplied together. Each term is raised to a power equal to its coefficient in the balanced chemical equation.

Equivalent (8.2) The number of moles of charge that a mole of ions contributes to a solution.

Ester (11.5) A compound that contains an alkoxy group (OR) bonded directly to the carbonyl carbon; general structure RCOOR.

Estrogen (19.9) A hormone that controls the development of secondary sex characteristics in females and regulates the menstrual cycle.

Ether (14.1) A compound that has two alkyl groups bonded to an oxygen atom; general structure ROR.

Evaporation (7.8) The conversion of liquid molecules to gas molecules.

Exact number (1.5) A number that results from counting objects or is part of a definition.

Exothermic reaction (6.2) A reaction in which energy is released and ΔH is negative (−).

F

Facilitated transport (19.7) The process by which some ions and molecules travel through the channels in a cell membrane created by integral proteins.

FAD (flavin adenine dinucleotide, 23.4) A biological oxidizing agent synthesized in cells from vitamin B_2, riboflavin. FAD is reduced by adding two hydrogen atoms, forming $FADH_2$.

$FADH_2$ (23.4) A biological reducing agent and coenzyme formed when FAD is reduced.

Fahrenheit scale (1.9) One of three temperature scales in which water freezes at 32 °F and boils at 212 °F.

Fat (13.3, 19.4) A triacylglycerol with few double bonds, making it a solid at room temperature.

Fat-soluble vitamin (11.7, 19.10) A vitamin that dissolves in an organic solvent but is insoluble in water. Vitamins A, D, E, and K are fat soluble.

Fatty acid (13.3, 19.2) A carboxylic acid (RCOOH) with a long carbon chain, usually containing 12–20 carbon atoms.

f Block (2.6) A group of elements consisting of the two rows of inner transition metals. The f subshell is filled last in these elements.

Fermentation (24.4) The anaerobic conversion of glucose to ethanol and CO_2.

Fibrous protein (21.7) A water-insoluble protein composed of long linear polypeptide chains that are bundled together to form rods or sheets.

Fischer esterification (17.8) Treatment of a carboxylic acid (RCOOH) with an alcohol (R'OH) and an acid catalyst to form an ester (RCOOR').

Fischer projection formula (15.6) A method of drawing chiral compounds with the chirality center at the intersection of a cross. The horizontal bonds are assumed to be wedges and the vertical bonds are assumed to be dashed wedges.

Formula weight (5.6) The sum of the atomic weights of all the atoms in a compound, reported in atomic mass units (amu).

Forward reaction (6.5) In equilibrium, a reaction that proceeds from left to right as drawn.

Freezing (7.11) The conversion of a liquid to a solid.

Freezing point depression (8.8) The decrease in the melting point of a liquid solution due to the presence of a nonvolatile solute.

Functional group (11.5) An atom or a group of atoms with characteristic chemical and physical properties.

G

Gamma (γ) ray (10.1) High-energy radiation released from a radioactive nucleus.

Gas (1.2) A state of matter that has no definite shape or volume. The particles of a gas move randomly and are separated by a distance much larger than their size.

Gas laws (7.3) A series of laws that relate the pressure, volume, and temperature of a gas.

Gay–Lussac's law (7.3) A gas law that states for a fixed amount of gas at constant volume, the pressure of the gas is proportional to its Kelvin temperature.

Geiger counter (10.4) A small portable device used for measuring radioactivity.

Gene (22.1) A portion of a DNA molecule responsible for the synthesis of a single protein.

Genetic code (22.7) The sequence of nucleotides in mRNA (coded in triplets) that specifies the amino acid sequence of a protein. Each triplet is called a codon.

Genetic disease (22.9) A disease resulting from a mutation that causes a condition to be inherited from one generation to another.

Genetic engineering (22.10) The process of manipulating DNA in the laboratory that allows a gene in one organism to be spliced into the DNA of another organism.

Globular protein (21.7) A protein that is coiled into a compact shape with a hydrophilic outer surface to make it water soluble.

Glucogenic amino acid (24.9) An amino acid that can be used to synthesize glucose.

Gluconeogenesis (24.6) The synthesis of glucose from noncarbohydrate sources—lactate, amino acids, or glycerol.

Glycol (14.3) A compound with two hydroxyl groups, also called a diol.

Glycolysis (24.3) A linear, 10-step pathway that converts glucose, a six-carbon monosaccharide, to two three-carbon pyruvate molecules.

α Glycoside (20.5) A monosaccharide with the OR group on the anomeric carbon oriented below the plane of the ring.

β Glycoside (20.5) A monosaccharide with the OR group on the anomeric carbon oriented above the plane of the ring.

Glycosidic linkage (20.5) The acetal C—O bond that joins two monosaccharides together.

Gram (1.4) The basic unit of mass in the metric system; abbreviated as g.

Gray (10.4) A unit that measures absorbed radiation; abbreviated as Gy.

Greenhouse gas (12.8) A gas that absorbs thermal energy that normally radiates from the earth's surface, and redirects it back to the surface.

Ground state (2.6) The lowest energy arrangement of electrons.

Group (2.4) A column in the periodic table.

Group number (2.4) A number that identifies a particular column in the periodic table.

H

Half-life (10.3) The time it takes for one-half of a sample to decay.

Half reaction (5.4) An equation written for an individual oxidation or reduction that shows how many electrons are gained or lost.

Halogen (2.4) An element located in group 7A (group 17) of the periodic table. Halogens include fluorine (F), chlorine (Cl), bromine (Br), iodine (I), and astatine (At).

Halogenation (12.9) The reaction of a compound with a halogen, X_2, such as the addition of X_2 to an alkene.

Hardening (13.7) The reaction of an unsaturated liquid vegetable oil with hydrogen to form a fat with a higher melting point.

Haworth projection (20.3) A planar, six-membered ring used to represent the cyclic hemiacetal of glucose and other sugars.

Heating curve (7.12) A graph that shows how the temperature of a substance changes as heat is added.

Heat of fusion (7.11) The amount of energy needed to melt one gram of a substance.

Heat of reaction (6.2) The energy absorbed or released in any reaction and symbolized by ΔH—also called the enthalpy change.

Heat of vaporization (7.11) The amount of energy needed to vaporize one gram of a substance.

α-Helix (21.6) A secondary structure of a protein formed when a peptide chain twists into a right-handed or clockwise spiral.

Heme (21.7) A complex organic compound containing an Fe^{2+} ion complexed with a large nitrogen-containing ring system.

Hemiacetal (16.8) A compound that contains an OH group (hydroxyl) and an OR group (alkoxy) bonded to the same carbon.

Henry's law (8.4) A law that states that the solubility of a gas in a liquid is proportional to the partial pressure of the gas above the liquid.

Heteroatom (11.2) Any atom in an organic compound that is not carbon or hydrogen.

Heterocycle (14.7) A ring that contains a heteroatom.

Heterogeneous mixture (8.1) A mixture that does not have a uniform composition throughout a sample.

Hexose (20.2) A monosaccharide with six carbons.

High-density lipoprotein (19.8) A spherical particle that transports cholesterol from the tissues to the liver.

Homogeneous mixture (8.1) A mixture that has a uniform composition throughout a sample.

Hormone (18.9, 19.9) A compound synthesized in one part of an organism, which then travels through the bloodstream to elicit a response at a target tissue or organ.

Hybrid (13.9) A composite of two or more resonance forms.

Hydration (13.6) The addition of water to a molecule.

Hydrocarbon (11.5) A compound that contains only the elements of carbon and hydrogen.

Hydrochlorofluorocarbon (14.9) A compound such as CF_3CHCl_2 that contains the elements of H, Cl, and F bonded to carbon.

Hydrofluorocarbon (14.9) A compound such as FCH_2CF_3 that contains the elements of H and F bonded to carbon.

Hydrogenation (13.6) The addition of hydrogen (H_2) to an alkene.

Hydrogen bonding (7.7) An attractive intermolecular force that occurs when a hydrogen atom bonded to O, N, or F is electrostatically attracted to an O, N, or F atom in another molecule.

Hydrohalogenation (13.6) The addition of HX (X = Cl or Br) to an alkene.

Hydrolase (21.9) An enzyme that catalyzes a hydrolysis reaction.

Hydrolysis (16.8) A cleavage reaction that uses water.

Hydrolyzable lipid (19.1) A lipid that can be converted to smaller molecules by hydrolysis with water.

Hydronium ion (3.6) The H_3O^+ ion.

Hydrophilic (19.2) The polar part of a molecule that is attracted to water.

Hydrophobic (19.2) The nonpolar part of a molecule (C—C and C—H bonds) that is not attracted to water.

Hydroxide (3.6) The OH^- ion.

α-Hydroxy acid (17.4) A compound that contains a hydroxyl group on the α carbon to a carboxyl group.

Hydroxyl group (11.5) An OH group.

Hypertonic solution (8.9) A solution that has a higher osmotic pressure than body fluids.

Hypotonic solution (8.9) A solution that has a lower osmotic pressure than body fluids.

I

Ideal gas law (7.5) A gas law that relates the pressure (P), volume (V), temperature (T), and number of moles (n) of a gas in a single equation; $PV = nRT$, where R is a constant.

Incomplete combustion (12.8) An oxidation reaction that forms carbon monoxide (CO) instead of carbon dioxide (CO_2) because insufficient oxygen is available.

Induced-fit model (21.10) The binding of a substrate to an enzyme such that the shape of the active site adjusts to fit the shape of the substrate.

Inexact number (1.5) A number that results from a measurement or observation and contains some uncertainty.

Inhibitor (21.10) A molecule that causes an enzyme to lose activity.

Inner transition metal elements (2.4) A group of elements consisting of the lanthanides and actinides.

Insertion mutation (22.9) The addition of one or more nucleotides to a DNA molecule.

Intermolecular forces (7.7) The attractive forces that exist between molecules.

Ion (3.2) A charged species in which the number of protons and electrons in an atom is not equal.

Ion–dipole interaction (8.3) The attraction of an ion to a dipole in another molecule.

Ionic bond (3.1) A bond that results from the transfer of electrons from one element to another.

Ionic solid (7.9) A solid composed of oppositely charged ions in a regular arrangement.

Ionization energy (2.8) The energy needed to remove an electron from a neutral atom.

Ion–product constant, K_w (9.5) The product of the concentrations of H_3O^+ and OH^- in water or an aqueous solution—symbolized by K_w and equal to 1×10^{-14}.

Irreversible inhibitor (21.10) An inhibitor that covalently binds to an enzyme, permanently destroying its activity.

Isoelectric point (21.3) The pH at which an amino acid exists primarily in its neutral form; abbreviated as pI.

Isomerase (21.9) An enzyme that catalyzes the conversion of one isomer to another.

Isomers (12.2) Two different compounds with the same molecular formula.

Isotonic solution (8.9) Two solutions with the same osmotic pressure.

Isotopes (2.3) Atoms of the same element having a different number of neutrons.

IUPAC nomenclature (12.3) A systematic method of naming compounds developed by the International Union of Pure and Applied Chemistry.

J

Joule (6.1) A unit of measurement for energy; abbreviated as J, where 1 cal = 4.184 J.

K

Kelvin scale (1.9) A temperature scale commonly used by scientists. The Kelvin scale is divided into kelvins (K); $T_K = T_C + 273$.

Ketogenesis (24.8) The synthesis of ketone bodies from acetyl CoA.

Ketogenic amino acid (24.9) An amino acid that cannot be used to synthesize glucose, but can be converted to ketone bodies.

Ketone (11.5) A compound that has two alkyl groups bonded to the carbonyl group; general structure RCOR.

Ketone bodies (24.8) Three compounds—acetoacetate, β-hydroxybutyrate, and acetone—formed when acetyl CoA levels exceed the capacity of the citric acid cycle.

Ketose (20.2) A monosaccharide with a carbonyl group at C2.

Ketosis (24.8) The accumulation of ketone bodies during starvation and uncontrolled diabetes.

Kinase (21.9) An enzyme that catalyzes the transfer of a phosphate group from one substrate to another.

Kinetic energy (6.1) The energy of motion.

Kinetic-molecular theory (7.2) A theory that describes the fundamental characteristics of gas particles.

L

Lactam (17.1) A cyclic amide.

Lactone (17.1) A cyclic ester.

Lagging strand (22.4) The strand of DNA synthesized in small fragments during replication, which are then joined together by a DNA ligase enzyme.

Lanthanides (2.4) A group of 14 elements in the periodic table beginning with the element cerium ($Z = 58$) and immediately following the element lanthanum (La).

Law of conservation of energy (6.1) A law that states that the total energy in the universe does not change. Energy cannot be created or destroyed.

Law of conservation of matter (5.1) A law that states that atoms cannot be created or destroyed in a chemical reaction.

LD_{50} (10.4) The lethal dose of radiation (or a poison) that kills 50% of a population.

Leading strand (22.4) The strand of DNA that grows continuously during replication.

Le Châtelier's principle (6.6) A principle that states that if a chemical system at equilibrium is disturbed or stressed, the system will react in the direction that counteracts the disturbance or relieves the stress.

Lecithin (19.6) A phosphoacylglycerol in which the identity of the R group esterified to the phosphodiester is $-CH_2CH_2N(CH_3)_3^+$. A lecithin is also called a phosphatidylcholine.

Leukotriene (19.11) A molecule synthesized in several steps from arachidonic acid, which contributes to the asthmatic response by constricting smooth muscles, especially in the lungs.

Levorotatory (15.7) Rotating plane-polarized light in the counterclockwise direction. The rotation is labeled as (–).

Lewis structure (4.1) An electron-dot structure for a molecule that shows the location of all valence electrons in the molecule, both the shared electrons in bonds and the nonbonded electron pairs.

Ligase (21.9) An enzyme that catalyzes bond formation accompanied by energy release from a hydrolysis reaction.

"Like dissolves like" (8.3, 11.6) The principle in solubility that compounds dissolve in solvents having similar types of intermolecular forces.

Limiting reactant (5.10) The reactant that is completely used up in a reaction.

Lipase (19.5) An enzyme that catalyzes ester hydrolysis in triacylglycerols.

Lipid (17.9, 19.1) A biomolecule that is soluble in organic solvents and insoluble in water.

Lipid bilayer (19.7) The basic structure of the cell membrane formed from two layers of phospholipids having their ionic heads oriented on the outside and their nonpolar tails on the inside.

Lipoprotein (19.8) A small water-soluble spherical particle composed of proteins and lipids.

Liquid (1.2) A state of matter that has a definite volume, but takes on the shape of the container it occupies. The particles of a liquid are close together but they can randomly move past each other.

Liter (1.4) The basic unit of volume in the metric system; abbreviated as L.

Lock-and-key model (21.10) The binding of a substrate to a rigid active site, such that the three-dimensional geometry of the substrate exactly matches the shape of the active site.

London dispersion forces (7.7) Very weak intermolecular interactions due to the momentary changes in electron density in a molecule.

Lone pair (4.1) An unshared electron pair.

Low-density lipoprotein (19.8) A spherical particle containing proteins and lipids, which transports cholesterol from the liver to the tissues.

Lyase (21.9) An enzyme that catalyzes the addition of a molecule to a double bond or the elimination of a molecule from a double bond.

M

Main group element (2.4) An element in groups 1A–8A of the periodic table.

Major mineral (macronutrient, 2.1) One of the seven elements present in the body in small amounts (0.1–2% by mass) and needed in the daily diet.

Markovnikov's rule (13.6) The rule that states that in the addition of HX to an unsymmetrical alkene, the H atom bonds to the less substituted carbon atom.

Mass (1.4) A measure of the amount of matter in an object.

Mass number (2.2) The total number of protons and neutrons in a nucleus; symbolized as A.

Matter (1.1) Anything that has mass and takes up volume.

Melting (7.11) The conversion of a solid to a liquid.

Melting point (mp, 7.7) The temperature at which a solid is converted to the liquid phase.

Messenger RNA (mRNA, 22.5) The carrier of information from DNA (in the cell nucleus) to the ribosomes (in the cell cytoplasm). Each gene of a DNA molecule corresponds to a specific mRNA molecule.

Metabolism (23.1) The sum of all of the chemical reactions that take place in an organism.

Meta isomer (13.10) A 1,3-disubstituted benzene.

Metal (2.1) A shiny element that is a good conductor of heat and electricity.

Metallic solid (7.9) A lattice of metal cations surrounded by a cloud of electrons that move freely.

Metalloid (2.1) An element with properties intermediate between a metal and a nonmetal. Metalloids include boron (B), silicon (Si), germanium (Ge), arsenic (As), antimony (Sb), tellurium (Te), and astatine (At).

Meter (1.4) A unit used to measure length; abbreviated as m.

Metric system (1.4) A measurement system in which each type of measurement has a base unit and all other units are related to the base unit by a prefix that indicates if the unit is larger or smaller than the base unit.

Micelle (17.6) A spherical droplet formed when soap is dissolved in water. The ionic heads of the soap molecules are oriented on the surface and the nonpolar tails are packed in the interior.

Millimeters of mercury (7.2) A unit used to measure pressure; abbreviated as mm Hg and also called "torr."

Mitochondrion (23.1) A small sausage-shaped organelle within a cell in which energy production takes place.

Mixture (1.3) Matter composed of more than one substance.

Molarity (8.6) The number of moles of solute per liter of solution; abbreviated as M.

Molar mass (5.6) The mass of one mole of any substance, reported in grams per mole.

Mole (5.5) A quantity that contains 6.02×10^{23} items—usually atoms, molecules, or ions.

Molecular formula (4.2) A formula that shows the number and identity of all of the atoms in a compound, but it does not indicate what atoms are bonded to each other.

Molecular solid (7.9) A solid composed of individual molecules arranged regularly.

Molecular weight (5.6) The formula weight of a covalent compound.

Molecule (4.1) A compound or element containing two or more atoms joined with covalent bonds.

Monomers (13.8) Small molecules that covalently bond together to form polymers.

Monoprotic acid (9.1) An acid that contains one acidic proton.

Monosaccharide (20.1) A carbohydrate that cannot be hydrolyzed to simpler compounds.

D Monosaccharide (20.2) A carbohydrate that has the OH group on the chirality center farthest from the carbonyl on the right in the Fischer projection.

L Monosaccharide (20.2) A carbohydrate that has the OH group on the chirality center farthest from the carbonyl on the left in the Fischer projection.

Multiple bond (4.2) A chemical bond that contains four or six electrons—that is, a double or a triple bond.

Mutarotation (20.3) The process by which a single anomer of a monosaccharide equilibrates to a mixture of anomers.

Mutation (22.9) A change in the nucleotide sequence in a molecule of DNA.

N

NAD⁺ (nicotinamide adenine dinucleotide, 16.6, 23.4) A biological oxidizing agent and coenzyme synthesized from the vitamin niacin. NAD⁺ and NADH are interconverted by oxidation and reduction reactions.

NADH (16.6, 23.4) A biological reducing agent and coenzyme formed when NAD⁺ is reduced.

Net ionic equation (9.7) An equation that contains only the species involved in a reaction.

Network solid (7.9) A solid composed of a vast number of atoms covalently bonded together, forming sheets or three-dimensional arrays.

Neuron (18.8) A nerve cell.

Neurotransmitter (18.8) A chemical messenger that transmits nerve impulses from one nerve cell to another cell.

Neutralization reaction (9.7) An acid–base reaction that produces a salt and water as products.

Neutral solution (9.5) Any solution that has an equal concentration of H_3O^+ and OH^- ions and a pH = 7.

Neutron (2.2) A neutral subatomic particle in the nucleus.

Nitration (13.13) Substitution of a nitro group (NO_2) for a hydrogen.

Nitro group (13.13) An NO_2 group.

Noble gases (2.4) Elements located in group 8A (group 18) of the periodic table. The noble gases are helium (He), neon (Ne), argon (Ar), krypton (Kr), xenon (Xe), and radon (Rn).

Nomenclature (3.4) The system of assigning an unambiguous name to a compound.

Nonbonded electron pair (4.1) An unshared electron pair or lone pair.

Noncompetitive inhibitor (21.10) An inhibitor that binds to an enzyme but does not bind at the active site.

Nonelectrolyte (8.2) A substance that does not conduct an electric current when dissolved in water.

Nonhydrolyzable lipid (19.1) A lipid that cannot be cleaved into smaller units by aqueous hydrolysis.

Nonmetal (2.1) An element that does not have a shiny appearance and poorly conducts heat and electricity.

Nonpolar bond (4.7) A bond in which electrons are equally shared.

Nonpolar molecule (11.6) A molecule that has no net dipole.

Nonreducing sugar (20.4) A sugar that does not react with Benedict's reagent.

Nonvolatile (8.8) Not readily vaporized.

Normal boiling point (7.8) The temperature at which the vapor pressure above a liquid equals 760 mm Hg.

N-Terminal amino acid (21.4) In a peptide, the amino acid with the free —NH_3^+ group on the α carbon.

Nuclear fission (10.6) The splitting apart of a nucleus into lighter nuclei and neutrons.

Nuclear fusion (10.6) The joining together of two nuclei to form a larger nucleus.

Nuclear reaction (10.1) A reaction that involves the subatomic particles of the nucleus.

Nuclease (21.9) An enzyme that catalyzes the hydrolysis of nucleic acids.

Nucleic acid (22.1, 22.2) An unbranched polymer composed of nucleotides. DNA and RNA are nucleic acids.

Nucleoside (22.1) A compound formed by joining the anomeric carbon of a monosaccharide with a nitrogen atom of a purine or pyrimidine base.

Nucleotide (22.1) A compound formed by adding a phosphate group to the 5'-OH of a nucleoside.

Nucleus (2.2) The dense core of the atom that contains protons and neutrons.

Nylon (17.10) A condensation polymer that contains many amide bonds.

O

Octet rule (3.2) The rule in bonding that states that main group elements are especially stable when they possess eight electrons (an octet) in the outer shell.

Oil (13.3, 19.4) A triacylglycerol that is liquid at room temperature.

Omega-*n* acid (19.2) An unsaturated fatty acid where *n* is the carbon at which the first double bond occurs in the carbon chain. The numbering begins at the end of the chain with the CH_3 group.

Optically active (15.7) Able to rotate the plane of polarized light.

Optically inactive (15.7) Not able to rotate the plane of polarized light.

Orbital (2.5) A region of space where the probability of finding an electron is high.

Organic chemistry (11.1) The study of compounds that contain the element carbon.

Ortho isomer (13.10) A 1,2-disubstituted benzene.

Osmosis (8.9) The selective diffusion of solvent, usually water, across a semipermeable membrane from a less concentrated solution to a more concentrated solution.

Osmotic pressure (8.9) The pressure that prevents the flow of additional solvent into a solution on one side of a semipermeable membrane.

Oxidase (21.9) An enzyme that catalyzes an oxidation.

Oxidation (5.4, 12.8) The loss of electrons from an atom. Oxidation may result in a gain of oxygen atoms or a loss of hydrogen atoms.

β-Oxidation (24.7) A process in which two-carbon acetyl CoA units are sequentially cleaved from a fatty acid.

Oxidative deamination (24.9) The process by which the C—H and C—NH_3^+ bonds on the α carbon of an amino acid are converted to C=O and an ammonium ion (NH_4^+).

Oxidative phosphorylation (23.6) The process by which the energy released from the oxidation of reduced coenzymes is used to convert ADP to ATP using the enzyme ATP synthase.

Oxidizing agent (5.4) A compound that gains electrons (i.e., is reduced), causing another compound to be oxidized.

Oxidoreductase (21.9) An enzyme that catalyzes oxidation–reduction reactions.

P

Para isomer (13.10) A 1,4-disubstituted benzene.

Parent name (12.4) The root that indicates the number of carbons in the longest continuous carbon chain in a molecule.

Partial hydrogenation (13.7) The hydrogenation of some, but not all, of the double bonds in a molecule.

Partial pressure (7.6) The pressure exerted by one component of a mixture of gases.

Parts per million (8.5) A concentration term (abbreviated ppm)—the number of "parts" in 1,000,000 parts of solution.

***p* Block** (2.6) The elements in groups 3A–8A (except helium) in the periodic table. The *p* subshell is filled last in these elements.

Penicillin (17.11) An antibiotic that contains a β-lactam and interferes with the synthesis of the bacterial cell wall.

Pentose (20.2) A monosaccharide with five carbons.

Peptide (21.4) A compound that contains many amino acids joined together by amide bonds.

Peptide bond (21.4) An amide bond in peptides and proteins.

Percent yield (5.9) The amount of product actually formed in a particular reaction divided by the theoretical yield, multiplied by 100%.

Period (2.4) A row in the periodic table.

Periodic table (2.1) A schematic arrangement of all known elements that groups elements with similar properties.

Petroleum (12.6) A complex mixture of compounds, most of which are hydrocarbons containing 1–40 carbon atoms.

Phenol (13.12) A compound that contains a hydroxyl group bonded to a benzene ring.

Pheromone (12.1) A chemical substance used for communication in a specific animal species, most commonly an insect population.

Phosphate (3.6) A PO_4^{3-} anion.

Phosphatidylcholine (19.6) A phosphoacylglycerol in which the identity of the R group esterified to the phosphodiester is —$CH_2CH_2N(CH_3)_3^+$; also called a lecithin.

Phosphatidylethanolamine (19.6) A phosphoacylglycerol in which the identity of the R group esterified to the phosphodiester is —$CH_2CH_2NH_3^+$; also called a cephalin.

Phosphoacylglycerol (19.6) A lipid with a glycerol backbone that contains two of the hydroxyls esterified with fatty acids and the third hydroxyl as part of a phosphodiester.

Phosphodiester (19.6) A derivative of phosphoric acid (H_3PO_4) that is formed by replacing two of the H atoms by R groups.

Phospholipid (19.6) A lipid that contains a phosphorus atom.

Phosphorylation (23.3) A reaction that adds a phosphate group to a molecule.

pH scale (9.6) The scale used to report the H_3O^+ concentration; $pH = -\log [H_3O^+]$.

Physical properties (1.2) Those properties of a substance that can be observed or measured without changing the composition of the material.

Plane-polarized light (15.7) Light that consists of waves that oscillate in a single plane. Plane-polarized light arises from passing ordinary light through a polarizer.

Plasmid (22.10) A circular, double-stranded DNA molecule isolated from bacteria.

β-Pleated sheet (21.6) A secondary structure formed when two or more peptide chains, called strands, line up side-by-side.

Point mutation (22.9) The substitution of one nucleotide for another.

Polar bond (4.7) A bond in which electrons are unequally shared and pulled towards the more electronegative element.

Polarimeter (15.7) An instrument that measures how much a compound rotates plane-polarized light.

Polar molecule (11.6) A molecule that contains a net dipole.

Polyamide (17.10) A class of condensation polymer that contains many amide bonds.

Polyatomic ion (3.6) A cation or anion that contains more than one atom.

Polycyclic aromatic hydrocarbon (13.11) A compound containing two or more benzene rings that share a carbon–carbon bond.

Polyester (17.10) A class of condensation polymer that contains many ester bonds.

Polymer (13.8) A large molecule made up of repeating units of smaller molecules—called monomers—covalently bonded together.

Polymerase chain reaction (22.10) A technique that produces exact copies of a fragment of DNA.

Polymerization (13.8) The joining together of monomers to make polymers.

Polynucleotide (22.2) A polymer of nucleotides that contains a sugar–phosphate backbone.

Polysaccharide (20.1) Three or more monosaccharides joined together.

***p* Orbital** (2.5) A dumbbell-shaped orbital higher in energy than an *s* orbital in the same shell.

Positron (10.1) A radioactive particle that has a negligible mass and a +1 charge.

Postsynaptic neuron (18.8) A nerve cell that contains the receptors that bind a neurotransmitter.

Potential energy (6.1) Energy that is stored.

Pressure (7.2) The force (F) exerted per unit area (A); symbolized by P.

Presynaptic neuron (18.8) A nerve cell that releases a neurotransmitter.

Primary (1°) alcohol (14.2) An alcohol having the general structure RCH_2OH.

Primary (1°) alkyl halide (14.9) An alkyl halide having the general structure RCH_2X.

Primary (1°) amide (17.1) A compound having the general structure $RCONH_2$.

Primary (1°) amine (18.1) A compound having the general structure RNH_2.

Primary (1°) carbon (12.2) A carbon atom bonded to one other carbon.

Primary structure (21.6) The particular sequence of amino acids that are joined together by peptide bonds in a protein.

Product (5.1) A substance formed in a chemical reaction.

Progestin (19.9) A hormone responsible for the preparation of the uterus for implantation of a fertilized egg.

Prostaglandins (17.4, 19.11) A group of carboxylic acids that contain a five-membered ring, are synthesized from arachidonic acid, and have a wide range of biological activities.

Protease (21.9) An enzyme that catalyzes the hydrolysis of the amide bonds in proteins.

Proteins (21.1) Biomolecules that contain many amide bonds, formed by joining amino acids together.

Proton (2.2) A positively (+) charged subatomic particle that resides in the nucleus of the atom.

Proton transfer reaction (9.2) A Brønsted–Lowry acid–base reaction in which a proton is transferred from an acid to a base.

Pure substance (1.3) A substance that contains a single component, and has a constant composition regardless of the sample size.

Q

Quaternary ammonium ion (18.1) A cation with the general structure R_4N^+.

Quaternary (4°) carbon (12.2) A carbon atom that is bonded to four other carbons.

Quaternary structure (21.6) The shape adopted when two or more folded polypeptide chains come together into one protein complex.

R

Racemic mixture (15.5) An equal mixture of two enantiomers.

Rad (10.4) The radiation absorbed dose; the amount of radiation absorbed by one gram of a substance.

Radioactive decay (10.2) The process by which an unstable radioactive nucleus emits radiation, forming a nucleus of new composition.

Radioactive isotope (10.1) An isotope that is unstable and spontaneously emits energy to form a more stable nucleus.

Radioactivity (10.1) The energy emitted spontaneously by an unstable radioactive isotope.

Radiocarbon dating (10.3) A method to date artifacts that is based on the ratio of the radioactive carbon-14 isotope to the stable carbon-12 isotope.

Reactant (5.1) The starting material in a reaction.

Reaction rate (6.3) A measure of how fast a chemical reaction occurs.

Recombinant DNA (22.10) Synthetic DNA that contains segments from more than one source.

Redox reaction (5.4) A reaction that involves the transfer of electrons from one element to another.

Reducing agent (5.4) A compound that loses electrons (i.e., is oxidized), causing another compound to be reduced.

Reducing sugar (20.4) A carbohydrate that is oxidized with Benedict's reagent.

Reductase (21.9) An enzyme that catalyzes a reduction.

Reduction (5.4, 12.8) The gain of electrons by an atom. Reduction may result in the loss of oxygen atoms or the gain of hydrogen atoms.

Refining (12.6) The distillation of crude petroleum to form usable fractions that differ in boiling point.

Rem (10.4) The radiation equivalent for man; the amount of radiation absorbed by a substance that also factors in its energy and potential to damage tissue.

Replication (22.4) The process by which DNA makes a copy of itself when a cell divides.

Resonance structures (4.4) Two Lewis structures having the same arrangement of atoms but a different arrangement of electrons.

Restriction endonuclease (22.10) An enzyme that cuts DNA at a particular sequence of bases.

Retrovirus (22.11) A virus that contains a core of RNA.

Reverse reaction (6.5) In equilibrium, a reaction that proceeds from right to left as drawn.

Reverse transcription (22.11) A process by which a retrovirus produces DNA from RNA.

Reversible inhibitor (21.10) An inhibitor that binds to an enzyme, but enzyme activity is restored when the inhibitor is released.

Reversible reaction (6.5) A reaction that can occur in either direction, from reactants to products or from products to reactants.

Ribonucleic acid (RNA, 22.1, 22.5) A polymer of ribonucleotides that translates genetic information to protein synthesis.

Ribonucleoside (22.1) A compound that contains the monosaccharide ribose and a purine or pyrimidine base.

Ribonucleotide (22.1) A compound that contains the monosaccharide ribose bonded to either a purine or pyrimidine base as well as a phosphate at the 5'-OH group.

Ribosomal RNA (rRNA, 22.5) The most abundant type of RNA. rRNA is found in the ribosomes of the cell and provides the site where polypeptides are assembled during protein synthesis.

S

Saponification (17.9, 19.5) The basic hydrolysis of an ester.

Saturated fatty acids (19.2) Fatty acids that have no double bonds in their long hydrocarbon chains.

Saturated hydrocarbon (12.1) An alkane with molecular formula C_nH_{2n+2} that contains a chain of carbon atoms but no rings.

Saturated solution (8.3) A solution that has the maximum number of grams of solute that can be dissolved.

s Block (2.6) Elements located in groups 1A and 2A of the periodic table as well as the element helium. The s subshell is filled last in these elements.

Scientific notation (1.6) A system in which numbers are written as $y \times 10^x$, where y is a number between 1 and 10 and x can be either positive or negative.

Secondary (2°) alcohol (14.2) An alcohol having the general structure R_2CHOH.

Secondary (2°) alkyl halide (14.9) An alkyl halide having the general structure R_2CHX.

Secondary (2°) amide (17.1) A compound that has the general structure RCONHR'.

Secondary (2°) amine (18.1) A compound that has the general structure R_2NH.

Secondary (2°) carbon (12.2) A carbon atom that is bonded to two other carbons.

Secondary structure (21.6) The three-dimensional arrangement of localized regions of a protein. The α-helix and β-pleated sheet are two kinds of secondary structure.

Semipermeable membrane (8.9) A membrane that allows only certain molecules to pass through.

Shell (2.5) A region where an electron that surrounds a nucleus is confined. A shell is also called a principal energy level.

Sievert (10.4) A unit that measures absorbed radiation; abbreviated as Sv.

Significant figures (1.5) All of the digits in a measured number, including one estimated digit.

Single replacement reaction (5.3) A reaction in which one element replaces another element in a compound to form a different compound and element as products.

SI units (1.4) The International System of Units formally adopted as the uniform system of units for the sciences.

Skeletal structure (11.4) A shorthand method used to draw organic compounds in which carbon atoms are assumed to be at the junction of any two lines or at the end of a line, and all H's on C's are omitted.

Soap (17.6, 19.5) A salt of a long-chain carboxylic acid.

Solid (1.2) A state of matter that has a definite shape and volume. The particles of a solid lie close together, and are arranged in a regular, three-dimensional array.

Solubility (8.3) The amount of solute that dissolves in a given amount of solvent.

Solute (8.1) The substance present in the lesser amount in a solution.

Solution (8.1) A homogeneous mixture that contains small particles. Liquid solutions are transparent.

Solvation (8.3) The process of surrounding particles of a solute with solvent molecules.

Solvent (8.1) The substance present in the larger amount in a solution.

s Orbital (2.5) A spherical orbital that is lower in energy than other orbitals in the same shell.

Specific gravity (1.10) A unitless quantity that compares the density of a substance with the density of water at 4 °C.

Specific heat (7.10) The amount of heat energy needed to raise the temperature of 1 g of a substance by 1 °C.

Specific rotation (15.7) A physical constant for the amount that a chiral compound rotates the plane of polarized light. Specific rotation is defined with a specific sample tube length (usually 10 cm), concentration, temperature (25 °C), and wavelength.

Spectator ion (9.7) An ion that appears on both sides of an equation but undergoes no change in a reaction.

Sphingomyelin (19.6) A phospholipid derived from sphingosine, which contains a single fatty acid bonded with an amide bond to the carbon backbone.

SSRI (18.8) A class of antidepressants that acts by inhibiting the reuptake of serotonin by the presynaptic neuron. SSRI is an abbreviation for "selective serotonin reuptake inhibitor."

Standard molar volume (7.4) The volume of one mole of any gas at STP—22.4 L.

States of matter (1.2) The forms in which most matter exists—that is, gas, liquid, and solid.

Stereochemistry (15.1) The three-dimensional structure of molecules.

Stereoisomers (13.3) Isomers that differ only in their three-dimensional arrangement of atoms.

Steroid (19.8) A lipid whose carbon skeleton contains three six-membered rings and one five-membered ring.

STP (7.4) Standard conditions of temperature and pressure—1 atm (760 mm Hg) for pressure and 273 K (0 °C) for temperature.

Straight-chain alkane (12.2) An alkane that has all of its carbons in one continuous chain.

Sublimation (7.11) A phase change in which the solid phase enters the gas phase without passing through the liquid state.

Subshell (2.5) A sublevel within a shell designated by the letters s, p, d, or f, and containing one type of orbital.

Substitution reaction (12.9) A reaction in which an atom is replaced by another atom or a group of atoms.

Sulfate (3.6) An SO_4^{2-} ion.

Sulfhydryl group (14.1) An SH group.

Sulfonation (13.13) The substitution of SO_3H for a hydrogen.

Supersaturated solution (8.4) A solution that contains more than the predicted maximum amount of solute at a given temperature.

Surface tension (7.8) A measure of the resistance of a liquid to spread out.

Suspension (8.1) A heterogeneous mixture that contains large particles suspended in a liquid.

Synapse (18.8) The gap between neurons across which neurotransmitters act.

Synthase (21.9) An enzyme that catalyzes the addition of a small molecule to a double bond.

T

Temperature (1.9) A measure of how hot or cold an object is.

Tertiary (3°) alcohol (14.2) An alcohol that has the general structure R_3COH.

Tertiary (3°) alkyl halide (14.9) An alkyl halide that has the general structure R_3CX.

Tertiary (3°) amide (17.1) A compound that has the general structure $RCONR'_2$.

Tertiary (3°) amine (18.1) A compound that has the general structure R_3N.

Tertiary (3°) carbon (12.2) A carbon atom that is bonded to three other carbons.

Tertiary structure (21.6) The three-dimensional shape adopted by an entire peptide chain.

Tetrose (20.2) A monosaccharide with four carbons.

Theoretical yield (5.9) The amount of product expected from a given amount of reactant based on the coefficients in the balanced chemical equation.

Thiol (11.5) A compound that contains a sulfhydryl group (SH group) bonded to a tetrahedral carbon atom; general structure RSH.

Titration (9.9) A technique for determining an unknown molarity of an acid by adding a base of known molarity to a known volume of acid.

Tollens reagent (16.5) An oxidizing agent that contains silver(I) oxide (Ag_2O) in aqueous ammonium hydroxide (NH_4OH).

Trace element (micronutrient, 2.1) An element required in the daily diet in small quantities—usually less than 15 mg.

Transaminase (21.9) An enzyme that catalyzes the transfer of an amino group.

Transamination (24.9) The transfer of an amino group from an amino acid to an α-keto acid.

Transcription (22.6) The process that synthesizes RNA from DNA.

Transferase (21.9) An enzyme that catalyzes the transfer of a group from one molecule to another.

Transfer RNA (tRNA, 22.5) The smallest type of RNA, which brings a specific amino acid to the site of protein synthesis on a ribosome.

Trans isomer (13.3) An alkene with two R groups on opposite sides of a double bond.

Transition metal element (2.4) An element contained in one of the 10 columns in the periodic table numbered 1B–8B.

Transition state (6.3) The unstable intermediate located at the top of the energy hill in an energy diagram.

Translation (22.8) The synthesis of proteins from RNA.

Triacylglycerol (17.9, 19.4) A triester formed from glycerol and three molecules of fatty acids.

Triol (14.3) A compound with three hydroxyl groups.

Triose (20.2) A monosaccharide with three carbons.

Tripeptide (21.4) A peptide that contains three amino acids joined together by two amide bonds.

Triple bond (4.2) A multiple bond that contains six electrons—that is, three two-electron bonds.

Triprotic acid (9.1) An acid that contains three acidic protons.

Tritium (2.3) A hydrogen atom that has one proton and two neutrons, giving it a mass number of three.

U

Universal gas constant (7.5) The constant, symbolized by R, that equals the product of the pressure and volume of a gas, divided by the product of the number of moles and Kelvin temperature; $R = PV/nT$.

Unpaired electron (2.6) A single electron.

Unsaturated fatty acid (19.2) A fatty acid that has one or more double bonds in its long hydrocarbon chain.

Unsaturated hydrocarbon (13.1) A compound that contains fewer than the maximum number of hydrogen atoms per carbon.

Unsaturated solution (8.3) A solution that has fewer than the maximum number of grams of solute.

Urea cycle (24.9) The process by which an ammonium ion is converted to urea, $(NH_2)_2C{=}O$.

V

Valence electron (2.7) An electron in the outermost shell that takes part in bonding and chemical reactions.

Valence shell electron pair repulsion (VSEPR) theory (4.6) A theory that predicts molecular geometry based on the fact that electron pairs repel each other; thus, the most stable arrangement keeps these groups as far away from each other as possible.

Vapor (7.8) Gas molecules formed from the evaporation of a liquid.

Vaporization (7.11) The conversion of a liquid to a gas.

Vapor pressure (7.8) The pressure above a liquid exerted by gas molecules in equilibrium with the liquid phase.

Vesicle (18.8) A small packet where neurotransmitters are stored, located in the filaments of the axon of a neuron near the synapse.

Virus (22.11) An infectious agent consisting of a DNA or RNA molecule that is contained within a protein coating.

Viscosity (7.8) A measure of a fluid's resistance to flow freely.

Vitamin (11.7) An organic compound that must be obtained in the diet and is needed in small amounts for normal cell function.

Volatile (8.8) Readily vaporized.

Volume/volume percent concentration (8.5) The number of milliliters of solute dissolved in 100 mL of solution.

W

Water-soluble vitamin (11.7) A vitamin with many polar bonds that dissolves in water.

Wax (19.3) An ester (RCOOR') formed from a fatty acid (RCOOH) and a high molecular weight alcohol (R'OH).

Weight (1.4) The force that matter feels due to gravity.

Weight/volume percent concentration (8.5) The number of grams of solute dissolved in 100 mL of solution.

X

X-ray (10.7) A high-energy form of radiation.

Z

Zaitsev rule (14.5) A rule that states that the major product in an elimination reaction is the alkene that has more alkyl groups bonded to the double bond.

Zwitterion (21.2) A neutral compound that contains both a positive and a negative charge.

Zymogen (21.10) The inactive precursor of an enzyme that is then converted to its active form when needed.

Index

Page numbers followed by *f* indicate figures; *mn*, marginal notes, and *t*, tables. Page numbers preceded by "A-" indicate pages in Appendix A.

A

a- (prefix), 426*mn*
ABO blood system, 738–739, 739*f*, 739*t*
Absolute zero, 26
Acceptor stem, of tRNA, 809, 809*f*
ACE. *See* Angiotensin-converting enzyme
Acetal(s)
 cyclic hemiacetal conversion to, 580
 definition of, 577
 disaccharides, 725–732
 drawing of, 578–579
 ethers versus, 579–580
 formation of, 577–583, 725
 hydrolysis of, 583
 identifying in complex molecule, 582
 locating, in cyclic compound, 581
Acetaldehyde, 130, 405, 563, 845, 873
Acetaminophen, 603
 covalent bonds in, 107
 dosage for children, 24–25, 24*mn*, 35
 oral suspension for children, 305
 percent yield of, 173–175
 structure of, 129, 483, 483*f*
 synthesis of, 173–174, 628
 therapeutic concentration of, 309
Acetate, 320*t*, 342–345, 344*t*
Acetic acid, 289, 289*mn*, 312*mn*, 313*t*, 314*f*, 405, 595, 597, 601
 acid dissociation constant for, 327*t*
 aspirin synthesis from, 29, 142–143
 in buffer, 342–345, 344*t*
 dissociation of, 320, 321*f*
 solubility of, 413
 structure of, 413, 414*f*
 as weak acid, 320, 320*t*
Acetoacetate, 882
Acetoacetyl CoA, 886
Acetone, 414, 565, 567, 882
Acetylcholine, 653
Acetylcholinesterase inhibitor, 784
Acetyl CoA, 846–847, 862
 amino acid conversion to, 886, 886*f*
 in citric acid cycle, 835*f*, 837, 848–852, 849*f*, 862
 conversion to ketone bodies, 882
 in fatty acid oxidation, 877–881, 878*f*
 formation of, 835*f*, 836–837, 862, 871
 in oxidative phosphorylation, 855
 pyruvate conversion to, 871
Acetylene, 182, 185, 388, 390, 454, 457
Acetyl groups, 836–837, 846–847
Acetylsalicylic acid, 609. *See also* Aspirin
Achiral molecule, 533–535, 548. *See also* Chirality
Acid(s)
 Arrhenius, 311
 Brønsted–Lowry, 311–314, 316
 buffers and, 342–348
 conjugate, 316–319
 definition of, 311

diprotic, 313
dissociation of, 319–324
 examples, in food products, 314, 314*f*
 monoprotic, 313
 names of common, 313, 313*t*
 pH scale of, 331–335
 titration of, 340–342, 340*f*
 triprotic, 313
Acid–base indicator, 332, 332*f*
Acid–base reactions, 311
 acid and amine, 644–648, 657
 acid and bicarbonate or carbonate, 337–338
 acid and hydroxide bases, 335–337
 Brønsted–Lowry acid with Brønsted–Lowry base, 316–319
 carboxylic acid, 604–605, 625
 common, 335–338
 equilibrium in, 325–328
  acid dissociation constant and, 326–328, 327*t*
  direction of, predicting from acid strength, 325–326
  weaker acid favored in, 327
 general, 316
 net charge in, 317
 net ionic equation for, 336
 water as acid and base in, 328
Acid dissociation constant (K_a), 326–328, 327*t*, 343
Acidic amino acids, 749, 751*t*, 752–754
Acidic solutions, 329–330, 329*mn*, 329*t*, 331, 331*mn*, 338–340, 339*t*
Acidosis, 347–348, 347*mn*
Acid rain, 62*mn*, 164*mn*, 182, 341–342, 342*mn*, 346, 346*f*, 353
Acid strength, 319–326
 acid dissociation constant and, 326–327
 determining, from extent of dissociation, 322–323
 dissociation and, 319–324, 321*f*
 predicting equilibrium direction from, 325–326
 relationship with base strength, 323–324
 relative, 320*t*
 and salt solutions, 338–340, 339*t*
Acne medications, 152*mn*
Aconitase, 849
Aconitate, 859
Acquired immune deficiency syndrome (HIV/AIDS), 786, 823–825, 824*f*
Acrylic acid, 478
Actin, 748*f*
Actinides, 51*f*, 52
Activation energy
 catalysts and, 201, 201*f*
 definition of, 199
 and reaction rate, 199, 200
Active site, of enzyme, 202, 202*f*, 779–780, 780*f*
Active transport, 688
Actual yield, 171–174, 171*mn*
Acyclic alkanes, 426–432
 bond rotation in, 431–432
 classifying carbon atoms in, 430–431
 definition of, 426
 with fewer than five carbons, 427–429
 with five or more carbons, 429–430
 isomers of, 428–429
 nomenclature for, 435–439
 as saturated hydrocarbons, 426, 454

skeletal structures of, 431–432
substitution reaction, 447
Acyl CoA, 878–881
Acyl compounds, 594
Acyl group, 594, 597, 598
Addiction
 alcoholism, 510–511
 amphetamine and methamphetamine, 654
 dopamine in, 651
 nicotine, 641*mn*, 642, 653
 opioid, 642–643
Addition, using significant figures in, 16–17, A-4
Addition reactions
 aldehyde and ketone, 569, 577–583
 alkene, 468–473, 468*f*
  halogenation, 468*f*, 470, 470*mn*
  hydration, 468*f*, 472–473
  hydrogenation, 468*f*, 469, 473–475
  hydrohalogenation, 468*f*, 470–471
 carbonyl, 571
 definition of, 468
Adenine, 796, 799*t*, 804, 806–808, 807*f*
Adenosine 5'-diphosphate. *See* ADP
Adenosine monophosphate (AMP), 878
Adenosine 5'-triphosphate. *See* ATP
-adiene (suffix), 457
Adipose cells, 678–679, 679*f*
ADP, 837–839, 839*f*, 852, 854–855, 865, 865*f*
Adrenal cortical steroids, 693
Adrenaline. *See* Epinephrine
Aerobic reactions, 842
Aerobic respiration, 852, 853
Aerosol propellants, 519–520, 519*mn*
AIDS (HIV), 786, 786*f*, 823–825, 824*f*
Air, as solution of gases, 273, 273*f*
Airbags, chemistry of, 145–146, 145*f*, 148, 271
Airplanes, de-icing of, 295*mn*
Air pollution, 37*mn*, 62*mn*, 149*mn*, 164*mn*. *See also*
  Acid rain
 automobile emissions, 203, 203*mn*
 carbon monoxide, 37*mn*
 catalytic converters to reduce, 203, 203*f*
 nitric oxide, 164*mn*
 nitrogen dioxide, 149*mn*
 nitrogen monoxide, 164*mn*, 203
 ozone, 164*mn*, 201
 smog, 201
 sulfur oxides, 62*mn*
-al (suffix), 562
Alanine, 550, 750*t*, 751–753
Alanine transaminase, 776
Albuterol, 174, 174*f*, 421, 536, 655, 697
Alcohol(s), 497–511
 aldehyde and ketone addition reactions with, 577–583
 aldehyde and ketone reduction to, 571–575
 bent shape of, 500
 boiling point of, 500, 501
 carboxylic acid reaction with, 611–613
 common names for, 502
 dehydration of, 505–507, 523, 526
 formation of, 472–473, 497
 functional group of, 402, 403, 403*t*, 497–499
 hydrogen bonding of, 500

Alcohol(s) (Continued)
interesting, 503–505
intermolecular forces of, 500
melting point of, 500
monosaccharide reduction to, 721–722
net dipole of, 500
nomenclature for, 501–503
oxidation of, 505, 507–510, 507f, 523
primary (1°), 499–500
properties of, 499–501
reactions of, 505–510
secondary (2°), 499–500
simple, 503–504, 504f
solubility of, 500–501
structure of, 497–501
tertiary (3°), 499–500, 508–509
Alcohol-based hand sanitizers, 286mn
Alcohol dehydrogenase, 511, 873
Alcoholic beverages, 873, 873mn
blood alcohol level, 309, 509–510, 510f
consumption/abuse, 510–511, 511mn
fermentation, 166–167, 166mn, 387, 503, 503f
health effects of, 511
metabolism of, 510–511
Alcoholism, 510
Aldehyde(s)
acetal hydrolysis to, 583
alcohol oxidation to, 508–511, 523
carbonyl group of, 404–405, 405t, 561–562, 721–724
in chemistry of vision, 575–577, 575mn, 576f
cucumber, 160mn
in health and medicine, 567–568
hydrogenation of, 572
monosaccharides, 709
naturally occurring, 562, 567, 568f
nomenclature for, 562–564
odor of, 564mn, 567, 568f, 569mn, 590
oxidation of, 569–571, 569mn, 584, 722–724
physical properties of, 565–567
polarity of, 565
polyhydroxy, 707 (See also Carbohydrates)
reactions of, 569–583
acetal formation in, 577–583, 584
addition, 569, 577–583
Tollens reagent and, 570–571, 570mn
reduction of, 571–575, 584, 721–722
structure of, 405, 405t, 561–562
-aldehyde (suffix), 563
Aldehyde dehydrogenase, 511
Alditols, 721–722, 740
Aldohexose, 709
Aldonic acid, 722–724, 740
Aldopentoses, 719–720
Aldoses, 709–710, 721–724
Aldosterone, 424, 693
Aldotriose, 709
Algal blooms, 512
Alkali metals (Group 1A elements), 51f, 52–53
cation formation by, 83–84, 84t
compounds of, 54
properties of, 53
valence electronic configuration of, 64, 65t
Alkaline batteries, 155, 155f
Alkaline earth elements (Group 2A), 51f, 53–54
cation formation by, 83–84, 84t
compounds of, 54
properties of, 53
valence electron configuration of, 65t
Alkaloids, 639–644
atropine, 642, 643–644
caffeine, 633, 639–641, 640f, 640mn, 640t
morphine and related alkaloids, 642–643, 642mn
nicotine, 633, 639, 641–642, 641f, 641mn

origin of term, 642mn
quinine, 642, 643
Alkalosis, 347–348
Alkanes, 402–403, 425–452
acyclic, 426–432, 435–439, 447
boiling point of, 444
bond rotation in, 431–432
branched-chain, 428, 451
classifying carbon atoms in, 430–431
combustion of, 426, 444–446
definition of, 402, 426
drawing, 427mn
fossil fuels, 442–443
functional group lacking in, 402–403, 426
halo, 517
halogenation of, 446–447
insolubility of, 444, 444mn
intermolecular forces in, 444
isomers of, 428–430
melting point of, 444
nomenclature for, 429, 429mn, 430t, 434–435, 435t
acyclic alkanes, 435–439
cycloalkanes, 439, 440–442
physical properties of, 444
physical states of, 444
ring structure (cycloalkanes), 426, 439–442, 447
simple, 427–432
skeletal structures of, 431–432
straight-chain, 428, 429–430, 430t, 434, 444
structure of, 402t
substituents in, 434–439, 435t, 441–442
tetrahedral, 427
Alkenes, 402–403, 402t, 454–475
bond angles in, 454
cis–trans isomers of, 460–463
constitutional isomers of, 460
definition of, 402, 454
in food and medicine, 466
formation in dehydration, 505–507
functional group of, 402–403, 402t
general formula for, 454
nomenclature for, 456–460
physical properties of, 454
reactions of, 468–475
addition, 468–473, 468f
halogenation, 468f, 470, 470mn
hydration, 468f, 472–473
hydrogenation, 468f, 469, 473–475
hydrohalogenation, 468f, 470–471
restricted bond rotation in, 460
structure of, 454–456, 459–460
Alkoxy group, 403t
Alkyl groups, 434, 435f
amide, 598
amine, 633–635
definition of, 434
ether, 497, 511–512, 514–515
nomenclature for, 434–435, 435t
Alkyl halides, 497–498, 516–520
environmental effects of, 519–520, 519f, 519mn
formation of, 446–447, 468f, 470–471
functional group of, 403, 403t, 497–498
insolubility of, 517
interesting, 518–519
nomenclature for, 517–518
physical properties of, 517
primary (1°), 516
secondary (2°), 516
simple, 518
structure of, 497–498
tertiary (3°), 516
Alkynes, 402–403, 454–460
definition of, 402, 454
functional group of, 402–403, 402t
general formula for, 454

nomenclature for, 456–460
physical properties of, 454
structure of, 454–456, 459–460
Allicin, 433, 433mn, 521mn
Allosteric control, 782–783, 782f
Allosteric enzyme, 782
All-trans-retinal, 575–577, 576f
All-trans-retinol, 575
Almonds, odor of, 590
Alpha emission, 359–360, 359mn, 364t
Alpha (α) particles, 358, 358t
definition of, 358
effects of and working with, 370
emission, 359–360, 359mn, 364t
Altitude, 243, 243mn, 268, 250
Aluminum, 53, 253t
Aluminum cans, 53mn
Aluminum foil, as element, 7, 7f
Aluminum oxide, 94mn
Aluminum sulfate, 99
Americium-241, decay of, 359mn
Amide(s), 591–631
carbonyl group of, 404, 405t, 561, 593–595
carboxylic acid conversion to, 611, 613–614, 625
cyclic (lactams), 594, 631
definition of, 593
hydrogen bonding in, 600, 600f
hydrolysis of, 614, 616–617, 625
interesting, 603
nomenclature for, 598–599
in penicillin, 623–624
physical properties of, 599–601
primary (1°), 593, 600
secondary (2°), 593, 598, 600
structure of, 593–595
synthetic polymers, 619–623
tertiary (3°), 593, 598
-amide (suffix), 598–599
Amide bonds, peptide, 754–760, 763, 772–773
Amine(s), 632–662
alkaloids, 639–644
atropine, 642, 643–644
caffeine, 633, 639–641, 640f, 640mn, 640t
morphine and related alkaloids, 642–643, 642mn
nicotine, 633, 639, 641–642, 641f, 641mn
origin of term, 642mn
quinine, 642, 643
aromatic, 637
as bases, 644–648, 657
carboxylic acid reaction with, 613–614
classification of, 633–634
definition of, 633
drugs, 633
functional group of, 403, 403t
heterocycle, 633
naturally occurring, 632, 634, 635mn, 639–644
neurotransmitters, 650–657
nomenclature for, 636–639
odor of, 634, 638
physical properties of, 638–639
polarity of, 638
primary (1°), 633, 633mn, 636, 638
secondary (2°), 633, 633mn, 636, 638
solubility of, 638, 647–648
structure and bonding of, 633–635
N-substituted primary, 636
tertiary (3°), 633, 633mn, 636, 638
-amine (suffix), 636
Amino acids, 749–754
acid–base behavior of, 752–754
acidic, 749, 751t, 752–754
alpha (α), 749
basic, 749, 751t, 752–754
bonding in peptides, 754–760, 763

D and L forms of, 751–752
essential, 749–751, 751*mn*, 752*mn*
functional groups of, 749
general features of, 749–751
glucogenic, 886, 886*f*
glucose synthesis from, 875–876, 876*f*
identifying in peptides, 758–760
ketogenic, 886, 886*f*
metabolism of, 835*f*, 836–837, 862, 883–887, 883*f*, 886*f*
    fate of amino group in, 883–885
    fate of carbon skeleton in, 886
naturally occurring, 749, 750*t*–751*t*
neutral, 749, 750*t*, 752–754
nomenclature and abbreviations, 749
nutritional requirements for, 749–751, 751*mn*
protein digestion to, 834–835, 836*f*
sequence of, 763, 768*f*, 816
side chain of, 749
stereochemistry of, 751–752
structure of, 749
triplet codes for (codons), 811–816, 812*t*, 814*t*, 815*f*
Aminobenzene (aniline), 480
p-Aminobenzoic acid (PABA), 483, 487
Amino group, 403*t*, 637, 749
    fate, in catabolism, 883–885
Ammonia
    as amphoteric compound, 319
    as Brønsted–Lowry base, 314–315, 315*f*
    carboxylic acid reaction with, 613–614
    as conjugate base, 320*t*
    as covalent molecule, 109
    household, pH of, 332*f*
    Lewis structure of, 122
    molecular formula for, 112
    molecular geometry of, 122–123
    nitrogen conversion to, 209, 209*mn*
    reaction with HCl, 317, 317*mn*
    as weak base, 323, 324*f*
    as weak electrolyte, 276
-ammonium (suffix), 646
Ammonium cation, 753
Ammonium hydrogen phosphate, 147*mn*
Ammonium hydroxide, 570–571
Ammonium ions, 97, 885
    acid dissociation constant for, 327*t*
    formation of, 643–644
    quaternary, 633, 649
    as weak acid, 320*t*
Ammonium nitrate, 105, 280
Ammonium salts, 646–649
    quaternary, 633, 649
    useful drugs, 648–649, 648*mn*
Amorphous solids, 252–253, 253*mn*
Amoxicillin (Amoxil), 24–25, 306, 624
AMP, 878
Amphetamine, 654
Amphoteric compound, 318–319
Amplification, DNA, 820–821
Amprenavir (Agenerase), 786, 823
amu. *See* Atomic mass unit
Amygdalin, 568, 856
Amylase, 833, 835*f*
Amylopectin, 734, 735*f*
Amylose, 504, 734, 735*f*
Anabolic steroids, 559, 692, 692*mn*, 693, 704
Anabolism, 833, 876
Anaerobic reactions, 842
Anaerobic respiration, 865, 870–871
Androgens, 692
Androsterone, 590, 692
-ane (suffix), 429, 429*mn*, 430*t*, 434, 457
Anesthetics, ethers as, 498, 515–516, 528
Anethole, 490
Angel's trumpets (plants), 420, 635*mn*
Angiotensin-converting enzyme (ACE), 785–786

Angiotensin-converting enzyme (ACE) inhibitors, 408, 408*mn*, 785–786
Aniline, 480
Animal fats, 671–676, 673*t*
Animal waste, methane from, 443, 443*f*
Anions, 79–87
    acid names derived from, 313
    carboxylate, 604, 605–607, 753
    definition of, 79
    formation of, 81, 84, 84*t*
    hydrogen in, 313
    important, in human body, 86–87
    in ionic compounds, 88–89
    naming of, 92, 92*t*, 97
    oxidation of, 153–154
    polyatomic, 97
    in salt solutions, 338–340
    size of, 81
    solubility and, 281–282
Anisaldehyde, 590
Anise, 490, 590
Anomer, 715–720
α Anomer, 716–720, 717*f*
β Anomer, 716–720, 717*f*
Anomeric carbon, 715–720
Antabuse, 511
Antacids, 35, 100, 185, 274, 315*f*, 336*mn*, 337, 337*mn*
Anthracene, 482
Anti-aging creams, 415*mn*
Antibiotics, 108, 386*f*. *See also specific drugs*
Anticodon, 809, 809*f*, 813–816, 814*t*, 815*f*
Antidepressants, 652
Antidiuretic hormone (ADH), 761–762, 762*f*
Antifreeze (ethylene glycol), 295–296, 308, 502, 502*mn*
Antihistamines, 54*mn*, 75, 648–649, 648*mn*, 656–657, 657*mn*
Anti-inflammatory agents, 602. *See also specific agents*
Antilogarithm, 333–334, 333*mn*, A-5–A-6
Antimony, 37*t*
Antioxidants, 466, 466*mn*, 484–485, 485*mn*
Antiseptics, 154
Anti-ulcer medication, 656
Ants, sting from, 116*mn*
APC (aspirin, phenacetin, caffeine), 614
Apple, waxy coating of, 448
Apple juice, pH of, 331*mn*
Apricots, 568, 603
Aqueous solution, 96, 96*mn*, 274
    dissociation of water in, 328–330
    seawater as, 272
    solubility in, 278–281
    symbol, in chemical equations, 141, 141*t*
Arachidic acid, 667*t*, 669
Arachidonic acid, 465, 667*t*, 669, 696–698
Archaeological dating, 360, 367, 368*f*
Arginine, 751*t*
Argon, 54, 245
Aripiprazole (Abilify), 658
Aromatic amines, 637
Aromatic compounds, 402–403, 454, 479–489
    carcinogens, 483–484
    definition of, 402
    drugs, 483–484, 483*f*
    functional group of, 402–403, 402*t*
    with more than one ring, 482
    nomenclature for, 480–482
    physical properties of, 480
    polycyclic, 483–484
    reactions of, 485–489
        chlorination, 486
        nitration, 486–487
        substitution, 480–482, 485–489
        sulfonation, 486, 487–488
    structure of, 402*t*, 479–480
    sunscreen, 482*mn*, 483–484

Arrhenius, Svante, 311
Arrhenius acids and bases, 311
Arsenic, 39*f*
Arsenic-74, 383
Artemether, 35
Artificial sweeteners, 133, 188, 631, 721–722, 721*mn*, 729–731, 730*f*, 730*t*, 731*mn*, 791
Aryl halide, 486
Ascorbic acid. *See* Vitamin C
-ase (suffix), 779
Asparagine, 750*t*
Aspartame, 188, 631, 729–731, 730*f*, 730*t*, 791
Aspartic acid, 751*t*
Asphalt, 452
Aspirin
    as carboxylic acid, 602, 609–610, 610*f*
    covalent bonds in, 108
    grams in tablet, 21–22
    hydrolysis of, 616
    mechanism of action, 696–697
    molarity of solution, 291
    molar mass of, 163
    mole/moles of, 157*mn*, 159
    reaction rate of, 200
    synthesis of, 29, 137, 138, 142–143, 170, 174, 612
Astatine, 54
Asthma, 655, 697–698
-ate (suffix), 313, 597, 606
Atenolol, 408*mn*
Atherosclerosis, 690, 690*f*
Athletes
    anabolic steroid use by, 692, 692*mn*, 704
    creatine supplement use by, 842–843, 842*mn*
Atkins, Robert, 882
Atkins diet, 882, 882*mn*
Atmosphere
    carbon dioxide in, 445, 446*f*
    oxygen in, 229
    ozone in, 119, 119*f*, 226
atmosphere (atm), 227
Atmospheric pressure, 227, 227*f*, 243, 250
Atom
    definition of, 37, 42
    electronic configurations of, 58–63
    electronic structure of, 56–58
    molecular shape around, 121–124, 123*t*, 390–394, 392*t*
    structure of, 42–46
Atomic mass, 49. *See also* Atomic weight
Atomic mass unit (amu), 43–44, 159–160
Atomic number, 44–46
    definition of, 44, 356
    isotope, 47–49, 356–357
    in nuclear equation, 359
    synthetic nuclei, 384
Atomic radius, 67–69
Atomic size, 66–69
Atomic weight, 49–50, 159–161
Atorvastatin, 174, 174*f*, 691
ATP
    cancer and, 870–871
    composition of, 837
    coupled reactions of, 839–842, 840*f*
    energy for glycolysis from, 865–867, 865*f*, 866*f*
    hydrolysis of, 777, 777*t*, 832, 838–842, 839*f*
    production of, 837–843
        in citric acid cycle, 848–852, 849*f*, 874–875, 874*f*, 888
        in electron transport chain, 852–854, 853*f*, 874–875, 874*f*, 888
        in fatty acid oxidation, 880–881
        in glycolysis, 865, 865*f*, 868–869, 868*f*, 874–875, 874*f*, 888
        in oxidative phosphorylation, 854–855, 874–875, 874*f*, 888
        yield from glucose, 874–875, 874*f*, 881, 888
    synthesis of, 837–839, 839*f*, 854–855

Atropine, 642, 643–644
Attention deficit hyperactivity disorder (ADHD), 654
Autoclave, 267
Automobiles
    antifreeze in, 295–296
    catalytic converters in, 75, 203, 203f
    chemistry of airbag, 145–146, 145f, 148, 271
    emissions from, 203, 203mn, 445–446, 445mn
    leaded gasoline for, 49mn, 75
Avobenzone, 567, 568
Avocados, 847mn
Avogadro, Amadeo, 157
Avogadro's law, 236–239, 237m, 264
Avogadro's number, 157–159
Axon, 649–650, 649f
AZT, 824, 824mn

B

Background radiation, 368
Baking, as chemical reaction, 138
Baking soda, 99
Balancing chemical equations, 141, 142–147
    for equations with odd–even relationship of atoms, 145–146, 145f
    for equations with polyatomic ions, 146–147
Balancing nuclear equations, 359
Ball-and-stick models, 41–42, 130, 399
Balsamic vinegar, carboxylic acids in, 414f
Bamboo, cyanide in, 856, 856mn
Barium, 53
Barium-142, 375
Barium carbonate, formation of, 151
Barium chloride, 93
Barium sulfate, 54, 98mn
Barometer, 227, 227f
Base(s). See also Acid–base reactions
    amines as, 644–648
    Arrhenius, 311
    Brønsted–Lowry, 311–312, 314–316, 315f
    buffers and, 342–348
    conjugate, 316–319, 320t, 323–324
        in buffer systems, 342–348
    definition of, 311
    examples, in consumer products, 315f
    pH scale of, 331–335
    strength of, 319, 323–324
        and direction of equilibrium, 325–326
        and dissociation, 323–324, 324f
        relationship with acid strength, 323–324
        and salt solutions, 338–340, 339t
Bases, nitrogen-containing, 795–800, 799t
    complementary pairs of, 804, 806–808
    sequence of, 802, 805, 815f
Basic amino acids, 749, 751t, 752–754
Basic solutions, 329–330, 329t, 331, 338–340, 339t
Batteries, 155–157, 155f, 157f, 183–184
Becquerel (Bq), 369, 369t
Bees
    pheromones of, 590
    venom of, 790
Beeswax, 669–670, 671
Benazepril, 658
Bends, 224, 243, 243mn, 282, 282mn
Benedict's reagent, 722–724
Bent shape, 123, 123t, 129, 392, 392t
    alcohol, 500
    ether, 512
Benzaldehyde, 406f, 563, 568, 586, 590
Benzene(s)
    boiling point of, 660
    disubstituted, 481
    molecular formula for, 479
    monosubstituted, 480
    polysubstituted, 481

    reactions of, 485–489
        chlorination, 486
        nitration, 486–487
        substitution, 480–482, 485–489
        sulfonation, 486, 487–488
    resonance structures of, 479
    structure of, 479–480
Benzene derivatives
    aromatic compounds, 402t, 479–489
    nomenclature for, 480–482
Benzenesulfonic acid, 487–488, 488f
Benzo[a]pyrene, 483–484
Benzocaine, 423, 603, 613
Benzoic acid, 595, 597
Benzoyl peroxide, 152mn
Benzphetamine, 661
Benzyl acetate, 629
2-Benzyl-4-chlorophenol, 485
Bergstrom, Sune, 602
Beryllium, 53, 61t, 64
Beta emission, 360–361, 361f, 364t
Beta (β) particles, 358, 358t
    definition of, 358
    effects of and working with, 370
    emission, 360–361, 361f, 364t
BHT (butylated hydroxy toluene), 485
Bi- (prefix), 97
Bicarbonate, 100
    acid dissociation constant for, 327t
    as conjugate base, 320t
    reaction with carbonate, 337–338
Bicarbonate/carbonate buffer, 344t, 345–348, 346f
Biochemical reactions, 862–864
Biodegradable polymers, 631
Biodiesel, 679
Biofuels, 679, 679mn
Biogas, 443, 443f
Biological catalysts, 202, 202f
Biologically active peptides, 760–762
Biological membranes, osmosis and, 299–300
Biomolecules, 664. See also Carbohydrates; DNA; Lipid(s); Proteins
Birth control pills, 386f, 467–468, 467f, 467mn
Bismuth-214, 381
1,3-Bisphosphoglycerate, 867–868, 867f
Blattellaquinone, 612, 612mn
Blimp, 60mn
Blocks, in periodic table, 61–62, 62f
Blood
    buffers in, 347–348
    covalent molecules in, 111–112, 111f
    glucose levels in, 714, 724–725, 724mn, 725f, 875
    pH of, 335f, 347, 347mn
    plasma electrolytes, 276–277
    as suspension, 274mn
Blood alcohol level, 309, 509–510, 510f
Blood gases, 271
Blood pressure, 228, 228f
Blood type, 707, 738–739, 738mn, 739f, 739t
Bodybuilders, anabolic steroid use by, 692, 692mn
Body fluids. See also specific types
    pH of, 335, 335f
Body mass index (BMI), 35
Body temperature, 216, 216mn, 217f
Boiling, physical change in state during, 4–5
Boiling point (bp), 4
    alcohol, 500, 501
    aldehyde, 566
    alkane, 444
    alkene and alkyne, 454
    alkyl halide, 517
    amide, 600
    amine, 638–639
    aromatic compound, 480
    atmospheric pressure and, 250

    carboxylic acid, 600
    definition of, 247
    dimethyl ether, 526
    enantiomer, 547
    ethanol, 526
    ether, 513–514
    intermolecular forces and, 247–249
    ionic compound, 96, 410, 410t
    ketone, 566
    organic compound, 410, 410t
    pyridine versus benzene, 660
    relative, predicting in two compounds, 248–249
    thiol, 520
    vapor pressure and, 250
Boiling point elevation, 294–295, 294f
Boldenone undecylenate, 704
Bombykol, 462, 462mn
Bond(s), 77–79. See also specific types
    delocalized, 479
    energy in breaking and forming, 192–197
    energy stored in, 190
    periodic table and, 77
Bond dissociation energy, 193–197, 193t
Bond polarity, 125–127, 126t
Bond rotation, 431–432, 460
Bone density, 100, 100mn
Bone scans, 372, 372f
Boron, 39f, 61t, 116
Boron-11, 362
Boron trifluoride, 122
Boyle's law, 229–231, 231f, 236t, 264
Bp. See Boiling point
Brachytherapy, 373, 373mn
Bradykinin, 791
Branched-chain alkanes, 428, 451
Breast milk, 731–732, 732mn
Breathing
    Boyle's law and, 231, 231f
    ideal gas law and, 240, 240f
Broad bean, L-Dopa from, 544–545, 545f
Bromide, 92t, 320t, 518
Bromine, 37t, 54, 446, 470, 470mn
Bromochlorofluoromethane, 534–536, 548
Bromochloromethane, 534, 548
Bromocyclohexane, 470
Bromomethane, 403
Brompheniramine, 75, 538
Bronchodilators, 655, 697–698
Brønsted, Johannes, 311
Brønsted–Lowry acid, 311–314
    carboxylic, 312, 312mn
    charge of, 313
    definition of, 311
    examples, in food products, 314, 314f
    identifying, 313–314, 316
    number of protons donated by, 313
    reaction with Brønsted–Lowry base, 316–319
Brønsted–Lowry base, 311–312, 314–316, 315f
    charge of, 314
    definition of, 311
    examples, in consumer products, 315f
    identifying, 315–316
    reaction with Brønsted–Lowry acid, 316–319
Bryson, Bill, 55
Buckminsterfullerene, 55, 55f
Bucky ball, 55, 55f
Buffer(s), 342–348
    acid rain and naturally buffered lake, 346, 346f
    in blood, 347–348
    calculating pH of, 345
    common, 344t
    definition of, 342
    effect on pH changes, 342, 343f
    general characteristics of, 342–345
Bufotenin, 652–653

Building-block elements, 39, 39f
Bupropion, 75
Buret, 340, 340f
1,3-Butadiene, 457
Butanal, 569mn
Butane
　boiling point of, 248, 410, 410t
　bond rotation in, 432
　as CFC alternative, 519mn
　intermolecular forces in, 248
　isomer of, 428
　melting point of, 248, 410, 410t
　natural gas, 442
　properties of, 410, 410t
　structure of, 428
2,3-Butanedione, 528, 588
Butanoic acid, 569mn, 628
2-Butanol, 505–506, 539, 546
2-Butanone, 564
Butene, 408–409, 460–462, 505–506
Butter, 464, 473–475, 473mn, 673t, 688t, 701
Butylated hydroxy toluene (BHT), 485
Butylbenzene, 480
Butyl group, 435f, 435t

C

Cabbage, hydrocarbon coating of, 424
Cadaverine, 638
Caffeine, 387, 387f, 633, 639–641, 640f, 640mn, 640t
Calcium, 37t, 53
　as major mineral (macronutrient), 39f, 40
　role in human body, 86, 87f
Calcium carbonate
　acid rain and, 346, 346f, 353
　in antacids, 100, 315f, 337, 337mn
　insolubility of, 105
　as ionic compound, 77, 100, 105
　reaction with acid, 337, 337mn
　in shells, 100mn
Calcium chloride, 280
Calcium fluoride, 88
Calcium hydroxide, 315
Calcium hypochlorite, 354
Calcium phosphate, 76, 146–147
Calcium propanoate, 607mn
Calcium sulfate, 97, 146–147
Calcium supplements, 76
Calculator, A-4–A-6
　for logarithms and antilogarithms, 333–334, 333mn, A-5–A-6
　for pH, 333–334, A-5–A-6
Caloric value, 191–192, 191t, 192mn
Calories (C), in nutrition, 191–192, 191t, 192mn, 218–219
Calories (cal), 190–191
Camphor, 549, 549mn
Cancer
　glycolysis and, 870–871
　PET imaging in, 374, 374f
　radiation therapy for, 355, 360, 363, 363f, 370, 373, 373mn, 374
Candlenuts (kukui nuts), 453, 475, 494
Canola oil, 673t
Caproic acid, 601
Caprolactam, 631
Capsaicin, 387, 387f, 594
Captopril, 542, 786
Caraway seeds, 553
Carbohydrates, 504–505, 706–746
　biological functions of, 707
　blood type, 707, 738–739, 738mn, 739f, 739t
　in blood type, 707
　caloric value of, 191, 191t, 192mn, 219
　classification of, 707–708

complex, 707
　as cyclic hemiacetals, 580–581
　definition of, 707
　digestion of, 834–835, 836f, 862
　disaccharides, 707–708, 725–732
　as energy source, 708
　Fischer projections of, 546–547
　human milk oligosaccharides, 731–732
　metabolism of, 833–835, 835f, 836f, 862, 864–877
　　ATP yield from, 874–875, 874f
　　gluconeogenesis, 875–877, 876f
　　glycolysis, 835f, 862, 864–875, 865f
　molecular formula of, 707
　monosaccharides, 707, 709–725
　nomenclature for, 709
　polysaccharides, 708, 732–736
　simple, 707
　useful derivatives of, 736–738
Carbon, 37t. See also Organic compounds; Organic molecules
　α (alpha), 596
　anomeric, 715–720
　atomic number of, 46
　β (beta), 596
　as building-block element, 39, 39f
　charcoal, 172mn
　classification of atoms, 430–431
　electronic configuration of, 60, 61t
　elemental forms of, 55, 55f, 252
　isotopes of, 75, 356
　　archaeological dating with, 360, 367, 368f
　　decay of, 360, 362
　linear, 454
　molar mass of, 161
　primary, 431
　quaternary, 431
　reactive intermediates, 136
　ring, chirality centers on, 540–542
　secondary, 431
　specific heat of, 253, 253t
　tertiary, 431
　tetrahedral, 535–539, 535mn (See also Chirality centers; Enantiomers)
Carbon-11, 75, 362, 373–374
Carbon-12, 367
Carbon-14, 360, 365, 367, 368f
Carbonate, 97, 97t
　in buffer, 344t, 345–348, 346f
　reaction with bicarbonate, 337–338
Carbonated beverages, 282, 283f, 314f
Carbon bonds
　nonpolarity of, 125
　patterns, in organic compounds, 388–390, 389f
　rotation around, 431–432
Carbon dating, 360, 367, 368f
Carbon dioxide, 386mn
　atmospheric concentration of, 445, 446f
　blood/blood gases, 271, 347–348
　in citric acid cycle, 848–852, 849f
　combustion as source of, 138–143, 142mn, 172mn, 445
　glucose metabolism as source of, 144, 144mn
　as greenhouse gas, 445
　molecular geometry of, 121
　nonpolarity of, 128
　partial pressure of, 242–243
　photosynthetic use of, 229
　propane–oxygen reaction as source of, 142mn, 143
　pyruvate reaction with, 777
　reversible reaction for, 204
　solid (dry ice), 32, 259
　sublimation of, 259
Carbon–heteroatom single bond, 403–404, 403t, 497–498

Carbonic acid, 313t
　acid dissociation constant for, 327t
　in blood, 347–348
　in carbonated beverages, 314f
　formation of, 337–338
　as weak acid, 320t
Carbon monoxide (CO)
　catalytic converters and, 203, 203f
　composition of, 37mn
　formation from ethane, 164
　hemoglobin and, 164, 445, 771
　incomplete combustion and, 445–446
　mole calculations, 164–165
　release from fossil fuels, 37mn
　reversible reaction with carbon dioxide, 204
　smoking and, 446
Carbon monoxide monitors, 164mn, 445mn
Carbon–oxygen double bond, 389, 404–409, 405t
Carbon skeleton, of amino acids, 886
Carbon tetrachloride, 280, 280f, 518
Carbonyl addition, 571
Carbonyl group (C=O), 404–405, 405t, 561–562, 593–595
　acetal and hemiacetal formation, 577–583, 584
　aldehydes, 404–405, 405t, 561–562, 721–724
　amides, 404, 405t, 593–595
　carboxylic acids, 404–405, 405t, 593–595
　esters, 404–405, 405t, 593–595
　fruit compounds, 405, 406f
　ketones, 404, 405t, 561–562
　monosaccharides, 709–710, 722–724
　oxidation of, 722–724
Carbonyl reductions, 571–575, 584
　in human body, 574–575
　in monosaccharides, 721–722
　in organic synthesis, 573–574
Carboxylate anions, 604, 605–607, 753
Carboxyl group, 749
Carboxylic acid(s), 312, 312mn, 561, 591–631
　acidity of, 604–609
　aldehyde oxidation to, 569–571
　amide hydrolysis to, 614, 616–617, 625
　aspirin as, 602, 609–610, 610f
　in balsamic vinegar and olive oil, 414f
　carbonyl group of, 404–405, 405t, 561, 593–595
　in consumer products and medicine, 601–602
　conversion to amides, 611, 613–614, 625
　conversion to esters, 611–613, 625
　definition of, 593
　ester hydrolysis to, 614–616, 617–618, 625
　fatty acids, 463–465, 666–669
　hydrogen bonding in, 599–600, 599f
　monosaccharide oxidation to, 721, 722–724
　nomenclature for, 595–596
　odor of, 601
　physical properties of, 599–601
　prostaglandins, 696–697
　reaction with bases, 604–605, 625
　salts of, 604–609
　structure of, 405, 405t, 561, 593–595
　in synthetic polymer preparation, 619–623
Carboxylic acid derivatives, 561
Carboxypeptidase A, 774
Carcinogens, aromatic compounds as, 483–484
Cardiovascular system
　covalent molecules and, 111–112, 111f
　dietary fats/oils and, 675–676
　pacemakers in, 156–157, 157f
β-Carotene, 416, 416mn, 473mn, 665, 694
Carvone, 553
Cassava, 122, 122mn
Catabolism, 833–837, 862
　acetyl CoA formation in, 835f, 836–837
　amino acid, 835f, 836–837, 862, 883–887, 883f, 886f
　carbohydrate, 833–835, 835f, 836f

Catabolism (*Continued*)
  citric acid cycle in, 835*f*, 837, 848–852, 848*f*, 849*f*
  definition of, 833
  digestion in, 834–835, 835*f*, 836*f*, 862
  electron transport chain in, 837, 852–854, 853*f*
  oxidative phosphorylation in, 837, 852, 854–855
  stages of, 834–837, 835*f*
  triacylglycerol, 833–835, 835*f*, 836*f*, 877–881
Catalase, 140, 140*f*, 774, 774*mn*
Catalysts, 201–203
  activation energy lowered by, 201, 201*f*
  biological, 202, 202*f*
  definition of, 201
  enzyme, 202, 202*f*, 774–775
  metal, 201, 469
Catalytic converters, 75, 203, 203*f*
Cations, 68, 79–87
  ammonium, 753
  battery, 155, 155*f*
  definition of, 79
  formation of, 80–81, 83–86, 84*t*
  important, in human body, 86–87
  in ionic compounds, 88–89
  from main group elements, naming ionic compound
    with, 93
  naming of, 91–92, 92*t*
  polyatomic, 97
  reduction of, 153–154
  in salt solutions, 338–340
  size of, 81
  solubility and, 281–282
  transition metals and, 85–86, 86*f*
Celecoxib (Celebrex), 697, 697*mn*
Celery ketone, 553, 553*mn*
Cell membranes, 686–688
  composition of, 686–687, 687*f*
  transport across, 687–688, 687*f*
Cellobiose, 727
Cellular metabolism, 834, 834*f*
Cellulose, 504–505, 707, 708, 732–734
Celsius temperature scale, 26–27, 26*f*
Centi- (prefix), 10*t*
Centimeter (cm), 10, 11*mn*
Cephalin, 682
Cereal
  iron-fortified, 40*mn*
  sold by weight, 161*mn*
Cesium, 53
Cetirizine, 657, 657*mn*
Cetyl laurate, 671
CFCs. *See* Chlorofluorocarbons
CFTR (cystic fibrosis transmembrane conductance
    regulation), 818
Chain reaction, 375
Chair form, of cycloalkane, 440
Charcoal, 172*mn*
Charge
  attraction versus repulsion, 43
  dipole, 126–128
  ion, 77, 79–87
  of metals, variable, 85–86, 93–94
  of subatomic particles, 42–43, 43*t*
  sum, in ionic compounds, 88
Charles's law, 229, 231–233, 232*mn*, 233*f*, 236*t*, 264
Chemical change, 5, 138–140
Chemical equations
  balanced, 142
  balancing of, 141, 142–147
    for equations with odd–even relationship of atoms,
      145–146, 145*f*
    for equations with polyatomic ions, 146–147
  coefficients in, 140–142
  definition of, 140
  mass calculations in, 165–171
  mole calculations in, 164–165

  subscripts in, 141–142
  symbols used in, 141, 141*t*
  writing, 140–142
Chemical formulas, 40. *See also* Formulas
Chemical properties, 4–5
Chemical reactions, 5, 137–188. *See also specific processes*
  actual yield of, 171–174, 171*mn*
  catalysts of, 201–203, 201*f*
  combination, 147–150, 148*t*
  conservation of matter in, 141
  coupled, 777, 839–842, 840*f*
  decomposition, 147–150, 148*t*
  in drug synthesis, 137, 138
  energy changes in, 192–197
  energy diagrams of, 198–200
  equilibrium in, 203–216
  go to completion, 203–204
  identifying in, 139–140
  limiting reactants in, 175–180
  molecular collisions in, 197–201
  oxidation–reduction, 152–156, 153*f*, 154*f*
  percent yield of, 171–175
  physical and chemical changes in, 138–140
  rates of, 199, 200–203
  reactants and products of, 138–139
  replacement, 147, 150–152, 151*t*
  reversible, 203–204
  substitution, 447
  theoretical yield of, 171–174, 171*mn*
  transition state in, 198–200, 199*f*
  types of, 147–152
Chemistry
  definition of, 2
  reactions at heart of, 138
  as science of everyday experience, 2–3
Chernobyl nuclear disaster, 75, 376, 382, 384
Chest physiotherapy, 818*mn*
Chickenpox vaccine, 823
Chiral compounds, 539–540
Chiral drugs, 543–545
Chirality, 533–559
  definition of, 533–534
  in nature, 530, 535, 535*f*
  origin of term, 533*mn*
  and sense of smell, 552–553, 553*f*
  testing of, 534–535
Chirality centers, 535–539
  amino acid, 751–752
  compounds with two or more, 550–552
  in cyclic compounds, 540–542
  definition of, 535, 535*mn*
  in enantiomers, 539–540, 711–713
  Fischer projections of, 546–547, 711–713
  locating, 536–538
  monosaccharide, 711–713
  rules for, 536
Chiral molecule, 533–535. *See also* Chirality
Chiral receptors, 543, 543*f*
Chitin, 736–738, 738*mn*
Chloral hydrate, 591
Chloride ion, 81, 86, 87*f*, 92*t*, 320*t*
Chlorination, 486
Chlorine, 37*t*, 54
  anion formation, 81
  energy for bond breaking and formation, 192–193
  isotopes of, 47
  as major mineral (macronutrient), 39–40, 39*f*
  methane reaction with, 446
  role in human body (chloride anion), 86, 87*f*
  valence electrons of, 64
Chlorobenzene, 480, 486
Chloroethane (ethyl chloride), 187, 249*mn*, 403, 470
Chlorofluorocarbons (CFCs), 136, 427*mn*, 519–520,
    519*f*, 519*mn*
Chloroform, 186, 411, 518

Chloromethane, 113, 113*mn*, 127, 446, 518*f*, 518*mn*
2-Chloropentane, 537
Chlorophyll, 708, 708*mn*
Chloropropane, 471
Chlorpheniramine, 54*mn*, 656, 662
Chlortrimeton, 662
Chocolate, 640*mn*, 663, 674*mn*
Cholesterol, 664, 688–691
  biological function of, 688
  blood levels of, 309, 464, 675–676, 689–691, 691*f*
  dietary, 688–689, 688*mn*, 688*t*
  home testing kits, 689*mn*
  serum testing for, 690*mn*
  solubility of, 413, 413*t*
  specific rotation of, 549
  synthesis of, 688
Cholesterol-lowering drugs, 174, 174*f*, 691, 704
Chondrochole A, 498
Chondroitin, 736, 737*f*, 737*mn*
Chromatin, 805, 805*f*
Chromium, 37*t*, 39*f*
Chromium ions, 92*t*
Chromosomes, 795, 805–806, 805*f*
Chymotrypsin, 784–785, 791, 833
Chymotrypsinogen, 784–785
Cigarette smoking, 185, 370, 370*mn*, 446, 641–642
Cimetidine, 656
Cinnamaldehyde, 491, 568*f*, 591
Cinnamon, 306, 491
Cirrhosis of liver, 511
Cis isomers, 460–463, 463*mn*, 531–532
Citrate, 848–849, 849*f*, 859, 869
Citrate synthase, 849
Citric acid, 310, 314*f*, 406*f*
Citric acid cycle, 835*f*, 837, 848–852, 862
  ATP yield from, 874–875, 874*f*
  intermediates, amino acid conversion to, 886, 886*f*
  overview of, 848, 848*f*
  steps in, 848–852, 849*f*
Citronellal, 568*f*, 588
CLAs (conjugated linoleic acids), 465
Cleaning products
  concentrated, 292*mn*
  pH of, 332*f*
Climate change, 445, 445*mn*
Clinical conversion factors, 24–25
Cloning, DNA, 820–821
Clopidogrel, 559
CMP, 798
Coal, sulfur content of, 62*mn*
Cobalt, 37*t*, 39*f*
Cobalt-59, 357
Cobalt-60, 355, 357, 363, 363*f*, 365*t*, 373
α-Cobratoxin, 790
Cocaine, 424, 616
Cocoa/cocoa butter, 663, 674, 674*mn*
Coconut oil, 673*mn*, 673*t*, 674, 681, 705, 889
Codeine, 642
Codons, 811–816, 812*t*, 814*t*, 815*f*
Coefficients
  in chemical equations, 140–142, 167
  in mole ratio formation, 164
  in scientific notation, 17–20, 158, 158*mn*, A-1–A-2
Coenzyme(s), 510, 775, 843–847. *See also specific*
    coenzymes
  definition of, 843
  FAD and FADH$_2$, 845–846
  NAD$^+$ and NADH, 775, 843–845
Coenzyme A, 836–837, 843, 846–847
  in citric acid cycle, 849–851, 849*f*
  in fatty acid oxidation, 878
Cofactor, 775
Coffee, 329, 329*mn*, 498, 640–641, 640*f*, 640*t*
Cold packs, 280
Collagen, 79*mn*, 163*mn*, 416, 748, 748*f*, 770, 770*f*

Colligative properties, 294–297
    boiling point elevation, 294–295, 294f
    definition of, 294
    freezing point depression, 295–297, 295mn
    osmotic pressure, 298
Collisions, molecular, 197–201
Colloids, 274–275, 274t
Combination reactions, 147–150, 148t
Combined gas law, 235–236, 236t, 264
Combustion
    acetylene, 182, 185
    alkane, 426, 444–446
    benzo[a]pyrene from, 483–484
    charcoal, 172mn
    chemical equation for, 140–142
    chemical reaction in, 138–139
    contribution to climate change, 445
    as exothermic reaction, 195, 195mn
    incomplete, 445–446
    methane, 138–142, 155–156, 195, 195mn, 445
    methanol, 186, 528
    nitrogen monoxide released in, 164mn
    oxidation–reduction reactions in, 155–156, 444–445
    propane, 142mn, 143
    triacylglycerol, 679, 679mn
Common names, 636. See also Nomenclature
Competitive inhibitor, 783–784
Complementary base pairs, 804, 806–808
Complexes I, II, III, and IV, 852–853, 853f
Compound(s), 7–8, 8f, 40–42. See also specific types
    chemical formulas for, 40
    definition of, 7, 40
    molecular art of, 40–42
    number of naturally occurring and synthetic, 7
    potential energy of, 190
Computed tomography (CT) scans, 378–379, 378f
Concentration
    brackets [ ] to symbolize, 205
    mole, and equilibrium, 205
    product, changes in and equilibrium, 211–213, 215t
    reactant, 200–201, 211–213, 211f, 215t
    solution, 283–293 [See also Solution(s), concentration]
    therapeutic, 309
Condensation, 249, 257–258, 259t
Condensation polymer, 619–623
Condensed structures, 395–398, 396f
    alkene and alkyne, 454–456
    converting ball-and-stick model to, 408–409
Conjugate acid, 316–319
    definition of, 316
    dissociation of water and, 328
    drawing of, 318
Conjugate acid–base pair, 317–319
Conjugate base, 316–320, 320t, 323–324
    in buffer systems, 342–348
    definition of, 316
    dissociation of water and, 328
    drawing of, 318
    strength of, 323–324
Conjugated linoleic acids (CLAs), 465
Conjugated proteins, 771
Conservation of energy, 190
Conservation of matter, 141
Constitutional isomers, 428–430, 460, 531–533, 541, 551f
    definition of, 428, 462
    dipeptide, 755–756
    in glycolysis, 867
    identifying, 428–429, 532–533
    monosaccharides, 709
    stereoisomers versus, 462–463, 531
Contact lens solution, 290, 290mn
Contractile proteins, 748
Conversion factors, 20–23
    Avogadro's number, 157–159
    definition of, 20

heat of fusion, 256–257
molarity, 289–290
mole ratios, 164
percent concentration, 285–286
problem solving with, 20–25
    using clinical conversion factors, 24–25
    using one conversion factor, 21–22
    using two or more conversion factors, 23
    relating grams to moles, 161–163
    writing, for pair of units, 20
Cooling curve, 260–261, 261f
Copper, 37t, 39f
    formation of metal, 152–153, 153f
    ions, 92t
    metabolism of, 105
    as metallic solid, 252, 252f
    as oxidizing agent, 153
    specific heat of, 253, 253t
Corey, E. J., 161mn
Cori cycle, 876, 876f
Corn, ethanol production of, 170mn, 189
Corn oil, 673, 673t, 701
Cortisol, 527, 693
Cortisone, 693
Cotton, 2f
Cottonwood tree, 734mn
Coupled reactions, 777, 839–842, 840f
Covalent bonds, 77–79, 108–112
    breaking, energy for, 193–197
    and cardiovascular system, 111–112, 111f
    definition of, 77, 108
    double, 115
    in drugs, 107, 108
    energy stored in, 190
    molecule formed by, 78, 108
    multiple, 114–116
    in organic compounds, 410–412
    and periodic table, 109–111
    polarity of, 125–127, 126t, 410–412
    solid line representing two-electron bond, 108
    triple, 115
Covalent compounds, 107–136
    drugs as, 107, 108, 128–131
    electronegativity and bond polarity in, 124–127
    formulas for, 112, 120
    intermolecular forces in, 244–245
    Lewis structures of, 110, 112–119
    molecular weight of, 160
    naming of, 120, 120t
    octet rule exceptions in, 116–117
    organic compounds as, 410
COX-1 and COX-2 enzymes/inhibitors, 697, 697mn
CPK (creatine phosphokinase), 785
Creatine, 842–843, 842mn
Creatine phosphate, 832, 842–843
Creatine phosphokinase (CPK), 785
Crenation, 300, 300f
Crick, Francis, 803
Critical mass, 375
Cross (Fischer projection) formula, 546–547
Crutzen, Paul, 519mn
Crystalline solids, 252, 252f
C-Terminal amino acid, 755–756
CT scans, 378–379, 378f
Cubic centimeter (cm³ or cc), 11, 11mn
Cucumber aldehyde, 160mn
Curcumin, 484–485
Curie (Ci), 368–369, 369mn, 369t
Curie, Marie Skłodowska, 369mn
Cyanide, 117, 320t, 855–856, 856mn
Cyclic amides (lactams), 594, 631
Cyclic compounds. See also specific compounds
    biological properties of, 440
    chirality centers in, 540–542

    locating acetal, hemiacetal, and ether in, 581
    skeletal structures of, 398–399, 398f
Cyclic esters (lactones), 594
Cyclic hemiacetals, 580–582
Cyclic ketones, 564
Cyclic metabolic pathway, 833, 848
Cyclic monosaccharides, 715–720
Cyclo- (prefix), 439, 440–441
Cycloalkanes, 439–442
    chair form of, 440
    definition of, 426
    nomenclature for, 439, 440–442
    simple, 439–440
    structure of, 439–440
    substitution reaction, 447
Cycloalkenes, 457
Cyclobutane, 439
Cyclohexane, 398, 426, 439–441
Cyclohexanone, 578
Cyclooctane, 552, 553f
Cyclooxygenase inhibitors, 697, 697mn
Cyclopentane, 439, 452
Cyclopentanol, 398
Cyclopropane, 136, 388, 439
Cysteine, 527, 750t, 752
Cystic fibrosis, 347mn, 818, 818mn
Cystic fibrosis transmembrane conductance regulation (CFTR), 818
Cytidine, 796
Cytochrome oxidase, 855–856
Cytoplasm, 834, 834f
Cytosine, 796, 799t, 804, 806–808, 807f

D

D (prefix), 711
Dacron. See Polyethylene terephthalate
Dalton's law, 242–243
dAMP, 798
Dashed lines, for transition state, 198
Dating, radiocarbon, 360, 367, 368f
Daughter DNA, 806–808
d block, of periodic table, 61–62, 62f
dCMP, 800–801
ddI (dideoxyinosine), 824
DDT, 187, 200, 287, 287mn, 415, 486, 486mn, 494
Deamination, 883, 885
Deca- (prefix), 120t
Decaffeinated coffee, 641
Decanal, 562
Decarboxylases, 777, 863
Decarboxylations, 848–852, 863, 873
Deci- (prefix), 10t
Deciliter (dL), 11
Decomposition reactions, 147–150, 148t
Decongestants, 136, 655, 655mn
DEET, 613, 613mn
Degrees, of temperature, 26–27, 26f
Dehydrase, 777
Dehydration, alcohol, 505–507, 523, 526
Dehydrogenases, 775
De-icing, airplane, 295mn
Deletion mutation, 817
Delocalized bonds, 479
Delta (Δ), for heat in chemical equation, 141, 141t
Delta (δ), in bond polarity, 126
Denaturation, protein, 773–774, 774mn
Dendrites, 649–650, 649f
Denominator, 20
Density, 27–29, 27t, 226t
    definition of, 27
    mass and volume determinations from, 29
    problem solving using, 28–29
    specific gravity, 29–30
    temperature and, 27
Deoxy- (prefix), 795mn, 797

Deoxyadenosine, 796
Deoxyribonucleic acid. *See* DNA
Deoxyribonucleoside, 796–798
Deoxyribonucleotides, 798
Deoxyribose, 591, 795–797
D-2-Deoxyribose, 795–797
Deposition, 259, 259*t*
Depression, serotonin in, 652
Dermabond, 628
Desflurane, 516
Desoxyn, 654
Detergents, 487–488, 488*f*, 630
Deuterium (D), 47, 377
Dexamethasone, 516, 516*mn*
Dextromethorphan, 662
Dextrorotatory compounds, 548–550
DHA. *See* Dihydroxyacetone; Docosahexaenoic acid
Di- (prefix), 120*t*, 514, 636–637
Diabetes ketoacidosis, 882
Diallyl disulfide, 521*mn*, 522
Dialysis, 300–301, 301*f*
Diamine, in polymer preparation, 619–623
1,4-Diaminobenzene, 620
Diamond, 55, 55*f*, 252
Diapers, disposable, 478*mn*
Diastereomers, 551–552, 551*f*
Diastolic pressure, 228–229, 228*f*
Diatomic molecule, 108–109
Dicarboxylic acid, in polymer preparation, 619–623
Dichloroacetylene, 412
1,1-Dichloroethylene, 422
Dichloromethane, 187, 412, 518*f*, 641
Dichromate, 106
Dideoxyinosine (ddI), 824
Dienes, 457
Diesel fuel, 442
Dietary supplements, 752*mn*
Diethyl ether, 187, 403–404, 413, 514, 515, 528
Diffusion, 688
Digestion, 834–835, 835*f*, 836*f*, 862
Digital thermometer, 26*mn*
Digoxin, 2*f*, 174, 582, 582*mn*
Dihalide, 470
Dihydrocapsaicin, 131, 131*mn*
Dihydrogen phosphate/hydrogen phosphate buffer, 344*t*, 345
Dihydrogen phosphate ion, 320*t*, 327*t*
Dihydroxyacetone (DHA), 124*mn*, 567, 709
Dihydroxyacetone phosphate, 867, 867*f*, 877
Dilution, 291–293
Dimers, 599
1,6-Dimethylcyclohexene, 457
Dimethyl ether, 392–393, 428, 526, 531
2,6-Dimethyl-3-heptanone, 590
Dinoprostone, 696–697
-diol (suffix), 502
Diols, 502
Dioxin (TCDD), 188
Dioxybenzone, 567, 568
Dipeptides, 754–760
Diphenhydramine, 648–649, 648*mn*, 656
Diphosphorus pentoxide, 120
Dipole, 126–128
  ion interaction with, 279
  organic compound, 411–412
Dipole–dipole interactions, 244, 245, 246*t*
Diprotic acid, 313
Disaccharides, 707–708, 725–732
  hydrolysis of, 707–708, 727–728, 740
  structure and formation of, 725–727
  sucrose, 729–731
Disintegrations per second, 368–370
Disparlure, 512
Disposable diapers, 478*mn*

Dissociation
  acid strength and, 319–324, 321*f*
  base strength and, 323–324, 324*f*
  definition of, 319
  water, 328–330
Dissociation constant, acid (K_a), 326–328, 327*t*, 343
Disubstituted benzenes, 481
Disulfide bonds, 522, 522*f*, 528, 762, 766–768, 766*mn*, 768*f*
Disulfides, 521–522
Division
  in scientific notation, 158, A-2
  using significant figures in, 14–16, A-4
DNA, 795
  chromosome, 795, 805–806, 805*f*
  complementary base pairs of, 804, 806–808
  composition of, 799*t*
  double helix of, 803–806, 803*f*, 804*f*
  human genome, 805, 823
  hydrogen bonding and, 246, 246*f*, 804, 804*f*
  monosaccharide of, 795–797
  mutation and, 816–818
  nitrogen-containing bases of, 796, 799*t*, 802
  nucleosides and nucleotides of, 795–800
  recombinant, 819–823, 819*f*
  replication of, 806–808, 807*f*
  RNA versus, 808
  sequence of, 802, 805, 815*f*
  transcription of, 806, 810–811, 810*f*
DNA amplification, 820–821
DNA analysis, 794
DNA fingerprinting, 822, 822*f*
DNA ligase, 807*f*, 808, 819*f*, 820
DNA polymerase, 807, 807*f*, 821
Dobutamine, 556
Docosahexaenoic acid (DHA), 669, 701
1-Dodecanol, 423
Donepezil, 421
L-Dopa, 184, 393–394, 544–545, 545*f*, 545*mn*, 650*f*, 651
Dopamine, 293, 421, 545, 545*f*, 650–651, 650*f*, 651
Doping, 692*mn*
d orbital, 56–58, 57*t*
Double bond, 115
  carbon–carbon, 388
  carbon–oxygen, 389, 404–409, 405*t*
Double-headed arrow, for resonance structures, 118, 479
Double helix of DNA, 803–806, 803*f*, 804*f*
Double replacement reactions, 147, 150–152, 151*t*
Drain cleaners, 315*f*, 705
Drugs. *See also specific drugs*
  amine, 633
  ammonium salts, 648–649, 648*mn*
  aromatic, 483–484, 483*f*
  calculating dosages of, 24–25, 35
  chiral, 543–545
  covalent, 107, 108, 128–131
  DNA interference by, 798
  enzyme-interacting, 785–786
  lipid-lowering, 691, 704
  naming new, 433
  neurotransmitters and, 650, 651, 652
  performance-enhancing, 692, 692*mn*
  sulfa, 486–487
  synthesis of, 137, 138, 174–175, 174*f*
  therapeutic concentration of, 309
Dry ice, 32, 259

E

Ecstasy (drug), 419, 634
Egg whites, denaturation of, 774, 774*mn*
Eicosanoids, 666, 696–698
Electrolytes, 275–278, 276*t*. *See also specific electrolytes*
Electron(s), 42–46, 56–66
  atomic structure, 56–58
  atomic weight of, 49–50

charge of, 42–43, 43*t*
configurations of (*See* Electronic configurations)
ionization energy for removing, 68
isotopes of, 46–49
mass number of, 45–46
mass of, 43–44, 43*t*
nonbonded (lone) pairs of, 108, 110
  in amphoteric compounds, 318–319
  in Brønsted–Lowry bases, 314–315
  in molecular geometry, 121–124, 123*t*
  in organic compounds, 389–394
number of, 44–46, 56
octet rule for, 81, 109
orbitals of, 56–58, 57*t*, 59*f*, 62–63
properties of, 43*t*
quantized energy of, 56
sharing, in covalent bond, 77–79, 108–112
shells of, 56–58, 57*t*, 63
transfer
  in ionic bond, 77–79
  in oxidation–reduction reactions, 152–156, 153*f*
unpaired, 59, 60
valence, 63–66, 110–119
  Lewis structures of, 112–119
  relationship to group number, 64–66, 65*t*
Electron cloud, 43
Electron-dot symbol, 66, 109–110. *See also* Lewis structures
Electronegativity, 124–127
  and amines, 638
  and bond polarity, 125–127, 126*t*
  and carbonyl groups, 561
  definition of, 124
  and hydrogen bonding, 245–246
  organic compound, 410–412
  periodic trends in, 125
  values for main group elements, 125, 125*f*
Electronic configurations, 58–66
  definition of, 58
  electron-dot symbols of, 66, 109–110
  first-row (period 1) elements, 59–60, 61*t*
  ground state, 58–59, 62–63
  group number and, 64–66, 65*t*
  ion, 79–87
  Lewis structures of, 110, 112–119
  and molecular shape, 121–124
  periodic table blocks and, 61–62, 62*f*
  second-row (period 2) elements, 60–61, 61*t*
  valence, 63–66
Electron transport chain, 837, 852–854, 853*f*, 874–875, 874*f*
Electrostatic attraction, 77
Electrostatic forces
  in ionic compounds, 79, 244
  in proteins, 766–768, 768*f*
Element(s), 7–8, 8*f*, 37–42
  atomic number of, 44–46
  atomic weight of, 49–50
  building-block, 39, 39*f*
  compound formation from, 40–42
  definition of, 7, 37
  electrons and chemical properties of, 56
  examples of, 7, 7*f*
  of life (human body), 39–40, 39*f*
  molecular art of, 7–8, 7*f*, 40–42, 41*f*
  naming of, 37*mn*
  naturally occurring, 37
  periodic table of, 38–39, 38*f*, 51–56, 51*f*
  symbols for, 37–38, 37*t*
  synthetic, 37
  trace, 39*f*, 40
Elemicin, 409, 409*mn*
Eleostearic acid, 494
Elimination reaction, 505–507, 523, 526
Eloxatin, 48*mn*

Emulsification, 833
Enalapril, 786
Enanthotoxin, 394, 394*mn*
Enantiomers, 535–553, 551*f*
  chiral drugs, 543–545
  compounds with two or more chirality centers, 550–552
  definition of, 535, 539
  diastereomers versus, 551–552, 551*f*
  drawing, for compound with chirality center on ring, 541
  drawing pair of, 539–540
  Fischer projections of, 546–547, 711–713
  monosaccharides, 711–713
  optical activity of, 547–550
  physical properties of, 547–550
  rotation of, 548–550
  and sense of smell, 552–553, 553*f*
  thalidomide, 542, 542*mn*
Endorphins, 761
Endothermic process
  evaporation as, 249, 258
  melting as, 256, 259*t*
  sublimation as, 259, 259*t*
  vaporization as, 257, 259*t*
Endothermic reactions, 193–197
  characteristics of, 196*t*
  classification, versus exothermic reactions, 193–194
  definition of, 193
  energy diagram of, 199, 199*f*
  photosynthesis as, 195, 195*mn*
  positive heat of reaction in, 193, 195, 199, 199*f*
  temperature changes and equilibrium in, 213–214
-ene (suffix), 456
Energy, 190–200. *See also* Metabolism
  bond storage of, 190
  changes in reactions, 192–197
  conservation of, 190
  definition of, 190
  kinetic, 190, 190*mn*, 198, 200–201, 225–226
  nutritional (Calories), 191–192, 191*t*, 192*mn*, 218–219
  phase changes and, 256–263
  potential, 190, 190*mn*
  release in bonding, 192–193
  required for breaking bonds, 192–197
  solvation and, 280
Energy of activation
  catalysts and, 201, 201*f*
  definition of, 199
  and reaction rate, 199, 200
Energy barrier, 199. *See also* Energy of activation
Energy bars, 106, 223
Energy diagrams, 197–200
Energy-generating phase, of glycolysis, 865, 865*f*, 868–869, 868*f*
Energy-investment phase, of glycolysis, 865–867, 865*f*, 866*f*, 867*f*
Enflurane, 411, 515
English system of measurement, 9, 12*t*
Enkephalins, 760–761
Enthalpy changes (Δ*H*), 193–197
  bond strength and, 195
  calculation of, 196–197
  on energy diagram, 198–200, 199*f*
  kilocalories per mole (kcal/mol), 195
  negative, in exothermic reactions, 193, 195
  positive, in endothermic reactions, 193, 195
  temperature changes and equilibrium in, 213–214
Environment, Focus on
  acid rain and naturally buffered lake, 346, 346*f*
  alkyl halides and ozone layer, 519–520, 519*f*, 519*mn*
  catalytic converters, 203, 203*f*
  combustion, 444–446
  fossil fuels, 442–443

organic pollutants, 414–415
  ozone, 119, 119*f*
  polymer recycling, 478–479, 478*mn*, 478*t*, 623, 623*mn*
  wind currents, 233, 233*f*
Enzymes, 748, 774–786. *See also specific enzymes*
  allosteric, 782
  allosteric control of, 782–783, 782*f*
  catalyst action of, 202, 202*f*, 774–775
  characteristics of, 774–775
  classification of, 775–778, 777*t*
  definition of, 202, 748, 774
  as diagnostic tools, 785, 785*t*
  digestive, 833, 835*f*
  factors affecting activity of, 781–782
  function of, 779–785
  inactive precursor of (zymogen), 784–785
  induced-fit model of, 779–780, 780*f*
  inhibitors of, 783–784
  lock-and-key model of, 779–780
  nomenclature for, 778–779
  pH and, 781–782, 781*f*
  restriction endonucleases, in DNA technology, 819–820, 819*f*, 821
  specificity of, 774, 779–780
  temperature and, 781–782, 781*f*
  therapeutic drugs interacting with, 785–786
Enzyme–substrate complex, 779–780
Ephedrine, 537, 550
Epinephrine, 645, 653–654, 654*f*
Epoxide, 512
Equations. *See* Chemical equations; *specific equations*
Equilibrium, 203–216
  in acid–base reactions, 325–328
    acid dissociation constant and, 326–328, 327*t*
    direction of, predicting from acid strength, 325–326
    weaker acid favored in, 327
  body temperature, 216, 217*f*
  concentration changes and, 211–213, 211*f*, 215*t*
  concentration of moles and, 205
  definition of, 204
  determining state of system, 210
  direction of, equilibrium constant and, 206–208, 206*t*, 207*f*
  disturbances or stresses in, 210
  Le Châtelier's principle and, 210–216
  molecular art of, 204, 204*f*
  pressure changes and, 214–216, 215*t*
  temperature changes and, 213–214, 215*t*
  vapor pressure and, 250
Equilibrium constant (*K*), 205–210
  calculation of, 208–210
  definition of, 205
  magnitude of, 206–210, 206*t*, 207*f*
  using to determine amount of product, 207–208
  writing expression for, 205
Equivalent (Eq), 276–278, 277*t*
Erythrocytes. *See* Red blood cells
Erythrulose, 537
Escherichia coli plasmids, 819–820, 819*f*
Essential amino acids, 749–751, 751*mn*, 752*mn*
Essential fatty acids, 464*mn*, 668*mn*
Ester(s), 591–631
  carbonyl group of, 404–405, 405*t*, 561, 593–595
  carboxylic acid conversion to, 611–613, 625
  cyclic, 594
  definition of, 593
  hydrolysis of, 614–618, 625
  hydrolyzable lipids, 665 [*See also* Lipid(s), hydrolyzable]
  interesting, 603–604
  lipid, 665
  nomenclature for, 597–598
  olestra as, 617–618, 617*mn*

physical properties of, 599–601
  structure of, 405, 405*t*, 561, 593–595
  synthetic polymers, 621–623
Esterification, 611–612, 621
Estimated numbers, 12–13
Estradiol, 400–401, 467, 692
Estragole, 422
Estrogens, 692
Estrone, 692, 693
Eth- (prefix), 429, 434
Ethambutol, 419
Ethane
  bond rotation in, 431–432
  carbon monoxide formation from, 164
  halogenation of, 446
  molecular shape of, 391
  natural gas, 164, 391*mn*, 442
  structure of, 388, 427
Ethanol, 387, 503–504
  blood alcohol level, 309, 509–510, 510*f*
  boiling point of, 526
  consumption/abuse, 510–511, 511*mn*
  conversions
    grams of reactant to grams of product, 168–169
    moles of reactant to grams of product, 166–167
  dehydration of, 505
  fermentation to form, 166–167, 166*mn*, 387, 503, 503*f*, 873, 873*mn*
  in fuel, 170*mn*, 187, 189, 220, 451, 472, 472*mn*, 503–504
  functional group of, 402
  health effects of, 511
  as hydration product, 472
  isomer of, 428, 531
  as laboratory solvent, 503–504
  metabolism of, 510–511
  oxidation of, 845
  pyruvate conversion to, 871, 873
  solubility of, 279, 413, 413*t*, 424, 501
  specific heat of, 253*t*
  structure of, 130
  volume/volume percent, 285, 285*mn*
Ethene. *See* Ethylene
Ethers, 497–498, 511–516
  acetals versus, 579–580
  as anesthetics, 498, 515–516, 528
  bent shape of, 512
  complex, 514
  functional group of, 403, 403*t*, 497–498, 511–512
  heterocycle of, 512
  intermolecular forces of, 513
  locating, in cyclic compound, 581
  net dipole of, 513
  nomenclature of, 514–515
  physical properties of, 513–514
  simple, 514
  solubility of, 513
  structure of, 497–498, 511–512
Ethyl acetate, 405, 611, 611*mn*
Ethylbenzene, 480
Ethyl butanoate, 406*f*, 603–604
Ethyl chloride (chloroethane), 187, 249*mn*, 403, 470
Ethylene
  formation of, 505
  hydration of, 472
  Lewis structure of, 115
  molecular shape of, 390
  nomenclature of, 457
  in plants and fruit, 454, 454*mn*
  polyethylene from, 390*mn*
  reaction with water, ethanol from, 168–169, 170*mn*
  structure of, 388, 454
Ethylene glycol, 295–296, 308, 502, 502*mn*
Ethylene monomers, 476

Ethyl formate, 598, 598*mn*
Ethyl group, 434, 435*f*, 435*t*
Ethyl heptanoate, 627
Ethyl methyl ketone, 564
Ethyl phenylacetate, 628
Ethyl propyl ether, 514
Ethyne. *See* Acetylene
Ethynylestradiol, 467, 467*f*
Eugenol, 185, 484–485
Evaporation, 249, 258
Exact number, 12
Exothermic process
    condensation as, 249, 257–258, 259*t*
    deposition as, 259, 259*t*
    freezing as, 256, 259*t*
Exothermic reactions, 193–197
    characteristics of, 196*t*
    classification, versus endothermic reactions, 193–194
    definition of, 193
    methane combustion as, 195, 195*mn*
    negative heat of reaction in, 193, 195
    temperature changes and equilibrium in, 213–214
Exponent, in scientific notation, 17–20, 158, 158*mn*, A-1–A-2
Extracts, flavor, 285*mn*, 306

F

Facilitated transport, 688
FAD and FADH$_2$, 845–846, 845*t*
    in citric acid cycle, 848–851, 849*f*
    in electron transport chain, 853–854, 853*f*
    in fatty acid oxidation, 878–879, 878*f*
    in oxidative phosphorylation, 855
    synthesis of, 846
Fahrenheit temperature scale, 26–27, 26*f*
Falcarinol, 490
Fat(s), 671–681. *See also* Triacylglycerols
    caloric value of, 191–192, 191*t*, 192*mn*, 219
    definition of, 464
    dietary, 675–676, 676*f*, 701
    fatty acid composition of, 672–674, 673*t*
    physical properties of, 672
    reaction rate of, 200
    storage in body, 192
    synthetic, 617–618
    trans, 475, 675–676, 676*f*
Fat-soluble vitamins, 279*mn*, 415–416, 417*f*, 666, 694–696, 694*t*
Fatty acids, 187, 463–465, 666–669
    ATP yield from, 880–881
    catabolism of, 877–881
    characteristics of, determining, 668–669
    cis bonds of, 464, 667–668
    common, 464*t*, 667, 667*t*, 668*mn*
    conversion to thioester, 878
    definition of, 463, 666
    essential, 464*mn*, 668*mn*
    melting point of, 464, 465, 668
    metabolism of, 836–837, 862
    metal salts (soap), 680–681
    naturally occurring, 667
    oxidation of, 835*f*, 877–881, 878*f*
    saturated, 463–465, 464*t*, 667, 667*t*, 671–676, 676*f*
    structure of, 464, 464*t*, 465*f*, 666–668
    in triacylgycerols (*See* Triacylglycerols)
    unsaturated, 453, 463–465, 464*t*, 667–668, 667*t*, 671–676, 676*f*
f block, of periodic table, 61–62, 62*f*
Fenfluramine (Fen-Phen), 419
Fenofibrate, 704
Fentanyl, 401, 658
Fermentation, 166–167, 166*mn*, 387, 503, 503*f*, 873, 873*mn*
Ferritin, 748*f*

Fertilizers, 105, 209*mn*
Fetal alcohol syndrome, 511
Fever, 216
Fexofenadine, 656
Fiber, dietary, 733–734
Fibroin protein, 768
Fibrous proteins, 748, 769
Fight-or-flight response, 653–654, 654*f*
Fingerprinting, DNA, 822, 822*f*
Fischer esterification, 611–612, 621
Fischer projection formula, 546–547, 711–713, 751–752
Fish, glycerol in, 296
Fish oil, 668–669, 668*mn*, 674, 674*mn*, 701
Fission, nuclear, 374–376, 375*f*
Flammability, of organic compounds, 410*t*
Flavin adenine dinucleotide. *See* FAD and FADH$_2$
Fleming, Alexander, 623
Flotation, density and, 27–28, 27*mn*
Fluoride, 92*t*, 320*t*
Fluorine, 37*t*, 54
    electronegativity of, 125
    electronic configuration of, 61*t*
    isotope of, 49, 380
    mass number of, 45
    as trace element (micronutrient), 39*f*, 40
Fluorine-18, 373–374
5-Fluorouracil, 798
Fluoxetine, 174, 174*f*, 538, 573–574, 652
Fluticasone, 519*mn*
Folic acid, 487
Food
    alkenes in, 466
    Brønsted–Lowry acids in, 314, 314*f*
    caffeine in, 640*mn*, 640*t*
    cholesterol in, 688–689, 688*mn*, 688*t*
    digestion of, 834–835, 836*f*
    fiber in, 733–734
    fructose versus sucrose in, 715*mn*
    genetically modified, 820*mn*
    hydrogenation in, 473–475, 473*mn*
    irradiation of, 370, 370*mn*
    metabolism of, 138, 834–835, 835*f*, 836*f*
    protein in, 748*mn*
f orbital, 56–58, 57*t*
Formaldehyde, 122, 122*mn*, 245, 411, 511, 563, 567
Formalin, 567
Formic acid, 116*mn*, 511, 595, 597, 601
Formulas
    chemical, 40
    for covalent compounds, 112, 120
    for ionic compounds, 88–90
        writing for compounds with polyatomic ions, 98–99
        writing from name of compound, 95
    molecular, 112
Formula weight, 160
Forward reaction, 204
Fossil fuels, 442–443
    carbon monoxide release from, 37*mn*
    nonrenewable energy from, 443
    refining of, 442, 442*f*
    sulfur dioxide release from, 136
    sulfur oxide release from, 62*mn*
Foxglove, 582*mn*
Francium, 53
Freeze-drying, 259, 259*mn*, 259*t*
Freezing, 256–257
Freezing point depression, 295–296, 296*mn*
Freon, 519. *See also* Chlorofluorocarbons
Fructose, 707, 710, 714, 870
    content in food, 715*mn*
    cyclic form of, 719–720
    moles and grams of, 185
    phosphorylation of, 841, 870
    sweetness of, 730*t*
Fructose 1,6-bisphosphate, 863, 866–867, 866*f*, 867*f*

Fructose 6-phosphate, 841, 863, 866–867, 866*f*, 870, 887
Fruits
    carbonyl compounds in, 405, 406*f*
    ethylene in, 454, 454*mn*
    pH of, 332*f*
Fucose, 738
2'-Fucosyllactose, 731–732
Fumarase, 776–777
Fumarate, 849*f*, 850–851
Functional groups, 401–409
    alcohol, 402, 403, 403*t*, 497–499
    aldehyde, 561–562
    alkoxy, 403*t*
    alkyl halide, 403, 403*t*, 497–498
    amine, 403, 403*t*
    amino, 403*t*, 637, 749, 883–885
    amino acid, 749
    behavior of, 401
    carbon–heteroatom single bond in, 403–404, 403*t*, 497–498
    carbonyl, 404–405, 405*f*, 561–562, 577–583, 584, 593–595, 709–710, 721–724
    definition of, 401
    ether, 403, 403*t*, 497–498, 511–512
    halo, 403*t*
    hydrocarbon, 402–403, 402*t*
    hydroxyl, 402, 403*t*, 497–499, 709
    identifying, 406–408
    ketone, 561–562
    sulfhydryl, 403*t*, 497–498, 520, 846–847
    thiol, 403, 403*t*, 497–498, 520
Funk, Casimir, 415*mn*
Fusion, nuclear, 374, 377–378

G

Gadoleic acid, 668–669, 668*mn*
GAGs (glycosaminoglycans), 736, 737*f*
Galactose, 714–715, 738, 870
Galactosemia, 714, 714*mn*, 818*t*, 870
Galactose 1-phosphate, 870
Gamma emission, 363–364, 363*f*, 364*t*
Gamma (γ) rays, 358, 358*t*
    definition of, 358
    effects of and working with, 370
    emission, 363–364, 363*f*, 364*t*
Garlic, 433, 433*mn*, 521*mn*, 522
Gas(es), 3–5, 4*f*, 225–243, 225*f*
    blood gases, 271
    condensation of, 249
    definition of, 3, 225
    evaporation to, 249
    kinetic energy in, 225–227
    kinetic–molecular theory of, 226–227
    mixture, 6, 6*f*, 242–243
    organic compounds as, 410
    partial pressure of, 242–243, 243*mn*, 268, 282, 283*f*
    phase changes of
        gas to liquid, 249, 257–258, 259*t*
        gas to solid, 259, 259*t*
        liquid to gas, 249, 257–258, 259*t*
        solid to gas, 259, 259*t*
    pressure and, 226–229
    properties of, 226–227, 226*t*
    solubility of, 282, 282*mn*, 283*f*
    solutions, 273, 273*f*
    symbol, in chemical equation, 141, 141*t*
Gas constant, universal (*R*), 239–242
Gas laws, 229–243, 264
    Avogadro's (volume–moles), 236–239, 237*mn*, 264
    Boyle's (pressure–volume), 229–231, 231*f*, 236*t*, 264
    Charles's (volume–temperature), 229, 231–233, 232*mn*, 233*f*, 236*t*, 264
    combined (pressure–volume–temperature), 235–236, 236*t*, 264

Dalton's (partial pressure), 242–243
Gay–Lussac's (pressure–temperature), 229, 233–235, 236t, 264
ideal (pressure–volume–temperature–moles), 239–242, 264
Gasohol, 170mn, 451, 472, 472mn, 503–504
Gasoline, 442
  combustion of, 138, 445, 445mn
  as covalent compound, 108
  density of, 27t
  ethanol in, 170mn, 451, 472, 472mn, 503–504
  leaded, 49mn, 75
  MTBE in, 414
  octane of, 223
  safety of, activation energy and, 200mn
  seasonal changes in, 452
Gastric juice, 320, 321f, 335, 335f
Gay–Lussac's law, 229, 233–235, 236t, 264
GDP (guanosine 5'-diphosphate), 849f, 850–851
Geckos, 244mn
Geiger counter, 368, 368mn
Gel electrophoresis, 822
Gene, 795, 806
Generic name, 433
Genetically modified crops, 820mn
Genetic code, 811–813, 812t
Genetic diseases, 818, 818t
Genetic engineering, 819
Genome, human, 805, 823
Geometric (cis–trans) isomers, 460–463, 463mn
Geranial, 568f
Geraniol, 404
German cockroach, pheromone of, 612, 612mn
GHB, 421
Giga- (prefix), 10t
Ginger, 136, 456, 456mn
Ginkgo, 161, 161mn, 601, 601mn
Global climate change, 445, 445mn
Globular proteins, 769, 771–772
Glucagon, 875
Glucogenic amino acids, 886, 886f
Gluconeogenesis, 875–877, 876f
Gluconic acid, 722
Glucosamine, 589, 736, 737mn, 738, 738mn
Glucose, 714–715
  ATP yield from, 874–875, 874f, 881, 888
  blood levels of, 714, 724–725, 724mn, 725f, 875
  catabolism of, 840–842
  chirality centers for, 712
  Cori cycle, 876, 876f
  cyclic forms of D-glucose, 715–717
  as cyclic hemiacetal, 580
  dilution of solution, 292–293
  enantiomers of, 712
  fermentation, 166–167, 166mn
  glycogen metabolism to, 736
  hydrolysis to, 504–505
  intravenous, 711mn
  metabolism of, 144, 144mn, 219, 451, 862, 864–877
  molarity of solution, 289–290
  osmotic pressure of solution, 297–299
  oxidation of, 722, 833
  in PET imaging, 373–374
  phosphorylation of, 840, 840f, 841, 866, 866f
  in polysaccharides, 732–734
  reduction of, 721
  solubility of, 279
  structure of, 707–709
  sweetness of, 730t
  synthesis from noncarbohydrate sources, 875–876, 876f
  osmotic pressure of solution, 297–299
Glucose 6-phosphate, 840, 840f, 866, 866f, 870
Glucuronate, 736
Glutamic acid, 751t

Glutamine, 750t
Glyceraldehyde, 546–547, 549, 709, 711
Glyceraldehyde 3-phosphate, 867–869, 867f, 868f, 870
Glycerol, 296, 504f, 671
  glucose synthesis from, 875–876, 876f
  phosphorylation of, 877
  from triacylglycerol hydrolysis, 677–681, 834–835, 836f, 877
Glycerol 3-phosphate, 877
Glycine, 111–112, 111f, 135, 749, 750t, 753–754
Glycogen, 714, 732, 735–736, 735f, 875, 876
Glycolic acid, 129, 622–623
Glycolipids, 687
Glycols, 502
Glycolysis, 835f, 862, 864–875, 865f
  ATP yield from, 874–875, 874f
  and cancer cells, 870–871
  energy-generating phase of, 865, 865f
  energy-investment phase of, 865–867, 865f, 866f, 867f
  equation summarizing, 869
  fate of pyruvate in, 871–873
  gluconeogenesis as reverse of, 876, 876f
  net result of, 869
Glycoproteins, 687
Glycosaminoglycans (GAGs), 736, 737f
β-Glycosidase, 733
α Glycoside, 726
β Glycoside, 726
Glycosidic linkage
  in chitin, 736–738
  in disaccharides, 725–728
  in polysaccharides, 732–736
Glyphosate, 117, 117mn
GMP (guanosine 5'-monophosphate), 800
Gold, 37t, 253t
Golden bamboo lemur, 856, 856mn
Gore, Al, 445mn
Gram (g), 9, 9t, 11
  relating moles to, 161–163
  relating number of atoms or molecules to, 163
Grapefruit, aroma of, 521mn
Grapes
  fermentation of, 166–167, 166mn
  tartaric acid from, 537
Graphite, 55, 55f, 252–253, 253t
Gravity, specific. See Specific gravity
Gray, 371
Greenhouse gases, 445
Ground state, 58–59, 62–63
Group 1A elements, 51f, 53–54. See also Alkali metals
Group 2A elements, 51f, 53–54. See also Alkaline earth elements
Group 3A elements, 65t, 83–84, 84t, 116
Group 4A elements, 65t
Group 5A elements, 65t, 84t
Group 6A elements, 65t, 84t
Group 7A elements, 51f, 54. See also Halogens
Group 8A elements, 51f, 54. See also Noble gases
Group number, on periodic table, 51f, 52
Groups, in periodic table, 51f, 52–53, 52f. See also specific groups
GTP (guanosine 5'-triphosphate), 839, 855
Guanine, 796, 799t, 804, 806–808, 807f
Guanosine 5'-diphosphate (GDP), 849f, 850–851
Guanosine 5'-monophosphate (GMP), 800
Guanosine 5'-triphosphate (GTP), 839, 848, 849f, 850–851, 855
Gypsy moth, 512

H

Haber, Fritz, 209mn
Haber process, 209mn
Hair, 19mn, 522, 522f, 748, 769, 770f
Half-life, 364–367, 365t

Half reactions, 153
Halo alkane, 517
Halogenation, 446–447, 468f, 470, 470mn
Halogens (Group 7A elements), 51f, 54
  addition to alkenes
    halogenation, 468f, 470, 470mn
    hydrohalogenation, 468f, 470–471
  in alkyl halides, 497–498, 516
  anion formation by, 84t
  atomic size of, 67
  compounds of, 54
  as heteroatoms, 389, 497–498
  in Lewis structures, 112
  substitution reaction, 446–447, 480
  valence electronic configuration of, 65t
Halo group, 403t
Halothane, 42, 393, 516
Handedness
  human, 531, 533, 533mn
  molecular, 531, 533–534 (See also Chirality)
  shell, 530
Hand sanitizers, 286mn
Hansen's disease (leprosy), 542mn
Hardening, 474
Haworth projections, 717–719, 717f, 726
HCFCs. See Hydrochlorofluorocarbons
HDL (high-density lipoprotein), 689–691, 689f, 691f
HDPE (high-density polyethylene), 475mn, 478t, 479
Health & Medicine, Focus on
  aldehydes and ketones, 567–568
  ammonium salts as useful drugs, 648–649, 648mn
  anti-inflammatory agents, 602
  aromatic drugs, sunscreens, and carcinogens, 483–484, 483f
  aspirin, 602, 609–610
  blood pressure, 228–229, 228f
  caffeine and nicotine, 639–642
  chiral drugs, 543–545
  cholesterol, 688–691, 688mn
  clinical conversion factors for problem solving, 24–25
  covalent drugs and medical products, 128–131
  dialysis, 300–301, 301f
  dissolving sutures, 622–623
  enzymes to diagnose and treat disease, 785–786
  ethanol consumption/abuse, 510–511
  ethers as anesthetics, 515–516
  fats and oil in diet, 675–676
  fat-soluble vitamins, 694–696, 694t
  glucose monitoring, 724–725, 724mn, 725f
  glycolysis and cancer cells, 870–871
  histamine and antihistamines, 656–657
  human milk oligosaccharides, 731–732
  hydrogen cyanide, 855–856, 856mn
  ionic compounds, 100
  ions in consumer products, 91, 91mn
  isotopes in medicine, 50, 50f
  lactate, 871–872
  lactose intolerance, 728, 728mn
  margarine or butter, 473–474, 473mn
  medical imaging without radioactivity, 378–379, 378f
  multiple sclerosis, 684, 684f
  naming new drugs, 433
  nitration and sulfa drugs, 486–487
  olestra (synthetic fat), 617–618
  oral contraceptives, 467–468, 467f, 467mn
  osteoporosis treatment, 100
  pacemakers, 156–157, 157f
  penicillin, 623–624, 623mn
  percent yield of drugs, 174–175, 174f
  phenols as antioxidants, 484–485, 485mn
  problem solving using clinical conversion factors, 24–25
  prostaglandins and leukotrienes, 696–698
  radioactivity effects, 370
  radioisotopes used in medicine, 371–374

Health & Medicine, Focus on (*Continued*)
saturated and unsaturated fatty acids, 463–465
skin care products, 601–602, 601*mn*
sucrose and artificial sweeteners, 729–731, 730*f*, 730*t*, 731*mn*
thalidomide, 542
viruses, 823–825
vitamins, 415–417
Heart
covalent molecules and, 111–112, 111*f*
fats/cholesterol and, 675–676, 689–691, 690*f*
pacemakers for, 156–157, 157*f*
Heart attack, lactate in, 872, 872*f*
Heart valves, synthetic, 386*f*
Heat
energy conversion to, 190
symbol, in chemical equations, 141, 141*t*
Heat of fusion, 256–257
Heating curve, 260, 260*f*
Heat of reaction (Δ*H*), 193–197
bond strength and, 195
calculation of, 196–197
on energy diagram, 198–200, 199*f*
kilocalories per mole (kcal/mol), 195
negative, in exothermic reactions, 193, 195
positive, in endothermic reactions, 193, 195, 199, 199*f*
temperature changes and equilibrium in, 213–214
Heat reservoir, water as, 254
Heat, specific. *See* Specific heat
Heat of vaporization, 257–258
Helium, 54
atomic number of, 45
electronic configuration of, 59–60, 61*t*
"lighter than air," 36, 60*mn*
London dispersion forces in, 245
properties of, 226
Helium balloons, 36, 266
α-Helix, 763–766, 764*f*, 766*f*, 768*f*
Heme, 771, 771*f*
Hemiacetals
cyclic, 580–582
definition of, 577, 715
drawing of, 578–579
formation of, 577–583
identifying, 579–580
locating, in cyclic compound, 581
monosaccharide, 715–720
Hemibrevetoxin B, 512
Hemlock, 394, 394*mn*, 633
Hemoglobin, 34, 40, 748, 748*f*, 771–772
carbon monoxide and, 164, 445, 771
as covalent molecule, 111, 111*f*
sickle cell, 771–772, 772*mn*
structure of, 768, 771, 771*f*
Hemolysis, 299, 300*f*
Henry's law, 282, 283*f*
Heparin, 736, 736*mn*, 737*f*
Hepatobiliary iminodiacetic acid (HIDA) scan, 371, 372*f*
Hepta- (prefix), 120*t*
Heptane, 451
2-Heptanone, 585, 590
Heroin, 642–643, 662, 760–761
Heteroatoms, 389–394
definition of, 389
ether (heterocycle), 512
in functional groups, 401–409
single bond of carbon atom to, 403–404, 403*t*, 497–498
Heterocycle, 512, 633, 637
Heterogeneous mixture, 273, 273*mn*
Hexa- (prefix), 120*t*
Hexachloroethane, 419, 552, 553*f*
Hexane, 399, 413, 413*t*
Hexanoic acid, 601
Hexokinase, 780*f*, 840, 840*f*, 866*f*

Hexose, 709, 870
Hexyl group, 435*t*
HFCs (hydrofluorocarbons), 520
Hibernation, 881*mn*
HIDA scan, 371, 372*f*
High-density lipoproteins (HDLs), 689–691, 689*f*, 691*f*
High-density polyethylene (HDPE), 475*mn*, 478*t*, 479
Histamine, 656–657
Histamine (H2) receptor, 656
Histidine, 751*t*
Histones, 805, 805*f*
HIV/AIDS, 786, 786*f*, 823–825, 824*f*
HIV protease inhibitors, 786, 786*f*, 823–825
HMOs. *See* Human milk oligosaccharides
Homogeneous mixture, 273. *See also* Solution(s)
Honey, 628, 707
Honeysuckle, 535, 535*f*
Hormones. *See also specific hormones*
definition of, 653
peptide, 761–762
protein, 748
sex, 692, 693
steroid, 692–693
Hot air balloons, 232*mn*
Hot pack, 280
Human Body, Focus on
biologically active peptides, 760–762
biological reductions, 574–575
blood type, 738–739, 738*mn*, 739*f*, 739*t*
body temperature, 216, 216*mn*, 217*f*
Boyle's law and breathing, 231, 231*f*
buffers in blood, 347–348
carbohydrate derivatives, 736–738
covalent molecules and cardiovascular system, 111–112, 111*f*
creatine and athletic performance, 842–843, 842*mn*
DNA fingerprinting, 822, 822*f*
elements of life, 39–40, 39*f*
energy and nutrition, 191–192, 191*t*, 192*mn*
epinephrine and related compounds, 653–655
hydrochloric acid in stomach, 321*f*
ions of importance, 86–87, 87*f*
lactase, 202, 202*f*
lungs, 240, 240*f*
osmosis and biological membranes, 299–300
oxidation and blood alcohol level, 509–510, 510*f*
pH of body fluids, 335, 335*f*
proteins, 769–772
sense of smell, 552–553, 553*f*
straight and curly hair, 522, 522*f*
triacylglycerol metabolism, 678–680
vision chemistry, 575–577, 575*mn*, 576*f*
Human genome, 805, 823
Human Genome Project, 823
Human immunodeficiency virus (HIV), 786, 786*f*, 823–825, 824*f*
Human milk oligosaccharides (HMOs), 731–732
Huntington's disease, 818*t*
Hyaluronate, 736, 737*f*
Hybrid, 118, 479
Hydration of alkenes, 468*f*, 472–473
Hydro- (prefix), 313
Hydrobromic acid, 312, 313*t*, 317, 320, 320*t*, 470–471
Hydrocarbons, 402–403, 402*t*. *See also specific types*
alkanes, 402–403, 402*t*, 425–452
alkenes, 402–403, 402*t*, 454–475
alkynes, 402–403, 402*t*, 454–460
aromatic compounds, 402–403, 402*t*, 454, 479–489
cabbage coating, 424
combustion of, 444–445
definition of, 402, 454
fatty acids, 463–465, 666–669
isomers, 428–430, 460–463
as nonpolar molecules, 411
polymers, 475–479

saturated, 426, 454 (*See also* Acyclic alkanes)
skin moisturizers, 424
structure of, 402*t*
unsaturated, 453–495
Hydrochloric acid, 311–313
in buffer, 342
digestive function of, 320, 321*f*
dissociation of, 320, 321*f*
hydrohalogenation with, 470–471
reaction with ammonia, 317, 317*mn*
reaction with sodium hydroxide, 336
as strong acid, 320, 320*t*
titration of, 340–341, 340*f*
Hydrochlorofluorocarbons (HCFCs), 520
Hydrocyanic acid, 320*t*, 327*t*
Hydrofluoric acid, 320*t*, 324, 327*t*
Hydrofluorocarbons (HFCs), 520
Hydrogen, 37*t*
addition to alkenes, 468*f*, 469, 473–475
addition to vegetable oil, 473–475, 473*mn*, 474*f*, 474*mn*
in anion, 97
as building-block element, 39, 39*f*
covalent bonding by, 109–110, 116
as diatomic molecule, 108–109
electronic configuration of, 59, 61*t*
as energy source, 176*mn*
exception to octet rule, 116
isotopes of, 47
in Lewis structures, 112
as limiting reactant, 176–177
in organic compounds, 388–390
teeth-whitening products, 129*mn*
Hydrogenation, 201, 468*f*, 469, 473–475, 473*mn*, 474*f*, 474*mn*, 572
Hydrogen bonding, 244, 245–247, 246*t*
alcohol, 500
amide, 600, 600*f*
amine, 638
carboxylic acid, 599–600, 599*f*
DNA, 246, 246*f*, 804, 804*f*
electronegativity and, 245–246
protein, 766, 768*f*
solubility and, 278–279
Hydrogen bromide, 148
Hydrogen chloride, 311
Hydrogen cyanide, 121, 122, 122*mn*, 568, 855–856, 856*mn*
Hydrogen fluoride, 108
Hydrogen halides, 446–447, 468*f*, 470–471
Hydrogen ions, 311–316
Hydrogen peroxide, 128–129, 774*mn*
decomposition of, 146
as oxidizing agent, 154
polarity of, 129
solution of, 275
structure of, 128–129
visible physical change with, 140, 140*f*
Hydrogen phosphate, 327*t*, 838–839, 839*f*
Hydrogen phosphate/phosphate buffer, 344*t*
Hydrogen sulfate, 320*t*, 327*t*
Hydrogen sulfide, 116–117
Hydrohalogenation, 468*f*, 470–471
Hydroiodic acid, 320, 320*t*
Hydrolase, 776, 777*t*
Hydrolysis
acetal, 583
amide, 614, 616–617, 625
aspirin, 616
ATP, 777, 777*t*, 832, 838–842, 839*f*
carbohydrate, 833, 835*f*, 862
cellulose, 504–505
creatine phosphate, 832, 842–843
disaccharide, 707–708, 727–728, 740
enzymes in, 776–777, 777*t*
ester, 614–618, 625

lipid, 665
  phosphoenolpyruvate, 840–842
  protein, 772–773, 833, 835*f*, 862
  starch, 504–505
  triacylglycerol, 677–681, 699, 776, 833, 835*f*,
    862, 877
  wax, 671, 699
Hydronium ion, 311–316, 311*mn*
  acid strength and, 319–323
  dissociation of water and, 328–330
  pH scale and, 331–335
  as polyatomic ion, 97
  solution concentration of, 329–330, 329*t*, 331
Hydrophilic portion, of lipid, 666–667
Hydrophobic portion, of lipid, 666–667
Hydroxide ion, 311, 314–315
  as conjugate base, 320*t*
  as polyatomic ion, 97*t*
  reaction of acids with hydroxide bases,
    335–337
  as strong base, 323
α-Hydroxy acids, 601–602, 601*mn*, 622–623
Hydroxyapatite, 100
Hydroxybenzenes (phenols), 393, 480, 484–485
β-Hydroxybutyrate, 882
Hydroxydihydrocitronellal, 558
Hydroxyl group, 402, 403*t*, 497–499, 709
Hygrine, 659
Hyperbaric chamber, 243, 243*mn*
Hypertension, 229, 785–786
Hyperthyroidism, 360, 361*f*
Hypertonic solution, 299–300, 300*f*
Hypochlorous acid, 354
Hypothalamus, in thermoregulation, 216, 217*f*
Hypotonic solution, 299, 300*f*

I

Ibuprofen
  as carboxylic acid, 602, 610
  chirality of, 543–544
  covalent bonds in, 108
  determining dosage of, 35
  mechanism of action, 696–697
  moles and molar mass of, 185
  names for, 433
  pain relief with, 544*mn*
  percent concentration, 286
  skeletal structure of, 401
  synthesis of, 138
-ic (suffix), 92, 94, 313, 595
Ice
  density of, 27–28, 27*t*
  melting of, 4–5, 138
  as molecular solid, 252, 252*f*
Ichthyothereol, 491
-ide (suffix), 92, 92*t*, 313, 518
Ideal gas law, 239–242, 264
Identical twins, 533*mn*, 805*mn*, 822
-idine (suffix), 797
Incomplete combustion, 445–446
Indoor pollution, 54, 54*mn*, 122*mn*, 164*mn*
Induced-fit model, of enzyme, 779–780, 780*f*
-ine (suffix), 517, 518
Inexact number, 12
Informational strand, of DNA, 810–811, 810*f*, 815*f*
Inhibitors, 783–784
Inner transition metals, 51*f*, 52
Inorganic phosphate, 838–839, 839*f*
Insect repellants, 613, 613*mn*
Insertion mutation, 817
Insulin, 714, 714*mn*, 748, 748*f*, 767, 767*f*, 820, 875
Integral proteins, 687
Intergovernmental Panel on Climate Change, 445*mn*
Intermembrane space, 834, 834*f*

Intermolecular forces, 244–249
  and alcohols, 500
  and aldehydes, 565–566
  and alkanes, 444
  and amides, 600
  and amines, 638–639
  and boiling point, 247–249, 250
  and carboxylic acids, 599–600
  determining types in compound, 246–247
  dipole–dipole forces, 244, 245, 246*t*
  and ethers, 513
  hydrogen bonding, 244, 246*f*, 246*t*
  and ketones, 565–566
  London dispersion forces, 244–245, 244*mn*, 246*t*, 686
    and boiling/melting points, 247–248
    and protein structure, 766–768, 768*f*
  and melting point, 247–249
  molecule size and, 245
  and organic compounds, 410
  and surface tension, 250, 250*f*
  and vapor pressure, 250
  and viscosity, 251
International System of Units, 9*mn*
International Union of Pure and Applied Chemistry
  (IUPAC). *See* IUPAC system of nomenclature
Intravenous (IV) solution, 35, 277–278, 304
Iodide, 92*t*, 320*t*
Iodine, 37*t*, 39*f*, 40, 54, 154
Iodine-123, 357
Iodine-131, 50, 50*f*, 357, 360, 361*f*, 365–366, 365*t*, 369,
  371, 373*f*, 382, 384
Iodine-125 seeds, 373, 373*mn*
Ion(s), 79–87
  definition of, 77
  electrolytes and, 275–278
  electrostatic attraction between, 79
  equivalent as measure of, 276–278, 277*t*
  formation of
    by metals, 80–81, 83–86, 84*t*
    by nonmetals, 81, 84, 84*t*
  important, in human body, 86–87, 87*f*
  in ionic compounds, 88–89
  naming of, 91–92, 92*t*
  periodic table groupings and, 83–85
  polyatomic, 97–99, 97*t*, 117–119, 146–147
  in salt solutions, 338–340
  spectator, 336
  symbols for, 81–83, 81*mn*
  types of, 79–83
Ion channels, 688
Ion–dipole interaction, 279
Ionic bonds, 77–79
  energy stored in, 190
  metal–nonmetal, 77, 78*f*, 88–89
  polarity of, 126–127, 126*t*
Ionic compounds, 76–106
  boiling point of, 96, 410, 410*t*
  in consumer products, 91, 91*mn*, 106
  definition of, 77
  electrostatic forces in, 77, 244
  examples of, 77
  formulas for, 88–90
    writing for compounds with polyatomic ions, 98–99
    writing from name of compound, 95
  formula weight of, 160
  in health and medicine, 100
  melting point of, 96, 410, 410*t*
  naming of, 91–95, 92*t*
  organic compounds versus, 410, 410*t*
  physical properties of, 96–97
  solubility of, 96, 96*f*, 278–279, 278*f*, 281–282, 410*t*
  zero overall charge of, 88–90, 89*f*
Ionic solids, 252, 252*f*
Ionization energy, 66, 68–69
Ion–product constant, 328–330

Iridium-192, 373, 373*f*
Iron, 37*t*
  catalyst, for chlorination, 486
  cations of, 85, 86, 87*f*, 92, 92*t*
  oxidation of, 155
  specific heat of, 253*t*
  as trace element (micronutrient), 39*f*, 40
Iron-fortified cereals, 40*mn*
Iron oxide, 155
Iron sulfate, 100, 160
Irradiated food, 370, 370*mn*
Irreversible inhibitor, 783
Isoamyl acetate, 406*f*
Isobutane, 428
Isobutyl cyanoacrylate, 136
Isocitrate, 844, 849, 849*f*, 859
Isoflurane, 515
Isoleucine, 750*t*
Isomaltose, 744
Isomer(s), 531–533, 551*f*. *See also specific types*
  cis–trans, 460–463, 463*mn*, 531–532
  constitutional, 428–430 (See also Constitutional
    isomers)
  definition of, 428, 460, 531
  diastereomers, 551–552, 551*f*
  enantiomers, 535–553, 551*f*
  identifying, 532–533
  stereoisomers, 462–463, 531–533, 551*f*
Isomerase, 776, 777*t*, 866, 866*f*
Isomerization, 776, 866–869, 866*f*, 867*f*, 868*f*
Isooctane, 445
Isopentane, 429
Isotonic solution, 299, 300, 300*f*
Isotopes, 46–50, 356–357
  atomic weight and, 49–50
  definition of, 46, 356
  naturally occurring, 47, 49
  radioactive, 50, 50*f*, 356–357
    decay of, 359–364
    half-life of, 364–367, 365*t*
    medical uses of, 50, 50*f*, 355, 360–363, 361*f*, 363*f*,
      369–374, 372*f*, 373*f*
  stable versus unstable, 356–357
Isotope symbol, 47
Isovaleric acid, 596, 596*mn*
-ite (suffix), 97, 313
IUPAC system of nomenclature, 433
  alcohols, 501–503
  aldehydes, 562–564
  alkanes, 434–439
    acyclic alkanes, 435–439
    cycloalkanes, 440–442
  alkenes and alkynes, 456–460
  alkyl halides, 517–518
  amides, 598–599
  benzene derivatives, 480–482
  carboxylic acids, 595–596
  esters, 597–598
  ethers, 514–515
  ketones, 564–565

J

Jicama, 853–854, 853*mn*
Jojoba oil (wax), 670, 670*mn*
Joule (J), 190–191, 190*mn*
Joule, James Prescott, 190*mn*

K

Kelp, 518*f*, 518*mn*
Kelvin temperature scale, 26–27, 26*f*, 231–232
Keratin, 522, 748, 748*f*, 769, 770*f*
α-Keratin, 769, 770*f*
Kerosene, 442
Ketamine, 285*mn*, 286, 293

α-Keto acid, 883–884
Ketoacidosis, 882
Ketogenic amino acids, 886, 886f
α-Ketoglutarate, 849, 849f, 859, 883–885
α-Ketoglutarate dehydrogenase, 849
Ketohexoses, 719–720
Ketone(s)
  acetal hydrolysis to, 583
  alcohol oxidation to, 508–509, 523
  carbonyl group of, 404, 405t, 561–562
  celery, 553, 553mn
  in health and medicine, 567–568
  hydrogenation of, 572
  monosaccharides, 709
  naturally occurring, 562
  nomenclature for, 564–565
  physical properties of, 565–567
  polarity of, 565
  polyhydroxy, 707 (See also Carbohydrates)
  reactions of, 569–583
    acetal formation in, 577–583, 584
    addition, 569, 577–583
    reduction, 571–575, 584
  structure of, 405t, 561–562
Ketone bodies, 882, 882mn
Ketose, 709–710
Ketosis, 882
Ketostix, 882mn
Ketotriose, 709
Kevlar, 620, 620mn
Kidney dialysis, 300–301, 301f
Kilo- (prefix), 10t
Kilocalories (kcal), 190–191
Kilocalories per mole (kcal/mol), 195
Kilojoules (kJ), 190–191
Kilometer (km), 10
Kinase, 776, 863
Kinetic energy, 190, 190mn
  gases and, 225–227
  molecular collision and, 198, 200–201
  states of matter and, 225–226
  temperature and, 200–201
Kinetic–molecular theory, 226–227
Krebs, Hans, 848
Krebs cycle. See Citric acid cycle
Krypton, 54
Krypton-91, 375
Kukui nuts, 453, 475, 494

L

ʟ (prefix), 711
Laboratory results, scientific notation for, 17–18, 18f
Lactam, 594, 631
β-Lactam, 623–624
Lactase, 202, 202f, 581, 728
Lactate
  conversion to pyruvate, 872
  glucose synthesis from, 875–876, 876f
  in heart attack, 872, 872f
  in muscle metabolism, 872, 872mn
  pyruvate conversion to, 845, 871–872
Lactate dehydrogenase, 575, 775
Lactic acid, 135, 325mn, 528, 558, 575, 622–623
Lactone, 594
Lactose, 202, 202f, 557, 581, 707–708, 728
Lactose intolerance, 581, 728, 728mn
Lagging strand, of DNA, 807f, 808
Lamivudine, 830
Landsteiner, Karl, 738
Lanolin, 669
Lanthanides, 51f, 52
Lard, 673t, 681
Latex, 3, 3f

Laughing gas, 119, 119mn
Lauric acid, 667t, 705
Lavandulol, 499, 499mn
Lavender oil, 496, 499, 499mn
Law of conservation of energy, 190
Law of conservation of matter, 141
LD₅₀, 371
LDPE (low-density polyethylene), 475mn, 478t
Lead, 37t, 49mn
Lead-210, 381
Leaded gasoline, 49mn, 75
Leading strand, of DNA, 807f, 808
Le Châtelier's principle, 210–216, 347, 611, 721
Lecithin, 682
Left-handedness, 531, 533mn
Length, 9–10, 9t, 12t
Leprosy, 542mn
Lethal dose (LD₅₀), 371
Leucine, 558, 750t, 752, 752mn
ᴅ-Leucine, 558
ʟ-Leucine, 558
Leu-enkephalin, 760, 773, 831
Leukotriene(s), 696, 697–698
Leukotriene C₄, 491, 696, 697–698
Levodopa, 544–545
Levonorgestrel, 424, 468
Levorotatory compounds, 548–550
Lewis structures, 110, 112–119
  differing in electron arrangement, 117–119
  drawing of, 112–116
  molecular shape determined from, 121–124
  multiple bonds in, 114–116
  octet rule exceptions in, 116–117
  rules for, 112
Licorice, 490
Lidocaine, 385, 394, 394mn, 658
Ligase, 777, 777t
Light, plane-polarized, 547–549
Lightning, ozone production in, 165mn
"Like dissolves like," 278, 412, 500, 566
Limestone, and acid rain, 346, 346f
Limiting reactants, 175–180
(R)-Limonene, 541
Linalool, 496, 499, 499mn
Linamarin, 122, 122mn
Linear carbon, 454
Linear geometry, 121–122, 123t, 124, 390, 392t
Linear metabolic pathway, 833
Linoleic acid, 453, 464mn, 464t, 465, 465f, 474, 494, 667t, 668
Linolenic acid, 187, 453, 464mn, 464t, 465f, 475, 667t, 668
Lipases, 618, 679, 776, 833, 835f, 877
Lipid(s), 617–618, 663–705. See also Triacylglycerols
  biological functions of, 666
  catabolism of, 834–836, 835f, 836f
  cell membrane, 686–688
  definition of, 664
  dietary, 675–676, 676f, 688–689, 688t, 701
  digestion of, 834–835, 836f
  emulsification of, 833
  hydrolyzable, 665–688
    fatty acids, 187, 463–465, 666–669
    phospholipids, 665, 681–688
    triacylglycerols, 617–618, 664, 665, 671–681
    waxes, 665, 669–671
  identifying, 665
  key reactions, 699
  metabolism of, 833–835, 835f, 836f, 861, 862, 877–881
  nonhydrolyzable, 665–666
    eicosanoids, 666, 696–698
    fat-soluble vitamins, 279mn, 415–416, 417f, 666, 694–696, 694t
    steroids, 666, 688–693

  origin of term, 664mn
  physical properties of, 664
  solubility and insolubility of, 664
  structure and bonding of, 664–666
Lipid bilayer, 686
Lipid-lowering drugs, 174, 174f, 691, 704
Lipoproteins, 689–691
Liposuction, 34
Lipoxygenase, 698
Liquefied petroleum gas (LPG), 427mn
Liquid(s), 3–5, 4f, 225–226, 225f, 249–251
  condensation to, 249, 257–258
  definition of, 3, 225
  evaporation of, 249, 258
  intermolecular forces and, 244–249
  kinetic energy in, 225–226
  organic compounds as, 410
  phase changes of
    gas to liquid, 249, 257–258, 259t
    liquid to gas, 249, 257–258, 259t
    liquid to solid, 252, 256–257, 259t
    solid to liquid, 256–257, 256mn, 259t
  properties of, 226t
  solubility of gas in, 282, 282mn, 283f
  surface tension of, 251, 251f
  symbol, in chemical equation, 141, 141t
  vaporization of, 257–258
  vapor pressure and, 249–251
  viscosity of, 251
Liquid nutritional supplements, 104–105
Lisinopril, 595, 595mn
Liter (L), 9, 9t, 10mn, 11
Lithium, 44mn, 53, 60, 61t
Lithium–iodine battery, in pacemakers, 156–157, 157f
Local mediators, 696
Lock-and-key model, of enzyme, 779–780
Logarithm, 331, 333–334, 333mn, A-5
London dispersion forces, 244–245, 244mn, 246t, 686
  and boiling/melting points, 247–248
  and protein structure, 766–768, 768f
Lone pairs, 108, 110
  in amphoteric compounds, 318–319
  in Brønsted–Lowry bases, 314–315
  in molecular geometry, 121–124, 123t
  in organic compounds, 389–394
Loratadine, 483, 483f
Lovastatin, 691, 691mn
Low-density lipoproteins (LDLs), 689–691, 689f, 691f
Low-density polyethylene (LDPE), 475mn, 478t
Lowry, Thomas, 311
LPG (liquefied petroleum gas), 427mn
Lucite, 493
Lungs, 240, 240f
Lupin, 632, 634
Lupinine, 634
Lyase, 776–777, 777t
Lycopene, 466, 466mn
Lysine, 42, 751t
Lysol, 485
Lysozyme, 764, 765f

M

Maalox, 35, 100, 185, 336mn
Macadamia nuts, 495
Macronutrients, 39–40, 39f
Magnesium, 37t, 53
  ions, 80
  isotopes of, 48
  as major mineral (macronutrient), 39f, 40
  reaction with water, heat from, 196–197, 196mn
  role in human body, 86, 87f
Magnesium cation, 80
Magnesium chloride, 93
Magnesium hydroxide, 100, 315

Magnesium sulfate, 54, 100, 280
Magnetic resonance imaging (MRI), 378–379, 378*f*
Ma huang, 537
Main group elements, 51*f*, 52
    cations from, naming ionic compounds with, 93
    covalent bonding by, 110
    electronegativity values for, 125, 125*f*
    ion formation by, 79–87, 85*t*
    ionic charges of, 83–85, 84*t*
    Lewis structures of, 112–116
    valence electron configuration of, 64–66, 65*t*
Major minerals, 39–40, 39*f*
Malaria, 35
Maltose, 726–727, 726*mn*
Mammogram, 384
Manganese, 37*t*, 39*f*, 87
Mangoes, 426, 589, 603–604
Mannitol, 308
Mannose, 870, 887
Mannose 6-phosphate, 870, 887
Manure, methane from, 443, 443*f*
Marble statues, 353
Margarine, 473–475, 473*mn*, 673*t*, 701
Marijuana, 403–404, 424
Markovnikov's rule, 471, 472
Mass
    calculations in chemical equations, 165–171
    conversions, 159–163
    critical, in nuclear fission, 375
    definition of, 11
    molar, 160–163
    relationship to volume (density), 27–29
    subatomic particles, 43–44, 43*t*
    units of measurement, 9, 9*t*, 11–12, 12*t*
    weight versus, 11
Mass number, 45–46
    definition of, 45, 356
    isotope, 47–49, 356–357
    in nuclear equation, 359
Mathematical concepts, A-1–A-6
Matrix, mitochondrial, 834, 834*f*
Matter
    chemical properties of, 4–5
    classification of, 5–8, 8*f*
    conservation of, 141
    definition of, 2
    naturally occurring materials, 2–3, 2*f*, 3*f*
    physical properties of, 4–5
    states of, 3–5, 4*f*, 225–226, 225*f*
    synthetic materials, 2–3, 2*f*, 3*f*
    transformation of, 3, 3*f*
MDMA (Ecstasy), 419, 634
Meadowsweet, 602, 609, 609*mn*
Measles vaccine, 823
Measurement, 9–12
    conversion factors, 20–25
    English system, 9, 12*t*
    International System of Units, 9*mn*
    metric system, 9–10, 9*t*, 10*t*
    newborn, 1, 9
    numbers and units of, 9
    rounding off numbers, 14–16, 15*t*, A-3
    scientific notation, 17–20, 18*f*, 158, A-1–A-2
    significant figures, 12–17, A-2–A-4
Meat tenderizers, 776*mn*
Medical imaging. *See also* specific types
    with radioactivity, 50, 50*f*, 362, 363, 371–373, 372*f*
    without radioactivity, 378–379, 378*f*
Mega- (prefix), 10*t*
Melatonin, 603
Melittin, 790
Melting, 256–257, 256*mn*, 259*t*
    organic compound, 410
    physical change in, 4–5, 138
    relative, predicting in two compounds, 248–249

Melting point (mp), 4
    alcohol, 500
    alkane, 444
    alkene and alkyne, 454
    alkyl halide, 517
    amide, 600
    aromatic compound, 480
    carboxylic acid, 600
    definition of, 247
    enantiomer, 547
    ether, 513
    fats and oils, 672
    fatty acid, 464, 465, 668
    freezing point depression and, 295–297, 295*mn*
    intermolecular forces and, 247–249
    ionic compound, 96, 410, 410*t*
    monosaccharide, 711
    organic compound, 410
    thiol, 520
Membrane
    biological, osmosis and, 299–300
    cell, 686–688, 687*f*
    dialysis, 300–301, 301*f*
    semipermeable, 297, 299–301
Membrane proteins, 748
Mendeleev, Dmitri, 51
Menthol, 485, 499, 587, 665
Menthone, 587
Mepivacaine, 419
Mercaptan, 521*mn*
Mercaptomethylfuran, 498
Mercury, 37*t*
    dental use of, 65*mn*, 273, 273*f*
    ions, 92*t*
    specific heat of, 253*t*
    toxicity of, 65*mn*
Mercury barometer, 227, 227*f*
Mercury thermometer, 26*mn*
Mescaline, 185, 655
Meselson, Matthew, 806
Messenger RNA (mRNA), 808–816, 809*t*
    DNA transcription to, 810–811, 810*f*
    sequence of, 811, 815*f*
    translation of, 813–816, 815*f*
    triplets in (genetic code), 811–813, 812*t*
Meta- (prefix), 481
Metabolic acidosis, 348
Metabolic alkalosis, 348
Metabolic pathways, 833, 848
Metabolism, 832–860
    acetyl CoA formation in, 835*f*, 836–837
    aerobic reactions in, 842
    amino acid, 835*f*, 836–837, 862, 883–887, 886*f*
    anabolism in, 833, 876
    anaerobic reactions in, 842
    biochemical reactions in, 862–864
    carbohydrate, 833–835, 835*f*, 836*f*, 862, 864–877
        ATP yield from, 874–875, 874*f*
        gluconeogenesis, 875–877, 876*f*
        glycolysis, 835*f*, 862, 864–875, 865*f*
    catabolism in, 833–837, 835*f*, 836*f*, 862
    cellular, 834, 834*f*
    citric acid cycle in, 835*f*, 837, 848–852, 848*f*, 849*f*
    coenzymes in, 843–847
    coupled reactions in, 839–842, 840*f*
    definition of, 833
    digestion in, 834–835, 835*f*, 836*f*
    electron transport chain in, 837, 852–854, 853*f*
    food, 138, 834–835, 835*f*, 836*f*
    overview of, 834–837
    oxidative phosphorylation in, 837, 854–855
    triacylglycerol, 678–680, 833–835, 835*f*, 836*f*, 877–881
Meta isomer, 481

Metal(s)
    catalyst, 201, 469
    in catalytic converters, 203, 203*f*
    cations of
        formation of, 80–81, 83–86, 84*t*
        naming of, 91–92, 92*t*
    definition of, 39
    ionic bonding with nonmetal, 77, 78*f*, 88–89
    oxidation of, 152–154, 153*f*, 154*f*
    in periodic table, 38–39, 38*f*
    specific heat of, 253
    with variable charges, 85–86, 93–94
Metallic solids, 252, 252*f*
Metalloid(s)
    covalent bonding with nonmetal, 109
    definition of, 39
    on periodic table, 38–39, 38*f*
Metal salts, 315, 323, 336–338
Metastable, 363*mn*
Met-enkephalin, 760, 831
Meter (m), 9–10, 9*t*
Meth- (prefix), 429, 434
Methadone, 648–649
Methamphetamine, 136, 411, 555, 635, 635*f*, 645, 654–655
Methane
    biogas, 443, 443*f*
    boiling point of, 247–248
    combustion of, 138–142, 155–156, 195, 195*mn*, 445
    as covalent molecule/compound, 77, 109
    halogenation of, 446
    melting point of, 247–248
    molecular geometry of, 122, 391
    natural gas, 387, 442
    nonpolarity of, 127
    properties of, 387
    structure of, 387, 388, 427
Methanol, 504*f*
    aspartame metabolism to, 188
    combustion of, 186, 528
    Lewis structure of, 114
    molecular shape of, 392, 412
    oxidation of, 511
    polarity of, 412
    toxicity of, 114, 188, 504*f*, 511
Methenolone, 704
Methionine, 750*t*
Methoxychlor, 494
Methoxyflurane, 132, 515
Methyl acetate, 593
Methyl acrylate, 477, 493
Methylamine, 391
Methyl anthranilate, 408–409, 408*mn*
Methylbenzene (toluene), 480
Methyl benzoate, 611
3-Methyl-1-butanethiol, 524
Methyl butanoate, 597
Methyl carbanion, 136
Methyl carbocation, 136
Methyl cinnamate, 490
3-Methylcyclohexene, 540–541
Methylcyclopentane, 540
1-Methylcyclopentene, 457
3-Methylcyclopentene, 457
Methylene chloride (dichloromethane), 187, 412, 518*f*
Methyl group, 434, 435*f*, 435*t*
5-Methyl-1,4-hexadiene, 457
3-Methyl-2-hexenoic acid, 136
6-Methyloctanal, 588
Methylparaben, 628
Methylphenidate, 662
Methyl salicylate, 424, 603
3-Methyl-3-sulfanyl-1-hexanol, 498, 521

Metric system, 9–12, 10*mn*, 10*t*, 12*t*
Micelles, 608, 608*f*
Micro- (prefix), 10*t*
Microcurie (μCi), 368, 369*t*
Microliter (μL), 11
Micronutrients (trace elements), 39*f*, 40
Migraine, serotonin in, 652
Milk, human, oligosaccharides in, 731–732
Milk of magnesia, 100, 274
Milk proteins, denaturation of, 774
Milli- (prefix), 10*t*
Millicurie (mCi), 368–369, 369*t*
Milliliter (mL), 11
Millimeter (mm), 10
Millimeters of mercury (mm Hg), 227
Millirem (mrem), 371
Mineral(s), 39–40, 39*f*
Mineral oil, 451, 452
Mirror images, molecular, 531, 533–534
Misoprostol, 697
Mitochondria, 834, 834*f*
    citric acid cycle in, 837, 848–852
    electron transport chain in, 852–854, 853*f*
    oxidative phosphorylation in, 854–855
Mixtures, 5–6, 6*f*, 8*f*, 273–275. *See also*
        Solution(s)
    definition of, 6, 273
    gas, 6, 6*f*, 242–243
    heterogeneous, 273, 273*mn*
    homogeneous, 273
    separation of, 6
    solid–liquid, 6, 6*f*
mm Hg (millimeters of mercury), 227
Moisturizers, 424
mol (one mole), 157
Molarity, 288–291
    calculating number of grams from, 291
    calculating volume from, 289–290
    calculation from grams of solute, 288–289
    as conversion factor, 289–290
    definition of, 288
    titration to determine, 340–342, 340*f*
Molar mass, 160–163
    calculating, 161
    calculating energy change from, 196–197
    calculations in chemical equations, 165–171
    definition of, 161
    periodic table and, 161
    relating grams to moles, 161–163
    relating grams to number of atoms or
        molecules, 163
Molar volume, standard, 238
Mole(s), 157–171
    Avogadro's number as conversion factor for,
        157–159
    calculations in chemical equations, 164–165
    concentration, and equilibrium, 205
    conversions
        mass to mole, 159–163
        moles to number of molecules, 158–159
        number of molecules to moles, 159
    definition of, 157
    equivalents and, 276–278, 277*t*
    examples of, 157*mn*
    gas laws
        Avogadro's (volume–moles), 236–239,
            237*mn*, 264
        ideal (pressure–volume–temperature–moles),
            230–242, 264
        kilocalories per, 195
        relating grams to, 161–163
Molecular art, 7–8, 7*f*, 40–42, 41*f*, 44–45, 68–69, 204,
        204*f*, 208–209
Molecular collisions, 197–201
Molecular formula, 112

Molecular shape, 121–124, 123*t*. *See also specific shapes*
    alcohol, 500
    four groups around an atom, 121, 122–123
    organic molecule, 390–394, 392*t*, 411–412
    and polarity, 127–128
    and sense of smell, 552–553, 553*f*
    three-dimensional, 530–559 (*See also* Chirality)
    three groups around an atom, 121, 122
    two groups around an atom, 121–122
Molecular solids, 252, 252*f*
Molecular weight, 160
Molecule
    covalent bonding in, 78, 108
    definition of, 78, 108
    diatomic, 108–109
    polarity of, 127–128, 127*f*
    resonance-stabilized, 118–119
Mole ratios, 164
Molina, Mario, 519*mn*
Molybdenum, 37*t*, 39*f*
Monensin, 591
Mono- (prefix), 120*t*
Monomers, 475–478
Monoprotic acid, 313
Monosaccharides, 707, 709–725
    blood type, 738–739
    carbohydrate digestion to, 834–835, 836*f*
    carbonyl group of, 709–710
    chirality centers of, 711–713
    common, 714–715
    cyclic forms of, 715–720
        of D-glucose, 715–717
        of fructose, 719–720
        Haworth projections of, 717–719, 717*f*, 726
    D and L forms of, 712
    disaccharide hydrolysis to, 707–708, 727–728, 740
    glycosidic linkage of
        in disaccharides, 725–728
        in polysaccharides, 732–736
    hydroxyl group of, 709
    melting point of, 711
    metabolism of, 836–837, 862, 864–875
    nucleoside and nucleotide, 795–800
    number of carbons in chain, 709–710
    oxidation of, 721, 722–724, 740
    reduction of, 721–722, 740
    structure of, 709–710
    sweet taste of, 711
Monosodium glutamate (MSG), 752*mn*
Monosubstituted benzenes, 480
Monounsaturated triacylglycerols, 672
Morphine, 642–643, 642*mn*, 662, 760–761
Morton, William, 515
Mp. *See* Melting point
MRIs, 378–379, 378*f*
mRNA. *See* Messenger RNA
MSG (monosodium glutamate), 752*mn*
MTBE (*tert*-butyl methyl ether), 414
Multiple bond, 114–116
Multiple sclerosis, 684, 684*f*
Multiplication
    in scientific notation, 158, A-2
    using significant figures in, 14–16, A-4
Mumps vaccine, 823
Muscalure, 491
Muscone, 573
Mutagens, 816
Mutarotation, 717
Mutation, 816–818
Myelin sheath, 684, 684*f*
Mylanta, 336*mn*
Mylar. *See* Polyethylene terephthalate
Myoglobin, 40, 747, 748*f*, 771–772, 771*f*, 771*mn*
Myosin, 748*f*
Myristic acid, 667*t*, 889

N

N- (prefix), 598–599
N-Acetyl-D-galactosamine, 738
N-Acetyl-D-glucosamine, 736, 738
NAD$^+$ and NADH, 574–575, 576*f*, 775,
        843–845, 845*t*
    in citric acid cycle, 848–851, 849*f*
    in electron transport chain, 853–854, 853*f*
    in fatty acid oxidation, 878–879, 878*f*
    in glycerol catabolism, 877
    in glycolysis, 865, 865*f*, 868–869, 868*f*
    in oxidative deamination, 885
    in oxidative phosphorylation, 855
    in pyruvate metabolism, 871–873
Naloxone, 643
Nandrolone, 559, 692, 693
Nano- (prefix), 10*t*
Nanometer, 10
Naphthalene, 482
Naproxen, 543–544, 544*mn*, 602, 630
Natural gas, 164, 387, 391*mn*, 442–443, 442*mn*
Naturally occurring materials, 2–3, 2*f*, 3*f*
Negative allosteric control, 782, 782*f*
Neon, 54, 60, 61*t*
Neopentane, 429
Neral, 422
Neroli oil, 408*mn*
Nerve gas (sarin), 784
Net dipole, 127–128, 500, 513
Net ionic equation, 336
Network solids, 252, 252*f*
Neuron, 649–650, 649*f*
Neuropeptides, 760–761
Neurotransmitters, 633, 649–657
    definition of, 649
    drugs affecting, 650
    function of, 649–650, 649*f*
Neutral amino acids, 749, 750*t*, 752–754
Neutralization reaction, 335–337
Neutral solutions, 329–330, 329*t*, 331,
        338–340, 339*t*
Neutron(s), 42–46
    mass of, 43–44, 43*t*
    number of, 44–46, 356
    number of, varying (isotopes), 46–49
    properties of, 43*t*
Niacin, 574, 574*mn*
Nickel, 39*f*
Nickel–cadmium batteries, 184
Nicotinamide adenine dinucleotide. *See* NAD$^+$ and
        NADH
Nicotine, 34–35, 75, 161, 185, 633, 639, 641–642, 641*f*,
        641*mn*, 653
Nightshade plant, 643–644
Nitrate, 97*t*, 320*t*
Nitration, of benzene (aromatic compound),
        486–487
Nitric acid, 312
    in acid rain, 164*mn*, 353
    benzene reaction with, 486–487
    dissociation of, 320, 322
    as strong acid, 320, 320*t*, 322
Nitride, 92*t*
Nitrobenzene, 486–487
Nitrogen, 37*t*
    as building-block element, 39, 39*f*
    conversion to ammonia, 209, 209*mn*
    electronic configuration of, 61*t*
    fertilizers containing, 105
    as heteroatom, 389
    isotopes of, 380
    partial pressure of, 242–243
Nitrogen-13, 373–374
Nitrogen-14, 360

Nitrogen compounds, 633–635.
    See also Amine(s)
Nitrogen-containing bases, 795–800, 799*t*
    complementary pairs of, 804, 806–808
    sequence of, 802, 805, 815*f*
Nitrogen dioxide, 149, 149*mn*
Nitrogen gas, 7, 7*f*, 114–115
Nitrogen heterocycles, 637
Nitrogen monoxide, 164, 164*mn*, 201, 203, 203*f*
Nitroglycerin, 111–112, 111*f*
Nitro group, 486–487
Nitrous acid, 313*t*
Nitrous oxide, 119, 119*mn*
Nitrox, 243, 268
Noble gases (Group 8A elements), 51*f*, 54
    covalent bonding relationship to, 108
    ion relationship to, 79
    London dispersion forces in, 245
    stability of, 54, 77
    valence electronic configuration of, 64, 65*t*
Nomenclature
    acid, 313, 313*t*
    alcohol, 501–503
    aldehyde, 562–564
    alkane, 429, 429*mn*, 430*t*, 434–435, 435*t*
        acyclic alkanes, 435–439
        cycloalkanes, 439, 440–442
    alkene and alkyne, 456–460
    alkyl halide, 517–518
    amide, 598–599
    amine, 636–639
    amino acid, 749
    ammonium salt, 646
    benzene derivatives, 480–482
    carbohydrate, 709
    carboxylic acid, 595–596
    covalent compound, 120, 120*t*
    definition of, 91
    drug, 433
    element, 37*mn*
    enzyme, 778–779
    ester, 597–598
    ether, 514–515
    ionic compound, 91–95, 99
    IUPAC system of, 433
    ketone, 564–565
    organic compound, 433
    peptide, 755
    polyatomic ion, 97, 97*t*
    thiol, 520–521
Nona- (prefix), 120*t*
Nonbonded electron pairs, 108. *See also* Lone pairs
Noncompetitive inhibitor, 783
Nonelectrolytes, 275–278, 276*t*
Nonmetals
    anions of, 81, 84, 84*t*, 92, 92*t*
    covalent bonding between, 77, 109
    covalent bonding with metalloid, 109
    definition of, 39
    electronegativity values of, 125
    ionic bonding with metal, 77, 78*f*, 88–89
    in periodic table, 38–39, 38*f*
    reduction of, 153–154
Nonpolar bonds, 125–127, 126*t*, 127*f*, 411–412
Nonpolar molecule, 127–128
Nonpolar solvents, 278, 280, 280*f*
Nonreducing sugar, 722
Nonrenewable energy, 443
Nonsteroidal anti-inflammatory drugs (NSAIDs),
    543–544, 697, 697*mn*. *See also specific drugs*
Nonvolatile solute, 294–295, 294*f*
Noradrenaline. *See* Norepinephrine
Norepinephrine, 650–651, 650*f*, 653
Norethindrone, 467, 467*f*
N-Terminal amino acid, 755–756

Nuclear chemistry, 355–384
    detecting and measuring radioactivity in, 368–371
    health effects of radioactivity in, 370, 370*mn*
    human exposure to radioactivity in, 371
    nuclear reactions in, 359–364 (*See also* Nuclear
        reactions)
    protective equipment in, 370, 370*mn*
    radioactive isotopes in, 50, 50*f*, 356–357
        decay of, 359–364
        half-life of, 364–367, 365*t*
        medical uses of, 50, 50*f*, 355, 360–363, 361*f*, 363*f*,
            369–374, 372*f*, 373*f*
    radiocarbon dating in, 360, 367, 368*f*
    types of radiation in, 358, 358*t*
Nuclear equations, 359–364
    alpha emission, 359–360
    balancing, 359
    beta emission, 361
    fission reaction, 376
    gamma emission, 364
    positron emission, 362
Nuclear fission, 374–376, 375*f*
Nuclear fusion, 374, 377–378
Nuclear power plants, 75, 374–376, 375*f*, 382
Nuclear reactions, 356, 359–364
    alpha emission, 359–360, 359*mn*, 364*t*
    beta emission, 360–361, 361*f*, 364*t*
    chain reaction in, 375
    critical mass in, 375
    fission, 374–376, 375*f*
    fusion, 374, 377–378
    gamma emission, 363–364, 363*f*, 364*t*
    positron emission, 362, 364*t*
Nuclear waste, 376
Nuclease, 776
Nucleic acids, 794–831. *See also* DNA; RNA
    definition of, 795
    formation of polymers, 800–803
    nucleosides and nucleotides of, 795–800
Nucleosides, 795–798, 799*t*
Nucleosomes, 805, 805*f*
Nucleotides, 795–800, 799*t*
    abbreviations for, 798, 799*t*
    genetic code (codon), 811–813, 812*t*
    mutation and, 816–818
    polymers of, 800–803
Nucleus, 43
Numbers
    Avogadro's, 157–159
    estimated, 12–13
    exact, 12
    inexact, 12
    mole, 157–171
    rounding off, 14–16, 15*t*, A-3
    scientific notation, 17–20, 18*f*, 158, A-1–A-2, A-4–A-5
    significant figures, 12–17, A-2–A-4
Numerator, 20
Nutmeg, 409, 409*mn*
Nutrition (diet)
    amino acids in, 749–751, 751*mn*
    cholesterol in, 688–689, 688*mn*, 688*t*
    energy (Calories) in, 191–192, 191*t*, 192*mn*, 218–219
    fats and oils in, 675–676, 676*f*, 701
    fiber in, 733–734
    protein in, 749, 749*t*
Nutritional supplements, liquid, 104–105
Nutrition labels, 892
Nylon, 2, 2*f*, 108, 138, 619–621, 619*mn*

O

-o (suffix), 480, 517
Octa- (prefix), 120*t*
Octanal, 562
Octane, 223, 280, 280*f*, 414

1-Octanol, 501
Octet rule, 81, 109
    exceptions to, 116–117
    and Lewis structures, 112–119
2-Octyl cyanoacrylate, 628
-oic (suffix), 595, 598
Oil(s), 671–681
    definition of, 464
    dietary, 675–676, 676*f*, 701
    fatty acid composition of, 672–674, 673*t*
    partially hydrogenated, 473–475, 473*mn*, 474*f*, 474*mn*
    physical properties of, 672
Oil refinery, 442, 442*f*
Oil spills, 425, 444, 444*mn*
-ol (suffix), 501, 502
Oleandrin, 581, 581*mn*
Oleic acid, 413, 414*f*, 464, 464*t*, 465*f*, 667, 667*t*, 668*mn*,
    674–675, 889
Olestra, 617–618, 617*mn*
Oligosaccharides, human milk, 731–732
Olive oil, 414*f*, 673, 673*t*, 889
Omega-3 fatty acids, 668, 668*mn*, 674, 674*mn*
Omega-6 fatty acids, 668
Omega-*n* acids, 668
-one (suffix), 564
Opioids, 642–643. *See also* Heroin; Morphine
Opsin, 575
Optical activity, 547–550
Orajel, 603
Oral contraceptives, 386*f*, 467–468, 467*f*, 467*mn*
Orange, flavor and color of, 562
Orbital(s), 56–63, 57*t*
    definition of, 56
    electron spin in, 56*mn*, 59
    number of, 57
    shape of, 58
Orbital diagrams, 58–59, 59*f*, 62–63
Organelles, 834
Organic chemistry, 385. *See also* Organic compounds;
        Organic molecules
    definition of, 385
    medical products of, 384, 385, 385*f*
Organic compounds, 386–390. *See also specific types*
    boiling point of, 410
    bonding patterns in, 388–390, 389*f*
    chains of atoms in, 388
    characteristic features of, 387–390
    covalent bonds in, 410–412
    environmental pollutants, 414–415
    examples of, 387, 387*f*
    flammability of, 410*t*
    heteroatoms in, 389–394
    hydrogen in, 388–390
    intermolecular forces in, 410
    ionic compounds versus, 410, 410*t*
    lone pairs in, 389–394
    melting point of, 410
    nomenclature for, 433
    oxidation of, 507–510, 507*f*
    physical states of, 410, 410*t*
    polarity of, 410–412
    properties of, 410–415, 410*t*
    ring structure of, 388, 398–401, 398*f*
    solubility of, 410*t*, 412–414, 413*t*
    vitamins, 415–417, 417*f*
Organic molecules, 385–424
    ball-and-stick models of, 395, 399, 408–409
    condensed structures of, 395–398, 396*f*, 408–409
    drawing, 395–401
    functional groups of, 401–409
    shapes of, 390–394, 392*t*, 411–412
    skeletal structures of, 395, 398–401, 398*f*,
        408–409
Organic solvents, 412–414
Ortho- (prefix), 481

-ose (suffix), 709
Oseltamivir (Tamiflu), 175, 406*mn*, 407–408
-osine (suffix), 797
Osmosis, 294, 297–301, 300*f*, 301*f*
Osmotic pressure, 297–300
Osteoporosis, 100, 100*mn*
-ous (suffix), 92, 94, 313
Ovalbumin, 774
Oxalic acid, 132, 594
Oxaloacetate, 777, 848–852, 849*f*
Oxalosuccinate, 844, 859
Oxidase, 775
Oxidation, 152, 445
 alcohol, 505, 507–510, 507*f*, 523
 aldehyde, 569–571, 584, 722–724
 blood alcohol screening, 509–510, 510*f*
 coenzymes and, 843–846, 845*f*
 fatty acid, 835*f*, 877–881, 878*f*
 glucose, 722, 833
 monosaccharide, 721, 722–724, 740
 thiol, 521–522
β-Oxidation, 877–881, 878*f*
Oxidation–reduction reactions, 152–156, 153*f*
 battery, 155–157, 155*f*, 157*f*, 183–184
 combustion, 155–156, 444–445
 electron transport chain, 853–854, 853*f*
 enzymes and coenzymes in, 775, 777*t*,
  843–846, 845*t*
 examples of, 154–156, 154*f*, 843–845
 guidelines for, 153
 identifying components of, 154
Oxidative deamination, 883, 885
Oxidative phosphorylation, 837, 852, 854–855,
 874–875, 874*f*
Oxide, 92*t*
Oxidizing agent, 153–154, 843–846
Oxidoreductase, 775, 777*t*
-oxy (suffix), 514
Oxybenzone, 567, 568
Oxycodone (OxyContin), 661
Oxygen, 37*t*, 229
 altitude and, 243, 243*mn*, 268
 blood gases, 271
 as building-block element, 39, 39*f*
 as covalent molecule, 111, 111*f*
 density of, 27*t*
 electronegativity of, 125
 electronic configuration of, 60, 61*t*
 glucose reaction with, 144
 hemoglobin binding of, 111, 111*f*
 as heteroatom, 389, 497–498
 hyperbaric, 243, 243*mn*
 as limiting reactant, 179
 partial pressure of, 242–243, 243*mn*, 268
 propane reaction with, 142*mn*, 143
Oxygen-15, 373–374
Oxygen debt, 872
Oxytocin, 761–762, 761*f*
Oyster mushrooms, 691, 691*mn*
Ozone
 as air pollutant, 164*mn*, 201
 atmospheric, 119, 119*f*, 226
  chlorofluorocarbons and, 519–520, 519*f*, 519*mn*
  function of, 520
 lightning production of, 165*mn*
 resonance structures of, 119

P

PABA (*p*-aminobenzoic acid), 483, 487
Pacemakers, 156–157, 157*f*
Packing peanuts, 734*mn*
Padimate O, 483
PAHs. *See* Polycyclic aromatic hydrocarbons
Pain relievers, 543–544, 544*mn*, 602, 760–761

Paired spins, 59
Palladium, 201, 203*f*, 469, 487, 572, 721
Palmitic acid, 666, 667*t*, 668*mn*, 675, 678, 881, 881*mn*
Palmitoleic acid, 495, 667*t*, 678
Palm oil, 673*t*, 674, 681
Pantothenic acid, 847, 847*mn*
Papain, 776*mn*
Papaya, genetically modified, 820*mn*
Para (prefix), 481
Paraldehyde, 591
Parent name, of alkane, 434
Parkinson's disease, 184, 393–394, 421, 544–545,
 545*f*, 651
Partial hydrogenation, 473–475, 473*mn*, 474*f*, 474*mn*
Partial pressure, 242–243, 243*mn*, 268, 282, 283*f*
Parts per million, 287
Paternity testing, 822
p block, of periodic table, 61–62, 62*f*
PCBs (4,4'-dichlorobiphenyls), 414–415
PCR. *See* Polymerase chain reaction
Peaches, 629
Peanut butter, 474*mn*, 751*mn*
Peanut oil, 673*t*
Pears, propyl acetate in, 594
Penguins, lipid metabolism in, 861
Penicillamine, 536
Penicillin, 623–624, 623*mn*, 624*mn*, 783, 785
Penicillin G, 624
Penta- (prefix), 120*t*
Pentane, 395, 429, 432
Pentose, 709
Pentyl butanoate, 603
Pentyl group, 435*t*
Pepsin, 833, 835*f*
Peptide(s), 754–762
 biologically active, 760–762
 constitutional isomers, 755–756
 drawing of dipeptides, 756–758
 hydrolysis of, 772–773
 identifying amino acids in, 758–760
 nomenclature for, 755
Peptide bonds, 754. *See also* Peptide(s)
Peptide hormones, 761–762
Percent concentration, 283–287
 as conversion factor, 285–286
 parts per million, 287
 volume determination from, 286
 volume/volume, 285, 285*mn*
 weight/volume, 283–284, 283*mn*
Percent yield, 171–175, 174*f*
Performance-enhancing drugs, 692, 692*mn*
Period 1 elements, 59–60, 61*t*, 65*t*
Period 2 elements, 60–61, 61*t*, 65*t*, 67
Period 3 elements, 52*f*, 53, 65*t*
Periodic table, 38–39, 38*f*, 51–56, 51*f*. *See also specific*
 elements and element groups
 actinides in, 51*f*, 52
 atomic number and, 44
 atomic size and, 67–69
 basic features of, 51–53
 blocks in, 61–62, 62*f*
 bond dissociation energy, 194
 bonding properties and, 77
 carbon in, 55–56
 covalent bonding and, 109–111
 electronic configuration and, 59–63
 Group 1A elements (alkali metals) in, 51*f*, 53–54,
  64, 65*t*
 Group 2A elements (alkaline earth elements) in, 51*f*,
  53–54, 65*t*
 Group 7A elements (halogens) in, 51*f*, 54, 65*t*, 67
 Group 8A elements (noble gases) in, 51*f*, 54, 64,
  65*t*, 77
 groups in, 51*f*, 52–53, 52*f*
 inner transition metals in, 51*f*, 52

 ion formation and, 83–85
 ionization energy and, 66, 68–69
 lanthanides in, 51*f*, 52
 main group elements in, 51*f*, 52, 64–66, 65*t*
 metalloids in, 38–39, 38*f*
 metals in, 38–39, 38*f*
 molar mass and, 161
 nonmetals in, 38–39, 38*f*
 periods in, 51*f*, 52–53, 52*f*
 transition metals in, 51*f*, 52
Periodic trends, 66–69
 atomic size, 66–69
 definition of, 66
 electronegativity, 125
 ionization energy, 66, 68–69
 molecular art of, 68–69
Periods, in periodic table, 51*f*, 52–53, 52*f*
Peripheral proteins, 686–687
Permanganate, 106
Pesticides, as covalent compounds, 108
PET. *See* Polyethylene terephthalate; Positron emission
 tomography
Petroleum, 2*f*, 28, 425, 442–444, 442*f*, 444*mn*
Petroleum gas, liquefied, 427*mn*
Petroleum jelly (Vaseline), 444, 444*mn*, 451
Peyote, 185
pH
 and amino acids, 752–754
 of blood, 335*f*, 347, 347*mn*
 of body fluids, 335, 335*f*
 buffers and, 342–348, 343*f*
 calculation of, 331–334, A-5–A-6
 of common substances, 332*f*
 and enzyme activity, 781–782, 781*f*
 measuring, 331–335, 332*f*
 of seawater, 333*mn*
Phase changes, 256–263
 cooling curve of, 260–261, 261*f*
 energy changes during, determining, 259–260,
  262–263
 gas to liquid, 249, 257–258, 259*t*
 gas to solid, 259, 259*t*
 heating curve of, 260, 260*f*
 liquid to gas, 249, 257–258, 259*t*
 liquid to solid, 252, 256–257, 259*t*
 solid to gas, 259, 259*t*
 solid to liquid, 256–257, 256*mn*, 259*t*
PHB. *See* Polyhydroxybutyrate
Phenacetin, 614
Phenanthrene, 482
Phenols, 393, 480, 484–485
Phentermine, 662
Phenylacetaldehyde, 590
Phenylalanine, 543*f*, 730, 750*t*
Phenylephrine, 136, 648–649, 655
2-Phenylethylamine, 654–655
Phenylketonuria, 730, 818*t*
Pheromones, 426, 462, 462*mn*, 512, 590, 612, 612*mn*
pH meter, 332, 332*f*
Phosgene, 133
Phosphate, 97, 97*t*
Phosphate buffer, 344*t*
Phosphate group, in nucleotides, 795, 798–800
Phosphate, inorganic, 838–839, 839*f*
Phosphatidylcholine, 682
Phosphatidylethanolamine, 682
Phosphide, 92*t*
Phosphoacylglycerols, 681–682
 comparison with triacylglycerols and sphingomyelins,
  681, 683, 685, 685*f*
 structure of, 681–682, 683*f*
Phosphodiester, 681, 800–801, 801*f*
Phosphoenolpyruvate, 840–842, 868*f*, 869
2-Phosphoglycerate, 868*f*, 869
3-Phosphoglycerate, 868–869, 868*f*

Phosphoglycerides. *See* Phosphoacylglycerols
Phospholipids, 665, 681–688, 689*f*
  cell membrane, 686–688
Phosphoric acid, 116–117, 146–147, 147*mn*, 313*t*
  acid dissociation constant for, 327*t*
  strength of, 320*t*, 324
Phosphorus, 37*t*
  exception to octet rule, 116–117
  as major mineral (macronutrient), 39*f*, 40
Phosphorus-32, 365, 365*t*, 373*f*, 382
Phosphorus trichloride, 116–117
Phosphorylation, 838–842
  coupled reactions, 840–842
  electron transport chain, 852–854
  fructose, 841, 870
  galactose, 870
  glucose, 840, 840*f*, 841, 866, 866*f*
  glycerol, 877
  glycolysis, 866–869, 866*f*, 868*f*
  oxidative, 837, 852, 854–855, 874–875, 874*f*
Photosynthesis, 138, 195, 195*mn*, 229, 708, 708*mn*
pH paper or indicators, 332, 332*f*
pH scale, 331–335
Phylloquinone. *See* Vitamin K
Physical change, 4–5, 138–140, 140*f*
Physical properties, 4–5. *See also specific substances*
  changes in state, 4–5, 4*f*
  mixture, 5–6, 6*f*
  pure substance, 5
Physiological saline solution, 299
Piperidine, 633
Piperitone, 562
Plan B (levonorgestrel), 424
Plane-polarized light, 547–549
Plaque, atherosclerotic, 690, 690*f*
Plasma, electrolytes in, 276–277
Plasmids, 819–820, 819*f*
Plastic, 386*f*, 475–478. *See also* Polyethylene
Platinum, 47–48, 48*mn*, 75, 203*f*
β-Pleated sheet, 763–766, 765*f*, 766*f*, 768*f*
Plexiglas, 493
Plumeria, 590
Point mutation, 817–818
Polar (polar covalent) bonds, 126–127, 126*t*,
    411–412
Polarimeter, 548
Polarity
  aldehyde and ketone, 565
  amine, 638
  bond, 125–127, 126*t*
  molecule, 127–128, 127*f*
  organic compound, 410–412
Polar molecule, 127–128, 127*f*
Polar solvents, 278–279, 278*f*
Polio vaccine, 823
Pollution
  air (*See* Air pollution)
  indoor, 54, 54*mn*, 122*mn*, 164*mn*
  organic pollutants in, 414–415
Polonium-210, 370
Polonium-214, 381
Polonium-218, 384
Poly(acrylic acid), 478, 478*mn*
Polyacrylonitrile, 476*f*
Polyamides, 619–621
Polyatomic ions, 97–99
  balancing equations with, 146–147
  common, 97*t*
  definition of, 97
  formulas for ionic compounds with, 98–99
  Lewis (resonance) structures of, 117–119
  naming of ionic compounds with, 99
  parentheses for, 98
Polycarbonate, 253*mn*
Polychlorinated biphenyls (PCBs), 414–415

Polychlorotrifluoroethylene, 493
Polycyclic aromatic hydrocarbons (PAHs), 483–484
Polyesters, 621–623
Polyethylene, 253*mn*, 390*mn*, 403, 452, 475
  formation of, 476
  high-density, 475*mn*, 478*t*, 479
  low-density, 475*mn*, 478*t*
  recycling of, 478–479, 478*mn*, 478*t*
Poly(ethylene glycol), 528
Polyethylene terephthalate (PET), 2*f*, 22*mn*, 478*t*, 479,
    619–622, 622*f*
Polyhydroxybutyrate (PHB), 631
Polyisobutylene, 444, 476*f*
Polymer(s), 475–479
  biodegradable, 631
  common products, 475, 476*f*
  condensation, 619–623
  definition of, 475
  formation of, 475–478
  in medicine and dentistry, 477*f*
  naturally occurring, 475
  nucleic acids as, 800–803
  proteins as, 754, 762
  recycling of, 478–479, 478*mn*, 478*t*, 623, 623*mn*
  synthetic, 475–478, 619–623
Polymerase chain reaction (PCR), 820–821
Polymerization, 475–478
Polynucleotide, 801–803, 801*f*
Polypeptides, 754, 766–768, 768*f*, 813–816, 815*f*
Polypropylene, 477*f*, 478*t*
Polysaccharides, 708, 732–736. *See also specific types*
  blood type, 738–739, 739*f*
  cellulose, 732–734, 733*f*
  glycogen, 732, 735–736, 736*f*
  starch, 732, 734, 734*f*
Polystyrene (Styrofoam), 2, 2*f*, 475, 476*f*, 478*t*
Polysubstituted benzenes, 481
Polytetrafluoroethylene (Teflon), 133, 475, 477*f*
Polytrimethylene terephthalate (PTT), 629
Polyunsaturated triacylglycerols, 672
Poly(vinyl chloride) (PVC), 475, 476*f*, 477*f*,
    478*t*, 528
Poppy seeds, 642*mn*
p orbitals, 56–58, 57*t*
  in fourth shell, 57, 57*t*
  in second shell, 57, 57*t*
  shape of, 58
  in third shell, 57, 57*t*
Positive allosteric control, 782, 782*f*
Positron (β⁺), 358, 358*t*
Positron emission, 362, 364*t*
Positron emission tomography (PET), 75, 362,
    373–374, 374*f*
Postsynaptic neuron, 649*f*, 650
Potassium, 37*t*
  as major mineral (macronutrient), 39–40, 39*f*
  properties of, 53
  role in human body, 86, 87*f*, 91*mn*
Potassium-40, 365*t*
Potassium chloride, 91, 277–278
Potassium dichromate, 507, 507*mn*, 509–510,
    569–570
Potassium hydroxide, 315, 323
Potassium iodide, 54, 91
Potassium sorbate, 607
Potential energy, 190, 190*mn*
Pounds per square inch (psi), 227
Prednisone, 693
Prefixes. *See also specific prefixes*
  in acids, 313
  in alkanes, 434
  in benzene derivatives, 481
  in covalent compounds, 120
  in ethers, 514
  in metric system, 9–10, 10*t*

Pressure
  atmospheric, 227, 227*f*, 243, 250
  blood, 228–229, 228*f*
  changes, and equilibrium, 214–216, 215*t*
  definition of, 227
  gas, 226–229
  gas laws, 229
    Boyle's (pressure–volume), 229–231, 231*f*,
      236*t*, 264
    combined (pressure–volume–temperature),
      235–236, 236*t*, 264
    Dalton's (partial pressure), 242–243
    Gay-Lussac's (pressure–temperature), 229,
      233–235, 236*t*, 264
    ideal (pressure–volume–temperature–moles),
      239–242, 264
  measurement of, 227, 227*f*
  osmotic, 297–299
  standard conditions of, 238–239
  units of, 227–228
  vapor, 249–251
Pressure cooker, 235*mn*
Pressure gauge, 227*mn*
Presynaptic neuron, 649*f*, 650
Primary (1°) alcohol, 499–500, 508–509
Primary (1°) alkyl halide, 516
Primary (1°) amide, 593, 600
Primary (1°) amine, 633, 633*mn*, 636, 638
Primary carbon, 431
Primary structure of polynucleotide, 802
Primary structure of protein, 762–763, 768*f*
Principal energy levels (shells), 56–58
Pristane, 450
Problem solving, with conversion factors, 20–25
  using clinical conversion factors, 24–25
  using one conversion factor, 21–22
  using two or more conversion factors, 23
Products, 138–139
  actual yield of, 171–174, 171*mn*
  in chemical equation, 140–142
  concentration, and equilibrium, 211–213, 215*t*
  equilibrium constant and, 206–208, 206*t*, 207*f*
  grams of
    calculating percent yield from, 172–174
    converting grams of reactants to, 167–171
    converting moles of reactants to, 165–167
  percent yield of, 171–175
  reversible reactions and, 203–204
  theoretical yield of, 171–174, 171*mn*
  using limiting reactant to determine amount of,
    178–179, 180
Proenzyme, 784–785
Progesterone, 467–468, 567, 692
Progestins, 692
Proline, 541, 750*t*
Prop- (prefix), 429
Propane
  boiling point of, 248
  as CFC alternative, 519*mn*
  combustion of, 445
  intermolecular forces in, 248
  liquefied petroleum gas, 427*mn*
  melting point of, 248
  natural gas, 442
  reaction with oxygen, 142*mn*, 143
  structure of, 388, 427
1,3-Propanediol, 629
1-Propanethiol, 524
2-Propanol, 253*t*, 255*mn*, 285, 404, 472*mn*, 504*f*
Propene, 393, 471, 472*mn*, 477*f*
Propoxyphene, 559
Propranolol, 544
Propyl acetate, 594
Propyl alcohol, 502
Propylene glycol, 528

Propyl group, 435t
Prostaglandin(s), 602, 696–697
Prostaglandin F$_{2\alpha}$, 696
Prostaglandin E$_2$, 696–697
Protease, 776
Protease inhibitors, 786, 786f, 823–825
Protective equipment, 370, 370mn
Proteins, 747–793
  amino acids of, 749–754
  caloric value of, 191–192, 191t, 192mn, 219
  cell membrane, 686–687
  conjugated, 771
  contractile, 748
  definition of, 748
  denaturation of, 773–774, 774mn
  digestion of, 834–835, 836f, 862
  disulfide bonds of, 522, 522f, 528, 762, 766–768,
    766mn, 768f
  drawing (representations) of, 764, 765f
  electrostatic interactions in, 766–768, 768f
  enzyme, 774–786
  fibrous, 748, 769
  food sources of, 748mn
  globular, 769, 771–772
  α-helix of, 763–766, 764f, 766f, 768f
  in human body, 748, 748f, 769–772
  hydrogen bonds of, 766, 768f
  hydrolysis of, 772–773
  integral, 687
  membrane, 748
  metabolism of, 833–835, 835f, 836f,
    883–887
  nutritional requirements for, 749, 749t
  origin of word, 748
  peptides and peptide bonds of, 754–763
  peripheral, 686–687
  β-pleated sheet of, 763–766, 765f, 766f, 768f
  as polymer, 754, 762
  primary structure of, 762–763, 768f
  quaternary structure of, 762, 768, 768f, 769f
  ribbon diagrams of, 764, 765f
  secondary structure of, 762–766, 768f
  shorthand symbols for structure, 764, 765f
  subunits of, 768
  synthesis of
    anabolism in, 833
    mutations and, 816–818
    translation in, 806, 813–816, 815f
  tertiary structure of, 762, 766–768, 768f
Proton(s), 42–46
  Brønsted–Lowry acids as donors of, 311–314,
    316–319
  Brønsted–Lowry bases as acceptors of, 311–312,
    314–319
  charge of, 42–43, 43t
  mass of, 43–44, 43t
  number of, 44–46, 356
  properties of, 43t
  transfer
    acid strength and, 319–324
    in Brønsted–Lowry acid–base reactions and,
      316–319
Pseudoephedrine, 136, 655, 655mn
psi (pounds per square inch), 227
Psilocin, 652–653
PTT. See Polytrimethylene terephthalate
Pure substance, 5, 8f, 273
  classification as element or compound, 7–8, 8f
  definition of, 5
Purine, 796–797
Putrescine, 404, 634
PVC. See Poly(vinyl chloride)
Pyrethrin I, 440
Pyridine, 660
Pyrimidine, 796–797

Pyruvate
  amino acid conversion to, 886, 886f
  conversion to acetyl CoA, 871
  conversion to ethanol, 871, 873
  conversion to lactate, 845, 871–872
  Cori cycle, 876, 876f
  fate of, 871–873
  formation of, 776, 840–842
  glucose conversion to, 835f, 862, 864–876
  lactate conversion to, 872
  oxaloacetate formation from, 777
Pyruvate carboxylase, 777
Pyruvate decarboxylase, 873
Pyruvic acid, 575

Q
Quadramet, 374mn
Quantized energy, of electron, 56
Quaternary ammonium ions (salts), 633, 649
Quaternary carbon, 431
Quaternary structure of protein, 762, 768, 769f
Queen substance, 491
Quinine, 35, 642, 643

R
Racemic mixture, 544
Racemic switches, 544–545
Rad (radiation absorbed dose), 371
Radiation. See also Radioactivity
  background, 368
  health effects of, 370, 370mn
  types of, 358, 358t
Radiation badges, 368, 368mn
Radiation therapy, 355, 360, 363, 363f, 373, 373mn, 374
Radioactive decay
  alpha emission in, 359–360, 359mn, 364t
  beta emission in, 360–361, 361f, 364t
  definition of, 359
  gamma emission in, 363–364, 363f, 364t
  measuring radioactivity in, 368–370
  positron emission in, 362, 364t
Radioactive decay series, 384
Radioactive isotopes, 50, 50f, 355, 356–357
  decay of, 359–364
  half-life of, 364–367, 365t
  medical uses of, 50, 371–374
    commonly used, 373f
    diagnostic, 50, 50f, 362, 363, 371–373, 372f
    dosage of, 369
    PET, 75, 362, 373–374, 374f
    therapeutic, 50, 355, 360, 361f, 363, 363f, 370,
      373, 374
Radioactive seeds, 373, 373mn
Radioactivity
  alpha emission, 359–360, 359mn, 364t
  beta emission, 360–361, 361f, 364t
  definition of, 357
  detecting and measuring, 368–371
  gamma emission, 363–364, 363f, 364t
  half-life, 364–367, 365t
  health effects of, 370, 370mn
  human exposure to, 371
  medical uses of, 50, 371–374
    commonly used, 373f
    diagnostic, 50, 50f, 362, 363, 371–373, 372f
    dosage of, 369
    PET, 75, 362, 373–374, 374f
    therapeutic, 50, 355, 360, 361f, 363, 363f, 370,
      373, 374
  positron emission, 362, 364t
  protective equipment for working with, 370, 370mn
  units of, 368–369, 369mn, 369t, 371
Radiocarbon dating, 360, 367, 368f
Radioisotopes. See Radioactive isotopes

Radium, 53
Radius, atomic, 67
Radon, 54, 360
Radon detector, 54, 54mn
Raffinose, 729, 729mn
Rasagiline, 651
Raspberries, 598, 598mn
Reactants, 138–139
  actual yield from, 171–174, 171mn
  in chemical equation, 140–142
  concentration of
    changes in, and equilibrium, 211–213, 211f, 215t
    and reaction rate, 200–201
  equilibrium constant and, 206–208, 206t, 207f
  grams of
    calculating energy change from, 196–197
    conversion to grams of product, 167–171
    determining limiting reactant from, 179
  limiting, 175–180
  moles of, conversion to grams of product,
    165–167
  percent yield from, 171–175
  reversible reactions and, 203–204
  theoretical yield from, 171–174, 171mn
Reaction(s). See also specific reactions
  chemical, 5, 137–188
  nuclear, 356, 359–364
Reaction arrow, 140
Reaction coordinate, 198
Reaction rates, 200–203
  activation energy and, 199, 200
  catalysts and, 201–203, 201f
  reactant concentration and, 200–201
  temperature and, 200–201
Rebaudioside A, 731, 731mn
Recombinant DNA, 819–823
  definition of, 819
  general principles of, 819–820
  preparation of, 819–820, 819f
Recycling code, 478, 478t, 623
Recycling, polymer, 478–479, 478mn, 478t,
  623, 623mn
Red blood cells
  and osmotic pressure, 299–300, 300f
  radioactive tagging of, 372
Redox reactions. See Oxidation–reduction reactions
"Red tides," 512
Reducing agent, 153–154, 843–846
Reducing sugars, 722
Reductase, 775
Reduction, 152, 445. See also Oxidation–reduction
  reactions
  aldehyde, 571–575, 584, 721–722
  coenzymes and, 843–846, 845t
  ketone, 571–575, 584
  monosaccharide, 721–722, 740
Refining, 442, 442f
Refrigeration, 201mn
Rem (radiation equivalent for man), 371
Replacement reactions, 147, 150–152, 151t
Replication
  DNA, 806–808, 807f
  virus, 823
Replication fork, 806, 807f
Resonance, 117–119
Resonance-stabilized molecule, 118–119
Resonance structures, 117–119
  for aromatic compounds, 479
  composite, in hybrid, 118
  definition of, 117
  double-headed arrow for, 118
  drawing, 117–118
  for neutral molecules, 119
  for polyatomic ions, 117–119
Respiratory acidosis, 347, 347mn

Respiratory alkalosis, 347
Restriction endonucleases, 819–820, 819f
11-*cis*-Retinal, 575–577, 575mn, 576f
Retinol (vitamin A), 415–416, 415mn, 416f
Retrovirus, 823–825, 824f
Reverse reaction, 204
Reverse transcription, 823–825, 824f
Reversible inhibitor, 783–784
Reversible reactions, 203–204
Rhenium-186, 383
Rhodium, in catalytic converters, 203f
Rhodopsin, 575, 576f
Ribbon diagrams, 764, 765f
Riboflavin, 846, 846mn
Ribonucleic acid. *See* RNA
Ribonucleoside, 796–798
Ribonucleotides, 798
Ribose, 710, 713, 795–797
D-Ribose, 795–797
Ribosomal RNA (rRNA), 808–809, 809t
Ribosomes, translation in, 813–816
Rickets, 694
Right-handedness, 531, 533mn
Ring carbons, chirality centers on, 540–542
Ringer's solution, 304
Rizatriptan, 652
RNA, 795, 808–809
  composition of, 799t
  DNA transcription to, 806, 810–811, 810f
  DNA versus, 808
  messenger (*See* Messenger RNA)
  monosaccharide of, 795–797, 808
  nitrogen-containing bases of, 796, 799t
  nucleosides and nucleotides of, 795–800, 808
  nucleotides of, 795
  ribosomal, 808–809, 809t
  sequence of, 815f
  transfer, 808–809, 809f, 809t, 813–814
  translation of, 806, 813–816, 815f
Rofecoxib, 697
Rolaids, 315f
Rosemary, 494
Rosmarinic acid, 494
Rotenone, 853–854, 853mn
Rounding off numbers, 14–16, 15t, A-3
Roundup (weed killer), 117, 117mn
Rowland, F. Sherwood, 519mn
rRNA (ribosomal RNA), 808–809, 809t
RU 486, 468
Rubber, 3, 3f, 253mn
Rubbing alcohol, 255mn, 285, 472mn, 504f
Rubidium, 53
Rust, 155

S

Saccharin, 133, 729–731, 730f, 730t
Safflower oil, 673t
Safrole, 591
Salicin, 589, 609, 609mn, 734mn
Salicylic acid, 142–143, 170, 612
Saline solution, 273, 273f, 275, 290, 290mn,
  299–300
Saliva, pH of, 335, 335f
Salmeterol, 498, 591, 655
Salt(s)
  ammonium, 646–649
  carboxylic acid, 604–609
  formation in acid–base reactions, 336–338
  metal, 315, 323, 336–338
  water–soluble, from acid–amine reactions, 644–648
  zwitterion, 749, 752–754
Salt solution
  acidity and basicity of, 338–340, 339t
  electrolytes in, 275

medical uses (saline solution), 273, 273f, 290, 290mn,
  299–300
number of moles in, determining, 290
osmotic pressure of, 299–300
Samarium-153, 374, 374mn
Samuelsson, Bengt, 602
Sand, 252, 252f, 253t
Saponification, 615, 680–681, 681mn, 699
Saponins, 607
Sarin, 784
Sassafras plant, 591
Saturated fatty acids, 463–465, 667, 676f
  common, 464t, 667, 667t, 668mn
  definition of, 464, 667
  sources of, 464
  triacylglycerol, 671–676
Saturated hydrocarbons, 426, 454. *See also* Acyclic
  alkanes
Saturated solution, 278
s block, of periodic table, 61–62, 62f
Scientific calculator, using, 333–334, 333mn,
  A-4–A-6
Scientific notation, 17–20, 18f, 158, 158mn, A-1–A-2,
  A-4–A-5
Scombroid fish poisoning, 656mn
Scopolamine, 635, 635mn
Scuba divers, 224, 227mn, 243, 243mn, 282, 282mn
Scurvy, 416, 416mn
Seashells, chirality in, 530, 535, 535f
Seawater, 272, 287, 333mn
Secondary (2°) alcohol, 499–500, 508–509
Secondary (2°) alkyl halide, 516
Secondary (2°) amide, 593, 598, 600
Secondary (2°) amine, 633, 633mn, 636, 638
Secondary carbon, 431
Secondary structure of protein, 762–766, 768f
Seldane, 662
Selective serotonin reuptake inhibitors (SSRIs), 652
Selenium, 39f, 40
Semiconservative replication, 806
Semipermeable membrane, 297
  dialysis, 300–301, 301f
  osmosis and biological membranes, 299–300
Serine, 750t
Serotonin, 136, 651–653
Sertraline, 483, 483f, 542, 652
Sevoflurane, 404, 498, 528
Sex hormones, 692, 693
Shark liver oil, 450
Shells, 56–58
  distance from nucleus and volume of, 56
  electron distribution in, 56
  maximum number of electrons in, 57, 57t
  numbering of, 56
  subshells of, 56
  valence, 63
Shivering, 216mn
Shortening, 673t
Shorthand symbols, for protein structure, 764, 765f
Sickle cell anemia, 772, 818t
Sickle cell hemoglobin, 771–772, 772mn
Side chain, of amino acid, 749
Side reactions, 171
Sievert, 371
Significant figures, 12–17, A-2–A-4
  in addition and subtraction, 16–17, A-4
  definition of, 13, A-2–A-3
  determining number of, 13–14, 13mn
  in multiplication and division, 14–16, A-4
  rounding off, 14–16, 15t, A-3
Silicon, 39f
Silicon dioxide, 252, 252f
Silicon tetrafluoride, 120
Silk, 619, 766, 766f, 768
Silkworm moth, 462, 462mn

Silver, 37t
  liquid mercury with, 273, 273f
  as metallic solid, 252
  specific heat of, 253t
  sterling, tarnish on, 90, 90mn
Silver(I) oxide, 570–571
Silver sulfide, 90, 90mn
Simvastatin, 691
Single replacement reactions, 147, 150–152, 151t
Sitagliptin, 401, 401mn
SI units, 9mn
Skeletal structures, 395, 398–401
  acyclic alkanes, 431–432
  conversion to complete structures, 398f
  converting ball-and-stick model to,
    408–409
  cyclic compound, 398–399, 398f
Skin care products, 601–602, 601mn
Skin moisturizers, 424
Skunks, 524
Smell, sense of, 552–553, 553f
Smog, 201, 203, 203mn
Smoke detectors, 359mn
Smoking, 185, 370, 370mn, 446, 641–642
Soap, 592, 607–609, 608f, 608mn, 680–681
Sodium, 37t
  atomic number of, 80
  dietary intake of, 87, 87mn, 87t
  electronic configuration of, 80
  ion formation, 80, 91
  as major mineral (macronutrient), 39–40, 39f
  properties of, 53
  role in human body, 86–87, 87f
Sodium-24, 382, 383
Sodium acetate, 342–344, 344t, 604, 606
Sodium alendronate, 100
Sodium amide, 124
Sodium azide, in automobile airbags, 145–146, 145f,
  148, 278
Sodium benzoate, 607, 607mn
Sodium bicarbonate, 99, 100, 337–339, 386mn
Sodium carbonate, 386mn
Sodium cation, 80
Sodium chloride
  as compound, 7, 7f, 40, 54
  formation of, 40, 336
  ionic bonding in, 77, 78f
  as ionic compound, 77, 88, 410, 410t
  as ionic solid, 252, 252f
  melting point of, 96
  molar mass of, 161
  molecular weight of, 160
  mole of, 157mn, 167, 168f
  osmotic pressure of solution, 298–299
  saline solution, 273, 273f, 275, 290, 290mn,
    299–300
  solubility of, 96, 96f, 278–279, 278f
  as strong electrolyte, 276
Sodium chloride (salt) solution
  acidity and basicity of, 338–340, 339t
  electrolytes in, 275
  medical uses (saline solution), 273, 273f, 290, 290mn,
    299–300
  number of moles in, determining, 290
  osmotic pressure of, 299–300
Sodium fluoride, 91, 93, 94mn
Sodium hydroxide, 311, 315, 315f, 323, 324f, 705
  in buffer, 342
  dissociation of, 323, 324f
  reaction with hydrochloric acid, 336
  as strong base, 323
Sodium iodide-131 (Na^{131}I), 369, 371
Sodium metal, reaction with water, 185, 186
Sodium selenite, 106
Solanine, 560, 582

Solid(s), 3–5, 4f, 225–226, 225f, 252–253
  amorphous, 252–253, 253mn
  crystalline, 252, 252f
  definition of, 3, 225
  intermolecular forces and, 244–249
  ionic, 252, 252f
  kinetic energy in, 225–226
  metallic, 252, 252f
  molecular, 252, 252f
  network, 252, 252f
  phase changes of
    gas to solid, 259, 259t
    liquid to solid, 252, 259t
    solid to gas, 259, 259t
    solid to liquid, 256–257, 256mn, 259t
  properties of, 226t
  solubility of, 282
  symbol, in chemical equation, 141, 141t
Solubility, 4, 278–283
  alcohol, 500–501
  aldehyde, 566
  amine, 638, 647–648
  basic principles of, 278–281
  carboxylic acid, 604–607
  definition of, 278
  enantiomer, 547
  ether, 513
  gas, 282, 282mn, 283f
  ionic compound, 96, 96f, 278–279, 278f, 410t
  ketone, 566–567
  "like dissolves like," 278, 412, 500, 566
  lipid, 664
  organic compound, 410t, 412–414, 413t
  temperature and, 282
  vitamin, 279mn, 415–417, 417f
Solute
  concentration of, 283–293
  definition of, 274
  electrolyte versus nonelectrolyte, 275–278, 276t
  nonvolatile, 294–295, 294f
  solubility of, 278–283
  volatile, 294
Solution(s), 272–309, 274t
  acidic, 329–330, 329mn, 329t, 331, 331mn,
    338–340, 339t
  aqueous, 96, 96mn, 274
    dissociation of water in, 328–330
    seawater as, 272
    solubility in, 278–281
    symbol, in chemical equations, 141, 141t
  basic, 329–330, 329t, 331, 338–340, 339t
  boiling point elevation of, 294–295, 294f
  colligative properties of, 294–297
  colloid, 274–275, 274t
  concentration, 283–293
    conversion factor, 285–286
    definition of, 283
    dilution and, 291–293
    making solution with particular, 283–284, 284f
    parts per million, 287
    percent, 283–287
    titration to determine, 340–342, 340f
    units of (molarity), 288–291, 340–342
    volume determination from, 286
    volume/volume percent, 285, 285mn
    weight/volume percent, 283–284, 283mn
  definition of, 273
  electrolytes versus nonelectrolytes in, 275–278, 276t
  freezing point depression of, 295–297, 295mn
  gas, 273, 273f
  as homogeneous mixture, 273
  ion–dipole interaction, 279
  neutral, 329–330, 329t, 331, 338–340, 339t
  osmosis and, 297–301
  pH of, 331–332

saturated, 278
supersaturated, 282
suspension, 274–275, 274mn, 274t
unsaturated, 278
Solvation, 279–280
Solvents
  addition of (dilution), 291–293
  definition of, 274
  nonpolar, 278, 280, 280f
  organic, 412–414
  polar, 278–279, 278f
  solubility in, 278–283
Sophorose, 745
s orbitals, 56–58, 57t
  in first shell, 57, 57t
  in fourth shell, 57, 57t
  in second shell, 57, 57t
  shape of, 58
  in third shell, 57, 57t
Sorbitol, 500mn, 665, 721, 730t
Sorona, 629
Soybean oil, 673, 673t
Space-filling representation, 41–42
Spam, 98mn
Spearmint, 553
Specific gravity, 29–30, 29mn
Specific heat (SH), 253–256, 253t
Specificity of enzymes, 774, 779–780
Specific rotation, 549
Spectator ions, 336
Spermaceti wax, 423, 669–670, 669mn
SPF (sun protection factor), 482mn
Sphingomyelins, 681, 683–685
  comparison with triacylglycerols and
    phosphoacylglycerol, 681, 683, 685, 685f
  structure of, 683–684
Sphygmomanometer, 228–229, 228f
Spider dragline silk, 766, 766f
Spider plants, as air purifier, 122mn
Spin, electron, 56mn, 59
Spinach, oxalic acid in, 594
Spiral pathway, 879
Sports drinks, 309, 334mn
SSRIs (selective serotonin reuptake inhibitors), 652
Stahl, Franklin, 806
Standard conditions of temperature and pressure (STP),
  238–239
Standard molar volume, 238
Stanozolol, 692
Starch, 504–505, 707–709, 732, 734, 734f
  hydrolysis of, 504–505
  structure of, 732, 734
States of matter, 3–5, 4f, 225–226, 225f. See also
  Gas(es); Liquids; Solids
Statins, 691
Stearic acid, 464, 464t, 667, 667t, 668mn, 674, 677–678
  butter from, 473
  β-oxidation of, 878–881
  solubility properties of, 279, 414
  structure of, 464t, 465f
Stereochemistry
  amino acid, 751–752
  chirality in, 533–559 (See also Chirality)
  definition of, 531
Stereoisomers, 462–463, 531–533
  constitutional isomers versus, 462–463, 531
  definition of, 462, 531
  diastereomers, 551–552, 551f
  enantiomers, 535–553 (See also Enantiomers)
  identifying, 532–533
Sterling silver, 90, 90mn
Steroids, 666, 688–693
  adrenal cortical, 693
  anabolic, 692, 692mn, 693, 704
  cholesterol, 688–691 (See also Cholesterol)

hormones, 692–693
  inhaled, for asthma, 697
  structure of, 688
Stevia, 731, 731mn
Sticky ends, 820
Stomach
  hydrochloric acid in, 320, 321f
  pH in, 335, 335f
Stop codons, 812
STP (standard conditions of temperature and pressure),
  238–239
Straight-chain alkanes, 428, 429–430, 430t,
  434, 444
Strands, in protein structure, 764
Stratospheric ozone, 119, 119f
Strong acids, 319–324, 320t
  acid dissociation constant of, 326–327
  buffering and, 342, 343f, 344
  definition of, 319
  dissociation in water, 320, 321f
  relative strengths, 320t
  and salt solutions, 338–340
Strong bases, 323–324
  buffering and, 342, 343f, 344
  definition of, 323
  dissociation in water, 323, 324f
  and salt solutions, 338–340
Strong electrolytes, 276, 276t
Strontium, 53
Strontium-89, 383
Strontium-90, 75, 384
Styrene, 404
Styrofoam (polystyrene), 2, 2f, 475, 476f, 478t
Subatomic particles, 42–46, 43t. See also Electron(s);
  Neutron(s); Proton(s)
Sublimation, 259, 259mn, 259t
Subscripts, in chemical equations, 141–142
Subshells, 56
Substituents
  definition of, 435
  naming of
    alcohols, 501–503
    alkanes, 434–439, 435t, 441–442
    alkyl halides, 517–518
    benzene derivatives, 480–482
    ethers, 514–515
Substitution reactions
  alkanes, 446–447
  aromatic compounds (benzene), 480–482, 485–489
  carboxylic acids, 611–614, 625
  chlorination, 486
  definition of, 447, 485
  esters and amides, 614–618
  nitration, 486–487
  sulfonation, 486, 487–488
Subtraction, using significant figures in,
  16–17, A-4
Subunit, of protein, 768
Succinate, 849f, 850–851
Succinyl CoA, 849–851, 849f
Sucralose, 729–731, 730f, 730t
Sucrose, 423, 707, 729–731
  content in food, 715mn
  ethanol production from, 187
  mole of, 167, 168f
Sudafed, 136, 648, 655, 655mn
Suffixes. See also specific suffixes
  for alcohols, 501–503
  for alkanes, 434
  for alkenes, 456
  for alkynes, 456
Sugar(s), 707–709. See also Carbohydrates
  artificial sweeteners versus, 729–731, 730t
  nonreducing, 722
  nucleoside and nucleotide, 795–800

reducing, 722
    table, 167, 168*f*, 706, 707, 729
"Sugar alcohol," 721
Sugarcane, 170*mn*, 187, 729
Sugar-free chewing gum, 500*mn*
Sulfa drugs, 486–487
Sulfamethoxazole, 487
Sulfanilamide, 487, 783–784, 785
Sulfate, 97, 97*t*
Sulfhydryl group, 403*t*, 497–498, 520, 846–847
Sulfide, 92*t*
Sulfisoxazole, 487
Sulfite, 97
Sulfonation, of benzene (aromatic compound), 486,
    487–488
Sulfur, 37*t*
    coal content of, 62*mn*
    exception to octet rule, 116–117
    as major mineral (macronutrient), 39*f*, 40
Sulfur-32, 365
Sulfur dioxide, 136
Sulfuric acid, 312–313
    in acid rain, 62*mn*, 182, 341–342, 342*mn*, 346, 346*f*
    balancing equation with polyatomic ions, 146–147
    exception to octet rule, 116–117
    industrial use of, 320
    as strong acid, 320, 320*t*
Sulfurous acid, 62*mn*, 313
Sulfur oxides, 62*mn*, 342*mn*
Sulfur trioxide, benzene reaction with, 487–488, 488*f*
Sumatriptan, 652
Sun, nuclear fusion in, 374, 377
Sun protection factor (SPF), 482*mn*
Sunscreen, 482*mn*, 483–484, 567, 568, 630
Supercoil, 769–770, 770*f*
Superhelix, 769–770, 770*f*
Supersaturated solution, 282
Surface tension, 251, 251*f*
Suspensions, 274–275, 274*mn*, 274*t*
Sutures, dissolving, 622–623
Sweat, 136, 216, 249, 258, 540*mn*, 569*mn*
Sweeteners, artificial, 133, 188, 631, 721–722, 721*mn*,
    729–731, 730*f*, 730*t*
Sweetness, of monosaccharides, 711
Swimming pools, 354
Symbols
    in chemical equation, 141, 141*t*
    electron-dot, 66, 109–110
    element, 37–38, 37*t*
    isotope, 47
Synapse, 649*f*, 650
Synthase, 777
Synthetic elements, 37
Synthetic materials, 2–3, 2*f*, 3*f*
Synthetic polymers, 475–478, 619–623
Systematic names, 433. *See also* Nomenclature
Systolic pressure, 228–229, 228*f*

T

Table salt. *See* Sodium chloride
Table sugar, 167, 168*f*, 706, 707, 729–731. *See also*
    Sucrose
Tallow, 681
Tamoxifen, 466
Tanning agents, 124*mn*, 537, 567
Taq polymerase, 821
Tarragon, 422
Tartaric acid, 537, 550
Tay–Sachs disease, 818*t*
3TC (lamivudine), 830
TCA. *See* Citric acid cycle
TCDD (dioxin), 188
Technetium-99m, 363, 363*mn*, 365*t*, 369–370, 371–372,
    372*f*, 373*f*, 382

Teeth-whitening products, 129*mn*
Teflon, 133, 475, 477*f*
Temperature
    body, 216, 216*mn*, 217*f*
    changes, and equilibrium, 213–214, 215*t*
    definition of, 26
    and density, 27
    and enzyme activity, 781–782, 781*f*
    gas laws, 229
        Charles's (volume–temperature), 229, 231–233,
            232*mn*, 233*f*, 236*t*, 264
        combined (pressure–volume–temperature),
            235–236, 236*t*, 264
        Gay–Lussac's (pressure–temperature), 229,
            233–235, 236*t*, 264
        ideal (pressure–volume–temperature–moles),
            239–242, 264
    and reaction rate, 200–201
    scales, 26–27, 26*f*
    and solubility, 282
    and specific heat, 253–256
    standard conditions of, 238–239
    and vapor pressure, 250–251
Template strand, of DNA, 810–811, 810*f*, 815*f*
Terephthalic acid, 620–623
Terfenadine (Seldane), 662
Tertiary (3°) alcohol, 499–500, 508–509
Tertiary (3°) alkyl halide, 516
Tertiary (3°) amide, 593, 598
Tertiary (3°) amine, 633, 633*mn*, 636, 638
Tertiary carbon, 431
Tertiary structure of protein, 762, 766–768, 768*f*
Terylene. *See* Polyethylene terephthalate
Testosterone, 692, 693
Tetra- (prefix), 120*t*
Tetrachloromethane (carbon tetrachloride), 280,
    280*f*, 518
Tetrafluoroethylene, 133
Tetrahedral carbon atoms, 535–539, 535*mn*, 536. *See
    also* Chirality centers; Enantiomers
Tetrahedral geometry, 121, 122–123, 123*t*, 124,
    391–392, 392*t*, 427
Tetrahydrocannabinol (THC), 403–404,
    403*mn*, 424
Tetrahydrogestrinone, 692
Tetrose, 709
Thalidomide, 542, 542*mn*
Thallium-201, 372–373, 373*f*
Thallium-210, 381
THC. *See* Tetrahydrocannabinol
Theobromine, 420
Theoretical yield, 171–174, 171*mn*
Therapeutic concentration, 309
Thermal cycler, 821
Thermometers, 26*mn*
Thermoregulation, 216, 216*mn*, 217*f*
THG (tetrahydrogestrinone), 692
Thioesters, 846–847, 862, 877–878
Thiol(s), 497–498, 520–522
    coenzyme A as, 846
    functional group of, 403, 403*t*, 497–498, 520
    nomenclature for, 520–521
    odor of, 498, 521, 521*mn*, 524, 527
    oxidation of, 521–522
    in proteins, 522, 522*f*
-thiol (suffix), 520–521
Thorium-234, 359
Three-dimensional shape, of molecules, 530–559.
    See also Chirality
Threonine, 550, 750*t*
Thymine, 796, 799*t*, 804, 806–808, 807*f*
Thyroid gland, 50, 50*f*
Thyrotropin-releasing hormone (TRH), 595
Tiger moth, 448
Time, units of measurement, 9*t*

Tin, 37*t*
    ions, 92*t*
    isotopes of, 47–48
Titration, 340–342, 340*f*
Tobacco, 448, 641–642, 641*f*
Tollens reagent, 570–571, 570*mn*
Toluene, 480, 485
Trace elements, 39*f*, 40
Trade name, 433
Trandolapril, 408, 408*mn*
Transaminase, 776, 883–884
Transamination, 883–885
Transcription, 806, 810–811, 810*f*
Transcription, reverse, 823–825, 824*f*
Trans fats, 475, 675–676, 676*f*
Transferase, 776, 777*t*
Transfer RNA (tRNA), 808–809, 809*f*, 809*t*,
    813–814
Trans isomers, 460–463, 463*mn*, 531–532
Transition metals
    cation formation by, 85–86, 86*f*
    in periodic table, 51*f*, 52
Transition state, 198–200, 199*f*
Translation, 806, 813–816, 815*f*
Transport, across cell membrane, 687–688
Tri- (prefix), 120*t*, 636–637
Triacylglycerols, 617–618, 664, 665, 671–681
    catabolism of, 833–835, 835*f*, 836*f*, 877–881
    combustion of, 679, 679*mn*
    compared with phospholipids, 681, 683,
        685, 685*f*
    definition of, 671
    dietary, 675–676, 676*f*, 701
    digestion of, 834–835, 836*f*, 862
    drawing structure of, 674
    fatty acid composition of, 671–674, 673*t*
    general features of, 672–675
    hydrolysis of, 677–681, 699, 776, 833, 835*f*, 862
    metabolism in body, 678–680
    mixed, 672
    monounsaturated, 672
    physical properties of, 672
    polyunsaturated, 672
    saponification of, 680–681, 699
    simple, 672
Tricarboxylic acid cycle (TCA). *See* Citric
    acid cycle
Trichloromethane (chloroform), 186, 411, 518
Triethylamine, 404
Trigonal planar geometry, 121, 122, 123*t*, 390, 392*t*,
    454, 479, 763
Trigonal pyramidal geometry, 123, 123*t*, 391,
    392*t*, 634
Trimethylamine, 638
Triols, 502
Triose, 709
Tripeptide, 754
Triple bond, 115, 388
Triprotic acid, 313
Tristearin, 452, 677
Tritium (T), 47, 377
tRNA (transfer RNA), 808–809, 809*f*, 809*t*, 813–814
Trypsin, 784–785, 791, 833
Trypsinogen, 784–785
Tryptophan, 651, 653, 750*t*
Tums, 100, 337, 337*mn*
Tuna fish oil, 668–669, 668*mn*
Tung oil, 494
Tungsten, 37*t*
Turmeric, 484–485
Twins, identical, 533*mn*, 805*mn*, 822
Tylenol. *See* Acetaminophen
Tympanic thermometer, 26*mn*
Tyrosine, 421, 650, 650*f*, 750*t*
Tyvek, 479

U

U-47700, 659
Ulcers, drug therapy for, 656
Undecane, 426
Units of concentration, 288–291
Units of energy, 190–191, 190*mn*
Units of measurement, 9–12
  conversion factors, 20–23
  English system, 9
  metric system, 9–10, 9*t*, 10*t*, 12*t*
  SI units, 9*mn*
Units of pressure, 227–228
Units of radioactivity, 368–369, 369*mn*, 369*t*, 371
Universal gas constant (*R*), 239–242
Unpaired electrons, 59, 60
Unsaturated fatty acids, 453, 463–465, 667–668, 676*f*
  common, 464*t*, 667, 667*t*, 668*mn*
  definition of, 464, 667
  sources of, 464
  triacylglycerol, 671–676
Unsaturated hydrocarbons, 453–495
  alkenes, 454–475
  alkenes and alkynes, 454–460
  alkynes, 454–460
  aromatic compounds, 454, 479–489
  definition of, 454
  fatty acids, 463–465
  polymers, 475–479
Unsaturated solution, 278
Uracil, 796, 799*t*, 808
Uranium-235, 365*t*, 375–376
Uranium-238, 359
Urea, 862, 885
Urea cycle, 885
Urine, 29*mn*, 30, 335*f*
Urushiol, 485

V

Vaccine, 823, 823*mn*
Valdecoxib, 697
Valence electrons, 63–66
  covalent bonding and, 110–119
  definition of, 63
  electron-dot symbol of, 66, 109–110
  Lewis structures of, 112–119
  and molecular shape, 121–124
  octet rule and, 81, 109, 112–116
  octet rule exceptions and, 116–117
  relationship to group number, 64–66, 65*t*
Valence shell electron pair repulsion (VSEPR) theory, 121–124, 390
Valerian, 596*mn*
Valeric acid, 596, 596*mn*
Valine, 750*t*
van der Waals forces. *See* London dispersion forces
Vane, John, 602
Vanillin, 484–485, 568*f*
Vapor, 249
Vaporization, 257–258, 259*t*
Vapor pressure, 249–251
  boiling point elevation and, 294, 294*f*
  definition of, 250
  temperature and, 250–251
Vaseline, 444, 444*mn*, 451
Vasopressin, 761–762, 762*f*
Vegetable oils, 473–475, 473*mn*, 474*f*, 474*mn*, 671–676, 673*t*

Venlafaxine, 422
Vesicles, 649*f*, 650
Vicia faba, L-Dopa from, 544–545, 545*mn*
Vinegar, acetic acid of, 289, 289*mn*, 314*f*, 320, 321*f*, 414*f*
Viruses, 823–825, 823*mn*
Viscosity, 251
Vision, chemistry of, 575–577, 575*mn*, 576*f*
Vitamin(s), 415–417
  definition of, 694
  fat-soluble, 279*mn*, 415–416, 417*f*, 666, 694–696, 694*t*
  origin of term, 415*mn*
  water-soluble, 279*mn*, 415, 416, 417*f*
Vitamin A, 415–416, 415*mn*, 416*mn*, 417*f*, 575, 694, 694*t*
Vitamin B, 415
Vitamin B$_2$ (riboflavin), 846, 846*mn*
Vitamin B$_3$, 416
Vitamin B$_5$ (pantothenic acid), 847, 847*mn*
Vitamin B$_6$, 130, 130*mn*, 423
Vitamin C, 79*mn*, 163, 163*mn*, 327, 327*mn*, 416, 416*mn*, 417*f*, 770
Vitamin D, 694–695, 694*t*
Vitamin D$_3$, 440
Vitamin E, 423, 485, 664, 694–695, 694*t*
Vitamin K, 417, 538, 538*mn*, 694–695, 694*t*
Volatile solute, 294
Volcanic emissions, 113, 113*mn*
Volume
  gas laws, 229
    Avogadro's (volume–moles), 236–239, 237*mn*, 264
    Boyle's (pressure–volume), 229–231, 231*f*, 236*t*, 264
    Charles's (volume–temperature), 229, 231–233, 232*mn*, 233*f*, 236*t*, 264
    combined (pressure–volume–temperature), 235–236, 236*t*, 264
    ideal (pressure–volume–temperature–moles), 239–242, 264
  relationship to mass (density), 27–29
  units of measurement, 9, 9*t*, 11, 11*mn*, 12*t*
Volumetric flask, 283–284, 284*f*
Volume/volume percent, 285, 285*mn*
VSEPR. *See* Valence shell electron pair repulsion (VSEPR) theory
Vulcanization, 3, 3*f*

W

Water. *See also* specific reactions
  as achiral molecule, 534
  as acid, 318, 320*t*, 328
  addition to alkenes, 468*f*, 472–473
  as base, 315, 318, 320*t*, 328
  boiling point of, 247–248
  cardiovascular function of, 111–112, 111*f*
  combination reaction for, 148
  as compound, 7, 7*f*, 40–41
  cooling curve for, 260–261, 261*f*
  as covalent molecule/compound, 77, 108, 109
  density of, 27–28, 27*t*
  dissociation of, 328–330
  heat of vaporization, 258
  as heat reservoir, 254
  intermolecular forces in, 247–248
  ion–product constant for, 328–330
  Lewis structure of, 123
  limiting reactant in formation of, 176–177
  loss, in dehydration reaction, 505–507, 523
  melting point of, 247–248

  molecular art of, 41
  molecular geometry of, 123
  mole of, 157*mn*, 167, 168*f*
  partial pressure of gas, 242–243
  polarity of, 128
  solubility in, 278–283
  specific heat of, 253–254, 253*t*
  states of, 4, 4*f*, 138
  as weak acid, 320*t*
Water-soluble salts, 644–648
Water-soluble vitamins, 279*mn*, 415, 416, 417*f*
Water vapor, 249
Watson, James, 803
Waxes, 665, 669–671, 669*mn*, 699
Weak acids, 319–323, 320*t*
  acid dissociation constant of, 326–327, 327*t*
  in buffer systems, 342–348
  definition of, 319
  dissociation in water, 320, 321*f*
  relative strengths, 320*t*
  and salt solutions, 338–340
Weak bases, 323–324, 324*f*
  definition of, 323
  dissociation in water, 323, 324*f*
  and salt solutions, 338–340
Weak electrolytes, 276, 276*t*
Weight, 11
Weight/volume percent, 283–284, 283*mn*
Whales
  myoglobin in, 747, 771*mn*
  spermaceti wax from, 423, 669–670, 669*mn*
Willow tree, 589, 609, 609*mn*
Wilson's disease, 105, 536
Wind currents, Charles's law and, 233, 233*f*
Wine, 166–167, 166*mn*
Wintergreen, oil of, 603
Wool, 619
World Anti-Doping Agency (WADA), 692*mn*

X

Xenon, 54
Xenon-133, 371, 373*f*
X-rays, 378, 378*f*, 384
Xylitol, 527, 721–722, 721*mn*
Xylose, 721–722

Y

-yl (suffix), 755
-yne (suffix), 456
Yogurt, Calories in, 192
Yuzu, 564, 564*mn*

Z

Zaitsev rule, 506, 526
Zero
  absolute, 26
  as significant figure, 13, A-3
Zidovudine (AZT), 824, 824*mn*
Zileuton, 698
Zinc, 37*t*, 39*f*, 40, 105, 153
Zinc chloride, formation of, 150
Zinc oxide, 91, 91*mn*
Zinc–silver oxide batteries, 183
Zingerone, 136
Zingiberene, 456, 456*mn*
Zwitterion, 749, 752–754
Zymogen, 784–785

Periodic Table of the Elements

1A 1																		8A 18
1 **H** 1.008	2A 2											3A 13	4A 14	5A 15	6A 16	7A 17	2 **He** 4.003
3 **Li** 6.941	4 **Be** 9.012												5 **B** 10.81	6 **C** 12.01	7 **N** 14.01	8 **O** 16.00	9 **F** 19.00	10 **Ne** 20.18
11 **Na** 22.99	12 **Mg** 24.31	3B 3	4B 4	5B 5	6B 6	7B 7	8	8B 9	10	1B 11	2B 12	13 **Al** 26.98	14 **Si** 28.09	15 **P** 30.97	16 **S** 32.07	17 **Cl** 35.45	18 **Ar** 39.95
19 **K** 39.10	20 **Ca** 40.08	21 **Sc** 44.96	22 **Ti** 47.88	23 **V** 50.94	24 **Cr** 52.00	25 **Mn** 54.94	26 **Fe** 55.85	27 **Co** 58.93	28 **Ni** 58.69	29 **Cu** 63.55	30 **Zn** 65.41	31 **Ga** 69.72	32 **Ge** 72.64	33 **As** 74.92	34 **Se** 78.96	35 **Br** 79.90	36 **Kr** 83.80
37 **Rb** 85.47	38 **Sr** 87.62	39 **Y** 88.91	40 **Zr** 91.22	41 **Nb** 92.91	42 **Mo** 95.94	43 **Tc** (98)	44 **Ru** 101.1	45 **Rh** 102.9	46 **Pd** 106.4	47 **Ag** 107.9	48 **Cd** 112.4	49 **In** 114.8	50 **Sn** 118.7	51 **Sb** 121.8	52 **Te** 127.6	53 **I** 126.9	54 **Xe** 131.3
55 **Cs** 132.9	56 **Ba** 137.3	57 **La** 138.9	72 **Hf** 178.5	73 **Ta** 180.9	74 **W** 183.8	75 **Re** 186.2	76 **Os** 190.2	77 **Ir** 192.2	78 **Pt** 195.1	79 **Au** 197.0	80 **Hg** 200.6	81 **Tl** 204.4	82 **Pb** 207.2	83 **Bi** 209.0	84 **Po** (209)	85 **At** (210)	86 **Rn** (222)
87 **Fr** (223)	88 **Ra** (226)	89 **Ac** (227)	104 **Rf** (267)	105 **Db** (268)	106 **Sg** (271)	107 **Bh** (272)	108 **Hs** (270)	109 **Mt** (276)	110 **Ds** (281)	111 **Rg** (280)	112 **Cn** (285)	113 **Nh** (284)	114 **Fl** (289)	115 **Mc** (289)	116 **Lv** (293)	117 **Ts** (294)	118 **Og** (294)

6	58 **Ce** 140.1	59 **Pr** 140.9	60 **Nd** 144.2	61 **Pm** (145)	62 **Sm** 150.4	63 **Eu** 152.0	64 **Gd** 157.3	65 **Tb** 158.9	66 **Dy** 162.5	67 **Ho** 164.9	68 **Er** 167.3	69 **Tm** 168.9	70 **Yb** 173.0	71 **Lu** 175.0
7	90 **Th** 232.0	91 **Pa** 231.0	92 **U** 238.0	93 **Np** (237)	94 **Pu** (244)	95 **Am** (243)	96 **Cm** (247)	97 **Bk** (247)	98 **Cf** (251)	99 **Es** (252)	100 **Fm** (257)	101 **Md** (258)	102 **No** (259)	103 **Lr** (262)

The Elements

Element	Symbol	Atomic Number	Relative Atomic Mass*	Element	Symbol	Atomic Number	Relative Atomic Mass*
Actinium	Ac	89	(227)	Mendelevium	Md	101	(258)
Aluminum	Al	13	26.98	Mercury	Hg	80	200.6
Americium	Am	95	(243)	Molybdenum	Mo	42	95.94
Antimony	Sb	51	121.8	Moscovium	Mc	115	(289)
Argon	Ar	18	39.95	Neodymium	Nd	60	144.2
Arsenic	As	33	74.92	Neon	Ne	10	20.18
Astatine	At	85	(210)	Neptunium	Np	93	(237)
Barium	Ba	56	137.3	Nickel	Ni	28	58.69
Berkelium	Bk	97	(247)	Nihonium	Nh	113	(284)
Beryllium	Be	4	9.012	Niobium	Nb	41	92.91
Bismuth	Bi	83	209.0	Nitrogen	N	7	14.01
Bohrium	Bh	107	(272)	Nobelium	No	102	(259)
Boron	B	5	10.81	Oganesson	Og	118	(294)
Bromine	Br	35	79.90	Osmium	Os	76	190.2
Cadmium	Cd	48	112.4	Oxygen	O	8	16.00
Calcium	Ca	20	40.08	Palladium	Pd	46	106.4
Californium	Cf	98	(251)	Phosphorus	P	15	30.97
Carbon	C	6	12.01	Platinum	Pt	78	195.1
Cerium	Ce	58	140.1	Plutonium	Pu	94	(244)
Cesium	Cs	55	132.9	Polonium	Po	84	(209)
Chlorine	Cl	17	35.45	Potassium	K	19	39.10
Chromium	Cr	24	52.00	Praseodymium	Pr	59	140.9
Cobalt	Co	27	58.93	Promethium	Pm	61	(145)
Copernicium	Cn	112	(285)	Protactinium	Pa	91	231.0
Copper	Cu	29	63.55	Radium	Ra	88	(226)
Curium	Cm	96	(247)	Radon	Rn	86	(222)
Darmstadtium	Ds	110	(281)	Rhenium	Re	75	186.2
Dubnium	Db	105	(268)	Rhodium	Rh	45	102.9
Dysprosium	Dy	66	162.5	Roentgenium	Rg	111	(280)
Einsteinium	Es	99	(252)	Rubidium	Rb	37	85.47
Erbium	Er	68	167.3	Ruthenium	Ru	44	101.1
Europium	Eu	63	152.0	Rutherfordium	Rf	104	(267)
Fermium	Fm	100	(257)	Samarium	Sm	62	150.4
Flerovium	Fl	114	(289)	Scandium	Sc	21	44.96
Fluorine	F	9	19.00	Seaborgium	Sg	106	(271)
Francium	Fr	87	(223)	Selenium	Se	34	78.96
Gadolinium	Gd	64	157.3	Silicon	Si	14	28.09
Gallium	Ga	31	69.72	Silver	Ag	47	107.9
Germanium	Ge	32	72.64	Sodium	Na	11	22.99
Gold	Au	79	197.0	Strontium	Sr	38	87.62
Hafnium	Hf	72	178.5	Sulfur	S	16	32.07
Hassium	Hs	108	(270)	Tantalum	Ta	73	180.9
Helium	He	2	4.003	Technetium	Tc	43	(98)
Holmium	Ho	67	164.9	Tellurium	Te	52	127.6
Hydrogen	H	1	1.008	Tennessine	Ts	117	(294)
Indium	In	49	114.8	Terbium	Tb	65	158.9
Iodine	I	53	126.9	Thallium	Tl	81	204.4
Iridium	Ir	77	192.2	Thorium	Th	90	232.0
Iron	Fe	26	55.85	Thulium	Tm	69	168.9
Krypton	Kr	36	83.80	Tin	Sn	50	118.7
Lanthanum	La	57	138.9	Titanium	Ti	22	47.88
Lawrencium	Lr	103	(262)	Tungsten	W	74	183.8
Lead	Pb	82	207.2	Uranium	U	92	238.0
Lithium	Li	3	6.941	Vanadium	V	23	50.94
Livermorium	Lv	116	(293)	Xenon	Xe	54	131.3
Lutetium	Lu	71	175.0	Ytterbium	Yb	70	173.0
Magnesium	Mg	12	24.31	Yttrium	Y	39	88.91
Manganese	Mn	25	54.94	Zinc	Zn	30	65.41
Meitnerium	Mt	109	(276)	Zirconium	Zr	40	91.22

*Values in parentheses represent the mass number of the most stable isotope.

Common Functional Groups in Organic Chemistry

Type of Compound	General Structure	Example	Functional Group
Alcohol	R—ÖH	CH_3—ÖH	—OH hydroxyl group
Aldehyde	R—C(=O)—H	CH_3—C(=O)—H	C=O carbonyl group
Alkane	R—H	CH_3CH_3	– –
Alkene	C=C	CH₂=CH₂	double bond
Alkyl halide	R—Ẍ: (X = F, Cl, Br, I)	CH_3—Br̈:	—X halo group
Alkyne	—C≡C—	H—C≡C—H	triple bond
Amide	R—C(=O)—N(H or R)(H or R)	CH_3—C(=O)—NH_2	—$CONH_2$, —CONHR, —$CONR_2$
Amine	R—NH_2 or R_2NH or R_3N	CH_3—NH_2	—NH_2 amino group
Aromatic compound	benzene ring	benzene ring	benzene ring
Carboxylic acid	R—C(=O)—ÖH	CH_3—C(=O)—ÖH	—COOH carboxyl group
Ester	R—C(=O)—ÖR	CH_3—C(=O)—OCH_3	—COOR
Ether	R—Ö—R	CH_3—Ö—CH_3	—OR alkoxy group
Ketone	R—C(=O)—R	CH_3—C(=O)—CH_3	C=O carbonyl group
Thiol	R—S̈H	CH_3—S̈H	—SH sulfhydryl group

Common Metric Prefixes

Prefix	Symbol	Numerical Value
giga-	G	10^9
mega-	M	10^6
kilo-	k	10^3
deci-	d	10^{-1}
centi-	c	10^{-2}
milli-	m	10^{-3}
micro-	μ	10^{-6}
nano	n	10^{-9}

Useful Conversion Factors

Length	Mass	Volume
1 m = 100 cm = 1,000 mm	1 kg = 1,000 g	1 L = 1,000 mL
1 cm = 10 mm	1 g = 1,000 mg	1 mL = 1 cm^3 = 1 cc
2.54 cm = 1 in.	1 kg = 2.20 lb	946 mL = 1 qt
1 m = 39.4 in.	454 g = 1 lb	1 L = 1.06 qt
1 km = 0.621 mi	28.3 g = 1 oz	29.6 mL = 1 fl oz
Temperature	Pressure	Energy
$T_F = 1.8(T_C) + 32$	1 atm = 14.7 psi	1 kcal = 1,000 cal
$T_C = (T_F - 32)/1.8$	1 atm = 760 mm Hg	1 cal = 4.184 J
$T_K = T_C + 273$	1 mm Hg = 1 torr	

Physical Constants

Avogadro's number	6.02×10^{23} particles/mol
Universal gas constant (R)	0.0821 L · atm/(mol · K) or 62.4 L · mm Hg/(mol · K)
Volume of one mole of gas at STP	22.4 L

Common Element Colors Used in Molecular Art

C   H   O   N   F   Cl   Br   I   S   P

Credits

i. About the Author: *Chapter from General, Organic, & Biological Chemistry, Fourth Edition by Smith, 2019* 1

ii. Preface: *Chapter from General, Organic, & Biological Chemistry, Fourth Edition by Smith, 2019* 2

iii. Learning Resources for Instructors and Students: *Chapter from General, Organic, & Biological Chemistry, Fourth Edition by Smith, 2019* 6

iv. Acknowledgments: *Chapter from General, Organic, & Biological Chemistry, Fourth Edition by Smith, 2019* 8

v. List of How To's: *Chapter from General, Organic, & Biological Chemistry, Fourth Edition by Smith, 2019* 9

vi. List of Applications: *Chapter from General, Organic, & Biological Chemistry, Fourth Edition by Smith, 2019* 11

1. Matter and Measurement: *Chapter 1 from General, Organic, & Biological Chemistry, Fourth Edition by Smith, 2019* 15

2. Atoms and the Periodic Table: *Chapter 2 from General, Organic, & Biological Chemistry, Fourth Edition by Smith, 2019* 50

3. Ionic Compounds: *Chapter 3 from General, Organic, & Biological Chemistry, Fourth Edition by Smith, 2019* 90

4. Covalent Compounds: *Chapter 4 from General, Organic, & Biological Chemistry, Fourth Edition by Smith, 2019* 121

5. Chemical Reactions: *Chapter 5 from General, Organic, & Biological Chemistry, Fourth Edition by Smith, 2019* 151

6. Energy Changes, Reaction Rates, and Equilibrium: *Chapter 6 from General, Organic, & Biological Chemistry, Fourth Edition by Smith, 2019* 203

7. Gases, Liquids, and Solids: *Chapter 7 from General, Organic, & Biological Chemistry, Fourth Edition by Smith, 2019* 238

8. Solutions: *Chapter 8 from General, Organic, & Biological Chemistry, Fourth Edition by Smith, 2019* 286

9. Acids and Bases: *Chapter 9 from General, Organic, & Biological Chemistry, Fourth Edition by Smith, 2019* 324

10. Nuclear Chemistry: *Chapter 10 from General, Organic, & Biological Chemistry, Fourth Edition by Smith, 2019* 369

11. Introduction to Organic Molecules and Functional Groups: *Chapter 11 from General, Organic, & Biological Chemistry, Fourth Edition by Smith, 2019* 399

12. Alkanes: *Chapter 12 from General, Organic, & Biological Chemistry, Fourth Edition by Smith, 2019* 439

13. Unsaturated Hydrocarbons: *Chapter 13 from General, Organic, & Biological Chemistry, Fourth Edition by Smith, 2019* 467

14. Organic Compounds That Contain Oxygen, Halogen, or Sulfur: *Chapter 14 from General, Organic, & Biological Chemistry, Fourth Edition by Smith, 2019* 510

15. The Three-Dimensional Shape of Molecules: *Chapter 15 from General, Organic, & Biological Chemistry, Fourth Edition by Smith, 2019* 544

16. Aldehydes and Ketones: *Chapter 16 from General, Organic, & Biological Chemistry, Fourth Edition by Smith, 2019* 574

17. Carboxylic Acids, Esters, and Amides: *Chapter 17 from General, Organic, & Biological Chemistry, Fourth Edition by Smith, 2019* 606

18. Amines and Neurotransmitters: *Chapter 18 from General, Organic, & Biological Chemistry, Fourth Edition by Smith, 2019* 646

19. Lipids: *Chapter 19 from General, Organic, & Biological Chemistry, Fourth Edition by Smith, 2019* 677

20. Carbohydrates: *Chapter 20 from General, Organic, & Biological Chemistry, Fourth Edition by Smith, 2019* 720

21. Amino Acids, Proteins, and Enzymes: *Chapter 21 from General, Organic, & Biological Chemistry, Fourth Edition by Smith, 2019* 761

22. Nucleic Acids and Protein Synthesis: *Chapter 22 from General, Organic, & Biological Chemistry, Fourth Edition by Smith, 2019* 808

23. Metabolism and Energy Production: *Chapter 23 from General, Organic, & Biological Chemistry, Fourth Edition by Smith, 2019* 846

24. Carbohydrate, Lipid, and Protein Metabolism: *Chapter 24 from General, Organic, & Biological Chemistry, Fourth Edition by Smith, 2019* 875

25. Body Fluids: *Chapter 25.Create from General, Organic, & Biological Chemistry, Fourth Edition by Smith, 2019* 907

26. Index for Body Fluids (Create Only): *Chapter from General, Organic, & Biological Chemistry, Fourth Edition by Smith, 2019* 929

A. Appendix: Useful Mathematical Concepts: *Chapter A from General, Organic, & Biological Chemistry, Fourth Edition by Smith, 2019* 931

B. Appendix: Answers to Selected In-Chapter and End-of-Chapter Problems: *Chapter B from General, Organic, & Biological Chemistry, Fourth Edition by Smith, 2019* 937

C. Glossary: *Chapter from General, Organic, & Biological Chemistry, Fourth Edition by Smith, 2019* 991

D. Index: *Chapter from General, Organic, & Biological Chemistry, Fourth Edition by Smith, 2019* 1003

E. Periodic Table of the Elements: *Chapter from General, Organic, & Biological Chemistry, Fourth Edition by Smith, 2019* 1027

F. Common Functional Groups in Organic Chemistry: *Chapter from General, Organic, & Biological Chemistry, Fourth Edition by Smith, 2019* 1029

Online Supplements 1033

Connect One Semester Online Access for General, Organic, & Biological Chemistry, Fourth Edition: *Media by Smith* 1034

Access Code for the Online Supplements 1035

Online Supplements

Connect One Semester Online Access for General, Organic, & Biological Chemistry, Fourth Edition

McGraw-Hill Connect is a digital teaching and learning environment that improves performance over a variety of critical outcomes. With Connect, instructors can deliver assignments, quizzes and tests easily online. Students can practice important skills at their own pace and on their own schedule.

HOW TO REGISTER

Using a <u>Print Book</u>?

To register and activate your Connect account, simply follow these easy steps:

1. **Go to the Connect course web address provided by your instructor or visit the Connect link set up on your instructor's course within your campus learning management system.**
2. **Click on the link to register.**
3. **When prompted, enter the Connect code found on the inside back cover of your book and click Submit. Complete the brief registration form that follows to begin using Connect.**

Using an <u>eBook</u>?

To register and activate your Connect account, simply follow these easy steps:

1. **Upon purchase of your eBook, you will be granted automatic access to Connect.**
2. **Go to the Connect course web address provided by your instructor or visit the Connect link set up on your instructor's course within your campus learning management system.**
3. **Sign in using the same email address and password you used to register on the eBookstore. Complete your registration and begin using Connect.**

Note: Access Code is for one use only. If you did not purchase this book new, the access code included in this book is no longer valid.

Need help? Visit mhhe.com/support